10

COMPENDIUM OF
SOIL FUNGI

COMPENDIUM OF SOIL FUNGI

Volume 2

K. H. DOMSCH
Institute of Soil Biology
Federal Agricultural Research Centre
Braunschweig
Federal Republic of Germany

W. GAMS
Centraalbureau voor Schimmelcultures,
Baarn
The Netherlands

TRAUTE-HEIDI ANDERSON
Institute of Soil Biology
Federal Agricultural Research Centre
Braunschweig
Federal Republic of Germany

1980

ACADEMIC PRESS

A Subsidiary of Harcourt Brace Jovanovich, Publishers

London   New York   Toronto   Sydney   San Francisco

WILLIAM MADISON RANDALL LIBRARY UNC AT WILMINGTON

ACADEMIC PRESS (LONDON) LTD
24/28 Oval Road
London NW1

United States Edition published by
ACADEMIC PRESS INC.
111 Fifth Avenue
New York, New York 10003

British Library Cataloguing in Publication Data

Domsch, Klaus Heinz
    Compendium of soil fungi.
    Vol. 2
    1. Soil fungi
    I. Title   II. Gams, Walter   III. Anderson, T-H
    589'.2'09148   QR111   80-41403
    ISBN 0-12-220402-6

Printed and bound in Great Britain
at The Pitman Press, Bath

Contents

VOLUME 1

VOLUME 2

Classification of and Keys to the Genera Treated

Pleomorphic fungi are keyed out according to both teleomorphic and anamorphic genera, though the text may refer only to one of them. (Figures in parentheses refer to numbered sketches).

I. OOMYCETES: Hyphae coenocytic, without regularly spaced septa; cell walls containing cellulose; zoospores with two unequal flagella; sexual organs immobile: oogonia and antheridia.

    A. Saprolegniales, Saprolegniaceae: Mycelium producing saccate or filamentous zoosporangia; zoospores in the first discharge ovoid with flagella inserted at the anterior end or encysting at once, subsequently reniform with laterally inserted flagella.

        1   Zoosporangia filamentous, forming a single row of zoospores which encyst at the mouth at emergence; oogonia without pits, containing a single oospore; aquatic and terrestrial species   *Aphanomyces* (p. 46)

    B. Peronosporales: Mycelium producing variously shaped zoosporangia; zoosporangia sometimes deciduous and acting as conidia; zoospores released either directly or from a thin-walled vesicle, reniform, with laterally inserted flagella; oogonia mostly containing a single oospore.

    a. Pythiaceae: Sporangiophores usually not differentiated from the mycelium.

        1   Sporangia usually ovoid or obpyriform with a distinct apical differentiation for zoospore discharge; antheridia amphigynous (1) or paragynous (2); oospores not filling the oogonium (aplerotic)   *Phytophthora* (p. 648)
           Sporangia filamentous, irregularly inflated or globose to ovoid, releasing their contents into a spherical vesicle in which the zoospores develop; antheridia paragynous in various modifications; oospores plerotic or aplerotic   *Pythium* (p. 678)

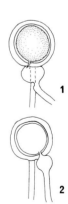

II. ZYGOMYCETES: Hyphae coenocytic; cell walls chitinous; asexual spores immobile, produced in many-spored sporangia, few- to 1-spored sporangioles, fragmenting merosporangia, or in clusters on sporocladia; sexual propagation through zygospores produced by fusion of hyphal gametangia.

    A. Mucorales: Hyphae forming indefinite coenocytic mycelia without regularly spaced septa; sporocarps absent; sporangiospores produced in many-spored sporangia, sporangioles, or merosporangia, which are not usually forcibly discharged. Mostly saprophytic, occasionally obligate mycoparasites or parasites on animals or plants.

1   Sporangioles or merosporangia produced synchronously on vesicles   **2**
     Sporangia or sporangioles not produced synchronously on vesicles   **3**

2(1)   Smooth-walled merosporangia fragmenting into a row of sporangiospores (3); saprophytic: Syncephalastraceae   *Syncephalastrum* (p. 750)
     Sporangioles 1-spored, ± ornamented (4); saprophytic: Cunninghamellaceae   *Cunninghamella* (p. 236)

3(1)   Sporangiophores producing often large, columellate, multispored sporangia with deliquescent walls, and always few- or 1-spored sporangioles with a persistent and separable wall on thin lateral branches: Thamnidiaceae
     All branchlets dichotomously dividing, straight, each bearing a sporangiole; sterile spines absent   *Thamnidium* (p. 762)
     Sporangioles, if present, not in dense clusters and with evanescent or inseparable walls   **4**

4(3)   Sporangia multispored and columellate; smell never garlic-like; zygospores pigmented, ornamented or smooth-walled, naked or surrounded by distinct appendages: Mucoraceae   **5**
     Sporangia many-, few- or 1-spored, lacking a columella; smell often garlic-like; zygospores hyaline, smooth-walled or indented, sometimes invested by a hyphal coat: Mortierellaceae   *Mortierella* (p. 431)

5(4)   Apophysis absent   **6**
     Apophysis (8, 9) below the sporangium present   **9**

6(5)   Stolons and rhizoids absent   **7**
     Stolons and rhizoids present   **8**

7(6)   Homothallic; zygospores with one suspensor strongly inflated (5), often borne at the base of a sporangiophore   *Zygorrhynchus* (p. 855)
     Mostly heterothallic and suspensors ± equal   *Mucor* (p. 461)

8(6)   Colonies usually more than 5 mm deep, pale; sporangiophores verticillately branched; not thermophilic   *Actinomucor* (p. 32)
     Colonies less than 5 mm deep, dark grey due to the sporangia; sporangiophores not regularly verticillate; thermophilic   *Rhizomucor* (p. 700)

9(5)   Sporangiophores mostly arising in groups from rhizoids (6), pigmented   *Rhizopus* (p. 703)
     Sporangiophores mostly arising from the stolons (7), hyaline, at least in the lower part   **10**

10(9)   Apophysis sharply delimited, hemispherical (8)   *Gongronella* (p. 381)
     Apophysis merging into the sporangiophore, funnel-shaped (9)   *Absidia* (p. 7)

B. Entomophthorales, Entomophthoraceae: Hyphal segments of limited growth, soon fragmenting, budding, or transformed into sporangia which are reduced to a single conidium; conidia forcibly discharged; mostly parasitic on insects or other invertebrates, sometimes saprophytic.

1   Primary conidia pyriform to spherical, multinucleate; zygospores formed within one of the gametangia; growing readily on ordinary media   *Conidiobolus* (p. 225)

III. ASCOMYCETES: Hyphae regularly septate, cells mostly uninucleate; walls containing chitin in varying amounts. Sexual propagation through ascospores produced in asci; fruiting-bodies (ascomata) mostly present. Asexual propagation often through conidia or hyphal fragments (cf. also V. Deuteromycetes).

1   Ascomata absent, true mycelium present; asci produced after the fusion of vegetative cells (10), forming irregular numbers of ascospores: Dipodascaceae
      Asci globose or elongate; ascospores ellipsoidal to subglobose, ornamented or surrounded by a gelatinous sheath; arthroconidia (30) (*Geotrichum*) present   (*Dipodascus*, cf. *Geotrichum*, p. 348)
      Ascomata present   **2**

2(1)   Ascomata non-ostiolate (cleistothecia)   **3**
      Ascomata ostiolate or discoid (perithecia or apothecia)   **28**

ASCOMATA NON-OSTIOLATE

3(2)   Ascoma wall mostly a loose network of hyphae (except *Aphanoascus*); anamorphs with arthroconidia (30, 32, 33) or solitary thalloconidia (31); racquet hyphae (11) generally present: Gymnoascaceae   **4**
      Ascoma wall continuous; anamorphs with phialoconidia, blastoconidia or absent; racquet hyphae absent   **12**

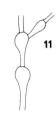

4(3)   Ascoma wall closed, consisting of brown polygonal cells; anamorph *Chrysosporium*   *Aphanoascus* (p. 44)
      Ascoma wall a loose network or almost absent   **5**

5(4)   Ascospores spherical, ornamented; peridal hyphae brown, thick-walled, often with long appendages   *Auxarthron* (p. 135)
      Ascospores lenticular or ellipsoidal, smooth-walled   **6**

6(5)   Peridial hyphae similar to the vegetative hyphae, scanty; ascospores lenticular or oblate, reddish or brownish, with an equatorial rim or furrow   *Arachniotus* (p. 54)
      Peridial hyphae ± differentiated from the vegetative hyphae; ascospores ellipsoidal, globose or oblate but without equatorial rim   **7**

7(6)   Peridial hyphae ± pigmented, with short, thin- or thick-walled appendages **8**
      Peridial hyphae with long, differentiated appendages   **9**

8(7)   Ascospores ellipsoidal to fusiform; ascoma initials consisting of coiled ascogonia without antheridia; peridial hyphae forming a network beset with short, blunt, thin-walled appendages *Pseudogymnoascus* (p. 676)
      Ascospores oblate; ascoma initials consisting of coiled ascogonia and swollen antheridia; peridial hyphae forming a network beset with thick-walled, hooked or spine-like appendages *Gymnoascus* (p. 385)

9(7)   Ascomata orange-brown; appendages thick-walled, comb-like (12)
                  Ctenomyces (p. 234)
      Ascomata white to cream; appendages thin-walled, never comb-like **10**

10(9)   Peridial hyphae sinuately branched, unconstricted, anastomosing, giving rise to several tight, cylindrical hyphal coils; anamorph *Histoplasma* (40)   *Emmonsiella* (p. 275)
      Peridial hyphae consisting of swollen cells, sometimes with straight or less tightly spiralled appendages   **11**

11(10) Peridial hyphae composed of dumb-bell-shaped cells with deep central
        constrictions (13); anamorph *Trichophyton*   *Arthroderma* (p. 65)
        Peridial hyphae consisting of swollen cells with one to several moderate
        constrictions (14), sometimes ending with coiled or straight appendages;
        anamorph *Microsporum*   *Nannizzia* (p. 488)

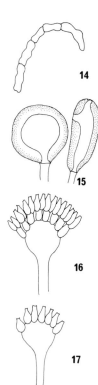

14

15

12(3)   Asci minute, irregularly scattered in the ascoma; anamorphs (if present)
        with catenulate phialoconidia: Trichocomaceae (Eurotiaceae)   **13**
        Asci of different sizes, irregularly scattered or fasciculate; anamorphs with
        slimy phialoconidia, blastoconidia or absent   **19**

13(12) Anamorph *Aspergillus* (16, 17)   **14**
        Anamorph *Penicillium* (72, 73), *Paecilomyces*, *Polypaecilum*, or absent **17**

14(13) Hülle cells (15) present; conidiophores mostly with both metulae and
        phialides (biseriate) (16)   **15**
        Hülle cells absent; conidiophores with phialides only (uniseriate) (17) **16**

16

17

15(14) Ascomata surrounded by several layers of yellow hyphae; ascospores ±
        hyaline, subglobose, smooth, with an inconspicuous equatorial groove;
        anamorph *Aspergillus flavipes* group   *Fennellia* (p. 303)
        Ascomata surrounded by hülle cells only; ascospores mostly orange-red to
        vinaceous, oblate, usually with equatorial crests; anamorph *Aspergillus
        nidulans* and *A. flavipes* groups   *Emericella* (p. 264)

16(14) Peridium one cell thick; conidiophores usually conspicuously roughened;
        conidial heads radiating (*Aspergillus glaucus* group); osmophilic
                                                            Eurotium (p. 289)
        Peridium several cells thick; conidiophores ± smooth-walled; conidial
        heads columnar (*Aspergillus fumigatus* group); not osmophilic
                                                            Neosartorya (p. 511)

17(13) Ascoma wall ± thin, consisting of a dense or loose hyphal network, ±
        yellow, soft; asci catenulate; phialides with an aculeate tip, mostly in
        symmetrical, one-stage-branched penicilli   *Talaromyces* (p. 752)
        Ascoma wall consisting of several layers of pseudoparenchymatous, ±
        thick-walled cells   **18**

18(17) Ascomata thick-walled, separate, sclerotium-like, with an ascigerous cav-
        ity, usually hyaline; asci borne singly or catenulate; phialides flask-
        shaped, borne in monoverticillate or divaricate penicilli; mesophilic
                                                            Eupenicillium (p. 283)
        Ascomata moderately thick-walled, often confluent, orange to brown; asci
        borne singly; anamorph *Paecilomyces*, *Polypaecilum*, or absent; ther-
        mophilic   *Thermoascus* (p. 776)

18

19(12) Ascomata stalked, enclosed in a membrane which is surrounded by some
        appressed hyphae (18); asci 8-spored, evanescent; conidia catenulate
        with a truncate base, produced in basipetal succession with concomitant
        shortening of the conidiogenous cell (*Basipetospora*)
                                                            Monascus (p. 425)
        Ascomata not stalked; asci not enclosed in a membrane; anamorphs
        different   **20**

20(19) Ascomata hyaline, containing a limited number of many-spored asci;
        ascospores hyaline   cf. *Thelebolus* (p. 772)
        Ascomata containing ± numerous asci which are mostly 8-spored   **21**

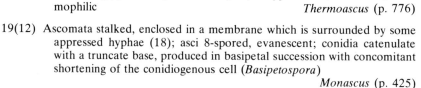

21(20) Ascomata surrounded by a dark amorphous mass, globose or obcampanulate; ascospores hyaline, later becoming brownish; anamorph *Cladosporium*-like   *Amorphotheca* (p. 40)

Ascomata wall pale or dark but not surrounded by an amorphous mass; ascospores brown   **22**

22(21) Asci bitunicate (19), ascospores 2-celled, brown, with inconspicuous apical germ-pores   cf. *Neotestudina* (p. 513)

Asci unitunicate; ascospores 1-celled   **23**

23(22) Ascomata with often long brown hairs; asci clavate, deliquescent; ascospores limoniform with one inconspicuous germ pore
                                            cf. *Chaetomidium* (p. 163)

Ascomata glabrous, brown   **24**

24(23) Ascospores ellipsoidal, provided with 3–6 conspicuous, pale to brown, often irregularly shaped, longitudinal wings (20); anamorph *Acremonium*   *Emericellopsis* (p. 272)

Ascospores smooth-walled   **25**

25(24) Ascomata with a thin wall of angular, flattened cells; ascospores globose or ellipsoidal, without germ pores   *Pseudeurotium* (p. 671)

Ascoma wall consisting of several cell layers; ascospores ellipsoidal or fusiform, with germ pores   **26**

26(25) Ascospores with two conspicuous germ pores; anamorph *Sepedonium*-like or *Myceliophthora* (62)   *Corynascus* (p. 232)

Ascospores with one germ pore   **27**

27(26) Ascospores with a conspicuous germ pore; anamorph absent or *Myceliophthora*; some species thermophilic   *Thielavia* (p. 780)

Ascospores with an inconspicuous germ pore; anamorph *Scedosporium* or synnematous; not thermophilic   *Petriellidium* (p. 614)

28(2) Ascomata with flat hymenium (apothecia)   **29**
Ascomata closed (perithecia etc.)   **33**

ASCOMATA APOTHECIA

29(28) Ascus tip provided with a narrow, amyloid pore (21); ascomata mostly supported on a long slender stalk; sclerotia commonly present: Helotiales, Sclerotiniaceae   **30**

Ascus tip opening by an operculum (22) or a slit (23): Pezizales   **31**

30(29) *Botrytis*-type conidia present; sclerotial medulla compact, gelatinized
                                (*Botryotinia*, cf. *Botrytis*, p. 149)

Botrytis-type conidia absent; sclerotial medulla consisting of thick-walled hyphae with some intercellular spaces   *Sclerotinia* (p. 712)

31(29) Asci few in number, ovoid to ellipsoidal, mostly many-spored, opening with a slit (23)   *Thelebolus* (p. 772)

Asci numerous, cylindrical, operculate (22)   **32**

32(31) Ascomata not hairy; asci turning blue in iodine in their upper part; synchronously produced blastoconidia often present   *Peziza* (p. 617)

Ascomata surrounded by pale brown, septate, rigid and acute setae; asci not turning blue in iodine; blastoconidia absent, but solitary, large conidia produced in the substratum on curved stalks
                                            Cheilymenia (p. 191)

ASCOMATA PERITHECIA

33(28) Asci unitunicate   **34**
        Asci bitunicate   **57**

34(33) Ascomata walls brown to black; asci cylindrical with a refractive apical ring
          or cylinder; ascospores brown; paraphyses absent: Sordariaceae   **35**
        Ascomata walls pale-coloured to brown or black, but not in the above
          combination; paraphyses present or absent; ascospores hyaline or
          brightly coloured   **37**

35(34) Ascospores unequally 2-celled, the upper larger cell dark brown and
          strongly ornamented   *Apiosordaria* (p. 50)
        Ascospores 1-celled   **36**

36(35) Ascospore wall smooth, usually surrounded by a gelatinous sheath
                                                                Sordaria (p. 734)
        Ascospore wall regularly pitted or reticulate   *Gelasinospora* (p. 346)

37(34) Ascomata walls mostly pale or in bright colours, fleshy; asci slender,
          clavate to cylindrical; ascospores often septate; paraphyses growing
          downwards in the ascomata   **38**
        Ascomata wall brown or black   **44**

38(37) Ascospores 1-celled, subglobose, ± colourless with an uneven hyaline coat;
          ascomata orange to red; anamorph *Acremonium*-like
                                                              Neocosmospora (p. 509)
        Ascospores septate   **39**

39(38) Ascospores 2-celled   **40**
        Ascospores more than 2-celled   **43**

40(39) Ascospores apiculate at both ends; anamorph *Sepedonium* (47),
          Mycogone, or *Cladobotryum*   *Hypomyces* (p. 398)
        Ascospores with rounded ends: Hypocreaceae   **41**

41(40) Ascomata mostly immersed in a stroma; part-spores falling apart at an
          early stage in the ascus (24); anamorph *Trichoderma* or *Gliocladium*
                                              (*Hypocrea*, cf. *Trichoderma*, p. 794)
        Ascomata free or aggregated on a stroma; part-spores not falling apart **42**

42(41) Ascomata brown, slender flask-shaped; anamorph *Fusarium*-like
                                                            Plectosphaerella (p. 660)
        Ascomata yellow-orange-red; anamorph *Acremonium, Verticillium, Glio-
          cladium, Fusarium, Cylindrocarpon, Volutella*, etc.   *Nectria* (p. 497)

43(39) Ascomata yellow-orange; anamorph *Fusarium* or *Cylindrocladium*
          (82)   (*Calonectria*, cf. *Cylindrocladium*, p. 249)
        Ascomata purple or bluish-black; anamorph *Fusarium* (83)
                                                              Gibberella (p. 352)

44(37) Asci without any apical apparatus, soon evanescent   **45**
        Asci with apical apparatus, persistent   **50**

45(44) Ascomata with conspicuous hairs or setae; asci clavate or cylindrical;
          ascospores mostly with one germ pore   **46**
        Ascomata ± glabrous; ascospores without germ pores   **48**

46(45) Ascomata non-ostiolate   *Chaetomidium* (p. 163)
        Ascomata ostiolate with protruding, often thread-like, ascospore masses **47**

24

47(46) Ascomata narrowly flask-shaped; setae fused around the ostiole, often forming a long tube, smooth-walled; pigmented chlamydospores regularly present *Farrowia* (p. 301)
Ascomata globose to ellipsoidal or lageniform; setae not fused into a tube, but spreading, usually ornamented; pigmented or hyaline chlamydospores sometimes produced *Chaetomium* (p. 165)

48(45) Ascomata globose with a short beak; anamorph *Scopulariopsis* or *Wardomyces* *Microascus* (p. 416)
Ascomata globose with a very long beak **49**

49(48) Anamorph with tubular phialide openings (74) (*Chalara*)
Ceratocystis (p. 161)
Anamorph with penicillate, pigmented conidiophores (*Verticicladiella, Graphium,* etc.) or simple hyaline conidiogenous cells with denticulate apex (57) (*Sporothrix*) (*Ophiostoma,* cf. *Sporothrix,* p. 737)

50(44) Apical apparatus of the asci mostly turning blue in iodine (amyloid); ascospores hyaline or brown, 1-celled or septate, mostly with a germ pore: Amphisphaeriaceae **51**
Apical apparatus of the asci not turning blue in iodine (not amyloid); ascospores without germ pores **54**

51(50) Ascospores 1-celled or unequally 2-celled **52**
Ascospores multicellular **53**

52(51) Ascospores 1-celled, at germination unequally 2-celled; anamorph *Nigrospora* (37, p. 515) *Khuskia* (p. 402)
Ascospores unequally 2-celled; anamorph *Arthrinium* (51, p. 55)
Apiospora (p. 52)

53(51) Ascospores hyaline; anamorph *Fusarium*-like *Monographella* (p. 428)
Ascospores brown, with hyaline end-cells; anamorph *Truncatella* (81) (*Pestalotia*) *Broomella* (p. 156)

25

54(50) Ascospores and phialoconidia often producing appressoria (25) on germination: Polystigmataceae
Ascomata immersed, singly or in groups, but not in a stroma; ascospores 1-celled, hyaline; anamorph *Colletotrichum* *Glomerella* (p. 378)
Ascospores and conidia not producing appressoria on germination; ascospores hyaline or brightly coloured **55**

55(54) Asci with a discrete refractive apical ring, often becoming detached in a slimy mass before ascospore discharge; Diaporthaceae
Ascomata thick-walled, with a cylindrical apical beak; ascospores filiform *Gaeumannomyces* (p. 342)
Asci without a refractive apical ring: Sphaeriaceae **56**

56(55) Colonies hyaline; conidia *Fusarium*-like, mostly 2-celled
Plectosphaerella (p. 660)
Colonies (olivaceous-)brown; conidiophores pigmented, *Chloridium*- (88), *Codinaea*-, or *Menispora*-like *Chaetosphaeria* (p. 184)

ASCI BITUNICATE

57(33) Ascomata superficial, globose, thick-walled, non-ostiolate, with irregularly scattered asci (26); ascospores 2-celled, brown, with inconspicuous germ pores: Zopfiaceae *Neotestudina* (p. 513)

26

Ascomata ± immersed in host tissue or stroma; asci fasciculate or parallel   **58**

58(57) Ascospores 4- or more-celled, constricted at the septa, and soon falling apart into part-spores; part-spores mostly with a germ slit: Sporormiaceae

Ascospores with transverse walls only; ascomata ostiolate or nonostiolate   *Preussia* (p. 666)

Ascospores 1-celled or septate, not falling apart within the ascus, without germ pores or germ slits   **59**

59(58) Ascomata immersed in stroma or host tissue; ascospores 1-celled, hyaline or brownish: Botryosphaeriaceae

Anamorphs *Lasiodiplodia, Botryodiplodia, Dothiorella*

Botryosphaeria (p. 143)

Ascospores more than 1-celled   **60**

60(59) Ascomata flattened, immersed in host tissue; ascospores 2-celled: Dothideaceae

Anamorphs *Cladosporium, Septoria*

(*Mycosphaerella*, cf. *Cladosporium*, p. 201)

Ascospores multicellular: Pleosporaceae   **61**

61(60) Ascospores muriform; anamorphs *Stemphylium, Alternaria, Dendryphion, Phoma*   *Pleospora* (p. 663)

Ascospores without longitudinal septa   **62**

62(61) Ascospores fusiform, ± pale brown, usually not coiled in the ascus; anamorphs *Phoma, Coniothyrium*   *Leptosphaeria* (p. 403)

Ascospores filiform, hyaline, somewhat coiled in the ascus; anamorphs *Bipolaris, Curvularia*   *Cochliobolus* (p. 213)

IV. BASIDIOMYCETES. Hyphae regularly septate, cells uninucleate or (mostly) binucleate, rarely plurinucleate; binucleate mycelia often forming clamp-connections at the septa. Sexual propagation through basidiospores produced on the sterigmata of basidia; fruiting-bodies (basidiomata) mostly present and, in those treated, resupinate or erect. Asexual propagation in some cases through conidia.

A. **Heterobasidiomycetidae:** Basidiospores germinating with secondary spores. Basidia often divided into as many cells as sterigmata (phragmobasidia).

Basidiomata resupinate; holobasidia differentiated into swollen metabasidia and long, slender sterigmata (27) which may be separated from the metabasidia by secondary septa: Tulasnellaceae

Basidia arising in loose cymes from tufts of ascending hyphae; sterigmata long, straight, divergent but not delimited by septa from the metabasidia; basidiospores hyaline, smooth-walled, not amyloid; hyphal cells often moniliform and forming irregular sclerotia (*Rhizoctonia*); hyphal cells multinucleate   *Thanatephorus* (p. 765)

27

B. **Homobasidiomycetidae:** Basidiospores germinating with hyphae; basidia not divided into several cells.

1   Basidiomata resupinate, effused, thin and mostly smooth; hyphal context of generative hyphae only, with or without clamp-connections: Corticiaceae

Basidiomata superficial, pellicular, white, often with a loose subiculum, clamp-connections usually present; basidia clavate, with 2–4 sterigmata; sclerotia present in some species   *Athelia* (p. 125)

Basidiomata erect, stalked, simple-clavate or branched; hyphal context of generative hyphae (rarely with skeletal hyphae), with or without clamp-connections; basidia clavate, with four sterigmata; spores hyaline, smooth-walled: Clavariaceae

28

Basidiomata minute, mostly simple, differentiated into clavula and stipe, mostly arising from a sclerotium (28)   *Typhula* (p. 820)

V. DEUTEROMYCETES. Hyphae regularly septate, cells mostly uninucleate. Sexual propagation unknown; asexual propagation through conidia which may be produced on single or aggregated conidiophores or within acervuli or pycnidia (conidiomata), or absent (sterile mycelia).

A. Sterile mycelia: Conidia absent, sclerotia or similar structures sometimes present.

1   Sclerotia or bulbils absent; colonies characteristically pigmented: the felted hyphal mat ochraceous-orange to brown, the reverse yellow-orange-red or greenish; chlamydospores absent   cf. *Epicoccum* (p. 279)

Sclerotia or bulbils present   **2**

29

2(1)   Bulbils or microsclerotia not exceeding 130 μm diam   **3**

Sclerotia exceeding 500 μm diam   **4**

3(2)   Bulbils ("papulaspores") developing from single hyphal branches (29), pale brown to reddish, consisting of a few large central and a larger number of cortical cells   *Papulaspora* (p. 537)

Bulbils (microsclerotia) developing from fasciculate hyphal branches, pale ochraceous, consisting of numerous polygonal cells

Minimedusa (p. 421)

4(2)   Sclerotia with a black rind and white medulla, irregular in shape
(*Sclerotium*, cf. *Sclerotinia*, p. 712, and *Botrytis*, p. 149)

Sclerotia brown   **5**

5(4)   Hyphal cells large, 100–250 × 7–12 μm, often moniliform and swollen to 30 μm diam; sclerotia very irregular in shape and size
(*Rhizoctonia*, cf. *Thanatephorus,* p. 765)

Hyphal cells not swollen, not exceeding 10 μm in width; sclerotia rounded   (*Sclerotium*, cf. *Athelia*, p. 125)

B. Hyphomycetes: Conidiophores single, sometimes aggregated into sporodochia (acervuli of the Melanconiales are not distinguishable from sporodochia in culture and so are treated here), or united into erect synnemata (coremia); not enclosed in pycnidia.

30

1   Conidia formed by fragmentation of hyphal branches (arthroconidia) (30) or by gradual transformation (solitary thalloconidia) (31)   **3**

Conidia blown out from a conidiogenous cell or a previously formed conidium   **2**

31

2(1)   Conidia formed singly at each conidiogenous opening   **12**

Conidia formed in basipetal succession at each conidiogenous opening **63**

ARTHROCONIDIA AND SOLITARY THALLOCONIDIA

3(1)   Solitary thalloconidia (31) present   **4**
         Arthroconidia formed in long or short chains (30, 32, 33)   **5**

4(3)   Conidia (macroconidia) smooth-walled, usually arising directly from the
         subtending hyphae   *Trichophyton* (p. 810)
         Conidia (macroconidia) finely roughened, usually arising from distinct
         stalk cells   *Microsporum* (p. 420)

5(3)   Arthroconidia ± rounded and broader than connecting empty portions
         (32), cohering in short chains   **6**
         Arthroconidia cylindrical, contiguous or connected by empty portions of
         equal width   **7**

6(5)   Conidiophore stipes pigmented   *Oidiodendron* (p. 517)
         Conidiophore stipes hyaline, often absent   *Chrysosporium* (p. 193)

7(5)   Arthroconidia ± pigmented   **8**
         Arthroconidia hyaline   **9**

8(7)   Arthroconidia dark brown, smooth-walled, formed by fragmentation of
         pluricellular chlamydospores; hyaline catenate phialoconidia also
         present   cf. *Chalara elegans* (p. 187)
         Arthroconidia pale brown, finely warted; formed by the division of
         successively formed meristematic portions into four cuboid cells
         (69)   *Wallemia* (p. 849)

9(7)   Arthroconidia generally formed in the aerial mycelium, separated by
         conspicuous empty hyphal portions (33) (*Malbranchea*)
         Spherules 15–80 μm diam, forming numerous endospores by cleavage
         (on glucose broth with partially coagulated egg albumin under semi-
         aerobic conditions)   *Coccidioides* (p. 211)
         Arthroconidia not separated by empty hyphal portions   **10**

10(9)   Arthroconidia chains ascendent; blastoconidia absent
                                                                  Geotrichum (p. 348)
         Arthroconidial chains generally prostrate   **11**

11(10)   Blastoconidia also present (34); endospores not formed within the
         arthroconidia   *Trichosporon* (p. 812)
         Blastoconidia absent or scanty; endospores formed within the arthro-
         conidia   (*Protendomycopsis*)

BLASTOCONIDIA AND POROCONIDIA

12(2)   Blastoconidia formed singly, in neither chains nor clusters   **13**
         Blastoconidia formed in acropetal chains or in clusters   **31**

13(12)   Conidia attached to the full width of the conidiogenous cell, not readily
         seceding   **14**
         Conidia mostly arising from a constriction in the conidiogenous cell, readily
         liberated   **22**

14(13)   Conidia pigmented, globose or elongate, borne on undifferentiated, mostly
         prostrate hyphae, in terminal, lateral or intercalary positions
                                                                  Humicola (p. 393)
         Conidia borne on stalk cells or conidiophores   **15**

15(14)   Conidia borne on simple stalks   **16**
         Conidia borne on branched conidiophores   **19**

16(15) Conidia hyaline, consisting of several thick-walled cells (35)
      Verticillium chlamydosporium and *V. catenulatum* (p. 834, 833)
  Conidia pigmented, 1- or few-celled   **17**

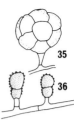

17(16) Conidia 2- or more-celled, smooth-walled or ornamented (36)
              Trichocladium (p. 790)
  Conidia 1-celled   **18**

18(17) Conidia borne on cylindrical stalk cells, brown, ± ornamented, without
  germ slits; often thermophilic   *Thermomyces* (p. 778)
  Conidia borne at the inflated tip of a stalk cell (37), black, smooth-walled,
  with an inconspicuous equatorial germ slit   *Nigrospora* (p. 515)

19(15) Conidiophores with a straight, pigmented stipe; conidia globose, pigmented, also produced on undifferentiated hyphae as in *Humicola*
          Staphylotrichum (p. 748)
  Conidiophores irregularly branched, hyaline   **20**

20(19) Conidiophores forming short, compact clusters (38); conidia with a longitudinal germ slit   *Wardomyces* (p. 851)
  Conidiophores sparsely branched, not forming clusters; conidia without a
  germ slit   **21**

21(20) Conidia hyaline or pale brown, thick-walled, minutely roughened, without
  a germ pore; straight erect brown setae sometimes present
           Botryotrichum (p. 146)
  Conidia dark brown, smooth-walled, with a conspicuous germ pore
           Gilmaniella (p. 366)

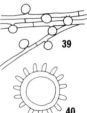

22(13) Conidia hyaline   **23**
  Conidia brown (or yellow)   **28**

23(22) Conidia 1-celled   **24**
  Conidia septate   **26**

24(23) Conidia minute (to 6 μm diam), globose, smooth-walled, arising
  pleurogenously from inconspicuous denticles on undifferentiated, creeping hyphae (39)   *Trichosporiella* (p. 811)
  Conidia larger, globose to ovoid, ± ornamented   **25**

25(24) Conidia (macroconidia) globose with conspicuous radiating protuberances
  (40); microconidia ovoid, smooth-walled
        (*Histoplasma*, cf. *Emmonsiella*, p. 275)
  Conidia ovoid, ± warted   *Chrysosporium* (p. 193)

26(23) Conidia fusiform with two or more transverse septa, the central cell
  markedly wider and longer than the others (41)
           Monacrosporium (p. 423)
  Conidia branched (aquatic Hyphomycetes)   **27**

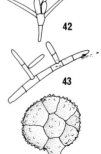

27(26) Conidia comprising 2–3 divergent tapering arms with a similarly tapering
  basal stipe and 2–3 central broader processes (42)
           Tetracladium (p. 760)
  Conidia comprising a cylindrical main axis from which 2–3 lateral branches
  arise rectangularly which may branch again but do not taper towards the
  ends (43)   *Varicosporium* (p. 826)

28(22) Conidiogenous cells and conidia aggregated in compact pustules, dark
  brown, globose, multicellular, warted (44)   *Epicoccum* (p. 279)
  Conidiogenous cells and conidia not aggregated in pustules   **29**

29(28) Conidia brown, 1- to many-septate, liberated by the fracture of the denticle, part often remaining attached to the base of the conidium (45)   *Pithomyces* (p. 657)
    Conidia pale brown, 1-celled, liberated at the basal septum, no part of the denticle remaining attached to the base   **30**

30(29) Conidia globose to ovoid, smooth-walled or ornamented, formed on repeatedly sympodially branched conidiophores (46); smaller hyaline phialoconidia produced on clustered phialides   *Harzia* (p. 387)
    Conidia formed on little-branched, long conidiophores, thick-walled, globose and conspicuously warted (or elongate and smooth); large phialoconidia produced on long conidiophores (47)
                      (*Sepedonium*, cf. *Hypomyces*, p. 398)

31(12) Conidia formed ± synchronously in dense clusters   **32**
    Conidia formed in succession in clusters or chains   **39**

32(31) Conidia hyaline to pale brown   **33**
    Conidia brown to dark brown   **36**

33(32) Conidia formed pleurogenously on creeping hyphae in slimy masses
                  Aureobasidium (p. 130)
    Conidia formed terminally on conidiophores   **34**

34(33) Short indistinct conidiophores arising from funiculose aerial hyphae; conidia subglobose with a broad basal scar; sclerotia at first light yellow, later becoming reddish brown, 1–2 mm diam, but often aggregated to larger clusters   *Phymatotrichopsis* (p. 644)
    Conidiophores distinct; conidia with inconspicuous basal scars   **35**

35(34) Conidiophores dichotomously branched, ending in long cylindrical conidiogenous cells (48); sclerotia absent
            (*Chromelosporium*, cf. *Peziza*, p. 617)
    Conidiophores in the upper part racemosely branched, ending in short, slightly swollen conidiogenous cells (49); sclerotia usually black, irregular in shape and size   *Botrytis* (p. 149)

36(32) Conidia verrucose, without germ slits (50); synnemata of *Doratomyces* mostly present   (*Echinobotryum*, cf. *Doratomyces*, p. 256)
    Conidia smooth-walled, with a germ slit   **37**

37(36) Conidia lenticular (fusiform, triangular, reniform or lunate), with an equatorial germ slit, produced on basauxically elongating conidiophores (51)   *Arthrinium* (p. 55)
    Conidia elongate with a longitudinal germ slit, produced pleurogenously on hyphae   **38**

38(37) Hyphae brown with darker septa; subglobose *Phialophora*-type conidia sometimes present   *Mammaria* (p. 407)
    Hyphae hyaline; ovoid *Scopulariopsis*-type conidia sometimes formed
              Wardomyces (p. 851)

39(31) Conidia formed on hyaline to pale brown conidiogenous cells, not leaving a pore after dehiscence   **40**
    Conidia formed on dark, thick-walled conidiogenous cells, leaving a pore after secession (poroconidia, tretic conidia)   **58**

40(39) Conidia formed in sympodial succession (52–61) but never in acropetal chains   **41**
    Conidia formed in long or short acropetal chains (62, 63)   **52**

41(40) Conidia formed some distance apart on a sympodially elongating, zig-zag-shaped rhachis (52); all parts hyaline   *Beauveria* (p. 136)
        Conidia formed in dense clusters; hyaline or pigmented   **42**

42(41) Conidia formed pleurogenously and terminally on short branches, lunate or fusiform; colonies pinkish (later becoming brown)
                                                          Microdochium (p. 418)
        Conidia formed terminally on distinct conidiogenous cells (cf. also **98**) **43**

43(42) Conidia borne on cylindrical denticles which break at maturity, a part remaining attached to the conidial base (53); conidia ± brown, septate
                                                        Scolecobasidium (p. 717)
        Conidia dehiscing at the basal septum, no part of the denticle remaining attached to the base   **44**

44(43) Conidiophores pigmented, conidia hyaline to subhyaline   **45**
        Conidiophores hyaline   **47**

45(44) Conidiophores verticillate, bearing stellate conidiiferous denticles at the tips of each branch (54)   *Pseudobotrytis* (p. 674)
        Conidiophores unbranched or with simple short branches   **46**

46(45) Conidiophores short, branched, little differentiated from the vegetative hyphae, bearing densely crowded conidiiferous denticles (55); conidia subglobose to ovoid; often associated with *Exophiala*-type conidia; colonies slow-growing, dark olivaceous-brown
                                        (*Rhinocladiella*, cf. *Exophiala*, p. 296)
        Conidiophores long, erect, brown, mostly unbranched, rarely verticillate, many-celled; conidia borne on scattered denticles (56), subglobose to fusiform; without any additional conidial type; colonies rather fast growing, pale brown, orange to olivaceous-green
                                                      Ramichloridium (p. 698)

47(44) Conidia 1-celled   **48**
        Conidia septate   **49**

48(47) Conidia ovoid to clavate (57)   *Sporothrix* (p. 737)
        Conidia lunate (58)   *Idriella* (p. 400)

49(47) Conidia once-branched, formed on short, repeatedly verticillate conidiophores (59)   *Tricellula* (p. 788)
        Conidia unbranched   **50**

50(49) Conidia formed on short, swollen conidiogenous cells (60)
                                                       Cephaliophora (p. 159)
        Conidia formed on long, slender conidiophores   **51**

51(50) Conidia obovate, mostly 2-celled (61)   *Arthrobotrys* (p. 57)
        Conidia fusiform with a rounded tip, 3- or more-celled, central cell longer and wider than the others (41)   *Monacrosporium* (p. 423)

52(40) Conidia mostly 1-celled   **53**
        Conidia regularly 1- to many-septate   **56**

53(52) Conidia formed on short swollen conidiogenous cells (62), sub-hyaline
                                       (*Myceliophthora*, cf. *Thielavia*, p. 780)
        Conidia formed from conidiogenous cells located on distinct conidiophores, mostly brown   **54**

54(53) Conidia formed in compact apical heads on long, brown conidiophores, in relatively short chains   *Periconia* (p. 612)

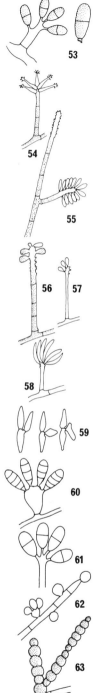

Conidia formed in repeatedly branching complexes   **55**

55(54) Conidia with truncate ends and prominent scars   *Cladosporium* (p. 201)
        Conidia with rounded ends and inconspicuous scars
                               (*Hormoconis*, cf. *Amorphotheca*, p. 40)

56(52) Conidia regularly 2-celled, (sub-)hyaline   *Hormiactis* (p. 391)
        Conidia mostly more-celled, pigmented   **57**

57(56) Conidia constricted at the septa, with paler end-cells, arising from subglo-
        bose lateral conidiogenous cells (63)   *Torula* (p. 784)
        Conidia ± fusiform, not constricted at the septa   *Heteroconium* (p. 389)

58(39) Conidia with transverse septa only   **59**
        Conidia with both transverse and longitudinal septa (muriform) **61**

59(58) Conidia cylindrical, many-celled, formed on sympodially proliferating
        conidiogenous cells and in acropetal chains (64); germination multi-
        lateral   *Dendryphion* (p. 254)
        Conidia not cylindrical, fewer-celled, not in chains; germination bipolar
        (65)   **60**

60(59) Conidia ellipsoidal or clavate, often curved, with larger central, and
        smaller, mostly paler, end-cells   *Curvularia* (p. 242)
        Conidia ellipsoidal to fusiform, straight, with little differentiation between
        the central and end-cells (65)   *Bipolaris* (p. 141)

61(58) Conidia formed singly at the swollen tip of the conidiogenous cell which
        may proliferate percurrently (66) (*Stemphylium,* cf. *Pleospora,* p. 663)
        Conidia formed singly or in acropetal chains by the conidiogenous cells
        which may proliferate sympodially   **62**

62(61) Conidia usually not in chains, base less rounded than the tip; conidiogen-
        ous cells with a strong tendency to geniculate sympodial proliferation
        (67)   *Ulocladium* (p. 824)
        Conidia formed singly or in acropetal chains, base broadly rounded, apex ±
        beaked (68); conidiogenous cells with little tendency to sympodial
        proliferation   *Alternaria* (p. 34)

CONIDIA FORMED IN BASIPETAL SUCCESSION (phialides, annellides, etc.)

63(2)   Conidiogenous cells phialides of constant length, releasing conidia through
        a conspicuous or inconspicuous collarette   **67**
        Conidiogenous cells not of constant length   **64**

64(63) Conidiogenous cell forming a succession of meristematic portions which
        subsequently divide like arthroconidia (69)   *Wallemia* (p. 849)
        Conidiogenous cell either elongating with annellations or progressively
        shortened   **65**

65(64) Conidiogenous cells annellides (annellophores) increasing in length; conidia
        brown or hyaline   **96**
        Conidiogenous cells progressively shortening; conidia (sub-)hyaline **66**

66(65) Conidiophores very long (to 2 mm), unbranched; conidia 2-celled, ellip-
        soidal to pyriform, thick-walled, forming imbricate columns (70)
                                                     Trichothecium (p. 814)
        Conidiophores short, irregularly branching; conidia 1-celled, globose, with
        broadly truncate base   (*Basipetospora,* cf. *Monascus,* p. 425)

67(63) Conidia dry, provided with connectives at both ends (71), in persistent
    chains (connected chains) **68**
    Conidia in slimy heads or dry chains, but then not provided with connec-
    tives at the tip (disconnected chains) **73**

68(67) Conidiophores unbranched **69**
    Conidiophores branched **70**

69(68) Conidiophores mostly consisting of a simple phialide, sometimes sympo-
    dially proliferating
        Sagenomella (p. 710), cf. also *Acremonium* (p. 16)
    Conidiophores consisting of a cylindrical stalk cell and a lageniform
    phialide *Torulomyces* (p. 786)

70(68) Conidiophores ending in a swollen vesicle with densely crowded phialides
    (17) or metulae and phialides (16) *Aspergillus* (p. 76)
    Phialides not crowded on a vesicle **71**

71(70) Phialides consisting of a ± cylindrical venter and a somewhat tapering tip,
    aggregated in ± compact penicilli which may be simple (72) or
    repeatedly branched (73) *Penicillium* (p. 540)
    Phialides flask-shaped with strongly tapering tip, aggregated in ± divergent
    clusters **72**

72(71) Brown hyphae and conidiophores present; phialides with a tendency to
    sympodial proliferation *Acrophialophora* (p. 30)
    Brown hyphae and conidiophores absent; phialides usually not sympodially
    proliferating *Paecilomyces* (p. 525)

73(67) Phialides with a long tubular collarette, forming long chains of ± cylindrical
    conidia (74) *Chalara* (p. 187)
    Phialides lacking a tubular collarette **74**

74(73) Conidiophores hyaline (sometimes with brown incrustations) **75**
    Conidiophores ± brown **91**

75(74) Conidia 1-celled; sporodochia absent **76**
    Conidia septate and/or sporodochia present **84**

76(75) Conidia green, forming compact dry columns *Metarrhizium* (p. 413)
    Conidia not green or not forming compact columns **77**

77(76) Conidiophores unbranched or basitonously (75) branched **78**
    Conidiophores mesotonously (76) to acrotonously (77) branched **79**

78(77) Phialide wall not thicker than that of the vegetative hyphae
    Acremonium (p. 16)
    Phialide wall thickened and refractive at least in the lower half
    Monocillium (p. 427)

79(77) Phialides with a ± strongly swollen venter and slender, often somewhat
    curved neck (78) **80**
    Phialides ± subulate or flask-shaped **81**

80(79) Colonies broadly spreading, sporulating in green or white pustules
    Trichoderma (p. 794)
    Colonies slow-growing, evenly sporulating, white *(Tolypocladium)*

81(79) Phialides at least partly in compacted penicilli; conidia pink or greenish,
    often cohering in loose columns *Gliocladium* (p. 368)
    Phialides always divergent; conidia hyaline to pink **82**

82(81) Conidia formed from both terminal phialides and subterminal cells with lateral openings (79), sometimes cohering in loose columns
Sesquicillium (p. 732)
Conidia formed only from terminal phialides **83**

83(82) Conidia in simple chains *Paecilomyces* (p. 525)
Conidia in imbricate chains (80) *Mariannaea* (p. 409)
Conidia in slimy heads *Verticillium* (p. 828)

84(75) All conidia 1-celled **85**
At least some conidia septate **88**

85(84) Conidia large (at least 12 × 3·5 μm), filled with granular plasma, cylindrical or falcate, forming appressoria on germination (25); brown setae often present *Colletotrichum* (p. 223)
Conidia smaller, contents not granular, not forming appressoria **86**

86(85) Sporodochia convex, with protruding hyaline (or pigmented) setae, without differentiated marginal hyphae *Volutella* (p. 846)
Sporodochia devoid of setae, or cupulate, or surrounded by differentiated marginal hyphae **87**

87(86) Sporodochia dark green, compacted, cupulate, surrounded by white marginal hyphae; hyaline setae sometimes present *Myrothecium* (p. 481)
Sporodochia pink or greenish, loosely defined, lacking setae
Gliocladium (p. 368)

88(84) Conidia fusiform, with two brown central and two hyaline end-cells; bearing filiform apical setulae (81) (*Truncatella*, cf. *Broomella*, p. 156)
Conidia hyaline throughout **89**

89(88) Conidiophores forming compact penicilli, mostly with a long sterile appendage (82); conidia regularly cylindrical, microconidia absent
Cylindrocladium (p. 249)
Conidiophores not forming compact penicilli with a sterile appendage; microconidia often present **90**

90(89) Conidia fusiform to falcate, mostly with a differentiated foot-cell (83)
Fusarium (p. 305)
Conidia ± cylindrical, straight or curved, without a differentiated foot-cell (84) *Cylindrocarpon* (p. 243)

91(74) Phialide openings pleurogenous, one each in intercalary hyphal cells, with a conspicuous collarette (85); fertile cells often aggregated into tufts
Cladorrhinum (p. 199)
Phialide openings terminal (or secondarily lateral after sympodial proliferation) **92**

92(91) Phialides in dense clusters at the slightly inflated tip of differentiated erect conidiophores (86) **93**
Phialides not in dense terminal clusters **94**

93(92) Conidia in slimy heads (86) *Stachybotrys* (p. 742)
Conidia in dry chains *Memnoniella* (p. 411)

94(92) Conidiophores simple or irregularly branched and forming a short, hyaline or slightly darkened stipe; conidia produced from a single conidiogenous locus within a ± conspicuous collarette (87) *Phialophora* (p. 620)
Conidiophores with long, brown stipes; phialides commonly producing conidia from several conidiogenous loci within the shallow collarette (88) **95**

95(94) Conidiophores unbranched   (*Chloridium*, cf. *Chaetosphaeria*, p. 84)
Conidiophore stipes giving rise to bent short lateral cells which form several phialides in an almost verticillate manner
Gonytrichum (p. 383)

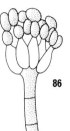

96(65) Conidia fusiform, septate, with 2 brown central and hyaline end-cells, bearing thread-like apical setulae (81)
(*Truncatella*, cf. *Broomella*, p. 156)
Conidia 1(–2)-celled   **97**

97(96) Annellations inconspicuous; conidia in irregular clusters   **98**
Annellations ± conspicuous; conidia in regular chains (89)   **99**

98(97) Colonies slow-growing, dark olivaceous-brown; conidiiferous openings on both intercalary and terminal conidiogenous cells and often also on germinating conidia   *Exophiala* (p. 296)
Colonies rather fast-growing, grey; conidiogenous cells discrete, lateral; dark synnemata with similar conidiogenesis sometimes present
(*Scedosporium*, cf. *Petriellidium*, p. 614)

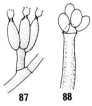

99(97) Conidiophores not aggregated in synnemata   **100**
Conidiophores aggregated in synnemata, sporulating over most of their length   **101**

100(99) Dark blastoconidia with a germ slit present   *Wardomyces* (p. 851)
Dark blastoconidia with a germ slit absent   *Scopulariopsis* (p. 724)

101(99) Sterile setae protruding between the conidiogenous cells
Trichurus (p. 817)
Sterile setae absent   *Doratomyces* (p. 256)

C. Coelomycetes: Conidiogenous cells enclosed in pycnidia or acervuli (conidiomata).

1   Conidiogenous cells aggregated in subcuticular or subepidermal acervuli: Melanconiales (keyed out under B. Hyphomycetes)
Conidiogenous cells enclosed in globose or flask-shaped pycnidia (90): Sphaeropsidales   **2**

2(1) Pycnidia aggregated in botryose clusters, thick-walled, dark brown; conidia dark brown at maturity, ellipsoidal, 1-septate, with longitudinal striations   (*Lasiodiplodia*, cf. *Botryosphaeria*, p. 143)
Pycnidia mostly separate   **3**

3(2) Conidia pigmented, 1(–2)-celled   *Coniothyrium* (p. 228)
Conidia hyaline   **4**

4(3) Conidia formed on elongate, branched conidiophores which bear short lateral and terminal phialides; conidia 1-celled; pycnidia usually covered with setae   (*Pyrenochaeta*)
Only shorter, unbranched conidiogenous cells present   **5**

5(4) Conidia fairly large (10 × 6 μm or more) or if smaller, subglobose, produced singly, enveloped in a gelatinous sheath and with a single apical appendage; usually biotrophic parasites   (*Phyllosticta*)
Conidia mostly smaller, elongate, without any distinctive gelatinous envelope and appendages   **6**

6(5)   Conidia normally 1-celled, but rarely secondarily 2-celled; saprophytes or
        weak parasites   *Phoma* (p. 630)
       Conidia normally 2-celled, septum formed by a secondary inner wall layer;
        plant parasites   (*Ascochyta*)

References

JOURNALS ARE ABBREVIATED ACCORDING TO THE WORLD LIST OF SCIENTIFIC PERIODICALS, FOURTH EDITION, 1963 AND THE BRITISH UNION CATALOGUE OF PERIODICALS (BUCOP). TRANSLATED TITLES OF PAPERS PUBLISHED IN LESS KNOWN LANGUAGES ARE GIVEN IN PARENTHESIS. ALTHOUGH THEY WERE FREQUENTLY USED, THE SECONDARY SOURCES OF TITLES HAD TO BE OMITTED.

1   AA, H.A.VAN DER & KESTEREN, H.A.VAN (1971) - THE IDENTITY OF PHYLLOSTICTA DESTRUCTIVA DESM. AND SIMILAR PHOMA-LIKE FUNGI DESCRIBED FROM MALVACEAE AND LYCIUM HALIMIFOLIUM. ACTA BOT.NEERL. 20, 552-563.

2   ABAWI, G.S. & GROGAN, R.G. (1975) - SOURCE OF PRIMARY INOCULUM AND EFFECTS OF TEMPERATURE AND MOISTURE ON INFECTION OF BEANS BY WHETZELINIA SCLEROTIORUM. PHYTOPATHOLOGY 65, 300-309.

3   ABAWI, G.S., POLACH, F.J. & MOLIN, W.T. (1975) - INFECTION OF BEAN BY ASCOSPORES OF WHETZELINIA SCLEROTIORUM. PHYTOPATHOLOGY 65, 673-678.

4   ABBAS, S.Q. & GHAFFAR, A. (1973) - INHIBITION OF CERTAIN FUNGI BY MEMNONIELLA ECHINATA. PAKIST.J.BOT. 5, 169.

5   ABDALLA, M.H. (1974) - MYCOFLORA OF GROUNDNUT KERNELS FROM THE SUDAN. TRANS.BR.MYCOL.SOC. 63, 353-359.

6   ABDEL-FATTAH, A.F., MABROUK, S.S. & EL-HAWWARY, N.M. (1972) - PRODUCTION AND SOME PROPERTIES OF RENNIN-LIKE MILK-CLOTTING ENZYME FROM PENICILLIUM CITRINUM. J.GEN.MICROBIOL. 70, 151-155.

7   ABDEL-FATTAH, A.F., MABROUK, S.S. & EL-HAWWARY, N.M. (1972) - DISTRIBUTION PATTERN OF MILK-CLOTTING AND PROTEOLYTIC ACTIVITIES IN SOME FUNGI. ACTA BIOL.ACAD.SCI.HUNG. 23, 55-60.

8   ABDEL-FATTAH, H.M., MOUBASHER, A.H. & ABDEL-HAFEZ, S.I. (1977) - STUDIES ON MYCOFLORA OF SALT MARSHES IN EGYPT. 1. SUGAR FUNGI. MYCOPATHOLOGIA 61, 19-26.

9   ABDUL-HAJJ, Y.J. (1972) - STEREOCHEMISTRY OF C-1,2-DEHYDROGENATION OF 5-BETA-PREGNANE-3,11,20-TRIONE BY SEPTOMYXA AFFINIS. J.BIOL.CHEM. 247, 686-691.

10 ABE, SH. (1956) - STUDIES ON THE CLASSIFICATION OF THE PENICILLIA. J.GEN. APPL.MICROBIOL., TOKYO 2, 1-344.

11 ABED, N.M. (1972) - THE SIDE CHAIN DEGRADATION OF PROGESTERONE BY ASPERGILLUS VERSICOLOR 79. PAKIST.J.BIOCHEM. 5, 5-7.

12 ABEYGUNAWARDENA, D.V.W. & WOOD, R.K.S. (1957) - FACTORS AFFECTING THE GERMINATION OF SCLEROTIA AND MYCELIAL GROWTH OF SCLEROTIUM ROLFSII SACC. TRANS.BR.MYCOL.SOC. 40, 221-231.

13 ABOTT, E.V. (1926) - A STUDY OF THE MICROBIAL ACTIVITIES IN SOME LOUISIANA SOILS - A PRELIMINARY SURVEY. BULL.LA AGRIC.EXP.STN 194, 1-25.

14 ABRAHAM, E.P. (1945) - THE EFFECT OF MYCOPHENOLIC ACID ON THE GROWTH OF
    STAPHYLOCOCCUS AUREUS IN BROTH. BIOCHEM.J. 39, 398-408.

15 ABRAMYAN, D.G. (1966) - (EFFECT OF THE CULTURE FILTRATES OF SOME RHIZO-
    SPHERE FUNGI ON THE GROWTH OF TOMATOES). BIOL.ZH.ARM. 19 (10), 43-49.

16 ABRAMYAN, G. (1968) - (DISTRIBUTION OF PENICILLIUM SPECIES IN THE RHIZO-
    SPHERE OF TOMATOES IN VARIOUS ECOLOGICAL AND CLIMATIC ZONES OF ARMENIA).
    UCHEN.ZAP.EREVANS.GOS.UNIV. 3, 137-143.

17 ACHA, I.G., AGUIRRE, M.J.R., URUBURU, F. & VILLANUEVA, J.R. (1966) - THE
    FINE STRUCTURE OF THE FUSARIUM CULMORUM CONIDIUM. TRANS.BR.MYCOL.SOC.
    49, 695-702.

18 ACHA, I.G., LEAL, J.A. & VILLANUEVA, J.R. (1965) - LYSIS OF UREDOSPORE GERM
    TUBES BY SPECIES OF VERTICILLIUM. PHYTOPATHOLOGY 55, 40-42.

19 ACHILLADELIS, B. & HANSON, J.R. (1969) - MINOR TERPENOIDS OF TRICHOTHECIUM
    ROSEUM. PHYTOCHEMISTRY 8, 765-767.

20 ACHILOVA, S. & KUCHAEVA, A.G. (1964) - (BIOLOGICAL METHODS OF CONTROLLING
    COTTON ROOT ROT CAUSED BY RHIZOCTONIA SOLANI). MIKROBIOLOGIYA 33, 900-
    903.

21 ADAIR, C.N. (1971) - INFLUENCE OF CONTROLLED-ATMOSPHERE STORAGE CONDITIONS
    ON CABBAGE POSTHARVEST DECAY. PL.DIS.REPTR 55, 864-868.

22 ADAMETZ, L. (1886) - UNTERSUCHUNGEN UEBER DIE NIEDEREN PILZE DER ACKERKRU-
    ME. DISS.UNIV.LEIPZIG.

23 ADAMS, P.B. (1967) - A BURIED MEMBRANE FILTER METHOD FOR STUDYING BEHAV-
    IOUR OF SOIL FUNGI. PHYTOPATHOLOGY 57, 602-603.

24 ADAMS, P.B. (1971) - EFFECT OF SOIL TEMPERATURE AND SOIL AMENDMENTS ON THIE-
    LAVIOPSIS ROOT ROT OF SESAME. PHYTOPATHOLOGY 61, 93-97.

25 ADAMS, P.B. (1971) - PYTHIUM APHANIDERMATUM OOSPORE GERMINATION AS AFFECT-
    ED BY TIME, TEMPERATURE, AND PH. PHYTOPATHOLOGY 61, 1149-1150.

26 ADAMS, P.B. LEWIS, J.A. & PAPAVIZAS, G.C. (1968) - SURVIVAL OF ROOT-INFECT-
    ING FUNGI IN SOIL. 9. MECHANISM OF CONTROL OF FUSARIUM ROOT ROT OF BEAN
    WITH SPENT COFFEE GROUNDS. PHYTOPATHOLOGY 58, 1603-1608.

27 ADAMS, P.B. & PAPAVIZAS, G.C. (1969) - SURVIVAL OF ROOT-INFECTING FUNGI IN
    SOIL. 10. SENSITIVITY OF PROPAGULES OF THIELAVIOPSIS BASICOLA TO SOIL
    FUNGISTASIS IN NATURAL AND ALFALFA-AMENDED SOIL. PHYTOPATHOLOGY 59,
    135-138.

28 ADAMS, P.M. & HANSON, J.R. (1972) - SESQUITERPENOID METABOLITES OF TRICHO-
    DERMA POLYSPORUM AND T. SPORULOSUM. PHYTOCHEMISTRY 11, 423.

29 ADAMS, P.R. & DEPLOEY, J.J. (1976) - AMYLASE PRODUCTION BY MUCOR MIEHEI AND
    M. PUSILLUS. MYCOLOGIA 68, 934-938.

30 ADENIJII, M.O. (1970) - INFLUENCE OF MOISTURE AND TEMPERATURE ON YAM DECAY
    ORGANISMS. PHYTOPATHOLOGY 60, 1698-1699.

31 ADOMAKO, D., KAYE, M.A.G. & LEWIS, D.H. (1971) - CARBOHYDRATE METABOLISM
    IN CHAETOMIUM GLOBOSUM. 1. CELLULAR CARBOHYDRATES OF RESTING MYCELIUM
    AND THEIR CHANGES FOLLOWING UTILIZATION OF HEXOSES. NEW PHYTOL. 70, 51-59.

32 ADOMAKO, D., KAYE, M.A.G. & LEWIS, D.H. (1972) - CARBOHYDRATE METABOLISM
    IN CHAETOMIUM GLOBOSUM. 3. THE METABOLISM OF MANNITOL. NEW PHYTOL. 71,
    467-476.

33 ADYE, J. & MATELES, R.I. (1964) - INCORPORATION OF LABELLED COMPOUNDS INTO
    AFLATOXIN. BIOCHIM.BIOPHYS.ACTA 86, 418-420.

34 AFANASYEVA, M.M. (1975) - FUNGISTATIC EFFECTS OF SOILS ON GROWTH AND SUR-
    VIVAL OF CONIDIA OF HELMINTHOSPORIUM SATIVUM PAMM., KING & BAKKE. MIKOL.
    FITOPAT. 9, 428-430.

35 AFIFI, A.F. (1975) - EFFECT OF VOLATILE SUBSTANCES FROM SPECIES OF LABIA-
    TAE ON RHIZOSPHERIC AND PHYLLOSPHERIC FUNGI OF PHASEOLUS VULGARIS. PHY-
    TOPATH.Z. 83, 296-302.

36 AGARWAL, C.P. (1975) - GILMANIELLA HUMICOLA - A SOIL INHABITING CELLULOLY-
    TIC HYPHOMYCETE. PROC.NATN.ACAD.SCI., INDIA, SECT.B, 41, 539-542.

37 AGARWAL, P.N., VERMA, G.M., VERMA, R.K. & RASTOGI, V.K. (1963) - ETHYLMA-
    LONATE AN INHIBITOR FOR FUNGAL CELLULOLYTIC ENZYMES. INDIAN J.EXPL BIOL.
    1, 162-163.

38 AGARWAL, P.N., VERMA, G.M., VERMA, R.K. & RASTOGI, V.K. (1963) - DECOMPO-
    SITION OF CELLULOSE BY THE FUNGUS CHAETOMIUM GLOBOSUM. 3. FACTORS AFFECT-
    ING ELABORATION OF CELLULOLYTIC ENZYMES. INDIAN J.EXPL BIOL. 1, 229-230.

39 AGARWAL, P.N., VERMA, G.M., VERMA, R.K. & SAHAL, D.D. (1963) - DECOMPOSI-
    TION OF CELLULOSE BY THE FUNGUS CHAETOMIUM GLOBOSUM. 1. STUDIES ON EN-
    ZYME ACTIVITY. INDIAN J.EXPL BIOL. 1, 46-50.

40 AGNIHOTHRUDU, V. (1957) - ASPERGILLI FROM THE SOILS OF SOUTH INDIA. NATUR-
    WISSENSCHAFTEN 44, 65.

41 AGNIHOTHRUDU, V. (1961) - RHIZOSPHERE MICROFLORA OF TEA (CAMELLIA SINEN-
    SIS) IN RELATION TO THE ROOT ROT CAUSED BY USTULINA ZONATA. SOIL SCI. 91,
    133-137.

42 AGNIHOTHRUDU, V. & BARUA, G.C.S. (1957) - A NEW RECORD OF A RARE FUNGUS
    FROM TEA RHIZOSPHERE. SCI.CULT. 22, 568-569.

43 AGNIHOTRI, V.P. (1963) - STUDIES ON ASPERGILLI. 10. UTILIZATION OF POLY-
    SACCHARIDES. CAN.J.MICROBIOL. 9, 703-707.

44 AGNIHOTRI, V.P. (1963) - ASPERGILLI FROM SOIL. NATURWISSENSCHAFTEN 15, 527.

45 AGNIHOTRI, V.P. (1964) - STUDIES ON ASPERGILLI. 14. EFFECT OF FOLIAR SPRAY
    OF UREA ON THE ASPERGILLI OF THE RHIZOSPHERE OF TRITICUM VULGARE L. PL.
    SOIL 20, 364-370.

46 AGNIHOTRI, V.P. (1964) - STUDIES ON ASPERGILLI. 16. EFFECT OF PH, TEMPERA-
    TURE, AND CARBON AND NITROGEN INTERACTION. MYCOPATH.MYCOL.APPL. 24,
    305-314.

47 AGNIHOTRI, V.P. (1969) - PRODUCTION AND GERMINATION OF APPRESSORIA IN PY-
    THIUM IRREGULARE. MYCOLOGIA 61, 967-980.

48 AGNIHOTRI, V.P. (1973) - EFFECT OF DEXON ON SOIL MICROFLORA AND THEIR AM-
    MONIFICATION AND NITRIFICATION ACTIVITIES. INDIAN J.EXPL BIOL. 11,
    213-216.

49   AGNIHOTRI, V.P. & MEHROTRA, B.S. (1961) – THE AMINO ACID COMPOSITION OF
       SOME ASCOSPORIC MEMBERS OF THE ASPERGILLUS NIDULANS GROUP. LLOYDIA 24,
       41-44.

50   AGNIHOTRI, V.P. & VAARTAJA, O. (1967) – ROOT EXUDATES FROM RED PINE SEED-
       LINGS AND THEIR EFFECTS ON PYTHIUM ULTIMUM. CAN.J.BOT. 45, 1031-1040.

51   AGNIHOTRI, V.P. & VAARTAJA, O. (1967) – EFFECTS OF AMENDMENTS, SOIL MOIS-
       TURE CONTENTS, AND TEMPERATURES ON GERMINATION OF PYTHIUM SPORANGIA UN-
       DER THE INFLUENCE OF SOIL MYCOSTASIS. PHYTOPATHOLOGY 57, 1116-1120.

52   AGRAWAL, G.W., KULHARA, D. & BISEN, P.S. (1974) – PRODUCTION OF CELLULOLY-
       TIC ENZYMES BY PLEOSPORA INFECTORIA (GROUP) AND NIGROSPORA SPHAERICA
       CAUSING POD SPOTS OF PEA (PISUM SATIVUM) AND BEAN (DOLICHOS LABLAB).
       BIOCHEM.PHYSIOL.PFL. 165, 401-405.

53   AGRAWAL, S.C. (1971) – THE CELLULOLYTIC CAPACITY OF SOME FOREST LITTER
       FUNGI. PHYTON, B.AIRES 28, 169-175.

54   AHARONI, Y. & STADELBACHER, G.J. (1973) – THE TOXICITY OF ALDEHYDE VAPOURS
       TO POSTHARVEST PATHOGENS OF FRUITS AND VEGETABLES. PHYTOPATHOLOGY 63,
       544-545.

55   AHEARN, D.G. & KAPLAN, W. (1969) – OCCURRENCE OF SPOROTRICHUM SCHENCKII ON
       A COLD-STORED MEAT PRODUCT. AM.J.EPID. 89, 116-124.

56   AHEARN, D.G. & MEYERS, S.P. (1972) – THE ROLE OF FUNGI IN THE DECOMPOSITION
       OF HYDROCARBONS IN THE MARINE ENVIRONMENT. IN: BIODETER.MATER., APPLIED
       SCIENCE PUBLISHERS, 12-18.

57   AHMED, M.A. & HUSAIN, S.SH. (1971) – STUDIES ON STORED GRAIN FUNGI. 3.
       FUNGI FROM CEREALS. PAKIST.J.SCIENT.IND.RES. 14, 237-240.

58   AHMED, S.A., SMITH, J.E. & ANDERSON, J.G. (1972) – MITOCHONDRIAL ACTIVITY
       DURING CITRIC ACID PRODUCTION BY ASPERGILLUS NIGER. TRANS.BR.MYCOL.SOC.
       59, 51-61.

59   AHMED, S.I. & CAIN, R.F. (1972) – REVISION OF THE GENERA SPORORMIA AND
       SPORORMIELLA. CAN.J.BOT. 50, 419-477.

60   AHMED, S.I. & MURTAZA, N. (1970) – REPORT ON ADDITIONS TO THE PENICILLIUM
       SPECIES FROM WEST PAKISTAN KARACHI. PAKIST.J.SCIENT.IND.RES. 12, 389-
       391.

61   AHMEDUNNISA, AHMED, S.I. & RIZIVI, N. (1968) – CONTRIBUTION TO SOIL FUNGI
       OF WEST PAKISTAN. 1. KARACHI. PAKIST.J.SCIENT.IND.RES. 11, 388-390.

62   AHRENS, CH. (1971) – UNTERSUCHUNGEN ZUR TAXONOMIE UND ZUR GEOGRAPHISCHEN
       VERBREITUNG DER GATTUNG PHYTHIUM PRINGSHEIM. DISS.UNIV.BONN.

63   AINSWORTH, G.C. & AUSTWICK, P.K.C. (1955) – A SURVEY OF ANIMAL MYCOSES IN
       BRITAIN – MYCOLOGICAL ASPECTS. TRANS.BR.MYCOL.SOC. 38, 369-386.

64   AINSWORTH, G.C. & REVELL, R.E. (1949) – THE INCIDENCE OF ASPERGILLOSIS IN
       CAPTIVE WILD BIRDS. J.COMP.PATH.THERAP. 59, 213-224.

65   AIST, J.R. & WILLIAMS, P.H. (1972) – ULTRASTRUCTURE AND TIME COURSE OF MI-
       TOSIS IN THE FUNGUS FUSARIUM OXYSPORUM. CELL BIOL. 55, 368-389.

66   AJELLO, L. (1952) – THE ISOLATION OF ALLESCHERIA BOYDII, AN ETIOLOGIC
       AGENT OF MYCETOMAS, FROM SOIL. AM.J.TROP.MED.HYG. 1, 227-238.

67 AJELLO, L. (1953) - THE DERMATOPHYTE, MICROSPORUM GYPSEUM, AS A SAPROPHYTE
    AND PARASITE. J.INVEST.DERM. 21, 157-171.

68 AJELLO, L. (1959) - A NEW MICROSPORUM AND ITS OCCURRENCE IN SOIL AND ON
    ANIMALS. MYCOLOGIA 51, 69-76.

69 AJELLO, L. (1960) - HISTOPLASMA CAPSULATUM SOIL STUDIES. MYKOSEN 3, 43-48.

70 AJELLO, L. (1961/62) - THE ASCIGEROUS STATE OF MICROSPORUM COOKEI. SABOU-
    RAUDIA 1, 173-177.

71 AJELLO, L. (1967) - COMPARATIVE ECOLOGY OF RESPIRATORY MYCOTIC DISEASE
    AGENTS. BACT.REV. 31, 6-24.

72 AJELLO, L. (1967) - COCCIDIOIDOMYCOSIS. UNIV.ARIZONA PRESS, TUCSON, 434 PP.

73 AJELLO, L. (1968) - A TAXONOMIC REVIEW OF THE DERMATOPHYTES AND RELATED
    SPECIES. SABOURAUDIA 6, 147-159.

74 AJELLO, L. (1971) - COCCIDIOIDOMYCOSIS AND HISTOPLASMOSIS, A REVIEW OF
    THEIR EPIDEMIOLOGY AND GEOGRAPHICAL DISTRIBUTION. MYCOPATH.MYCOL.APPL.
    45, 221-230.

75 AJELLO, L. & ALPERT, E.M. (1972) - SURVEY OF EASTER ISLAND SOILS FOR KE-
    RATINOPHILIC FUNGI. MYCOLOGIA 64, 161-166.

76 AJELLO, L., CHICK, E.W. & FURCOLOW, H.L. (1971) - HISTOPLASMOSIS. SPRING-
    FIELD, ILLINOIS, U.S.A.

77 AJELLO, L. & COCKSHOTT, W.P. (1962) - OCCURRENCE OF MICROSPORUM COOKEI IN
    AFRICA. MYCOLOGIA 54, 110-111.

78 AJELLO, L., LAZARUS, A.S., CORNEJO, A. & MOORE, J.C. (1961/62) - STUDIES
    ON THE OCCURRENCE OF HISTOPLASMA CAPSULATUM IN PERU. SABOURAUDIA 1, 83-
    86.

79 AJELLO, L., VARSAVSKY, E. & DELVINGT, W. (1965) - KERATINOPHILIC FUNGI FROM
    BELGIAN SOILS. TRANS.BR.MYCOL.SOC. 48, 417-421.

80 AJELLO, L., VARSAVSKY, E., SOTGIU, G., MAZZONI, A. & MANTOVANI, A. (1965) -
    SURVEY OF SOILS FOR HUMAN PATHOGENIC FUNGI FROM THE EMILIA-ROMAGNA REGION
    OF ITALY. 1. ISOLATION OF KERATINOPHILIC FUNGI. MYCOPATH.MYCOL.APPL. 26,
    65-71.

81 AKAI, S., OGURA, H. & SATO, T. (1960) - STUDIES ON PELLICULARIA FILAMENTO-
    SA. 1. ON THE RELATION BETWEEN PATHOGENICITY AND SOME CHARACTERS ON CUL-
    TURE MEDIA. ANN.PHYTOPATH.SOC.JAPAN 25, 125-130.

82 AKIN, D.E. & MICHAELS, G.E. (1972) - MICROSPORUM GYPSEUM MACROCONIDIAL DE-
    VELOPMENT REVEALED BY TRANSMISSION AND SCANNING ELECTRON MICROSCOPY.
    SABOURAUDIA 10, 52-55.

83 AKSENOVA, V.A. (1962) - ON THE TOXICITY OF THE POLYSACCHARIDE FRACTION OF
    THE TOXIN OF BOTRYTIS CINEREA. DOKL.AKAD.NAUK SSSR, SER.BIOL. 147, 496-
    498.

84 ALASOADURA, S.O. (1970) - CULTURE STUDIES ON BOTRYODIPLODIA THEOBROMAE PAT.
    MYCOPATH.MYCOL.APPL. 42, 153-160.

85 ALBITSKAYA, O.N. & SHAPOSHNIKOVA, N.A. (1960) - (THE EFFECT OF MOLDS ON THE
    CORROSION OF METALS). MIKROBIOLOGIYA 29, 725-730.

86   ALBRIGHT, J.L., AUST, S.D., BYERS, J.H., FRITZ, T.E., BRODIE, B.O., OLSON,
     R.E., LINK, R.P., SIMON, J., RHOADES, H.E. & BREWER, R.L. (1964) - MOL-
     DY CORN TOXICOSIS IN CATTLE. J.AM.VET.MED.ASSOC. 144, 1013-1019.

87   ALCONERO, R. (1969) - MYCORRHIZAL SYNTHESIS AND PATHOLOGY OF RHIZOCTONIA
     SOLANI IN VANILLA ORCHID ROOTS. PHYTOPATHOLOGY 59, 426-430.

88   AL-DOORY, Y. (1967) - THE OCCURRENCE OF KERATINOPHILIC FUNGI IN TEXAS SOIL.
     MYCOPATH.MYCOL.APPL. 33, 105-112.

89   AL-DOORY, Y. (1968) - THE ISOLATION OF KERATINOPHILIC FUNGI FROM AFRICAN
     SOILS. MYCOPATH.MYCOL.APPL. 36, 113-116.

90   AL-DOORY, Y. (1969) - FURTHER STUDIES OF THE KERATINOPHILIC FUNGI IN AFRI-
     CAN SOILS. MYCOPATH.MYCOL.APPL. 39, 287-392.

91   AL-DOORY, Y. & PAIRON, REV.R. (1972) - A BIBLIOGRAPHY OF COCCIDIOIDOMYCOSIS.
     MYCOPATH.MYCOL.APPL. 46, 113-188.

92   AL-DOORY, Y. TOLBA, M.K. & AL-ANI, H. (1959) - ON THE FUNGAL FLORA OF IRAQI
     SOILS. MYCOLOGIA 51, 429-439.

93   ALDRIDGE, D.C., ARMSTRONG, J.J., SPEAKE, R.N. & TURNER, W.B. (1967) - CY-
     TOCHALASINS, A NEW CLASS OF BIOLOGICALLY ACTIVE MOLD METABOLITES. CHEM.
     COMMUN., 1967, 26-27.

94   ALDRIDGE, D.C., BORROW, A., FOSTER, R.G., LARGE, M.S., SPENCER, H. & TURNER,
     W.B. (1972) - METABOLITES OF NECTRIA COCCINEA. J.CHEM.SOC.PERKIN TRANS.
     I, 1972 (17), 2136-2141.

95   AL HAFFAR, S. (1967) - RECHERCHE DE L'EQUILIBRE CATIONIQUE LE PLUS FAVORA-
     BLE A LA CROISSANCE DE PENICILLIUM CHRYSOGENUM. ANNLS PHYSIOL.VEG., BRUX.
     12, 57-67.

96   AL-HASSAN, K.K. & FERGUS, C.L. (1968) - THE INFLUENCE OF OILS AND STEROLS
     ON SEXUAL REPRODUCTION OF SPECIES OF PYTHIUM. MYCOLOGIA 60, 1243-1246.

97   ALDWINCKLE, H.S., POLACH, F.J., MOLIN, W.T. & PEARSON, R.C. (1975) - PATH-
     OGENICITY OF PHYTOPHTHORA CACTORUM ISOLATES FROM NEW YORK APPLE TREES
     AND OTHER SOURCES. PHYTOPATHOLOGY 65, 989-994.

98   ALFIERI, S.A., SEYMOUR, C.P. & SOBERS, E.K. (1970) - BROWN LEAF NECROSIS
     OF MAHONIA BEALEI CAUSED BY CYLINDROCLADIUM ELLIPTICUM SP.NOV. PHYTO-
     PATHOLOGY 60, 1212-1215.

99   ALI, B.S., HEITEFUSS, R. & FUCHS, W.H. (1965) - DIE PRODUKTION VON CHITI-
     NASE DURCH ENTOMOPHTHORA CORONATA. Z.PFLKRANKH.PFLSCHUTZ 72, 201-207.

100 ALI, M.I., BATANOUNY, K.H. & SALAMA, A.M. (1975) - STUDIES ON THE FUNGAL
     FLORA OF EGYPTIAN SOILS. 2. DIFFERENT HABITATS IN THE WADI HOF. PEDO-
     BIOLOGIA 15, 13-19.

101 ALI, M.M. & ISLAM, M.A. (1965) - PECTIC ENZYME OF PENICILLIUM FREQUENTANS
     INVOLVED IN THE RETTING OF JUTE. PAKIST.J.SCIENT.IND.RES. 8, 47-51.

102 ALICBUSAN, R.V., ICHITANI, T. & TAKAHASHI, M. (1965) - ECOLOGIC AND TAXO-
     NOMIC STUDIES ON PYTHIUM AS PATHOGENIC SOIL FUNGI. 3. POPULATION OF PY-
     THIUM ULTIMUM AND OTHER MICRO-ORGANISMS IN THE RHIZOSPHERE. BULL.UNIV.
     OSAKA PREFECT., SER.B, 16, 59-64.

103 ALILOU, M. & ASGARI, M. (1973) - RECHERCHE SUR L'ISOLEMENT DES DERMATO-
     PHYTES DU SOL EN IRAN. NOTE PRELIMINAIRE. BULL.SOC.PATH.EXOT. 66, 74-77.

104 ALLAM, M.E. & YUSEF, H.M. (1974) - BIOTIN DEFICIENCY IN NIGROSPORA ORYZAE.
    MYCOPATH.MYCOL.APPL. 52, 65-74.

105 ALLAWAY, A.F. & JENNINGS, D.H. (1971) - THE EFFECT OF CATIONS ON GLUCOSE
    UTILIZATION BY, AND ON THE GROWTH OF, THE FUNGUS DENDRYPHIELLA SALINA.
    NEW PHYTOL. 70, 511-518.

106 ALLEN, CH.M. (1972) - BIOSYNTHESIS OF ECHINULIN. ISOPRENYLATION OF CYCLO-
    L-ALANYL-L-TRYPTOPHANYL. BIOCHEMISTRY 11, 2154-2160.

107 ALLEN, CH.M.JR. (1972) - ISOPRENE-CONTAINING METABOLITES OF ASPERGILLUS
    AMSTELODAMI. CAN.J.MICROBIOL. 18, 1275-1282.

108 ALLEN, J. & STROBEL, G.A. (1966) - THE ASSIMILATION OF H(14) CN BY A VARIE-
    TY OF FUNGI. CAN.J.MICROBIOL. 12, 414-416.

109 ALLEN, M.C. & HAENSELER, C.M. (1935) - ANTAGONISTIC ACTION OF TRICHODERMA
    ON RHIZOCTONIA AND OTHER SOIL FUNGI. PHYTOPATHOLOGY 25, 244-252.

110 ALLEN, R.N. & HARVEY, J.D. (1974) - NEGATIVE CHEMOTAXIS OF ZOOSPORES OF PHY-
    TOPHTHORA CINNAMOMI. J.GEN.MICROBIOL. 84, 28-38.

111 ALLEN, R.N. & NEWHOOK, F.J. (1973) - CHEMOTAXIS OF ZOOSPORES OF PHYTOPHTHO-
    RA CINNAMOMI TO ETHANOL IN CAPILLARIES OF SOIL PORE DIMENSIONS. TRANS.
    BR.MYCOL.SOC. 61, 287-302.

112 ALLEN, R.N. & NEWHOOK, F.J. (1974) - SUPPRESSION BY ETHANOL OF SPONTANEOUS
    TURNING ACTIVITY IN ZOOSPORES OF PHYTOPHTHORA CINNAMOMI. TRANS.BR.MYCOL.
    SOC. 63, 383-385.

113 ALLINGTON, W.B. (1936) - SCLEROTIAL FORMATION IN RHIZOCTONIA SOLANI AS AF-
    FECTED BY NUTRITIONAL AND OTHER FACTORS. PHYTOPATHOLOGY 26, 831-844.

114 ALMEIDA, F.DE (1939) - ASPERGILLUS DO GRUPO OCHRACEUS ISOLADO DE ESCARRO.
    ANAIS FAC.MED.UNIV.S.PAULO 15, 141-149.

115 ALPERDEN, I., MINTZLAFF, H.-J., TAUCHMANN, F. & LEISTNER, L. (1973) - UN-
    TERSUCHUNGEN UEBER DIE BILDUNG DES MYKOTOXINS PATULIN IN ROHWURST.
    FLEISCHWIRTSCHAFT 53, 566-568.

116 ALSBERG, C.L. & BLACK, O.F. (1913) - CONTRIBUTIONS TO THE STUDY OF MAIZE
    DETERIORATION. BULL.U.S.DEP.AGRIC., BUR.PL.IND. 270, 48 PP.

117 ALTERAS, I. (1971) - ON THE LONG-TERM SURVIVAL OF KERATINOPHILIC FUNGI IN
    NONSTERILE SOIL. MYCOPATH.MYCOL.APPL. 44, 177-181.

118 ALTERAS, I. & EVOLCEANU, R. (1969) - A TEN YEARS SURVEY OF ROMANIAN SOIL
    SCREENING FOR KERATINOPHILIC FUNGI. MYCOPATH.MYCOL.APPL. 38, 151-159.

119 ALTERAS, I., NESTEROV, V. & CIOLOFAN, I. (1966) - THE OCCURRENCE OF DERMA-
    TOPHYTES IN WILD ANIMALS FROM RUMANIA. SABOURAUDIA 4, 215-217.

120 ALUKO, M.O. & HERING, T.F. (1970) - THE MECHANISMS ASSOCIATED WITH THE AN-
    TAGONISTIC RELATIONSHIP BETWEEN CORTICIUM SOLANI AND GLIOCLADIUM VIRENS.
    TRANS.BR.MYCOL.SOC. 55, 173-179.

121 ALVAREZ-GARCIA, L.A. & CORTES-MONLLOR, A. (1971) - CURRUTACA - A PYTHIUM
    SOFT ROT OF XANTHOSOMA AND COLOCASIA SPP. IN PUERTO RICO. J.AGRIC.UNIV.
    P.RICO 55, 78-84.

122 AMBRUS, G., SZARKA, E., BARTA, I., HORVATH, C., RADIOS, L. & KAJTAR, M.
    (1975) - MICROBIOLOGICAL 1-ALPHA-HYDROXYLATION OF NORETHISTERONE. STER-
    OIDS 24, 99-106.

123 AMEMURA, A. & TERUI, G. (1965) - STUDIES ON FUNGAL CELLULASES. 1. DEGRADA-
     TION OF WOOD PULP BY PENICILLIUM VARIABILE CELLULASE. J.FERMENT.TECHNOL.,
     OSAKA 43, 275-280.

124 AMES, L.M. (1963) - A MONOGRAPH OF THE CHAETOMIACEAE. U.S.ARMY RES.DEVEL.,
     SER.2, REPRINT CRAMER, LEHRE (1968).

125 AMMER, U. & LIESE, W. (1966) - UNTERSUCHUNGEN UEBER DAS ABBAUVERMOEGEN
     HOLZZERSTOERENDER PILZE. IN: HOLZ UND ORGANISMEN; BECKER, G. & LIESE, W.
     (ED.), BEIH. MATER. ORG. 1, 291-299.

126 AMMON, H.U. (1963) - UEBER EINIGE ARTEN AUS DEN GATTUNGEN PYRENOPHORA FRIES
     UND COCHLIOBOLUS DRECHSLER MIT HELMINTHOSPORIUM ALS NEBENFRUCHTFORM. PHY-
     TOPATH.Z. 47, 244-300.

127 ANDERSON, A.B., MCCRINDLE, R. & TURNBULL, J.K. (1973) - MICROBIOLOGICAL
     TRANSFORMATIONS OF 17-NORKAURAN-16-ONE AND 16-NORPHYLLOCLADAN-16-ONE BY
     ASPERGILLUS NIGER. CHEM.COMMUN., 1973 (4), 143-144.

128 ANDERSON, E.J. (1951) - A SIMPLE METHOD FOR DETECTING THE PRESENCE OF PHY-
     TOPHTHORA CINNAMOMI RANDS IN SOIL. PHYTOPATHOLOGY 41, 187-189.

129 ANDERSON, J.G. & SMITH, J.E. (1971) - THE PRODUCTION OF CONIDIOPHORES AND
     CONIDIA BY NEWLY GERMINATED CONIDIA OF ASPERGILLUS NIGER (MICROCYCLE CO-
     NIDIATION). J.GEN.MICROBIOL. 69, 185-197.

130 ANDERSON, J.G. & SMITH, J.E. (1972) - THE EFFECTS OF ELEVATED TEMPERATURES
     ON SPORE SWELLING AND GERMINATION IN ASPERGILLUS NIGER. CAN.J.MICROBIOL.
     18, 289-297.

131 ANDERSON, J.P.E. & DOMSCH, K.H. (1973) - QUANTIFICATION OF BACTERIAL AND
     FUNGAL CONTRIBUTIONS TO SOIL RESPIRATION. ARCH.MIKROBIOL. 93, 113-127.

132 ANDERSON, J.P.E. & DOMSCH, K.H. (1976) - MICROBIAL DEGRADATION OF THE THIOL-
     CARBAMATE HERBICIDE, DIALLATE, IN SOILS AND BY PURE CULTURES OF SOIL MI-
     CROORGANISMS. ARCHS ENVIRON.CONTAM.TOXICOL. 4, 1-7.

133 ANDERSON, J.P.E. & DOMSCH, K.H. (1978) - MINERALIZATION OF BACTERIA AND FUN-
     GI IN CHLOROFORM-FUMIGATED SOILS. SOIL BIOL.BIOCHEM. 10, 207-213.

134 ANDERSON, J.P.E. & LICHTENSTEIN, E.P. (1972) - EFFECTS OF VARIOUS SOIL FUN-
     GI AND INSECTICIDES ON THE CAPACITY OF MUCOR ALTERNANS TO DEGRADE DDT.
     CAN.J.MICROBIOL. 18, 553-560.

135 ANDERSON, K.L. & MARCUS, S. (1968) - SPORULATION CHARACTERISTICS OF HISTO-
     PLASMA CAPSULATUM. MYCOPATH.MYCOL.APPL. 36, 179-187.

136 ANDERSON, K.L., WHEAT, R.W., COUANT, N.F. & CLINGENPEEL, W. (1974) - COM-
     POSITION OF THE CELL WALL AND OTHER FRACTIONS OF THE AUTOLYZED YEAST
     FORM OF HISTOPLASMA CAPSULATUM. MYCOPATH.MYCOL.APPL. 54, 439-451.

137 ANDERSON, N., FRENCH, D.W. & TAYLOR, D.P. (1962) - CYLINDROCLADIUM ROOT
     ROT OF CONIFERS IN MINNESOTA. FOREST SCI. 8, 378-382.

138 ANDERSON, N.A., STRETTON, H.M., GROTH, J.V. & FLENTJE, N.T. (1972) - GENET-
     ICS OF HETEROKARYOSIS IN THANATEPHORUS CUCUMERIS. PHYTOPATHOLOGY 62,
     1057-1065.

139 ANDERSON, P.J. (1919) - ROSE CANKER AND ITS CONTROL. BULL.MASS.AGR.EXP.STN
     183, 11-46.

140 ANDO, T. (1968) - INTERRELATION BETWEEN KINDS OF FOREST ECOSYSTEM AND POPU-
     LATIONS OF LITTER AND SOIL MICROFUNGI. 1. LITTER AND SOIL MICROFUNGAL
     POPULATIONS IN SIX FOREST ECOSYSTEMS IN GIFU PREFECTURE. RES.BULL.FAC.
     AGRIC.GIFU UNIV. 26, 204-221.

141 ANDREEVA, N.A., USHAKOVA, V.I. & EGOROV, N.S. (1972) - STUDY OF PROTEOLYT-
     IC ENZYMES OF DIFFERENT STRAINS OF PENICILLIUM LILACINUM THOM IN CON-
     NECTION WITH THEIR FIBRINOLYTIC ACTIVITY. MICROBIOLOGY (TRANSL. MIKROBIO-
     LOGIYA) 41, 364-368.

142 ANDRIEU, S., BIGUET, J. & MASSAMBA, S. (1971) - ETUDE IMMUNOLOGIQUE COMPA-
     REE DE SPOROTHRIX SCHENCKII ET DES SOUCHES SAPROPHYTES VOISINES. SABOU-
     RAUDIA 9, 206-209.

143 ANEKWE, G.E. & DUBAL, B.C. (1971) - FATTY ACID COMPOSITION OF TRIGLYCERIDES
     AND PHOSPHOGLYCERIDES DURING GROWTH IN GLOMERELLA CINGULATA. LIPIDS 6,
     856-857.

144 ANEKWE, G.E. & LEE, L.L. (1973) - THE CHARACTERIZATION OF A CEREBROSIDE
     SULFATE FROM THE MYCELIA OF GLOMERELLA CINGULATA. PHYSIOLOGIA PL. 29,
     134-136.

145 ANGLESEA, D. & SWIFT, M.J. (1971) - THE KERATINOPHILIC ABILITY OF MONODIC-
     TYS LEVIS AND TRICHOPHYTON AJELLOI. TRANS.BR.MYCOL.SOC. 57, 333-337.

146 ANKE, H. & DIEKMANN, H. (1974) - STOFFWECHSELPRODUKTE VON MIKROORGANISMEN.
     125. BIOSYNTHESE VON SIDERAMINEN IN PILZEN. ARCH.MICROBIOL. 95, 213-
     225.

147 ANKE, T. & DIEKMANN, H. (1974) - STOFFWECHSELPRODUKTE VON MIKROORGANISMEN.
     126. EINBAU VON DELTA-N-HYDROXY-L-ORNITHIN UND DELTA-N-ACYL-DELTA-N-HY-
     DROXY-L-ORNITHINEN IN SIDERAMINE VON PILZEN. ARCH.MICROBIOL. 95, 227-
     236.

148 ANNE, J., EYSSEN, H. & SONER, P.DE (1974) - FORMATION AND REGENERATION OF
     PENICILLIUM CHRYSOGENUM PROTOPLASTS. ARCH.MICROBIOL. 98, 159-166.

149 ANSEL, M. & THIBAUT, M. (1973) - DISTINCTION DES ESPECES DE SIPHOMYCETES
     PAR L'EXAMEN EN MICROSCOPIE ELECTRONIQUE A BALAYAGE. ANNLS PARASIT.HUM.
     COMP. 48, 387-397.

150 ANSLOW, W.K., BREEN, J. & RAISTRICK, H. (1940) - STUDIES IN THE BIOCHEM-
     ISTRY OF MICRO-ORGANISMS. 64. EMODIC ACID AND CO-HYDROXY-EMODIN, META-
     BOLIC PRODUCTS OF A STRAIN OF PENICILLIUM CYCLOPIUM. BIOCHEM.J. 34, 159-
     168.

151 ANSLOW, W.K. & RAISTRICK, H. (1938) - STUDIES IN THE BIOCHEMISTRY OF MICRO-
     ORGANISMS. 57. FUMIGATIN AND SPINULOSIN, METABOLIC PRODUCTS RESPECTIVE-
     LY OF ASPERGILLUS FUMIGATUS AND PENILLIUM SPINULOSUM. BIOCHEM.J. 32, 687-
     696.

152 ANSLOW, W.K., RASTRICK, H. & SMITH, G. (1943) - ANTI-FUNGAL SUBSTANCES FROM
     MOULDS. 1. PATULIN, A METABOLIC PRODUCT OF PENICILLIUM PATULUM AND P. EX-
     PANSUM. J.SOC.CHEM.IND., LOND. 62, 236-238.

153 ANTOINE, H.M., NICOLLE, R., EPARDEAU, B. & VOIGT, J.J. (1973) - DIAGNOSTIC
     AU LABORATOIRE D'UNE MYCOSE RARE A ENTOMOPHTHORA CORONATA. LYON MED. 230,
     785-788.

154 AOKI, H., SASSA, T. & TAMURA, T. (1963) - PHYTOTOXIC METABOLITES OF RHIZOC-
     TONIA SOLANI. NATURE, LOND. 200, 575.

155 AOKI, J. (1971) - BEAUVERIA BASSIANA ISOLATED FROM SOME LEPIDOPTEROUS SPE-
     CIES IN JAPAN. JAPAN.J.APPL.ENT.ZOOL. 15, 222-227.

156 AOKI, J. & CHIGUSA, K. (1968) - STUDIES ON THE NUTRITION AND METABOLISM OF
     PATHOGENIC FUNGI IN MUSCARDINE DISEASES. 1. NITROGEN UTILIZATION BY SYN-
     THETIC MEDIA OF BEAUVERIA BASSIANA, ISARIA FARINOSA, AND I.FUMOSO-ROSEA.
     J.SERIC.SCI., TOKYO 37, 288-294.

157 AOKI, J., KATAGIRI, K. & KUSHIDA, T. (1975) - THREE PATHOGENIC FUNGI ISO-
     LATED IN JAPAN FROM MIMELA COSTATA HOPE (COLEOPTERA - SCARABAEIDAE).
     JAPAN. J.APPL.ENT.ZOOL. 19, 17-22.

158 AOKI, J. & TANADA, Y. (1974) - SURVIVAL OF ENTOMOPHTHORA SPP. IN LABORATO-
     RY CULTURES. APPL.ENT.ZOOL. 9, 80-86.

159 APINIS, A.E. (1958) - DISTRIBUTION OF MICROFUNGI IN SOIL PROFILES OF CER-
     TAIN ALLUVIAL GRASSLANDS. ANGEW.PFLSOZIOL. 15, 83-90.

160 APINIS, A.E. (1963) - OCCURRENCE OF THERMOPHILOUS MICROFUNGI IN CERTAIN
     ALLUVIAL SOILS NEAR NOTTINGHAM. NOVA HEDWIGIA 5, 57-78.

161 APINIS, A.E. (1963) - THERMOPHILOUS FUNGI OF COASTAL GRASSLANDS. IN: SOIL
     ORGANISMS; DOEKSEN, J. & DRIFT, J. VAN DER (ED.), NORTH HOLLAND PUBL.
     CO., AMSTERDAM, 427-437.

162 APINIS, A.E. (1964) - REVISION OF BRITISH GYMNOASCACEAE. MYCOL.PAP. 96, 1-
     56.

163 APINIS, A.E. (1964) - ON FUNGI ISOLATED FROM SOILS AND AMMOPHILA DEBRIS.
     KEW BULL. 19, 127-131.

164 APINIS, A.E. (1964) - CONCERNING OCCURRENCE OF PHYCOMYCETES IN ALLUVIAL
     SOILS OF CERTAIN PASTURES, MARSHES, AND SWAMPS. NOVA HEDWIGIA 8, 103-
     126.

165 APINIS, A.E. (1966) - GROWTH PATTERNS OF SOIL FUNGI IN ALLUVIAL PASTURES
     AND MARSHES. IN: PROGRESS IN SOIL BIOLOGY, PROC.COLLOQUIUM ON DYNAMICS
     OF SOIL COMMUNITIES; GRAFF, O. & SATCHELL, J.E. (ED.), VIEWEG & SOHN,
     BRAUNSCHWEIG, NORTH HOLLAND PUBL.CO., AMSTERDAM, P. 211-232.

166 APINIS, A.E. (1972) - THERMOPHILOUS FUNGI IN CERTAIN GRASSLANDS. MYCOPATH.
     MYCOL.APPL. 48, 63-74.

167 APINIS, A.E. & CHESTERS, C.G.C. (1964) - ASCOMYCETES OF SOME SALT MARSHES
     AND SAND DUNES. TRANS.BR.MYCOL.SOC. 47, 419-435.

168 APINIS, A.E. & PUGH, G.J.F. (1967) - THERMOPHILOUS FUNGI OF BIRDS' NESTS.
     MYCOPATH.MYCOL.APPL. 33, 1-9.

169 APPLEGARTH, D.A. (1967) - THE CELL WALL OF PENICILLIUM NOTATUM. ARCHS BIO-
     CHEM.BIOPHYS. 120, 471-478.

170 APPLEGARTH, D.A. & BOZOIAN, G. (1969) - THE CELL WALL OF HELMINTHOSPORIUM
     SATIVUM. ARCHS BIOCHEM.BIOPHYS. 134, 285-289.

171 ARAI, T., MIKAMI, Y., FUKUSHIMA, K., UTSUMI, T. & YAZAWA, K. (1973) - A
     NEW ANTIBIOTIC, LEUCINOSTATIN, DERIVED FROM PENICILLIUM LILACINUM. J.
     ANTIBIOT., TOKYO 26, 157-161.

172 ARGOUDELIS, A.D., DIETZ, A. & JOHNSON, L.E. (1974) - ZERVAMICIN-I AND ZER-
     VAMICIN-II, POLYPEPTIDE ANTIBIOTICS PRODUCED BY EMERICELLOPSIS SALMOSYN-
     NEMATA. J.ANTIBIOT., TOKYO 27, 321-328.

173 ARGOUDELIS, A.D. & JOHNSON, L.E. (1974) - EMERIMICINS-II, -III, AND -IV,
     ANTIBIOTICS PRODUCED BY EMERICELLOPSIS MICROSPORA IN MEDIA SUPPLEMENTED
     WITH TRANS-4N-PROPYL-L-PROLINE. J.ANTIBIOT., TOKYO 27, 274-282.

174 ARGOUDELIS, A.D., MIZSAK, S.A. & BACZYNSKYJ, L. (1975) - N-ACETYL-L-PHENYL-
     ALANYL-L-PHENYLALANINOL, A METABOLITE OF EMERICELLOPSIS SALMOSYNNEMATA.
     J.ANTIBIOT., TOKYO 28, 733-736.

175 ARGOUDELIS, A.D. & ZIESERL, J.F. (1966) - THE STRUCTURE OF U-13,933, A NEW
     ANTIBIOTIC. TETRAHEDRON LETTERS, 1966 (18), 1969-1973.

176 ARIMA, K., IWASAKI, S. & TAMURA, G. (1967) - MILK CLOTTING ENZYME FROM MI-
     CROORGANISMS. 1. SCREENING TEST AND THE IDENTIFICATION OF THE POTENT
     FUNGUS. AGRIC.BIOL.CHEM., TOKYO 31, 540-545.

177 ARIMA, K., LIU, W.H. & BEPPU, T. (1972) - ISOLATION AND IDENTIFICATION OF
     THE LIPOLYTIC AND THERMOPHILIC FUNGUS. AGRIC.BIOL.CHEM., TOKYO 36, 1913-
     1917.

178 ARINZE, A.E., NAQVI, S.H.Z. & EKUNDAYO, J.A. (1976) - PRODUCTION OF EXTRA-
     CELLULAR CELLULOLYTIC AND PECTIC ENZYMES BY LASIODIPLODIA THEOBROMAE
     ON SWEET POTATO (IPOMOEA BATATAS) TUBERS. INT.BIODETERIOR.BULL. 12, 15-
     18.

179 ARKLEY, V., DEAN, F.M., JONES, P., ROBERTSON, A. & TETAZ, J. (1957) - SOME
     METABOLITES OF CHAETOMIUM AFFINE CORDA. CROAT.CHEM.ACTA 29, 141-151.

180 ARMENTROUT, V.M., HAENSSLER, G. & MAXWELL, D.P. (1976) - ACID PHOSPHATASE
     LOCALIZATION IN THE FUNGUS WHETZELINIA SCLEROTIORUM. ARCH.MICROBIOL.
     107, 7-14.

181 ARMSTRONG, F.H. & SAVORY, J.G. (1959) - THE INFLUENCE OF FUNGAL DECAY ON
     THE PROPERTIES OF TIMBER. EFFECT OF PROGRESSIVE DECAY BY THE SOFT ROT
     FUNGUS CHAETOMIUM GLOBOSUM ON THE STRENGTH OF BEECH. HOLZFORSCHUNG 13,
     84-89.

182 ARNESON, P.A. & DURBIN, R.D. (1968) - THE SENSITIVITY OF FUNGI TO ALPHA-
     TOMATINE. PHYTOPATHOLOGY 58, 536-537.

183 ARNETT, J.C.JR. & HATCH, H.B.JR. (1975) - PULMONARY ALLESCHERIASIS. REPORT
     OF A CASE AND REVIEW OF THIS LITERATURE. ARCH.INTERN.MED. 135, 1250-
     1253.

184 ARNOLD, G.R.W. (1967) - SPOREN AQUATISCHER HYPHOMYCETEN AUS DEM PARADIES
     BEI WEIMAR. WESTFAELISCHE PILZBRIEFE 6, 156-159.

185 ARNOLD, G.R.W. (1970) - BEITRAEGE ZUR KENNTNIS DER PILZFLORA THUERINGENS.
     1. AQUATISCHE HYPHOMYCETEN. MYKOL.MITTBL., HALLE 13, 11-18.

186 ARNOLD, G.W. (1970) - KULTURVERSUCHE MIT HYPHOMYCETAZEEN. SYDOWIA 24, 183-
     190.

187 ARNOLD, W.R. & PETTIT, R.E. (1969) - INTERRELATIONSHIP BETWEEN PEANUT KER-
     NEL MOISTURE AND STORAGE GASES WITH GROWTH OF ASPERGILLUS FLAVUS AND
     AFLATOXIN PRODUCTION. PHYTOPATHOLOGY 59, 111 (ABS.).

188 ARNSTEIN, H.R.V. & COOK, A.H. (1947) - PRODUCTION OF ANTIBIOTICS BY FUNGI.
     3. JAVANICIN, AN ANTIBACTERIAL PIGMENT FROM FUSARIUM JAVANICUM. J.CHEM.
     SOC., 1947, 1021-1028.

189   ARRIETA, L. & GREZ, R. (1971) - SOLUBILIZATION OF IRON-CONTAINING MINERALS
      BY SOIL MICROORGANISMS. APPL.MICROBIOL. 22, 487-490.

190   ARSENAULT, G.P. (1965) - FUNGAL METABOLITES. 2. STRUCTURE OF BOSTRYCOIDIN,
      A BETA-AZA-ANTHRAQUINONE FROM FUSARIUM SOLANI D2 PURPLE. TETRAHEDRON
      LETTERS, 1965, 4033-4037.

191   ARSVOLL, K. (1975) - FUNGI CAUSING WINTER DAMAGE ON CULTIVATED GRASSES IN
      NORWAY. MELD.NORG.LANDBRHOEISK. 54, 49 PP.

192   ARSVOLL, K. (1976) - MUTUAL ANTAGONISM BETWEEN ISOLATES OF TYPHULA ISHI-
      KARIENSIS AND TYPHULA INCARNATA. MELD.NORG.LANDBRHOEISK. 55, 1-6.

193   ARSVOLL, K. & SMITH, J.D. (1978) - TYPHULA ISHIKARIENSIS AND ITS VARIETIES,
      VAR. IDAHOENSIS COMB.NOV. AND VAR. CANADENSIS VAR.NOV. CAN.J.BOT. 56,
      348-364.

194   ARX, J.A.VON (1949) - BEITRAEGE ZUR KENNTNIS DER GATTUNG MYCOSPHAERELLA.
      SYDOWIA 3, 28-100.

195   ARX, J.A.VON (1950) - UEBER DIE ASCUSFORM VON CLADOSPORIUM HERBARUM. SYDO-
      WIA 4, 320-324.

196   ARX, J.A.VON (1957) - DIE ARTEN DER GATTUNG COLLETOTRICHUM. PHYTOPATH.Z.
      29, 413-468.

197   ARX, J.A.VON (1970) - A REVISION OF THE FUNGI CLASSIFIED AS GLOEOSPORIUM.
      J.CRAMER, LEHRE, 203 PP.

198   ARX, J.A.VON (1971) - UEBER DIE TYPUSART, ZWEI NEUE UND EINIGE WEITERE AR-
      TEN DER GATTUNG SPOROTRICHUM. PERSOONIA 6, 179-184.

199   ARX, J.A.VON (1971) - TESTUDINACEAE, A NEW FAMILY OF ASCOMYCETES. PERSOO-
      NIA 6, 365-369.

200   ARX, J.A.VON (1971) - ON ARACHNIOTUS AND RELATED GENERA OF THE GYMNOASCA-
      CEAE. PERSOONIA 6, 371-380.

201   ARX, J.A.VON (1972) - ON ENDOMYCOPSIS AND RELATED YEAST-LIKE FUNGI. ANTONIE
      VAN LEEUWENHOEK 38, 289-309.

202   ARX, J.A.VON (1973) - CENTRAALBUREAU VOOR SCHIMMELCULTURES BAARN AND DELFT.
      PROGRESS REPORT 1972. VERH.K.NED.AKAD.WET., AFD.NATUURK. 61 (4), 59-81.

203   ARX, J.A.VON (1973) - THE GENERA PETRIELLIDIUM AND PITHOASCUS (MICROASCA-
      CEAE). PERSOONIA 7, 367-375.

204   ARX, J.A.VON (1973) - OSTIOLATE AND NONOSTIOLATE PYRENOMYCETES. PROC.K.NED.
      AKAD.WET., SER.C, 76, 289-296.

205   ARX, J.A.VON (1974) - THE GENERA OF FUNGI SPORULATING IN PURE CULTURE. J.
      CRAMER, VADUZ, 2ND ED., 315 PP.

206   ARX, J.A.VON (1975) - REVISION OF MICROASCUS WITH THE DESCRIPTION OF A NEW
      SPECIES. PERSOONIA 8, 191-197.

207   ARX, J.A.VON (1975) - ON THIELAVIA AND SOME SIMILAR GENERA OF ASCOMYCETES.
      STUD.MYCOL., BAARN 8, 31 PP.

208   ARX, J.A.VON (1978) - NOTES ON DIPODASCUS, ENDOMYCES AND GEOTRICHUM WITH
      THE DESCRIPTION OF TWO NEW SPECIES. ANTONIE VAN LEEUWENHOEK 43, 301-309.

209 ARX, J.A.VON & GAMS, W. (1966) - UEBER PLEURAGE VERRUCULOSA UND DIE ZUGE-
     HOERIGE CLADORRHINUM-KONIDIENFORM. NOVA HEDWIGIA 13, 199-208.

210 ARX, J.A.VON & MUELLER, E. (1954) - DIE GATTUNGEN DER AMEROSPOREN PYRENO-
     MYCETEN. BEITR.KRYPT.FL.SCHWEIZ 11 (1), 434 PP.

211 ARX, J.A.VON & MUELLER, E. (1975) - A RE-EVALUATION OF THE BITUNICATE AS-
     COMYCETES WITH KEYS TO FAMILIES AND GENERA. STUD.MYCOL., BAARN 9, 159
     PP.

212 ARX, J.A.VON & OLIVIER, D.L. (1952) - THE TAXONOMY OF OPHIOBOLUS GRAMINIS.
     TRANS.BR.MYCOL.SOC. 35, 29-33.

213 ARX, J.A.VON, RODRIGUES DE MIRANDA, L., SMITH, M.TH. & YARROW, D. (1977) -
     THE GENERA OF YEASTS AND THE YEAST-LIKE FUNGI. STUD.MYCOL., BAARN 14,
     42 PP.

214 ARX, J.A.VON & STORM, P.K. (1967) - UEBER EINIGE AUS DEM ERDBODEN ISOLIER-
     TE, ZU SPORORMIA, PREUSSIA UND WESTERDYKELLA GEHOERENDE ASCOMYCETEN.
     PERSOONIA 4, 407-415.

215 ASAI, T. HOSHI, S. MIYASAKA, S. & IZUMIDA, M. (1952) - THE AMYLASE PRODUC-
     TION BY SUBMERGED CULTURE OF ASPERGILLUS. 1. THE CULTURAL ENVIRONMENTS
     AFFECTING THE AMYLASE PRODUCTION. J.AGRIC.CHEM.SOC.JAPAN 25, 352-357.

216 ASHLEY, J.N., HOBBS, B.C. & RAISTRICK, H. (1937) - STUDIES IN THE BIOCHEM-
     ISTRY OF MICROORGANISMS. 53. THE CRYSTALLINE COLOURING MATTERS OF FUSA-
     RIUM CULMORUM AND RELATED FORMS. BIOCHEM.J. 31, 385-397.

217 ASHOUR, W.E. (1954) - PECTINASE PRODUCTION BY BOTRYTIS CINEREA AND PYTHIUM
     DEBARYANUM. TRANS.BR.MYCOL.SOC. 37, 343-352.

218 ASHWOOD-SMITH, M.J. & HORNE, B. (1972) - RESPONSE OF ASPERGILLUS AND PENI-
     CILLIUM SPORES TO ULTRAVIOLET IRRADIATION AT LOW TEMPERATURES. PHOTO-
     CHEM.PHOTOBIOL. 15, 89-92.

219 ASHWORTH, L.J., HARPER, D.M. & ANDRIS, H.L. (1974) - THE INFLUENCE OF MIL-
     LING OF AIR-DRY SOIL UPON APPARENT INOCULUM DENSITY AND PROPAGULE SIZE
     OF VERTICILLIUM ALBO-ATRUM. PHYTOPATHOLOGY 64, 629-632.

220 ASHWORTH, L.J., HUISMAN, O.C., HARPER, D.M. & STROMBERG, L.K. (1974) - FREE
     AND BOUND MICROSCLEROTIA OF VERTICILLIUM ALBO-ATRUM IN SOILS. PHYTOPA-
     THOLOGY 64, 563-564.

221 ASHWORTH, L.J., MCCUTCHEON, O.D. & GEORGE, A.G. (1972) - VERTICILLIUM AL-
     BO-ATRUM. THE QUANTITATIVE RELATIONSHIP BETWEEN INOCULUM DENSITY AND IN-
     FECTION OF COTTON. PHYTOPATHOLOGY 62, 901-903.

222 ASHWORTH, L.J., WATERS, J.E., GEORGE, A.G. & MCCUTCHEON, O.D. (1972) -
     ASSESSMENT OF MICROSCLEROTIA OF VERTICILLIUM ALBO-ATRUM IN FIELD SOILS.
     PHYTOPATHOLOGY 62, 715-719.

223 ASKAROVA, S.A. & MAMADALIEV, A.K. (1974) - (DYNAMICS OF THE CONTENT OF MI-
     CROBIAL ANTAGONISTS OF VERTICILLIUM DAHLIAE IN THE RHIZOSPHERE OF COT-
     TON). UZBEK.BIOL.ZH. 18 (5), 67-68.

224 ASPIRAS, R.B. ALLEN, O.N. CHESTERS, G. & HARRIS, R.F. (1971) - CHEMICAL
     AND PHYSICAL STABILITY OF MICROBIAL STABILIZED AGGREGATES. PROC.SOIL
     SCI.SOC.AM. 35, 283-285.

225 ASPIRAS, R.B., ALLEN, O.N., HARRIS, R.F. & CHESTER, G. (1971) - AGGREGATE
     STABILIZATION BY FILAMENTOUS MICROORGANISMS. SOIL SCI. 112, 282-284.

226   ATHERTON, J., BYCROFT, B.W., ROBERTS, J.C., ROFFEY, P. & WILCOX, M.E.
      (1968) - STUDIES IN MYCOLOGICAL CHEMISTRY. 23. THE STRUCTURE OF FLAVO-
      MANNIN, A METABOLITE OF PENICILLIUM WORTMANNI KLOECK. J.CHEM.SOC.(C),
      1968, 2560-2564.

227   ATKIN, C., WITTER, L.D. & ORDAL, Z.J. (1967) - CONTINUOUS PROPAGATION OF
      TRICHOSPORON CUTANEUM IN CHEESE WHEY. APPL.MICROBIOL. 15, 1339-1344.

228   ATKINSON, R.G. (1961) - PRELIMINARY STUDIES ON THE UTILIZATION AND RELEASE
      OF AMINO ACIDS BY CYLINDROCARPON RADICICOLA. CAN.J.BOT. 39, 1531-1536.

229   ATTWOOD, M.M. (1971) - THE PRODUCTION OF BETA-CAROTENE IN MORTIERELLA RA-
      MANNIANA VAR. RAMANNIANA M29. THE EFFECT OF CHANGES IN THE ENVIRONMENT
      UPON GROWTH AND PIGMENTATION. ANTONIE VAN LEEUWENHOEK 37, 369-378.

230   ATTWOOD, M.M. (1973) - ATP-CITRATE LYASE ACTIVITY IN FUNGAL EXTRACTS. AN-
      TONIE VAN LEEUWENHOEK 39, 539-544.

231   ATWAL, A.S., SINGH, B. & BATTU, G.S. (1973) - CHILO PARTELLUS (SWINHOE) A
      NEW HOST OF ASPERGILLUS FLAVUS AND FUSARIUM SP. CURR.SCI. 42, 585.

232   AUBE, C. (1967) - ANTAGONISME DES CHAMPIGNONS DU SOL ENVERS VERTICILLIUM
      ALBO-ATRUM R. & B., AGENT DE LA FLETRISSURE VERTICILLIENNE DE LA LU-
      ZERNE. CAN.J.MICROBIOL. 13, 227-233.

233   AUBE, C. & GAGNON, C. (1970) - INFLUENCE OF CERTAIN SOIL FUNGI ON ALFALFA.
      CAN.J.PL.SCI. 50, 159-162.

234   AUBE, C. & GAGNON, C. (1971) - FUNGI AND THEIR ECOLOGY IN A SOIL SEEDED
      WITH RED CLOVER. CAN.J.MICROBIOL. 17, 921-927.

235   AUBE, C. & PELLETIER, G. (1968) - FORMATION OF ENDOSPORES IN VERTICILLIUM
      ALBO-ATRUM R. & B. CAN.J.MICROBIOL. 14, 606-607.

236   AUBE, C. & SACKSTON, W.E. (1965) - BIOLOGICAL CONTROL OF VERTICILLIUM WILT
      OF ALFALFA BY GLIOCLADIUM ROSEUM AND OTHER FUNGI. PROC.CAN.PHYTOPATH.
      SOC. 32, 11 (ABS.).

237   AUBE, C. & SACKSTON, W.E. (1965) - DISTRIBUTION AND PREVALENCE OF VERTICIL-
      LIUM SPECIES PRODUCING SUBSTANCES WITH GIBBERELLIN-LIKE BIOLOGICAL PROP-
      ERTIES. CAN.J.BOT. 43, 1335-1342.

238   AUCAMP, P.J. & HOLZAPFEL, C.W. (1970) - POLYHYDROXYANTHRAQUINONES FROM AS-
      PERGILLUS VERSICOLOR, ASPERGILLUS NIDULANS AND BIPOLARIS SP. THEIR SIG-
      NIFICANCE IN RELATION TO BIOGENETIC THEORIES ON AFLATOXIN-B1. JL S.AFR.
      CHEM.INST. 23, 40-56.

239   AUDHYA, T.K. & RUSSEL, D.W. (1973) - PRODUCTION OF ENNIATIN-A. CAN.J.MI-
      CROBIOL. 19, 1051-1054.

240   AUDHYA, T.K. & RUSSEL, D.W. (1974) - PRODUCTION OF ENNIATINS BY FUSARIUM
      SAMBUCINUM. SELECTION OF HIGH-YIELD CONDITIONS FROM LIQUID SURFACE CUL-
      TURES. J.GEN.MICROBIOL. 82, 181-190.

241   AUE, R., MUELLER, E. & STOLL, CH. (1969) - PSEUDOPHAEOTRICHUM SUDANENSE
      NOV.GEN. ET NOV.SPEC. NOVA HEDWIGIA 17, 83-91.

242   AUGER-BARREAU, R. & POUGNARD, N. (1968) - PREMIERES OBSERVATIONS SUR LA
      MICROFLORE FONGIQUE DES SOLS DE SAUTERNES ET DE SAINT-EMILION. BOTA-
      NISTE 51, 221-226.

243 AUSTIN, B. (1968) - EFFECTS OF AIRSPEED AND HUMIDITY CHANGES ON SPORE DIS-
CHARGE IN SORDARIA FIMICOLA. ANN.BOT. 32, 251-260.

244 AUSTIN, B. (1968) - AN ENDOGENOUS RHYTHM OF SPORE DISCHARGE IN SORDARIA
FIMICOLA. ANN.BOT. 32, 261-278.

245 AUSTIN, D.J. & MEYERS, M.B. (1964) - 3-O-METHYLVIRIDICATIN, A NEW METABO-
LITE FROM PENICILLIUM PUBERULUM. J.CHEM.SOC., 1964, 1197-1198.

246 AUSTWICK, P.K.C. (1962) - THE PRESENCE OF ASPERGILLUS FUMIGATUS IN THE
LUNGS OF DAIRY COWS. LAB.INVESTIG. 11, 1065-1072.

247 AUSTWICK, P.K.C. (1976) - ENVIRONMENTAL ASPECTS OF MORTIERELLA WOLFII IN-
FECTION IN CATTLE. N.Z.JL AGRIC.RES. 19, 25-33.

248 AVILA, R. & LACEY, J. (1974) - THE ROLE OF PENICILLIUM FREQUENTANS IN
SUBEROSIS (RESPIRATORY DISEASE IN WORKERS IN THE CORK INDUSTRY). CLIN.
ALLERGY 4, 109-117.

249 AVIZOHAR-HERSHENZON, Z. & SHACKED, P. (1968) - A BAITING METHOD FOR ESTI-
MATING THE SAPROPHYTIC ACTIVITY OF SCLEROTIUM ROLFSII IN SOIL. PHYTO-
PATHOLOGY 58, 410-413.

250 AVIZOHAR-HERSHENZON, Z. & SHACKED, P. (1969) - STUDIES ON THE MODE OF AC-
TION OF INORGANIC NITROGENOUS AMENDMENTS ON SCLEROTIUM ROLFSII IN SOIL.
PHYTOPATHOLOGY 59, 288-292.

251 AWAO, T., KOMAGATA, K., YOSHIMURA, I. & MITSUKI, K. (1972) - DETERIORATION
OF SYNTHETIC RESINS BY FUNGI. J.FERMENT.TECHNOL., OSAKA 49, 188-194.

252 AWAO, T. & MITSUGI, K. (1973) - NOTES ON THERMOPHILIC FUNGI IN JAPAN. 1.
TRANS.MYCOL.SOC.JAPAN 14, 145-160.

253 AWAO, T. & OTSUKA, S. (1973) - NOTES ON THERMOPHILIC FUNGI IN JAPAN. 2.
TRANS.MYCOL.SOC.JAPAN 14, 221-236.

254 AXELROD, D.E. (1972) - KINETICS OF DIFFERENTIATION OF CONIDIOPHORES AND
CONIDIA BY COLONIES OF ASPERGILLUS NIDULANS. J.GEN.MICROBIOL. 73, 181-
184.

255 AYANABA, A. & ALEXANDER, M. (1973) - MICROBIAL FORMATION OF NITROSAMINES
IN VITRO. APPL.MICROBIOL. 25, 862-868.

256 AYCOCK, R. (1961) - SYMPOSIUM ON SCLEROTIUM ROLFSII. SUMMATION. PHYTOPA-
THOLOGY 51, 107-108.

257 AYCOCK, R. (1966) - STEM ROT AND OTHER DISEASES CAUSED BY SCLEROTIUM ROLF-
SII. TECH.BULL.N.CAROL.AGRIC.EXP.STN 174, 202 PP.

258 AYERS, W.A. & LUMSDEN, R.D. (1975) - FACTORS AFFECTING PRODUCTION AND GER-
MINATION OF SPORES OF THREE PYTHIUM SPECIES. PHYTOPATHOLOGY 65, 1094-
1100.

259 AYERS, W.A., PAPAVIZAS, G.C. & LUMSDEN, R.D. (1969) - PURIFICATION AND
PROPERTIES OF THE ENDOPOLYGALACTURONASE OF APHANOMYCES EUTEICHES. PHY-
TOPATHOLOGY 59, 925-930.

260 AYERS, W.A. & ZENTMYER, G.A. (1971) - EFFECT OF SOIL SOLUTION AND TWO SOIL
PSEUDOMONADS ON SPORANGIUM PRODUCTION BY PHYTOPHTHORA CINNAMOMI. PHYTO-
PATHOLOGY 61, 1188-1193.

261 AYERST, G. (1969) - THE EFFECTS OF MOISTURE AND TEMPERATURE ON GROWTH AND
SPORE GERMINATION IN SOME FUNGI. J.STORED PROD.RES. 5, 127-141.

262 AYTOUN, R.S.C. (1953) - THE GENUS TRICHODERMA. ITS RELATIONSHIP WITH AR-
     MILLARIA MELLEA AND POLYPORUS SCHWEINITZII, TOGETHER WITH PRELIMINARY
     OBSERVATIONS ON ITS ECOLOGY IN WOODLAND SOILS. TRANS.PROC.BOT.SOC.EDINB.
     36, 99-114.

263 BAARD, S.W. (1970) - THE CARBON/NITROGEN REQUIREMENTS OF HELMINTHOSPORIUM
     SATIVUM AND THE INFLUENCE OF ORGANIC RESIDUES ON DISEASE INCIDENCE. PL.
     SOIL 32, 169-176.

264 BABUSHKINA, I.N. (1971) - (AN INFLUENCE OF RHIZOSPHERE FUNGI ON THE VARIA-
     BILITY OF VERTICILLIUM WILT CAUSAL AGENTS). MIKOL.FITOPAT. 5, 345-351.

265 BABUSHKINA, I.N. (1974) - (THE INTERACTION OF SOIL MICROFUNGI AND VERTI-
     CILLIUM DAHLIAE). MIKOL.FITOPAT. 8, 395-401.

266 BACKMAN, P.A. & RODRIGUEZ-KABANA, R. (1976) - DEVELOPMENT OF A MEDIUM FOR
     SELECTIVE ISOLATION OF SCLEROTIUM ROLFSII. PHYTOPATHOLOGY 66, 234-236.

267 BACON, J.S.D., GORDON, A.H. & JONES, D. (1972) - DEGRADATION OF SCLEROTAN,
     A BETA-(1-3)-GLUCAN BY ENZYMES FROM FUNGI PARASITIC ON SCLEROTIA. BIO-
     CHEM.J. 129, 27-28.

268 BADAR, Y., LOCKLEY, W.J.S., TOUBE, T.P. & WEEDON, B.C.L. (1973) - NATURAL
     AND SYNTHETIC PYRROL-2-YLPOLYENES. J.CHEM.SOC.PERKIN TRANS.I, 1973 (13),
     1416-1424.

269 BADURA, L. (1960) - SOME OBSERVATIONS ON THE MYCOFLORA FROM THE LITTER AND
     SOIL IN THE PINE FOREST IN THE RADUNIA (SEPIA GORA) REGION. ACTA MICRO-
     BIOL.POL. 9, 33-58.

270 BADURA, L. (1963) - RICERCHE SULLA MICOFLORA DEL SUOLO SOTTO I FAGGI DELL
     'ORTO BOTANICO DELL'UNIVERSITA DI TORINO. ALLIONIA 9, 65-74.

271 BADURA, L. (1965) - INVESTIGATIONS ON THE SOIL MYCOFLORA OF A BEECH COM-
     MUNITY IN THE BOTANICAL GARDEN OF THE TURIN UNIVERSITY (ITALY). FRAGM.
     FLOR.GEOBOT. 2, 197-208.

272 BADURA, L. AND BADUROVA, M. (1964) - (SOME OBSERVATIONS ON THE MYCOFLORA
     BOT.POL. 33, 507-525.

273 BADUROVA, M. & BADURA, L. (1967) - FURTHER INVESTIGATIONS ON THE RELATION-
     SHIP BETWEEN SOIL FUNGI AND THE MACROFLORA. ACTA SOC.BOT.POL. 36, 515-
     529.

274 BAERLOCHER, F. & KENDRICK, B. (1974) - DYNAMICS OF THE FUNGAL POPULATION
     ON LEAVES IN A STREAM. J.ECOL. 62, 761-791.

275 BAERLOCHER, F., KENDRICK, B. & MICHAELIDES, J. (1977) - COLONIZATION OF
     RESIN-COATED SLIDES BY AQUATIC HYPHOMYCETES. CAN.J.BOT. 55, 1163-1166.

276 BAERWALD, G., JAHN, G. & VOLZKE, K. (1973) - MIKROBIOLOGISCHE GEWINNUNG
     EINER PROTEASE MIT FIBRINOLYTISCHER WIRKUNG AUS ASPERGILLUS OCHRACEUS.
     PHARMAZIE 28, 798 (ABS.).

277 BAGDADI, V.K. (1967) - (DISTRIBUTION OF MICROMYCETES IN VARIOUS TYPES OF
     SYRIAN SOILS). VEST.MOSK.GOS.UNIV., SER.BIOL.POCHV. 1973 (2), 87.

278 BAGDASARYAN, Z.N., GRISHCHENKO, V.M., NOVGORODOVA, T.V. & BEZBORODOVA, S.I.
     (1973) - (COMPAPATIVE STUDIES OF SOME PROPERTIES OF EXTRACELLULAR ACID
     RNA-SES FROM PENICILLIUM CLAVIFORME). MIKROBIOLOGIYA 42, 413-417.

279 BAHADUR, K. & MALVIYA, A.N. (1966) - BIOSYNTHESIS OF CITRIC ACID. 1. THE
     ROLE OF HYDROGEN ION-CONCENTRATION AND FERMENTATION PERIOD ON THE PRO-
     DUCTION OF ACIDS BY ASPERGILLUS NIGER. ZENTBL.BAKT.PARASITKDE, ABT.2,
     120, 616-619.

280 BAHADUR, K. & MALVIYA, A.N. (1966) - BIOSYNTHESIS OF CITRIC ACID. 3. DYNAM-
     IC ROLE OF METAL IONS IN THE PRODUCTION OF CITRIC ACID BY ASPERGILLUS
     NIGER. ZENTBL.BAKT.PARASITKDE, ABT.2, 120, 726-733.

281 BAHADUR, K. & MALVIYA, A.N. (1966) - BIOSYNTHESIS OF CITRIC ACID. 4. THE
     INFLUENCE OF MINERAL NUTRIENTS ON THE MICROBIAL PRODUCTION OF CITRIC
     ACID. ZENTBL.BAKT.PARASITKDE, ABT.2, 120, 734-739.

282 BAIJAL, U. (1969) - SPECIES OF MORTIERELLA FROM INDIA. 7. SYDOWIA 21, 269-
     271.

283 BAIMATAEVA, B.K. (1970) - (SOME BIOLOGICAL CHARACTERISTICS OF THE FUNGUS
     ALTERNARIA TENUIS). IZV.AKAD.NAUK KAZAKH.SSR., SER.BIOL. NAUK 4, 37-41.

284 BAINBRIDGE, A. (1970) - SPORULATION BY PYTHIUM ULTIMUM AT VARIOUS SOIL
     MOISTURE TENSIONS. TRANS.BR.MYCOL.SOC. 55, 485-488.

285 BAINBRIDGE, B.W. (1971) - MACROMOLECULAR COMPOSITION AND NUCLEAR DIVISION
     DURING SPORE GERMINATION IN ASPERGILLUS NIDULANS. J.GEN.MICROBIOL. 66,
     319-325.

286 BAINBRIDGE, B.W. (1974) - A SIMPLE AND RAPID TECHNIQUE FOR OBTAINING A
     HIGH PROPORTION OF HYBRID CLEISTOTHECIA IN ASPERGILLUS NIDULANS. GENET.
     RES. 23, 115-117.

287 BAINBRIDGE, B.W., BULL, A.T., PIRT, S.J., ROWLEY, B.I. & TRINCI, A.P.J.
     (1971) - BIOCHEMICAL AND STRUCTURAL CHANGES IN NON-GROWING MAINTAINED
     AND AUTOLYSING CULTURES OF ASPERGILLUS NIDULANS. TRANS.BR.MYCOL.SOC.
     56, 371-385.

288 BAINIER, G. (1908) - MYCOTHEQUE DE L'ECOLE DE PHARMACIE. 24. PERICONIA ET
     DENDRYPHIUM. BULL.TRIMEST.SOC.MYCOL.FR. 24, 73-84.

289 BAINIER, G. (1908) - CEPHALIOPHORA TROPICA ET C. IRREGULARIS. BULL.TRIMEST.
     SOC.MYCOL.FR. 24, 147-151.

290 BAINIER, G. (1910) - MONOGRAPHIE DES CHAETOMIDIUM ET CHAETOMIUM. BULL.TRI-
     MEST.SOC.MYCOL.FR. 25, 191-231.

291 BAJAN, C. & KMITOWA, K. (1974) - THE EFFECT OF THE MEDIUM AND TEMPERATURE
     ON THE DEVELOPMENT OF INSECT PATHOGENIC FUNGI ISOLATED FROM THE COLO-
     RADO BEETLE (LEPTINOTARSA DECEMLINEATA SAY). EKOL.POL. 21, 657-686.

292 BAK, T.G. (1967) - STUDIES ON GLUCOSE DEHYDROGENASE OF ASPERGILLUS ORYZAE.
     3. GENERAL ENZYMATIC PROPERTIES. BIOCHIM.BIOPHYS.ACTA 146, 317-327.

293 BAKALIVANOV, D. (1966) - (STIMULATING AND INHIBITING PROPERTIES OF CERTAIN
     SOIL MICROSCOPIC FUNGI ON PLANT GROWTH). IZV.BULG.AKAD.NAUK INST.FIZIOL.
     RAST.M.POPOV. 15, 133-142.

294 BAKALIVANOV, D. (1968) - INDOLE DERIVATIVES IN SOIL MICROSCOPIC FUNGI.
     POCHV.AGROKHIM. 3, 81-86.

295 BAKER, E.E., MRAK, E.M. & SMITH, C.E. (1943) - THE MORPHOLOGY, TAXONOMY,
     AND DISTRIBUTION OF COCCIDIOIDES IMMITIS RIXFORD & GILCHRIST 1896.
     FARLOWIA 1, 199-244.

296 BAKER, G.E., DUNNS, P.H. & SAKAI, W.A. (1974) - THE ROLES OF FUNGI IN HAWAIIAN ISLAND ECOSYSTEMS. 1. FUNGAL COMMUNITIES ASSOCIATED WITH LEAF SURFACES OF THREE ENDEMIC VASCULAR PLANTS IN KILAUEA FOREST RESERVE AND HAWAII VOLCANOES NATIONAL PARK, HAWAII. IN: ISLAND ECOSYSTEMS IRP, U.S. INTERNATIONAL BIOLOGICAL PROGRAM (ED.).

297 BAKER, J. & NORRIS, D.M. (1968) - A COMPLEX OF FUNGI MUTUALISTICALLY INVOLVED IN THE NUTRITION OF THE AMBROSIA BEETLE XYLEBORUS FERRUGINEUS. J.INVERTEBR.PATH. 11, 246-250.

298 BAKER, K.F. (1970) - TYPES OF RHIZOCTONIA DISEASES AND THEIR OCCURRENCE. IN: RHIZOCTONIA SOLANI, BIOLOGY AND PATHOLOGY; PARMETER, J.R.JR. (ED.), UNIV.CALIFORNIA PRESS, BERKELEY, 125-147.

299 BAKER, K.F. & COOK, R.J. (1974) - BIOLOGICAL CONTROL OF PLANT PATHOGENS. FREEMAN & CO., SAN FRANCISCO, P. 229.

300 BAKER, K.F., FLENTJE, N.T., OLSEN, C.M. & STRETTON, H.M. (1967) - EFFECT OF ANTAGONISTS ON GROWTH AND SURVIVAL OF RHIZOCTONIA SOLANI IN SOIL. PHYTOPATHOLOGY 57, 591-597.

301 BAKER, R. & NASH, SH.M. (1965) - ECOLOGY OF PLANT PATHOGENS IN SOIL. 6. INOCULUM DENSITY OF FUSARIUM SOLANI F.SP. PHASEOLI IN BEAN RHIZOSPHERE AS AFFECTED BY CELLULOSE AND SUPPLEMENTAL NITROGEN. PHYTOPATHOLOGY 55, 1381-1382.

302 BAKER, R.D. (1975) - MUCORMYCOSIS (OPPORTUNISTIC ZYGOMYCOSIS). IN: OPPORTUNISTIC FUNGAL INFECTIONS; CHICK, E.W., BALOWS, A. & FURCOLOW, M.L. (ED.), THOMAS, C.C. PUBLISHER, U.S.A., P. 204-214.

303 BAKERSPIGEL, A. (1970) - THE ISOLATION OF PHOMA HIBERNICA FROM A LESION ON A LEG. SABOURAUDIA 7, 261-264.

304 BAKERSPIGEL, A. (1971) - FUNGI ISOLATED FROM KERATOMYCOSIS IN ONTARIO, CANADA. 1. MONOSPORIUM APIOSPERMUM (ALLESCHERIA BOYDII). SABOURAUDIA 9, 109-112.

305 BAKERSPIGEL, A. (1974) - THE KERATINOPHILIC FUNGI OF ONTARIO, CANADA. MYCOPATH.MYCOL.APPL. 53, 1-11.

306 BALABANOFF, V.A. (1967) - ETUDES COMPAREES DES DERMATOPHYTES ISOLES DE GROTTES ET D'ETABLES EN BULGARIE. MYCOPATH.MYCOL.APPL. 32, 237-248.

307 BALASOORIYA, I. & PARKINSON, D. (1967) - STUDIES ON FUNGI IN PINE WOOD SOIL. 2. SUBSTRATE RELATIONSHIPS OF FUNGI IN THE MINERAL HORIZONS OF THE SOIL. REVUE ECOL.BIOL.SOL 4, 639-643.

308 BALASUBRAMANIAN, K.A. & SRIVASTAVA, D.N. (1972) - RELATIONSHIP OF NUTRITION TO GERMINATION AND PATHOGENICITY OF SPORES OF RHIZOPUS STOLONIFER. INDIAN J.EXPL BIOL. 10, 445-447.

309 BALATSOURAS, G.D. & VAUGHN, R.H. (1958) - SOME FUNGI THAT MIGHT CAUSE SOFTENING OF STORAGE OLIVES. FD RES. 23, 235-243.

310 BALAZY, S. (1965) - ENTOMOPATHOGENOUS FUNGI FROM THE ORDER HYPHOMYCETES DAMAGING FOREST INSECTS IN POLAND. ROCZN.WYZ.SZK.ROLN.POZNAN. 27, 21-30.

311 BALDACCI, E. (1960) - ATTENZIONE ALLE IMPORTAZIONI DEL RISO IN ITALIA. RISO, 1960, 3-7.

312 BALL, C. (1973) - THE GENETICS OF PENICILLIUM CHRYSOGENUM. PROG.INDUST. MICROBIOL. 12, 47-72.

313 BALLANTINE, J.A., FERRITO, V. & HASSALL, C.H. (1971) - THE BIOSYNTHESIS OF ASPERUGIN IN ASPERGILLUS RUGULOSUS. PHYTOCHEMISTRY 10, 1309-1313.

314 BALLANTINE, J.A., FERRITO, V., HASSALL, C.H. & JENKINS, M.L. (1973) - THE BIOSYNTHESIS OF PHENOLS. 24. ARUGOSIN-C, A METABOLITE OF A MUTANT STRAIN OF ASPERGILLUS RUGULOSUS. J.CHEM.SOC.PERKIN TRANS.I, 1973 (17), 1825-1830.

315 BALLANTINE, J.A., FERRITO, V., HASSALL, C.H. & JONES, V.I.P. (1969) - ASPERTETRONIN-A AND -B, TWO NOVEL TETRONIC ACID DERIVATIVES PRODUCED BY A BLOCKED MUTANT OF ASPERGILLUS RUGULOSUS. J.CHEM.SOC.(C), 1969, 56-61.

316 BALLANTINE, J.A., FRANCIS, D.J., HASSALL, C.H. & WRIGHT, J.L.C. (1970) - THE BIOSYNTHESIS OF PHENOLS. 21. THE MOLECULAR STRUCTURE OF ARUGOSIN, A METABOLITE OF A WILD-TYPE STRAIN OF ASPERGILLUS RUGULOSUS. J.CHEM.SOC. (C), 1970, 1175-1182.

317 BAMBURG, J.R., MARASAS, W.F., RIGGS, N.V., SMALLEY, E.B. & STRONG, F.M. (1968) - TOXIC SPIROEPOXY COMPOUNDS FROM FUSARIA AND OTHER HYPHOMYCETES. BIOTECHNOL.BIOENG. 10, 445-455.

318 BAMBURG, J.R., RIGGS, N.V. & STRONG, F.M. (1968) - THE STRUCTURE OF TOXINS FROM TWO STRAINS OF FUSARIUM TRICINCTUM. TETRAHEDRON 24, 3329-3336.

319 BAMBURG, J.R. & STRONG, F.M. (1969) - MYCOTOXINS OF THE TRICHOTHECANE FAMILY PRODUCED BY FUSARIUM TRICINCTUM AND TRICHODERMA LIGNORUM. PHYTOCHEMISTRY 8, 2405-2410.

320 BAMFORD, P.C., NORRIS, G.L.F. & WARD, G. (1961) - FLAVIPIN PRODUCTION BY EPICOCCUM SPECIES. TRANS.BR.MYCOL.SOC. 44, 354-356.

321 BANDONI, R.J. (1972) - TERRESTRIAL OCCURRENCE OF SOME AQUATIC HYPHOMYCETES. CAN.J.BOT. 50, 2283-2288.

322 BANDONI, R.J. & TOWERS, G.H.M. (1967) - DEGRADATION OF USNIC ACID BY MICROORGANISMS. CAN.J.BIOCHEM. 45, 1197-1201.

323 BANIECKI, J.F. & BLOSS, H.E. (1969) - THE BASIDIAL STAGE OF PHYMATOTRICHUM OMNIVORUM. MYCOLOGIA 61, 1054-1060.

324 BANIECKI, J.F. & BLOSS, H.E. (1969) - EFFECTS OF STEROLS AND LIGHT ON SPORULATION AND GERMINATION OF CONIDIA OF PHYMATOTRICHUM OMNIVORUM. PHYTOPATHOLOGY 59, 680-684.

325 BANIHASHEMI, Z. (1970) - A NEW TECHNIQUE FOR ISOLATION OF PHYTOPHTHORA AND PYTHIUM SPECIES FROM SOIL. PL.DIS.REPTR 54, 261-262.

326 BANIHASHEMI, Z. & MITCHELL, J.E. (1975) - USE OF SAFFLOWER SEEDLINGS FOR THE DETECTION AND ISOLATION OF PHYTOPHTHORA CACTORUM FROM SOIL AND ITS APPLICATION TO POPULATION STUDIES. PHYTOPATHOLOGY 65, 1424-1430.

327 BANIHASHEMI, Z. & MITCHELL, J.E. (1976) - FACTORS AFFECTING OOSPORE GERMINATION IN PHYTOPHTHORA CACTORUM, THE INCITANT OF APPLE COLLAR ROT. PHYTOPATHOLOGY 66, 443-448.

328 BANKS, G.T., BUCK, K.W., CHAIN, E.B., DARBYSHIRE, J.E. & HIMMELWEIT, F. (1969) - VIRUSLIKE PARTICLES IN PENICILLIN PRODUCING STRAINS OF PENICILLIUM CHRYSOGENUM. NATURE, LOND. 222, 89-90.

329 BANKS, G.T., BUCK, K.W., CHAIN, E.B., DARBYSHIRE, J.E. & HIMMELWEIT, F. (1969) - PENICILLIUM CYANEO-FULVUM VIRUS AND INTERFERON STIMULATION. NATURE, LOND. 223, 155-158.

330 BANKS, G.T., BUCK, K.W., CHAIN, E.B., HIMMELWEIT, F., MARKS, J.E., TYLER,
     J.M., HOLLINGS, M., LAST, F.T. & STONE, O.M. (1968) - VIRUSES IN FUNGI
     AND INTERFERON STIMULATION. NATURE, LOND. 218, 542-545.

331 BANSAL, R.D. & GROVER, R.K. (1971) - EFFECT OF ALCOHOLS AND ORGANIC ACIDS
     ON GROWTH, SPORULATION AND SUBSEQUENT SPORE GERMINATION OF ASPERGILLUS
     FLAVUS. SYDOWIA 25, 167-171.

332 BARACHO, I.R. & AZEVEDO, J.L. (1972) - QUANTITATIVE ANALYSIS OF CLEISTO-
     THECIA IN ASPERGILLUS NIDULANS. EXPERIENTIA 28, 855-856.

333 BARACHO, I.R., VENCOVSKY, R. & AZEVEDO, J.L. (1970) - CORRELATION BETWEEN
     SIZE AND HYBRID OR SELFED STATE OF THE CLEISTOTHECIA IN ASPERGILLUS NI-
     DULANS. TRANS.BR.MYCOL.SOC. 54, 109-116.

334 BARASH, I. (1968) - LIBERATION OF POLYGALACTURONASE DURING SPORE GERMINA-
     TION BY GEOTRICHUM CANDIDUM. PHYTOPATHOLOGY 58, 1364-1371.

335 BARASH, I., KARR, A.L. & STROBEL, G.A. (1975) - ISOLATION AND CHARACTERI-
     ZATION OF STEMPHYLIN, A CHROMONE GLUCOSIDE FROM STEMPHYLIUM BOTRYOSUM.
     PL.PHYSIOL., LANCASTER 55, 646-651.

336 BARASH, I. LOWY, I. & POMERANTZ, S. (1972) - EFFECT OF UREA ON AMMONIUM-
     DEPENDENT SYNTHESIS OF CARBAMYL PHOSPHATE DURING SPORE GERMINATION OF
     GEOTRICHUM CANDIDUM. PL.PHYSIOL., LANCASTER 50, 642-644.

337 BARASH, I. & MOR, H. (1972) - STUDIES ON THE CONTROL AND PROPERTIES OF OR-
     NITHINE TRANSCARBAMYLASE IN GERMINATED SPORES OF GEOTRICHUM CANDIDUM.
     PL.CELL PHYSIOL. 13, 119-130.

338 BARASH, I. & MOR, H. (1973) - REGULATION OF NICOTINAMIDE ADENINE DINUCLEO-
     TIDE PHOSPHATE-SPECIFIC GLUTAMATE DEHYDROGENASE IN GERMINATED SPORES OF
     GEOTRICHUM CANDIDUM. PL.PHYSIOL., LANCASTER 51, 852-858.

339 BARBETTA, M., CASNATI, G., POCHINI, A. & SELVA, A. (1969) - NEOECHINULINE.
     A NEW INDOLE METABOLITE FROM ASPERGILLUS AMSTELODAMI. TETRAHEDRON LET-
     TERS, 1969 (51), 4457-4460.

340 BARHAM, R.O., MARX, D.H. & RUEHLE, J.L. (1974) - INFECTION OF ECTOMUCORRHI-
     ZAL AND NONMYCORRHIZAL ROOTS OF SHORTLEAF PINE BY NEMATODES AND PHYTOPH-
     THORA CINNAMOMI. PHYTOPATHOLOGY 64, 1260-1264.

341 BARINOVA, S.A. (1953) - (INFLUENCE OF CARBON DIOXIDE ON MOLD GROWTH). MI-
     KROBIOLOGIYA 22, 391-398.

342 BARKAI-GOLAN, R. (1974) - SPECIES OF PENICILLIUM CAUSING DECAY OF STORED
     FRUITS AND VEGETABLES IN ISRAEL. MYCOPATH.MYCOL.APPL. 54, 141-145.

343 BARKAI-GOLAN, R., KAHAN, R.S. & PADOVA, R. (1969) - SYNERGISTIC EFFECTS OF
     GAMMA RADIATION AND HEAT ON THE DEVELOPMENT OF PENICILLIUM DIGITATUM IN
     VITRO AND IN STORED CITRUS FRUITS. PHYTOPATHOLOGY 59, 922-924.

344 BARKER, K.I. (1964) - ON THE DISEASE REDUCTION AND REPRODUCTION OF THE NEM-
     ATODE APHELENCHUS AVENAE ON ISOLATES OF RHIZOCTONIA SOLANI. PL.DIS.
     REPTR 48, 428-432.

345 BARKER, K.R. & WALKER, J.C. (1962) - RELATIONSHIP OF PECTOLYTIC AND CELLU-
     LOLYTIC ENZYME PRODUCTION BY STRAINS OF PELLICULARIA FILAMENTOSA TO
     THEIR PATHOGENICITY. PHYTOPATHOLOGY 52, 1119-1125.

346 BARNES, G.L. (1971) - MYCOFLORA OF DEVELOPING PEANUT PODS IN OKLAHOMA.
     MYCOPATH.MYCOL.APPL. 45, 85-92.

347 BARNES, R.A. & GERBER, N.N. (1955) - THE ANTIFUNGAL AGENT FROM OSAGE ORANGE
     WOOD. J.AM.CHEM.SOC. 77, 3259-3262.

348 BARNETT, E.A. & FERGUS, C.L. (1971) - THE RELATION OF EXTRACELLULAR AMYL-
     ASE, MYCELIUM, AND TIME, IN SOME THERMOPHILIC AND MESOPHILIC HUMICOLA
     SPECIES. MYCOPATH.MYCOL.APPL. 44, 131-141.

349 BARNETT, H.L. (1964) - HIGH MANGANESE REQUIREMENTS AND DEFICIENCY SYMPTOMS
     IN CERTAIN FUNGI. PHYTOPATHOLOGY 52, 746.

350 BARNETT, H.L. & LILLY, V.G. (1962) - A DESTRUCTIVE MYCOPARASITE, GLIOCLA-
     DIUM ROSEUM. MYCOLOGIA 54, 72-77.

351 BARNETT, H.L. & LILLY, V.G. (1966) - MANGANESE REQUIREMENTS AND DEFICIENCY
     SYMPTOMS OF SOME FUNGI. MYCOLOGIA 58, 585-591.

352 BARNUM, C. (1924) - THE PRODUCTION OF SUBSTANCES TOXIC TO PLANTS BY PENI-
     CILLIUM EXPANSUM. PHYTOPATHOLOGY 14, 238-243.

353 BARR, D.J.S. & KEMP, W.G. (1976) - OLPIDIUM BRASSIACE, TOBACCO NECROSIS
     VIRUS AND PYTHIUM SPP. IN RELATION TO RUSTY ROOT OF CARROTS IN ONTARIO
     AND QUEBEC. CAN.PL.DIS.SURV. 55, 77-82.

354 BARR, M.E. (1958) - LIFE HISTORY STUDIES OF MYCOSPHAERELLA TASSIANA AND M.
     TYPHAE. MYCOLOGIA 50, 501-513.

355 BARRAS, S.J. (1969) - PENICILLIUM IMPLICATUM ANTAGONISTIC TO CERATOCYSTIS
     MINOR AND C. IPS. PHYTOPATHOLOGY 59, 520.

356 BARRETT, J.T. & HARDMAN, D.A. (1947) - MYROTHECIUM LEAF SPOT AND CANKER OF
     GARDENIA. PHYTOPATHOLOGY 37, 360 (ABS.).

357 BARRON, G.L. (1961) - MONOCILLIUM HUMICOLA AND PAECILOMYCES VARIABILIS FROM
     SOIL. CAN.J.BOT. 39, 1573-1578.

358 BARRON, G.L. (1961) - STUDIES ON SPECIES OF OIDIODENDRON, HELICODENDRON,
     AND STACHYBOTRYS FROM SOIL. CAN.J.BOT. 39, 1563-1571.

359 BARRON, G.L. (1962) - STACHYBOTRYS AURANTIA SP.NOV. FROM SOIL. CAN.J.BOT.
     40, 257-261.

360 BARRON, G.L. (1962) - NEW SPECIES AND NEW RECORDS OF OIDIODENDRON. CAN.J.
     BOT. 40, 589-607.

361 BARRON, G.L. (1964) - A NEW GENUS OF THE HYPHOMYCETES FROM SOIL. MYCOLOGIA
     56, 514-518.

362 BARRON, G.L. (1964) - THE PARASEXUAL CYCLE AND LINKAGE RELATIONSHIPS IN
     THE STORAGE ROT FUNGUS PENICILLIUM EXPANSUM. CAN.J.BOT. 40, 1603-1613.

363 BARRON, G.L. (1967) - TORULOMYCES AND MONOCILLIUM. MYCOLOGIA 59, 716-718.

364 BARRON, G.L. (1968) - THE GENERA OF HYPHOMYCETES FROM SOIL. WILLIAMS & WIL-
     KINS, BALTIMORE, 364 PP.

365 BARRON, G.L. & BUSCH, L.V. (1962) - STUDIES ON THE SOIL HYPHOMYCETE SCOLE-
     COBASIDIUM. CAN.J.BOT. 40, 77-84.

366 BARRON, G.L., CAIN, R.F. & GILMAN, J.C. (1961) - THE GENUS MICROASCUS. CAN.
     J.BOT. 39, 1609-1631.

367 BARRON, G.L. & FLETCHER, J.T. (1970) - VERTICILLIUM ALBO-ATRUM AND V. DAHLIAE AS MYCOPARASITES. CAN.J.BOT. 48, 1137-1139.

368 BARRON, G.L. & ONIONS, A.H.S. (1966) - VERTICILLIUM CHLAMYDOSPORIUM AND ITS RELATIONSHIPS TO DIHETEROSPORA, STEMPHYLIOPSIS, AND PAECILOMYCES. CAN.J. BOT. 44, 861-870.

369 BARTLETT, G.W. & MOSES, V. (1957) - THE PATHWAY OF GLUCOSE METABOLISM IN ZYGORRHYNCHUS MOELLERI. J.GEN.MICROBIOL. 16, 550-560.

370 BARTNICKI-GARCIA, S. & LIPPMANN, E. (1972) - THE BURSTING TENDENCY OF HYPHAL TIPS OF FUNGI. J.GEN.MICROBIOL. 73, 487-500.

371 BARTON, D.H.R., DE MAYO, P., MORRISON, G.A. & RAISTRICK, H. (1959) - THE CONSTITUTION OF ATROVENETIN AND SOME RELATED HERQUEINONE DERIVATIVES. TETRAHEDRON 6, 48-62.

372 BARTON, L.L., GEORGI, C.E. & LINEBACK, D.R. (1972) - EFFECT OF MALTOSE ON GLUCOAMYLASE FORMATION BY ASPERGILLUS NIGER. J.BACT. 111, 771-777.

373 BARTON, R. (1957) - GERMINATION OF OOSPORES OF PYTHIUM MAMILLATUM IN RESPONSE TO EXUDATES FROM LIVING SEEDLINGS. NATURE, LOND. 180, 613-614.

374 BARTON, R. (1958) - OCCURRENCE AND ESTABLISHMENT OF PYTHIUM IN SOILS. TRANS. BR.MYCOL.SOC. 41, 207-222.

375 BARTON, R. (1960) - SAPROPHYTIC ACTIVITY OF PYTHIUM MAMILLATUM IN SOILS. 1. INFLUENCE OF SUBSTRATE COMPOSITION AND SOIL ENVIRONMENT. TRANS.BR. MYCOL.SOC. 43, 529-540.

376 BARTOSHEVICH, YU, E., PETRUKHINA, T.YU., DMITRIEVA, S.V., NOVIKOVA, N.D. & GOL'DSHTEIN, V.L. (1973) - (DEGRADATION OF CULTURAL INDICES IN FUSIDIUM COCCINEUM DURING SELECTION). ANTIBIOTIKI 18, 981-986.

377 BARZ, W. (1971) - UEBER DEN ABBAU AROMATISCHER VERBINDUNGEN DURCH FUSARIUM OXYSPORUM SCHLECHT. ARCH.MIKROBIOL. 78, 341-352.

378 BARZ, W., SCHLEPPHORST, R. & LAIMER, J. (1976) - UEBER DEN ABBAU VON POLYPHENOLEN DURCH PILZE DER GATTUNG FUSARIUM. PHYTOCHEMISTRY 15, 87-90.

379 BARZA RAMOS, T.M. & UPADHYAY, H.P. (1966) - FUNGOS DOS SOLOS DO NORDESTE DO BRASIL. 4. ATAS INST.MICOL. 3, 328-335.

380 BASSETT, C. (1961) - SOME SOIL-BORNE FUNGI IN FOREST NURSERIES. N.Z.SCI. REV. 19, 24.

381 BASSIR, O. & ADEKUNLE, A. (1968) - TWO NEW METABOLITES OF ASPERGILLUS FLAVUS. FEBS LETTERS, 1968 (2), 23-25.

382 BASU, R. & MAJUMDAR, S.K. (1969) - EFFECTS OF CARBON AND NITROGEN SOURCES ON ANTIBIOTIC PRODUCTION BY PENICILLIUM WORTMANNI. J.FERMENT.TECHNOL., OSAKA 47, 185-188.

383 BASU, R. & MAJUMDAR, S.K. (1969) - DETERMINATION OF OPTIMUM CULTURAL CONDITIONS FOR THE PRODUCTION OF A NEW ANTIFUNGAL ANTIBIOTIC BY PENICILLIUM WORTMANNI. J.FERMENT.TECHNOL., OSAKA 47, 189-193.

384 BASU, S.N. (1951) - SIGNIFICANCE OF CALCIUM IN THE FRUITING OF CHAETOMIUM SPECIES, PARTICULARLY CHAETOMIUM GLOBOSUM. J.GEN.MICROBIOL. 5, 231-238.

385 BASU, S.N. & BOSE, R.G. (1950) - FACTORS AFFECTING THE FRUITING OF CHAETO-
     MIUM SPECIES. J.GEN.MICROBIOL. 4, 132-140.

386 BASU, S.N. & GHOSE, S.N. (1960) - THE PRODUCTION OF CELLULASE BY FUNGI ON
     MIXED CELLULOSIC SUBSTRATES. CAN.J.MICROBIOL. 6, 265-282.

387 BASYOUNI, S.H., BREWER, D. & VINING, L.C. (1968) - PIGMENTS OF THE GENUS
     BEAUVERIA. CAN.J.BOT. 46, 441-448.

388 BATEMAN, D.F. (1961) - THE EFFECT OF SOIL MOISTURE UPON DEVELOPMENT OF
     POINSETTIA ROOT ROTS. PHYTOPATHOLOGY 51, 445-451.

389 BATEMAN, D.F. (1962) - RELATION OF SOIL PH TO DEVELOPMENT OF POINSETTIA
     ROOT ROTS. PHYTOPATHOLOGY 52, 559-566.

390 BATEMAN, D.F. (1963) - INFLUENCE OF HOST AND NONHOST PLANTS UPON POPULA-
     TION OF THIELAVIOPSIS BASICOLA IN SOIL. PHYTOPATHOLOGY 53, 1174-1177.

391 BATEMAN, D.F. (1964) - CELLULASE AND THE RHIZOCTONIA DISEASE OF BEAN. PHY-
     TOPATHOLOGY 54, 1372-1377.

392 BATEMAN, D.F. (1969) - SOME CHARACTERISTICS OF THE CELLULASE SYSTEM PRO-
     DUCED BY SCLEROTIUM ROLFSII SACC. PHYTOPATHOLOGY 59, 37-42.

393 BATEMAN, D.F. (1972) - THE POLYGALACTURONASE COMPLEX PRODUCED BY SCLERO-
     TIUM ROLFSII. PHYSIOL.PL.PATH. 2, 175-184.

394 BATEMAN, D.F. & BEER, S.V. (1965) - SIMULTANEOUS PRODUCTION AND SYNERGIS-
     TIC ACTION OF OXALIC ACID AND POLYGALACTURONASE DURING PATHOGENESIS BY
     SCLEROTIUM ROLFSII. PHYTOPATHOLOGY 55, 204-211.

395 BATESON, J.H. & CROSS, B.E. (1972) - NEW METABOLITES OF GIBBERELLA FUJIKU-
     ROI. 19. 3-BETA,7-BETA-DIHYDROXYKAURENOLIDE. J.CHEM.SOC., 1972, 1117-
     1120.

396 BATESON, J.H. & CROSS, B.E. (1974) - THE MICROBIOLOGICAL PRODUCTION OF
     ANALOGUES OF MOLD METABOLITES. 1. PRODUCTION OF FLUOROGIBBERELLIC ACID
     AND FLUOROGIBBERELLIN-A9 BY GIBBERELLA FUJIKUROI. J.CHEM.SOC.PERKIN
     TRANS.I, 1974 (10), 1131-1136.

397 BATIKYAN, S.G. (1968) - (SOME SPECIFIC CYTOLOGICAL FEATURES OF FUSARIUM
     FUNGI AND AN EVALUATION OF THEIR SIGNIFICANCE FOR TAXONOMY). BIOL.ZH.
     ARM. 21, 45-52.

398 BATISTA, A.C., OLIVEIRA DA SILVA, J., PEREZ MACIEL, M.J., AMERICO DE LIMA,
     J. & RAMOS DE MOURA, N. (1967) - MICROPOPULACOES FUNGICAS DOS SOLOS DO
     TERRITORIO FEDERAL DO AMAPA. ATAS INST.MICOL. 4, 117-121.

399 BATISTA, A.CH., OLIVEIRA DA SILVA, J., PEREZ MACIEL, M.J. & GONZAGA DE AL-
     MEIDA, A. (1967) - ASPERGILLACEAE DOS SOLOS DAS ZONAS FISIOGRAFICAS DE
     BRAGANCA E DO BAIXO AMAZONAS, ESTADO DO PARA. ATAS INST.MICOL. 4, 185-
     189.

400 BATISTA, A.CH., PEREZ MACIEL, M.J., ALVES, M.S.E. & BARROS REGO, S. (1967)
     - FUNGOS PHIALOPHORA MEDLAR - SUA DISPERSAO NOS SOLOS CANAVIEIROS DO ES-
     TADO DO RIO GRANDE DO NORTE. ATAS INST.MICOL. 4, 261-263.

401 BATRA, L.R. (1975) - ASCOMYCETES OF PAKISTAN - PLECTOMYCETES. BIOLOGIA,
     LAHORE 21, 1-37.

402 BATRA, L.R., BATRA, S.W.T. & BOHART, G.E. (1973) - THE MYCOFLORA OF DOMES-
     TICATED AND WILD BEES (APOIDEA). MYCOPATH.MYCOL.APPL. 49, 13-44.

403 BATTELLI, G., BIANCHEDI, M., FRIGO, W., AMORATI, P., MANTOVANI, A. & PAG-
     LIANI, A. (1975) - RICERCA DI DERMATOFITI IN TERRENI DI TANE DI MAR-
     MOTTA (MARMOTA MARMOTA) E IN TERRENI LIMITROFI DI ZONE ALPINE. VET.ITAL.
     26 (SUPPL. 9-12), 28.

404 BAUDET, E.A.R.F. (1932) - MUCOR PUSILLUS LINDT ALS OORZAAK VAN MYCOSE BIJ
     HET VARKEN. TIJDSCHR.DIERGENEESK. 59, 1163-1164.

405 BAUM, G.L. & ARTIS, D. (1966) - ISOLATION OF FUNGI FROM JUDEAN DESERT SOIL.
     MYCOPATH.MYCOL.APPL. 29, 350-354.

406 BAUMANN, F., BRUNNER, R. & ROEHR, M. (1971) - DIE SUBSTRATSPEZIFITAET DER
     PENICILLIN-AMIDASE AUS FUSARIUM SEMITECTUM. HOPPE-SEYLER'S Z.PHYSIOL.
     CHEM. 352, 853-858.

407 BAUMGART, G. (1973) - RASTERELEKTRONENMIKROSKOPISCHE UNTERSUCHUNGEN AN SCO-
     PULARIOPSIS BREVICAULIS. OEST.BOT.Z. 122, 121-124.

408 BAUSOR, S.C. (1974) - CHANGES IN THE QUIESCENT STATE IN RHIZOCTONIA SOLANI.
     AM.J.BOT. 61, 20 (ABS.).

409 BAUTE, R., DEFFIEUX, G., BAUTE, M.-A., FILLEAU, M.-J. & NEVEU, A. (1976) -
     UN NOUVEAU METABOLITE FONGIQUE DU GROUPE DES EPIDITHIO-3,6-DIOXO-2,5-
     PIPERAZINES L'EPICORAZINE-A, ISOLEE D'UNE SOUCHE D'EPICOCCUM NIGRUM
     LINK (ADELOMYCETES). TETRAHEDRON LETTERS, 1976 (44), 3943-3944.

410 BAWDON, R.E., GARRISON, R.G. & FINA, L.R. (1972) - DEOXYRIBONUCLEIC ACID
     BASE COMPOSITION OF THE YEASTLIKE AND MYCELIAL PHASES OF HISTOPLASMA
     CAPSULATUM AND BLASTOMYCES DERMATITIDIS. J.BACT. 111, 593-596.

411 BAXTER, L.W. & FAGAN, S.G. (1974) - A SIMPLIFIED METHOD OF INDUCING ASEX-
     UAL SPORULATION IN GLOMERELLA CINGULATA. PL.DIS.REPTR 58, 300-303.

412 BAYLET, R., LACOSTE, CAMAIN, BASSET,A. CHABAL & IZARN (1968) - ASPERGILLUS
     NIDULANS, AGENT DE MYCETOMES. BULL.SOC.PATH.EXOT. 61, 359-365.

413 BAYLISS-ELLIOTT, J.S. (1930) - THE SOIL FUNGI OF THE DOVEY SALT MARSHES.
     ANN.APPL.BIOL. 17, 284-305.

414 BEAN, G.A., KLARMAN, W.L., RAMBO, G.W. & SANFORD, J.B. (1971) - DIMETHYL
     SULFOXIDE INHIBITION OF AFLATOXIN SYNTHESIS BY ASPERGILLUS FLAVUS.
     PHYTOPATHOLOGY 61, 380-382.

415 BEARDER, J.R., MACMILLAN, J. & PHINNEY, B.O. (1973) - 3-HYDROXYLATION OF
     GIBBERELLIN A12-ALDEHYDE IN GIBBERELLA FUJIKUROI REC-193A. PHYTOCHEM-
     ISTRY 12, 2173-2179.

416 BEAUVERIE, M.J. (1914) - LES MUSCARDINES. LE GENRE BEAUVERIA VUILLEMIN.
     REVUE GEN.BOT. 26, 81-157.

417 BECHTOL, M.K. & THRONEBERRY, G.O. (1966) - CHARACTERISTICS OF RESPIRATION
     BY CONIDIA OF VERTICILLIUM ALBO-ATRUM. PHYTOPATHOLOGY 56, 963-966.

418 BECKMAN, C.H. (1973) - THE INCIDENCE OF VERTICILLIUM SPECIES IN SOILS,
     VINES AND TUBERS OF RHODE ISLAND-GROWN POTATOES. PL.DIS.REPTR 57, 928-
     932.

419 BEDFORD, C.T., KNITTEL, P., MONEY, T., PHILLIPS, G.T. & SALISBURY, P.
     (1973) - BIOSYNTHESIS OF MYCOPHENOLIC ACID. CAN.J.CHEM. 51, 694-697.

420 BEDI, K.S. (1961) - FACTORS AFFECTING THE VIABILITY OF SCLEROTIA OF SCLE-
     ROTINIA SCLEROTIORUM. INDIAN J.AGRIC.SCI. 31, 236-245.

421 BEDI, K.S. (1962) - EFFECT OF TEMPERATURE ON THE FORMATION OF SCLEROTIA OF SCLEROTINIA SCLEROTIORUM. INDIAN PHYTOPATH. 15, 55-60.

422 BEDI, K.S. (1963) - SOME CHEMICAL AND BIOLOGICAL FACTORS AFFECTING THE FOR- MATION OF APOTHECIA OF SCLEROTINIA SCLEROTIORUM. J.INDIAN BOT.SOC. 42, 66-73.

423 BEDI, K.S. (1963) - THE AGE AND THE SIZE OF SCLEROTIA OF SCLEROTINIA SCLE- ROTIORUM IN RELATION TO THE FORMATION OF APOTHECIA. J.INDIAN BOT.SOC. 42, 204-207.

424 BEECHAM, A.F., FRIDRICHSONS, J. & MATHIESON, A.MCL. (1966) - THE STRUCTURE AND ABSOLUTE CONFIGURATION OF GLIOTOXIN AND THE ABSOLUTE CONFIGURATION OF SPORIDESMIN. TETRAHEDRON LETTERS, 1966 (27), 3131-3138.

425 BEER, J.V. (1963) - THE INCIDENCE OF ASPERGILLUS FUMIGATUS IN THE THROATS OF WILD GEESE AND GULLS. SABOURAUDIA 2, 238-247.

426 BEGA, R.V. (1974) - PHYTOPHTHORA CINNAMOMI - ITS DISTRIBUTION AND POSSIBLE ROLE IN OHIA DECLINE ON THE ISLAND OF HAWAII. PL.DIS.REPTR 58, 1069- 1073.

427 BEHERA, N., RIKHY, M., SHARMA, K.R. & MUKERJI, K.G. (1973) - FUNGI OF DELHI. 23. SOME INTERESTING RECORDS. PROC.NATN.ACAD.SCI., INDIA, SECT.B, 39, 710-718.

428 BEHMER, D.E. & MCCALLA, T.M. (1963) - THE INHIBITION OF SEEDLING GROWTH CROP RESIDUES IN SOIL INOCULATED WITH PENICILLIUM URTICAE. PL.SOIL 18, 199- 206.

429 BEHR, L. (1963) - UEBER EINEN DURCH COLLETOTRICHUM DEMATIUM F. CIRCINANS (BERK.) V.ARX (COMB.NOV.) VERURSACHTEN TOTALSCHADEN AN KEIMENDEN KUE- CHENZWIEBELN (ALLIUM CEPA L.). ZENTBL.BAKT.PARASITKDE, ABT.2, 116, 552- 561.

430 BEHR, L. (1966) - UEBER BOTRYTIS CINEREA PERS. AM LEIN UND SEIN VERHALTEN GEGENUEBER ANTAGONISTEN IM BODEN. NACHRBL.DT.PFLSCHUTZDIENST, BERL. 20, 41-44.

431 BEKHTEREVA, M.N., GERASIMOVA, N.M. & KISELEVA, S.I. (1973) - (PRODUCTION OF LIPIDS AND THEIR COMPOSITION IN CUNNINGHAMELLA ELEGANS GROWING ON MEDIA WITH DIFFERENT SUGARS). MIKROBIOLOGIYA 42, 234-239.

432 BEKKER, S.E. & SUPRUN, T.P. (1960) - (STUDY OF THE FUNGUS FLORA OF THE FOREST SOILS OF THE AMUR REGION). BOT.ZH.SSSR. 45, 404-410.

433 BELL, A.M., JONES, E.R.H., MEAKINS, G.D., MINERS, J.O. & WILKINS, A.L. (1975) - MICROBIOLOGICAL HYDROXYLATION. 20. HYDROXYLATION OF DIOXYGENATED 5-ALPHA-ANDROSTANES WITH THE FUNGI ABSIDIA REGNIERI AND SYNCEPHALASTRUM RACEMOSUM. J.CHEM.SOC.PERKIN TRANS.I, 1975 (20), 2040-2043.

434 BELL, D.K. & CRAWFORD, J.L. (1967) - A BOTRAN-AMENDED MEDIUM FOR ISOLATING ASPERGILLUS FLAVUS FROM PEANUTS AND SOIL. PHYTOPATHOLOGY 57, 939-941.

435 BELL, J.V. & HAMALLE, R.J. (1974) - VIABILITY AND PATHOGENICITY OF ENTOMO- GENOUS FUNGI AFTER PROLONGED STORAGE ON SILICA GEL AT -20 C. CAN.J.MI- CROBIOL. 20, 639-642.

436 BELL, M.R., JOHNSON, J.R., WILDI, B.S. & WOODWARD, R.B. (1958) - THE STRUC- TURE OF GLIOTOXIN. J.AM.CHEM.SOC. 80, 1001.

437   BELL, R.G. (1976) - THE DEVELOPMENT ON BEEF CATTLE MANURE OF PETRIELLIDIUM
      BOYDII, A POTENTIAL PATHOGEN FOR MAN AND CATTLE. CAN.J.MICROBIOL. 22,
      552-556.

438   BELLET, P. & THUONG, T.VAN (1970) - HYDROXYLATION MICROBIOLOGIQUE D'ALCA-
      LOIDES INDOLIQUES. ANNLS PHARM.FR. 28, 119-122.

439   BELLIS, D.M. (1958) - METABOLISM OF COUMARIN AND RELATED COMPOUNDS IN CUL-
      TURES OF PENICILLIUM SPECIES. NATURE, LOND. 182, 806-807.

440   BELYAKOVA, L.A. (1974) - (THIELAVIA KIRILENKOAE SP.NOV. AND A KEY TO SPE-
      CIES BELONGING TO THE GENUS THIELAVIA). MIKOL.FITOPAT. 8, 73-77.

441   BELYAKOVA, L.A. (1974) - (THE GENUS EMERICELLOPSIS VAN BEYMA (EUROTIACEAE)).
      MIKOL.FITOPAT. 8, 385-395.

442   BENEDEK, T. (1969) - PARTHENOGENETIC PRODUCTION OF FERTILE CLEISTOTHECIA
      IN NANNIZZIA INCURVATA STOCKD. UNDER THE INFLUENCE OF CHRYSOSPORIUM SPE-
      CIES. MYCOPATH.MYCOL.APPL. 37, 193-214.

443   BENEDICT, W.G. & MOUNTAIN, W.B. (1954) - STUDIES ON THE ASSOCIATION OF RHI-
      ZOCTONIA SOLANI AND NEMATODES IN A ROOT-ROT DISEASE COMPLEX OF WINTER
      WHEAT IN SOUTH-WESTERN ONTARIO. PROC.CAN.PHYTOPATH.SOC. 22, 12 (ABS.).

444   BENEZET, H.J. & MATSUMURA, F. (1974) - FACTORS INFLUENCING THE METABOLISM
      OF MEXACARBATE BY MICROORGANISMS. J.AGRIC.FD CHEM. 22, 427-430.

445   BENITEZ, T., VILLA, T.G. & GARCIA ACHA, I. (1976) - SOME CHEMICAL AND STRUC-
      TURAL FEATURES OF THE CONIDIAL WALL OF TRICHODERMA VIRIDE. CAN.J.MICRO-
      BIOL. 22, 318-321.

446   BENJAMIN, C.R. (1955) - ASCOCARPS OF ASPERGILLUS AND PENICILLIUM. MYCOLO-
      GIA 47, 669-687.

447   BENJAMIN, C.R. & HESSELTINE, C.W. (1957) - THE GENUS ACTINOMUCOR. MYCOLO-
      GIA 49, 240-249.

448   BENJAMIN, C.R. & STODOLA, F.H. (1960) - RAMULOSIN, A C10 H14 O3 COMPOUND
      PRODUCED BY THE FUNGUS PESTALOTIA RAMULOSA. NATURE, LOND. 188, 662-663.

449   BENJAMIN, R.K. (1956) - A NEW GENUS OF THE GYMNOASCACEAE WITH A REVIEW OF
      THE OTHER GENERA. ALISO 3, 301-328.

450   BENJAMIN, R.K. (1959) - THE MEROSPORANGIFEROUS MUCORALES. ALISO 4, 321-433.

451   BENKEN, A.A. & DOTSENKO, A.S. (1971) - (SUPPRESSION OF VERTICILLIUM DAHLIAE
      KLEB. INOCULUM IN SOIL). MIKOL.FITOPAT. 5, 351-358.

452   BENKOVIC, S.J., VERGARA, E.V. & HEVEY, R.C. (1971) - PURIFICATION AND PROP-
      ERTIES OF AN ARYLSULFATASE FROM ASPERGILLUS ORYZAE. J.BIOL.CHEM. 246,
      4926-4933.

453   BENNETT, F.T. (1928) - ON TWO SPECIES OF FUSARIUM, F. CULMORUM AND F. AVE-
      NACEUM, AS PARASITES OF CEREALS. ANN.APPL.BIOL. 15, 213-244.

454   BENNY, G.L. & BENJAMIN, R.K. (1975) - OBSERVATIONS ON THAMNIDIACEAE (MU-
      CORALES). NEW TAXA, NEW COMBINATIONS, AND NOTES ON SELECTED SPECIES.
      ALISO 8, 301-351.

455   BENOIT, M.A. & MATHUR, S.B. (1970) - IDENTIFICATION OF SPECIES OF CURVULA-
      RIA ON RICE SEED. PROC.INT.SEED TEST.ASS. 35, 99-119.

456 BENSON, B.W. & GROSKLAGS, J.H. (1969) - NUCLEI OF THE GENUS EMERICELLOPSIS. MYCOLOGIA 61, 718-725.

457 BENSON, D.M. & BAKER, R. (1974) - EPIDEMIOLOGY OF RHIZOCTONIA SOLANI PRE-EMERGENCE DAMPING-OFF OF RADISH - INOCULUM POTENTIAL AND DISEASE POTENTIAL INTERACTION. PHYTOPATHOLOGY 64, 957-962.

458 BENSON, D.M. & BAKER, R. (1974) - EPIDEMIOLOGY OF RHIZOCTONIA SOLANI PRE-EMERGENCE DAMPING-OFF OF RADISH - SURVIVAL. PHYTOPATHOLOGY 64, 1163-1168.

459 BENT, K.J. (1964) - SIGNIFICANCE OF THE AMINO ACID POOL IN NITROGEN METABOLISM OF PENICILLIUM GRISEOFULVUM. BIOCHEM.J. 92, 280-289.

460 BENTLEY, R. & KEIL, J.G. (1961) - THE ROLE OF ACETATE AND MALONATE IN THE BIOSYNTHESIS OF PENICILLIC ACID. PROC.CHEM.SOC., 1961, 111-112.

461 BEN-YEPHET, Y. & PINKAS, Y. (1976) - CESIUM CHLORIDE FLOTATION TECHNIQUE FOR ISOLATION OF VERTICILLIUM DAHLIAE MICROSCLEROTIA FROM SOIL. PHYTOPATHOLOGY 66, 1252-1254.

462 BENZONANA, G. (1974) - SOME PROPERTIES OF AN EXOCELLULAR LIPASE FROM RHIZOPUS ARRHIZUS. LIPIDS 9, 166-172.

463 BERAHA, L., GARBER, E.D. & STROMNAES, O. (1964) - GENETICS OF PHYTOPATHOGENIC FUNGI. VIRULENCE OF COLOR AND NUTRITIONALLY DEFICIENT MUTANTS OF PENICILLIUM ITALICUM AND PENICILLIUM DIGITATUM. CAN.J.BOT. 42, 429-436.

464 BERBEC, J., JEZIORSKA, Z. & MICZYNSKA, Z. (1971) - INFLUENCE OF SOME CULTIVATED PLANTS ON THE CHANGE OF THE DEGREE OF SOIL INFECTION BY THIELAVIOPSIS BASICOLA (BERK. & BR.) FERR. PAM.PULAWSKI 43, 151-167.

465 BERG, B. (1976) - THE ULTRASTRUCTURE OF THE FUNGUS TRICHODERMA VIRIDE AND INVESTIGATION OF ITS GROWTH ON CELLULOSE. J.APPL.BACT. 41, 395-399.

466 BERG, L.VAN DEN & LENTZ, C.P. (1968) - THE EFFECT OF RELATIVE HUMIDITY AND TEMPERATURE ON SURVIVAL AND GROWTH OF BOTRYTIS CINEREA AND SCLEROTINIA SCLEROTIORUM. CAN.J.BOT. 46, 1477-1481.

467 BERGEL, F., MORRISON, A.L., MOSS, A.R. & RINDERKNECHT, H. (1944) - AN ANTIBACTERIAL SUBSTANCE FROM ASPERGILLUS CLAVATUS. J.CHEM.SOC., 1944, 415-421.

468 BERGEN, L. & WAGNER-MERNER, D.T. (1977) - COMPARATIVE SURVEY OF FUNGI AND POTENTIAL PATHOGENIC FUNGI FROM SELECTED BEACHES IN THE TAMPA BAY AREA. MYCOLOGIA 69, 299-308.

469 BERGESON, G.B. (1972) - CONCEPTS OF NEMATODE-FUNGUS ASSOCIATIONS IN PLANT DISEASE COMPLEXES - A REVIEW. EXP.PARASITOL. 32, 301-314.

470 BERGHEM, L.E.R. (1974) - THE MECHANISM OF ENZYMATIC CELLULOSE DEGRADATION BY TRICHODERMA VIRIDE. ACTA UNIV.UPSAL. NO.317, 1-17.

471 BERGHEM, L.E.R., PETTERSSON, L.G. & AXIO-FREDRIKSSON, U.-B. (1975) - THE MECHANISM OF ENZYMATIC CELLULOSE DEGRADATION. CHARACTERIZATION AND ENZYMATIC PROPERTIES OF A BETA-1,4-GLUCAN CELLOBIOHYDROLASE FROM TRICHODERMA VIRIDE. EUR.J.BIOCHEM. 53, 55-62.

472 BERGHEM, L.E.R., PETTERSSON, L.G. & AXIO-FREDRIKSSON, U.-B. (1976) - THE MECHANISM OF ENZYMATIC CELLULOSE DEGRADATION. PURIFICATION AND SOME PROPERTIES OF TWO DIFFERENT 1,4-BETA-GLUCAN GLUCANOHYDROLASES FROM TRICHODERMA VIRIDE. EUR.J.BIOCHEM. 61, 621-630.

473 BERK, S., EBERT, H. & TEITELL, L. (1957) - UTILIZATION OF PLASTICIZERS AND RELATED ORGANIC COMPOUNDS BY FUNGI. IND.ENGNG CHEM. 49, 1115-1124.

474 BERLINER, M.D. (1968) - PRIMARY SUBCULTURES OF HISTOPLASMA CAPSULATUM. 1. MACRO AND MICROMORPHOLOGY OF THE MYCELIAL TYPE. SABOURAUDIA 6, 111-118.

475 BERLINER, M.D. (1973) - HISTOPLASMA CAPSULATUM. EFFECTS OF PH ON THE YEAST AND MYCELIAL PHASES IN VITRO. SABOURAUDIA 11, 267-270.

476 BERLINER, M.D. (1973) - VITAL STAINING FOR THE DIFFERENTIATION OF THE ALBINO AND BROWN PHENOTYPES IN VITRO. SABOURAUDIA 11, 271-273.

477 BERLINER, M.D. & BIUNDO, N. (1973) - EFFECTS OF CONTINUOUS LIGHT AND TOTAL DARKNESS ON CULTURES OF HISTOPLASMA CAPSULATUM. SABOURAUDIA 11, 48-51.

478 BERNARDINI, M., CARILLI, A., PACIONI, G. & SANTURBANO, B. (1975) - ISOLATION OF BEAUVERICIN FROM PAECILOMYCES FUMOSO-ROSEUS. PHYTOCHEMISTRY 14, 1865-1866.

479 BERNAT, J. & BRAUNOVA, O. (1976) - (THE NITRITE PRODUCTION OF THE GENUS CHAETOMIUM). ACTA FAC.RER.NAT.UNIV.COMENIANAE, MICROBIOL., 1967 (4), 127-134.

480 BERNDT, H. & LIESE, W. (1971) - UNTERSUCHUNGEN UEBER DIE ENZYME VON BLAEUEPILZEN. 3. PECTINTRANSELIMINASE UND MANNANASE BEI AUREOBASIDIUM PULLULANS. ARCH.MIKROBIOL 79, 140-146.

481 BERTHE, M.C., BONALY, R. & REISINGER, O. (1970) - CHEMICAL AND ENZYMATIC DEGRADATION OF THE WALLS OF HELMINTHOSPORIUM SPICIFERUM, PROTECTIVE ROLE OF PIGMENTS. CAN.J.MICROBIOL. 22, 929-936.

482 BERTHIER, J. (1974) - LE GENRE TYPHULA (CLAVARIACEES) ET LES GENRES AFFINES - CLASSIFICATION - ESPECES NOUVELLES. BULL.SOC.LINN.LYON 43, 182-188.

483 BERTHIER, J. (1976) - MONOGRAPHIE DES TYPHULA, PISTILLARIA ET GENRES VOISINS. BULL.SOC.LINN.LYON 45, (NUMERO SPECIAL), 213 PP.

484 BERTINI, S. (1955) - AZIONE STIMOLATRICE DI PENICILLIUM NOTATUM E DI ALTRI PENICILLIUM SU LO SVILUPPO E LA FORMAZIONE DI SCLEROZI DI SCLEROTIUM ROLFSII. ANNALI SPER.AGR. 1955 (1-5).

485 BERTOLDI, M.DE (1972) - NUCLEAR DISTRIBUTION IN SOME STRAINS REFERRED TO THE GENUS HUMICOLA. ANNALI BOT. 31, 187-196.

486 BERTOLDI, M.DE, LEPIDI, A.A. & NUTI, M.P. (1972) - CLASSIFICATION OF THE GENUS HUMICOLA TRAAEN. 1. PRELIMINARY REPORTS AND INVESTIGATIONS. MYCOPATH.MYCOL.APPL. 46, 289-304.

487 BERTOLDI, M.DE, MARIOTTI, F. & FILIPPI, C. (1974) - THE FINE STRUCTURE OF SOME STRAINS OF HUMICOLA. CAN.J.MICROBIOL. 20, 237-239.

488 BERTOLDI, M.DE & VERONA, O. (1970) - MICROMICETI NUOVI O RARI PER L'ITALIA ISOLATI DA TERRENI DI SARDEGNA. AGRICOLTURA ITAL., PISA 70, 349-370.

489 BERTONI, M.D., GODEAS, A.M., LOEWENBAUM, M.E. & WRIGHT, J.E. (1973) - MICOFLORA DEL SUELO DE LA ARGENTINA. 4. FORMAS ASCOSPORICAS ADICIONALES DE LA REGION CHAQUENA. BOLN SOC.ARGENT.BOT. 15, 93-105.

490 BERTRAND, M.D. (1941) - LE VANADIUM COMME FACTEUR DE CROISSANCE POUR L'ASPERGILLUS NIGER. BULL.SOC.CHIM.BIOL. 23, 467-471.

491   BERTUS, A.L. (1976) - CYLINDROCLADIUM SCOPARIUM ON AUSTRALIAN NATIVE PLANTS
      IN CULTIVATION. PHYTOPATH.Z. 85, 15-25.

492   BESRI, M. (1975) - INFLUENCE DU PRECEDENT CULTURAL SUR L'EVOLUTION DE LA
      POPULATION DE FUSARIUM OXYSPORUM DANS LA RHIZOSPHERE DE QUELQUES PLAN-
      TES. ANNLS PHYTOPATH. 7, 1-8.

493   BESSEY, E.A. (1939) - VARICOSPORIUM ELODEAE KEGEL, AN UNCOMMON SOIL FUNGUS.
      PAP.MICH.ACAD.SCI. 25, 15-17.

494   BEYMA THOE KINGMA, F.H.VAN (1939/40) - UEBER EINIGE FORMEN VON VERTICILLIUM
      DAHLIAE KLEBAHN. ANTONIE VAN LEEUWENHOEK 6, 33-47.

495   BEYMA THOE KINGMA, F.H.VAN (1943) - BESCHREIBUNG DER IM CENTRAALBUREAU
      VOOR SCHIMMELCULTURES VORHANDENEN ARTEN DER GATTUNGEN PHIALOPHORA UND
      MARGARINOMYCES, NEBST SCHLUESSEL ZU IHRER BESTIMMUNG. ANTONIE VAN LEEU-
      WENHOEK 9, 51-76.

496   BEZBORODOVA, S.I. & BAGDASARYAN, Z.N. (1972) - (STUDY OF EXTRACELLULAR
      RNAASES FROM PENICILLIUM CLAVIFORME). MIKROBIOLOGIYA 41, 684-690.

497   BEZBORODOVA, S.I. & GORBUNOVA, V.V. (1973) - (PURIFICATION AND PROPERTIES
      OF THE EXTRACELLULAR ALKALINE PHOSPHODIESTERASE OF PENICILLIUM CHRYSO-
      GENUM). MIKROBIOLOGIYA 42, 29-34.

498   BEZBORODOVA, S.I. & ILINA, T.V. (1970) - (EXTRACELLULAR PHOSPHOMONOESTER-
      ASES OF FUNGI BELONGING TO THE FUSARIUM GENUS). MIKROBIOLOGIYA 39, 741-
      747.

499   BHARDWAJ, K.K.R. & GAUR, A.C. (1971) - ISOLATION AND CHARACTERIZATION OF
      SOME HUMIC ACID DECOMPOSING BACTERIA AND FUNGI FROM SOIL. ZENTBL.BAKT.
      PARASITKDE, ABT.2, 126, 307-312.

500   BHARGAVA, S.N. (1972) - RELATION BETWEEN DECOMPOSITION RATES FOR CELLULOSE
      AND WHEAT STRAW IN FIVE CEREAL FOOT-ROT FUNGI. TRANS.BR.MYCOL.SOC. 58,
      348-350.

501   BHATIA, I.S., RAHEJA, R.K. & SUKHIJA, P.S. (1973) - FUNGAL LIPIDS. 2. EF-
      FECTS OF VARYING CONCENTRATION OF NITROGEN IN THE MEDIUM AND INCUBATION
      PERIOD ON THE CHEMICAL COMPOSITION OF LIPIDS OF PYTHIUM IRREGULARE BUIS-
      MAN. J.SCI.FD AGRIC. 24, 779-788.

502   BHATNAGAR, G.M. & KRISHNAN, P.S. (1960) - ENZYMATIC STUDIES ON THE SPORES
      OF ASPERGILLUS NIGER. 1. CATALASE. ARCH.MIKROBIOL. 36, 131-138.

503   BHATNAGAR, G.M. & KRISHNAN, P.S. (1960) - ENZYMATIC STUDIES ON THE SPORES
      OF ASPERGILLUS NIGER. 2. PHOSPHATASE. ARCH.MIKROBIOL. 36, 169-174.

504   BHATNAGAR, G.M. & KRISHNAN, P.S. (1960) - ENZYMATIC STUDIES ON THE SPORES
      OF ASPERGILLUS NIGER. 3. ENZYMES OF THE EMBDEN-MEYERHOF-PARNAS PATHWAY
      IN GERMINATING SPORES OF ASPERGILLUS NIGER. ARCH.MIKROBIOL. 37, 211-214.

505   BHATT, G.C. (1970) - THE SOIL MICROFUNGI OF WHITE CEDAR FOREST IN ONTARIO.
      CAN.J.BOT. 48, 333-339.

506   BHATTACHARYYA, S.K. & BANERJEE, A.B. (1972) - FREE D-AMINO ACIDS IN THE
      CELL POOL OF FUNGI AND ACTINOMYCETES. ACTA MICROBIOL.POL. 4, 63-68.

507   BHELWA, P.W., PHILLIPS, D.V. & ALLISON, C.C. (1962) - MITIGATION OF FU-
      SARIUM WILT SYMPTOMS OF TOMATO SEEDLINGS BY SEED INOCULATION WITH A SPE-
      CIES OF CEPHALOSPORIUM. PHYTOPATHOLOGY 52, 725.

508   BHUYAN, B.K. & JOHNSON, M.J. (1958) - CHEMICALLY DEFINED MEDIA FOR SYNNE-
      MATIN PRODUCTION. J.BACT. 76, 376-384.

509   BIDAULT, C. (1921) - SUR LES MOISISSURES DES VIANDES CONGELEES. C.R.SEANC.
      SOC.BIOL. 85, 1017-1018.

510   BIESBROCK, J.A. & HENDRIX, F.F. (1967) - A TAXONOMIC STUDY OF PYTHIUM
      IRREGULARE AND RELATED SPECIES (PYTHIUM DEBARYANUM, PYTHIUM SPINOSUM,
      PYTHIUM ULTIMUM, PYTHIUM MAMILLATUM, PYTHIUM OLIGANDRUM, PYTHIUM APHA-
      NIDERMATUM). MYCOLOGIA 59, 943-952.

511   BIESBROCK, J.A. & HENDRIX, F.F. (1970) - INFLUENCE OF SOIL WATER AND TEM-
      PERATURE ON ROOT NECROSIS OF PEACH CAUSED BY PYTHIUM SPP. PHYTOPATHOLOGY
      60, 880-882.

512   BILAI, V.I. (1963) - ANTIBIOTIC-PRODUCING MICROSCOPIC FUNGI. ELSEVIER PUBL.
      CO., AMSTERDAM, LONDON, NEW YORK, 215 PP.

513   BILAI, V.I., BASARAB, B.M., HAVRYUSHINA, A.I. & NENYUCHENKO, I.T. (1968) -
      (PROTEOLYTIC PROPERTIES OF MUCORALES FUNGI). MYKROBIOL.ZH. 30, 304-308.

514   BILAI, V.I. & GORBIK, L.T. (1972) - A CYTOLOGICAL STUDY OF NUCLEI IN CONI-
      DIUM AND HYPHAL CELLS OF FUSARIUM SPECIES. MYKROBIOL.ZH. 34 (4), 441-
      443.

515   BILAI, V.I., PIDOPLICHKO, N.M. & DYMOVICH, V.A. (1964) - (ANTIBACTERIAL
      PROPERTIES OF PENICILLIUM SPECIES FROM THE RHIZOSPHERE OF AGRICULTURAL
      PLANTS). MYKROBIOL.ZH. 26 (1), 31-37.

516   BILAI, V.I., PIDOPLICHKO, N.M., NIKOLSKAYA, E.A. & DYMOVICH, V.A. (1964) -
      (ANTIFUNGOUS PROPERTIES OF THE SPECIES OF PENICILLIUM). MYKROBIOL.ZH.
      26 (1), 42-45.

517   BILAI, V.I. & ZAKHARCHENKO, V.A. (1971) - (RANGE OF SOIL MICROMYCETE GROWTH
      TEMPERATURE). MYKROBIOL.ZH. 33 (1), 30-34.

518   BILAI, V.I. & ZAKORDONETS, L.A. (1971) - DYNAMICS OF AMINO ACID CONTENT IN
      FUSARIUM MONILIFORME 51070 IN THE PROCESS OF GROWTH. MYKROBIOL.ZH. 33
      (3), 306-309.

519   BILAI, V.I., ZANEVICH, V.E. & MALASHENKO, YU.R. (1961) - (A COMPARATIVE
      STUDY OF DIFFERENT STRAINS OF GIBBERELLA FUJIKUROI WHICH SYNTHESIZED
      GIBBERELLINOID PLANT GROWTH STIMULATORS). MYKROBIOL.ZH. 23 (3), 34-38.

520   BILAI, V.I., ZANEVICH, V.E. & VYUN, A.A. (1959) - (ANTIBIOTIC PROPERTIES
      OF PENICILLIUM SPECIES FROM THE RHIZOSPHERE OF AGRICULTURAL CROP PLANTS
      IN THE UKRAINE). MYKROBIOL.ZH. 21 (2), 35-39.

521   BILGRAMI, K.S. & VERMA, R.N. (1972) - SOME ADDITIONS TO INDIAN FUNGI. CURR.
      SCI. 41, 504.

522   BINDER, M., TAMM, C., TURNER, W.B. & MINATO, H. (1973) - NOMENCLATURE OF A
      CLASS OF BIOLOGICALLY ACTIVE MOULD METABOLITES. THE CYTOCHALASINS, PHO-
      MINS, AND ZYGOSPORINS. J.CHEM.SOC.PERKIN TRANS.I, 1973 (11), 1146-1147.

523   BINYAMINI, N. & SCHIFFMANN-NADEL, M. (1972) - THE UTILIZATION IN VITRO OF
      DIFFERENT AVOCADO FRUIT CONSTITUENTS BY COLLETOTRICHUM GLOEOSPORIOIDES.
      MYCOLOGIA 64, 916-919.

524   BIRCH, A.J. & RUSSELL, R.A. (1972) - STUDIES IN RELATION TO BIOSYNTHESIS.
      14. STRUCTURAL ELUCIDATIONS OF BREVIANAMIDES-B, -C, -D, AND -F. TETRA-
      HEDRON 28, 2999-3008.

525 BIRD, G.W., MCCARTER, S.M. & RONCADORI, R.W. (1971) - ROLE OF NEMATODES AND SOIL-BORNE FUNGI IN COTTON STUNT. J.NEMATOL. 3, 17-22.

526 BIRD, M.L. & CHALLENGER, F. (1939) - THE FORMATION OF ORGANO-METALLOIDAL AND SIMILAR COMPOUNDS BY MICRO-ORGANISMS. 7. DIMETHYLTELLURIDE. J.CHEM. SOC., 1939, 163-168.

527 BIRKENBEIL, H. (1973) - EIN PILZWIRKSAMES ANTIBIOTIKUM VON FUSARIUM OXY-SPORUM. MIKROKOSMOS 62, 232-234.

528 BIRKINSHAW, J.H., BRACKEN, A. & RAISTRICK, H. (1943) - STUDIES IN THE BIO-CHEMISTRY OF MICROORGANISMS. 72. GENTISYL ALCOHOL (2,5-DIHYDROXYBENZYL ALCOHOL), A METABOLIC PRODUCT OF PENICILLIUM PATULUM. BIOCHEM.J. 37, 726-728.

529 BIRKINSHAW, J.H., BRACKEN, A. & RAISTRICK, H. (1945) - STUDIES IN THE BIO-CHEMISTRY OF MICRO-ORGANISMS. 73. METABOLIC PRODUCTS OF ASPERGILLUS FU-MIGATUS FRESENIUS. BIOCHEM.J. 39, 70-72.

530 BIRKINSHAW, J.H., CHARLES, J.H.V., LILLY, C. & RAISTRICK, H. (1931) - STUD-IES IN THE BIOCHEMISTRY OF MICRO-ORGANISMS. 7. KOJIC ACID (5-HYDROXY-2-HYDROXY-METHYL-GAMMA-PYRONE). PHIL.TRANS.B. 220, 127-138.

531 BIRKINSHAW, J., CHARLES, J.H.V. & RAISTRICK, H. (1931) - STUDIES IN THE BIOCHEMISTRY OF MICRO-ORGANISMS. 18. BIOCHEMICAL CHARACTERISTICS OF SPECIES OF PENICILLIUM RESPONSIBLE FOR THE ROT OF CITRUS FRUITS. PHIL. TRANS.B. 220, 355-362.

532 BIRKINSHAW, J.H., OXFORD, A.E. & RAISTRICK, H. (1936) - STUDIES IN THE BIO-CHEMISTRY OF MICROORGANISMS. 48. PENICILLIC ACID, A METABOLIC PRODUCT OF PENICILLIUM PUBERULUM AND P. CYCLOPIUM. BIOCHEM.J. 30, 394-411.

533 BIRKINSHAW, J.H. & RAISTRICK, H. (1931) - STUDIES IN THE BIOCHEMISTRY OF MICROORGANISMS. 12. ON A NEW METHOXY-DIHYDROXYTOLUQUINONE PRODUCED FROM GLUCOSE BY SPECIES OF PENICILLIUM OF THE P. SPINULOSUM SERIES. TRANS.R. SOC., SER.B, 220, 245-254.

534 BIRKINSHAW, J.H. & RAISTRICK, H. (1931) - STUDIES IN THE BIOCHEMISTRY OF MICROORGANISMS. 17. PRODUCTS OF DEXTROSE METABOLISM FORMED BY VARIOUS SPECIES OF FUNGI. TRANS.R.SOC., SER.B, 220, 331-354.

535 BIRKINSHAW, J.H. & RAISTRICK, H. (1936) - STUDIES IN THE BIOCHEMISTRY OF MICROORGANISMS. 49. PALITANTIN, $C_{14} H_{22} O_4$, A HITHERTO UNDESCRIBED META-BOLIC PRODUCT OF PENICILLIUM PALITANS. BIOCHEM.J. 30, 801-808.

536 BIRKINSHAW, J.H., RAISTRICK, H. & ROSS, D.J. (1952) - STUDIES IN THE BIO-CHEMISTRY OF MICROORGANISMS. 86. THE MOLECULAR CONSTITUTION OF MYCOPHE-NOLIC ACID, A METABOLIC PRODUCT OF PENICILLIUM BREVI-COMPACTUM. 3. FUR-THER OBSERVATIONS ON THE STRUCTURAL FORMULA FOR MYCOPHENOLIC ACID. BIO-CHEM.J. 50, 630-634.

537 BIRKINSHAW, J.H., RAISTRICK, H., ROSS, D.J. & STICKINGS, C.E. (1952) - STUDIES IN THE BIOCHEMISTRY OF MICROORGANISMS. 85. CYCLOPIC ACID AND CYCLOPALDIC ACID, METABOLIC PRODUCTS OF PENICILLIUM CYCLOPIUM. BIOCHEM. J. 50, 610-628.

538 BIRKINSHAW, J.H., ROBERTS, J.C. & ROFFEY, P. (1966) - MYCOLOGICAL CHEM-ISTRY. 19. PRODUCT B (AVERANTIN), A PIGMENT FROM ASPERGILLUS VERSICOLOR. J.CHEM.SOC.(C), 1966, 855-857.

539   BIRKINSHAW, J.H. & SAMANT, M.S. (1960) - STUDIES IN THE BIOCHEMISTRY OF
      MICROORGANISMS. 107. METABOLITES OF PENICILLIUM VIRIDICATUM WESTLING.
      VIRIDICATIC ACID (ETHYLCARLOSIC ACID). BIOCHEM.J. 74, 369-373.

540   BISBY, G.R., TIMONIN, M.I. & JAMES, M. (1935) - FUNGI ISOLATED FROM SOIL
      PROFILES IN MANITOBA. CAN.J.RES., SECT.C, 13, 47-65.

541   BIXBY, M.W., BOUSH, G.M. & MATSUMURA, F. (1971) - DEGRADATION OF DIELDRIN
      TO CARBON DIOXIDE BY A SOIL FUNGUS, TRICHODERMA KONINGI. BULL.ENVIRON.
      CONTAM.TOXICOL. 6, 491-494.

542   BJOERLING, K. (1936) - UEBER DIE GATTUNGEN MORTIERELLA UND HAPLOSPORANGIUM.
      BOT.NOTISER 1936, 116-126.

543   BJOERNSSON, I.P. (1959) - RESPONSES OF CERTAIN FUNGI, PARTICULARLY TRICHO-
      DERMA SP., TO LIGHT. J.WASH.ACAD.SCI. 49, 317-323.

544   BLACK, R.L.B. & DIX, N.J. (1968) - UTILIZATION OF FERULIC ACID BY MICRO-
      FUNGI FROM LITTER AND SOIL. TRANS.BR.MYCOL.SOC. 66, 313-317.

545   BLACKBURN, F. & HAYES, W.A. (1963) - A CHEMICALLY DEFINED MEDIUM FOR THE
      CULTIVATION OF NEMATOPHAGOUS HYPHOMYCETES. TRANS.BR.MYCOL.SOC. 46, 449-
      452.

546   BLACKBURN, F. & HAYES, W.A. (1966) - STUDIES ON THE NUTRITION OF ARTHROBO-
      TRYS OLIGOSPORA AND A. ROBUSTA. 1. THE SAPROPHYTIC PHASE. ANN.APPL.BIOL.
      58, 43-50.

547   BLACKWELL, E. (1943) - THE LIFE HISTORY OF PHYTOPHTHORA CACTORUM. TRANS.
      BR.MYCOL.SOC. 26, 71-89.

548   BLAIR, I.D. (1942) - STUDIES ON THE GROWTH IN SOIL AND THE PARASITIC ACTION
      OF CERTAIN RHIZOCTONIA ISOLATES FROM WHEAT. CAN.J.RES., SECT.C, 20, 174-
      185.

549   BLAIR, I.D. (1943) - BEHAVIOUR OF THE FUNGUS RHIZOCTONIA SOLANI IN THE
      SOIL. ANN.APPL.BIOL. 30, 118-127.

550   BLAIR, I.D. (1945) - TECHNIQUES FOR SOIL FUNGUS STUDIES. N.Z.JL SCI.TECH-
      NOL. 26A, 258-271.

551   BLAKEMAN, J.P. & SZTEJNBERG, A. (1974) - GERMINATION OF BOTRYTIS CINERA
      SPORES ON BEETROOT LEAVES TREATED WITH ANTIBIOTICS. TRANS.BR.MYCOL.SOC.
      62, 537-545.

552   BLANK, L.M. & TALLEY, P.J. (1941) - ARE AMMONIUM SALTS TOXIC TO THE COTTON
      ROOT ROT FUNGUS? PHYTOPATHOLOGY 31, 926-935.

553   BLANK, L.M. & TALLEY, P.J. (1941) - THE CARBON UTILIZATION AND CARBOHYDRA-
      SE ACTIVITY OF PHYMATOTRICHOPSIS OMNIVORA. AM.J.BOT. 28, 564-569.

554   BLASER, P. (1975) - SYSTEMATISCHE UNTERSUCHUNGEN UEBER DIE ASPERGILLUS
      GLAUCUS-GRUPPE. MYKOSEN 18, 87-89.

555   BLASER, P. (1976) - TAXONOMISCHE UND HISTOLOGISCHE UNTERSUCHUNGEN UEBER
      DIE GATTUNG EUROTIUM. SYDOWIA 28, 1-49 (1974/75).

556   BLISS, D.E. (1951) - THE DESTRUCTION OF ARMILLARIA MELLEA IN CITRUS SOIL.
      PHYTOPATHOLOGY 41, 665-683.

557   BLOCH, P., TAMM, C., BOLLINGER, P., PETCHER, T.J. & WEBER, H.P. (1976) -
      PSEUROTIN, A NEW METABOLITE OF PSEUDEUROTIUM OVALIS STOLK HAVING AN UN-
      USUAL HETERO-SPIROCYCLIC SYSTEM. HELV.CHIM.ACTA 59, 133-137.

558 BLOCHWITZ, A. (1914) - BOTRYOTRICHUM PILULIFERUM. MORPHOLOGIE, ENTWICKLUNGS-
     GESCHICHTE, PHYSIOLOGIE, OEKOLOGIE. ANNLS MYCOL. 12, 315-334.

559 BLOK, I. (1970) - PATHOGENICITY OF PYTHIUM SYLVATICUM. NETH.J.PL.PATH. 76,
     296-298.

560 BLOK, I. (1973) - A GROWTH-REGULATING SUBSTANCE PRODUCED BY PYTHIUM SYLVA-
     TICUM. NETH.J.PL.PATH. 79, 266-276.

561 BLOOM, J.R. & COUCH, H.B. (1960) - INFLUENCE OF ENVIRONMENT ON DISEASES OF
     TURFGRASSES. 1. EFFECT OF NUTRITION, PH, AND SOIL MOISTRURE ON RHIZO-
     CTONIA BROWN PATCH. PHYTOPATHOLOGY 50, 532-535.

562 BLOOMFIELD, B.J. & ALEXANDER, M. (1967) - MELANINS AND THE RESISTANCE OF
     FUNGI TO LYSIS. J.BACT. 93, 1276-1280.

563 BLOSS, H.E. (1970) - OBSERVATIONS ON SPECIES OF PHYMATOTRICHUM. J.ARIZ.
     ACAD.SCI. 6, 102-108.

564 BLOSS, H.E. & WHEELER, J.E. (1975) - INFLUENCE OF NUTRIENTS AND SUBSTRATA
     ON FORMATION OF STRANDS AND SCLEROTIA BY PHYMATOTRICHUM OMNIVORUM. MY-
     COLOGIA 67, 303-310.

565 BLUMER, S. (1944) - BEITRAEGE ZUR PHYSIOLOGIE VON TRICHODERMA VIRIDE. BER.
     SCHWEIZ.BOT.GES. 54, 605-624.

566 BLUMER, S. (1945) - BODENPILZE AUS DEN SCHIEFERSCHUTTHALDEN VON ENGI (GLA-
     RUS). MITT.NATF.GES.KT.GLARUS 7, 185-203.

567 BLUMER, S. (1952) - UEBER ZWEI SCHIMMELPILZE AUF DEN BLUETENSTAENDEN VON
     POINSETTIA PULCHERRIMA. PHYTOPATH.Z. 19, 417-422.

568 BLUMER, S. (1953) - UEBER DIE EIGNUNG VON PENICILLIUM EXPANSUM FUER EINE
     BIOLOGISCHE BEKAEMPFUNG VON SCHWARZFUSSPILZEN (RHIZOCTONIA SOLANI).
     PHYTOPATH.Z. 21, 163-188.

569 BLUNT, F.L. & BAKER, G.E. (1968) - ANTIMYCOTIC ACTIVITY OF FUNGI ISOLATED
     FROM HAWAIIAN SOILS. MYCOLOGIA 60, 559-570.

570 BLYTH, W. (1971) - MODIFICATION IN THE ULTRASTRUCTURE OF ASPERGILLUS FUMI-
     GATUS DUE TO THE PRESENCE OF LIVING CELLS OF PSEUDOMONAS AERUGINOSA.
     SABOURAUDIA 9, 283-286.

571 BLYTH, W. & FOREY, A. (1971) - THE INFLUENCE OF RESPIRATORY BACTERIA AND
     THEIR BIOCHEMICAL FRACTIONS ON ASPERGILLUS FUMIGATUS. SABOURAUDIA 9,
     273-282.

572 BOCCAS, B. & ZENTMYER, G.A. (1976) - GENETICAL STUDIES WITH INTERSPECIFIC
     CROSSES BETWEEN PHYTOPHTHORA CINNAMOMI AND PHYTOPHTHORA PARASITICA. PHY-
     TOPATHOLOGY 66, 477-484.

573 BOCHEVA, S.S. (1973) - (UREA OF ASPERGILLUS ORYZAE). BIOL.NAUKI 16, 90-94.

574 BOCHOW, H. & SEIDEL, D. (1964) - BEITRAEGE ZUR FRAGE DES EINFLUSSES EINER
     ORGANISCHEN DUENGUNG AUF DEN BEFALL VON PFLANZEN DURCH PARASITISCHE
     PILZE. 4. WIRKUNGEN EINER STALLMIST- BZW. STROHDUENGUNG AUF PLASMODIO-
     PHORA BRASSICAE WOR., OPHIOBOLUS GRAMINIS SACC. UND HELMINTHOSPORIUM
     SATIVUM P., K. & B. PHYTOPATH.Z. 51, 291-310.

575 BOCKS, S.M., LINDSAY SMITH, J.R. & NORMAN, R.O.C. (1964) - HYDROXYLATION
     OF PHENOXYACETIC ACID AND ANISOLE BY ASPERGILLUS NIGER. NATURE, LOND.
     201, 398.

576 BODANSZKY, M. & STAHL, G.L. (1974) - THE STRUCTURE AND SYNTHESIS OF MAL-FORMIN-A. PROC.NATN.ACAD.SCI., U.S.A. 71, 2791-2794.

577 BODIN, E. & GAUTIER, L. (1906) - NOTE SUR UNE TOXINE PRODUITE PAR L'ASPER-GILLUS FUMIGATUS. ANNLS INST.PASTEUR, PARIS 20, 209-224.

578 BOEDIJN, K.B. (1958) - NOTES ON THE MUCORALES OF INDONESIA. SYDOWIA 12, 321-362.

579 BOEDIJN, K.B. & REITSMA, J. (1950) - NOTES ON THE GENUS CYLINDROCLADIUM. REINWARDTIA 1, 51-60.

580 BOEHME, H. (1967) - VORKOMMEN VON TRICHOPHYTON VANBREUSEGHEMII RIOUX, JARRY & JUMINER IM ERDBODEN VON DEUTSCHLAND. MYKOSEN 10, 117-120.

581 BOEHME, H. (1972) - UEBER DEN STOFFWECHSEL DER GATTUNG MICROSPORUM GRUBY 1943. 4. VERGLEICHENDE UNTERSUCHUNGEN UEBER DEN ABBAU VON TRIGLYCERIDEN UND WACHSEN DURCH FUENF ARTEN DER GATTUNG MICROSPORUM. MYCOPATH.MYCOL. APPL. 46, 221-232.

582 BOEHME, H., RAWALD, W. & STOHR, G. (1969) - UEBER OEKOLOGISCHE, INSBESON-DERE BODENMIKROBIOLOGISCHE ASPEKTE DES VORKOMMENS KERATINOPHILER PILZE IN VERSCHIEDENEN BODENTYPEN. ZENTBL.BAKT.PARASITKDE, ABT.2, 123, 116-137.

583 BOEHME, H. & SCHMOLLACK, E. (1969) - ABBAU VON VERNIX CASEOSA DURCH MIKRO-SPORUM GYPSEUM (BODIN) GUIART & GRIGORAKI IN VITRO. DERM.MSCHR. 155, 171-177.

584 BOEHME, H. & ZIEGLER, H. (1965) - VERBREITUNG UND KERATINOPHILIE VON ANIXI-OPSIS STERCORARIA (HANSEN) HANSEN. ARCH.KLIN.EXP.DERM. 223, 422-428.

585 BOEHME, H. & ZIEGLER, H. (1967) - KERATINABBAU DURCH PILZE. ARCH.MIKROBIOL. 57, 93-110.

586 BOEHNER, B., FETZ, E., HAERRI, E., SIGG, H.P., STOLL, CH. & TAMM, CH. (1965) - UEBER DIE ISOLIERUNG VON VERRUCARIN-H, VERRUCARIN-J, RORIDIN-D UND RORIDIN-E AUS MYROTHECIUM-ARTEN. HELV.CHIM.ACTA 48, 1079-1087.

587 BOEHNER, B. & TAMM, CH. (1966) - DIE KONSTITUTION VON RORIDIN-D, VERRUCA-RIN UND RORIDIN. 12. HELV.CHIM.ACTA 49, 2547-2554.

588 BOER, S.DE (1940) - NITRATE ASSIMILATION OF ASPERGILLUS NIGER. PROC.K.NED. AKAD.WET. 43, 1-8.

589 BOER, S.DE (1962) - DE INVLOED VAN HET TOEVOEGEN VAN ORGANISCH MATERIAAL AAN DE GROND OP HET OPTREDEN VAN RHIZOCTONIA ZIEKTE EN SCHURFT BIJ AARDAPPELEN. TIJDSCHR.PLZIEKT. 68, 268-277.

590 BOEREMA, G.H. (1964) - PHOMA HERBARUM, THE TYPE-SPECIES OF THE FORM-GENUS PHOMA. PERSOONIA 3, 9-16.

591 BOEREMA, G.H. (1970) - ADDITIONAL NOTES ON PHOMA HERBARUM. PERSOONIA 6, 15-48.

592 BOEREMA, G.H. (1976) - THE PHOMA SPECIES STUDIED IN CULTURE BY DR. R.W.G. DENNIS. TRANS.BR.MYCOL.SOC. 67, 289-319.

593 BOEREMA, G.H. & BOLLEN, G.J. (1975) - CONIDIOGENESIS AND CONIDIAL SEPTATION AS DIFFERENTIATING CRITERIA BETWEEN PHOMA AND ASCOCHYTA. PERSOONIA 8, 111-144.

594 BOEREMA, G.H. & DORENBOSCH, M.M.J. (1973) - THE PHOMA AND ASCOCHYTA SPECIES
     DESCRIBED BY WOLLENWEBER AND HOCHAPFEL IN THEIR STUDY ON FRUIT-ROTTING.
     STUD.MYCOL., EAARN 3, 50 PP.

595 BOEREMA, G.H., DORENBOSCH, M.M.J. & KESTEREN, H.A.VAN (1965) - REMARKS ON
     SPECIES OF PHOMA REFERRED TO PEYRONELLAEA. PERSOONIA 4, 47-68.

596 BOEREMA, G.H., DORENBOSCH, M.M.J. & KESTEREN, H.A.VAN (1968) - REMARKS ON
     SPECIES OF PHOMA REFERRED TO PEYRONELLAEA. 2. PERSOONIA 5, 201-205.

597 BOEREMA, G.H., DORENBOSCH, M.M.J. & KESTEREN, H.A.VAN (1971) - REMARKS ON
     SPECIES OF PHOMA REFERRED TO PEYRONELLAEA. 3. PERSOONIA 6, 171-177.

598 BOEREMA, G.H., DORENBOSCH, M.M.J. & KESTEREN, H.A.VAN (1977) - REMARKS ON
     SPECIES OF PHOMA REFERRED TO PEYRONELLAEA. 5. KEW BULL. 31, 533-544.

599 BOEREMA, G.H., DORENBOSCH, M.M.J. & LEFFRING, L. (1965) - A COMPARATIVE
     STUDY OF THE BLACK STEM FUNGI ON LUCERNE AND RED CLOVER AND THE FOOTROT
     FUNGUS ON PEA. NETH.J.PL.PATH. 71, 79-89.

600 BOEREMA, G.H. & HOEWELER, L.H. (1967) - PHOMA EXIGUA AND ITS VARIETIES.
     PERSOONIA 5, 15-28.

601 BOEREMA, G.H. & KESTEREN, H.A.VAN (1961) - PHOMA-ACHTIGE SCHIMMELS BIJ
     AARDAPPEL. MEDED.PLZIEKTENK.DIENST WAGENINGEN 136 (JAARB.1961), 201-209.

602 BOEREMA, G.H. & KESTEREN, H.A.VAN (1964) - THE NOMENCLATURE OF TWO FUNGI
     PARASITIZING BRASSICA. PERSOONIA 3, 17-28.

603 BOERNER, H. (1963) - UNTERSUCHUNGEN UEBER DIE BILDUNG ANTIPHYTOTISCHER UND
     ANTIMIKROBIELLER SUBSTANZEN DURCH MIKROORGANISMEN IM BODEN. 1. BILDUNG
     VON PATULIN UND EINER PHENOLISCHEN VERBINDUNG DURCH PENICILLIUM EXPAN-
     SUM. PHYTOPATH.Z. 48, 370-396.

604 ROESENBERG, H. (1972) - DIAGNOSTISCHE MOEGLICHKEITEN ZUM NACHWEIS VON AFLA-
     TOXIN-VERGIFTUNGEN. ZENTBL.BAKT.PARASITKDE, ABT.1, 220, 252-257.

605 BOESEWINKEL, H.J. (1976) - STORAGE OF FUNGAL CULTURES IN WATER. TRANS.BR.
     MYCOL.SOC. 66, 183-185.

606 BOGLIOLO, L. & ARVEIRA NEVES, J. (1953) - RESEARCHES ON THE ETIOLOGIC
     AGENTS OF THE AMERICAN BLASTOMYCOSIS. 2. MORPHOLOGY AND SYSTEMATIC OF
     THE AGENT OF POSADAS-WERNICKE'S DISEASE. MYCOPATH.MYCOL.APPL. 6, 137-
     160.

607 BOGOMOLOVA, L.A. (1969) - (FORMATION OF FUSARIC ACID OF F. MONILIFORME AND
     F. OXYSPORUM). MYKROBIOL.ZH. 31 (4), 314-318.

608 BOJOVIC-CVETIC, B. & VUJICIC, R. (1974) - ULTRASTRUCTURE OF CONIDIOPHORES
     IN ASPERGILLUS FLAVUS. TRANS.BR.MYCOL.SOC. 63, 131-135.

609 BOLKAN, H.A. & BUTLER, E.E. (1974) - STUDIES ON HETEROKARYOSIS AND VIRU-
     LENCE OF RHIZOCTONIA SOLANI. PHYTOPATHOLOGY 64, 513-522.

610 BOLLAG, J.-M. & LIU, S.-Y. (1972) - HYDROXYLATIONS OF CARBARYL BY SOIL FUN-
     GI. NATURE, LOND. 236, 177-178.

611 BOLLAG, J.-M. & LIU, S.-Y. (1972) - FUNGAL DEGRADATION OF 1-NAPHTHOL. CAN.
     J.MICROBIOL. 18, 1113-1117.

612   BOLLAG, J.-M. & TUNG, G. (1972) - NITROUS OXIDE RELEASE BY SOIL FUNGI. SOIL
      BIOL.BIOCHEM. 4, 271-276.

613   BOLLEN, G.J. (1969) - THE SELECTIVE EFFECT OF HEAT TREATMENT ON THE MICRO-
      FLORA OF A GREENHOUSE SOIL. NETH.J.PL.PATH. 75, 157-163.

614   BOLLEN, G.J. (1974) - FUNGAL RECOLONIZATION OF HEAT-TREATED GLASSHOUSE
      SOILS. AGRO-ECOSYSTEMS 1, 139-155.

615   BOLLEN, G.J. & POL-LUITEN, B.VAN DER (1975) - MESOPHILIC HEAT-RESISTANT
      SOIL FUNGI. ACTA BOT.NEERL. 24, 254-255.

616   BOLLEN, G.J. & SCHOLTEN, G. (1971) - ACQUIRED RESISTANCE TO BENOMYL AND
      SOME OTHER SYSTEMIC FUNGICIDES IN A STRAIN OF BOTRYTIS CINEREA IN CYCLA-
      MEN. NETH.J.PL.PATH. 77, 83-90.

617   BOLLER, R.A. & SCHROEDER, H.W. (1972) - SELF-PARASITISM IN ASPERGILLUS FLA-
      VUS. MYCOLOGIA 64, 433-437.

618   BOLLER, R.A. & SCHROEDER, H.W. (1973) - INFLUENCE OF ASPERGILLUS CHEVALIE-
      RI ON PRODUCTION OF AFLATOXIN IN RICE BY ASPERGILLUS PARASITICUS. PHY-
      TOPATHOLOGY 63, 1507-1510.

619   BOLLER, R.A. & SCHROEDER, H.W. (1974) - PRODUCTION OF AFLATOXIN BY CUL-
      TURES DERIVED FROM CONIDIA STORED IN THE LABORATORY. MYCOLOGIA 66, 61-
      66.

620   BOLLER, R.A. & SCHROEDER, H.W. (1974) - INFLUENCE OF RELATIVE HUMIDITY ON
      PRODUCTION OF AFLATOXIN IN RICE BY ASPERGILLUS PARASITICUS. PHYTOPATHOL-
      OGY 64, 17-21.

621   BOLLER, R.A. & SCHROEDER, H.W. (1974) - INFLUENCE OF ASPERGILLUS CANDIDUS
      ON PRODUCTION OF AFLATOXIN IN RICE BY ASPERGILLUS PARASITICUS. PHYTO-
      PATHOLOGY 64, 121-123.

622   BOLLER, R.A. & SCHROEDER, H.W. (1974) - INFLUENCE OF TEMPERATURE ON PRODUC-
      TION OF AFLATOXIN IN RICE BY ASPERGILLUS PARASITICUS. PHYTOPATHOLOGY 64,
      283-286.

623   BOLLIGER, G. & TAMM, CH. (1972) - VIER NEUE METABOLITEN VON GIBBERELLA
      ZEAE, 5-FORMYL-ZEARALENON, 7-DEHYDROZEARALENON, 8-HYDROXY UND 8-EPI-HY-
      DROXY-ZEARALENON. HELV.CHIM.ACTA 55, 3030-3048.

624   BOLLINGER, P., SIGG, H.-P. & WEBER, H.-P. (1973) - DIE STRUKTUR VON OVALI-
      CIN. HELV.CHIM.ACTA 56, 819-830.

625   BONDARCHUK, A.A. (1964) - (AMYLASE FROM THE MYCELIUM OF PENICILLIUM CHRY-
      SOGENUM, STRAIN 194). MYKROBIOL.ZH. 26, 40-44.

626   BONDARCHUK, A.A. (1966) - (ISOLATION OF ALPHA-AMYLASE FROM THE MYCELIA OF
      PENICILLIUM CHRYSOGENUM, STRAIN 194). MYKROBIOL.ZH. 28 (1), 3-6.

627   BONDARCHUK, A.A., NOVIKOVA, S.I., REDCHITS, T.I. & PAVLOVA, I.N. (1971) -
      (ISOLATION AND PURIFICATION OF ENZYME, SPLITTING HEXADECANE, FROM FU-
      SARIUM MONILIFORME). MYKROBIOL.ZH. 33 (5), 544-547.

628   BONDAREVSKAYA, E.G., PRAVENKAYA, A.TH., BOROVKOV, A.V. & MIRCHINK, M.G.
      (1972) - (THE ISOLATION AND DESCRIPTION OF A PHYTOTOXIN IN PENICILLIUM
      PURPUROGENUM STOLL). SEL'.KHOZ.BIOL. 7, 113-116.

629   BONDAREVSKAYA, F.G. & MIRCHINK, T.G. (1968) - (PHYTOTOXIC AND INSECTICIDAL
      PROPERTIES OF SOIL FUNGI). VEST.MOSK.GOS.UNIV., SER.BIOL.POCHV., (5),
      93-104.

55

630 BONDIETTI, E., MARTIN, J.P. & HAIDER, K. (1971) - INFLUENCE OF NITROGEN
     SOURCE AND CLAY ON GROWTH AND PHENOLIC POLYMER PRODUCTION BY STACHY-
     BOTRYS SPECIES, HEDERSONULA TORULOIDEA, AND ASPERGILLUS SYDOWI. PROC.
     SOIL SCI.SOC.AM. 36, 917-922.

631 BONEH, SH. (1953) - CONTRIBUTION TO THE KNOWLEDGE OF SOME TEXTILE DESTROY-
     ING FUNGI IN ISRAEL. PALEST.J.BOT., SER.J, 6, 107-113.

632 BONFANTE, P.F., CERUTI SCURTI, J. & OBERT, F. (1972) - INTERAZIONE DI TUBER
     MELANOSPORUM VITT. CON MICELI DI ALTRI FUNGHI. ALLIONIA 18, 53-59.

633 BOOIS, H.M.DE & JANSEN, F. (1976) - LYTIC AND FUNGISTATIC EFFECTS OF MULL
     AND MOR SOIL UPON DIFFERENT FUNGI. TRANS.BR.MYCOL.SOC. 67, 349-351.

634 BOOSALIS, M.G. (1956) - EFFECT OF SOIL TEMPERATURE AND GREEN-MANURE AMEND-
     MENT OF UNSTERILIZED SOIL ON PARASITISM OF RHIZOCTONIA SOLANI BY PENI-
     CILLIUM VERMICULATUM AND TRICHODERMA SP. PHYTOPATHOLOGY 46, 473-478.

635 BOOSALIS, M.G. (1964) - HYPERPARASITISM. A.REV.PHYTOPATH. 2, 363-376.

636 BOOTH, C. (1959) - STUDIES OF PYRENOMYCETES. 4. NECTRIA (PART I). MYCOL.
     PAP. 73, 1-115.

637 BOOTH, C. (1960) - STUDIES OF PYRENOMYCETES. 5. NOMENCLATURE OF SOME FU-
     SARIA IN RELATION TO THEIR NECTRIOID PERITHECIAL STATES. MYCOL.PAP. 74,
     1-16.

638 BOOTH, C. (1961) - STUDIES OF PYRENOMYCETES. 6. THIELAVIA, WITH NOTES ON
     SOME ALLIED GENERA. MYCOL.PAP. 83, 1-15.

639 BOOTH, C. (1966) - THE GENUS CYLINDROCARPON. MYCOL.PAP. 104, 1-56.

640 BOOTH, C. (1971) - THE GENUS FUSARIUM. COMMONW.MYCOL.INST., KEW, 237 PP.

641 BOOTH, C. (1977) - FUSARIUM LABORATORY GUIDE TO THE IDENTIFICATION OF THE
     MAJOR SPECIES. COMMONW.MYCOL.INST., KEW, 58 PP.

642 BOOTH, J.A. (1974) - EFFECT OF COTTON ROOT EXUDATE CONSTITUTENTS ON GROWTH
     AND PECTOLYTIC ENZYME PRODUCTION BY VERTICILLIUM ALBO-ATRUM. CAN.J.BOT.
     52, 2219-2224.

643 BOOTH, R.H. & TAYLOR, G.S. (1976) - FUSARIUM DISEASES OF CEREALS. 11. GROWTH
     AND SAPROPHYTIC ACTIVITY OF FUSARIUM NIVALE IN SOIL. TRANS.BR.MYCOL.SOC.
     66, 77-83.

644 BORDER, D.J. & TRINCI, A.P.J. (1970) - FINE STRUCTURE OF THE GERMINATION
     OF ASPERGILLUS NIDULANS CONIDIA. TRANS.BR.MYCOL.SOC. 54, 143-152.

645 BORECKA, H. (1962) - PENICILLIUM EXPANSUM AS AN PATHOGEN ON APPLE IN THE
     STORAGE TIME. ACTA AGROBOT. 12, 67-78.

646 BORECKA, H. & MILLIKAN, D.F. (1973) - STIMULATORY EFFECT OF POLLEN AND
     PISTILLATE PARTS OF SOME HORTICULTURAL SPECIES UPON THE GERMINATION OF
     BOTRYTIS CINEREA SPORES. PHYTOPATHOLOGY 63, 1431-1432.

647 BORECKI, Z. & PROFIC, H. (1962) - (THE FUNGI TRICHOTHECIUM ROSEUM LINK,
     PEZICULA MALICORTICIS (CORD.) NANNF., AND PENICILLIUM EXPANSUM (LINK)
     THOM AS PRIMARY OR SECONDARY PATHOGENS OF APPLES). ACTA AGROBOT. 12, 79-
     94.

648   BORKER, E., INSALATA, N.F., LEVI, C.P. & WITZEMAN, J.S. (1966) - MYCOTOXINS
      IN FEED AND FOODS. ADV.APPL.MICROBIOL. 8, 315-351.

649   BORN, G.L. (1971) - HEAT TREATMENT OF SOIL ENHANCES VERTICILLIUM WILT IN-
      FECTION OF BARBERRY AND REDBUD. PL.DIS.REPTR 55, 996-997.

650   BOROWSKA, A. (1966) - (LITTER FUNGI OF THE DEBRINA RESERVATION). ACTA MY-
      COL., WARSZAWA 2, 79-105.

651   BOROWSKA, A. & DEMIANOWICZ, Z. (1972) - FUNGI ON FIR HONEY-DEW. ACTA MYCOL.,
      WARSZAWA 8, 175-189.

652   BORROW, A., JEFFERYS, E.G., KESSELL, R.H.J., LLOYD, E.C., LLOYD.P.B. &
      NIXON, I.S. (1961) - THE METABOLISM OF GIBBERELLA FUJIKUROI IN STIRRED
      CULTURE. CAN.J.MICROBIOL. 7, 227-276.

653   BORTELS, H. (1927) - UEBER DIE BEDEUTUNG VON EISEN, ZINK UND KUPFER FUER
      MIKROORGANISMEN, UNTER BESONDERER BERUECKSICHTIGUNG VON ASPERGILLUS NI-
      GER. BIOCHEM.Z. 182, 301-358.

654   BORUT, SH. (1960) - AN ECOLOGICAL AND PHYSIOLOGICAL STUDY ON SOIL FUNGI OF
      THE NORTHERN NEGEV (ISRAEL). BULL.RES.COUN.ISRAEL 8D, 65-80.

655   BORUT, SH.Y. & JOHNSON, R.W.JR. (1962) - SOME BIOLOGICAL OBSERVATIONS ON
      FUNGI IN ESTUARINE SEDIMENTS. MYCOLOGIA 54, 181-193.

656   BOSE, R.G. (1962) - DECOMPOSITION OF CELLULOSE BY PAECILOMYCES ELEGANS.
      TEXT.RES.J. 32, 426-427.

657   BOSE, R.K. (1953) - STUDY OF POLYGALACTURONASE ACTIVITY OF JUTE-ROTTING
      FUNGI BY PAPER-CHROMATOGRAPHY. SCI.CULT. 18, 394-395.

658   BOSMANN, H.B. (1973) - PROTEIN CATABOLISM. 2. IDENTIFICATION OF NEUTRAL
      AND ACIDIC PROTEOLYTIC ENZYMES IN ASPERGILLUS NIGER. BIOCHIM.BIOPHYS.
      ACTA 293, 476-489.

659   BOSMANS, P., COOLEN, W.A. & VULSTEKE, G. (1974) - THE OCCURRENCE AND SPREAD
      OF CIGAR DISEASE IN SCORZONERA. MEDED.FAC.LANDBWET.RIJKSUNIV.GENT 39,
      1001-1006.

660   BOSTICK, P.E. (1968) - THE DISTRIBUTION OF SOME SOIL FUNGI ON A GEORGIA
      GRANITE OUTCROP. BULL.GA ACAD.SCI. 26, 149-154.

661   BOTHAST, R.J. & FENNEL, D.I. (1974) - A MEDIUM FOR RAPID IDENTIFICATION
      AND ENUMERATION OF ASPERGILLUS FLAVUS AND RELATED ORGANISMS. MYCOLOGIA
      66, 365-369.

662   BOTHAST, R.J., LANCASTER, E.P. & HESSELTINE, C.W. (1975) - SCOPULARIOPSIS
      BREVICAULIS - EFFECT OF PH AND SUBSTRATE ON GROWTH. EUR.J.APPL.MICRO-
      BIOL. 1, 55-66.

663   BOTTELIER, H.P. (1952) - OVER DE VORMING VAN VETTEN DOOR MICRO-ORGANISMEN.
      VAKBL.BIOL. 32, 147-156.

664   BOUHET, J.-C., CHOUNG, P.PH.VAN, TOMA, F., KIRSZENBAUM, M. & FROMAGOET, P.
      (1976) - ISOLATION AND CHARACTERIZATION OF LUTEOSKYRIN AND RUGULOSIN,
      TWO HEPATOTOXIC ANTHRAQUINONOIDS FROM PENICILLIUM ISLANDICUM SOPP AND
      PENICILLIUM RUGULOSUM THOM. J.AGRIC.FD CHEM. 24, 964-972.

665   BOUHOT, D. (1972) - UNE TECHNIQUE DE PRODUCTION DES MACROCONIDIES DE FU-
      SARIUM OXYSPORUM. ANNLS PHYTOPATH. 4, 183-186.

666   BOUHOT, D. (1975) - RECHERCHES SUR L'ECOLOGIE DES CHAMPIGNONS PARASITES
      DANS LE SOL. 5. UNE TECHNIQUE SELECTIVE D'ESTIMATION DU POTENTIEL IN-
      FECTIEUX DES SOLS, TERREAUX ET SUBSTRATS INFESTES PAR PYTHIUM SP.,
      ETUDES QUALITATIVES. ANNLS PHYTOPATH. 7, 9-18.

667   BOUHOT, D. & BILLOTTE, J.M. (1964) - RECHERCHE SUR L'ECOLOGIE DES CHAM-
      PIGNONS PARASITES DANS LE SOL. 2. CHOIX D'UN MILIEU NUTRITIF POUR
      L'ISOLEMENT SELECTIF DE FUSARIUM OXYSPORUM ET F. SOLANI DU SOL. ANNLS
      EPIPHYT. 15, 45-56.

668   BOUHOT, D. & ROUXEL, F. (1971) - TECHNIQUE SELECTIVE ET QUANTITATIVE D'ANA-
      LYSE DES FUSARIUM OXYSPORUM ET FUSARIUM SOLANI DANS LE SOL. ANNLS PHY-
      TOPATH. 3, 251-254.

669   BOUSQUET, J.-F. & BARBIER, M. (1972) - SUR L'ACTIVITE PHYTOTOXIQUE DE
      TROIS SOUCHES DE PHOMA EXIGUA ET LA PRESENCE DE LA CYTOCHALASINE-B (OU
      PHOMINE) DANS LEUR MILIEU DE CULTURE. PHYTOPATH.Z. 75, 365-367.

670   BOUSQUET, J.-F., VEGH, I., POUTEAU-THOUVENOT, M. & BARBIER, M. (1971) -
      ISOLEMENT DE L'ASPERGILLOMARASMINE-A DE CULTURES DE COLLETOTRICHUM
      GLOEOSPORIOIDES PENZ., AGENT PATHOGENE DES SAULES. ANNLS PHYTOPATH. 3,
      407-408.

671   BOWDEN, J.P. & SCHANTZ, E.J. (1955) - THE ISOLATION AND CHARACTERIZATION
      OF DERMATIC COMPOUNDS PRODUCED BY MYROTHECIUM VERRUCARIA. J.BIOL.CHEM.
      214, 365-372.

672   BOWMAN, R.D. & MUMMA, R.O. (1967) - THE LIPIDS OF PYTHIUM ULTIMUM. BIOCHIM.
      BIOPHYS.ACTA 144, 501-510.

673   BOYCE, A.M. & FAWCETT, H.S. (1948) - A PARASITIC ASPERGILLUS ON MEALY BUGS.
      J.ECON.ENT. 40, 702-705.

674   BOZARTH, R.F. (1972) - MYCOVIRUSES, A NEW DIMENSION IN MICROBIOLOGY. EN-
      VIRON.HLTH PERSPECT. 2, 23-39.

675   BOZARTH, R.F. & GOENAGA, A. (1972) - PURIFICATION AND PROPERTIES OF MUCO-
      FERRITIN FROM MORTIERELLA ALPINA. CAN.J.MICROBIOL. 18, 619-622.

676   BOZARTH, R.F., WOOD, H.A. & MANDELBROT, A. (1971) - THE PENICILLIUM STOLO-
      NIFERUM VIRUS COMPLEX - TWO SIMILAR DOUBLE-STRANDED RNA VIRUS-LIKE PAR-
      TICLES IN A SINGLE CELL. VIROLOGY 45, 516-523.

677   BRACKEN, A., POCKER, A. & RAISTRICK, H. (1954) - STUDIES IN THE BIOCHEM-
      ISTRY OF MICRO-ORGANISMS. 93. CYCLOPENIN, A NITROGEN-CONTAINING META-
      BOLIC PRODUCT OF PENICILLIUM CYCLOPIUM. BIOCHEM.J. 57, 587-595.

678   BRACKEN, A. & RAISTRICK, H. (1947) - STUDIES IN THE BIOCHEMISTRY OF MICRO-
      ORGANISM. 75. DEHYDROCAROLIC ACID, A METABOLIC PRODUCT OF PENICILLIUM
      CINERASCENS. BIOCHEM.J. 41, 569.

679   BRANCATO, F.P. & GOLDING, N.S. (1953) - GAS REQUIREMENTS OF MOLDS - THE
      IMPORTANCE OF DISSOLVED OXYGEN IN THE MEDIUM FOR GERMINATION AND GROWTH
      OF SEVERAL MOLDS. NORTHWEST SCI. 27, 33-38.

680   BRANDAENGE, S., JOSEPHSON, S., MAHLEN, L.M. & VALLEN, S. (1976) - (-)DECYL-
      CITRIC ACID AND (+)ISOCITRIC ACID AS METABOLITES FROM PENICILLIUM SPI-
      CULISPORUM - A CORRECTION. ACTA CHEM.SCAND. B30, 177-178.

681   BRANDSBERG, J.W. (1967) - A STUDY OF FUNGI ASSOCIATED WITH THE DECOMPOSI-
      TION OF CONIFEROUS LITTER. DISS.WASHINGTON STATE UNIV., AND MYCOLOGIA
      61, 373-381.

682   BRANDSBERG, J.W., WEEKS, R.J., HILL, W.B. & PIGGOTT, W.R. (1969) - A STUDY
       OF FUNGI FOUND IN ASSOCIATION WITH HISTOPLASMA CAPSULATUM - THREE BIRD
       ROOSTS IN S.E. MISSOURI, U.S.A. MYCOPATH.MYCOL.APPL. 38, 71-81.

683   BRANDT, W.H. (1962) - MANGANESE STIMULATION OF MELANIN SYNTHESIS AND MI-
       CROSCLEROTIAL DEVELOPMENT IN VERTICILLIUM. PL.PHYSIOL., LANCASTER 37,
       30 (ABS.).

684   BRANDT.W.H. & REESE, J.E. (1964) - MORPHOGENESIS IN VERTICILLIUM. A SELF-
       PRODUCED DIFFUSIBLE MORPHOGENIC FACTOR. AM.J.BOT. 51, 922-927.

685   BRASIER, C.M. (1971) - INDUCTION OF SEXUAL REPRODUCTION IN SINGLE A2 ISO-
       LATES BY PHYTOPHTHORA SPECIES BY TRICHODERMA VIRIDE. NATURE, LOND. 231,
       283.

686   BRASIER, C.M. (1975) - STIMULATION OF SEX ORGAN FORMATION IN PHYTOPHTHORA
       BY ANTAGONISTIC SPECIES OF TRICHODERMA. 1. THE EFFECT IN VITRO. NEW
       PHYTOL. 74, 183-194.

687   BRASIER, C.M. (1975) - STIMULATION OF SEX ORGAN FORMATION IN PHYTOPHTHORA
       BY ANTAGONISTIC SPECIES OF TRICHODERMA. 2. ECOLOGICAL IMPLICATIONS. NEW
       PHYTOL. 74, 195-198.

688   BRASIER, C.M. & SANSOME, E. (1975) - DIPLOIDY AND GAMETANGIAL MEIOSIS IN
       PHYTOPHTHORA CINNAMOMI, P. INFESTANS AND P. DRECHSLERI. TRANS.BR.MYCOL.
       SOC. 65, 49-65.

689   BRAUN, H. & SCHWINN, F.J. (1963) - FORTGEFUEHRTE UNTERSUCHUNGEN UEBER DEN
       ERREGER DER KRAGENFAEULE DES APFELBAUMES (PHYTOPHTHORA CACTORUM). PHY-
       TOPATH.Z. 47, 327-370.

690   BRAUN, R. & FROMAGEOT, P. (1962) - DESAMINATION DE LA TAURINE PAR ASPER-
       GILLUS NIGER. BIOCHIM.BIOPHYS.ACTA 62, 548-555.

691   BRAVERMAN, S.W. & CROSIER, W.F. (1966) - LONGEVITY AND PATHOGENICITY OF
       SEVERAL HELMINTHOSPORIUM SPECIES STORED UNDER MINERAL OIL. PL.DIS.REPTR
       50, 321-323.

692   BREEN, J., DACRE, J.C., RAISTRICK, H. & SMITH, G. (1955) - STUDIES IN THE
       BIOCHEMISTRY OF MICRO-ORGANISMS. 95. RUGULOSIN, A CRYSTALLINE COLOURING
       MATTER OF PENICILLIUM RUGULOSUM THOM. BIOCHEM.J. 60, 618-626.

693   BREFELD, O. (1881) - BOTANISCHE UNTERSUCHUNGEN UEBER SCHIMMELPILZE. UN-
       TERSUCHUNGEN AUS DEM GESAMMTGEBIETE DER MYKOLOGIE. HEFT 4, 112-121,
       LEIPZIG.

694   BRETON, A. (1969) - CROISSANCE DU MYCELIUM ET FRUCTIFICATION CHEZ DORATO-
       MYCES NANUS (EHRENB.) MORTON & SMITH. C.R.HEBD.SEANC.ACAD.SCI., PARIS,
       SER.D, 268, 2674-2677.

695   BRETON, A. (1971) - ACTION DE LA TEMPERATURE SUR LA CROISSANCE ET LA FRUC-
       TIFICATION DU DORATOMYCES NANUS (EHRENB.) MORTON & SMITH. BULL.MENS.
       SOC.LINN.LYON 40, 270-275.

696   BRETON, A. (1971) - CROISSANCE ET DEVELOPPEMENT DES COREMIES DU GENRE DO-
       RATOMYCES CORDA. MEM.SOC.BOT.FR. 1971, 19-27.

697   BRETON, A. (1971) - MORPHOGENESE DES COREMIES DU GENRE DORATOMYCES CORDA.
       RELATIONS ENTRE LE MYCELIUM VEGETATIF ET LES FRUCTIFICATIONS. ANNLS SCI.
       NAT.BOT., SER.12, (12), 9-16.

698 BRETON, A. (1975) - MORPHOGENESE DESCRIPTIVE ET EXPERIMENTALE DES COREMIES
     DU GENRE DORATOMYCES CORDA (FUNGI IMPERFECTI). DISS.UNIV.CLERMONT-FER-
     RAND, SER.E, 213, 242 PP.

699 BREWER, D. (1958) - STUDIES ON SLIME ACCUMULATION IN PULP AND PAPER MILLS.
     1. SOME FUNGI ISOLATED FROM MILLS IN NEW BRUNSWICK AND NEWFOUNDLAND.
     CAN.J.BOT. 36, 941-946.

700 BREWER, D. (1959) - STUDIES ON SLIME ACCUMULATIONS IN PULP AND PAPER MILLS.
     2. PHYSIOLOGICAL STUDIES OF PHIALOPHORA FASTIGIATA AND P. RICHARDSIAE.
     CAN.J.BOT. 37, 339-343.

701 BREWER, D., ARSENAULT, G.P., WRIGHT, J.L.C. & VINING, L.C. (1973) - PRO-
     DUCTION OF BIKAVERIN BY FUSARIUM OXYSPORUM AND ITS IDENTITY WITH LYCO-
     PERSIN. J.ANTIBIOT.,TOKYO 26, 778-781.

702 BREWER, D. & DUNCAN, J.M. (1968) - CYTOLOGICAL STUDIES OF CHAETOMIUM COCH-
     LIODES. CAN.J.BOT. 46, 773-775.

703 BREWER, D., DUNCAN, J.M., JERRAM, W.A., LEACH, C.K., SAFE, S., TAYLOR, A.,
     VINING, L.C., ARCHIBALD, R.MCG., STEVENSON, R.G., MIROCHA, C.J. &
     CHRISTENSEN, C.M. (1972) - OVINE ILL-THRIFT IN NOVA SCOTIA. 5. THE
     PRODUCTION AND TOXICOLOGY OF CHETOMIN, A METABOLITE OF CHAETOMIUM SPP.
     CAN.J.MICROBIOL. 18, 1129-1137.

704 BREWER, D., JERRAM, W.A., MEILER, D. & TAYLOR, A. (1970) - THE TOXICITY OF
     COCHLIODINOL, AN ANTIBIOTIC METABOLITE OF CHAETOMIUM SPP. CAN.J.MICRO-
     BIOL. 16, 433-440.

705 BREWER, D., JERRAM, W.A. & TAYLOR, A. (1968) - THE PRODUCTION OF COCHLIO-
     DINOL AND A RELATED METABOLITE BY CHAETOMIUM SPECIES. CAN.J.MICROBIOL.
     14, 861-866.

706 BRIAN, P.W. (1956) - PRODUCTION OF PATULIN IN APPLE FRUITS BY PENICILLIUM
     EXPANSUM. NATURE, LOND. 178, 263-264.

707 BRIAN, P.W. (1960) - GRISEOFULVIN. TRANS.BR.MYCOL.SOC. 43, 1-13.

708 BRIAN, P.W., CURTIS, P.J. & HEMMING, H.G. (1946) - BIOLOGICAL ASSAY, PRO-
     DUCTION AND ISOLATION OF CURLING FACTOR. TRANS.BR.MYCOL.SOC. 29, 173-
     186.

709 BRIAN, P.W., CURTIS, P.J. & HEMMING, H.G. (1947) - GLUTINOSIN, A FUNGISTA-
     TIC METABOLIC PRODUCT OF THE MOULD METARRHIZIUM GLUTINOSUM. PROC.R.SOC.,
     B, 135, 106-119.

710 BRIAN, P.W., CURTIS, P.J., HEMMING, H.G. & MCGOWAN, J.C. (1946) - THE PRO-
     DUCTION OF VIRIDIN BY PIGMENT-FORMING STRAINS OF TRICHODERMA VIRIDE.
     ANN.APPL.BIOL. 33, 190-200.

711 BRIAN, P.W., CURTIS, P.J., HEMMING, H.G. & NORRIS, G.L.F. (1957) - WORT-
     MANNIN, AN ANTIBIOTIC PRODUCED BY PENICILLIUM WORTMANNI. TRANS.BR.MYCOL.
     SOC. 40, 365-368.

712 BRIAN, P.W., DAWKINS, A.W., GROVE, J.F., HEMMING, H.G., LOWE, D. & NORRIS,
     G.L.F. (1961) - PHYTOTOXIC COMPOUNDS PRODUCED BY FUSARIUM EQUISETI. J.
     EXP.BOT. 12, 1-12.

713 BRIAN, P.W., ELSON, G.W., HEMMING, H.G. & RADLEY, M. (1954) - THE PLANT
     GROWTH PROMOTING PROPERTIES OF GIBBERELLIC ACID, A METABOLIC PRODUCT OF
     THE FUNGUS GIBBERELLA FUJIKUROI. J.SCI.FD AGRIC. 5, 602-612.

714 BRIAN, P.W., ELSON, G.W., HEMMING, H.G. & RADLEY, M. (1965) - AN INHIBITOR
     OF PLANT GROWTH PRODUCED BY ASPERGILLUS WENTII WEHMER. NATURE, LOND.
     207, 998-999.

715 BRIAN, P.W. & HEMMING, H.G. (1945) - GLIOTOXIN, A FUNGISTATIC METABOLIC
     PRODUCT OF TRICHODERMA VIRIDE. ANN.APPL.BIOL. 32, 214-220.

716 BRIAN, P.W. & HEMMING, H.G. (1947) - PRODUCTION OF ANTIFUNGAL AND ANTI-
     BACTERIAL SUBSTANCES BY FUNGI, PRELIMINARY EXAMINATION OF 166 STRAINS
     OF FUNGI IMPERFECTI. J.GEN.MICROBIOL. 1, 158-167.

717 BRIAN, P.W. & HEMMING, H.G. (1950) - SOME NUTRITIONAL CONDITIONS AFFECTING
     SPORE PRODUCTION BY TRICHODERMA VIRIDE. TRANS.BR.MYCOL.SOC. 33, 132-141.

718 BRIAN, P.W., HEMMING, H.G. & JEFFERYS, E.G. (1948) - PRODUCTION OF ANTI-
     BIOTICS BY SPECIES OF MYROTHECIUM. MYCOLOGIA 40, 363-368.

719 BRIAN, P.W., HEMMING, H.G. & MCGOWAN, J.C. (1945) - ORIGIN OF A TOXICITY
     TO MYCORRHIZA IN WAREHAM HEATH SOIL. NATURE, LOND. 155, 637-638.

720 BRIAN, P.W., HEMMING, H.G., MOFFATT, J.S. & UNWIN, C.H. (1953) - CANESCIN,
     AN ANTIBIOTIC PRODUCED BY PENICILLIUM CANESCENS. TRANS.BR.MYCOL.SOC.
     36, 243-247.

721 BRIAN, P.W. & MCGOWAN, J.C. (1945) - VIRIDIN, A HIGHLY FUNGISTATIC SUB-
     STANCE PRODUCED BY TRICHODERMA VIRIDE. NATURE, LOND. 156, 144-145.

722 BRIAN, P.W. & MCGOWAN, J.C. (1946) - BIOLOGICALLY ACTIVE METABOLIC PROD-
     UCTS OF THE MOULD METARRHIZIUM GLUTINOSUM. NATURE, LOND. 157, 334.

723 BRIAN, P.W., WRIGHT, J.M, STUBBS, J. & WAY, A.M. (1966) - UPTAKE OF ANTI-
     BIOTIC METABOLITES OF SOIL MICRO-ORGANISMS BY PLANTS. NATURE, LOND. 167,
     347-348.

724 BRINKERHOFF, L.A. (1969) - THE INFLUENCE OF TEMPERATURE, AERATION, AND
     SOIL MICROFLORA ON MICROSCLEROTIAL DEVELOPMENT OF VERTICILLIUM ALBO-
     ATRUM IN ABSCISED COTTON LEAVES. PHYTOPATHOLOGY 59, 805-808.

725 BROADBENT, D. (1966) - ANTIBIOTICS PRODUCED BY FUNGI. BOT.REV. 32, 219-242.

726 BROADBENT, D., HEMMING, H.G. & LEHAN, M. (1974) - PRODUCTION OF GRISEO-
     FULVIN BY KHUSKIA ORYZAE. TRANS.BR.MYCOL.SOC. 62, 625-626.

727 BROADBENT, P. & BAKER, K.F. (1974) - ASSOCIATION OF BACTERIA WITH SPORAN-
     GIUM FORMATION AND BREAKDOWN OF SPORANGIA IN PHYTOPHTHORA SPP. AUST.J.
     AGRIC.RES. 25, 139-145.

728 BROADBENT, P. & BAKER, K.F. (1975) - SOILS SUPPRESSIVE TO PHYTOPHTHORA
     ROOT ROT IN EASTERN AUSTRALIA. IN: BIOLOGICAL CONTROL OF SOIL-BORNE
     PLANT-PATHOGENS; BRUEHL, G.W. (ED.), ST.PAUL, MINNESOTA, 152-157.

729 BRODIE, I.D.S. & BLAKEMAN, J.P. (1975) - COMPETITION FOR CARBON COMPOUNDS
     BY A LEAF SURFACE BACTERIUM AND CONIDIA OF BOTRYTIS CINEREA. PHYSIOL.
     PL.PATH. 6, 125-136.

730 BROEKHOVEN, L.W.VAN, MAARSCHALKERWEERD, M.W.VAN, LOUSBERG, R.J.J.CH. &
     SALEMINK, C.A. (1974) - ISOMERIZATION AND TRANSFORMATION OF TRANS-TRANS-
     EPOXYFARNESOL BY DRECHSLERA SOROKINIANA. TETRAHEDRON LETTERS, 1974 (34),
     2909-2910.

731 BROEMMELHUES, M. (1935) - DIE WECHSELSEITIGE BEEINFLUSSUNG VON PILZEN UND
     DIE BEDEUTUNG DER PILZKONKURRENZ FUER DAS AUSMASS DER SCHAEDIGUNG AN
     WEIZEN DURCH OPHIOBOLUS GRAMINIS. ZENTBL.BAKT.PARASITKDE, ABT.2, 92,
     81-116.

732   BROOK, P.J. (1963) - ECOLOGY OF THE FUNGUS PITHOMYCES CHARTARUM (BERK. &
       CURT.) M.B. ELLIS IN PASTURE IN RELATION TO FACIAL ECZEMA DISEASE OF
       SHEEP. N.Z.JL AGRIC.RES. 6, 147-228.

733   BROOK, P.J. & WHITE, E.P. (1966) - FUNGUS TOXINS AFFECTING MAMMALS. A.REV.
       PHYTOPATH. 4, 171-194.

734   BROOKS, CH. & COOLEY, J.S. (1917) - TEMPERATURE RELATIONS OF APPLE-ROT FUN-
       GI. J.AGRIC.RES. 8, 139-163.

735   BROOKS, CH., FISHER, D.F. & COOLEY, J.S. (1914) - APPLE ROTS. PHYTOPATHOL-
       OGY 4, 403 (ABS.).

736   BROOKS, D.H. (1964) - INFECTION OF WHEAT ROOTS BY ASCOSPORES OF OPHIOBOLUS
       GRAMINIS. NATURE, LOND. 203, 203.

737   BROOKS, D.H. (1965) - ROOT INFECTION BY ASCOSPORES OF OPHIOBOLUS GRAMINIS
       AS A FACTOR IN EPIDEMIOLOGY OF THE TAKE-ALL DISEASE. TRANS.BR.MYCOL.
       SOC. 48, 237-248.

738   BROOKS, D.H. (1965) - WILD AND CULTIVATED GRASSES AS CARRIERS OF THE TAKE-
       ALL FUNGUS (OPHIOBOLUS GRAMINIS). ANN.APPL.BIOL. 55, 307-316.

739   BROOKS, F.T. (1945) - NOTES ON THE PATHOGENICITY OF MYROTHECIUM RORIDUM.
       TRANS.BR.MYCOL.SOC. 27, 155-157.

740   BROOKS, F.T. & HANSFORD, C.G. (1923) - MOULD GROWTH UPON COLD-STORED MEAT.
       TRANS.BR.MYCOL.SOC. 8, 113-142.

741   BROOKS, J.S. & MORRISON, G.A. (1972) - NATURALLY OCCURRING COMPOUNDS RE-
       LATED TO PHENALENONE. 3. THE STRUCTURE OF HERQUEINONE AND NORHERQUEIN-
       ONE AND THEIR RELATIONSHIPS WITH ISOHERQUEINONE AND ISONORHERQUEINONE.
       J.CHEM.SOC.PERKIN TRANS.I, 1972 (3), 421-437.

742   BROWN, A.G. (1970) - VERSIMIDE, A METABOLITE OF ASPERGILLUS VERSICOLOR.
       J.CHEM.SOC.(C), 1970, 2572-2573.

743   BROWN, A.H.S. & SMITH, G. (1957) - PAECILOMYCES AND BYSSOCHLAMYS. TRANS.BR.
       MYCOL.SOC. 40, 17-89.

744   BROWN, D.E. & HALSTED, D.J. (1975) - THE EFFECT OF ACID PH ON THE GROWTH
       KINETICS OF TRICHODERMA VIRIDE. BIOTECHNOL.BIOENG. 17, 1199-1210.

745   BROWN, J.C. (1958) - SOIL FUNGI OF SOME BRITISH SAND DUNES IN RELATION TO
       SOIL TYPE AND SUCCESSION. J.ECOL. 46, 641-664.

746   BROWN, M.E. & HORNBY, D. (1971) - BEHAVIOUR OF OPHIOBOLUS GRAMINIS ON
       SLIDES BURIED IN SOIL IN THE PRESENCE OR ABSENCE OF WHEAT SEEDLINGS.
       TRANS.BR.MYCOL.SOC. 56, 95-103.

747   BROWN, M.E., HORNBY, D. & PEARSON, V. (1973) - MICROBIAL POPULATIONS AND
       NITROGEN IN SOIL GROWING CONSECUTIVE CEREAL CROPS INFECTED WITH TAKE-
       ALL. J.SOIL.SCI. 24, 296-310.

748   BROWN, M.F. & WYLLIE, T.D. (1970) - ULTRASTRUCTURE OF MICROSCLEROTIA OF
       VERTICILLIUM ALBO-ATRUM. PHYTOPATHOLOGY 60, 538-542.

749   BROWN, R.G. (1972) - STIMULATION OF BETA-(1,6)-GLUCANASE PRODUCTION BY OXI-
       DIZED PUSTULAN. CAN.J.MICROBIOL. 18, 1543-1550.

750   BROWN, R.G., HANIC, L.A. & HSIAO, M. (1973) - STRUCTURE AND CHEMICAL COMPO-
      SITION OF YEAST CHLAMYDOSPORES OF AUREOBASIDIUM PULLULANS. CAN.J.MICRO-
      BIOL. 19, 163-168.

751   BROWN, R.G. & LINDBERG, B. (1967) - POLYSACCHARIDES FROM CELL WALLS OF
      AUREOBASIDIUM (PULLULARIA) PULLULANS. 2. HETEROPOLYSACCHARIDES. ACTA
      CHEM.SCAND. 21, 2383-2389.

752   BRUEHL, G.W. & CUNFER, B. (1971) - PHYSIOLOGIC AND ENVIRONMENTAL FACTORS
      THAT AFFECT THE SEVERITY OF SNOW MOLD OF WHEAT. PHYTOPATHOLOGY 61, 792-
      799.

753   BRUEHL, G.W. & LAI, P. (1966) - PRIOR-COLONIZATION AS A FACTOR IN THE SAP-
      ROPHYTIC SURVIVAL OF SEVERAL FUNGI IN WHEAT STRAW. PHYTOPATHOLOGY 56,
      766-768.

754   BRUEHL, G.W., MACHTMES, R. & KIYMOTO, R. (1975) - TAXONOMIC RELATIONSHIPS
      AMONG TYPHULA SPECIES AS REVEALED BY MATING EXPERIMENTS. PHYTOPATHOLOGY
      65, 1108-1114.

755   BRUMMELEN, J.VAN (1967) - A WORLD-MONOGRAPH OF THE GENERA ASCOBOLUS AND
      SACCOBOLUS. PERSOONIA, SUPPL.1, 260 PP.

756   BRUNNER, R., ROEHR, M. & BRUNNER, H. (1971) - EVIDENCE OF AN INTRACELLULAR
      PROTEINASE OF PENICILLIUM CHRYSOGENUM. ENZYMOLOGIA 40, 209-216.

757   BRUSHABER, J.A. & HASKINS, R.H. (1973) - CELL WALL STRUCTURES OF EPICOCCUM
      NIGRUM (HYPHOMYCETES). CAN.J.BOT. 51, 1071-1073.

758   BRUSHABER, J.A., WILSON, C.L. & AIST, J.R. (1967) - ASEXUAL NUCLEAR BEHAV-
      IOUR OF SOME PLANT PATHOGENIC FUNGI. PHYTOPATHOLOGY 57, 43-46.

759   BRYGOO, E.R. & DESTOMBES, P. (1976) - EPIDEMIOLOGIE DE LA CHROMOBLASTOMY-
      COSE HUMAINE. BULL.INST.PASTEUR 74, 219-243.

760   BUCHANAN, J.R., SOMMER, N.F., FORTLAGE, R.J., MAXIE, E.C., MITCHELL, F.G.
      & HSIEH, D.P.H. (1974) - PATULIN FROM PENICILLIUM EXPANSUM IN STONE
      FRUITS AND PEARS. J.AM.SOC.HORT.SCI. 99, 262-265.

761   BUCHNICEK, J. (1973) - LIGHT RESISTANCE IN GEOPHILIC DERMATOPHYTES. INT.
      SYMP.MED.MYCOL.BUCHAREST, 1973, 64-65 (ABS.).

762   BUCHVALD, J. KLOBUSICKY, M. & CHMEL, L. (1972) - ZUR FRAGE DES UEBERLEBENS
      DER FADENPILZE IM BIOTOP DES FELDES VOM GESICHTSPUNKT DES NATURHERDES
      DER MYKOTISCHEN INFEKTION. MYKOSEN 15, 275-283.

763   BUCKLEY, P.M., SJAHOLM, V.E. & SOMMER, N.F. (1966) - ELECTRON MICROSCOPY
      OF BOTRYTIS CINEREA CONIDIA. J.BACT. 91, 2037-2044.

764   BUCKLEY, P.M., SOMMER, N.F. & MATSUMOTO, T.T. (1968) - ULTRASTRUCTURAL DE-
      TAILS IN GERMINATING SPORANGIOSPORES OF RHIZOPUS STOLONIFER AND RHIZO-
      PUS ARRHIZUS. J.BACT. 95, 2365-2373.

765   BUCKLEY, P.M., WYLLIE, T.D. & DEVAY, J.E. (1969) - FINE STRUCTURE OF CONID-
      IA AND CONIDIUM FORMATION IN VERTICILLIUM ALBO-ATRUM AND V. NIGRESCENS.
      MYCOLOGIA 61, 240-249.

766   BUCKNALL, R.A., MOORES, H., SIMMS, R. & HESP, B. (1973) - ANTIVIRAL EFFECTS
      OF APHIDICOLIN, A NEW ANTIBIOTIC PRODUCED BY CEPHALOSPORIUM APHIDICOLA.
      ANTIMICROB.AGENTS.CHEMOTHER. 4, 294-298.

767 BUDDENHAGEN, I.W. (1958) - INDUCED MUTATIONS AND VARIABILITY IN PHYTOPHTHO-
     RA CACTORUM. AM.J.BOT. 45, 355-365.

768 BUDIARSO, I.T., CARLTON, W.W. & TUITE, J. (1971) - INVESTIGATIONS OF DOSE,
     AGE, AND DURATION OF ADMINISTRATION ON THE HEPATORENAL DAMAGE INDUCED
     IN MICE BY CULTURAL PRODUCTS OF PENICILLIUM VIRIDICATUM. TOXICOL.APPL.
     PHARMACOL. 20, 357-379.

769 BUECHI, G., KITAURA, Y., YUAN, S.-S., WRIGHT, H.E., CLARDY, J., DEMAIN,
     A.L., GLINSUKON, T., HUNT, N. & WOGAN, G.N. (1973) - STRUCTURE OF CYTO-
     CHALASIN-E, A TOXIC METABOLITE OF ASPERGILLUS CLAVATUS. J.AM.CHEM.SOC.
     95, 5423-5425.

770 BUECHI, G., WHITE, J.D. & WOGAN, G.N. (1965) - THE STRUCTURES OF MITORU-
     BRIN AND MITORUBRINOL. J.AM.CHEM.SOC. 87, 3484-3489.

771 BUENNING, E. & ETZOLD, H. (1958) - UEBER DIE WIRKUNG VON POLARISIERTEM
     LICHT AUF KEIMENDE SPOREN VON PILZEN, MOOSEN UND FARNEN. BER.DT.BOT.GES.
     71, 304-306.

772 BUGBEE, W.M. & ANDERSON, N.A. (1963) - INFECTION OF SPRUCE SEEDLINGS BY
     CYLINDROCLADIUM SCOPARIUM. PHYTOPATHOLOGY 53, 1267-1271.

773 BUGBEE, W.M. & ANDERSON, N.A. (1963) - HOST RANGE AND DISTRIBUTION OF CY-
     LINDROCLADIUM SCOPARIUM IN THE NORTH-CENTRAL STATES. PL.DIS.REPTR 47,
     512-515.

774 BUKHALO, A.S., MARTYNENKO, M.M. & ARTISHKOVA, L.V. (1975) - (MYCOLOGICAL
     CHARACTERISTIC OF SOILS IN PADDY FIELDS OF THE UKRAINE). UKR.BOT.ZH.
     32 (6), 717-722.

775 BULIT, J. & LOUVET, J. (1960) - UNE TECHNIQUE D'ETUDE DE L'ACTION DU GAZ
     CARBONIQUE SUR LES CHAMPIGNONS PARASITES DES ORGANES VEGETAUX SOUTER-
     RAINS. ANNLS INST.PASTEUR 98, 557-561.

776 BULL, A.T. (1970) - CHEMICAL COMPOSITION OF WILD-TYPE AND MUTANT ASPERGIL-
     LUS NIDULANS CELL WALLS - THE NATURE OF POLYSACCHARIDE AND MELANIN CON-
     STITUENTS. J.GEN.MICROBIOL. 63, 75-94.

777 BULL, A.T. & CARTER, B.L.A. (1973) - THE ISOLATION OF TYROSINASE FROM AS-
     PERGILLUS NIDULANS, ITS KINETIC AND MOLECULAR PROPERTIES AND SOME CON-
     SIDERATION OF ITS ACTIVITY IN VIVO. J.GEN.MICROBIOL. 75, 61-73.

778 BULLOCK, E., KIRKALDY, D., ROBERTS, J.C. & UNDERWOOD, J.G. (1963) - STUD-
     IES IN MYCOLOGICAL CHEMISTRY. 12. TWO NEW METABOLITES FROM A VARIANT
     STRAIN OF ASPERGILLUS VERSICOLOR. J.CHEM.SOC., 1963, 829-835.

779 BULLOCK, E., ROBERTS, J.C. & UNDERWOOD, J.G. (1962) - STUDIES IN MYCOLOG-
     ICAL CHEMISTRY. 11. THE STRUCTURE OF ISOSTERIGMATOCYSTIN AND AN AMENDED
     STRUCTURE FOR STERIGMATOCYSTIN. J.CHEM.SOC., 1962, 4179-4183.

780 BU'LOCK, J.D., DRAKE, D. & WINSTANLEY, D.J. (1972) - SPECIFICITY AND TRANS-
     FORMATIONS OF THE TRISPORIC ACID SERIES OF FUNGAL SEX HORMONES. PHYTO-
     CHEMISTRY 11, 2011-2018.

781 BUMBIERIS, M. (1969) - EFFECT OF SOIL AMENDMENTS ON NUMBERS OF SOIL MICRO-
     ORGANISMS AND ON THE ROOT-ROT FUSARIUM WILT COMPLEX OF PEAS. AUST.J.BIOL.
     SCI. 22, 1329-1336.

782 BUMBIERIS, M. (1972) - OBSERVATIONS ON SOME PYTHIACEOUS FUNGI ASSOCIATED
     WITH GRAPEVINE DECLINE IN SOUTH AUSTRALIA. AUST.J.AGRIC.RES. 23, 651-657.

783   BURGE, M.N. & ISAAC, I. (1974) - PHIALOPHORA ASTERIS, CAUSAL AGENT OF AS-
      TER WILT. TRANS.BR.MYCOL.SOC. 62, 367-376.

784   BURGES, A. & FENTON, E. (1953) - THE EFFECT OF CARBON DIOXIDE ON THE GROWTH
      OF CERTAIN SOIL FUNGI. TRANS.BR.MYCOL.SOC. 36, 104-108.

785   BURGESS, L.W. & GRIFFIN, D.M. (1967) - COMPETITIVE SAPROPHYTIC COLONIZA-
      TION OF WHEAT STRAW. ANN.APPL.BIOL. 60, 137-142.

786   BURGESS, L.W. & GRIFFIN, D.M. (1968) - THE RECOVERY OF GIBBERELLA ZEAE
      FROM WHEAT STRAWS. AUST.J.EXP.AGRIC.ANIM.HUSB. 8, 364-370.

787   BURGESS, L.W. & GRIFFIN, D.M. (1968) - THE RELATIONSHIP BETWEEN THE SPORE
      DENSITY OF COCHLIOBOLUS SATIVUS IN SOIL AND ITS SAPROPHYTIC ACTIVITY
      AND PARASITISM. AUST.J.EXP.AGRIC.ANIM.HUSB. 8, 371-373.

788   BURGESS, L.W. & GRIFFIN, D.M. (1968) - THE INFLUENCE OF DIURNAL TEMPERATURE
      FLUCTUATIONS ON THE GROWTH OF FUNGI. NEW PHYTOL. 67, 131-137.

789   BURKHARDT, H.J., LUNDIN, R.E. & MCFADDEN, W.H. (1968) - MYCOTOXINS PRO-
      DUCED BY FUSARIUM NIVALE (FRIES) CESATI ISOLATED FROM TALL FESCUE (FE-
      STUCA ARUNDINACEA SCHREB.). SYNTHESIS OF 4-ACETAMIDO-4-HYDROXY-2-BUTE-
      NOIC ACID-GAMMA-LACTONE. TETRAHEDRON 24, 1225-229.

790   BURMEISTER, H.R., ELLIS, J.J. & HESSELTINE, C.W. (1972) - SURVEY FOR FU-
      SARIA THAT ELABORATE T-2 TOXIN. APPL.MICROBIOL. 23, 1165-1166.

791   BURNETT, C. & RAMBO, G.W. (1972) - AFLATOXIN INHIBITION AND DETOXIFICATION
      BY A CULTURE FILTRATE OF ASPERGILLUS NIGER. PHYTOPATHOLOGY 62, 749 (ABS.).

792   BURNSIDE, J.E., SIPPEL, W.L., FORGACS, J., CARLL, W.T., ATWOOD, M.B. &
      DOLL, E.R. (1957) - A DISEASE OF SWINE AND CATTLE CAUSED BY EATING MOL-
      DY CORN. 2. EXPERIMENTAL PRODUCTION WITH PURE CULTURES OF MOLDS. AM.J.
      VET.RES. 18, 817-824.

793   BURR, T.J. (1973) - A SELECTIVE MEDIUM FOR THE ISOLATION OF PYTHIUM APHA-
      NIDERMATUM FROM FIELD SOIL. PHYTOPATHOLOGY 63, 1215 (ABS.).

794   BURR, T.J. & STANGHELLINI, M.E. (1973) - PROPAGULE NATURE AND DENSITY OF
      PYTHIUM APHANIDERMATUM IN FIELD SOIL. PHYTOPATHOLOGY 63, 1499-1501.

795   BURROUGHS, R. & SAUER, D.B. (1971) - GROWTH OF FUNGI IN SORGHUM GRAIN STORED
      AT HIGH MOISTURE CONTENTS. PHYTOPATHOLOGY 61, 767-772.

796   BURROUGHS, R., SEITZ, L.M., SAUER, D.B. & MOHR, H.E. (1976) - EFFECT OF
      SUBSTRATE ON METABOLITE PRODUCTION BY ALTERNARIA ALTERNATA. APPL.ENVIRON.
      MICROBIOL. 31, 685-690.

797   BURROWS, B.F. & TURNER, W.B. (1966) - 1-AMINO-2-NITROCYCLOPENTANECARBOXYLIC
      ACID. A NEW NATURALLY OCCURRING NITRO COMPOUND. J.CHEM.SOC., 1966, 255-
      260.

798   BURSNALL, L.A. & TRIBE, H.T. (1974) - FUNGAL PARASITISM IN CYSTS OF HETE-
      RODERA. 2. EGG PARASITES OF H. SCHACHTII. TRANS.BR.MYCOL.SOC. 62, 595-
      601.

799   BURTON, H.S. (1949) - ANTIBIOTICS FROM PENICILLIA. BR.J.EXP.PATH. 30, 151-
      158.

800   BURTON, K.A., CADMUS, M.C., LAGODA, A.A., SANDFORD, P.A. & WATSON, P.R.
      (1976) - A UNIQUE BIOPOLYMER FROM RHINOCLADIELLA MANSONII NRRL Y-6272.
      PRODUCTION IN 20 LITER FERMENTORS. BIOTECHNOL.BIOENG. 18, 1669-1678.

801   BURWOOD, R. & SPENCER, D.M. (1970) - METABOLISM BY PHYTOPATHOGENIC FUNGI.
      THE DEGRADATION OF HYDROXYBENZOIC ACIDS BY GLOMERELLA CINGULATA. PHY-
      TOCHEMISTRY 9, 333-335.

802   BUSH, D.A. & CODNER, R.C. (1968) - THE NATURE OF MACERATING FACTOR OF PE-
      NICILLIUM DIGITATUM SACCARDO. PHYTOCHEMISTRY 7, 863-869.

803   BUSH, M.T., TOUSTER, O. & BROCKMAN, J.E. (1951) - THE PRODUCTION OF BETA-
      NITROPROPIONIC ACID BY A STRAIN OF ASPERGILLUS FLAVUS. J.BIOL.CHEM. 188,
      685-693.

804   BUSSEL, J., SOMMER, N.F. & KOSUGE, T. (1969) - EFFECT OF ANAEROBIOSIS UPON
      GERMINATION AND SURVIVAL OF RHIZOPUS STOLONIFER SPORANGIOSPORES. PHY-
      TOPATHOLOGY 59, 946-952.

805   BUSTON, H.W. & BASU, S.N. (1948) - SOME FACTORS AFFECTING THE GROWTH AND
      SPORULATION OF CHAETOMIUM GLOBOSUM AND MEMNONIELLA ECHINATA. J.GEN.MI-
      CROBIOL. 2, 162-172.

806   BUSTON, H.W., JABBAR, A. & ETHERIDGE, D.F. (1953) - THE INFLUENCE OF HEXOSE
      PHOSPHATES, CALCIUM AND JUTE EXTRACT ON THE FORMATION OF PERITHECIA BY
      CHAETOMIUM GLOBOSUM. J.GEN.MICROBIOL. 8, 302-306.

807   BUSTON, H.W. & KHAN, A.H. (1956) - THE INFLUENCE OF CERTAIN MICROORGANISMS
      ON THE PRODUCTION OF PERITHECIA BY CHAETOMIUM GLOBOSUM. J.GEN.MICROBIOL.
      14, 655-660.

808   BUSTON, H.W. & KING, E.J. (1951) - FURTHER OBSERVATIONS ON THE SPORULATION
      OF CHAETOMIUM GLOBOSUM. J.GEN.MICROBIOL. 5, 766-771.

809   BUSTON, H.W., MOSS, M.O. & TYRRELL, D. (1966) - THE INFLUENCE OF CARBON
      DIOXIDE ON GROWTH AND SPORULATION OF CHAETOMIUM GLOBOSUM. TRANS.BR.MY-
      COL.SOC. 49, 387-396.

810   BUSTON, H.W. & RICKARD, B. (1956) - THE EFFECT OF A PHYSICAL BARRIER ON
      SPORULATION OF CHAETOMIUM GLOBOSUM. J.GEN.MICROBIOL. 15, 194-197.

811   BUTIN, H. (1963) - UEBER SCLEROPHOMA PITYOPHILA (CORDA) V. HOEHN. ALS
      BLAEUEPILZ AN VERARBEITETEM HOLZ. PHYTOPATH.Z. 48, 298-305.

812   BUTIN, H. (1965) - UNTERSUCHUNGEN ZUR OEKOLOGIE EINIGER BLAEUEPILZE AN
      VERARBEITETEM KIEFERNHOLZ. FLORA, JENA 155, 400-440.

813   BUTLER, E.E. (1957) - RHIZOCTONIA SOLANI AS A PARASITE OF FUNGI. MYCOLOGIA
      49, 354-373.

814   BUTLER, E.E. (1960) - PATHOGENICITY AND TAXONOMY OF GEOTRICHUM CANDIDUM.
      PHYTOPATHOLOGY 50, 665-672.

815   BUTLER, E.E. & BOLKAN, H. (1973) - A MEDIUM FOR HETEROKARYON FORMATION IN
      RHIZOCTONIA SOLANI. PHYTOPATHOLOGY 63, 542-543.

816   BUTLER, E.E. & BRACKER, C. (1970) - MORPHOLOGY AND CYTOLOGY OF RHIZOCTONIA
      SOLANI. IN: RHIZOCTONIA SOLANI, BIOLOGY AND PATHOLOGY; PARMETER, J.R.,
      JR. (ED.), UNIV.CALIFORNIA PRESS, BERKELEY, 32-51.

817   BUTLER, E.E. & ECKERT, J.W. (1963) - A SENSITIVE METHOD FOR THE ISOLATION
      OF GEOTRICHUM CANDIDUM FROM SOIL. MYCOLOGIA 54, 106-109.

818 BUTLER, E.E. & PETERSEN, L.J. (1972) - ENDOMYCES GEOTRICHUM, A PERFECT
     STATE OF GEOTRICHUM CANDIDUM. MYCOLOGIA 64, 365-374.

819 BUTLER, E.E., WEBSTER, R.K. & ECKERT, J.W. (1965) - TAXONOMY, PATHOGENICI-
     TY, AND PHYSIOLOGICAL PROPERTIES OF THE FUNGUS CAUSING SOUR ROT OF CI-
     TRUS. PHYTOPATHOLOGY 55, 1262-1268.

820 BUTLER, F.C. (1953) - SAPROPHYTIC BEHAVIOUR OF SOME CEREAL ROOT ROT FUNGI.
     1. SAPROPHYTIC COLONIZATION OF WHEAT STRAW. ANN.APPL.BIOL. 40, 284-297.

821 BUTLER, F.C. (1953) - SAPROPHYTIC BEHAVIOUR OF SOME CEREAL ROOT ROT FUNGI.
     2. FACTORS INFLUENCING SAPROPHYTIC COLONIZATION OF WHEAT STRAW. ANN.
     APPL.BIOL. 40, 298-304.

822 BUTLER, F.C. (1959) - SAPROPHYTIC BEHAVIOUR OF SOME CEREAL ROOT ROT FUNGI.
     4. SAPROPHYTIC SURVIVAL IN SOILS OF HIGH AND LOW FERTILITY. ANN.APPL.
     BIOL. 47, 28-36.

823 BUTT, Z.L. & GHAFFAR, A. (1972) - INHIBITION OF FUNGI, ACTINOMYCETES AND
     BACTERIA BY STACHYBOTRYS ATRA. MYCOPATH.MYCOL.APPL. 47, 241-252.

824 BUTT, Z.L. & GHAFFAR, A. (1974) - EFFECT OF CERTAIN PHYSICO-CHEMICAL FAC-
     TORS ON GROWTH AND ANTIFUNGAL PROPERTY OF STACHYBOTRYS ATRA. Z.PFLPHY-
     SIOL. 71, 463-466.

825 BUTZKE, H., FRANZ, G., REHAGEN, H.-W. & WICHTMANN, H. (1972) - VERGLEI-
     CHENDE OEKOLOGISCHE UNTERSUCHUNGEN AN ZWEI BOEDEN UNTER NATURNAHER WALD-
     BESTOCKUNG IM WESTFAELISCHEN MUENSTERLAND. FORTSCHR.GEOL.RHEINLD WESTF.
     21, 205-256.

826 BUXTON, E.W. (1955) - THE TAXONOMY AND VARIATION IN CULTURE OF FUSARIUM
     OXYSPORUM FROM GLADIOLUS. TRANS.BR.MYCOL.SOC. 38, 202-212.

827 BUXTON, E.W. (1959) - PRODUCTION OF A PERFECT STAGE IN A NUTRITIONALLY DE-
     FICIENT MUTANT OF PATHOGENIC FUSARIUM OXYSPORUM AFTER ULTRA-VIOLET IRRA-
     DIATION. NATURE, LOND. 184, 1258.

828 BUXTON, E.W., KHALIFA, O. & WARD, V. (1965) - EFFECT OF SOIL AMENDMENT
     WITH CHITIN ON PEA WILT CAUSED BY FUSARIUM OXYSPORUM F. PISI. ANN.APPL.
     BIOL. 55, 83-88.

829 BYE, A. & KING, H.K. (1970) - THE BIOSYNTHESIS OF 4-HYDROXYCOUMARIN AND
     DICOUMAROL BY ASPERGILLUS FUMIGATUS. BIOCHEM.J. 117, 237-245.

830 BYRDE, R.J.W. & WOODCOCK, D. (1957) - FUNGAL DETOXICATION. 2. THE METABO-
     LISM OF SOME PHENOXY-N-ALKYLCARBOXYLIC ACIDS BY ASPERGILLUS NIGER. BIO-
     CHEM.J. 65, 682-686.

831 BYRNE, P.J. & EATON, R.A. (1972) - FUNGAL ATTACK OF WOOD SUBMERGED IN WA-
     TERS OF DIFFERENT SALINITY. INT.BIODETERIOR.BULL. 8, 127-134.

832 BYRNE, P. & JONES, E.B.G. (1975) - EFFECT OF SALINITY ON SPORE GERMINATION
     OF TERRESTRIAL AND MARINE FUNGI. TRANS.BR.MYCOL.SOC. 64, 497-503.

833 BYRNE, P.J. & JONES, E.B.G. (1975) - EFFECT OF SALINITY ON THE REPRODUC-
     TION OF TERRESTRIAL AND MARINE FUNGI. TRANS.BR.MYCOL.SOC. 65, 185-200.

834 CAGLEVIC, M. (1961) - IMPORTANCIA QUE TIENE LA TIERRA INFECTADA EN LA PRO-
     PAGACION DEL MAL DEL PIE DEL TRIGO. BOLN TEC.DEP.INVEST.AGRIC.CHILI 9,
     15-17.

835 CAGNOLI-BELLAVITA, N., CECCHERELLI, P. & FRINGUELLI, R. (1975) - ASCOCHLO-
     RIN, A TERPENOID METABOLITE FROM ACREMONIUM LUZULAE. PHYTOCHEMISTRY 14,
     807.

836 CAGNOLI-BELLAVITA, N., CECCHERELLI, P. & MARIANI, R. (1970) - STRUCTURE DU VIRESCENOSIDE-C, NOUVEAU METABOLITE DE OOSPORA VIRESCENS. EUR.J.BIOCHEM. 15, 356-359.

837 CAILLEUX, R. (1971) - RECHERCHES SUR LA MYCOFLORE COPROPHILE CENTRAFRICAINE. BULL.TRIMEST.SOC.MYCOL.FR. 87, 461-567.

838 CAIN, R.F. (1934) - STUDIES OF COPROPHILOUS SPHAERIALES IN ONTARIO. STUD. UNIV.TORONTO, BIOL.SER. 38, 126 PP., REPRINT CRAMER, LEHRE (1968).

839 CAIN, R.F. (1950) - STUDIES OF COPROPHILOUS ASCOMYCETES. 1. GELASINOSPORA. CAN.J.RES., SECT.C, 28, 566-576.

840 CAIN, R.F. (1957) - STUDIES OF COPROPHILOUS ASCOMYCETES. 6. SPECIES FROM THE HUDSON BAY AREA. CAN.J.BOT. 35, 255-268.

841 CAIN, R.F. (1961) - STUDIES OF COPROPHILOUS ASCOMYCETES. 7. PREUSSIA. CAN. J.BOT. 39, 1633-1666.

842 CAIN, R.F. & GROVES, J.W. (1948) - NOTES ON SEED-BORNE FUNGI. 6. THE GENUS SORDARIA. CAN.J.RES., SECT.C, 26, 486-495.

843 CAJORI, F.A., OTANI, TH.T. & HAMILTON, M.A. (1954) - THE ISOLATION AND SOME PROPERTIES OF AN ANTIBIOTIC FROM FUSARIUM BOSTRYCOIDES. J.BIOL.CHEM. 208, 107-114.

844 CALAM, C.T., CLUTTERBUCK, P.W., OXFORD, A.E. & RAISTRICK, H. (1947) - STUDIES IN THE BIOCHEMISTRY OF MICRO-ORGANISMS. 74. THE MOLECULAR CONSTITUTION OF GEODIN AND ERDIN, TWO CHLORINE-CONTAINING METABOLIC PRODUCTS OF ASPERGILLUS TERREUS THOM. 3. POSSIBLE STRUCTURAL FORMULAE FOR GEODIN AND ERDIN. BIOCHEM.J. 41, 458-462.

845 CALAM, CH.T., OXFORD, A.E. & RAISTRICK, H. (1939) - STUDIES IN THE BIOCHEMISTRY OF MICRO-ORGANISMS. 63. ITACONIC ACID, A METABOLIC PRODUCT OF A STRAIN OF ASPERGILLUS TERREUS THOM. BIOCHEM.J. 33, 1488-1495.

846 CALDERONE, R.A. & NORMAN, C. (1976) - THE ACTIVITY OF SOME RESPIRATORY ASSOCIATED ENZYMES IN STEROL AND NONSTEROL GROWN CULTURES OF PHYTOPHTHORA CACTORUM. MYCOLOGIA 68, 440-446.

847 CALDWELL, I.Y. & TRINCI, A.P.J. (1973) - KINETIC ASPECTS OF GROWTH OF GEOTRICHUM CANDIDUM ON VARIOUS CARBON SOURCES. TRANS.BR.MYCOL.SOC. 61, 411-416.

848 CALDWELL, J. (1963) - EFFECTS OF HIGH PARTIAL PRESSURES OF OXYGEN ON FUNGI. NATURE, LOND. 197, 772-774.

849 CALDWELL, R. (1958) - FATE OF SPORES OF TRICHODERMA VIRIDE INTRODUCED INTO SOIL. NATURE, LOND. 181, 1144-1145.

850 CALDWELL, R. (1963) - OBSERVATIONS ON THE FUNGAL FLORA OF DECOMPOSING BEECH LITTER IN SOIL. TRANS.BR.MYCOL.SOC. 46, 249-261.

851 CALDWELL, R.W., TUITE, J., STOB, M. & BALDWIN, R. (1970) - ZEARALENONE PRODUCTION BY FUSARIUM SPECIES. APPL.MICROBIOL. 20, 31-34.

852 CALLAGHAN, A.A. (1969) - LIGHT AND SPORE DISCHARGE IN ENTOMOPHTHORALES. TRANS.BR.MYCOL.SOC. 53, 87-97.

853 CALONGE, F.D. (1970) - NOTES ON THE ULTRASTRUCTURE OF THE MICROCONIDIUM
     AND STROMA IN SCLEROTINIA SCLEROTIORUM. ARCH.MIKROBIOL. 71, 191-195.

854 CAMERON, H.R. (1962) - EFFECT OF HYDROGEN ION CONCENTRATION ON GROWTH
     RATES OF PHYTOPHTHORA SP. PHYTOPATHOLOGY 52, 727 (ABS.).

855 CAMERON, H.R. & MILBRATH, G.M. (1965) - VARIABILITY IN THE GENUS PHYTOPHTHO-
     RA. 1. EFFECTS OF NITROGEN SOURCES AND PH ON GROWTH. PHYTOPATHOLOGY 55,
     653-657.

856 CAMERON, R.E., KING, J. & DAVID, C.N. (1970) - SOIL MICROBIAL ECOLOGY OF
     WHEELER VALLEY, ANTARCTICA. SOIL SCI. 109, 110-120.

857 CAMPBELL, C.C. (1947) - REVERTING HISTOPLASMA CAPSULATUM TO THE YEAST PHASE.
     J.BACT. 54, 263-264.

858 CAMPBELL, C.K. (1970) - FINE STRUCTURE OF VEGETATIVE HYPHAE OF ASPERGILLUS
     FUMIGATUS. J.GEN.MICROBIOL. 64, 373-376.

859 CAMPBELL, C.K. (1971) - FINE STRUCTURE AND PHYSIOLOGY OF CONIDIAL GERMINA-
     TION IN ASPERGILLUS FUMIGATUS. TRANS.BR.MYCOL.SOC. 57, 393-402.

860 CAMPBELL, I.M., CALZADILLA, C.H. & MCCORKINDALE, N.J. (1966) - SOME NEW
     METABOLITES RELATED TO MYCOPHENOLIC ACID. TETRAHEDRON LETTERS, 1966
     (42), 5107-5111.

861 CAMPBELL, M.E. (1938) - AN INVESTIGATION OF THE MUCORALES IN THE SOIL.
     TRANS.R.SOC.EDINB. 59, 411-436.

862 CAMPBELL, R. (1972) - ULTRASTRUCTURE OF CONIDIUM ONTOGENY IN THE DEUTERO-
     MYCETE FUNGUS STACHYBOTRYS ATRA CORDA. NEW PHYTOL. 71, 1143-1149.

863 CAMPBELL, R. (1975) - THE ULTRASTRUCTURE OF THE FORMATION OF CHAINS OF CO-
     NIDIA IN MEMNONIELLA ECHINATA. MYCOLOGIA 67, 760-769.

864 CAMPBELL, R. (1975) - THE ULTRASTRUCTURE OF THE ARTHRINIUM STATE OF APIO-
     SPORA MONTAGNEI SACC. PROTOPLASMA 83, 51-60.

865 CAMPBELL, W.A. (1947) - A NEW SPECIES OF CONIOTHYRIUM PARASITIC ON SCLERO-
     TIA. MYCOLOGIA 39, 190-195.

866 CAMPBELL, W.A. & HENDRIX, F.F. (1967) - PYTHIUM AND PHYTOPHTHORA SPECIES
     IN FOREST SOILS IN THE SOUTHEASTERN UNITES STATES. PL.DIS.REPTR 51, 929-
     932.

867 CAMPBELL, W.A. & HENDRIX, F.F. (1967) - A NEW HETEROTHALLIC PYTHIUM FROM
     SOUTHERN UNITED STATES. MYCOLOGIA 59, 274-278.

868 CAMPBELL, W.P. (1956) - THE INFLUENCE OF ASSOCIATED MICROORGANISMS ON THE
     PATHOGENICITY OF HELMINTHOSPORIUM SATIVUM. CAN.J.BOT. 34, 865-874.

869 CAMPBELL, W.P. & GRIFFITHS, D.A. (1974) - MORPHOLOGICAL VARIATION IN ISO-
     LATES OF VERTICILLIUM ALBO-ATRUM. CAN.J.MICROBIOL. 20, 163-166.

870 CAMPBELL, W.P. & GRIFFITHS, D.A. (1974) - DEVELOPMENT OF ENDOCONIDIAL CHLA-
     MYDOSPORES IN FUSARIUM CULMORUM. TRANS.BR.MYCOL.SOC. 63, 221-228.

871 CAMPBELL, W.P. & GRIFFITHS, D.A. (1975) - THE DEVELOPMENT AND STRUCTURE OF
     THICK-WALLED, MULTICELLULAR, AERIAL SPORES IN DIHETEROSPORA CHLAMYDOSPO-
     RIA (VERTICILLIUM CHLAMYDOSPORIUM). CAN.J.MICROBIOL. 21, 963-971.

872 CANE, D.E. & IYENGAR, R. (1977) - THE ABSOLUTE CONFIGURATION OF CYCLONE-
     RODIOL. TETRAHEDRON LETTERS, 1977 (40), 3511-3514.

873 CANE, D.E. & LEVIN, R.H. (1975) - APPLICATION OF CARBON-13 MAGNETIC RESO-
     NANCE TO ISOPRENOID BIOSYNTHESIS. 1. OVALICIN. J.AM.CHEM.SOC. 97, 1282-
     1284.

874 CANTRELL, H.F. & DOWLER, W.M. (1971) - EFFECTS OF TEMPERATURE AND PH ON
     GROWTH AND COMPOSITION OF PYTHIUM IRREGULARE AND PYTHIUM VEXANS. MYCO-
     LOGIA 63, 31-37.

875 CAPEK, A. & FASSATIOVA, O. (1977) - SOME BIOCHEMICAL CHARACTERISTICS OF
     SPECIES OF GENUS BEAUVERIA. FOLIA MICROBIOL. 22, 308-310.

876 CAPEK, A., FASSATIOVA, O. & HANC, O. (1974) - PROGESTERONE TRANSFORMATIONS
     AS A DIAGNOSTIC FEATURE IN THE GENERA ALTERNARIA, STEMPHYLIUM AND CLA-
     DOSPORIUM. FOLIA MICROBIOL. 19, 378-380.

877 CAPEK, A., FASSATIOVA, O. & HANC, O. (1975) - PROGESTERONE TRANSFORMATION
     AS A DIAGNOSTIC FEATURE OF THE GENERA HUMICOLA AND GILMANIELLA. FOLIA
     MICROBIOL. 20, 166-167.

878 CAPEK, A., FASSATIOVA, O. & HANC, O. (1975) - PROGESTERONE TRANSFORMATIONS
     AS A BIOCHEMICAL FEATURE OF SPECIES OF THE GENUS SCOPULARIOPSIS. FOLIA
     MICROBIOL. 20, 517-518.

879 CAPEK, A. & SIMEK, A. (1971) - ANTIMICROBIAL AGENTS. 11. MICROBIAL DEGRA-
     DATION OF FUNGICIDIN. FOLIA MICROBIOL. 16, 364-366.

880 CAPEK, A., SIMEK, A., LEINER, J. & WEICHET, J. (1970) - ANTIMICROBIAL
     AGENTS. 7. MICROBIAL DEGRADATION OF THE ANTIFUNGAL AGENT 2-CHLORO-4-
     NITROPHENOL (NITROFUNGIN). FOLIA MICROBIOL. 15, 350-353.

881 CAPPELLINI, R.A. (1960) - FIELD INOCULATION OF FORAGE LEGUMES AND TEMPERA-
     TURE STUDIES WITH ISOLATES OF SCLEROTINIA TRIFOLIORUM AND SCLEROTINIA
     SCLEROTIORUM. PL.DIS.REPTR 44, 862-864.

882 CAPPELLINI, R.A. (1966) - GROWTH AND POLYGALACTURONASE PRODUCTION BY RHI-
     ZOPUS STOLONIFER. PHYTOPATHOLOGY 56, 734-737.

883 CAPPELLINI, R.A. & PETERSON, J.L. (1965) - MACROCONIDIUM FORMATION IN SUB-
     MERGED CULTURES BY A NON-SPORULATING STRAIN OF GIBBERELLA ZEAE. MYCO-
     LOGIA 57, 962-966.

884 CAPPELLINI, R.A. & PETERSON, J.L. (1966) - PRODUCTION, IN VITRO, OF CER-
     TAIN PECTOLYTIC AND CELLULOLYTIC ENZYMES BY FUNGI ASSOCIATED WITH CORN
     STALK ROT. BULL.TORREY BOT.CLUB 93, 52-55.

885 CAPPELLINI, R.A. & PETERSON, J.L. (1969) - SPORULATION OF GIBBERELLA ZEAE.
     2. THE EFFECTS OF PH ON MACROCONIDIUM PRODUCTION. MYCOLOGIA 61, 481-485.

886 CAPRILLI, F., NAZZARO, P., MERCANTINI, R. & TONOLO, A. (1971) - MORPHOLOG-
     ICAL AND CYTOLOGICAL OBSERVATIONS ON CONIDIAL FORMATION OF THE GENERA
     EPIDERMOPHYTON AND MICROSPORON. MYCOPATH.MYCOL.APPL. 45, 137-150.

887 CARDILLO, R., FUGANTI, C., GATTI, G., GHIRINGHELLI, D. & GRASSELLI, P.
     (1974) - MOLECULAR STRUCTURE OF CRYPTOECHINULINE-A, A NEW METABOLITE OF
     ASPERGILLUS AMSTELODAMI, ISOLATED DURING INVESTIGATIONS ON ECHINULINE
     BIOSYNTHESIS. TETRAHEDRON LETTERS, 1974 (36), 3163-3166.

888 CARDOSO, E.J.B.N. & SCHMITTHENNER, A.F. (1975) - INFLUENCE OF LIGHT ON THE
     GERMINATION OF PHYTOPHTHORA CACTORUM OOSPORES. SUMMA PHYTOPATH. 1, 23-
     30.

889   CARELS, M. & SHEPHERD, D. (1975) – SEXUAL REPRODUCTIVE CYCLE OF MONASCUS
      IN SUBMERGED SHAKEN CULTURE. J.BACT. 122, 288-294.

890   CARELS, M. & SHEPHERD, D. (1977) – THE EFFECT OF DIFFERENT NITROGEN SOUR-
      CES ON PIGMENT PRODUCTION AND SPORULATION OF MONASCUS SPECIES IN SUB-
      MERGED, SHAKEN CULTURE. CAN.J.MICROBIOL. 23, 1360-1372.

891   CARETTA, G. (1963) – NUOVI SINONIMI DI GEOTRICHUM CANDIDUM E CHIAVE ANALI-
      TICA DELLE SPECIE SINORA AMMESSE. ATTI IST.BOT.UNIV.LAB.CRITTOGAM.PAVIA,
      SER.5, 20, 282-291.

892   CARETTA, G. (1966) – OSSERVAZIONI MORFOLOGICHE COMPARATIVE SU ALCUNE SPE-
      CIE DEL GENERE RHIZOPUS. ATTI.IST.BOT.UNIV.LAB.CRITTOGAM.PAVIA, SER.6,
      2, 117-165.

893   CARETTA, G. & PIONTELLI, E. (1975) – ISOLATION OF KERATINOPHILIC FUNGI
      FROM SOIL IN PAVIA, ITALY. SABOURAUDIA 13, 33-37.

894   CAREY, M.C. & SMALL, D.M. (1971) – MICELLAR PROPERTIES OF SODIUM FUSIDATE,
      A STEROID ANTIBIOTIC STRUCTURALLY RESEMBLING THE BILE SALTS. J.LIPID
      RES. 12, 604-613.

895   CARITO, S.L. & PISANO, M.A. (1966) – PRODUCTION OF ALANINE BY FUSARIUM MO-
      NILIFORME. APPL.MICROBIOL. 14, 39-44.

896   CARLEY, H.E., WATSON, R.D. & HUBER, D.M. (1967) – INHIBITION OF PIGMENTA-
      TION IN ASPERGILLUS NIGER BY DIMETHYLSULFOXIDE. CAN.J.BOT. 45, 1451-
      1453.

897   CARLILE, M.J. (1956) – A STUDY OF THE FACTORS INFLUENCING NON-GENETIC VARI-
      ATION IN A STRAIN OF FUSARIUM OXYSPORUM. J.GEN.MICROBIOL. 14, 643-654.

898   CARLL, W.T. & FORGACS, J. (1954) – THE SIGNIFICANCE OF FUNGI IN HYPERKERA-
      TOSIS. MILITARY SURGEON 115, 187-193.

899   CARLTON, W.W. & TUITE, J. (1971) – TOXIC EFFECTS IN MICE OF CORN CULTURES
      OF PENICILLIUM CYCLOPIUM AND PENICILLIUM FREQUENTANS. TOXIC.APPL.PHAR-
      MACOL. 20, 538-547.

900   CARMEN, L.M. & LOCKWOOD, J.L. (1959) – FACTORS AFFECTING ZOOSPORE PRODUC-
      TION BY APHANOMYCES EUTEICHES. PHYTOPATHOLOGY 49, 535 (ABS.).

901   CARMICHAEL, J.W. (1957) – GEOTRICHUM CANDIDUM. MYCOLOGIA 49, 820-830.

902   CARMICHAEL, J.W. (1962) – CHRYSOSPORIUM AND SOME OTHER ALEURIOSPORIC HY-
      PHOMYCETES. CAN.J.BOT. 40, 1137-1174.

903   CARMICHAEL, J.W., SEKHON, A.S. & SIGLER, L. (1973) – CLASSIFICATION OF
      SOME DERMATOPHYTES BY PYROLYSIS-GAS-LIQUID CHROMATOGRAPHY. CAN.J.MICRO-
      BIOL. 19, 403-407.

904   CARMO-SOUSA, L.DO (1970) – TRICHOSPORON BEHREND. IN: THE YEASTS; LODDER,
      J. (ED.), NORTH HOLLAND PUBL.CO., AMSTERDAM, 1309-1352.

905   CARR, A.J.H. & OLIVE, L.S. (1959) – GENETICS OF SORDARIA FIMICOLA. 3. CROSS-
      COMPATIBILITY AMONG SELF-FERTILE AND SELF-STERILE CULTURES. AM.J.BOT.
      46, 81-91.

906   CARROLL, F.E. (1972) – A FINE-STRUCTURAL STUDY OF CONIDIUM INITIATION IN
      STEMPHYLIUM BOTRYOSUM. J.CELL SCI. 11, 33-47.

907 CARROLL, F.E. & CARROLL, G.C. (1973) - SENESCENCE AND DEATH OF THE CONIDIO-
GENOUS CELL IN STEMPHYLIUM BOTRYOSUM. ARCH.MIKROBIOL. 94, 109-124.

908 CARROLL, F.E. & CARROLL, G.C. (1974) - THE FINE STRUCTURE OF CONIDIUM INI-
TIATION IN ULOCLADIUM ATRUM. CAN.J.BOT. 52, 443-446.

909 CARROLL, R.B. & ELLIOTT, E.S. (1964) - SIMILARITY OF SPECIES OF FUNGI ISO-
LATED FROM ROOTS OF ALFALFA AND RED CLOVER. PHYTOPATHOLOGY 54, 746 (ABS.).

910 CARTER, B.L.A. & BULL, A.T. (1971) - THE EFFECT OF OXYGEN TENSION IN THE
MEDIUM ON THE MORPHOLOGY AND GROWTH KINETICS OF ASPERGILLUS NIDULANS.
J.GEN.MICROBIOL. 65, 265-273.

911 CARTER, B.L.A., BULL, A.T., PIRT, S.J. & ROWLEY, B.I. (1971) - RELATIONSHIP
BETWEEN ENERGY SUBSTRATE UTILIZATION AND SPECIFIC GROWTH RATE IN ASPER-
GILLUS NIDULANS. J.BACT. 108, 309-313.

912 CARTER, M.E., CORDES, D.O., MENNA, M.E.DI & HUNTER, R. (1973) - FUNGI ISO-
LATED FROM BOVINE MYCOTIC ABORTION AND PNEUMONIA WITH SPECIAL REFERENCE
TO MORTIERELLA WOLFII. RES.VET.SCI. 14, 201-206.

913 CARTER, M.V. & PRICE, T.V. (1974) - BIOLOGICAL CONTROL OF EUTYPA ARMENIA-
CAE. 2. STUDIES OF THE INTERACTION BETWEEN E. ARMENIACAE AND FUSARIUM
LATERITIUM, AND THEIR RELATIVE SENSITIVITIES TO BENZIMIDAZOLE CHEMICALS.
AUST.J.AGRIC.RES. 25, 105-119.

914 CARTER, S.B. (1967) - EFFECTS OF CYTOCHALASINS ON MAMMALIAN CELLS. NATURE,
LOND. 213, 261-264.

915 CASIDA, L.E. (1959) - PHOSPHATASE ACTIVITY OF SOME COMMON SOIL FUNGI. SOIL
SCI. 87, 305-310.

916 CASNATI, G., POCHINI, A. & UNGARO, R. (1973) - NEOECHINULINE - A NEW ISO-
PRENYL-INDOLE METABOLITE FROM ASPERGILLUS AMSTELODAMI. GAZETTA CHIM.
ITAL. 103, 141-151.

917 CASPER, S.J. (1966) - HYPHOMYCETEN-STUDIEN. 2. SUESSWASSER-HYPHOMYCETEN
AUS DEM THUERINGER WALD, DEM ERZGEBIRGE UND DEM RIESENGEBIRGE. LIMNOLO-
GIA 4, 471-481.

918 CASSINI, R., CASSINI, R. & MASSENOT, M. (1966) - MYCOFLORE D'UN SOL CUL-
TIVE EN BLE DEPUIS 1900 A L'ECOLE NATIONALE SUPERIEURE AGRONOMIQUE DE
GRIGNON. BULL.ASS.FR.ETUDE SOL 12, 355-365.

919 CATANI-CATOVIC, S. & PETERSON, J.L. (1966) - PHYTOTOXICITY OF THE METABO-
LITES OF A SOIL FUNGUS. SOIL SCI. 101, 57-62.

920 CATANI, S.C. & PETERSON, J.L. (1967) - ANTAGONISTIC RELATIONSHIPS BETWEEN
VERTICILLIUM DAHLIAE AND FUNGI ISOLATED FROM THE RHIZOSPHERE OF ACER
PLATANOIDES. PHYTOPATHOLOGY 57, 363-366.

921 CATEN, C.E. (1971) - HETEROKARYON INCOMPATIBILITY IN IMPERFECT SPECIES OF
ASPERGILLUS. HEREDITY 26, 299-312.

922 CATCHINGS, B.M. & GUIDRY, D.J. (1973) - EFFECTS OF PH AND TEMPERATURE ON
THE IN VITRO GROWTH OF SPOROTHRIX SCHENCKII. SABOURAUDIA 11, 70-76.

923 CATLEY, B.J. (1971) - UTILIZATION OF CARBON SOURCES BY PULLULARIA PULLU-
LANS FOR THE ELABORATION OF EXTRACELLULAR POLYSACCHARIDES. APPL.MICRO-
BIOL. 22, 641-649.

924 CATLEY, B.J. (1971) - ROLE OF PH AND NITROGEN LIMITATION IN THE ELABORA-
TION OF THE EXTRACELLULAR POLYSACCHARIDE PULLULAN BY PULLULARIA PULLU-
LANS. APPL.MICROBIOL. 22, 650-654.

925 CATLEY, B.J. (1972) - PULLULAN ELABORATION, AN INDUCIBLE SYSTEM OF PULLU-
     LARIA PULLULANS. FEBS LETTERS, 1972 (20), 174-176.

926 CATLEY, B.J. (1973) - THE RATE OF ELABORATION OF THE EXTRACELLULAR POLY-
     SACCHARIDE, PULLULAN, DURING GROWTH OF PULLULARIA PULLULANS. J.GEN.MI-
     CROBIOL. 78, 33-38.

927 CATLEY, B.J. & KELLY, P.J. (1975) - METABOLISM OF TREHALOSE AND PULLULAN
     DURING THE GROWTH CYCLE OF AUREOBASIDIUM PULLULANS. BIOCHEM.SOC.TRANS.
     NO.3, 1079-1081.

928 CATLEY, B.J. & WHELAN, W.J. (1971) - OBSERVATIONS ON THE STRUCTURE OF PUL-
     LULAN. ARCHS BIOCHEM.BIOPHYS. 143, 138-142.

929 CECCHERELLI, P., CAGNOLI-BELLAVITA, N., POLONSKY, J. & BASKEVITCH, Z.
     (1973) - STRUCTURES DES VIRESCENOSIDES-F ET -G, NOUVEAUXMETABOLITES DE
     OOSPORA VIRESCENS. TETRAHEDRON 29, 449-454.

930 CECCHERELLI, P., FRINGUELLI, R. & MADRUZZA, G.F. (1975) - CEREVISTEROL AND
     ERGOSTEROL PEROXIDE FROM ACREMONIUM LUZULAE. PHYTOCHEMISTRY 14, 1434.

931 CEJP, K. (1962) - PYTHIUM SPECIES OF THE GROUP PYTHIUM DEBARYANUM FROM
     CZECHOSLOVAKIA. ACTA UNIV.CAROL., BIOLOGICA 1962, 205-218.

932 CERUTI SCURTI, J. & FIUSSELLO, N. (1970) - ATTIVITA CELLULOSOLITICA DI MI-
     CETI ISOLATI DA MANGIMI E DA INSILATI. ALLIONIA 16, 7-16.

933 CERUTI SCURTI, J., FIUSSELLO, N. & CANTINI, G. (1971) - METABOLITI AD AZIO-
     NE ESTROGENA PRODOTTI DA MICETI. ALLIONIA 17, 55-58.

934 CERUTI SCURTI, J., FIUSSELLO, N. & JODICE, R. (1972) - INFLUENZA DEI FUN-
     GHI NEI PROCESSI DI UMIFICAZIONE. 3. UTILIZZAZIONE DELLA LIGNINA, LIG-
     NOSULFONATO, ACIDI UMICI E FULVICI DA PARTE DI MICETI IN RELAZIONE ALLA
     PRESENZA DI FENOLOSSIDASI. ALLIONIA 18, 117-128.

935 CHACKO, C.I. & LOCKWOOD, J.L. (1966) - CHLORINATED HYDROCARBON PESTICIDES.
     DEGRADATION BY MICROBES. SCIENCE, N.Y. 154, 893-895.

936 CHADEFAUD, M. & AVELLANAS, L. (1967) - REMARQUES SUR L'ONTOGENIE ET LA
     STRUCTURE DES PERITHECES DES CHAETOMIUM GLOBOSUM ET CH. SENEGALENSIS.
     BOTANISTE, 50, 59-88.

937 CHAHAL, D.S. & GRAY, W.D. (1971) - GROWTH OF CELLULOLYTIC FUNGI ON WOOD
     PULP. 3. EFFECT OF ORGANIC ACIDS. INDIAN PHYTOPATH. 24, 320-324.

938 CHAIET, L., KEMPF, A.J., HARMAN, R., KACZKA, E., WESTON, R., NOLLSTADT, K.
     & WOLF, F.J. (1970) - ISOLATION OF A PURE DEXTRANASE FROM PENICILLIUM
     FUNICULOSUM. APPL.MICROBIOL. 20, 421-426.

939 CHAIN, E., FLOREY, H.W., JENNINGS, M.A. & CALLOW, D. (1942) - AN ANTIBAC-
     TERIAL SUBSTANCE PRODUCED BY PENICILLIUM CLAVIFORME. BR.J.EXP.PATH. 23,
     202-205.

940 CHAIN, E., FLOREY, H.W., JENNINGS, M.A. & WILLIAMS, T.I. (1943) - HELVOLIC
     ACID, AN ANTIBIOTIC PRODUCED BY ASPERGILLUS FUMIGATUS MUT. HELVOLA YUILL.
     BR.J.EXP.PATH. 24, 108-119.

941 CHALLENGER, F., LISLE, D.B. & DRANSFIELD, P.B. (1954) - BIOLOGICAL METHYL-
     ATION. 14. THE FORMATION OF TRIMETHYLARSINE AND DIMETHYL SELENIDE IN
     MOULD CULTURES FROM METHYL SOURCES CONTAINING 14C. J.CHEM.SOC., 1954,
     1760-1771.

942 CHALUTZ, E. & DEVAY, J.E. (1969) - PRODUCTION OF ETHYLENE IN VITRO AND IN VIVO BY CERATOCYSTIS FIMBRIATA IN RELATION TO DISEASE DEVELOPMENT. PHYTOPATHOLOGY 59, 750-755.

943 CHAMBERS, S.C. (1970) - NUCLEAR DISTRIBUTION IN VEGETATIVE CELLS OF OPHIOBOLUS GRAMINIS AND OTHER CEREAL ROOT PATHOGENS. AUST.J.BIOL.SCI. 23, 1105-1107.

944 CHAMBERS, S.C. (1971) - SOME FACTORS AFFECTING THE SURVIVAL OF THE CEREAL ROOT PATHOGEN OPHIOBOLUS GRAMINIS IN WHEAT STRAW. AUST.J.EXP.AGRIC.ANIM. HUSB. 11, 90-93.

945 CHAMBERS, S.C. (1972) - FUSARIUM SPECIES ASSOCIATED WITH WHEAT IN VICTORIA. AUST.J.EXP.AGRIC.ANIM.HUSB. 12, 433-436.

946 CHAMBERS, S.C. & FLENTJE, N.T. (1967) - STUDIES ON VARIATION WITH OPHIOBOLUS GRAMINIS. AUST.J.BIOL.SCI. 20, 941-951.

947 CHAMBERS, S.C. & FLENTJE, N.T. (1968) - SAPROPHYTIC SURVIVAL OF OPHIOBOLUS GRAMINIS ON VARIOUS HOSTS. AUST.J.BIOL.SCI. 21, 1153-1161.

948 CHAMBERS, S.C. & FLENTJE, N.T. (1969) - RELATIVE EFFECTS OF SOIL NITROGEN AND SOIL ORGANISMS ON SURVIVAL OF OPHIOBOLUS GRAMINIS. AUST.J.BIOL.SCI. 22, 275-278.

949 CHANG, CH.-F., MYOKEI, R., SAKURAI, A., TAKAHASHI, N. & TAMURA, S. (1969) - ASPOCHRACIN, A NEW INSECTICIDAL METABOLITE OF ASPERGILLUS OCHRACEUS. 2. SYNTHESIS OF HEXAHYDROASPOCHRACIN. AGRIC.BIOL.CHEM., TOKYO 33, 1501-1506.

950 CHANG, I. & KOMMEDAHL, T. (1968) - BIOLOGICAL CONTROL OF SEEDLING BLIGHT OF CORN BY COATING KERNELS WITH ANTAGONISTIC MICROORGANISMS. PHYTOPATHOLOGY 58, 1395-1401.

951 CHANG, S.T., SHEPHERD, C.J. & PRATT, B.H. (1974) - CONTROL OF SEXUALITY IN PHYTOPHTHORA CINNAMOMI. AUST.J.BOT. 22, 669-680.

952 CHANG, Y. (1967) - THE FUNGI OF WHEAT STRAW COMPOST. 2. BIOCHEMICAL AND PHYSIOLOGICAL STUDIES. TRANS.BR.MYCOL.SOC. 50, 667-677.

953 CHANG, Y. & HUDSON, H.J. (1967) - THE FUNGI OF WHEAT STRAW COMPOST. 1. ECOLOGICAL STUDIES. TRANS.BR.MYCOL.SOC. 50, 649-666.

954 CHANG-HO, Y. (1970) - THE EFFECT OF PEA ROOT EXUDATE ON THE GERMINATION OF PYTHIUM APHANIDERMATUM ZOOSPORE CYSTS. CAN.J.BOT. 48, 1501-1514.

955 CHANG-HO, Y. (1974) - OXYGEN UPTAKE BY MOTILE AND GERMINATING ZOOSPORES OF PYTHIUM APHANIDERMATUM. CAN.J.BOT. 52, 669-671.

956 CHANG MEW, I. & KOMMEDAHL, T. (1972) - INTERACTION AMONG MICROORGANISMS OCCURRING NATURALLY AND APPLIED TO PERICARPS OF CORN KERNELS. PL.DIS. REPTR 56, 861-863.

957 CHANNELL, S., BLYTH, W., LLOYD, M., WEIR, D.M., AMOS, W.M.G., LITTLEWOOD, A.P., RIDDLE, H.F.V. & GRANT, I.W.B. (1969) - ALLERGIC ALVEOLITIS IN MALTWORKERS. Q.JL MED. 38, 351-376.

958 CHAPMAN, E.S. (1974) - EFFECT OF TEMPERATURE ON GROWTH RATE OF SEVEN THERMOPHILIC FUNGI. MYCOLOGIA 66, 542-546.

959   CHAPMAN, E.S. & FERGUS, C.L. (1975) - GERMINATION OF ASCOSPORES OF CHAE-
      TOMIUM GLOBOSUM. MYCOLOGIA 67, 1048-1052.

960   CHARLES, V.K. (1941) - A PRELIMINARY CHECK-LIST OF THE ENTOMOGENOUS FUNGI
      OF NORTH AMERICA. BULL.INS.PEST SURV. 21, SUPPL.9, 707-785.

961   CHASTUKHIN, V.Y. (1967) - (THE MICROMYCETES OF OLIGOTROPHIC BOGS AND MAR-
      SHY FORESTS, AND THEIR ROLE IN VEGETATIONAL CHANGES DURING DRAINAGE).
      BOT.ZH.SSR 52, 214-222.

962   CHASTUKHIN, V.Y. (1967) - (DECOMPOSITION OF PEAT MOSSES BY FUNGI). MIKOL.
      FITOPAT. 1, 294-303.

963   CHASTUKHIN, V.YA. & NIKOLAEVSKAYA, M.A. (1962) - (THE MICROFLORA OF DECAY-
      ING ROOT RESIDUES AND OF THE RHIZOSPHERE OF OAK). VEST.LENINGR.GOS.UNIV.,
      SER.BIOL. 17, 43-53.

964   CHATTERJI, B.C. (1966) - SOME OBSERVATIONS ON THE GROWTH AND SPORULATION
      OF CHAETOMIUM GLOBOSUM IN MEDIA CONTAINING AMMONIUM TARTRATE. TRANS.BR.
      MYCOL.SOC. 49, 397-401.

965   CHATURVEDI, C. (1966) - UTILIZATION OF OLIGOSACCHARIDES BY THREE IMPERFECT
      FUNGI. MYCOPATH.MYCOL.APPL. 29, 323-330.

966   CHAUDHURI, H. (1923) - A STUDY OF THE GROWTH IN CULTURE OF VERTICILLIUM
      ALBO-ATRUM R. & B. ANN.BOT. 37, 519-539.

967   CHAUDHURI, H. (1938) - MOLDS OF THE PUNJAB. 2. THE PENICILLIA. PROC.INDIAN
      ACAD.SCI., SECT.B, 8, 93-99.

968   CHAUDHURI, H. & SACHAR, G.S. (1934) - A STUDY OF THE FUNGUS FLORA OF THE
      PUNJAB SOILS. ANNLS MYCOL. 32, 90-100.

969   CHAUDHURI, H. & UMAR, M. (1938) - MOLDS OF THE PUNJAB. 1. THE ASPERGILLI.
      PROC.INDIAN ACAD.SCI., SECT.B, 8, 79-92.

970   CHAUHAN, M.S. & GROVER, R.K. (1973) - PATHOLOGICAL STUDIES ON HELMINTHO-
      SPORIUM SPICIFERUM LEAF BLIGHT OF TOBACCO. INDIAN J.MYCOL.PL.PATH. 3,
      55-62.

971   CHAUHAN, M.S. & GROVER, R.K. (1973) - MYCO-PHYLLO-FLORA OF TOBACCO AND
      THEIR ANTAGONISM AGAINST HELMINTHOSPORIUM SPICIFERUM. INDIAN J.MYCOL.
      PL.PATH. 3, 169-176.

972   CHAUHAN, M.S. & SURYANARAYANA, D. (1970) - PHYSIOLOGICAL STUDIES ON THE
      FUNGUS CAUSING MYROTHECIUM LEAF SPOT IN HARYANA, INDIA. COTT.GR.REV.
      47, 29-35.

973   CHAVEZ, H.B., BLOSS, H.E., BOYLE, A.M. & GRIES, G.A. (1976) - EFFECTS OF
      CROP RESIDUES IN SOIL ON PHYMATOTRICHUM ROOT ROT OF COTTON. MYCOPATHO-
      LOGIA 58, 1-7.

974   CHEE, K.-H. & NEWHOOK, F.J. (1965) - IMPROVED METHODS FOR USE IN STUDIES
      ON PHYTOPHTHORA CINNAMOMI RANDS AND OTHER PHYTOPHTHORA SPECIES. N.Z.JL
      AGRIC.RES. 8, 88-95.

975   CHEE, K.-H. & NEWHOOK, F.J. (1965) - VARIABILITY IN PHYTOPHTHORA CINNAMOMI
      RANDS. N.Z.JL AGRIC.RES. 8, 96-103.

976   CHEN, A.W. (1964) - SOIL FUNGI WITH HIGH SALT TOLERANCE. TRANS.KANS.ACAD.
      SCI. 67, 36-40.

977   CHEN, A.W. (1966) - SOIL PHYSICAL FACTORS AND THE ECOLOGY OF FUNGI. 5. FUR-
      THER STUDIES IN RELATIVELY DRY SOILS. TRANS.BR.MYCOL.SOC. 49, 419-426.

978   CHEN, A.W. & GRIFFIN, D.M. (1966) - SOIL PHYSICAL FACTORS AND THE ECOLOGY
      OF FUNGI. 6. INTERACTION BETWEEN TEMPERATURE AND SOIL MOISTURE. TRANS.
      BR.MYCOL.SOC. 49, 551-561.

979   CHEN, D.-W. & ZENTMYER, G.A. (1969) - AXENIC PRODUCTION OF SPORANGIA BY
      PHYTOPHTHORA CINNAMOMI. PHYTOPATHOLOGY 59, 1021 (ABS.).

980   CHEPENKO, L.I., VASIL'EVA, E.A., BORODIN, G.I. & RUNOV, V.I. (1974) -
      (NATURE OF SOME PIGMENTS OF VERTICILLIUM LATERITIUM). UZBEK.BIOL.ZH.
      18, 8-10.

981   CHEREPANOVA, N.P. (1975) - (EFFECTS OF ENVIRONMENTAL CONDITIONS ON THE PRO-
      DUCTION OF FRUIT BODIES BY SPECIES OF CHAETOMIUM FR.). MIKOL.FITOPAT.
      9, 391-396.

982   CHESTERS, C.G.C. (1948) - A CONTRIBUTION TO THE STUDY OF FUNGI IN THE SOIL.
      TRANS.BR.MYCOL.SOC. 30, 100-117.

983   CHESTERS, C.G.C. (1960) - CERTAIN PROBLEMS ASSOCIATED WITH THE DECOMPOSI-
      TION OF SOIL ORGANIC MATTER BY FUNGI. IN: ECOLOGY OF SOIL FUNGI; PAR-
      KINSON, D. & WAID, J.S. (ED.), LIVERPOOL, 223-238.

984   CHESTERS, C.G.C. & HICKMAN, C.J. (1944) - ON PYTHIUM VIOLAE N.SP. AND P.
      OLIGANDRUM DRECHSLER FROM CULTIVATED VIOLA. TRANS.BR.MYCOL.SOC. 27, 55-
      62.

985   CHESTERS, C.G.C. & MATHISON, G.E. (1963) - THE DECOMPOSITION OF WOOL KERA-
      TIN BY KERATINOMYCES AJELLOI. SABOURAUDIA 2, 225-237.

986   CHESTERS, C.G.C. & PARKINSON, D. (1959) - ON THE DISTRIBUTION OF FUNGI IN
      THE RHIZOSPHERES OF OATS. PL.SOIL 11, 145-156.

987   CHESTERS, C.G.C. & PEBERDY, J.F. (1965) - NUTRITIONAL FACTORS IN RELATION
      TO GROWTH AND FAT SYNTHESIS IN MORTIERELLA VINACEA. J.GEN.MICROBIOL. 41,
      127-134.

988   CHESTERS, C.G.C. & ROLINSON, G.N. (1951) - ZINC IN THE METABOLISM OF A
      STRAIN OF ASPERGILLUS NIGER. J.GEN.MICROBIOL. 5, 553-558.

989   CHESTERS, C.G.C. & THORNTON, R.H. (1956) - A COMPARISON OF TECHNIQUES FOR
      ISOLATING SOIL FUNGI. TRANS.BR.MYCOL.SOC. 39, 301-313.

990   CHET, I. (1969) - THE ROLE OF SCLEROTIAL RIND IN THE GERMINABILITY OF SCLE-
      ROTIA OF SCLEROTIUM ROLFSII. CAN.J.BOT. 47, 593-595.

991   CHET, I. & HENIS, Y, (1967) - X-RAY ANALYSIS OF HYPHAL AND SCLEROTIAL WALLS
      OF SCLEROTIUM ROLFSII. CAN.J.MICROBIOL. 14, 815-816.

992   CHET, I. & HENIS, Y. (1972) - THE RESPONSE OF TWO TYPES OF SCLEROTIUM ROLF-
      SII TO FACTORS AFFECTING SCLEROTIUM FORMATION. J.GEN.MICROBIOL. 73, 483-
      486.

993   CHET, I., HENIS, Y. & KISLEV, N. (1969) - ULTRASTRUCTURE OF SCLEROTIA AND
      HYPHAE OF SCLEROTIUM ROLFSII. J.GEN.MICROBIOL. 57, 143-147.

994   CHET, I., RETIG, N. & HENIS, Y. (1972) - CHANGES IN TOTAL SOLUBLE PROTEINS
      AND IN SOME ENZYMES DURING MORPHOGENESIS OF SCLEROTIUM ROLFSII. J.GEN.
      MICROBIOL. 72, 451-456.

995 CHET, I., TIMAR, D. & HENIS, Y. (1977) - PHYSIOLOGICAL AND ULTRASTRUCTURAL CHANGES OCCURRING DURING GERMINATION OF SCLEROTIA OF SCLEROTIUM ROLFSII. CAN.J.BOT. 55, 1137-1142.

996 CHEUNG, S.-S.C., KOBAYASHI, G.S., SCHLESSINGER, D. & MEDOFF, G. (1974) - RNA METABOLISM DURING MORPHOGENESIS IN HISTOPLASMA CAPSULATUM. J.GEN. MICROBIOL. 82, 301-307.

997 CHI, C.C. (1960) - EFFECTS OF STREPTOMYCES AND TRICHODERMA ON FUSARIUM. PHYTOPATHOLOGY 50, 631 (ABS.).

998 CHI, C.C. (1963) - FUNGISTATIC AND FUNGICIDAL EFFECTS OF STREPTOMYCES RIMOSUS ON SOME SOIL-INHABITING PATHOGENIC FUNGI IN VITRO. PHYTOPATHOLOGY 53, 872.

999 CHI, C.C. & HANSON, E.W. (1964) - RELATION OF TEMPERATURE, PH AND NUTRITION TO GROWTH AND SPORULATION OF FUSARIUM SPP. FROM RED CLOVER. PHYTOPATHOLOGY 54, 1053-1058.

1000 CHIARI, D. (1968) - STUDIEN ZUR ERNAEHRUNGSPHYSIOLOGIE DER GATTUNG FUSARIUM. OEST.BOT.Z. 115, 105-112.

1001 CHICK, E.W, HUDNELL, A.B.JR. & SHARP, D.G. (1963) - ULTRAVIOLET SENSITIVITY OF FUNGI ASSOCIATED WITH MYCOTIC KERATITIS AND OTHER MYCOSES. SABOURAUDIA 2, 195-200.

1002 CHIDAMBARAM, P., MATHUR, S.B. & NEERGAARD, P. (1973) - IDENTIFICATION OF SEED-BORNE DRECHSLERA SPECIES. FRIESIA 10, 165-207.

1003 CHIEN, C.-Y., KUHLMAN, E.G. & GAMS, W. (1974) - ZYGOSPORES IN TWO MORTIERELLA SPECIES WITH STYLOSPORES. MYCOLOGIA 66, 114-121.

1004 CHILD, J.J. & HASKINS, R.H. (1971) - INDUCTION OF SEXUALITY IN HETEROTHALLIC PYTHIUM SPP. BY CHOLESTEROL. CAN.J.BOT. 49, 329-332.

1005 CHILTON, J.E. (1954) - VOLUTELLA SPECIES ON ALFALFA. MYCOLOGIA 46, 800-809.

1006 CHINN, S.H.F. (1953) - A SLIDE TECHNIQUE FOR THE STUDY OF FUNGI AND ACTINOMYCETES IN SOIL WITH SPECIAL REFERENCE TO HELMINTHOSPORIUM SATIVUM. CAN. J.BOT. 31, 718-724.

1007 CHINN, S.H.F. (1973) - PREVALENCE OF DENDRYPHION NANUM IN FIELD SOILS IN SASKATCHEWAN WITH SPECIAL REFERENCE TO RAPE IN THE CROP ROTATION. CAN. J.BOT. 51, 2253-2258.

1008 CHINN, S.H.F. & LEDINGHAM, R.J. (1958) - APPLICATION OF A NEW LABORATORY METHOD FOR THE DETERMINATION OF SURVIVAL OF HELMINTHOSPORIUM SATIVUM SPORES IN SOIL. CAN.J.BOT. 36, 289-295.

1009 CHINN, S.H.F., LEDINGHAM, R.J. & SALLANS, B.J. (1961) - POPULATION AND VIABILITY STUDIES OF HELMINTHOSPORIUM SATIVUM IN FIELD SOILS. CAN.J.BOT. 38, 533-539.

1010 CHINN, S.H.F., SALLANS, B.J. & LEDINGHAM, R.J. (1962) - SPORE POPULATIONS OF HELMINTHOSPORIUM SATIVUM IN SOILS IN RELATION TO THE OCCURRENCE OF COMMON ROOT ROT OF WHEAT. CAN.J.PL.SCI. 42, 720-727.

1011 CHINN, S.H.F. & TINLINE, R.D. (1963) - SPORE GERMINABILITY IN SOIL AS AN INHERENT CHARACTER OF COCHLIOBOLUS SATIVUS. PHYTOPATHOLOGY 53, 1109-1112.

1012   CHMEL, L. & BUCHVALD, J. (1970) - ECOLOGY AND TRANSMISSION OF MICROSPORIUM
       GYPSEUM FROM SOIL TO MAN. SABOURAUDIA 8, 149-156.

1013   CHMEL, L., HASILIKOVA, A., HRASKO, J. & VLACILIKOVA, A. (1972) - THE IN-
       FLUENCE OF SOME ECOLOGICAL FACTORS ON KERATINOPHILIC FUNGI IN THE SOIL.
       SABOURAUDIA 10, 26-34.

1014   CHMEL, L. & VLACILIKOVA, A. (1975) - THE ECOLOGY OF KERATINOPHILIC FUNGI
       AT DIFFERENT DEPTHS OF SOIL. SABOURAUDIA 13, 185-191.

1015   CHODAT, F. & FLEURY, C. (1944) - ACTION DE LA SULFO-UREE SUR LE METABOLISME
       ET LE MELANISME DE L'ASPERGILLUS NIGER. C.R.SEANC.SOC.PHYS.HIST.NAT.,
       GENEVE 61, 94-99.

1016   CHOHAN, J.S., GUPTA, V.K. & SUNAR, M.S. (1973) - FUNGI IN GROUNDNUT. FAO
       PL.PROT.BULL. 21, 66-67.

1017   CHOHAN, J.S. & SINGH, T. (1974) - BIOLOGICAL CONTROL OF SEED-BORNE PATHO-
       GENS OF GROUNDNUT. INDIAN J.MYCOL.PL.PATH. 3, 193-194.

1018   CHOLLET, M.-M. & MOREAU, C. (1967) - ETUDE COMPAREE DE QUELQUES ASPERGIL-
       LUS DU GROUPE GLAUCUS - MORPHOLOGIE, CARACTERES CULTURAUX, NUTRITION
       CARBONEE ET PIGMENTS. BULL.TRIMEST.SOC.MYCOL.FR. 83, 293-317.

1019   CHONG, R., GRAY, R.W., KING, R.R. & WHALLEY, W.B. (1971) - THE CHEMISTRY
       OF FUNGI. 62. THE SYNTHESIS OF (+,-)-MITORUBRIN, A METABOLITE OF PENI-
       CILLIUM RUBRUM. J.CHEM.SOC.(C), 1971, 3571-3575.

1020   CHOO, Y.SEN & HOLLAND, A.A. (1970) - DIRECT AND INDIRECT FLUORESCENT ANTI-
       BODY STAINING OF OPHIOBOLUS GRAMINIS SACC. IN CULTURE AND IN THE RHIZO-
       SPHERE OF CEREAL PLANTS. ANTONIE VAN LEEUWENHOEK 36, 549-554.

1021   CHOU, C.K. & STEPHEN, R.C. (1969) - SOIL FUNGI. THEIR OCCURRENCE, DISTRI-
       BUTION AND ASSOCIATION WITH DIFFERENT MICROHABITATS TOGETHER WITH A
       COMPARATIVE STUDY OF ISOLATION TECHNIQUES. NOVA HEDWIGIA 15, 393-409.

1022   CHOU, L.G. (1972) - THE EFFECT OF LEAF AND PLANT LEACHATES FROM FIVE TOMA-
       TO CULTIVARS VARYING IN RESISTANCE TO BOTRYTIS CINEREA ON GERMINATION
       OF BOTRYTIS CINEREA SPORES. PHYTOPATHOLOGY 62, 750 (ABS.).

1023   CHOU, L.G. (1972) - EFFECT OF DIFFERENT CONCENTRATIONS OF CARBOHYDRATES,
       AMINO ACIDS AND GROWTH SUBSTANCES ON SPORE GERMINATION OF BOTRYTIS CI-
       NEREA. PHYTOPATHOLOGY 62, 1107 (ABS.).

1024   CHOU, L.G. & SCHMITTHENNER, A.F. (1974) - EFFECT OF RHIZOBIUM JAPONICUM
       AND ENDOGONE MOSSEAE ON SOYBEAN ROOT ROT CAUSED BY PYTHIUM ULTIMUM AND
       PHYTOPHTHORA MEGASPERMA VAR. SOJAE. PL.DIS.REPTR 58, 221-225.

1025   CHOU, M.C. & PREECE, T.F. (1968) - THE EFFECT OF POLLEN GRAINS ON INFEC-
       TIONS CAUSED BY BOTRYTIS CINEREA FR. ANN.APPL.BIOL. 62, 11-22.

1026   CHOY, Y.M. & UNRAU, A.M. (1971) - METABOLITES OF VERTICILLIUM DAHLIAE. THE
       ISOLATION AND STRUCTURE ELUCIDATION OF SOME DISACCHARIDES AND A TRISAC-
       CHARIDE. CAN.J.BIOCHEM. 49, 894-899.

1027   CHRISTEN, A.A. (1975) - SOME FUNGI ASSOCIATED WITH COLLEMBOLA. REVUE ECOL.
       BIOL.SOL 12, 723-728.

1028   CHRISTENBERRY, G.A. (1940) - A TAXONOMIC STUDY OF THE MUCORALES IN THE
       SOUTHEASTERN UNITED STATES. J.ELISHA MITCHELL SCIENT.SOC. 56, 333-366.

1029   CHRISTENSEN, C.M. (1951) - FUNGI ON AND IN WHEAT SEED. CEREAL CHEM. 28,
       408-415.

78 COMPENDIUM OF SOIL FUNGI

1030 CHRISTENSEN, M. (1960) - THE SOIL MICROFUNGI OF CONIFER-HARDWOOD FORESTS IN WISCONSIN. DISS.UNIV.WISCONSIN.

1031 CHRISTENSEN, C.M. (1967) - A NOTE ON INVASION OF DURUM WHEAT BY STORAGE FUNGI. CEREAL CHEM. 44, 100-102.

1032 CHRISTENSEN, M. (1969) - SOIL MICROFUNGI OF DRY TO MESIC CONIFER-HARD-WOOD FORESTS IN NORTHERN WISCONSIN. ECOLOGY 50, 9-27.

1033 CHRISTENSEN, C.M. (1972) - MOISTURE CONTENT OF SUNFLOWER SEEDS IN RELATION TO INVASION BY STORAGE FUNGI. PL.DIS.REPTR 56, 173-175.

1034 CHRISTENSEN, M. & BACKUS, M.P. (1961) - NEW OR NOTEWORTHY PENICILLIA FROM WISCONSIN SOILS. MYCOLOGIA 53, 451-463.

1035 CHRISTENSEN, M. & BACKUS, M.P. (1964) - TWO VARIETIES OF MONOCILLIUM HU-MICOLA IN WISCONSIN FOREST SOIL. MYCOLOGIA 56, 498-504.

1036 CHRISTENSEN, C.M. & GORDON, D.R. (1948) - THE MOLD FLORA OF STORED WHEAT AND CORN AND ITS RELATION TO HEATING OF MOIST GRAIN. CEREAL CHEM. 25, 417-418.

1037 CHRISTENSEN, C.M., KAUFERT, F.H., SCHMITZ, H. & ALLISON, J.L. (1942) - HORMODENDRUM RESINAE (LINDAU), AN INHABITANT OF WOOD IMPREGNATED WITH CREOSOTE AND COAL TAR. AM.J.BOT. 29, 552-558.

1038 CHRISTENSEN, C.M., NELSON, G.H., MIROCHA, C.J., BATES, F. & DORWORTH, C.E. (1966) - TOXICITY TO RATS OF CORN INVADED BY CHAETOMIUM GLOBOSUM. APPL. MICROBIOL. 14, 774-777.

1039 CHRISTENSEN, M. & WHITTINGHAM, W.F. (1965) - THE SOIL MICROFUNGI OF OPEN BOGS AND CONIFER SWAMPS IN WISCONSIN. MYCOLOGIA 57, 882-896.

1040 CHRISTENSEN, M., WHITTINGHAM, W.F. & NOVAK, R.O. (1962) - THE SOIL MICRO-FUNGI OF WET-MESIC FORESTS IN SOUTHERN WISCONSIN. MYCOLOGIA 54, 374-388.

1041 CHRISTENSEN, J.J. (1926) - PHYSIOLOGIC SPECIALISATION AND PARASITISM OF HELMINTHOSPORIUM SATIVUM. TECH.BULL.MINN.AGRIC.EXP.STN 37, 1-101.

1042 CHRISTIAS, C. (1975) - SPECIFIC INHIBITION OF SCLEROTIUM FORMATION BY 2-MERCAPTOETHANOL AND RELATED SULFHYDRYL COMPOUNDS IN SCLEROTIUM ROLFSII. CAN.J.MICROBIOL. 21, 1541-1547.

1043 CHRISTIAS, C. & BAKER, K.F. (1967) - CHITINASE AS A FACTOR IN THE GERMINA-TION OF CHLAMYDOSPORES OF THIELAVIOPSIS BASICOLA. PHYTOPATHOLOGY 57, 1363-1367.

1044 CHRISTIAS, C. & BAKER, K.F. (1969) - DEVELOPMENT AND MACRO- AND MICROSTRUC-TURE OF CHLAMYDOSPORES OF THIELAVIOPSIS BASICOLA. PHYTOPATHOLOGY 59, 1021 (ABS.).

1045 CHRISTIAS, C. & BAKER, K.F. (1970) - ULTRASTRUCTURE AND CLEAVAGE OF CHLA-MYDOSPORE CHAINS OF THIELAVIOPSIS BASICOLA. CAN.J.BOT. 48, 2305-2308.

1046 CHRISTIE, T. (1958) - NUTRITIONAL STUDIES OF PHYTOPHTHORA CACTORUM (LEB. & COHN) SCHROET. 1. UTILISATION OF NITROGEN AND CARBON COMPOUNDS. N.Z. JL SCI. 1, 83-90.

1047 CHU, H.T. & HSU, S.C. (1965) - STUDIES ON THE NEMATODE-TRAPPING FUNGI IN TAIWAN SUGAR CANE SOILS. REP.TAIWAN SUG.EXP.STN 37, 81-88.

1048 CHU, M. & STEPHEN, R.C. (1963) - A STUDY OF THE FREE-LIVING AND ROOT-SUR-
      FACE FUNGI IN CULTIVATED AND FALLOW SOILS IN HONG KONG. NOVA HEDWIGIA
      14, 301-311.

1049 CHU, S.B. & ALEXANDER, M. (1972) - RESISTANCE AND SUSCEPTIBILITY OF FUNGAL
      SPORES TO LYSIS. TRANS.BR.MYCOL.SOC. 58, 489-497.

1050 CHUNG, H.S. (1975) - STUDIES ON CYLINDROCARPON DESTRUCTANS CAUSING ROOT
      ROT OF GINSENG. REP.TOTTORI MYCOL.INST. 12, 127-138.

1051 CHUNG, H.S. & WILCOXSON, R.D. (1969) - EFFECT OF CONIDIAL NUMBER AND MA-
      TRIX ON GERMINATION OF CONIDIA IN PHOMA MEDICAGINIS. PHYTOPATHOLOGY 59,
      440-442.

1052 CHUNG, H.S. & WILCOXSON, R.D. (1971) - EFFECTS OF TEMPERATURE, LIGHT, CAR-
      BON AND NITROGEN NUTRITION ON REPRODUCTION IN PHOMA MEDICAGINIS. MYCO-
      PATH.MYCOL.APPL. 44, 297-308.

1053 CHURCHLAND, L.M. & MCCLAREN, M. (1973) - MARINE FUNGI ISOLATED FROM A KRAFT
      PULP MILL OUTFALL AREA. CAN.J.BOT. 51, 1703-1710.

1054 CIEGLER, A. (1969) - TREMORGENIC TOXIN FROM PENICILLIUM PALITANS. APPL.MI-
      CROBIOL. 18, 128-129.

1055 CIEGLER, A. (1972) - BIOPRODUCTION OF OCHRATOXIN-A AND PENICILLIC ACID BY
      MEMBERS OF THE ASPERGILLUS OCHRACEUS GROUP. CAN.J.MICROBIOL. 18, 631-
      636.

1057 CIEGLER, A., FENNELL, D.J., MINTZLAFF, H.-J. & LEISTNER, L. (1972) - OCHRA-
      TOXIN SYNTHESIS BY PENICILLIUM SPECIES. NATURWISSENSCHAFTEN 59, 365-366.

1058 CIEGLER, A. & HOU, CH.T. (1970) - ISOLATION OF VIRIDICATIN FROM PENICILLIUM
      PALITANS. ARCH.MIKROBIOL. 73, 261-267.

1059 CIEGLER, A. & PITT, J.I. (1970) - SURVEY OF THE GENUS PENICILLIUM FOR TRE-
      MORGENIC TOXIN PRODUCTION. MYCOPATH.MYCOL.APPL. 42, 119-124.

1060 CIFERRI, R. (1958) - MAUGINIELLA A SYNONYM OF SPORENDONEMA. ATTI IST.BOT.
      UNIV.LAB.CRITTOGAM.PAVIA, SER.5, 15, 126-133.

1061 CIFERRI, R., RIBALDI, M. & CORTE, A. (1957) - REVISION OF 23 STRAINS OF
      AUREOBASIDIUM PULLULANS (DE BARY) ARN. (=PULLULARIA PULLULANS). ATTI
      IST.BOT.UNIV.LAB.CRITTOGAM.PAVIA, SER.5, 14, 78-90.

1062 CLARDY, J., SPRINGER, J.P., BUECHI, G., MATSUO, K. & WIGHTMAN, R. (1975) -
      TRYPTOQUIVALINE AND TRYPTOQUIVALONE, TWO TREMORGENIC METABOLITES OF AS-
      PERGILLUS CLAVATUS. J.AM.CHEM.SOC. 97, 663.

1063 CLARE, B.G. (1963) - STARCH-GEL ELECTROPHORESIS OF PROTEINS AS AN AID IN
      IDENTIFYING FUNGI. NATURE, LOND. 200, 803-804.

1064 CLARE, B.G. & ZENTMYER, G.A. (1966) - STARCH GEL ELECTROPHORESIS OF PRO-
      TEINS FROM SPECIES OF PHYTOPHTHORA. PHYTOPATHOLOGY 56, 1334-1335.

1065 CLARE, N.T. (1944) - PHOTOSENSITIVITY DISEASES IN NEW ZEALAND. 3. THE PHO-
      TOSENSITIZING AGENT IN FACIAL ECZEMA. N.Z.JL SCI.TECHNOL. 25, 202-220.

1066 CLARK, B.M. (1968) - THE EPIDEMIOLOGY OF PHYCOMYCOSIS. IN: SYSTEMIC MYCO-
      SES; WOLSTENHOLME, G.E.W. & PORTER, R. (ED.), CHURCHILL LTD., LONDON,
      179.

1067 CLARK, F.E. & PAUL, E.A. (1970) - THE MICROFLORA OF GRASSLAND. ADV.AGRON. 22, 375-435.

1068 CLARK, R.V. (1971) - INFLUENCE OF SOME NITROGEN AND VITAMIN SOURCES ON GROWTH, SPORULATION, AND PATHOGENICITY OF COCHLIOBOLUS SATIVUS. CAN.J. BOT. 49, 2175-2186.

1069 CLARK, R.V. (1972) - INFLUENCE OF SOME CARBON SOURCES ON GROWTH OF COCHLIO-BOLUS SATIVUS. CAN.J.BOT. 50, 683-685.

1070 CLARK, T.B., KELLEN, W.R., FUKUDA, T. & LINDEGREN, J.E. (1968) - FIELD AND LABORATORY STUDIES ON THE PATHOGENICITY OF THE FUNGUS BEAUVERIA BASSIA-NA TO THREE GENERA OF MOSQUITOES. J.INVERTEBR.PATH. 11, 1-8.

1071 CLARKE, A.E. & STONE, B.A. (1965) - BETA-GLUCAN HYDROLASES FROM ASPERGIL-LUS NIGER. ISOLATION OF A BETA-(1-4)-GLUCAN HYDROLASE AND SOME PROPER-TIES OF THE BETA-(1-3)-GLUCAN-HYDROLASE COMPONENTS. BIOCHEM.J. 96, 793 801.

1072 CLARKE, J.H. (1966) - STUDIES ON FUNGI IN THE ROOT REGION. 5. THE ANTIBIO-TIC EFFECTS OF ROOT EXTRACTS OF ALLIUM ON SOME ROOT SURFACE FUNGI. PL. SOIL 25, 32-40.

1073 CLARKE, J.H. & GRIFFITHS, D.A. (1970) - ASCOSPORES OF SOME COMMON SPECIES OF EUROTIUM (ASPERGILLUS GLAUCUS) AS SHOWN BY SCANNING-ELECTRON MICROS-COPY. TRANS.BR.MYCOL.SOC. 55, 117-122.

1074 CLAUS, L. (1961) - UNTERSUCHUNGEN UEBER DIE CHITINASEWIRKUNG DES INSEKTEN-TOETENDEN PILZES BEAUVERIA BASSIANA (BALS.) VUILL. ARCH.MIKROBIOL. 40, 17-46.

1075 CLERK, G.C. (1969) - INFLUENCE OF SOIL EXTRACTS ON THE GERMINATION OF CO-NIDIA OF THE FUNGI BEAUVERIA BASSIANA AND PAECILOMYCES FARINOSUS. J.IN-VERTEBR.PATH. 13, 120-124.

1076 CLERK, G.C. & MADELIN, M.F. (1965) - THE LONGEVITY OF CONIDIA OF THREE IN-SECT-PARASITIZING HYPHOMYCETES. TRANS.BR.MYCOL.SOC. 48, 193-209.

1077 CLIFFORD, D.R. & WOODCOCK, D. (1964) - METABOLISM OF PHENOXYACETIC ACID BY ASPERGILLUS NIGER VAN TIEGH. NATURE, LOND. 203, 763.

1078 CLINTON, P.K.S. (1957) - A NOTE ON A WILT OF GROUNDNUTS DUE TO SCLEROTIUM ROLFSII SACC. IN TANGANYIKA. E.AFR.AGRIC.J. 22, 137-141.

1079 CLOSSE, A. & HAUSER, D. (1973) - ISOLIERUNG UND KONSTITUTIONSERMITTLUNG VON CHRYSODIN. HELV.CHIM.ACTA 56, 2694-2698.

1080 CLOUGH, K.S. & PATRICK, Z.A. (1972) - NATURALLY OCCURRING PERFORATIONS IN CHLAMYDOSPORES OF THIELAVIOPSIS BASICOLA IN SOIL. CAN.J.BOT. 50, 2251-2254.

1081 CLOUGH, K.S. & PATRICK, Z.A. (1976) - BIOTIC FACTORS AFFECTING THE VIABIL-ITY OF CHLAMYDOSPORES OF THIELAVIOPSIS BASICOLA (BERK. & BR.) FERRARIS IN SOIL. SOIL BIOL.BIOCHEM. 8, 465-472.

1082 CLUTTERBUCK, A.J. (1969) - A MUTATIONAL ANALYSIS OF CONIDIAL DEVELOPMENT IN ASPERGILLUS NIDULANS. GENETICS 63, 317-327.

1083 CLUTTERBUCK, A.J. (1970) - SYNCHRONOUS NUCLEAR DIVISION AND SEPTATION IN ASPERGILLUS NIDULANS. J.GEN.MICROBIOL. 60, 133-135.

1084 CLUTTERBUCK, A.J. (1974) - ASPERGILLUS NIDULANS. IN: HANDBOOK OF GENETICS, VOL.1.; KING, R.C. (ED.), PLENUM PRESS, NEW YORK, LONDON, 447-510.

1085 CLUTTERBUCK, A.J. & ROPER, J.A. (1966) - A DIRECT DETERMINATION OF NUCLEAR
      DISTRIBUTION IN HETEROKARYONS OF ASPERGILLUS NIDULANS. GENET.RES. 7,
      185-194.

1086 CLUTTERBUCK, P.W., LOVELL, R. & RAISTRICK, H. (1931) - STUDIES IN THE BIO-
      CHEMISTRY OF MICRO-ORGANISMS. 26. THE FORMATION FROM GLUCOSE BY MEMBERS
      OF THE PENICILLIUM CHRYSOGENUM SERIES OF A PIGMENT, AN ALKALI-SOLUBLE
      PROTEIN, AND PENICILLIN, THE ANTIBACTERIAL SUBSTANCE OF FLEMING. CHEM.
      IND. 50, 1045.

1087 CLUTTERBUCK, P.W., OXFORD, A.E., RAISTRICK, H. & SMITH, G. (1932) - STUD-
      IES IN THE BIOCHEMISTRY OF MICRO-ORGANISMS. 24. THE METABOLIC PRODUCTS
      OF THE PENICILLIUM BREVICOMPACTUM SERIES. BIOCHEM.J. 26, 1441-1458.

1088 CLUTTERBUCK, P.W. & RAISTRICK, H. (1933) - STUDIES IN THE BIOCHEMISTRY OF
      MICRO-ORGANISMS. 31. THE MOLECULAR CONSTITUTION OF THE METABOLIC PROD-
      UCTS OF PENICILLIUM BREVICOMPACTUM AND RELATED SPECIES. 2. MYCOPHENOLIC
      ACID. BIOCHEM.J. 27, 654-667.

1089 COCHRANE, V.W. (1958) - PHYSIOLOGY OF FUNGI. JOHN WILEY & SONS, NEW YORK,
      524 PP.

1090 COCHRANE, V.W. & COCHRANE, J.C. (1970) - CHLAMYDOSPORE DEVELOPMENT IN THE
      ABSENCE OF PROTEIN SYNTHESIS IN FUSARIUM SOLANI. DEV.BIOL. 23, 345-354.

1091 COCHRANE, V.W. & COCHRANE, J.C. (1971) - CHLAMYDOSPORE INDUCTION IN PURE
      CULTURE IN FUSARIUM SOLANI. MYCOLOGIA 63, 462-477.

1092 CODIGNOLA, A. & GALLINO, M. (1974/1975) - SU ALCUNI MICROMICETI ISOLATI DA
      INSILATI DI MAIS. 1. ATTIVITA ANTIBIOTICA. ALLIONIA 20, 43-46.

1093 COFONE, L., WALKER, J.D. & COONEY, J.J. (1973) - UTILIZATION OF HYDROCAR-
      BONS BY CLADOSPORIUM RESINAE. J.GEN.MICROBIOL. 76, 243-246.

1094 COHEN, B.L. (1973) - REGULATION OF INTRACELLULAR AND EXTRACELLULAR NEUTRAL
      AND ALKALINE PROTEASES IN ASPERGILLUS NIDULANS. J.GEN.MICROBIOL. 79,
      311-320.

1095 COHEN, H. (1967) - THE EFFECT OF EXTERNAL CONDITIONS ON COREMIUM PRODUC-
      TION IN PAECILOMYCES FARINOSUS. ANN.BOT. 31, 455-468.

1096 COLE, A.L.J. & BATEMAN, D.F. (1969) - ARABANASE PRODUCTION BY SCLEROTIUM
      ROLFSII AND ITS ROLE IN TISSUE MACERATION. PHYTOPATHOLOGY 59, 1750-1753.

1097 COLE, A.L.J. & WOOD, R.K.S. (1970) - PRODUCTION OF HEMICELLULASES BY PENI-
      CILLIUM DIGITATUM. PHYTOCHEMISTRY 9, 695-699.

1098 COLE, G.T. (1972) - MICROFIBRILS IN THE CYTOPLASM OF FERTILE HYPHAE OF THE
      IMPERFECT FUNGUS, DRECHSLERA SOROKINIANA. J.ULTRASTRUCT.RES. 41, 563-
      571.

1099 COLE, G.T. (1973) - ULTRASTRUCTURE OF CONIDIOGENESIS IN DRECHSLERA SOROKI-
      NIANA. CAN.J.BOT. 51, 629-638.

1100 COLE, G.T. (1973) - A CORRELATION BETWEEN RODLET ORIENTATION AND CONIDIO-
      GENESIS IN HYPHOMYCETES. CAN.J.BOT. 51, 2413-2422.

1101 COLE, G.T. (1975) - THE THALLIC MODE OF CONIDIOGENESIS IN THE FUNGI IMPER-
      FECTI. CAN.J.BOT. 53, 2983-3001.

1102 COLE, G.T. (1976) - CONIDIOGENESIS IN PATHOGENIC HYPHOMYCETES. 1. SPORO-
      THRIX, EXOPHIALA, GEOTRICHUM AND MICROSPORUM. SABOURAUDIA 14, 81-98.

1103 COLE, G.T. & ALDRICH, H.C. (1971) - ULTRASTRUCTURE OF CONIDIOGENESIS IN
      SCOPULARIOPSIS BREVICAULIS. CAN.J.BOT. 49, 745-755.

1104 COLE, G.T. & KENDRICK, W.B. (1968) - CONIDIUM ONTOGENY IN HYPHOMYCETES.
      THE IMPERFECT STATE OF MONASCUS RUBER AND ITS MERISTEM ARTHROSPORES.
      CAN.J.BOT. 46, 987-992.

1105 COLE, G.T. & KENDRICK, W.B. (1969) - CONIDIUM ONTOGENY IN HYPHOMYCETES. 5.
      THE PHIALIDES OF PHIALOPHORA, PENICILLIUM, AND CERATOCYSTIS. CAN.J.BOT.
      47, 779-789.

1106 COLE, G.T. & KENDRICK, W.B. (1969) - CONIDIUM ONTOGENY IN HYPHOMYCETES.
      THE ANNELLOPHORES OF SCOPULARIOPSIS BREVICAULIS. CAN.J.BOT. 47, 925-929.

1107 COLE, G.T. & KENDRICK, W.B. (1969) - CONIDIUM ONTOGENY IN HYPHOMYCETES -
      THE ARTHROSPORES OF OIDIODENDRON AND GEOTRICHUM, AND THE ENDOARTHROSPO-
      RES OF SPORENDONEMA. CAN.J.BOT. 47, 1773-1780.

1108 COLE, G.T. & KENDRICK, W.B. (1973) - TAXONOMIC STUDIES OF PHIALOPHORA. MY-
      COLOGIA 65, 661-690.

1109 COLE, G.T. & SAMSON, R.A. (1979) - PATTERNS OF DEVELOPMENT IN CONIDIAL FUN-
      GI. PITTMAN, LONDON.

1110 COLE, H., BRAVERMAN, S.W. & DUICH, J. (1968) - FUSARIA AND OTHER FUNGI
      FROM SEEDS AND SEEDLINGS OF MERION AND OTHER TURF-GRASS BLUEGRASSES.
      PHYTOPATHOLOGY 58, 1415-1419.

1111 COLE, M. & ROLINSON, G.N. (1961) - 6-AMINOPENICILLANIC ACID. 2. FORMATION
      OF 6-AMINOPENICILLANIC ACID BY EMERICELLOPSIS MINIMA AND RELATED FUNGI.
      PROC.R.SOC.B, 154, 490-497.

1112 COLE, M. & ROLINSON, G.N. (1972) - MICROBIAL METABOLITES WITH INSECTICIDAL
      PROPERTIES. APPL.MICROBIOL. 24, 660-662.

1113 COLE, R.J. & KIRKSEY, J.W. (1970) - DIHYDRO-O-METHYLSTERIGMATOCYSTIN, A
      NEW METABOLITE FROM ASPERGILLUS FLAVUS. TETRAHEDRON LETTERS, 1970 (35),
      3109-3112.

1114 COLE, R.J. & KIRKSEY, J.W. (1971) - AFLATOXIN-G1 METABOLISM BY RHIZOPUS
      SPECIES. J.AGRIC.FD CHEM. 19, 222-223.

1115 COLE, R.J., KIRKSEY, J.W. & BLANKENSHIP, B.R. (1972) - CONVERSION OF AFLA-
      TOXIN-B1 TO ISOMERIC HYDROXY COMPOUNDS BY RHIZOPUS SPP. J.AGRIC.FD CHEM.
      20, 1100-1102.

1116 COLE, R.J., KIRKSEY, J.W., CUTLER, H.G., DOUPNIK, B.L. & PECKHAM, J.C.
      (1973) - TOXIN FROM FUSARIUM MONILIFORME. EFFECTS ON PLANTS AND ANIMALS.
      SCIENCE, N.Y. 179, 1324-1325.

1117 COLE, R.J., MOORE, J.H., DAVIS, N.D., KIRKSEY, J.W. & DIENER, U.L. (1971) -
      4-HYDROXYMELLEIN - A NEW METABOLITE OF ASPERGILLUS OCHRACEUS. J.AGRIC.
      FD CHEM. 19, 909-911.

1118 COLHOUN, J. (1970) - EPIDEMIOLOGY OF SEED-BORNE FUSARIUM DISEASES OF CE-
      REALS. ANN.ACAD.SCI.FENN., SER.A, IV, 168, 31-36.

1119 COLHOUN, J. & PARK, D. (1964) - FUSARIUM DISEASES OF CEREALS. 1. INFECTION
      OF WHEAT PLANTS, WITH PARTICULAR REFERENCE TO THE EFFECTS OF SOIL MOIS-
      TURE AND TEMPERATURE ON SEEDLING INFECTION. TRANS.BR.MYCOL.SOC. 47, 559-
      572.

1120 COLHOUN, J., TAYLOR, G.S. & TOMLINSON, R. (1968) - FUSARIUM DISEASE OF CE-
     REALS. 2. INFECTION OF SEEDLINGS BY F. CULMORUM AND F. AVENACEUM IN RE-
     LATION TO ENVIRONMENTAL FACTORS. TRANS.BR.MYCOL.SOC. 51, 397-404.

1121 COLL, J. & LEAL, J.A. (1972) - UTILIZATION OF L-LEUCINE AS NITROGEN SOURCE
     BY FUNGI. TRANS.BR.MYCOL.SOC. 59, 107-114.

1122 COLL, J. & LEAL, J.A. (1972) - THE UTILISATION OF L-TRYPTOPHAN AS NITROGEN
     SOURCE BY FUSARIUM CULMORUM, ASPERGILLUS NIDULANS, AND PENICILLIUM ITA-
     LICUM. CAN.J.MICROBIOL. 18, 1353-1356.

1123 COLLINS, R.P. & HALIM, A.F. (1972) - CHARACTERIZATION OF THE MAJOR AROMA
     CONSTITUENT OF THE FUNGUS TRICHODERMA VIRIDE (PERS.). J.AGRIC.FD CHEM.
     20, 437-438.

1124 COLOTELO, N. (1973) - PHYSIOLOGICAL AND BIOCHEMICAL PROPERTIES OF THE EXU-
     DATE ASSOCIATED WITH DEVELOPING SCLEROTIA OF SCLEROTINIA SCLEROTIORUM
     (LIB.). CAN.J.MICROBIOL. 19, 73-79.

1125 COLOTELO, N. (1974) - A SCANNING ELECTRON MICROSCOPE STUDY OF DEVELOPING
     SCLEROTIA OF SCLEROTINIA SCLEROTIORUM. CAN.J.BOT. 52, 1127-1130.

1126 CONGLY, H. & HALL, R. (1976) - EFFECTS OF OSMOTIC POTENTIAL ON GERMINATION
     OF MICROSCLEROTIA AND GROWTH OF COLONIES OF VERTICILLIUM DAHLIAE. CAN.
     J.BOT. 54, 1214-1220.

1127 CONTARDI, A. & ERCOLI, A. (1933) - UEBER DIE ENZYMATISCHE SPALTUNG DER LE-
     CITHINE UND LYSOCITHINE. BIOCHEM.Z. 261, 275-302.

1128 CONWAY, K.E. (1969) - SOME AQUATIC HYPHOMYCETES OF FLORIDA. Q.JL FLA ACAD.
     SCI. 32, 210-220.

1129 CONWAY, K.E. (1970) - THE AQUATIC HYPHOMYCTES OF CENTRAL NEW YORK. MYCOLO-
     GIA 62, 516-530.

1130 COOK, A.H. & LACEY, M.S. (1944) - AN ANTIBIOTIC FROM ASPERGILLUS PARASITI-
     CUS. NATURE, LOND. 153, 460.

1131 COOK, G.E., STEADMAN, J.R. & BOOSALIS, M.G. (1975) - SURVIVAL OF WHETZELI-
     NIA SCLEROTIOPUM AND INITIAL INFECTION OF DRY EDIBLE BEANS IN WESTERN
     NEBRASKA. PHYTOPATHOLOGY 65, 250-255.

1132 COOK, H.A., CROMWELL, D.L. & WILSON, H.A. (1967) - MICROORGANISMS IN HOUSE-
     HOLD REFUSE AND SEEPAGE WATER FROM SANITARY LANDFILLS. PROC.W.VA ACAD.
     SCI. 39, 107-114.

1133 COOK, M.T. & TAUBENHAUS, J.J. (1911) - TRICHODERMA KONINGI, THE CAUSE OF A
     DISEASE OF SWEET POTATOES. PHYTOPATHOLOGY 1, 184-189.

1134 COOK, R.J. (1955-1970) - PROPAGULE GERMINATION AND MYCELIAL GROWTH IN SOIL.
     IN: NATURE OF THE INFLUENCE OF CROP RESIDUES ON FUNGUS-INDUCED ROOT DIS-
     EASES; COOK, R.J. & WATSON, R.D. (ED.), BULL.WASH.AGRIC.EXP.STN 716,
     14-18.

1135 COOK, R.J. (1967) - GIBBERELLA AVENACEA SP.N., PERFECT STAGE OF FUSARIUM
     ROSEUM F.SP. CEREALIS AVENACEUM. PHYTOPATHOLOGY 57, 732-736.

1136 COOK, R.J. & BRUEHL, G.W. (1966) - CALONECTRIA NIVALIS, PERFECT STAGE OF
     FUSARIUM NIVALE, OCCURS IN THE FIELD IN NORTH AMERICA. PHYTOPATHOLOGY
     56, 1100-1101.

1137   COOK, R.J. & BRUEHL, G.W. (1968) - RELATIVE SIGNIFICANCE OF PARASITISM VER-
        SUS SAPROPHYTISM IN COLONIZATION OF WHEAT STRAW BY FUSARIUM ROSEUM CUL-
        MORUM IN THE FIELD. PHYTOPATHOLOGY 58, 306-308.

1138   COOK, R.J., PAPENDICK, R.I. & GRIFFIN, D.M. (1972) - GROWTH OF TWO ROOT-
        ROT FUNGI AS AFFECTED BY OSMOTIC AND MATRIC WATER POTENTIALS. PROC.SOIL
        SCI.SOC.AM. 36, 78-82.

1139   COOK, R.J. & ROVIRA, A.D. (1976) - THE ROLE OF BACTERIA IN THE BIOLOGICAL
        CONTROL OF GAEUMANNOMYCES GRAMINIS BY SUPPRESSIVE SOILS. SOIL BIOL.BIO-
        CHEM. 8, 269-273.

1140   COOKE, J.C. (1969) - MORPHOLOGY OF CHAETOMIUM FUNICOLUM. MYCOLOGIA 61, 1060-
        1065.

1141   COOKE, P.M. & STEVENSON, J.W. (1965) - AN ANTIVIRAL SUBSTANCE FROM PENICIL-
        LIUM CYANEO-FULVUM BIOURGE. 1. PRODUCTION AND PARTIAL PURIFICATION. CAN.
        J.MICROBIOL. 11, 913-919.

1142   COOKE, R.C. (1963) - THE PREDACEOUS ACTIVITY OF NEMATODE-TRAPPING FUNGI
        ADDED TO SOIL. ANN.APPL.BIOL. 51, 295-299.

1143   COOKE, R.C. (1963) - ECOLOGICAL CHARACTERISTICS OF NEMATODE-TRAPPING HYPHO-
        MYCETES. 1. PRELIMINARY STUDIES. ANN.APPL.BIOL. 52, 431-437.

1144   COOKE, R.C. (1963) - SUCCESSION OF NEMATOPHAGOUS FUNGI DURING THE DECOMPO-
        SITION OF ORGANIC MATTER IN THE SOIL. NATURE, LOND. 197, 205.

1145   COOKE, R.C. (1964) - ECOLOGICAL CHARACTERISTICS OF NEMATODE-TRAPPING HY-
        PHOMYCETES. 2. GERMINATION OF CONIDIA IN SOIL. ANN.APPL.BIOL. 54, 375-
        379.

1146   COOKE, R.C. (1969) - CHANGES IN SOLUBLE CARBOHYDRATES DURING SCLEROTIUM
        FORMATION BY SCLEROTINIA SCLEROTIORUM AND S. TRIFOLIORUM. TRANS.BR.MY-
        COL.SOC. 53, 77-86.

1147   COOKE, R.C. (1970) - PHYSIOLOGICAL ASPECTS OF SCLEROTIUM GROWTH IN SCLERO-
        TINIA SCLEROTIORUM. TRANS.BR.MYCOL.SOC. 54, 361-365.

1148   COOKE, R.C. (1971) - PHYSIOLOGY OF SCLEROTIA OF SCLEROTINIA SCLEROTIORUM
        DURING GROWTH AND MATURATION. TRANS.BR.MYCOL.SOC. 56, 51-59.

1149   COOKE, R.C. (1971) - UPTAKE OF (C14) GLUCOSE AND LOSS OF WATER BY SCLERO-
        TIA OF SCLEROTINIA SCLEROTIORUM DURING DEVELOPMENT. TRANS.BR.MYCOL.SOC.
        57, 379-384.

1150   COOKE, R.C. & DICKINSON, C.H. (1965) - NEMATODE-TRAPPING SPECIES OF DAC-
        TYLELLA AND MONACROSPORIUM. TRANS.BR.MYCOL.SOC. 48, 621-629.

1151   COOKE, R.C. & GODFREY, B.E.S. (1964) - A KEY TO THE NEMATODE-DESTROYING
        FUNGI. TRANS.BR.MYCOL.SOC. 47, 61-74.

1152   COOKE, W.B. (1955) - SOME FUNGI FROM ALASKA. NW.SCI. 29, 127-137.

1153   COOKE, W.B. (1957) - NUTRITIONAL REQUIREMENTS OF NINE COMMON SEWAGE FUNGI.
        SEWAGE IND.WASTES 29, 1243-1251.

1154   COOKE, W.B. (1957) - CHECK LIST OF FUNGI ISOLATED FROM POLLUTED WATER AND
        SEWAGE. SYDOWIA, BEIH. 1, 146-175.

1155   COOKE, W.B. (1959) - FUNGI IN POLLUTED WATER AND SEWAGE. 4. THE OCCURRENCE
       OF FUNGI IN A TRICKLING FILTER-TYPE SEWAGE TREATMENT PLANT. 13TH PURDUE
       IND.WASTE CONF., SER.96, VOL.43 (3), 26-45.

1156   COOKE, W.B. (1959) - AN ECOLOGICAL LIFE HISTORY OF AUREOBASIDIUM PULLULANS
       (DE BARY) ARNAUD. MYCOPATH.MYCOL.APPL. 12, 1-45.

1157   COOKE, W.B. (1961) - POLLUTION EFFECTS ON THE FUNGUS POPULATION OF A STREAM.
       ECOLOGY 42, 1-18.

1158   COOKE, W.B. (1961) - THE NATURAL OCCURRENCE OF AUREOBASIDIUM. RECENT ADV.
       BOT., SECT.4, 1961, 330-334.

1159   COOKE, W.B. (1962) - A TAXONOMIC STUDY IN THE BLACK YEASTS. MYCOPATH.MYCOL.
       APPL. 17, 1-43.

1160   COOKE, W.B. (1962) - SPECIES OF FUSARIUM ISOLATED FROM A WASTE STABILIZA-
       TION POND SYSTEM. MYCOPATH.MYCOL.APPL. 18, 225-233.

1161   COOKE, W.B. (1963) - FUNGI ASSOCIATED WITH SPENT SULFITE LIQUOR DISPOSAL
       IN NATURAL SAND BED. TAPPI 46, 573-578.

1162   COOKE, W.B. (1968) - SOME FUNGI OF THE CACHE LA POUDRE RIVER, COLORADO.
       MYCOPATH.MYCOL.APPL. 35, 361-372.

1163   COOKE, W.B. (1969) - FUNGI IN SOILS OVER WHICH DIGESTED SEWAGE SLUDGE HAS
       BEEN SPREAD. MYCOPATH.MYCOL.APPL. 39, 209-229.

1164   COOKE, W.B. (1970) - FUNGI IN BURNED AND UNBURNED CHAPARRAL SOILS. SYDOWIA
       24, 164-168.

1165   COOKE, W.B. (1970) - FUNGI IN THE LEBANON SEWAGE TREATMENT PLANTS AND IN
       TURTLE CREEK, WARREN CO., OHIO. MYCOPATH.MYCOL.APPL. 42, 89-111.

1166   COOKE, W.B. (1970) - OUR MOULDY EARTH. A STUDY IN THE FUNGI OF OUR ENVI-
       RONMENT WITH EMPHASIS ON WATER. U.S. DEPARTMENT OF THE INTERIOR, FEDER-
       AL WATER POLLUTION CONTROL ADMINISTRATION, ROBERT A.TAFT WATER RESEARCH
       CENTER, ADV.WASTE TREATMENT RESEARCH LABORATORY, CINCINNATI, OHIO.

1167   COOKE, W.B. (1971) - THE EFFECT OF SLUDGE ADDITIVES ON SOIL FUNGUS POPULA-
       TIONS. MYCOPATH.MYCOL.APPL. 44, 205-220.

1168   COOKE, W.B. & BUSCH, K.A. (1957) - ACTIVITY OF CELLULOSE-DECOMPOSING FUNGI
       ISOLATED FROM SEWAGE-POLLUTED WATER. SEWAGE IND.WASTES 29, 210-217.

1169   COOKE, W.B. & FOURNELLE, H.T. (1960) - SOME SOIL FUNGI FROM ALASKAN TUNDRA
       AREA. ARCTIC 13, 266-270.

1170   COOKE, W.B. & KABLER, P. (1955) - ISOLATION OF POTENTIALLY PATHOGENIC FUN-
       GI FROM POLLUTED WATER AND SEWAGE. PUBL.HLTH REP., U.S.DEP.HLTH, EDUC.
       WELF. 70, 689-694.

1171   COOKE, W.B. & LAWRENCE, D.B. (1959) - SOIL MOULD FUNGI ISOLATED FROM RE-
       CENTLY GLACIATED SOILS IN SOUTH-EASTERN ALASKA. J.ECOL. 47, 529-549.

1172   COOKE, W.B. & PIPES, W.O. (1970) - THE OCCURRENCE OF FUNGI IN ACTIVATED
       SLUDGE. MYCOPATH.MYCOL.APPL. 40, 249-270.

1173   COOMBE, R.G., JACOBS, J.J. & WATSON, T.R. (1970) - METABOLITES OF SOME AL-
       TERNARIA SPECIES. THE STRUCTURES OF ALTENUSIN AND DEHYDROALTENUSIN. AUST.
       J.CHEM. 23, 2343-2351.

1174 COONEY, D.G. & EMERSON, R. (1964) - THERMOPHILIC FUNGI. W.H.FREEMAN & CO.,
      SAN FRANCISCO, LONDON.

1175 COONEY, J.J. & PROBY, C.M. (1971) - FATTY ACID COMPOSITION OF CLADOSPORIUM
      RESINAE GROWN ON GLUCOSE AND ON HYDROCARBONS. J.BACT. 108, 777-778.

1176 COOPER, B.A. & ARONSON, J.M. (1967) - CELL WALL STRUCTURE OF PYTHIUM DE-
      BARYANUM. MYCOLOGIA 59, 658-670.

1177 COOPER, B.H. (1969) - A SEROLOGICAL COMPARISON OF PHIALOPHORA VERRUCOSA,
      HORMODENDRUM PEDROSOI, AND CLADOSPORIUM CARRIONII USING IMMUNODIFFUSION
      AND IMMUNOELECTROPHORESIS. DISS.ABSTR. 29, 3415-3416.

1178 COOPER, B.H., GROVE, S., MIMS, C. & SZANISZLO, P.J. (1973) - SEPTAL ULTRA-
      STRUCTURE IN PHIALOPHORA PEDROSOI, PHIALOPHORA VERRUCOSA AND CLADOSPORIUM
      CARRIONII. SABOURAUDIA 11, 127-130.

1179 COOPER, R.M. & WOOD, K.S. (1975) - REGULATION OF SYNTHESIS OF CELL WALL
      DEGRADING ENZYMES BY VERTICILLIUM ALBO-ATRUM AND FUSARIUM OXYSPORUM F.
      SP. LYCOPERSICI. PHYSIOL.PL.PATH. 5, 135-156.

1180 COOPER, W.E. & CHILTON, S.J.P. (1949) - ANTIBIOSIS OF ACTINOMYCES STRAINS
      TO PYTHIUM ARRHENOMANES, P. ULTIMUM AND RHIZOCTONIA SOLANI. PHYTOPATHOL-
      OGY 39, 5 (ABS.).

1181 CORAZZA, E. (1975) - THE CRYSTAL STRUCTURE OF ISOVIRESCENO-B, C20 O2 H32.
      ACTA CRYST. B31, 1445-1450.

1182 CORBEL, M.J. (1972) - THE SEROLOGICAL RESPONSE TO ASPERGILLUS FUMIGATUS
      ANTIGENS IN BOVINE MYCOTIC ABORTION. BR.VET.J. 128, LXXIII-LXXV.

1183 CORBETT, D.C.M. & HIDE, G.A. (1971) - INTERACTION BETWEEN HETERODERA ROS-
      TOCHIENSIS WOLL. AND VERTICILLIUM DAHLIAE KLEB. ON POTATOES AND THE EF-
      FECT OF CCC ON BOTH. ANN.APPL.BIOL. 68, 71-80.

1184 CORBETTA, G. (1965) - RASSEGNA DELLE SPECIE DEL GENERE CURVULARIA. RISO
      1-23.

1185 CORDES, D.O., DI MENNA, M.E. & CARTER, M.E. (1972) - MYCOTIC PNEUMONIA AND
      PLACENTITIS CAUSED BY MORTIERELLA WOLFII. 1. EXPERIMENTAL INFECTIONS IN
      CATTLE AND SHEEP. VET.PATH. 9, 131-141.

1186 CORLETT, M. (1963) - THE DEVELOPMENTAL MORPHOLOGY OF TWO SPECIES OF MICRO-
      ASCUS. CAN.J.BOT. 41, 253-262.

1187 CORLETT, M. (1973) - SURFACE STRUCTURE OF THE CONIDIUM AND CONIDIOPHORE OF
      STEMPHYLIUM BOTRYOSUM. CAN.J.MICROBIOL. 19, 392-393.

1188 CORMACK, M.W. (1937) - CYLINDROCARPON EHRENBERGI AND OTHER SPECIES, AS
      ROOT PARASITES OF ALFALFA AND SWEET CLOVER IN ALBERTA. CAN.J.RES., SECT.
      C, 15, 403-424.

1189 CORMACK, M.W. (1951) - VARIATION IN THE CULTURAL CHARACTERISTICS AND PA-
      THOGENICITY OF FUSARIUM AVENACEUM AND F. ARTHROSPORIOIDES. CAN.J.BOT.
      29, 32-45.

1190 CORNER, E.J.H. (1950) - CLAVARIA AND ALLIED GENERA. OXFORD UNIV.PRESS, OX-
      FORD.

1191 CORNFORTH, J.W., RYBACK, G., ROBINSON, P.M. & PARK, D. (1971) - ISOLATION
      AND CHARACTERIZATION OF A FUNGAL VACUOLATION FACTOR (BIKAVERIN). J.CHEM.
      SOC.(C), 1971, 2786-2788.

1192   CORRY, J.E.L. (1973) — THE WATER RELATIONS AND HEAT RESISTANCE OF MICROOR-
       GANISMS. PROGR.INDUST.MICROBIOL. 12, 73-108.

1193   CORSINI, D.L. & LE TOURNEAU, D. (1973) — ORGANIC ACID METABOLISM IN SCLE-
       ROTINIA SCLEROTIORUM. ARCH.MIKROBIOL. 90, 59-64.

1194   COSCARELLI, W. & PRAMER, D. (1962) — NUTRITION AND GROWTH OF ARTHROBOTRYS
       CONOIDES. J.BACT. 84, 60-64.

1195   COSTA ALECRIM, J.DA & VITAL, A.F. (1955) — O ASPERGILLUS SYDOWI NUMA LESAO
       UNGUEAL. ANAIS FAC.MED.UNIV.RECIFE 1955, 229-240.

1196   COSTA PLA, L. (1973) — MICROBIAL TRANSFORMATION OF STEROIDS. 1-DEHYDROGEN-
       ATION OF 17,21-DIHYDROXYPREGN-4-ENE-3,20-DIONE WITH GLOMERFLLA CINGULA-
       TA. BIOCHEM.J. 136, 501-502.

1197   COUDERT, M.J., MICHEL-BRUN, J. & BATTESTI, M.R. (1968) — RECHERECHES SUR
       LES MICROMYCETES KERATINOPHILES DU SOL DANS LA REGION LYONNAISE. MYCO-
       PATH.MYCOL.APPL. 34, 253-262.

1198   COULOMBE, L.J. (1976) — ACREMONIUM KILIENSE GRUETZ ET ALTERNARIA ALTERNATA
       (FR.) KEISSLER, DEUX AGENTS DE POURRITURE D'ENTROPOSAGE CHEZ LA POMME
       MCINTOSH. PHYTOPROTECTION 57, 33-35.

1199   COURTOIS, H. (1963) — BEITRAG ZUR FRAGE HOLZABBAUENDER ASCOMYCETEN UND FUN-
       GI IMPERFECTI. HOLZFORSCHUNG 17, 176-183.

1200   COUTELEN, F., COCHET, G. & BIGUET, J. (1948) — LES CEPHALOSPORIOSES HU-
       MAINES. REVUE CRITIQUE A PROPOS D'UN CAS. ANNLS PARASIT.HUM.COMP. 23,
       364-398.

1201   COUTTS, A.D. & SMITH, R.E. (1976) — FACTORS INFLUENCING THE PRODUCTION OF
       CELLULASES BY SPOROTRICHUM THERMOPHILUM. APPL.ENVIRONM.MICROBIOL. 31,
       819-825.

1202   COVE, D.J. (1966) — THE INDUCTION AND REPRESSION OF NITRATE REDUCTASE IN
       THE FUNGUS ASPERGILLUS NIDULANS. BIOCHIM.BIOPHYS.ACTA 113, 51-56.

1203   COVEY, R.P. (JR.) (1970) — EFFECT OF OXYGEN TENSION ON THE GROWTH OF PHY-
       TOPHTHORA CACTORUM. PHYTOPATHOLOGY 60, 358-359.

1204   COWLEY, G.T. (1963) — CONTRIBUTION TO A STUDY OF THE PHYSIOLOGICAL BASIS
       FOR DISTRIBUTIONAL PATTERNS OF SOIL MICROFUNGI IN WISCONSIN. DISS.UNIV.
       WISCONSIN.

1205   COWLEY, G.T. & LICHTENSTEIN, E.P. (1970) — GROWTH INHIBITION OF SOIL FUNGI
       BY INSECTICIDES AND ANNULMENT OF INHIBITION BY YEAST EXTRACT OR NITRO-
       GENOUS NUTRIENTS. J.GEN.MICROBIOL. 62, 27-34.

1206   COWLEY, G.T. & WHITTINGHAM, W.F. (1961) — THE EFFECT OF TANNIN ON THE
       GROWTH OF SELECTED SOIL MICROFUNGI IN CULTURE. MYCOLOGIA 53, 539-542.

1207   COX, D.P. & ALEXANDER, M. (1973) — PRODUCTION OF TRIMETHYLARSINE GAS FROM
       VARIOUS COMPOUNDS BY THREE SEWAGE FUNGI. BULL.ENVIRON.CONTAM.TOXICOL.
       9, 84-89.

1208   CRACKOWER, S.H.B. (1972) — MITOSIS IN CLADOSPORIUM HERBARUM. CAN.J.MICRO-
       BIOL. 18, 692-694.

1209   CRACKOWER, S.H.B. & BAUER, H. (1971) — MITOSIS IN PENICILLIUM CHRYSOGENUM
       AND PENICILLIUM NOTATUM. CAN.J.MICROBIOL. 17, 605-608.

1210 CRAKER, L.E. & MANNING, W.J. (1974) - SO2 UPTAKE BY SOIL FUNGI. ENVIRON.
      POLLUTION 6, 309-311.

1211 CRAM, W.T. (1972) - THE FUNGI BEAUVERIA BASSIANA AND METARRHIZIUM ANISOP-
      LIAE IN CULTURES OF THE ROOT WEEVIL NEMOCESTES INCOMPTUS HORN (COLEO-
      PTERA CURCULIONIDAE). J.ENT.SOC., B.C. 69, 21-22.

1212 CRANDALL, B.S. & GRAVATT, G.F. (1967) - THE DISTRIBUTION OF PHYTOPHTHORA
      CINNAMOMI. CEIBA 13, 43-53.

1213 CRANE, J.L. (1968) - FRESHWATER HYPHOMYCETES OF THE NORTHERN APPALACHIAN
      HIGHLAND INCLUDING NEW ENGLAND, AND THREE COASTAL PLAIN STATES. AM.J.
      BOT. 55, 996-1002.

1214 CRAWLEY, W.E. & DODD, D.C. (1959) - A BACTERIUM WITH FUNGICIDAL ACTIVITY.
      NATURE, LOND. 183, 63-64.

1215 CREELMAN, D.W. (1960) - A SUMMARY OF THE PREVALENCE OF PLANT DISEASES IN
      CANADA. A.REP.CAN.PL.DIS.SURV. 38, 1-123.

1216 CRESPO GALIANA, J., ARCE, PASTOR, FEDERICO DE, CRESPO ERCHIGA & SOLO DE
      ZALDIVAR, P. (1972) - ESTUDIO DE LOS HONGOS DEL SUELO EN ESTRATOS GEO-
      LOGICOS. REVTA SAN.HIG.PUBL. 46, 927-948.

1217 CRISAN, E.V. (1962/63) - GROWTH AND PIGMENTATION OF MONOTOSPORA LANUGINOSA.
      DISS.ABSTR. 23, 808.

1218 CRISAN, E.V. (1964) - ISOLATION AND CULTURE OF THERMOPHILIC FUNGI. CONTR.
      BOYCE THOMPSON INST. 22, 291-302.

1219 CRISAN, E.V. (1969) - THE PROTEINS OF THERMOPHILIC FUNGI. CURR.TOPICS PL.
      SCI. 1969, 32-33.

1220 CRISAN, E.V. (1973) - CURRENT CONCEPTS OF THERMOPHILISM AND THE THERMOPHI-
      LIC FUNGI. MYCOLOGIA 65, 1171-1189.

1221 CRISAN, E.V. (1973) - EFFECTS OF AFLATOXIN ON SEEDLING GROWTH AND ULTRA-
      STRUCTURE IN PLANTS. APPL.MICROBIOL. 26, 991-1000.

1222 CROFT, J.H. (1966) - A RECIPROCAL PHENOTYPIC INSTABILITY AFFECTING DEVELOP-
      MENT IN ASPERGILLUS NIDULANS. HEREDITY 21, 565-579.

1223 CROOK, E.M. & JOHNSTON, J.R. (1962) - THE QUALITATIVE ANALYSIS OF THE CELL
      WALLS OF SELECTED SPECIES OF FUNGI. BIOCHEM.J. 83, 325-331.

1224 CROOK, F.M. & HINDSON, W.R. (1955) - AN AUSTRALIAN RECORD OF CEPHALIOPHORA
      TROPICA. TRANS.BR.MYCOL.SOC. 38, 218-220.

1225 CROSIER, W.F. & WEIMER, D. (1939) - SOME FUNGI ASSOCIATED WITH GRASS SEED.
      PROC.ASS.SEED ANALYSTS N.AM. 31, 120-124.

1226 CROSS, B.E., GALT, R.H.B. & HANSON, J.R. (1962) - SOME NEW METABOLITES OF
      GIBBERELLA FUJIKUROI AND THE STEREOCHEMISTRY OF (-)-KAURENE. TETRAHEDRON
      LETTERS, 1962 (4), 145-150.

1227 CROSS, B.E. & MARKWELL, R.E. (1971) - NEW METABOLITES OF GIBBERELLA FUJI-
      KUROI. 18. 4-B BETA,7-DIHYDROXY-1-METHYL-8-METHYLENEGIBBA-1,3,4A(10A)-
      TRIEN-10-ONE. J.CHEM.SOC.(C), 1971, 2980-2983.

1228 CROSS, B.E., MARKWELL, R.E. & STEWART, J.C. (1971) - NEW METABOLITES OF
      GIBBERELLA FUJIKUROI. 16. CYCLONERODIOL. TETRAHEDRON 27, 1663.

1229   CROSSE, R. & MASON, P.J. (1974) - VIRUS-LIKE PARTICLES IN PENICILLIUM CHRY-
        SOGENUM. TRANS.BR.MYCOL.SOC. 62, 603-634.

1230   CROWFOOT, D.M. & LOW, B.W. (1943) - A NOTE ON THE CHRYSTALLOGRAPHY OF HEL-
        VOLIC ACID AND THE METHYLESTER OF HELVOLIC ACID. BR.J.EXP.PATH. 24, 120.

1231   CSUTI, E., LEMAIRE, J.M., PONCHET, J. & RAPILLY, F. (1965) - EXEMPLES D'IN-
        TERACTIONS FONGIQUES AU NIVEAU DE PLANTULES DE BLE CONTAMINEES PAR L'HEL-
        MINTHOSPORIUM SATIVUM. ANNLS EPIPHYT. 16, 37-44.

1232   CUNFER, B.M. (1974) - SEXUAL INCOMPATIBILITY AND ASPECTS OF THE MONO- AND
        DIKARYOTIC PHASES OF TYPHULA IDAHOENSIS. PHYTOPATHOLOGY 64, 123-127.

1233   CUNFER, B.M. & BRUEHL, G.W. (1973) - ROLE OF BASIDIOSPORES AS PROPAGULES
        AND OBSERVATIONS ON SPOROPHORES OF TYPHULA IDAHOENSIS. PHYTOPATHOLOGY
        63, 115-120.

1234   CUNFER, B.M., GRAHAM, J.H. & LUKEZIC, F.L. (1969) - STUDIES ON THE BIOLOGY
        OF MYROTHECIUM RORIDUM AND M. VERRUCARIA PATHOGENIC ON RED CLOVER. PHY-
        TOPATHOLOGY 59, 1306-1309.

1235   CUNFER, B.M. & LUKEZIC, F.L. (1970) - A TOXIN FROM MYROTHECIUM RORIDUM AND
        ITS POSSIBLE ROLE IN MYROTHECIUM LEAF SPOT OF RED CLOVER. PHYTOPATHOLO-
        GY 60, 341-344.

1236   CUNNINGHAM, J.L. & HAGEDORN, D.J. (1960) - NOTES ON THE FLAGELLATION OF
        ZOOSPORES OF APHANOMYCES EUTEICHES. MYCOLOGIA 52, 652-654.

1237   CUNNINGHAM, J.L. & HAGEDORN, D.J. (1962) - ATTRACTION OF APHANOMYCES EU-
        TEICHES ZOOSPORES TO HOST AND NONHOST ROOTS. PHYTOPATHOLOGY 52, 7 (ABS.).

1238   CUNNINGHAM, K.G. & FREEMAN, G.G. (1953) - THE ISOLATION AND SOME CHEMICAL
        PROPERTIES OF VIRIDICATIN, A METABOLIC PRODUCT OF PENICILLIUM VIRIDICA-
        TUM WESTLING. BIOCHEM.J. 53, 328-332.

1239   CURL, E.A., RODRIGUEZ-KABANA, R. & FUNDERBURK, H.H. (1968) - INFLUENCE OF
        ATRAZINE AND VARIED CARBON AND NITROGEN AMENDMENTS ON GROWTH OF SCLE-
        ROTIUM ROLFSII AND TRICHODERMA VIRIDE IN SOIL. PHYTOPATHOLOGY 58, 323-
        328.

1240   CURRAN, P.M.T. (1971) - SPORULATION IN SOME MEMBERS OF THE ASPERGILLUS
        GLAUCUS GROUP IN RESPONSE TO OSMOTIC PRESSURE, ILLUMINATION AND TEMPER-
        ATURE. TRANS.BR.MYCOL.SOC. 57, 201-211.

1241   CURRIE, J.N. & THOM, CH. (1915) - AN OXALIC ACID PRODUCING PENICILLIUM.
        J.BIOL.CHEM. 22, 287-293.

1242   CURTIS, C.R. (1967) - RESPONSE OF FUNGI TO DIURNAL TEMPERATURE EXTREMES.
        NATURE, LOND. 213, 738-739.

1243   CURTIS, C.R. (1972) - ACTION SPECTRUM OF THE PHOTOINDUCED SEXUAL STAGE IN
        THE FUNGUS NECTRIA HAEMATOCOCCA BERK. & BR. VAR. CUCURBITAE (SNYDER &
        HANSEN) DINGLEY. PL.PHYSIOL., LANCASTER 49, 235-239.

1244   CURTIS, P.J. (1969) - ANAEROBIC GROWTH OF FUNGI. TRANS.BR.MYCOL.SOC. 53,
        299-302.

1245   CURTIS, P.J. & DUNCANSON, L.A. (1952) - A STRUCTURAL RELATIONSHIP BETWEEN
        FREQUENTIN AND PALITANTIN. BIOCHEM.J. 51, 276-278.

1246   CURTIS, P.J., HEMMING, H.G. & SMITH, W, K. (1951) - FREQUENTIN, AN ANTIBIO-
        TIC PRODUCED BY SOME STRAINS OF PENICILLIUM FREQUENTANS WESTLING. NA-
        TURE, LOND. 167, 557-558.

1247   CURTIS, R.F., HARRIS, P.C., HASSALL, C.H. & LEVI, J.D. (1964) - THE BIO-
       SYNTHESIS OF PHENOLS. 5. THE RELATION OF SOME PHENOLIC METABOLITES OF
       MUTANTS OF ASPERGILLUS TERREUS THOM, IMI 16043. BIOCHEM.J. 90, 43-51.

1248   CURTIS, R.F., HASSALL, C.H. & LEE, W.C. (1971) - THE SYNTHESIS OF THE SPI-
       RODIENONE-LACTONE, GEODOXIN. PHYTOCHEMISTRY 10, 3271-3273.

1249   CURTIS, R.F., HASSALL, C.H. & NAZAR, M. (1966) - 6-METHYL-5-(1-METHYL-2-
       FORMYL-OXYPROPYL)-RESORCINOL, A NOVEL METABOLITE OF PENICILLIUM CITRI-
       NUM. CHEM.IND., 1966, 702.

1250   CURTIS, R.F., HASSALL, C.H. & NAZAR, M. (1968) - THE BIOSYNTHESIS OF PHE-
       NOLS. 15. SOME METABOLITES OF PENICILLIUM CITRINUM RELATED TO CITRININ.
       J.CHEM.SOC.(C), 1968, 85-93.

1251   CURTIS, R.W., STEVENSON, W.R. & TUITE, J. (1974) - MALFORMIN IN ASPERGIL-
       LUS NIGER-INFECTED ONION PULBS (ALLIUM CEPA). APPL.MICROBIOL. 28, 362-
       365.

1252   CURZI, M. (1932) - STUDI SU LO SCLEROTIUM ROLFSII. BOLL.STAZ.PATOL.VEG.,
       ROMA 11, 306-373.

1253   CUTTER, V.M. (1946) - THE GENUS CUNNINGHAMELLA. FARLOWIA 2, 321-345.

1254   CYBIS, J. & WEGLENSKI, P. (1972) - ARGINASE INDUCTION IN ASPERGILLUS NI-
       DULANS. THE APPEARANCE AND DECAY OF THE CODING CAPACITY OF MESSENGER.
       EUR.J.BIOCHEM. 30, 262-268.

1255   DABINETT, P.E. & WELLMAN, A.M. (1973) - NUMERICAL TAXONOMY OF THE GENUS
       RHIZOPUS. CAN.J.BOT. 51, 2053-2064.

1256   DABROWA, N., LANDAU, J.W., NEWCOMER, V.D. & PLUNKETT, O.A. (1964) - A SUR-
       VEY OF TIDE-WASHED COASTAL AREAS OF SOUTHERN CALIFORNIA FOR FUNGI PO-
       TENTIALLY PATHOGENIC TO MAN. MYCOPATH.MYCOL.APPL. 24, 137-150.

1257   DADALAURI, T.G. (1973) - (NEW SPECIES OF SOIL FUNGI UNKNOWN IN GEORGIA).
       SOOBSHCH.AKAD.NAUK GRUZIN.SSR 71, 433-435.

1258   DAFTARI, L.N. (1966) - EFFECT OF TRACE ELEMENTS ON RHIZOCTONIA SPP. INDIAN
       PHYTOPATH. 19, 118-119.

1259   DALE, E. (1914) - ON THE FUNGI OF THE SOIL. 2. ANNLS MYCOL. 12, 33-62.

1260   DALVI, P.D. (1930) - BIOCHEMISTRY OF TAN-LIQUOR FERMENTATION. J.INDIAN
       INST.SCI. 13A, 173-192.

1261   DANA, B.F. (1931) - SOIL CULTURES FOR THE LABORATORY PRODUCTION OF SCLERO-
       TIA IN PHYMATOTRICHUM OMNIVORUM. PHYTOPATHOLOGY 21, 551-556.

1262   DANCE, M.H., NEWHOOK, F.J. & COLE, J.S. (1975) - BIOASSAY OF PHYTOPHTHORA
       SPP. IN SOIL. PL.DIS.REPTR 59, 523-527.

1263   DANEW, P., FRIEDRICH, E. & MANNSFELDT, H.-G. (1971) - UNTERSUCHUNGEN ZUR
       PEPTIDASEAKTIVITAET HAUTPATHOGENER PILZE. 1. BESTIMMUNGEN DER AKTIVI-
       TAET DER LEUCINAMINOPEPTIDASE, ARYLAMIDASE, CARBOXYPEPTIDASE UND ACYLA-
       SE BEI TRICHOPHYTON RUBRUM UND MICROSPORUM GYPSEUM. DERM.MSCHR. 157,
       232-238.

1264   DANIELS, G. (1954) - ISOLATION OF KERATINOMYCES AJELLOI FROM SOILS IN GREAT
       BRITAIN. NATURE, LOND. 174, 224-226.

1265 DANIELS, J. (1961) - CHAETOMIUM PILULIFERUM SP.NOV., THE PERFECT STATE OF
      BOTRYOTRICHUM PILULIFERUM. TRANS.BR.MYCOL.SOC. 44, 79-86.

1266 DANIELS, J. (1963) - SAPROPHYTIC AND PARASITIC ACTIVITIES OF SOME ISOLATES
      OF CORTICIUM SOLANI. TRANS.BR.MYCOL.SOC. 46, 485-502.

1267 DANIELSON, R.M. (1977) - ECOLOGY OF TRICHODERMA. PAPER PRESENTED AT 2ND
      INT.CONGR.MYCOL., TAMPA, 1977.

1268 DANIELSON, R.M. & DAVEY, C.B. (1970) - MICROBIAL RECOLONIZATION OF A FUMI-
      GATED NURSERY SOIL. FOREST SCI. 15, 368-380.

1269 DANIELSON, R.M. & DAVEY, C.B. (1973) - THE ABUNDANCE OF TRICHODERMA PROPA-
      GULES AND THE DISTRIBUTION OF SPECIES IN FOREST SOILS. SOIL BIOL.BIOCHEM.
      5, 485-494.

1270 DANIELSON, R.M. & DAVEY, C.B. (1973) - NON NUTRITIONAL FACTORS AFFECTING
      THE GROWTH OF TRICHODERMA IN CULTURE. SOIL BIOL.BIOCHEM. 5, 495-504.

1271 DANIELSON, R.M. & DAVEY, C.B. (1973) - CARBON AND NITROGEN OF TRICHODERMA.
      SOIL BIOL.BIOCHEM. 5, 505-515.

1272 DANIELSON, R.M. & DAVEY, C.B. (1973) - EFFECTS OF NUTRIENTS AND ACIDITY ON
      PHIALOSPORE GERMINATION OF TRICHODERMA IN VITRO. SOIL BIOL.BIOCHEM. 5,
      517-524.

1273 DANQUAH, O.A. (1975) - OCCURRENCE OF PHOMA GLOMERATA ON RICE (ORYZA SATIVA).
      A FIRST RECORD IN GHANA. PL.DIS.REPTR 59, 844-845.

1274 DARBY, R.T. & GODDARD, D.R. (1950) - STUDIES OF THE RESPIRATION OF THE MY-
      CELIUM OF THE FUNGUS MYROTHECIUM VERRUCARIA. AM.J.BOT. 37, 379-387.

1275 DARBY, R.T. & MANDELS, G.R. (1954) - INORGANIC NUTRITION OF MYROTHECIUM
      VERRUCARIA. MYCOLOGIA 46, 276-288.

1276 DARLING, W.M., CAMPBELL, P.J. & MCARDLE, M. (1963) - ANTIBIOTICS FROM AS-
      PERGILLUS AMSTELODAMI. J.GEN.MICROBIOL. 33, 191-204.

1277 DART, R.K. (1975) - LONG-CHAIN FATTY ACIDS IN SPORES OF PENICILLIUM. TRANS.
      BR.MYCOL.SOC. 65, 312-315.

1278 DART, R.K. (1976) - EFFECT OF TEMPERATURE ON THE FATTY ACID COMPOSITION OF
      SPOROTRICHUM THERMOPHILE. TRANS.BR.MYCOL.SOC. 66, 532-533.

1279 DART, R.K., LEE, J.D. & STRETTON, R.J. (1976) - CLASSIFICATION OF CERATO-
      CYSTIS AND SPOROTRICHUM BASED ON THEIR LONG-CHAIN FATTY ACIDS. TRANS.
      BR.MYCOL.SOC. 67, 327-328.

1280 DART, R.K. & STRETTON, R.J. (1976) - FATTY ACID COMPOSITION OF SPOROTRI-
      CHUM SPECIES. TRANS.BR.MYCOL.SOC. 66, 529-532.

1281 DART, R.K., STRETTON, R.J. & LEE, J.D. (1976) - RELATIONSHIPS OF PENICIL-
      LIUM SPECIES BASED ON THEIR LONG-CHAIN FATTY ACIDS. TRANS.BR.MYCOL.SOC.
      66, 525-529.

1282 DAS, A.C. (1963) - ECOLOGY OF SOIL FUNGI OF RICE FIELDS. 1. SUCCESSION OF
      FUNGI ON RICE ROOTS. 2. ASSOCIATION OF SOIL FUNGI WITH ORGANIC MATTER.
      TRANS.BR.MYCOL.SOC. 46, 431-443.

1283 DAS, C.R. & PAL, A. (1968) - INFLUENCE OF RHIZOPUS NIGRICANS ON THE DEVEL-
      OPMENT OF ALTERNARIA SOLANI (ELL. & MART.) JONES & GROUT. PHYTOPATH.Z.
      63, 40-46.

1284 DATUNASHVILI, E.N., PAVLENKO, N.M., LIFSHITS, D.B. & PATSENKER, E.S. (1970)
      - PROTEOLYTIC ACTIVITY OF ASPERGILLUS ACID PROTEASES. APPL.BIOCHEM.MI-
      CROBIOL. 6, 217-220.

1285 DAVET, P. (1969) - OBSERVATIONS SUR LA MYCOFLORE DES RACINES DE QUELQUES
      PLANTES MARAICHERES DU LIBAN. REVUE MYCOL. 34, 62-78.

1286 DAVEY, C.B. & PAPAVIZAS, G.C. (1960) - EFFECT OF DRY MATURE PLANT MATERIALS
      AND NITROGEN ON RHIZOCTONIA SOLANI IN SOIL. PHYTOPATHOLOGY 50, 522-525.

1287 DAVEY, C.B. & PAPAVIZAS, G.C. (1962) - GROWTH AND SEXUAL REPRODUCTION OF
      APHANOMYCES EUTEICHES AS AFFECTED BY THE OXIDATION STATE OF SULFUR. AM.
      J.BOT. 49, 400-404.

1288 DAVEY, C.B. & PAPAVIZAS, G.C. (1963) - SAPROPHYTIC ACTIVITY OF RHIZOCTONIA
      AS AFFECTED BY THE CARBON-NITROGEN BALANCE OF CERTAIN ORGANIC SOIL AMEND-
      MENTS. PROC.SOIL SCI.SOC.AM. 27, 164-167.

1289 DAVEY, G. & KALMAKOFF, J. (1974) - EVIDENCE THAT THE NEPHROTOXIN FROM THE
      FUNGUS MORTIERELLA WOLFII IS A PROTEIN. CAN.J.MICROBIOL. 20, 1513-1516.

1290 DAVEY, G., SMITH, J.M.B. & KALMAKOFF, J. (1973) - PURIFICATION AND PROPER-
      TIES OF A TOXIN ISOLATED FROM MORTIERELLA WOLFII. INFECT.IMMUN. 8, 882-
      886.

1291 DAVID, K.A.V. & RAO, A.S. (1965) - INHIBITION OF AN ANTAGONISTIC BACTERIUM
      BY SCLEROTIUM ROLFSII. PHYTOPATHOLOGY 55, 121 (ABS.).

1292 DAVIDSON, D.E. (1974) - WOOD-INHABITING AND MARINE FUNGI FROM A SALINE LAKE
      IN WYOMING. TRANS.BR.MYCOL.SOC. 63, 143-149.

1293 DAVIDSON, D.E. (1974) - SALINITY TOLERANCE AND ECOLOGICAL ASPECTS OF SOME
      MICROFUNGI FROM SALINE AND NON-SALINE SOILS IN WYOMING. MYCOPATH.MYCOL.
      APPL. 54, 181-188.

1294 DAVIDSON, D.E. & CHRISTENSEN, M. (1971) - EMERICELLOPSIS STOLKIAE SP.NOV.
      FROM SALINE SOILS IN WYOMING. TRANS.BR.MYCOL.SOC. 57, 385-391.

1295 DAVIDSON, J-G. & LORTI, M. (1970) - RELEVE DE MICROORGANISMES DANS LE BOIS
      DE QUELQUES ARBRES FEUILLUS PORTEURS DE DEFAUTS SUR LE TRONC. NATURA-
      LISTE CAN. 97, 43-50.

1296 DAVIDSON, R.M. & BRUEHL, G.W. (1972) - FACTORS AFFECTING THE EFFECTIVENESS
      OF SCLEROTIA OF TYPHULA IDAHOENSIS AS INOCULUM. PHYTOPATHOLOGY 62, 1040-
      1045.

1297 DAVIES, F.L., LIN, F.K. & GOTTLIEB, D. (1974) - SYNTHESIS OF RNA WITH RE-
      LATION TO AGING IN RHIZOCTONIA SOLANI. ARCH.MICROBIOL. 95, 145-152.

1298 DAVIES, J.S., WELLMANN, A.M. & ZAJIC, J.E. (1973) - HYPHOMYCETES UTILIZING
      NATURAL GAS. CAN.J.MICROBIOL. 19, 81-85.

1299 DAVIES, R.R. (1957) - STUDIES ON AIR-BORNE CLADOSPORIUM. TRANS.BR.MYCOL.
      SOC. 40, 409-414.

1300 DAVIES, R.R. & ISAAC, I. (1958) - DISSEMINATION OF VERTICILLIUM ALBO-ATRUM
      THROUGH THE ATMOSPHERE. NATURE, LOND. 181, 649.

1301 DAVIS, D. (1970) - CARBOHYDRATE SPECIFICITY FOR FUSARIC ACID SYNTHESIS.
      PHYTOPATHOLOGY 60, 111-113.

1302   DAVIS, J.D. (1969) - A SELECTIVE ISOLATION TECHNIQUE FOR DETERMINING CHAE-
       TOMIUM IN SOIL. PL.SOIL 31, 179-181.

1303   DAVIS, N.D., WAGENER, R.E., DALBY, D.K., MORGAN-JONES, G. & DIENER, U.L.
       (1975) - TOXIGENIC FUNGI IN FOOD. APPL.MICROBIOL. 30, 159-161.

1304   DAVIS, N.D., WAGENER, R.E., MORGAN-JONES, G. & DIENER, U.L. (1975) - TOXI-
       GENIC, THERMOPHILIC AND THERMOTOLERANT FUNGI. APPL.MICROBIOL. 29, 455-
       457.

1305   DAVIS, P.L. & SMOOT, J.J. (1965) - INDUCEMENT OF GERMINATION OF PENICIL-
       LIUM DIGITATUM SPORES BY ORANGE RIND COMPONENTS AND EFFECT OF PH OF SUB-
       STRATE. PHYTOPATHOLOGY 55, 1216-1218.

1306   DAVISON, E.M. & BUMBIERIS, M. (1973) - PHYTOPHTHORA AND PYTHIUM SPP. FROM
       PINE PLANTATIONS IN SOUTH AUSTRALIA. AUST.J.BIOL.SCI. 26, 163-169.

1307   DAVISON, S. & MARBROOK, J. (1965) - THE EFFECT OF TEMPERATURE ON THE TOXIC-
       ITY OF SPORES OF PITHOMYCES CHARTARUM (BERK. & CURT.) M.B. ELLIS. N.Z.JL
       AGRIC.RES. 8, 126-130.

1308   DAWKINS, A.W. (1966) - PHYTOTOXIC COMPOUNDS PRODUCED BY FUSARIUM EQUISETI.
       2. THE CHEMISTRY OF DIACETOXYSCIRPENOL. J.CHEM.SOC.ORG., 1966, 116-123.

1309   DAWKINS, A.W., GROVE, J.F. & TIDD, B.K. (1965) - DIACETOXYSCIRPENOL AND
       SOME RELATED COMPOUNDS. CHEM.COMMUN., 1965, 27-28.

1310   DAWSON, C.O. (1963) - TWO NEW SPECIES OF ARTHRODERMA ISOLATED FROM SOIL
       FROM RABBIT BURROWS. SABOURAUDIA 2, 185-191.

1311   DAWSON, C.O. & GENTLES, J.C. (1959) - PERFECT STATE OF KERATINOMYCES AJEL-
       LOI. NATURE, LOND. 183, 1345-1346.

1312   DAWSON, C.O. & GENTLES, J.C. (1961/62) - THE PERFECT STATES OF KERATINO-
       MYCES AJELLOI VANBREUSEGHEM, TRICHOPHYTON TERRESTRE DURIE & FREY AND
       MICROSPORUM NANUM FUENTES. SABOURAUDIA 1, 49-57.

1313   DAWSON, C.O., GENTLES, J.C. & BROWN, E.M. (1963/64) - ENVIRONMENTAL CON-
       DITIONS AFFECTING SEXUAL REPRODUCTION IN SPECIES OF ARTHRODERMA AND NAN-
       NIZZIA. SABOURAUDIA 3, 245-250.

1314   DAYAL, R. & BARRON, G.L. (1970) - VERTICILLIUM PSALLIOTAE AS A PARASITE OF
       RHOPALOMYCES. MYCOLOGIA 62, 826-830.

1315   DAYAL, R. & GUPTA, O.S.D. (1967) - THE SOIL FUNGI OF VARANASI, INDIA, IN
       RELATION TO THE EDAPHIC FACTORS. OIKOS 18, 76-81.

1316   DAYAL, R. & GUPTA, O.S.D. (1970) - SOME NEW RECORDS OF SOIL FUNGI FROM IN-
       DIA. SYDOWIA 24, 345-349.

1317   DAYAL, R. & LALLAL GIRI (1971) - SOIL FUNGI IN LEGUMINOUS FIELDS OF VARA-
       NASI, INDIA. OIKOS 22, 122-127.

1318   DEACON, J.W. (1973) - BEHAVIOUR OF CERCOSPORELLA HERPOTRICHOIDES AND OPHIO-
       BOLUS GRAMINIS ON BURIED WHEAT PLANT TISSUES. SOIL BIOL.BIOCHEM. 5, 339-
       353.

1319   DEACON, J.W. (1973) - PHIALOPHORA RADICICOLA AND GAEUMANNOMYCES GRAMINIS
       ON ROOTS OF GRASSES AND CEREALS. TRANS.BR.MYCOL.SOC. 61, 471-485.

1320 DEACON, J.W. (1973) - FACTORS AFFECTING OCCURRENCE OF OPHIOBOLUS PATCH DIS-
      EASE OF TURF AND ITS CONTROL BY PHIALOPHORA RADICICOLA. PL.PATH. 22,
      149-155.

1321 DEACON, J.W. (1974) - FURTHER STUDIES ON PHIALOPHORA RADICICOLA AND GAEU-
      MANNOMYCES GRAMINIS ON ROOTS AND STEM BASES OF GRASSES AND CEREALS.
      TRANS.BR.MYCOL.SOC. 63, 307-327.

1322 DEACON, J.W. (1976) - BIOLOGICAL CONTROL OF THE TAKE-ALL FUNGUS, GAEUMAN-
      NOMYCES GRAMINIS, BY PHIALOPHORA RADICICOLA AND SIMILAR FUNGI. SOIL BIOL.
      BIOCHEM. 8, 275-283.

1323 DEACON, J.W. (1976) - STUDIES ON PYTHIUM OLIGANDRUM, AN AGGRESSIVE PARA-
      SITE OF OTHER FUNGI. TRANS.BR.MYCOL.SOC. 66, 383-391.

1324 DE BIEVRE, C. (1969) - COMPOSITION EN PROTEINES, ARN, ADN, LIPIDES ET PO-
      LYOSIDES DES PHASES LEVURE ET FILAMENTEUSE DE SPOROTHRIX SCHENCKII.
      REVUE MYCOL. 34, 220-230.

1325 DE BIEVRE, C. (1974) - LIPIDES DE QUELQUES SOUCHES DE ENTOMOPHTHORA CORO-
      NATA ET DE BASIDIOBOLUS MERISTOSPORUS. ANNLS MICROBIOL. 125A, 309-321.

1326 DE BIEVRE, C. & MARIAT, F. (1975) - COMPOSITION EN ACIDES GRAS DES LIPIDES
      POLAIRES ET NEUTRES DE SPOROTHRIX SCHENCKII ET DE CERATOCYSTIS STENOCE-
      RAS. SABOURAUDIA 13, 226-230.

1327 DE BOER, J.J., BRIGHT, D., DALLINGER, G. & HEWITT, T.G. (1971) - CRYSTAL
      AND MOLECULAR STRUCTURE OF THE CHLOROFORM SOLVATE OF BIKAVERIN. J.CHEM.
      SOC.(C), 1971, 2788-2791.

1328 DEBRIT, F.P. (1950) - BEITRAG ZUR WIRKSTOFFPHYSIOLOGIE VON MUCOR RAMANNIA-
      NUS UND MUCOR RAMANNIANUS VAR. ANGULISPORUS. DISS.UNIV.BERN.

1329 DEBRIT, F.P. & SCHOPFER, W.H. (1946) - LES BESOINS EN FACTEURS DE CROIS-
      SANCE DE MUCOR RAMANNIANUS VAR. ANGULISPORUS NAOUMOFF. EXPERIENTIA 11,
      312.

1330 DEEMS, R.E. & YOUNG, H.C. (1956) - BLACK ROOT OF SUGAR BEETS AS INFLUENCED
      BY VARIOUS CROPPING SEQUENCES AND THEIR ASSOCIATED MYCOFLORAS. J.AM.SOC.
      SUG.BEET TECHNOL. 9, 32-43.

1331 DEFAGO, G. & KERN, H. (1975) - ABSORPTION ET TRANSPORT DU CHOLESTEROL PAR
      LE PYTHIUM PAROECANDRUM. PHYTOPATH.Z. 84, 34-46.

1332 DEFAGO, G., MEMMEN, K.F. & KERN, H. (1975) - INFLUENCE DU CHOLESTEROL ET
      DES SAPONINES SUR LE POUVOIR PATHOGENE DU PYTHIUM PAROECANDRUM. PHYTO-
      PATH.Z. 83, 167-184.

1333 DEGROOT, R.C. (1972) - GROWTH OF WOOD-INHABITING FUNGI IN SATURATED ATMOS-
      PHERES OF MONOTERPENOIDS. MYCOLOGIA 64, 863-870.

1334 DEJARDIN, R.A. & WARD, E.W.B. (1971) - GROWTH AND RESPIRATION OF PSYCHRO-
      PHILIC SPECIES OF THE GENUS TYPHULA. CAN.J.BOT. 49, 339-347.

1335 DEJARDIN, R.A. & WARD, E.W.B. (1971) - STUDIES ON THE ENDOGENOUS RESPIRA-
      TION OF THE PSYCHROPHILIC FUNGUS, TYPHULA IDAHOENSIS. CAN.J.BOT. 49,
      2081-2087.

1336 DELMOTTE-PLAQUEE, MR., DELMOTTE-PLAQUEE, MME. & BASTIN, R. (1956) - UN
      NOUVEL ANTIBIOTIQUE CHLORE VOISIN DE LA GEODINE. J.PHARM.BELG. 11, 200-
      205.

1337   DEL PRADO, F.A. & CHRISTENSEN, C.M. (1952) - GRAIN STORAGE STUDIES. 12.
        THE FUNGUS FLORA OF STORED RICE SEED. CEREAL CHEM. 29, 456-462.

1338   DELVECCHIO, V.G., CORBAZ, R. & TURIAN, G. (1969) - AN ULTRASTRUCTURAL STUDY
        OF THE HYPHAE, ENDOCONIDIA AND CHLAMYDOSPORES OF THIELAVIOPSIS BASICOLA.
        J.GEN.MICROBIOL. 58, 23-27.

1339   DEMETRIADES, S.D. (1953) - ETUDES SUR LA BIOLOGIE DU SCEROTINIA SCLEROTI-
        ORUM. 3. L'ACTION DU MAGNESIUM ET DU SOUFRE SUR LE DEVELOPPEMENT DU
        CHAMPIGNON ET LA FORMATION DE SES SCLEROTES. ANNLS INST.PHYTOPATH.BENAKI
        7, 15-20.

1340   DEMETRIADES, S.D. & EMMANOUIL, V.N. (1971) - SUR L'HYDROLYSE DE L'ARBUTINE
        PAR QUELQUES CHAMPIGNONS. ANNLS INST.PHYTOPATH.BENAKI 10, 106-209.

1341   DENNIS, C. (1972) - BREAKDOWN OF CELLULOSE BY YEAST SPECIES. J.GEN.MICRO-
        BIOL. 71, 409-411.

1342   DENNIS, C. & BUHAGIAR, R.W.M. (1973) - COMPARATIVE STUDY OF AUREOBASIDIUM
        PULLULANS, A. PRUNORUM SP.NOV. AND TRICHOSPORON PULLULANS. TRANS.BR.MY-
        COL.SOC. 60, 567-575.

1343   DENNIS, C. & WEBSTER, J. (1971) - ANTAGONISTIC PROPERTIES OF SPECIES-GROUPS
        OF TRICHODERMA. 1. PRODUCTION OF NON-VOLATILE ANTIBIOTICS. TRANS.BR.MY-
        COL.SOC. 57, 25-39.

1344   DENNIS, C. & WEBSTER, J. (1971) - ANTAGONISTIC PROPERTIES OF SPECIES-GROUPS
        OF TRICHODERMA. 2. PRODUCTION OF VOLATILE ANTIBIOTICS. TRANS.BR.MYCOL.
        SOC. 57, 41-48.

1345   DENNIS, C. & WEBSTER, J. (1971) - ANTAGONISTIC PROPERTIES OF SPECIES-GROUPS
        OF TRICHODERMA. 3. HYPHAL INTERACTION. TRANS.BR.MYCOL.SOC. 57, 363-369.

1346   DENNIS, R.W.G. (1946) - NOTES ON SOME BRITISH FUNGI ASCRIBED TO PHOMA AND
        RELATED GENERA. TRANS.BR.MYCOL.SOC. 29, 11-42.

1347   DENNIS, R.W.G. (1956) - A REVISION OF THE BRITISH HELOTIACEAE IN THE HER-
        BARIUM OF THE ROYAL BOTANIC GARDENS, KEW, WITH NOTES ON RELATED EURO-
        PEAN SPECIES. MYCOL.PAP. 62, 216 PP.

1348   DENNIS, R.W.G. (1978) - BRITISH ASCOMYCETES. J.CRAMER, LEHRE.

1349   DEPLOEY, J.J. (1976) - CARBOHYDRATE NUTRITION OF MUCOR MIEHEI AND MUCOR
        PUSILLUS. MYCOLOGIA 68, 190-194.

1350   DEPLOEY, J.J. & FERGUS, C.L. (1975) - GROWTH AND SPORULATION OF THERMOPHIL-
        IC FUNGI AND ACTINOMYCETES IN O2-N2 ATMOSPHERES. MYCOLOGIA 67, 780-797.

1351   DESAI, B., GEYPENS, M. & ASSCHE, C.VAN (1973) - INFLUENCE OF THREE FUNGI-
        CIDES ON THE PRODUCTION OF CELLULOLYTIC AND PECTINOLYTIC ENZYMES IN THE
        CULTURE FILTRATES OF PYTHIUM SPP. MEDED.FAC.LANDBWET.RIJKSUNIV.GENT 38,
        1455-1466.

1352   DESAI, B.M., MODI, V.V. & SHAH.V.K. (1967) - INDUCTION OF SORBITOL DEHYDRO-
        GENASE BY SORBITOL IN ASPERGILLUS NIGER. ARCH.MIKROBIOL. 56, 300-304.

1353   DESHPANDE, K.B. (1959) - NITROGEN METABOLISM OF RHIZOCTONIA SOLANI. J.BIOL.
        SCI. 2, 1-5.

1354   DESHPANDE, K.B. (1961) - ANTAGONISM BETWEEN RHIZOCTONIA SOLANI AND CERTAIN
        SAPROPHYTES. A LABORATORY STUDY. BIOL.PL.ACAD.SCI.BOHEMOSLOV. 3, 192-
        199.

1355 DESHPANDE, K.B. & SARJE, B.D. (1966) – CARBON METABOLISM AND MORPHOGENESIS OF PENICILLIUM FREQUENTANS. GLUCOSE CONSUMPTION. BIOL.PL.ACAD.SCI.BOHEMOSLOV. 8, 29-35.

1356 DETROY, R.W. & CIEGLER, A. (1971) – AFLATOXIN BIOSYNTHESIS IN ASPERGILLUS PARASITICUS. EFFECT OF METHIONINE ANALOGS. CAN.J.MICROBIOL. 17, 569-574.

1357 DETROY, R.W. & CIEGLER, A. (1971) – INDUCTION OF YEAST-LIKE DEVELOPMENT IN ASPERGILLUS PARASITICUS. J.GEN.MICROBIOL. 65, 259-264.

1358 DETROY, R.W., FREER, S.N. & FENNELL, D.I. (1973) – RELATIONSHIP BETWEEN THE BIOSYNTHESIS OF VIRUS-LIKE PARTICLES AND MYCOPHENOLIC ACID IN PENICILLIUM STOLONIFERUM AND PENICILLIUM BREVI-COMPACTUM. CAN.J.MICROBIOL. 19, 1459-1462.

1359 DETROY, R.W. & HESSELTINE, C.W. (1969) – TRANSFORMATION OF AFLATOXIN-B1 BY STEROID HYDROXYLATING FUNGI. CAN.J.MICROBIOL. 15, 495-500.

1360 DETROY, R.W., LILLEHOJ, E.B. & CIEGLER, A. (1971) – AFLATOXIN AND RELATED COMPOUNDS. IN: MICROBIAL TOXINS, VOL.6, FUNGAL TOXINS; CIEGLER, A., KADIS, S. & AJL, S.J. (ED.), ACADEMIC PRESS, N.Y., LONDON, 3-178.

1361 DETROY, R.W., LILLEHOJ, E.B. & HESSELTINE, C.W. (1974) – REPLICATION OF VIRUS-LIKE PARTICLES IN PENICILLIUM STOLONIFERUM MYCELIA. CAN.J.MICROBIOL. 20, 113-117.

1362 DEVAUX, A.L. & SACKSTON, W.E. (1966) – TAXONOMY OF VERTICILLIUM SPECIES CAUSING WILT OF HORTICULTURAL CROPS IN QUEBEC. CAN.J.BOT. 44, 803-811.

1363 DEVAY, J.E., FORRESTER, L.L., GARBER, R.H. & BUTTERFIELD, E.J. (1974) – CHARACTERISTICS AND CONCENTRATION OF PROPAGULES OF VERTICILLIUM DAHLIAE IN AIR-DRIED FIELD SOILS IN RELATION TO THE PREVALENCE OF VERTICILLIUM WILT IN COTTON. PHYTOPATHOLOGY 64, 22-29.

1364 DEWAR, M.D. & WALKER, G.J. (1973) – HYDROLYSIS OF ALPHA-1,3-GLUCOSIDIC LINKAGES BY EXTRACELLULAR ENZYMES OF CLADOSPORIUM RESINAE. J.DENT.RES. 52, 573 (ABS.).

1365 DEY, N.C. (1971) – PROPOSAL FOR A REVISED CLASSIFICATION OF DERMATOPHYTES. INDIAN J.DERM. 16, 79-97.

1366 DHAR, A.K. & BOSE, S.K. (1968) – A NEW ANTIFUNGAL ANTIBIOTIC FROM ASPERGILLUS VERSICOLOR. J.ANTIBIOT., TOKYO 21, 156-157.

1367 DHAR, A.K. & BOSE, S.K. (1968) – MUTAGENS FOR REGENERATION OF AN ANTIBIOTIC-PRODUCING STRAIN OF ASPERGILLUS VERSICOLOR. APPL.MICROBIOL. 16, 340-342.

1368 DHAR, A.K. & BOSE, S.K. (1969) – STUDIES ON VERSICOLIN, A NEW ANTIFUNGAL ANTIBIOTIC FROM ASPERGILLUS VERSICOLOR. 1. STRUCTURE OF VERSICOLIN. TETRAHEDRON LETTERS, 1969 (55), 4871-4874.

1369 DHINGRA, O.D. & KHARE, M.N. (1973) – BIOLOGICAL CONTROL OF RHIZOCTONIA BATATICOLA ON URID BEAN. PHYTOPATH.Z. 76, 23-29.

1370 DHINGRA, O.D., NICHOLSON, J.F. & SINCLAIR, J.B. (1973) – INFLUENCE OF TEMPERATURE ON RECOVERY OF ASPERGILLUS FLAVUS FROM SOYBEAN SEED. PL.DIS.REPTR 57, 185-187.

1371 DICK, C.M. & HUTCHINSON, S.A. (1966) – BIOLOGICAL ACTIVITY OF VOLATILE FUNGAL METABOLITES. NATURE, LOND. 211, 868.

1372 DICKINSON, C.H. (1965) - THE MYCOFLORA ASSOCIATED WITH HALIMIONE PORTULA-
COIDES. 3. FUNGI ON GREEN AND MORIBUND LEAVES. TRANS.BR.MYCOL.SOC. 48,
603-610.

1373 DICKINSON, C.H. (1967) - FUNGAL COLONIZATION OF PISUM LEAVES. CAN.J.BOT.
57, 915-927.

1374 DICKINSON, C.H. (1968) - GLIOMASTIX GUEGUEN. MYCOL.PAP. 115, 1-24.

1375 DICKINSON, C.H. & BOARDMAN, F. (1970) - PHYSIOLOGICAL STUDIES OF SOME FUN-
GI ISOLATED FROM PEAT. TRANS.BR.MYCOL.SOC. 55, 293-305.

1376 DICKINSON, C.H. & DOOLEY, M. (1969) - FUNGI ASSOCIATED WITH IRISH PEAT
BOGS. PROC.R.IR.ACAD., SECT.B, 68, 109-137.

1377 DICKINSON, C.H. & KENT, J.W. (1972) - CRITICAL ANALYSIS OF FUNGI IN TWO
SAND DUNE SOILS. TRANS.BR.MYCOL.SOC. 58, 269-280.

1378 DICKINSON, C.H. & PUGH, G.J.F. (1965) - THE MYCOFLORA ASSOCIATED WITH HA-
LIMIONE PORTULACOIDES. TRANS.BR.MYCOL.SOC. 48, 381-390.

1379 DICKINSON, C.H. & PUGH, G.J. (1965) - USE OF A SELECTIVE CELLULOSE AGAR
FOR ISOLATION OF SOIL FUNGI. NATURE, LOND. 207, 440-441.

1380 DIEKMANN, H. (1967) - STOFFWECHSELPRODUKTE VON MIKROORGANISMEN. 56. FUSI-
GEN - EIN NEUES SIDERAMIN AUS PILZEN. ARCH.MIKROBIOL. 58, 1-5.

1381 DIEKMANN, H. & KREZDORN, E. (1975) - STOFFWECHSELPRODUKTE VON MIKROORGA-
NISMEN. 150. FERRICROCIN, TRIACETYLFUSIGEN UND ANDERE SIDERAMINE AUS
PILZEN DER GATTUNG ASPERGILLUS, GRUPPE FUMIGATUS. ARCH.MICROBIOL. 106,
191-194.

1382 DIELEMAN-VAN ZAAYEN, A. (1967) - VIRUS-LIKE PARTICLES IN A WEED MOULD GROW-
ING ON MUSHROOM TRAYS. NATURE, LOND. 216, 595-596.

1383 DIELEMANN-VAN ZAAYEN, A. (1970) - INTRACELLULAR APPEARANCE AND SOME MOR-
PHOLOGICAL FEATURES OF VIRUS-LIKE PARTICLES IN AN ASCOMYCETE FUNGUS.
VIROLOGY 42, 534-537.

1384 DIEM, H.G. (1975) - AFFACTION ET REPULSION DES BACTERIES PAR LES SPORES DE
CLADOSPORIUM CLADOSPORIOIDES AU COURS DE GERMINATION. CAN.J.BOT. 53,
1092-1096.

1385 DIENER, U.L. & DAVIS, N.D. (1966) - AFLATOXIN PRODUCTION BY ISOLATES OF AS-
PERGILLUS FLAVUS. PHYTOPATHOLOGY 56, 1390-1393.

1386 DIENER, U.L. & DAVIS, N.D. (1968) - EFFECT OF ENVIRONMENT ON AFLATOXIN PRO-
DUCTION IN FRESHLY DUG PEANUTS. TROP.SCI. 10, 22-28.

1387 DIENER, U.L., MORGAN-JONES, G., HAGLER, W.M. & DAVIS, N.D. (1976) - MYCO-
FLORA OF ACTIVATED SEWAGE SLUDGE. MYCOPATHOLOGIA 58, 115-116.

1388 DIENER, U.L., WAGENER, R.E., MORGAN-JONES, G. & DAVIS, N.D. (1976) - TOXI-
GENIC FUNGI FROM COTTON. PHYTOPATHOLOGY 66, 514-516.

1389 DIETRICH, S.M.C. (1973) - CARBOHYDRATES FROM THE HYPHAL WALLS OF SOME
OOMYCETES. BIOCHIM.BIOPHYS.ACTA 313, 95-98.

1390 DIETRICH, S.M.C. (1976) - PRESENCE OF POLYPHOSPHATE OF LOW MOLECULAR WEIGHT
IN ZYGOMYCETES. J.BACT. 127, 1408-1413.

1391 DIETRICH, S.M.C. & VALIO, I.F.M. (1973) - EFFECT OF COUMARIN AND ITS DERI-
VATIVES ON THE GROWTH OF PYTHIUM AND OTHER FUNGI. TRANS.BR.MYCOL.SOC.
61, 461-469.

1392 DIJCK, P.J.VAN (1969) - OCCURRENCE OF RAMYCIN IN STRAINS OF MORTIERELLA
      RAMANNIANA. TRANS.BR.MYCOL.SOC. 53, 142-143.

1393 DIJCK, P.J.VAN & DESOMER, P. (1958) - RAMYCIN - A NEW ANTIBIOTIC. J.GEN.
      MICROBIOL. 18, 377-381.

1394 DIJKSTRA, M.J. (1974) - AN ULTRASTRUCTURAL EXAMINATION OF THE STRUCTURE
      AND GERMINATION OF ASEXUAL PROPAGULES OF FOUR MUCORALEAN FUNGI. MYCO-
      LOGIA 66, 477-489.

1395 DILL, B.C., LEIGHTON, T.J. & STOCK, J.J. (1972) - PHYSIOLOGICAL AND BIO-
      CHEMICAL CHANGES ASSOCIATED WITH MACROCONIDIAL GERMINATION IN MICROSPO-
      RUM GYPSEUM. APPL.MICROBIOL. 24, 977-985.

1396 DI MENNA, M.E. (1959) - SOME PHYSIOLOGICAL CHARACTERS OF YEASTS FROM SOILS
      AND ALLIED HABITATS. J.GEN.MICROBIOL. 20, 13-23.

1397 DI MENNA, M.E. (1962) - THE ANTIBIOTIC RELATIONSHIPS OF SOME YEASTS FROM
      SOIL AND LEAVES. J.GEN.MICROBIOL. 27, 249-257.

1398 DI MENNA, M.E. & BAILEY, J.R. (1973) - PITHOMYCES CHARTARUM SPORE COUNTS
      IN PASTURE. N.Z.JL AGRIC.RES. 16, 343-352.

1399 DI MENNA, M.E., CARTER, M.E. & CORDES, D.O. (1972) - THE IDENTIFICATION OF
      MORTIERELLA WOLFII ISOLATED FROM CASES OF ABORTION AND PNEUMONIA IN
      CATTLE AND A SEARCH FOR ITS INFECTION SOURCE. RES.VET.SCI. 13, 439-442.

1400 DI MENNA, M.E., MORTIMER, P.H., SMITH, B.L. & TULLOCH, M. (1973) - THE IN-
      CIDENCE OF THE GENUS MYROTHECIUM IN NEW ZEALAND PASTURES AND ITS RELA-
      TION TO ANIMAL DISEASE. J.GEN.MICROBIOL. 79, 81-87.

1401 DI MENNA, M.E. & PARLE, J.N. (1970) - MOULDS ON LEAVES OF PERENNIAL RYE-
      GRASS AND WHITE CLOVER. N.Z.JL AGRIC.RES. 13, 51-68.

1402 DINGLEY, J.M. (1951) - THE HYPOCREALES OF NEW ZEALAND. 2. THE GENUS NEC-
      TRIA. TRANS.R.SOC.N.Z. 79, 177-202.

1403 DINGLEY, J.M. (1957) - LIFE HISTORY STUDIES IN THE GENUS HYPOCREA. TRANS.
      R.SOC.N.Z. 84, 689-693.

1404 DINGLEY, J.M. (1962) - PITHOMYCES CHARTARUM, ITS OCCURRENCE, MORPHOLOGY,
      AND TAXONOMY. N.Z.JL AGRIC.RES. 5, 49-61.

1405 DIVAKARAN, P. & MODAK, M.J. (1968) - FATTY ACID COMPOSITION OF MYCELIUM OF
      PENICILLIUM CHRYSOGENUM GROWN IN DIFFERENT CARBOHYDRATES AS A SOLE
      SOURCE OF CARBON. EXPERIENTIA 24, 1102.

1406 DIX, N.J. (1964) - COLONIZATION AND DECAY OF BEAN ROOTS. TRANS.BR.MYCOL.
      SOC. 47, 285-292.

1407 DIX, N.J. (1967) - MYCOSTASIS AND ROOT EXUDATION. FACTORS INFLUENCING THE
      COLONIZATION OF BEAN ROOTS BY FUNGI. TRANS.BR.MYCOL.SOC. 50, 23-31.

1408 DIX, N.J. (1972) - EFFECT OF SOIL FUNGISTASIS ON SPORE GERMINATION AND
      GERMTUBE GROWTH IN PENICILLIUM SPECIES. TRANS.BR.MYCOL.SOC. 58, 59-66.

1409 DIXON, M. (1968) - TRICHOCLADIUM PYRIFORMIS SP.NOV. TRANS.BR.MYCOL.SOC.
      51, 160-164.

1410 DIXON-STEWART, D. (1932) - SPECIES OF MORTIERELLA ISOLATED FROM SOIL. TRANS. BR.MYCOL.SOC. 27, 208-220.

1411 DODMAN, R.L. (1972) - HETEROKARYON FORMATION AND GENETIC RECOMBINATION BE-TWEEN AUXOTROPHIC AND MORPHOLOGICAL MUTANTS OF THANATEPHORUS CUCUMERIS. AUST.J.BIOL.SCI. 25, 739-748.

1412 DOGUET, G. (1956) - MORPHOLOGIE ET ORGANOGENIE DU NEOCOSMOSPORA VASINFECTA ET DU NEOCOSMOSPORA AFRICANA. ANNLS SCI.NAT., BOT., SER.11, 17, 353-370.

1413 DOGUET, G. (1956) - LE GENRE THIELAVIA. REVUE MYCOL. 21, SUPPL.COLON., 1-21.

1414 DOI, Y. (1972) - REVISION OF THE HYPOCREALES WITH CULTURAL OBSERVATIONS. 4. THE GENUS HYPOCREA AND ITS ALLIES IN JAPAN. 2. ENUMERATION OF THE SPECIES. BULL.NATN.SCI.MUS., TOKYO 15, 649-751.

1415 DOIDGE, E.M. (1950) - THE SOUTH AFRICAN FUNGI AND LICHENS. BOTHALIA 5, 1-1094.

1416 DOMER, J.E., HAMILTON, J.G. & HARKIN, J.C. (1967) - COMPARATIVE STUDY OF THE CELL WALLS OF THE YEAST-LIKE AND MYCELIAL PHASES OF HISTOPLASMA CAP-SULATUM. J.BACT. 94, 466-474.

1417 DOMER, J.E. & HARMON, R.D. (1972) - LIPID, MONOSACCHARIDE AND CHITIN CON-TENT OF CELL WALLS OF SEPEDONIUM. SABOURAUDIA 10, 56-62.

1418 DOMINIK, T. (1967) - CHRYSOSPORIUM CORDA. ZESZ.NAUK.WYZSZ.SZK.ROLN.SZCZEC. 24, 37-66.

1419 DOMINIK, T. (1968) - (RARE OR FOR EUROPE NEW FUNGI ISOLATED FROM THE SOILS IN SZCZECIN PROVINCE). ZESZ.NAUK.WYZSZ.SZK.ROLN.SZCZEC. 28, 11-32.

1420 DOMINIK, T. & IHNATOWICZ, A. (1975) - SOIL FUNGI FROM ELOKA NEAR APIDJAN IN EQUATORIAL WEST AFRICA. ZESZ.NAUK.AKAD.ROLN.SZCZEC. 50, 13-27.

1421 DOMINIK, T., IHNATOWICZ, A., KOPYLOW, H. & MIETKIEWSKI, R. (1973) - MYCO-FLORA OF SAND-BOXES IN KINDERGARDENS IN SZCZECIN. EKOL.POL. 21, 901-923.

1422 DOMINIK, T. & MAJCHROWICZ, I. (1964) - A TRIAL FOR ISOLATING KERATINOLYTIC AND KERATINOPHILIC FUNGI FROM THE SOILS OF THE CEMETERIES AND FORESTS OF SZCZECIN. EKOL.POL., SER.A, 12, 79-105.

1423 DOMINIK, T. & MAJCHROWICZ, I. (1965) - SECOND CONTRIBUTION TO THE KNOWL-EDGE OF KERATINOLYTIC AND KERATINOPHILIC SOIL FUNGI IN THE REGION OF SZCZECIN. EKOL.POL., SER.A, 13, 415-447.

1424 DOMSCH, K.H. (1960) - DAS PILZSPEKTRUM EINER BODENPROBE. 1. NACHWEIS DER HOMOGENITAET. ARCH.MIKROBIOL. 35, 181-195.

1425 DOMSCH, K.H. (1960) - DAS PILZSPEKTRUM EINER BODENPROBE. 3. NACHWEIS DER EINZELPILZE. ARCH.MIKROBIOL. 35, 310-339.

1426 DOMSCH, K.H. (1960) - DIE WIRKUNG VON BODENFUNGICIDEN. 4. VERAENDERUNGEN IM SPEKTRUM DER BODENPILZE. Z.PFLKRANKH.PFLSCHUTZ 67, 129-150.

1427 DOMSCH, K.H. (1963) - DER EINFLUSS SAPROPHYTISCHER BODENPILZE AUF DIE JU-GENDENTWICKLUNG HOEHERER PFLANZEN. Z.PFLKRANKH.PFLSCHUTZ 70, 470-475.

1428 DOMSCH, K.H. (1975) - DISTRIBUTION OF SOIL FUNGI. PROC. 1ST INTERSECT. CONGR.IAMS, JAPAN 2, 340-353.

1429   DOMSCH, K.H. & BANSE, H.-J. (1972) - MYKOLOGISCHE UNTERSUCHUNGEN AN REGEN-
       WURMEXKREMENTEN. SOIL BIOL.BIOCHEM. 4, 31-38.

1430   DOMSCH, K.H. & GAMS, W. (1968) - DIE BEDEUTUNG·VORFRUCHTABHAENGIGER VER-
       SCHIEBUNGEN IN DER BODENMIKROFLORA. 1. DER EINFLUSS VON BODENPILZEN AUF
       DIE WURZELENTWICKLUNG VON WEIZEN, ERBSEN UND RAPS. PHYTOPATH.Z. 63, 64-
       74.

1431   DOMSCH, K.H. & GAMS, W. (1968) - DIE BEDEUTUNG VORFRUCHTABHAENGIGER VER-
       SCHIEBUNGEN IN DER BODENMIKROFLORA. 2. ANTAGONISTISCHE EINFLUESSE AUF
       PATHOGENE BODENPILZE. PHYTOPATH.Z. 63, 165-176.

1432   DOMSCH, K.H. & GAMS, W. (1969) - VARIABILITY AND POTENTIAL OF A SOIL FUN-
       GUS POPULATION TO DECOMPOSE PECTIN, XYLAN AND CARBOXYMETHYL-CELLULOSE.
       SOIL BIOL.BIOCHEM. 1, 29-36.

1433   DOMSCH, K.H., GAMS, W. & WEBER, E. (1968) - DER EINFLUSS VERSCHIEDENER VOR-
       FRUECHTE AUF DAS BODENPILZSPEKTRUM IN WEIZENFELDERN. Z.PFLERNAEHR.DUENG.
       BODENK. 119, 134-149.

1434   DOMSCH, K.H. & SCHWINN, F.J. (1965) - NACHWEIS UND ISOLIERUNG VON PFLAN-
       ZENPATHOGENEN BODENPILZEN MIT SELEKTIVEN VERFAHREN. ZENTBL.BAKT.PARA-
       SITKDE, ABT.1, SUPPL.1, 461-485.

1435   DONE, J., MORTIMER, P.H. & TAYLOR, A. (1961) - THE PRODUCTION OF SPORI-
       DESMIN AND SPORIDESMOLIDES BY PITHOMYCES CHARTARUM. J.GEN.MICROBIOL. 26,
       207-222.

1436   DOOLEY, M. (1970) - THE MICROBIOLOGY OF CUT-AWAY PEAT. 4. AUTECOLOGICAL
       STUDIES. PL.SOIL 33, 145-160.

1437   DOOLEY, M. & DICKINSON, C.H. (1970) - THE MICROBIOLOGY OF CUT-AWAY PEAT.
       2. THE ECOLOGY OF FUNGI IN CERTAIN HABITATS. PL.SOIL 32, 454-467.

1438   DOOLEY, M. & DICKINSON, C.H. (1971) - THE ECOLOGY OF FUNGI IN PEAT. IR.J.
       AGRIC.RES. 10, 195-206.

1439   DORENBOSCH, M.J. (1970) - KEY TO NINE UBIQUITOUS PHOMA-LIKE FUNGI. PERSOO-
       NIA 6, 1-14.

1440   DORN, F. & ARIGONI, D. (1974) - EIN BICYCLISCHER ABKOEMMLING VON (-)-LON-
       GIFOLEN AUS HELMINTHOSPORIUM SATIVUM UND H. VICTORIAE. EXPERIENTIA 30,
       851-852.

1441   DORN, F. & ARIGONI, D. (1975) - ZWEI NEUE SESQUITERPENE MIT ISOSATIVANGE-
       RUEST AUS HELMINTHOSPORIUM SATIVUM. EXPERIENTIA 31, 753-754.

1442   DORN, M. (1955) - UNTERSUCHUNGEN UEBER DAS AUFTRETEN VON SEKTOREN IN PILZ-
       KOLONIEN (INSBESONDERE BEI ALTERNARIA TENUIS). ARCH.MIKROBIOL. 21, 310-
       328.

1443   DOSSENA, A., MARCHELLI, R. & POCHINI, A. (1973) - NEOECHINULINE-D, A NEW
       ISOPRENYLATE DEHYDROTRYPTOPHYL METABOLITE FROM ASPERGILLUS AMSTELODAMI.
       EXPERIENTIA 31, 1249.

1444   DOUPNIK, B. & FECKHAM, J.C. (1970) - MYCOTOXICITY OF ASPERGILLUS OCHRACEUS
       TO CHICKS. APPL.MICROBIOL. 19, 594-597.

1445   DOWDING, P. & ROYLE, M.C.I. (1972) - UPTAKE AND PARTITIONING OF NITRATE
       AND PHOSPHATE BY CULTURES OF BOTRYTIS CINEREA. TRANS.BR.MYCOL.SOC. 59,
       193-203.

1446 DOWDING, P. & WIDDEN, P. (1974) - SOME RELATIONSHIPS BETWEEN FUNGI AND
THEIR ENVIRONMENT IN TUNDRA REGIONS. IN: SOIL ORGANISMS AND DECOMPOSI-
TION IN TUNDRA; HOLDING, A.J. ET AL. (ED), TUNDRA BIOME STEERING COM-
MITTEE (STOCKHOLM), 123-150.

1447 DOWNES, M.J. (1972) - OBSERVATIONS ON SOME FUSARIUM POPULATION IN CO. DO-
NEGAL OAT SOILS. SCIENT.PROC.R.DUBL.SOC., SER.B, 3, 127-135.

1448 DOWNES, M.J. & LOUGHNANE, J.B. (1965) - A BAITING MATERIAL FOR THE ISOLA-
TION OF RHIZOCTONIA SOLANI FROM SOIL. EUR.POTATO J. 8, 190.

1449 DOWNES, M.J. & LOUGHNANE, J.B. (1967) - THE BEHAVIOUR AND PERSISTENCE OF
RHIZOCTONIA SOLANI IN IRISH SOILS. SCIENT.PROC.R.DUBL.SOC., SER.B, 2,
67-73.

1450 DOWNING, M.H. (1953) - BOTRYOTRICHUM AND COCCOSPORA. MYCOLOGIA 45, 934-940.

1451 DOWNS, S.C., MCCALLA, T.M. & HASKINS, F.A. (1955) - STACHYBOTRYS ATRA, AN
EFFECTIVE AGGREGATOR OF PEORIAN LOESS. PROC.SOIL SCI.SOC.AM. 19, 179-
181.

1452 DOX, A.W. & NEIDIG, R.E. (1914) - THE SOLUBLE POLYSACCHARIDES OF LOWER
FUNGI. 1. MYCO-DEXTRAN, A NEW POLYSACCHARIDE IN PENICILLIUM EXPANSUM.
J.BIOL.CHEM. 18, 167-175.

1453 DOXTADER, K.G. & ALEXANDER, M. (1966) - NITRIFICATION BY GROWING AND RE-
PLACEMENT CULTURES OF ASPERGILLUS. CAN.J.MICROBIOL. 12, 807-815.

1454 DOXTADER, K.G. & ALEXANDER, M. (1966) - ROLE OF 3-NITROPROPANOIC ACID IN
NITRATE FORMATION BY ASPERGILLUS FLAVUS. J.BACT. 91, 1186-1191.

1455 DOXTADER, K.G. & ROVIRA, A.D. (1968) - NITRIFICATION BY ASPERGILLUS FLAVUS
IN STERILIZED SOIL. AUST.J.SOIL RES. 6, 141-147.

1456 DRABKIN, B.S. & JOFFE, A.Z. (1952) - (PROTISTOCIDAL ACTIVITY OF SOME
MOULDS). MIKROBIOLOGIYA 21, 700-704.

1457 DRECHSLER, C. (1934) - ORGANS OF CAPTURE IN SOME FUNGI PREYING ON NEMATO-
DES. MYCOLOGIA 26, 135-144.

1458 DRECHSLER, C. (1937) - SOME HYPHOMYCETES THAT PREY ON FREE-LIVING TERRICO-
LOUS NEMATODES. MYCOLOGIA 29, 447-552.

1459 DRECHSLER, C. (1940) - THREE SPECIES OF PYTHIUM ASSOCIATED WITH ROOT ROTS.
PHYTOPATHOLOGY 30, 189-213.

1460 DRECHSLER, C. (1944) - THREE HYPHOMYCETES THAT CAPTURE NEMATODES IN ADHE-
SIVE NETWORKS. MYCOLOGIA 36, 138-171.

1461 DRECHSLER, C. (1946) - SEVERAL SPECIES OF PYTHIUM PECULIAR IN THEIR SEXUAL
DEVELOPMENT. PHYTOPATHOLOGY 36, 781-864.

1462 DRECHSLER, C. (1952) - WIDESPREAD DISTRIBUTION OF DELACROIXIA CORONATA AND
OTHER SAPROPHYTIC ENTOMOPHTHORACEAE IN PLANT DETRITUS. SCIENCE, N.Y.
115, 575-576.

1463 DRECHSLER, C. (1952) - PRODUCTION OF ZOOSPORES FROM GERMINATING OOSPORES
OF PYTHIUM ULTIMUM AND PYTHIUM DEBARYANUM. BULL.TORREY BOT.CLUB. 79,
431-450.

1464 DRECHSLER, C. (1953) - DEVELOPMENT OF PYTHIUM DEBARYANUM ON WET SUBSTRA-
TUM. J.WASH.ACAD.SCI. 43, 213-225.

1465 DRECHSLER, C. (1960) - A PYTHIUM CAUSING STEM ROT OF TOBACCO IN NICARAGUA
      AND INDONESIA. SYDOWIA 14, 4-20.

1466 DRECHSLER, C. (1960) - TWO ROOT ROT FUNGI CLOSELY RELATED TO PYTHIUM UL-
      TIMUM. SYDOWIA 14, 106-115.

1467 DRECHSLER, C. (1962) - TWO ADDITIONAL SPECIES OF DACTYLELLA PARASITIC ON
      PYTHIUM OOSPORES. SYDOWIA 15, 92-97.

1468 DRECHSLER, C. (1963) - A SLENDER-SPORED DACTYLELLA PARASITIC ON PYTHIUM
      OOSPORES. PHYTOPATHOLOGY 53, 1050-1052.

1469 DREYFUSS, M. (1976) - TAXONOMISCHE UNTERSUCHUNGEN INNERHALB DER GATTUNG
      CHAETOMIUM. SYDOWIA 28, 50-132.

1470 DROUHET, E. & MARIAT, F. (1952) - ETUDE DES FACTEURS DETERMINANT LE DE-
      VELOPPEMENT DE LA PHASE LEVURE DE SPOROTRICHUM SCHENCKII. ANNLS INST.
      PASTEUR, PARIS 83, 506-514.

1471 D'SILVA, T.D.J. & HERRETT, R.A. (1971) - NEW FURANOID METABOLITES FROM
      RHIZOCTONIA SOLANI. EXPERIENTIA 27, 1143-1144.

1472 DUBE, A.J., DODMAN, R.L. & FLENTJE, N.T. (1971) - THE INFLUENCE OF WATER
      ACTIVITY ON THE GROWTH OF RHIZOCTONIA SOLANI. AUST.J.BIOL.SCI. 24, 57-
      65.

1473 DUBE, H.C. & BILGRAMI, K.S. (1966) - PESTALOTIA OR PESTALOTIOPSIS. MYCO-
      PATH.MYCOL.APPL. 29, 33-54.

1474 DUBERNET, M. & RIBEREAU-GAYON, P. (1973) - LES PHENOLOXIDASES DU RAISIN
      SAIN ET DU RAISIN PARASITE PAR BOTRYTIS CINEREA. C.R.HEBD.SEANC.ACAD.
      SCI., PARIS, SER.D, 277, 975-978.

1475 DUBOST, D. (1966/69) - LES CHAMPIGNONS DES SOLS SALES DE L'OUEST ALGERIEN.
      2. TOLERANCE AU CLNA. BULL.SOC.HIST.NATUR.AFR.NORD 57, 130-144.

1476 DUBOUCHET, J., MOREAU, M., MOROT-GAUDRY, J.-F. & PUGIN, A. (1971) - ACTI-
      VITE AUXINOLYTIQUE DU PHIALOPHORA CINERESCENS (WR.) VAN BEYMA. C.R.HEBD.
      SEANC.ACAD.SCI., PARIS, SER.D, 272, 1857-1860.

1477 DUCHE, J. & HEIM, R. (1931) - RECHERCHES SUR LA FLORE MYCOLOGIQUE DES SOLS
      SABLEUX. 1. MICROMYCETES DES DUNES LITTORALES DE BIVILLE-VAUVILLE (CO-
      TENTIN). TRAV.CRYPTOGAM.PARIS, 431-458.

1478 DUCKWORTH, R.B. & HARRIS, G.C. (1950) - THE MORPHOLOGY OF PENICILLIUM CHRY-
      SOGENUM IN SUBMERGED FERMENTATIONS. TRANS.BR.MYCOL.SOC. 32, 224-236.

1479 DUDDINGTON, C.L. (1951) - FURTHER RECORDS OF BRITISH PREDACIOUS FUNGI. 2.
      TRANS.BR.MYCOL.SOC. 34, 194-209.

1480 DUDDINGTON, C.L. (1951) - THE ECOLOGY OF PREDACIOUS FUNGI. 1. PRELIMINARY
      SURVEY. TRANS.BR.MYCOL.SOC. 34, 322-331.

1481 DUDDINGTON, C.L. (1954) - NEMATODE-DESTROYING FUNGI IN AGRICULTURAL SOIL.
      NATURE, LOND. 173, 500-501.

1482 DUDKA, I.A. (1966) - (COMPOSITION OF THE MYCOFLORA OF POLLUTED BASINS IN
      THE VICINITY OF KIEV). UKR.BOT.ZH. 23 (1), 71-74.

1483 DUDKA, I.A. (1966) - (AQUATIC HYPHOMYCETES OF THE SOUTHERN PART OF THE
      WOODLAND IN THE KIEV REGION). UKR.BOT.ZH. 51, 562-566.

1484 DUDKA, I.A. (1968) - (AQUATIC MONILIALES OF NORTH-EASTERN ESTONIA). IZV. AKAD.NAUK ESTON.SSR, SER.BIOL.NAUK 17, 394-403.

1485 DUDKA, I.A. (1974) - VODN GYFOMYTSETY UKRAINY. NAUKOVA DUMKA, KIEV, 240 PP.

1486 DUDKA, I.A. & ISACHENKO, A.A. (1975) - (CULTURAL CHARACTERISTICS OF AQUA- TIC HYPHOMYCETES. 1. COMPARATIVE CHARACTERISTIC). UKR.BOT.ZH. 32, 431- 439.

1487 DUDKA, I.A. & PARSHIKOV, V.N. (1975) - (FATTY ACID COMPOSITION OF TOTAL LIPIDS OF AQUATIC HYPHOMYCETES UNDER ARTIFICIAL CULTIVATION CONDITIONS). MIKOL.FITOPAT. 9, 298-303.

1488 DUJARRIC DE LA RIVIERE, B.P. (1951) - POUVOIR ANTIBIOTIQUE D'UN CHAMPIGNON PROVENANT D'UNE TERRE DE TRUFFIERE. C.R.HEBD.SEANC.ACAD.SCI., PARIS, SER.D, 232, 454-455.

1489 DULANEY, E.L. (1947) - PENICILLIN PRODUCTION BY THE ASPERGILLUS NIDULANS GROUP. MYCOLOGIA 39, 582-586.

1490 DULANEY, E.L., STAPLEY, E.O. & HLAVAC, C. (1955) - HYDROXYLATION OF STER- OIDS, PRINCIPALLY PROGESTERONE, BY A STRAIN OF ASPERGILLUS OCHRACEUS. MYCOLOGIA 47, 464-474.

1491 DUNCAN, B. (1973) - NUTRITION AND FAT PRODUCTION IN SUBMERGED CULTURES OF A STRAIN OF PENICILLIUM LILACINUM. MYCOLOGIA 65, 211-214.

1492 DUNCAN, B. & HERALD, SR.A.C. (1974) - SOME OBSERVATIONS ON THE ULTRASTRUC- TURE OF EPICOCCUM NIGRUM. MYCOLOGIA 66, 1028-1039.

1493 DUNCAN, B., SHAH, D.N. & HERALD, SR.A.C. (1976) - FAT PRODUCTION IN EPICOC- CUM NIGRUM. MYCOLOGIA 68, 412-418.

1494 DUNCAN, C.G. (1960) - WOOD-ATTACKING CAPACITIES AND PHYSIOLOGY OF SOFT-ROT FUNGI. REP.U.S.DEP.AGRIC., FOR.PROD.LAB., MADISON, NO. 2173.

1495 DUNCAN, C.G. (1965) - DETERMINING RESISTANCE TO SOFT-ROT FUNGI. RES.PAP. U.S.FOR.SERV., FPL 48.

1496 DUNCAN, C.G. & ESLYN, W.E. (1966) - WOOD-DECAYING ASCOMYCETES AND FUNGI IM- PERFECTI. MYCOLOGIA 58, 642-645.

1497 DUNN, E. & HUGHES, W.A. (1964) - INTERRELATIONSHIP OF THE POTATO ROOT EEL- WORM, HETERODERA ROSTOCHIENSIS, RHIZOCTONIA SOLANI AND COLLETOTRICHUM ATRAMENTARIUM, ON THE GROWTH OF TOMATO PLANT. NATURE, LOND. 201, 413- 414.

1498 DUNN, G., NEWBOLD, G.T. & SPRING, F.S. (1949) - SYNTHESIS OF FLAVACOL, A NEW METABOLIC PRODUCT OF ASPERGILLUS FLAVUS. J.CHEM.SOC., 1949, 2586- 2587.

1499 DUNN, P.H. & MECHALAS, B.J. (1963) - THE POTENTIAL OF BEAUVERIA BASSIANA AS A MICROBIAL INSECTICIDE. J.INSECT PATH. 5, 451-459.

1500 DUPONT, P.F. & HEDRICK, L.R. (1971) - DEOXYRIBONUCLEIC ACID BASE COMPOSI- TION AND NUMERICAL TAXONOMY OF YEASTS IN THE GENUS TRICHOSPORON. J.GEN. MICROBIOL. 66, 349-359.

1501 DURAN, F., ROBERBSTAD, G.W. & DONOWHO, E. (1973) - THE DISTRIBUTION OF COC- CIDIOIDES IMMITIS IN THE SOIL IN EL PASO, TEXAS. SABOURAUDIA 11, 143- 148.

1502   DURBIN, R.D. (1955) - STRAIGTH-LINE FUNCTION OF GROWTH OF MICRO-ORGANISMS
       AT TOXIC LEVELS OF CARBON DIOXIDE. SCIENCE, N.Y. 121, 734-735.

1503   DURBIN, R.D. (1959) - SOME EFFECTS OF LIGTH ON THE GROWTH AND MORPHOLOGY
       OF RHIZOCTONIA SOLANI. PHYTOPATHOLOGY 49, 59-60.

1504   DURBIN, R.D. (1959) - FACTORS AFFECTING THE VERTICAL DISTRIBUTION OF RHI-
       ZOCTONIA SOLANI WITH SPECIAL REFERENCE TO CO2 CONCENTRATION. AM.J.BOT.
       46, 22-25.

1505   DURBIN, R.D. & UCHYTIL, T.F. (1971) - PURIFICATION AND PROPERTIES OF ALLI-
       IN LYASE FROM THE FUNGUS PENICILLIUM CORYMBIFERUM. BIOCHIM.BIOPHYS.ACTA
       229, 518-520.

1506   DURIE, E.B. & FREY, D. (1957) - A NEW SPECIES OF TRICHOPHYTON FROM NEW
       SOUTH WALES. MYCOLOGIA 49, 401-411.

1507   DURIEZ, T., WALBAUM, S., TAILLIEZ, R. & BIGUET, J. (1976) - ETUDE ENZYMO-
       LOGIQUE COMPAREE DE SOUCHES DE ASPERGILLUS FUMIGATUS ET DE A. FISCHERI
       D'ORIGINE SAPROPHYTIQUE OU ISOLEES DE LESIONS HUMAINES OU ANIMALES.
       REPERCUSSIONS PRATIQUES D'ORDRE DIAGNOSTIQUE. MYCOPATHOLOGIA 59, 81-90.

1508   DURLEY, R.C., MACMILLAN, J. & SIMPSON, T.J. (1975) - FUNGAL PRODUCTS. 13.
       XANTHOMEGNIN, VIOMELLIN, RUBROSULPHIN AND VIOPURPURIN, PIGMENTS FROM
       ASPERGILLUS SULPHUREUS AND ASPERGILLUS MELLEUS. J.CHEM.SOC.PERKIN TRANS.
       I, 1975 (2), 163-169.

1509   DURRELL, L.W. (1959) - SOME STUDIES OF EMERICELLOPSIS. MYCOLOGIA 51, 31-
       43.

1510   DURRELL, L.W. (1968) - STUDIES OF AUREOBASIDIUM PULLULANS (DE BARY) AR-
       NAUD. MYCOPATH.MYCOL.APPL. 35, 113-120.

1511   DURRELL, L.W. (1968) - HYPHAL INVASION BY TRICHODERMA VIRIDE. MYCOPATH.
       MYCOL.APPL. 35, 138-144.

1512   DURRELL, L.W. & SHIELDS, L.M. (1960) - FUNGI ISOLATED IN CULTURE FROM
       SOILS OF THE NEVADA TEST SITE. MYCOLOGIA 52, 636-641.

1513   DURYNINA, E.P. & VELIKANOV, L.L. (1974) - (EFFECT OF MINERAL NUTRITION ON
       SPRING WHEAT INFECTION BY THE FUNGUS HELMINTHOSPORIUM SATIVUM). BIOL.
       NAUKI 17, 74-80.

1514   DUTHOIT, C.M. & GODFREY, B.E.S. (1963) - EFFECT OF GREEN MANURE AND PRE-
       DACIOUS FUNGI ON CEREAL ROOT EELWORM IN OATS. PL.PATH. 12, 18-19.

1515   DU TOIT, J.J. (1968) - ROOT ROT OF YOUNG MAIZE PLANTS. THE CAUSAL FUNGI.
       S.AFR.J.AGRIC.SCI. 11, 595-604.

1516   DUTT, B.L., RAJ, S. & KISHORE, H. (1974) - RELATIONSHIP AMONG ISOLATES OF
       RHIZOCTONIA SOLANI KUEHN. MYCOPATH.MYCOL.APPL. 52, 77-84.

1517   DUTT, S. & BEDI, P.S. (1974) - EFFECT OF CARBON AND NITROGEN NUTRITION ON
       THE GROWTH AND SPORULATION OF HELMINTHOSPORIUM SPICIFERUM. INDIAN J.MY-
       COL.PL.PATH. 4, 190-193.

1518   DUTT, S. & BEDI, P.S. (1974) - THE EFFECT OF VARIOUS FACTORS ON THE PRO-
       DUCTION OF MACERATING ENZYMES BY HELMINTHOSPORIUM SPICIFERUM IN VITRO.
       INDIAN PHYTOPATH. 27, 427.

1519 DUTTA, B.G. & GHOSH, G.R. (1964) - SOIL FUNGI FROM ORISSA (INDIA). 4. SOIL
      FUNGI OF PADDY FIELDS. MYCOPATH.MYCOL.APPL. 25, 316-322.

1520 DUTTON, M.F. & HEATHCOTE, J.G. (1966) - TWO NEW HYDROXYAFLATOXINS. BIOCHEM.
      J. 101, 21-22.

1521 DVORAK, J. & OTCENASEK, M. (1969) - MYCOLOGICAL DIAGNOSIS OF ANIMAL DERMA-
      TOPHYTOSES. ACADEMIA, PRAHA, 213 PP.

1522 DVORNIKOVA, T.P., SKRYABIN, G.K. & SUVOROV, N.N. (1970) - (ENZYMATIC TRANS-
      FORMATION OF TRYPTAMINE BY FUNGI). MIKROBIOLOGIYA 39, 42-46.

1523 DWIVEDI, R. & DWIVEDI, R.S. (1972) - RHIZOSPHERE OF CORIANDER WITH EMPHA-
      SIS ON FUNGISTASIS. ANNLS INST.PASTEUR 122, 455-461.

1524 DWIVEDI, R.S. (1966) - ECOLOGY OF THE SOIL FUNGI OF SOME GRASSLANDS OF VA-
      RANASI. 2. DISTRIBUTION OF SOIL MYCOFLORA. BULL.INT.SOC.TROP.ECOL. 7,
      84-99.

1525 DWIVEDI, R.S. & DWIVEDI, R. (1971) - ECOLOGY OF SOIL FUNGI OF A SAL FOREST
      WITH EMPHASIS ON FUNGISTASIS. PL.SOIL 34, 33-42.

1526 DWIVEDI, R.S. & GARRETT, S.D. (1968) - FUNGAL COMPETITION IN AGAR PLATE
      COLONIZATION FROM SOIL INOCULA. TRANS.BR.MYCOL.SOC. 51, 95-101.

1527 DWORSCHACK, R.G., KOEPSELL, H.J. & LAGODA, A.A. (1952) - PROTEOLYTIC EN-
      ZYMES OF MICROORGANISMS. EVALUATION OF PROTEINASES PRODUCED BY MOLDS
      OF THE ASPERGILLUS FLAVUS-ORYZAE GROUP IN SUBMERGED CULTURE. ARCHS BIO-
      CHEM.BIOPHYS. 41, 48-60.

1528 EASTWOOD, D.J. (1952) - THE FUNGUS FLORA OF COMPOSTS. TRANS.BR.MYCOL.SOC.
      35, 215-220.

1529 EATON, E.D. & KING, C.J. (1934) - A STUDY OF THE COTTON ROOT-ROT FUNGUS
      (PHYMATOTRICHUM OMNIVORUM) IN THE SOIL BY THE CHOLODNY METHOD. J.AGRIC.
      RES. 49, 1109-1113.

1530 EATON, E.D. & RIGLER, N.E. (1946) - INFLUENCE OF CARBOHYDRATE LEVELS AND
      ROOT-SURFACE MICROFLORAS ON PHYMATOTRICHUM ROOT ROT IN COTTON AND MAIZE
      PLANTS. J.AGRIC.RES. 72, 137-161.

1531 EBBEN, M.H. & WILLIAMS, P.H. (1956) - BROWN ROOT ROT OF TOMATOES. 1. THE
      ASSOCIATED FUNGAL FLORA. ANN.APPL.BIOL. 44, 425-436.

1532 EBERLE-HAEGI, R.-M. (1966) - UEBER DIE BILDUNG VON FERRICHRYSIN, EINEM SI-
      DERAMIN AUS ASPERGILLUS MELLEUS, UND IHRE VERKNUEPFUNG MIT DEM INTERME-
      DIAERSTOFFWECHSEL. BER.SCHWEIZ.BOT.GES. 76, 279-306.

1533 EBERSOLE, R.C., GODTFREDSEN, W.O., VANGEDAL, S. & CASPI, E. (1973) - MECH-
      ANISM OF OXIDATIVE CYCLIZATION OF SQUALENE. EVIDENCE FOR CYCLIZATION OF
      SQUALENE FROM EITHER END OF THE SQUALENE MOLECULE IN THE IN VIVO BIO-
      SYNTHESIS OF FUSIDIC ACID BY FUSIDIUM COCCINEUM. J.AM.CHEM.SOC. 95,
      8133-8140.

1534 EBERSOLE, R.C., GODTFREDSEN, W.O., VANGEDAL, S. & CASPI, E. (1974) - MECH-
      ANISM OF OXIDATIVE CYCLIZATION OF SQUALENE. CONCERNING THE MODE OF FOR-
      MATION OF THE 17(20)DOUBLE BOND IN THE BIOSYNTHESIS OF FUSIDIC ACID BY
      FUSIDIUM COCCINEUM. J.AM.CHEM.SOC. 96, 6499-6507.

1535 EBERT, E. & ZENK, M.H. (1966) - UNTERSUCHUNGEN ZUR STRUKTUR UND BIOGENESE
      DES SAUREN POLYSACCHARIDS VON PENICILLIUM ISLANDICUM (ISLANDSAEURE).
      ARCH.MIKROBIOL. 54, 276-296.

1536   EBNER, U. (1968) - WECHSELWIRKUNGEN ZWISCHEN ASPERGILLACEEN UND KULTUR-
       PFLANZEN IN MISCHKULTUR. BER.SCHWEIZ.BOT.GES. 78, 66-94.

1537   ECHANDI, E. & WALKER, J.C. (1957) - PECTOLYTIC ENZYMES PRODUCED BY SCLERO-
       TINIA SCLEROTIORUM. PHYTOPATHOLOGY 47, 303-306.

1538   ECKBLAD, F.-E. & TORKELSEN, A.-E. (1974) - CONTRIBUTIONS TO THE HYPOCREA-
       CEAE AND FUNGICOLOUS NECTRIACEAE OF NORWAY. NORW.J.BOT. 21, 5-15.

1539   ECKERT, J.W., RAHM, M.L. & HALL, G. (1968) - NEUTRAL CARBOHYDRATES OF CO-
       NIDIA OF PENICILLIUM DIGITATUM. PHYTOPATHOLOGY 58, 1406-1411.

1540   ECKERT, J.W. & TSAO, P.H. (1962) - A SELECTIVE MEDIUM FOR ISOLATION OF PHY-
       TOPHTHORA AND PYTHIUM FROM PLANT ROOTS. PHYTOPATHOLOGY 52, 771-777.

1541   EDGINGTON, L.V., KHEW, K.L. & BARRON, G.L. (1971) - FUNGITOXIC SPECTRUM OF
       BENZIMIDAZOLE COMPOUNDS. PHYTOPATHOLOGY 61, 42-44.

1542   EDMUNDS, J.E. (1964) - EFFECT OF TRICHODERMA VIRIDE AND FUSARIUM OXYSPORUM
       UPON INGRESS OF ALFALFA ROOTS BY PRATYLENCHUS PENETRANS. PHYTOPATHOLOGY
       54, 892 (ABS.).

1543   EDMUNDS, J.E. (1966) - NEMATODE-FUNGUS INTERACTIONS WITH ALFALFA ROOTS
       WITH SPECIAL REFERENCE TO PRATYLENCHUS PENETRANS, FUSARIUM OXYSPORUM
       AND TRICHODERMA VIRIDE. DISS.ABSTR. 26, 5637-5638.

1544   EDWARDS, L.B., ACQUAVIVA, F.A. & LIVESAY, T. (1973) - FURTHER OBSERVATIONS
       ON HISTOPLASMIN SENSITIVITY IN THE UNITED STATES. AM.J.EPIDEMIOL. 98,
       315-325.

1545   EDWARDS, M.R., HAZEN, E.L. & EDWARDS, G.A. (1960) - THE MICROMORPHOLOGY OF
       THE TUBERCULATE SPORES OF HISTOPLASMA CAPSULATUM. CAN.J.MICROBIOL. 6,
       65-70.

1546   EFREMOVA, L.L., KOSTYK, F.D. & OSYPOVA, R.A. (1971) - (EXOPOLYGALACTURON-
       ASE OF THE FUNGUS RHIZOPUS ARRHIZUS FISCHER). IZV.AKAD.NAUK MOLDAV.SSR,
       SER.BIOL.NAUK 4, 36-40.

1547   EGE, O. (1965) - EIN BEITRAG ZUR BIOLOGIE EINIGER APHIDIVORER ENTOMOPHTHO-
       RACEEN. ARCH.MIKROBIOL. 52, 20-48.

1548   EGEBERG, R.O., ELCONIN, A.E. & EGEBERG, M.C. (1964) - EFFECT OF SALINITY
       AND TEMPERATURE ON COCCIDIOIDES IMMITIS AND THREE ANTAGONISTIC SOIL SAP-
       ROPHYTES. J.BACT. 88, 473-476.

1549   EGEBERG, R.O. & ELY, A.F. (1956) - COCCIDIOIDES IMMITIS IN THE SOIL OF THE
       SOUTHERN SAN JOAQUIN VALLEY. AM.J.MED.SCI. 231, 151-154.

1550   EGGINS, H.O.W. & COURSEY, D.G. (1964) - THERMOPHILIC FUNGI ASSOCIATED WITH
       NIGERIAN OIL PALM PRODUCE. NATURE, LOND. 203, 1083-1084.

1551   EGGINS, H.O.W. & MALIK, K.A. (1969) - THE OCCURRENCE OF THERMOPHILIC CELLU-
       LOLYTIC FUNGI IN PASTURE LAND SOIL. ANTONIE VAN LEEUWENHOEK 35, 178-184.

1552   EHLE, H. (1966) - EINFLUSS EINER SUPERINFEKTION MIT ANTAGONISTISCHEN ACTI-
       NOMYCETEN AUF DIE OPHIOBOLOSE IM GEFAESSVERSUCH. Z.PFLKRANKH.PFLSCHUTZ
       73, 321-326.

1553   EHLE, H. (1966) - EINFLUSS DER GRUENDUENGUNG AUF DIE ACTINOMYCETENPOPULA-
       TION DES BODENS UNTER BESONDERER BERUECKSICHTIGUNG DER GEGEN OPHIOBOLUS
       GRAMINIS WIRKSAMEN ANTAGONISTEN. Z.PFLKRANKH.PFLSCHUTZ 73, 326-334.

1554 EHRMANN, G. & THURNER, J. (1962) - HUMAN-INFEKTION MIT KERATINOMYCES AJEL-LOI. MYKOSEN 5, 63-66.

1555 EICKER, A. (1969) - MICROFUNGI FROM SURFACE SOIL OF FOREST COMMUNITIES IN ZULULAND. TRANS.BR.MYCOL.SOC. 53, 381-392.

1556 EICKER, A. (1970) - VERTICAL DISTRIBUTION OF FUNGI IN ZULULAND SOILS. TRANS.BR.MYCOL.SOC. 55, 45-57.

1557 EICKER, A. (1972) - OCCURRENCE AND ISOLATION OF SOUTH AFRICAN THERMOPHILIC FUNGI. S.AFR.J.SCI. 68, 150-155.

1558 EICKER, A. (1973) - THE MYCOFLORA OF EUCALYPTUS MACULATA LEAF LITTER. SOIL BIOL.BIOCHEM. 5, 441-448.

1559 EICKER, A. (1974) - THE MYCOFLORA OF AN ALKALINE SOIL OF THE OPEN-SAVANNAH OF THE TRANSVAAL. TRANS.BR.MYCOL.SOC. 63, 281-288.

1560 EICKER, A. (1976) - NON-PARASITIC MYCOFLORA OF THE PHYLLOPLANE AND LITTER OF PANICUM COLORATUM. TRANS.BR.MYCOL.SOC. 67, 275-281.

1561 EICKMAN, N., CLARDY, J., COLE, R.J. & KIRKSEY, J.W. (1975) - THE STRUCTURE OF FUMITREMORGIN-A. TETRAHEDRON LETTERS, 1975 (12), 1051-1054.

1562 EIJK, G.W.VAN (1975) - BOSTRYCIN, A TETRAHYDROANTHRAQUINONE PIGMENT AND SOME OTHER METABOLITES FROM THE FUNGUS ARTHRINIUM PHAEOSPERMUM. EX-PERIENTIA 31, 783-784.

1563 EIJK, G.W.VAN & ROEYMANS, H.J. (1977) - CYNODONTIN, THE TETRAHYDROXYANTHRA-QUINONE OF CURVULARIA AND DRECHSLERA SPECIES. EXPERIENTIA 33, 1283-1284.

1564 EKA, O.U. (1970) - STUDIES ON EPICOCCUM NIGRUM. 1. INFLUENCE OF ENVIRON-MENTAL FACTORS ON GROWTH AND PIGMENTATION. W.AFR.J.BIOL.APPL.CHEM. 13, 3-12.

1565 EKA, O.U. (1970) - A NOTE ON PROPERTIES OF PIGMENTS PRODUCED BY EPICOCCUM NIGRUM. EXPERIENTIA 26, 924.

1566 EKUNDAYO, J.A. (1973) - NUTRIENT REQUIREMENTS FOR PRODUCTION OF PYCNIDIA OF BOTRYODIPLODIA THEOBROMAE PAT. J.GEN.MICROBIOL. 77, 227-228.

1567 EKUNDAYO, J.A. & CARLILE, M.J. (1964) - THE GERMINATION OF SPORANGIOSPORES OF RHIZOPUS ARRHIZUS. SPORE SWELLING AND GERM-TUBE EMERGENCE. J.GEN.MI-CROBIOL. 35, 261-269.

1568 EKUNDAYO, J.A. & DANIEL, T.M. (1973) - CASSAVA ROT AND ITS CONTROL. TRANS.BR.MYCOL.SOC. 61, 27-32.

1569 EKUNDAYO, J.A. & HASKINS, R.H. (1969) - PYCNIDIUM PRODUCTION BY BOTRYODI-PLODIA THEOBROMAE. 1. THE RELATION OF LIGHT TO THE INDUCTION OF PYCNI-DIA. CAN.J.BOT. 47, 1153-1156.

1570 EL-ANI, A.S. (1974) - ALLESCHERIA BOYDII. WILD TYPE AND A VARIANT FROM HU-MAN PULMONARY ALLESCHERIASIS. MYCOLOGIA 66, 661-668.

1571 EL-ANI, A.S. (1975) - VARIATION IN VIVO AND ISOLATION OF ASPERGILLUS FU-MIGATUS FROM A CASE OF HUMAN ASPERGILLOSIS. MYCOLOGIA 67, 1114-1118.

1572 EL-ANI, A.S. & OLIVE, L.S. (1975) - GENETICS OF SORDARIA FIMICOLA. 9. LINK-AGE GROUP II. AM.J.BOT. 62, 166-171.

1573 ELAROSI, H. (1957) - FUNGAL ASSOCIATIONS. 1. SYNERGISTIC RELATION BETWEEN
      RHIZOCTONIA SOLANI AND FUSARIUM SOLANI IN CAUSING A POTATO TUBER ROT.
      ANN.BOT. 21, 555-567.

1574 ELAROSI, H. (1957) - FUNGAL ASSOCIATIONS. 2. CULTURAL STUDIES ON RHIZOCTO-
      NIA SOLANI, FUSARIUM SOLANI AND OTHER FUNGI AND THEIR INTERACTIONS. ANN.
      BOT. 21, 569-585.

1575 ELBAKYAN, M. (1970) - (A LITTLE KNOWN DISEASE OF CUCUMBER PLANTS). TRUDY
      VSES.NAUCHNO-ISSLED.INST.ZASHCH.RAST. 29, 116-120.

1576 ELCONIN, A.F., EGEBERG, R.O. & EGEBERG, M.C. (1964) - SIGNIFICANCE OF SOIL
      SALINITY ON THE ECOLOGY OF COCCIDIOIDES IMMITIS. J.BACT. 87, 500-503.

1577 ELIASON, E.J. (1928) - COMPARATIVE VIRULENCE OF CERTAIN STRAINS OF PYTHIUM
      IN DIRECT INOCULATION OF CONIFERS. PHYTOPATHOLOGY 18, 361-367.

1578 ELINOV, N.P. & MATVEEVA, A.K. (1972) - (EXTRACELLULAR GLUCAN PRODUCED BY
      A. PULLULANS). BIOKHIMIYA 37, 256-257.

1579 ELKAN, E. & PHILPOT, C.M. (1973) - MYCOTIC INFECTIONS IN FROGS DUE TO A
      PHIALOPHORA-LIKE FUNGUS. SABOURAUDIA 11, 99-105.

1580 EL-KERSH, T.A., TOAMA, M.A. & EL-AZIZ, M. (1973) - CELLULASE PRODUCTION BY
      PHOMA GLOMERATA AND RHIZOCTONIA SOLANI. 1. OPTIMAL CONDITIONS FOR THE
      PRODUCTION OF THE ENZYME. CHEM.MIKROBIOL.TECHNOL.LEBENSM. 2, 102-106.

1581 ELLIOTT, C.G. (1972) - STEROLS AND THE PRODUCTION OF OOSPORES BY PHY-
      TOPHTHORA CACTORUM. J.GEN.MICROBIOL. 72, 321-327.

1582 ELLIOTT, C.G. (1972) - CALCIUM CHLORIDE AND GROWTH AND REPRODUCTION OF PHY-
      TOPHTHORA CACTORUM. TRANS.BR.MYCOL.SOC. 58, 169-172.

1583 ELLIOTT, C.G. & KNIGHTS, B.A. (1974) - UPTAKE AND METABOLISM OF CHOLESTEROL
      AND CHOLESTERYL OLEATE BY PHYTOPHTHORA CACTORUM. BIOCHIM.BIOPHYS.ACTA
      360, 78-87.

1584 ELLIOTT, C.G. & MACINTYRE, D. (1973) - GENETICAL EVIDENCE ON THE LIFE-HIS-
      TORY OF PHYTOPHTHORA. TRANS.BR.MYCOL.SOC. 60, 311-316.

1585 ELLIS, D.H. (1978) - FINE STRUCTURE OF CONIDIA IN TRICHOCLADIUM OPACUM
      (SYN. TORULA ALLII). TRANS.BR.MYCOL.SOC. 70, 67-71.

1586 ELLIS, D.H. (1978) - FINE STRUCTURE OF SPORE GERMINATION IN EPICOCCUM PUR-
      PURASCENS. TRANS.BR.MYCOL.SOC. 70, 170-173.

1587 ELLIS, D.H. & GRIFFITHS, D.A. (1974) - THE LOCATION AND ANALYSIS OF MELA-
      NIN IN THE CELL WALLS OF SOME SOIL FUNGI. CAN.J.MICROBIOL. 20, 1379-
      1386.

1588 ELLIS, D.H. & GRIFFITHS, D.A. (1975) - THE FINE STRUCTURE OF CONIDIAL DE-
      VELOPMENT IN THE GENUS TORULA. 1. T. HERBARUM (PERS.) LINK EX S.F. GRAY
      AND T. HERBARUM F. QUATERNELLA SACC. CAN.J.MICROBIOL. 20, 1661-1675.

1589 ELLIS, E.A. (1977) - ULTRASTRUCTURE OF VEGETATIVE HYPHAE OF THE THERMO-
      PHILE MUCOR PUSILLUS AT ITS CARDINAL TEMPERATURES. ABS.2ND INT.MYCOL.
      CONGR., TAMPA, 1977.

1590 ELLIS, J.J. (1956) - A NOTE ON EPICOCCUM. PROC.IOWA ACAD.SCI. 63, 307-310.

1591 ELLIS, J.J., BULLA, L.A., JULIAN, G. & HESSELTINE, C.W. (1970) - SCANNING
      ELECTRON MICROSCOPY OF FUNGAL AND BACTERIAL SPORES. PROC.3RD A.SCANNING
      EL.MICR.SYMPOS., IIT RES.INST., CHICAGO, 145-152.

1592   ELLIS, J.J. & HESSELTINE, C.W. (1965) - THE GENUS ABSIDIA - GLOBOSE-SPORED
        SPECIES. MYCOLOGIA 57, 222-235.

1593   ELLIS, J.J., RHODES, L.J. & HESSELTINE, C.W. (1976) - THE GENUS AMYLOMYCES.
        MYCOLOGIA 68, 131-143.

1594   ELLIS, J.J., WANG, H.L. & HESSELTINE, C.W. (1974) - RHIZOPUS AND CHLAMYDO-
        MUCOR STRAINS SURVEYED FOR MILK-CLOTTING, AMYLOLYTIC AND ANTIBIOTIC AC-
        TIVITIES. MYCOLOGIA 66, 593-599.

1595   ELLIS, J.J. & YATES, S.G. (1971) - MYCOTOXINS OF FUNGI FROM FESCUE. ECON.
        BOT. 25, 1-5.

1596   ELLIS, L.F. & KLEINSCHMIDT, W.J. (1967) - VIRUS-LIKE PARTICLES OF FRACTION
        OF STATOLON, A MOULD PRODUCT. NATURE, LOND. 215, 649-650.

1597   ELLIS, M. (1931) - SOME EXPERIMENTAL STUDIES ON PLEOSPORA HERBARUM (PERS.)
        RABENH. TRANS.BR.MYCOL.SOC. 16, 102-114.

1598   ELLIS, M. (1940) - SOME FUNGI ISOLATED FROM PINEWOOD SOIL. TRANS.BR.MYCOL.
        SOC. 24, 87-97.

1599   ELLIS, M.A., ILYAS, M.B. & SINCLAIR, J.B. (1974) - EFFECT OF CULTIVAR AND
        GROWING REGION ON INTERNALLY SEEDBORNE FUNGI AND ASPERGILLUS MELLEUS
        PATHOGENICITY IN SOYBEAN. PL.DIS.REPTR 58, 332-334.

1600   ELLIS, M.B. (1960) - DEMATIACEOUS HYPHOMYCETES. 1. MYCOL.PAP. 76, 1-36.

1601   ELLIS, M.B. (1965) - DEMATIACEOUS HYPHOMYCETES. 6. MYCOL.PAP. 103, 1-46.

1602   ELLIS, M.B. (1966) - DEMATIACEOUS HYPHOMYCETES. 7. CURVULARIA, BRACHYSPO-
        RIUM, ETC. MYCOL.PAP. 106, 1-57.

1603   ELLIS, M.B. (1971) - DEMATIACEOUS HYPHOMYCETES. COMMONW.MYCOL.INST. 608 PP.

1604   ELLIS, M.B. (1976) - MORE DEMATIACEOUS HYPHOMYCETES. COMMONW.MYCOL.INST.
        507 PP.

1605   ELLIS, M.B., ELLIS, E.A. & ELLIS, J.P. (1951) - BRITISH MARSH AND FEN FUN-
        GI. 2. TRANS.BR.MYCOL.SOC. 34, 497-514.

1606   ELLIS, T.T., REYNOLDS, D.R. & ALEXOPOULOS, C.J. (1973) - HUELLE CELL DEVEL-
        OPMENT IN EMERICELLA NIDULANS. MYCOLOGIA 65, 1028-1035.

1607   EL-REFAI, A.-M., SALLAM, L.A.R. & EL-KADY, I.A.R. (1974) - BIOCHEMICAL AS-
        PECTS OF 17ALPHA-HYDROXYLATION OF PROGESTERONE WITH TRICHOTHECIUM ROSE-
        UM. J.GEN.APPL.MICROBIOL., TOKYO 20, 129-135.

1608   EL-REFAI, A.-M., SALLAM, L.A.R. & NAIM, N. (1970) - THE ALKALOIDS OF FUN-
        GI. 5. STUDIES ON THE BIOSYNTHESIS OF ALKALOIDS IN GEOTRICHUM CANDIDUM.
        PAKIST.J.BIOCHEM. 3, 8-13.

1609   EL-REFAI, A.-M., SALLAM, L.A.R. & NAIM, N. (1970) - THE ALKALOIDS OF FUN-
        GI. 1. THE FORMATION OF ERGOLINE ALKALOIDS BY REPRESENTATIVE MOLD FUNGI.
        JAPAN.J.MICROBIOL. 14, 91-97.

1610   EL-REFAI, A.-M., SALLAM, L.A.R. & NAIM, N. (1974) - TRANSFORMATION OF COR-
        TISOL WITH REPRESENTATIVE FUNGI. J.GEN.APPL.MICROBIOL., TOKYO 20, 111-
        115.

1611 ELSWORTHY, G.C., HOLKER, J.S.E., MCKEOWN, J.M., ROBINSON, J.B. & MULHEIRN, L.J. (1970) - THE BIOSYNTHESIS OF THE AFLATOXINS. CHEM.COMMUN., 1970, 1069-1070.

1612 EL-TOBSHY, Z.M. & SINCLAIR, J.B. (1965) - GEOTRICHUM CANDIDUM - PLANT AND ANIMAL ISOLATES PATHOGENIC TO CERTAIN PLANT TISSUES. PHYTOPATHOLOGY 55, 1210-1212.

1613 EL ZORGANI, G.A. & OMER, M.E.H. (1974) - METABOLISM OF ENDOSULFAN ISOMERS BY ASPERGILLUS NIGER. BULL.ENVIRON.CONTAM.TOXICOL. 12, 182-185.

1614 EMDEN, J.H.VAN (1971) - THE SOIL AS A SOURCE OF HYPHOMYCETES AND SOME OTHER FUNGI READILY ISOLATED BY PLATING OUT WASHED SOIL PARTICLES. PAPER PRESENTED AT 1ST INT.MYCOL.CONGR., EXETER (MIMEOGRAPHED).

1615 EMDEN, J.H.VAN (1972) - SOIL MYCOFLORA IN RELATION TO SOME CROP-PLANTS. EPPO BULL. 7, 17-26.

1616 EMDEN, J.H.VAN, TICHELAAR, G.M. & VEENBAAS-RIJKS, J.W. (1969) - ONDERZOEK NAAR DE RHIZOSFEER MYCOFLORA VAN DIVERSE GEWASSEN EN ONKRUIDEN IN VERBAND MET DE MOGELIJKHEID VAN HARMONISCHE BESTRIJDING VAN PLANTE-PARASITAIRE BODEMSCHIMMELS. JVERSL.INST.PLZIEKTENK.ONDERZ. 45-49.

1617 EMDEN, J.H.VAN, TICHELAAR, G.M. & VEENBAAS-RIJKS, J.W. (1972) - ONDERZOEK NAAR DE RHIZOSFEER MYCOFLORA VAN DIVERSE GEWASSEN EN ONKRUIDEN IN VERBAND MET DE MOGELIJKHEID VAN HARMONISCHE BESTRIJDING VAN PARASITAIRE BODENSCHIMMELS. JVERSL.INST.PLZIEKTENK.ONDERZ. 43-53.

1618 EMEH, C.O. & MARTH, E.H. (1977) - YIELDS OF RUBRATOXIN FROM PENICILLIUM RUBRUM. TRANS.BR.MYCOL.SOC. 68, 112-115.

1619 EMMATTY, D.A. & GREEN, R.J. (1969) - FUNGISTASIS AND THE BEHAVIOR OF THE MICROSCLEROTIA OF VERTICILLIUM ALBO-ATRUM IN SOIL. PHYTOPATHOLOGY 59, 1590-1595.

1620 EMMENEGGER, T. (1954) - VERGLFICHENDE UNTERSUCHUNGEN UEBER DAS BILDUNGSVERMOEGEN VERSCHIEDENER ARTEN VON ASPERGILLUS FUER LACTOFLAVIN. BER.SCHWEIZ. BOT.GES. 64, 453-487.

1621 EMMONS, C.W. (1944) - ALLESCHERIA BOYDII AND MONOSPORIUM APIOSPERMUM. MYCOLOGIA 36, 188-193.

1622 EMMONS, C.W. (1949) - ISOLATION OF HISTOPLASMA CAPSULATUM FROM SOIL. U.S. PUBL.HLTH REP. 64, 892-896.

1623 EMMONS, C.W. (1966) - PATHOGENIC DEMATIACEOUS FUNGI. JAPAN J.MED.MYCOL. 7, 233-245.

1624 EMMONS, C.W., BINFORD, CH.H., UTZ, J.P. & KWON-CHNUNG, K.J. (1977) - MEDICAL MYCOLOGY. LEA & FEBIGER, PHILADELPHIA, 3RD ED. 592 PP.

1625 EMMONS, C.W. & BRIDGES, C.H. (1961) - ENTOMOPHTHORA CORONATA, THE ETIOLOGIC AGENT OF A PHYCOMYCOSIS OF HORSES. MYCOLOGIA 53, 307-312.

1626 EMOTO, Y. (1966) - FUNGI GROWN ON OIL-PAINTING. TRANS.MYCOL.SOC.JAPAN 7, 367-368.

1627 ENDE, G.VAN DEN (1958) - UNTERSUCHUNGEN UEBER DEN PFLANZENPARASITEN VERTICILLIUM ALBO-ATRUM. ACTA BOT.NEERL. 7, 665-740.

1628 ENDE, H.VAN DEN & STEGWEE, D. (1971) - PHYSIOLOGY OF SEX IN MUCORALES. BOT. REV. 37, 22-36.

1629 ENDE, H.VAN DEN, WIECHMANN, A.H.C.A., REYNGOUD, D.J. & HENDRIKS, T. (1970)
      - HORMONAL INTERACTIONS IN MUCOR.MUCEDO AND BLAKESLEA TRISPORA. J.BACT.
      101, 423-428.

1630 ENGEL, B.G. & BRZESKI, W. (1947) - UEBER DIE ISOLIERUNG EINES CHINHYDRONS
      VON GENTISINALKOHOL UND OXYMETHYL-P-BENZOCHINON (GENTISIN-CHINON) AUS
      DEM KULTURFILTRAT VON PENICILLIUM URTICAE BAINIER. HELV.CHIM.ACTA 30,
      1472-1478.

1631 ENGHUSEN, H. (1956) - BODENKUNDLICH-MYKOLOGISCHE STUDIE AN STUTTGARTER
      STEPPENSCHWARZERDEN IM VERGLEICH MIT WALDBOEDEN. ZENTBL.BAKT.PARASITKDE,
      ABT.2, 109, 157-177.

1632 ENGLAND, C.M. & RICE, E.L. (1957) - A COMPARISON OF THE SOIL FUNGI OF A
      TALL-GRASS PRAIRIE AND OF AN ABANDONED FIELD IN CENTRAL OKLAHOMA. BOT.
      GAZ. 118, 186-190.

1633 ENGLISH, M.P. (1965) - THE SAPROPHYTIC GROWTH OF NON-KERATINOPHILIC FUNGI
      ON KERATINIZED SUBSTRATA, AND A COMPARISON WITH KERATINOPHILIC FUNGI.
      TRANS.BR.MYCOL.SOC. 48, 219-235.

1634 ENGLISH, M.P., SMITH, R.J. & HARMAN, R.R.M. (1971) - THE FUNGAL FLORA OF
      ULCERATED LEGS. BR.J.DERM. 84, 567-581.

1635 ENGST, R., KUJAWA, M. UND MUELLER, G. (1967) - ENZYMATISCHER ABBAU DES DDT
      DURCH SCHIMMELPILZE. 1. ISOLIERUNG UND IDENTIFIZIERUNG EINES DDT ABBAU-
      ENDEN SCHIMMELPILZES. NAHRUNG 11, 401-403.

1636 ENGSTROM, G.W., DELANCE, J.V., RICHARD, J.L. & BAETZ, A.L. (1975) - PURI-
      FICATION AND CHARACTERIZATION OF ROSEOTOXIN-B, A TOXIC CYCLODEPSIPEP-
      TIDE FROM TRICHOTHECIUM ROSEUM. J.AGRIC.FD CHEM. 23, 244-252.

1637 ENIKEEVA, M.G., RUDNEVA, V.L. & SIZOVA, T.P. (1970) - (MYCOFLORA OF PINE
      FORESTS OF VARIOUS TYPES). VEST.MOSK.GOS.UNIV., SER.BIOL.POCHV. 25,
      100-103.

1638 ENOMOTO, M. & SAITO, M. (1972) - CARCINOGENS PRODUCED BY FUNGI. A.REV.MI-
      CROBIOL. 26, 279-312.

1639 ENTWISTLE, A.R. (1971) - THE INFECTION OF POTATOES BY PHOMA EXIGUA. ANN.
      APPL.BIOL. 69, 213-222.

1640 ENTWISTLE, A.R. (1972) - STUDY OF PHOMA EXIGUA POPULATIONS IN THE FIELD.
      TRANS.BR.MYCOL.SOC. 58, 217-223.

1641 ENTWISTLE, A.R. (1972) - FACTORS AFFECTING THE SPORE GERMINATION OF PHOMA
      EXIGUA. NORTH.IR.MINIST.AGRIC.REC.AGRIC. 20, 13-16.

1642 EPPLEY, R.M. & BAILEY, W.J. (1973) - 12,13-EPOXY-DELTA-9-TRICHOTHECENES AS
      THE PROBABLE MYCOTOXINS RESPONSIBLE FOR STACHYBOTRYOTOXICOSIS. SCIENCE,
      N.Y. 181, 758-760.

1643 EPPS, W.M., PATTERSON, J.C. & FREEMAN, I.E. (1951) - PHYSIOLOGY AND PARA-
      SITISM OF SCLEROTIUM ROLFSII. PHYTOPHATOLOGY 41, 245-256.

1644 EPPSTEIN, S.H., MEISTER, P.D., PETERSON, D.H., MURRAY, H.C., OSBORN, H.M.
      L., WEINTRAUB, A., REINEKE, L.M. & MEEKS, R.C. (1958) - MICROBIOLOGICAL
      TRANSFORMATIONS OF STEROIDS. 15. TERTIARY HYDROXYLATION OF STEROIDS BY
      FUNGI OF THE ORDER MUCORALES. J.AM.CHEM.SOC. 80, 3382-3389.

1645 EREN, J. & PRAMER, D. (1965) - GROWTH AND ACTIVITY OF ARTHROBOTRYS CONO-
      IDES IN SOIL. BACT.PROC. 21, 4.

1646 EREN, J. & PRAMER, D. (1966) - APPLICATION OF IMMUNOFLUORESCENT STAINING
      TO STUDIES OF THE ECOLOGY OF SOIL MICROORGANISMS. SOIL SCI. 101, 39-45.

1647 ERIKSSON, O. (1967) - ON GRAMINICOLOUS PYRENOMYCETES FROM FENNOSCANDIA. 2.
      PHRAGMOSPOROUS AND SCOLECOSPOROUS SPECIES. ARK.BOT. 6, 381-440.

1648 ERNEST, J.T. & RIPPON, J.W. (1966) - KERATITIS DUE TO ALLESCHERIA BOYDII
      (MONOSPORIUM APIOSPERMUM). AM.J.OPHTHAL. 62, 1202-1204.

1649 ERSHAD, D. (1971) - BEITRAG ZUR KENNTNIS DER PHYTOPHTHORA-ARTEN IN IRAN
      UND IHRER PHYTOPATHOLOGISCHEN BEDEUTUNG. MITT.BIOL.BUNDANST.LD-U.FORSTW.
      140, 5-84.

1650 ERSKAYA, G.G. (1972) - (EFFECT OF SOIL CONDITIONS ON THE DEVELOPMENT OF
      MYCOSIS OF THE FIELD MAY BEETLE CAUSED BY BEAUVERIA TENELLA). IZV.VYSSH.
      UCHEB.ZAVED.LES.ZH. 1, 19-23.

1651 ERVIOE, L.-R. (1965) - CERTAIN PARASITES OF FUNGAL SCLEROTIA. J.SCIENT.
      AGRIC.SOC.FINL. 37, 1-6.

1652 ERVIOE, L.-R., HALKILAHTI, A.-M. & POHJAKALLIO, O. (1964) - THE SURVIVAL
      IN THE SOIL OF SCLEROTIA OF TWO SCLEROTINIA SPECIES AND THEIR ABILITY
      TO FORM MYCELIA. ADVG.FRONT.PL.SCI. 8, 121-134.

1653 ESSER, K. & KUENEN, R. (1967) - GENETICS OF FUNGI. SPRINGER, BERLIN, HEI-
      DELBERG, NEW YORK.

1654 ETZOLD, H. (1960) - DIE WIRKUNG DES LICHTES AUF EINIGE PILZE UND IHRE SPEK-
      TRALE GRENZE ZUM LANGWELLIGEN HIN. ARCH.MIKROBIOL. 37, 226-244.

1655 EVANS, E. (1955) - SURVIVAL AND RECOLONIZATION BY FUNGI IN SOIL TREATED
      WITH FORMALIN OR CARBON DISULPHIDE. TRANS.BR.MYCOL.SOC. 38, 335-346.

1656 EVANS, E.H. (1971) - STUDIES ON MORTIERELLA RAMANNIANA. 1. RELATIONSHIP
      BETWEEN MORPHOLOGY AND CULTURAL BEHAVIOUR OF CERTAIN ISOLATES. TRANS.
      BR.MYCOL.SOC. 56, 201-216.

1657 EVANS, E.H. (1972) - STUDIES ON MORTIERELLA RAMANNIANA. 2. ASPECTS OF THE
      ECOLOGY OF TWO VARIETIES. TRANS.BR.MYCOL.SOC. 58, 197-203.

1658 EVANS, G., CARTWRIGHT, J.B. & WHITE, N.H. (1967) - THE PRODUCTION OF A PHY-
      TOTOXIN, NECTROLIDE, BY SOME ROOT-SURFACE ISOLATES OF CYLINDROCARPON RA-
      DICICOLA. PL.SOIL 26, 253-260.

1659 EVANS, G. & GLEESON, A.C. (1973) - OBSERVATIONS ON THE ORIGIN AND NATURE
      OF VERTICILLIUM DAHLIAE COLONIZING PLANT ROOTS. AUST.J.BIOL.SCI. 26,
      151-161.

1660 EVANS, G. & MCKEEN, C.D. (1975) - INFLUENCE OF CROPS ON NUMBERS OF MICRO-
      SCLEROTIA OF VERTICILLIUM DAHLIAE IN SOILS AND THE DEVELOPMENT OF WILT
      IN SOUTHWESTERN ONTARIO. CAN.J.PL.SCI. 55, 827-834.

1661 EVANS, G., MCKEEN, C.D. & GLEESON, A.C. (1974) - A QUANTITATIVE BIOASSAY
      FOR DETERMINING LOW NUMBERS OF MICROSCLEROTIA OF VERTICILLIUM DAHLIAE
      IN FIELD SOILS. CAN.J.MICROBIOL. 20, 119-124.

1662 EVANS, G., SNYDER, W.C. & WILHELM, S. (1967) - QUANTITATIVE STUDIES BY
      PLATE COUNTS OF PROPAGULES OF THE VERTICILLIUM WILT FUNGUS IN COTTON
      FIELD SOILS. PHYTOPATHOLOGY 57, 1250-1255.

1663   EVANS, G. & WHITE, N.H. (1966) - RADICICOLIN AND RADICICOL, TWO NEW ANTI-
        BIOTICS PRODUCED BY CYLINDROCARPON RADICICOLA. TRANS.BR.MYCOL.SOC. 49,
        563-576.

1664   EVANS, H.C. (1971) - THERMOPHILOUS FUNGI OF COAL SPOIL TIPS. 1. TAXONOMY.
        TRANS.BR.MYCOL.SOC. 57, 241-254.

1665   EVANS, H.C. (1971) - THERMOPHILOUS FUNGI OF COAL SPOIL TIPS. 2. OCCURRENCE,
        DISTRIBUTION AND TEMPERATURE RELATIONSHIPS. TRANS.BR.MYCOL.SOC. 57, 255-
        266.

1666   EVANS, H.C. (1972) - THERMOPHILOUS FUNGI ISOLATED FROM THE AIR. TRANS.BR.
        MYCOL.SOC. 59, 516-519.

1667   EVANS, R. & HANSON, J.R. (1975) - THE FORMATION OF TRICHODIENE FROM ALL-
        TRANS-FARNESYL PYROPHOSPHATE BY TRICHOTHECIUM ROSEUM. CHEM.COMMUN., 1975
        (6), 231-232.

1668   EVANS, R., HANSON, J.R. & NYFELER, R. (1976) - STUDIES IN TERPENOID BIO-
        SYNTHESIS. 17. BIOSYNTHESIS OF THE SESQUITERPENOIDS CYCLONERODIOL AND
        CYCLONEROTRIOL. J.CHEM.SOC.PERKIN TRANS.I, 1976, 1214.

1669   EVELEIGH, D.E. (1961) - THE GROWTH REQUIREMENTS OF PHOMA VIOLACEA, WITH
        REFERENCE TO ITS DISFIGURATION OF PAINTED SURFACES. ANN.APPL.BIOL. 49,
        412-423.

1670   EVELEIGH, D.E. (1961) - PHOMA SPECIES ASSOCIATED WITH PAINTED SURFACES.
        TRANS.BR.MYCOL.SOC. 44, 573-585.

1671   EVELEIGH, D.E. (1970) - FUNGAL DISFIGUREMENT OF PAPER, AND SOFT ROT OF CE-
        DAR SHINGLES. APPL.MICROBIOL. 19, 872-874.

1672   EVELEIGH, D.E. & BREWER, D. (1963) - ECOLOGICAL OBSERVATIONS ON THE FUNGI
        AND BACTERIA IN SLIME ACCUMULATIONS IN A PAPER MILL. CAN.J.BOT. 42, 35-
        43.

1673   EVELEIGH, D.E. & BREWER, D. (1964) - NUTRITIONAL REQUIREMENTS OF THE MICRO-
        FLORA OF A SLIME ACCUMULATION IN A PAPER MILL. CAN.J.BOT. 42, 341-350.

1674   EVREINOVA, T.N. & MIROSHNICHENKO, G.P. (1962) - FREE NUCLEOTIDES OF THE
        THERMOPHILIC AND MESOPHILIC VARIANTS OF ASPERGILLUS FUMIGATUS. MIKRO-
        BIOLOGIYA (ENGL.TRANSL.) 31, 350-354.

1675   EYLAR, O.R. & SCHMIDT, E.L. (1959) - A SURVEY OF HETEROTROPHIC MICROORGAN-
        ISMS FROM SOIL FOR ABILITY TO FORM NITRITE AND NITRATE. J.GEN.MICROBIOL.
        20, 473-481.

1676   EYRE, J.C. (1932) - CULTURAL STUDIES ON THE ASPERGILLI, WITH SPECIAL REF-
        ERENCE TO LIPASE PRODUCTION OF STRAINS ISOLATED FROM STORED COPRA AND
        CACAO. ANN.APPL.BIOL. 19, 351-369.

1677   EZEKIEL, W.N., TAUBENHAUS, J.J. & FUDGE, J.F. (1934) - NUTRITIONAL REQUIRE-
        MENTS OF THE ROOT-ROT FUNGUS, PHYMATOTRICHUM OMNIVORUM. PL.PHYSIOL.,
        LANCASTER 9, 187-216.

1678   EZRUCH, E.N. & BABUSHKINA, I.N. (1973) - (SOME PHYSIOLOGICAL FEATURES OF
        PATHOGENIC SPECIES OF THE GENUS VERTICILLIUM). MIKOL.FITOPAT. 7, 536-
        539.

1679   FAHMY, F.A. & YUSEF, H.M. (1974) - DEVELOPMENT AND MORPHOLOGY OF SYNNEMA
        IN TRICHURUS SPIRALIS HASSELBRING. ACTA PHYTOPATH.ACAD.SCI.HUNG. 9,
        81-87.

1680   FAHMY, F.A. & YUSEF, H.M. (1974) - A STUDY ON CERTAIN FACTORS AFFECTING SYNNEMA LENGTH IN TRICHURUS SPIRALIS HASSELBRING. ACTA PHYTOPATH.ACAD. SCI.HUNG. 9, 89-98.

1681   FAIRBAIRN, D. (1958) - THE PREPARATION AND PROPERTIES OF A LYSOPHOSPHO- LIPASE FROM PENICILLIUM NOTATUM. J.BIOL.CHEM. 173, 705-714.

1682   FAJOLA, A.O. & ALASOADURA, S.O. (1975) - ANTAGONISTIC EFFECTS OF TRICHO- DERMA HARZIANUM ON PYTHIUM APHANIDERMATUM CAUSING THE DAMPING-OFF DIS- EASE OF TOBACCO IN NIGERIA. MYCOPATHOLOGIA 57, 47-52.

1683   FAKIR, G.A., WELTY, R.E. & COWLING, E.B. (1971) - PREVALENCE AND PATHOGEN- ICITY OF FUNGI ASSOCIATED WITH ACHENES OF SYCAMORE IN THE FIELD AND IN STORAGE. PHYTOPATHOLOGY 61, 660-668.

1684   FAKIROVA, V. (1972) - STUDIES ON THE COPROPHILOUS ASCOMYCETES IN BULGARIA. IZV.BOT.INST., SOF. 22, 189-191.

1685   FANDIALAN, I. & ILAG, I.L. (1972) - MORPHOLOGY OF ISOLATES IN THE ASPER- GILLUS FLAVUS GROUP. KALIKASAN PHILIPP.J.BIOL. 1, 69-73.

1686   FANDIALAN, I.M. & ILAG, L.L. (1972) - TEMPERATURE AND THE GROWTH OF ISO- LATES IN THE ASPERGILLUS FLAVUS GROUP. KALIKASAN PHILIPP.J.BIOL. 1, 229- 233.

1687   FANELLI, C., CACACE, M.G. & CERVONE, F. (1977) - POLYGALACTURONASE FROM TRICHODERMA KONINGII. ABS.2ND INT.MYCOL.CONGR., TAMPA, 1977.

1688   FANELLI, C. & CERVONE, F. (1977) - POLYGALACTURONASE AND CELLULASE PRODUC- TION BY TRICHODERMA KONINGII AND TRICHODERMA PSEUDO-KONINGII. TRANS.BR. MYCOL.SOC. 68, 291-294.

1689   FANTINI, A.A. (1962) - GENETICS AND ANTIBIOTIC PRODUCTION OF EMERICELLOP- SIS SPECIES. GENETICS 47, 161-177.

1690   FARAJ SALMAN, A.-G. (1970) - EINFLUSS VON LICHT AUF DIE KOREMIENBILDUNG UND IHRE KREISFOERMIGE ANORDNUNG. 2. BEI PENICILLIUM CLAVIFORME MUT. OLIVICOLOR ABE & URA UND EINER VARIETAET DAVON. KULTURPFLANZE 18, 89- 97.

1691   FARAJ SALMAN, A.-G. (1971) - DAS WIRKUNGSSPEKTRUM DER LICHTABHAENGIGEN ZO- NIERUNG DER KOREMIEN VON ZWEI MUTANTEN VON PENICILLIUM CLAVIFORME BAI- NIER. PLANTA 101, 117-121.

1692   FARGUES, J., DURIEZ, T., ANDRIEU, S. & POPEYE, R. (1974) - ANALYSE SERO- LOGIQUE COMPAREE DE DEUX CHAMPIGNONS ENTOMOPATHOGENES, BEAUVERIA BAS- SIANA (BALS.)VUILL. ET BEAUVERIA TENELLA (DELACR.)SIEM. C.R.HEBD.SEANC. ACAD.SCI., PARIS, SER.D, 278, 2245-2247.

1693   FARGUES, J., DURIEZ, T., ANDRIEU, S., POPEYE, R. & ROBERT, P. (1975) - ETUDE IMMUNOLOGIQUE COMPAREE DE SOUCHES DE METARRHIZIUM ANISOPLIAE (DE- LACR.) SIEM., CHAMPIGNON HYPHOMYCETE ENTOMOPATHOGENE. C.R.HEBD.SEANC. ACAD.SCI., PARIS, SER.D, 281, 1781-1784.

1694   FARLEY, J.D., WILHELM, S. & SNYDER, W.C. (1971) - REPEATED GERMINATION AND SPORULATION OF MICROSCLEROTIA OF VERTICILLIUM ALBO-ATRUM IN SOIL. PHY- TOPATHOLOGY 61, 260-264.

1695   FARLEY, J.F., JERSILD, R.A. & NIEDERPRUEM, D.J. (1975) - ORIGIN AND ULTRA- STRUCTURE OF INTRA-HYPHAL HYPHAE IN TRICHOPHYTON TERRESTRE AND T. RU- BRUM. ARCH.MICROBIOL. 106, 195-200.

1696 FARLEY, J.F., JERSILD, R.A. & NIEDERPRUEM, D.J. (1976) - ULTRASTRUCTURAL
      ASPECTS OF ASCOSPORULATION IN ARTHRODERMA QUADRIFIDUM. SABOURAUDIA 14,
      337-341.

1697 FARROW, W.M. (1954) - TROPICAL SOIL FUNGI. MYCOLOGIA 46, 632-646.

1698 FASSATIOVA, O. (1964) - (BEOBACHTUNGEN UEBER DIE GATTUNG HUMICOLA). CESKA
      MYKOL. 18, 102-108.

1699 FASSATIOVA, O. (1965) - (ON THE VARIABILITY OF THE IMPERFECT SPECIES CHRY-
      SOSPORIUM PANNORUM). CESKA MYKOL. 19, 223-225.

1700 FASSATIOVA, O. (1966) - BODENMIKROMYCETEN AM HUEGEL DOUTNAC IM BOEHMISCHEN
      KARST. PRESLIA 38, 1-14.

1701 FASSATIOVA, O. (1967) - NOTES ON THE GENUS HUMICOLA. 2. CESKA MYKOL. 21,
      78-89.

1702 FASSATIOVA, O. (1969) - BODENMIKROMYCETEN IM GEBIRGE ZDANICKY LES (STEI-
      NITZER WALD) UND IN DER STEPPE BEI POUZDRANY (PAUSRAN). CESKA MYKOL.
      23, 243-252.

1703 FASSATIOVA, O. (1970) - MICROMYCETES INHABITING THE MINES OF PRIBRAM (CZE-
      CHOSLOVAKIA). CESKA MYKOL. 24, 162-165.

1704 FATEMI, J. (1971) - PHYTOPHTHORA AND PYTHIUM ROOT ROT OF SUGAR BEET IN
      IRAN. PHYTOPATH.Z. 71, 25-28.

1705 FAULKNER, J.K. & WOODCOCK, D. (1964) - METABOLISM OF 2,4-DICHLOROPHENOXY
      ACETIC ACID ('2,4,-D') BY ASPERGILLUS NIGER VAN TIEGH. NATURE, LOND.
      203, 865.

1706 FAULKNER, J.K. & WOODCOCK, D. (1965) - FUNGAL DETOXICATION. 7. METABOLISM
      OF 2,4-DICHLOROPHENOXYACETIC AND 4-CHLORO-2-METHYLPHENOXYACETIC ACIDS
      BY ASPERGILLUS NIGER. J.CHEM.SOC., 1965, 1187-1191.

1707 FAULKNER, J.K. & WOODCOCK, D. (1968) - THE METABOLISM OF PHENYLACETIC ACID
      BY ASPERGILLUS NIGER. PHYTOCHEMISTRY 7, 1741-1742.

1708 FAULKNER, L.R. & SKOTLAND, C.B. (1965) - INTERACTIONS OF VERTICILLIUM DAH-
      LIAE AND PRATYLENCHUS MINYUS IN VERTICILLIUM WILT OF PEPPERMINT. PHYTO-
      PATHOLOGY 55, 583-586.

1709 FAWCETT, P.A., LODER, P.B., DUNCAN, M.J., BEESLEY, T.J. & ABRAHAM, E.P.
      (1973) - FORMATION AND PROPERTIES OF PROTOPLASTS FROM ANTIBIOTIC-PRO-
      DUCING STRAINS OF PENICILLIUM CHRYSOGENUM AND CEPHALOSPORIUM ACREMONIUM.
      J.GEN.MICROBIOL. 79, 293-309.

1710 FEDORINCHIK, N.S. (1961) - DIE VERWENDUNG DES PILZES TRICHODERMA LIGNORUM
      ZUR BEKAEMPFUNG PHYTOPATHOGENER PILZE IM BODEN. TAGBER.DT.AKAD.LANDWWISS.
      41, 109-118.

1711 FEDORINCHIK, N.S. & VANDERFLAAS, L.K. (1954) - (EFFECT OF THE ANTAGONISTIC
      ACTIVITY OF THE SOIL FUNGUS TRICHODERMA LIGNORUM ON INCREASE IN YIELDS
      OF AGRICULTURAL CROPS). TRUDY VSES.INST.ZASHCH.RAST. 5, 17-37.

1712 FEHER, D. (1933) - MIKROBIOLOGIE DES WALDBODENS. J.SPRINGER, BERLIN, 272
      PP.

1713 FEHER, D. & BESENYEI, Z. (1933) - UNTERSUCHUNGEN UEBER DIE MIKROSKOPISCHEN
      PILZE DES WALDBODENS. FORSTL.VERSUCHE 35, 55-77.

1714 FEHLHABER, H.-W., GEIPEL, R., MERCKER, H.-J., TSCHESCHE, R., WELMAR, K. &
      SCHOENBECK, F. (1974) - BOTRYDIAL, EIN SESQUITERPEN-ANTIBIOTIKUM AUS
      DER NAEHRLOESUNG DES PILZES BOTRYTIS CINEREA. CHEM.BER. 107, 1720-1730.

1715 FEINSTEIN, G. & GERTLER, A. (1973) - ISOLATION OF ALKALINE PROTEINASES
      FROM ASPERGILLUS ORYZAE BY ONE-STEP AFFINITY CHROMATOGRAPHY ON OVOIN-
      HIBITOR-SEPHAROSE COLUMN. BIOCHIM.BIOPHYS.ACTA 309, 196-202.

1716 FELLOWS, H. (1937) - THE INFESTATION OF SOIL WITH OPHIOBOLUS GRAMINIS AND
      ITS SUBSEQUENT INCREASE AND SPREAD IN THE SOIL. PHYTOPATHOLOGY 27, 956
      (ABS.).

1717 FENIKSOVA, R.V. & ULEZLO, I.V. (1965) - (THE BIOSYNTHESIS OF MYROTHECIUM
      VERRUCARIA CELLULASE). PRIKL.BIOKHIM.MIKROBIOL. 1, 406-413.

1718 FENNELL, D.I., ST.JULIAN, G., BULLA, L.A.JR. & BAKER, F.L. (1974) - SCAN-
      NING ELECTRON MICROSCOPY OF CONIDIOPHORE ORNAMENTATIONS IN ASPERGILLUS
      SPP. IN: SCANNING ELECTRON MICROSCOPY; JOHARI, OM & CORVIN, I. (ED.),
      PROC.SYMP.ASSOC.WORKSHOPS, CHICAGO, ILL., U.S.A.

1719 FERGUS, C.L. (1952) - THE NUTRITION OF PENICILLIUM DIGITATUM SACC. MYCOLO-
      GIA 44, 183-199.

1720 FERGUS, C.L. (1954) - THE PRODUCTION OF ETHYLENE BY PENICILLIUM DIGITATUM.
      MYCOLOGIA 46, 543-545.

1721 FERGUS, C.L. (1957) - MYROTHECIUM RORIDUM ON GARDENIA. MYCOLOGIA 49, 124-
      127.

1722 FERGUS, C.L. (1960) - A NOTE ON THE OCCURRENCE OF PEZIZA OSTRACODERMA. MY-
      COLOGIA 52, 959-961.

1723 FERGUS, C.L. (1964) - THERMOPHILIC AND THERMOTOLERANT MOLDS AND ACTINOMY-
      CETES OF MUSHROOM COMPOST DURING PEAK HEATING. MYCOLOGIA 56, 267-284.

1724 FERGUS, C.L. (1966) - PARAFFIN UTILIZATION BY THERMOPHILIC FUNGI. CAN.J.
      MICROBIOL. 12, 1067-1068.

1725 FERGUS, C.L. (1969) - THE CELLULOLYTIC ACTIVITY OF THERMOPHILIC FUNGI AND
      ACTINOMYCETES. MYCOLOGIA 61, 120-129.

1726 FERGUS, C.L. (1971) - GERMINATION OF THE CONIDIA OF PEZIZA OSTRACODERMA.
      MYCOPATH.MYCOL.APPL. 45, 211-216.

1727 FERGUS, C.L. & AMELUNG, R.M. (1971) - THE HEAT RESISTANCE OF SOME THERMO-
      PHILIC FUNGI ON MUSHROOM COMPOST. MYCOLOGIA 63, 675-679.

1728 FERREIRA, N.P. (1968) - THE EFFECT OF AMINO ACIDS ON THE PRODUCTION OF
      OCHRATOXIN-A IN CHEMICALLY DEFINED MEDIA. ANTONIE VAN LEEUWENHOEK 34,
      433-440.

1729 FERRERA-CERRATO, R. (1976) - HIPERPARASITISMO DE TRICHODERMA VIRIDE (FUNGI
      HYPHOMYCETES) SOBRE HONGOS FITOPATOGENOS Y SAPROFITICOS. REVTA LAT.-AM.
      MICROBIOL. 18, 77-81.

1730 FERRIS, J.P., FASCO, M.J., STYLIANOPOULOU, F.L., JERINA, D.M., DALY, J.W.
      & JEFFREY, A.M. (1973) - MONOOXYGENASE ACTIVITY IN CUNNINGHAMELLA BAI-
      NIERI. EVIDENCE FOR A FUNGAL SYSTEM SIMILAR TO LIVER MICROSOMES. ARCHS
      BIOCHEM.BIOPHYS. 156, 97-103.

1731 FERRON, P. (1967) - LES POSSIBILITES DE LUTTE MICROBIOLOGIQUE CONTRE MELO-
      LONTHA MELOLONTHA L. AU MOYEN DE LA MYCOSE A BEAUVERIA TENELLA (DELACR.)
      SIEMASZKO. IN: INSECT PATHOLOGY AND MICROBIAL CONTROL; LAAN, P.A. VAN
      DER (ED.), NORTH HOLLAND PUBL.CO., AMSTERDAM, 204-209.

1732 FEUERMAN, E.J., ALTERAS, I., BASHAN, D. & LEHRER, N.B. (1976) - ISOLATION OF SPOROTHRIX SCHENCKII IN THE SOIL IN ISRAEL IN RELATION TO A NEW CASE IN MAN. SABOURAUDIA 14, 217-222.

1733 FEUERMAN, E., ALTERAS, I., HOENIG, E. & LEHRER, N. (1975) - THE ISOLATION OF KERATINOPHILIC FUNGI FROM SOILS IN ISRAEL. A PRELIMINARY REPORT. MYCOPATHOLOGIA 56, 41-46.

1734 FEZER, K.D. (1961) - COMMON ROOT ROT OF RED CLOVER. PATHOGENICITY OF ASSOCIATED FUNGI AND ENVIRONMENTAL FACTORS AFFECTING SUSCEPTIBILITY. MEM. CORNELL UNIV.AGRIC.EXP.STN 377, 3-38.

1735 FIDDY, C. & TRINCI, A.P.J. (1977) - SEPTATION IN MYCELIA OF MUCOR HIEMALIS AND MUCOR RAMANNIANUS. TRANS.BR.MYCOL.SOC. 68, 118-120.

1736 FIEDLER, H.J. & KAESTNER, CH. (1970) - MIKROBIOLOGISCHE EIGENSCHAFTEN EINER GNEIS-BRAUNERDE UNTER LAUB- UND NADELWALD. ZENTBL.BAKT.PARASITKDE, ABT.2, 124, 292-300.

1737 FILER, T.H. (1967) - DAMPING-OFF OF SWEETGUM BY PYTHIUM SYLVATICUM. PHYTOPATHOLOGY 57, 1284.

1738 FILIP, Z. (1970) - WACHSTUM UND HUMINSTOFFBILDUNG EINIGER BODENPILZE UNTER DEM EINFLUSS VON TONMINERALIEN. DISS.JUSTUS LIEBIG UNIV.GIESSEN.

1739 FILIP, Z., HAIDER, K. & MARTIN, J.P. (1972) - INFLUENCE OF CLAY MINERALS ON GROWTH AND METABOLIC ACTIVITY OF EPICOCCUM NIGRUM AND STACHYBOTRYS CHARTARUM. SOIL BIOL.BIOCHEM. 4, 135-145.

1740 FILIP, Z., HAIDER, K. & MARTIN, J.P. (1972) - INFLUENCE OF CLAY MINERALS ON THE FORMATION OF HUMIC SUBSTANCES BY EPICOCCUM NIGRUM AND STACHYBOTRYS CHARTARUM. SOIL BIOL.BIOCHEM. 4, 147-154.

1741 FINDLAY, J.A. & RADICS, L. (1972) - FLAVIPUCINE, AN ANTIBIOTIC FROM ASPERGILLUS FLAVIPES. J.CHEM.SOC.PERKIN TRANS.I, 1972 (16), 2071-2074.

1742 FIRPI, M. & VERONA, O. (1971) - INFLUENZA DELLA LUCE SULLO SVILUPPO DI ALTERNARIA TENUIS ED ULOCLADIUM CHARTARUM, AGENTI DI DETERIORAMENTO DI CARTA E CARTONI. CELLULOSA E CARTA, 25-29.

1743 FISCHER, B. (1974) - ISOLIERUNG UND UNTERSUCHUNGEN EINES ARGININ-ANTAGONISTEN (SIGMA-N-HYDROXY-L-ARGININ) UND EINES GLUTAMIN-ANTAGONISTEN AUS NANNIZZIA GYPSEA. DISS.UNIV.TUEBINGEN.

1744 FISCHER, G. (1953) - UNTERSUCHUNGEN UEBER DEN BIOLOGISCHEN ABBAU DES LIGNINS DURCH MIKROORGANISMEN. ARCH.MIKROBIOL. 18, 397-424.

1745 FISHBACH, R.S., WHITE, M.L. & FINEGOLD, S.M. (1973) - BRONCHOPULMONARY GEOTRICHOSIS. AM.REV.RESPIR.DIS. 108, 1388-1392.

1746 FISHER, E.E. (1962) - FACIAL ECZEMA. 4. INVESTIGATIONS ON FACIAL ECZEMA CONDUCTED BY THE BIOLOGY BRANCH. J.AGRIC.VICT.DEP.AGRIC. 60, 54-58.

1747 FISHER, E.E., KELLOCK, A.W. & WELLINGTON, N.A.M. (1967) - TOXIC STRAIN OF FUSARIUM CULMORUM (W.G.SM.) SACC. FROM ZEA MAYS L., ASSOCIATED WITH SICKNESS IN DAIRY CATTLE. NATURE, LOND. 215, 322.

1748 FISHER, K.D. (1961) - SOME PHYSIOLOGICAL COMPARISONS OF THE FUSARIUM SURFACE ROT AND FUSARIUM WILT PATHOGENS OF SWEET POTATO. DISS.ABSTR. 22, 21.

1749 FLADOS, N.D. (1958) - ECOLOGICAL FACTORS AFFECTING THE GROWTH OF SCLERO-
      TIUM ROLFSII. PHYTOPATHOLOGY 48, 343.

1750 FLANAGAN, P.W. & SCARBOROUGH, A.M. (1974) - PHYSIOLOGICAL GROUPS OF DECOM-
      POSER FUNGI ON TUNDRA PLANT REMAINS. IN: SOIL ORGANISMS AND DECOMPOSI-
      TION IN TUNDRA; HOLDING, A.J. ET AL. (ED.), TUNDRA BIOME STEERING COM-
      MITTEE (STOCKHOLM), 159-181.

1751 FLANNIGAN, B. (1969) - MICROFLORA OF DRIED BARLEY GRAIN. TRANS.BR.MYCOL.
      SOC. 53, 371-379.

1752 FLANNIGAN, B. (1970) - COMPARISON OF SEED-BORNE MYCOFLORAS OF BARLEY, OATS
      AND WHEAT. TRANS.BR.MYCOL.SOC. 55, 267-276.

1753 FLANNIGAN, B. (1970) - DEGRADATION OF ARABINOXYLAN AND CARBOXYMETHYL CEL-
      LULOSE BY FUNGI ISOLATED FROM BARLEY KERNELS. TRANS.BR.MYCOL.SOC. 55,
      277-281.

1754 FLANNIGAN, B. (1974) - DISTRIBUTION OF SEED-BORNE MICRO-ORGANISMS IN NAKED
      BARLEY AND WHEAT BEFORE HARVEST. TRANS.BR.MYCOL.SOC. 62, 51-58.

1755 FLANNIGAN, B. & DICKIE, N.A. (1972) - DISTRIBUTION OF MICRO-ORGANISMS IN
      FRACTIONS PRODUCED DURING PEARLING OF BARLEY. TRANS.BR.MYCOL.SOC. 59,
      377-391.

1756 FLANNIGAN, B. & SAGOO, G.S. (1977) - DEGRADATION OF WOOD BY ASPERGILLUS
      FUMIGATUS ISOLATED FROM SELF-HEATED WOOD CHIPS. MYCOLOGIA 69, 514-523.

1757 FLANNIGAN, B. & SELLARS, P.N. (1972) - ACTIVITIES OF THERMOPHILOUS FUNGI
      FROM BARLEY KERNELS AGAINST ARABINOXYLAN AND CARBOXYMETHYL CELLULOSE.
      TRANS.BR.MYCOL.SOC. 58, 338-341.

1758 FLANNIGAN, B. & SELLARS, P.N. (1977) - AMYLASE, BETA-GLUCOSIDASE AND BETA-
      XYLOSIDASE ACTIVITY OF THERMOTOLERANT AND THERMOPHILIC FUNGI ISOLATED
      FROM BARLEY. TRANS.BR.MYCOL.SOC. 69, 316-317.

1759 FLASHINSKI, S.J. & LICHTENSTEIN, E.P. (1974) - DEGRADATION OF DYFONATE IN
      SOIL INOCULATED WITH RHIZOPUS ARRHIZUS. CAN.J.MICROBIOL. 20, 871-875.

1760 FLEGLER, S., MCNABB, C.D. & FIELDS, W.G. (1974) - ANTIBIOTIC TREATMENT OF
      LAKE SEDIMENTS TO DETERMINE THE EFFECT OF FUNGI ON DECOMPOSITION. WATER
      RES. 8, 307-310.

1761 FLEISCHMAN, A.I. & PISANO, M.A. (1961) - STUDIES ON THE RESPIRATION OF
      EMERICELLOPSIS SALMOSYNNEMATA - THE OXIDATION OF AMINO COMPOUNDS. BACT.
      PROC., 1961, 112.

1762 FLEISCHMAN, A.I. & PISANO, M.A. (1962) - STUDIES ON THE RESPIRATION OF
      EMERICELLOPSIS SALMOSYNNEMATA - THE OXIDATION OF FATTY ACIDS. BACT.PROC.,
      1962, 105.

1763 FLEMING, A. (1929) - ON THE ANTIBACTERIAL ACTION OF CULTURES OF A PENICIL-
      LIUM WITH SPECIAL REFERENCE TO THEIR USE IN THE ISOLATION OF B. INFLU-
      ENZAE. BR.J.EXP.PATH. 10, 226-236.

1764 FLENTJE, N.T. (1956) - STUDIES ON PELLICULARIA FILAMENTOSA. 1. FORMATION
      OF THE PERFECT STAGE. TRANS.BR.MYCOL.SOC. 39, 343-356.

1765 FLENTJE, N.T. & SAKSENA, H.K. (1957) - STUDIES ON PELLICULARIA FILAMENTO-
      SA. 2. OCCURRENCE AND DISTRIBUTION OF PATHOGENIC STRAINS. TRANS.BR.MY-
      COL.SOC. 40, 95-108.

1766   FLENTJE, N.T. & STRETTON, H.M. (1964) - MECHANISM OF VARIATION IN THANATE-
       PHORUS CUCUMERIS AND T. PRATICOLUS. AUST.J.BIOL.SCI. 17, 686-704.

1767   FLENTJE, N.T., STRETTON, H.M. & HAWN, E.J. (1963) - NUCLEAR DISTRIBUTION
       AND BEHAVIOUR THROUGHOUT THE LIFE CYCLES OF THANATEPHORUS, WAITEA, AND
       CERATOBASIDIUM SPECIES. AUST.J.BIOL.SCI. 16, 450-467.

1768   FLENTJE, N.T., STRETTON, H.M. & MCKENZIE, A.R. (1970) - MECHANISMS OF VAR-
       IATION IN RHIZOCTONIA SOLANI. IN: RHIZOCTONIA SOLANI, BIOLOGY AND PA-
       THOLOGY, SYMPOSIUM 1965; PARMETER, J.JR. (ED.), UNIV.CALIFORNIA PRESS,
       BERKELEY, LOS ANGELES, LONDON, 52-65.

1769   FLETCHER, J. (1969) - MORPHOLOGY AND NUCLEAR BEHAVIOUR OF GERMINATING CO-
       NIDIA OF PENICILLIUM GRISEOFULVUM. TRANS.BR.MYCOL.SOC. 53, 425-432.

1770   FLETCHER, J. (1970) - PHYSIOLOGY OF GERMINATION OF PENICILLIUM GRISEO-FUL-
       VUM CONIDIA. TRANS.BR.MYCOL.SOC. 54, 65-81.

1771   FLETCHER, J. (1971) - CONIDIUM ONTOGENY IN PENICILLIUM. J.GEN.MICROBIOL.
       67, 207-214.

1772   FLETCHER, J. (1971) - FINE-STRUCTURAL CHANGES DURING GERMINATION OF CONID-
       IA OF PENICILLIUM GRISEOFULVUM DIERCKX. ANN.BOT. 35, 441-449.

1773   FLETCHER, J. (1972) - FINE STRUCTURE OF DEVELOPING MEROSPORANGIA AND SPO-
       RANGIOSPORES OF SYNCEPHALASTRUM RACEMOSUM. ARCH.MIKROBIOL. 87, 269-284.

1774   FLETCHER, J. (1973) - ULTRASTRUCTURAL CHANGES ASSOCIATED WITH SPORE FOR-
       MATION IN SPORANGIA AND SPORANGIOLA OF THAMNIDIUM ELEGANS LINK. ANN.BOT.
       37, 963-971.

1775   FLETCHER, J. (1976) - ELECTRON MICROSCOPY OF GENESIS, MATURATION AND WALL
       STRUCTURE OF CONIDIA OF ASPERGILLUS TERREUS. TRANS.BR.MYCOL.SOC. 66,
       27-34.

1776   FLETCHER, J. & MORTON, A.G. (1970) - PHYSIOLOGY OF GERMINATION OF PENICIL-
       LIUM GRISEOFULVUM CONIDIA. TRANS BR.MYCOL.SOC. 54, 65-81.

1777   FLETCHER, J.T. (1973) - SHAGGY STIPE, A NEW MUSHROOM DISEASE. MUSHROOM J.
       1, 114-115.

1778   FLETCHER, J.T. (1973) - SHAGGY STIPE, A NEW DISEASE OF CULTIVATED MUSHROOM
       CAUSED BY MORTIERELLA BAINIERI. PL.PATH. 22, 25-27.

1779   FLETCHER, J.T. & SCHOLEFIELD, S.M. (1976) - BENOMYL TOLERANCE IN ISOLATES
       OF BOTRYTIS CINEREA FROM TOMATO PLANTS. ANN.APPL.BIOL. 82, 529-536.

1780   FLIERMANS, C.B. (1973) - INHIBITION OF HISTOPLASMA CAPSULATUM BY GARLIC.
       MYCOPATH.MYCOL.APPL. 50, 227-231.

1781   FLORANCE, E.R., DENISON, W.C. & ALLEN, T.H.JR. (1972) - ULTRASTRUCTURE OF
       115-123.

1782   FLOREY, H.W., GILLIVER.K., JENNINGS, M.A. & SANDERS.A.G. (1946) - MYCOPHE-
       NOLIC ACID, AN ANTIBIOTIC FROM PENICILLIUM BREVICOMPACTUM. LANCET 250,
       46-49.

1783   FLOWERS, R.A. & HENDRIX, J.W. (1969) - GALLIC ACID IN A PROCEDURE FOR ISO-
       LATION OF PHYTOPHTHORA PARASITICA VAR. NICOTIANAE AND PYTHIUM SPP. FROM
       SOIL. PHYTOPATHOLOGY 59, 725-731.

1784   FLOWERS, R.A. & LITTRELL, R.H. (1972) - OOSPORE GERMINATION OF PYTHIUM
       APHANIDERMATUM AS AFFECTED BY CASEIN, GALLIC ACID AND PH LEVELS IN A
       SELECTIVE AGAR MEDIUM. PHYTOPATHOLOGY 62, 757.

1785   FLOWERS, R.A. & LITTRELL, R.H. (1973) - OOSPORE GERMINATION OF PYTHIUM
       APHANIDERMATUM AS INFLUENCED BY NITROGEN SOURCES AND CONCENTRATION.
       PHYTOPATHOLOGY 63, 441 (ABS.).

1786   FLUECK, V. (1955) - UNTERSUCHUNGEN UEBER DIE PATHOGENITAET VON ERREGERGE-
       MISCHEN BEI GETREIDEFUSSKRANKHEITEN. PHYTOPATH.Z. 23, 177-208.

1787   FLURY, E., MAULI, R. & SIGG, H.P. (1965) - THE CONSTITUTION OF DIACETOXY-
       SCIRPENOL. CHEM.COMMUN., 1965 (2), 26-27.

1788   FOKKEMA, N.J. (1973) - THE ROLE OF SAPROPHYTIC FUNGI IN ANTAGONISM AGAINST
       DRECHSLERA SOROKINIANA (HELMINTHOSPORIUM SATIVUM) ON AGAR PLATES AND ON
       RYE LEAVES WITH POLLEN. PHYSIOL.PL.PATH. 3, 195-205.

1789   FOKKEMA, N.J., LAAR, J.A.J.VAN DE, NELIS-BLOMBERG, A.L. & SCHIPPERS, B.
       (1975) - THE BUFFERING CAPACITY OF THE NATURAL MYCOFLORA OF RYE LEAVES
       TO INFECTION BY COCHLIOBOLUS SATIVUS, AND ITS SUSCEPTIBILITY TO BENOMYL
       NETH.J.PL.PATH. 81, 176-186.

1790   FOKKEMA, N.J. & LORBEER, J.W. (1974) - INTERACTIONS BETWEEN ALTERNARIA
       PORRI AND THE SAPROPHYTIC MYCOFLORA OF ONION LEAVES. PHYTOPATHOLOGY 64,
       1128-1133.

1791   FOLEY, D.C. (1959) - THE PRESENCE OF CELLULASE IN CORN STALKS INFECTED WITH
       FUSARIUM MONILIFORME. PHYTOPATHOLOGY 49, 538 (ABS.).

1792   FOLLIN, J.C. (1968) - SUR LE DETERMINISME DE LA FORMATION DU PERITHECE CHEZ
       GLOMERELLA CINGULATA (STONEM.) SPAULD. & VON SCHRENK F.SP. GOSSYPII.
       COTON FIBR.TROP. 23, 447-451.

1793   FOLLSTAD, M.N. (1966) - MYCELIAL GROWTH RATE AND SPORULATION OF ALTERNARIA
       TENUIS, BOTRYTIS CINEREA, CLADOSPORIUM HERBARUM, AND RHIZOPUS STOLONI-
       FER IN LOW-OXYGEN ATMOSPHERES. PHYTOPATHOLOGY 56, 1098-1099.

1794   FONTANA, A. & LUPPI, A.-M. (1966) - FUNGHI SAPROFITI ISOLATI DA ECTOMICOR-
       RIZE. ALLIONIA 12, 38-46.

1795   FORBES, R.S. & DICKINSON, C.H. (1977) - EFFECTS OF TEMPERATURE, PH AND NI-
       TROGEN ON CELLULOLYTIC ACTIVITY OF FUSARIUM AVENACEUM. TRANS.BR.MYCOL.
       SOC. 68, 229-235.

1796   FORBES, R.S. & DICKINSON, C.H. (1977) - BEHAVIOUR OF FUSARIUM AVENACEUM IN
       SOIL GROWTH ANALYSIS PLATES. TRANS.BR.MYCOL.SOC. 69, 197-205.

1797   FORDYCE, C. & GREEN, R.J. (1964) - MECHANISMS OF VARIATION IN VERTICILLIUM
       ALBO-ATRUM. PHYTOPATHOLOGY 54, 795-798.

1798   FORGACS, J. (1972) - STACHYBOTRYOTOXICOSIS. IN: MICROBIAL TOXINS, VOL. 8;
       KADIS, S., CIEGLER, A. & AJL, S.J. (ED.), ACADEMIC PRESS, NEW YORK, P.
       95-128.

1799   FORGACS, J. & CARLL, W.T. (1962) - MYCOTOXICOSES. ADV.VET.SCI. 7, 273-382.

1800   FORGACS, J., CARLL, W.T., HERRINGS, A.S. & HINSHAW, W.R. (1958) - TOXICITY
       OF STACHYBOTRYS ATRA FOR ANIMALS. TRANS.N.Y.ACAD.SCI., SECT.2, 20, 787-
       808.

1801   FORNO, L.S. & BILLINGHAM, M.E. (1972) - ALLESCHERIA BOYDII INFECTION OF
       THE BRAIN. J.PATH. 106, 195-198.

1802   FORRESTER, P.I. & GAUCHER, G.M. (1972) - M-HYDROXYBENZYL ALCOHOL DEHYDRO-
       GENASE FROM PENICILLIUM URTICAE. BIOCHEMISTRY 11, 1108-1114.

1803   FORRESTER, P.I. & GAUCHER, G.M. (1972) - CONVERSION OF 6-METHYLSALICYLIC
       ACID INTO PATULIN BY PENICILLIUM URTICAE. BIOCHEMISTRY 11, 1102-1107.

1804   FOSTER, F.W. & WAKSMAN, S.A. (1939) - THE SPECIFIC EFFECT OF ZINC AND OTHER
       HEAVY METALS ON GROWTH AND FUMARIC ACID PRODUCTION BY RHIZOPUS. J.BACT.
       37, 599-617.

1805   FOSTER, J.W., MCDANIEL, L.E., WOODRUFF, H.B. & STOKES, J.L. (1945) - MICRO-
       BIOLOGICAL ASPECTS OF PENICILLIN. 5. CONIDIOSPORE FORMATION IN SUBMERGED
       CULTURES OF PENICILLIUM NOTATUM. J.BACT. 50, 365-368.

1806   FOTHERGILL, P.G. & HIDE, D. (1962) - COMPARATIVE NUTRITIONAL STUDIES OF
       PYTHIUM SPECIES. J.GEN.MICROBIOL. 29, 325-334.

1807   FOTHERGILL, P.G. & JONES, M. (1958) - NUTRITIONAL STUDIES OF ZYGORHYNCHUS
       SPECIES. J.GEN.MICROBIOL. 19, 298-304.

1808   FOTHERGILL, P.G. & RAINE, L.C.D.P. (1954) - THE MINERAL NUTRITIONAL REQUIRE-
       MENTS OF MUCOR HIEMALIS. J.GEN.MICROBIOL. 10, 17-26.

1809   FOWLER, M. (1970) - NEW ZEALAND PREDACIOUS FUNGI. N.Z.JL BOT. 8, 283-302.

1810   FOWLKS, E.R., LEBEN, C. & SNELL, J.F. (1967) - STEROLS IN RELATION TO THE
       INFLUENCE OF NYSTATIN ON PYTHIUM APHANIDERMATUM AND COLLETOTRICHUM LA-
       GENARIUM. PHYTOPATHOLOGY 57, 246-249.

1811   FOX, R.A. (1953) - HETEROTHALLISM IN CHAETOMIUM. NATURE, LOND. 172, 165-
       166.

1812   FRAGNER, P. (1970) - (SPANNWEITE DER ART TRICHOSPORON CUTANEUM). CESKA MY-
       KOL. 24, 153-161.

1813   FRAGNER, P. & BELSAN, I. (1974) - SCOPULARIOPSIS BAIN. AS CAUSATIVE AGENT
       OF ONYCHOMYCOSES - MYCOLOGICAL AND CLINICAL STUDY. 1. MYCOLOGICAL STUDY.
       ACTA UNIV.CAROL., MED. 20, 305-331.

1814   FRAGNER, P., VITOVEC, J. & VLADIK, P. (1975) - (MUCOR PUSILLUS AS A CAUSA-
       TIVE AGENT OF NODOSE MUCORMYCOSIS IN A YOUNG BULL). CESKA MYKOL. 29,
       59-60.

1815   FRANK, H.K. (1967) - MYKOTOXINE UND IHRE PRODUZENTEN. MEDSCHE KLIN. 62,
       1933-1941.

1816   FRANK, J.A. & FRANCIS, S.K. (1976) - THE EFFECT OF A RHIZOCTONIA SOLANI
       PHYTOTOXIN ON POTATOES. CAN.J.BOT. 54, 2536-2540.

1817   FRANK, W., ROESTER, U. & SCHOLER, H.J. (1974) - SPHAERULEN-BILDUNG BEI EI-
       NER MUCOR-SPEZIFS IN INNEREN ORGANEN VON AMPHIBIEN. ZENTBL.BAKT.PARA-
       SITKDE, ABT.1, 226, 405-417.

1818   FRANK, Z.R. (1972) - PYTHIUM MYRIOTYLUM AND FUSARIUM SOLANI AS COFACTORS
       IN A POD-ROT COMPLEX OF PEANUT. PHYTOPATHOLOGY 62, 1331-1334.

1819   FRANKE, W., JILGE, G. & EICHHORN, G. (1961) - ZUM ENZYMATISCHEN UMSATZ VON
       C2-SAEUREN DURCH MIKROORGANISMEN. 1. UEBER GLYOXYLATTRANSAMINASEN AUS
       SCHIMMELPILZEN, INSBESONDERE ASPERGILLUS NIGER. ARCH.MIKROBIOL. 39,
       58-87.

1820 FRANKE, W., MOECHEL, L. & HEYE, K. (1965) - ZUR KENNTNIS DER SOGENANNTEN GLUCOSEOXYDASE. 8. EINFLUSS EINER VARIATION VON C- UND N-QUELLEN AUF DIE INDUZIERTE ENZYMBILDUNG DURCH ASPERGILLUS NIGER. ARCH.MIKROBIOL. 51, 323-350.

1821 FRANKLAND, J.C. (1966) - SUCCESSION OF FUNGI ON DECAYING PETIOLES OF PTERIDIUM AQUILINUM. J.ECOL. 54, 41-63.

1822 FRANKLAND, J. (1969) - FUNGAL DECOMPOSITION OF BRACKEN PETIOLES. J.ECOL. 57, 25-36.

1823 FRANZ, G. (1960) - DIE MIKROFLORA EINIGER STANDORTE IM LEITHAGEBIRGE IN IHRER ABHAENGIGKEIT VON BODEN UND VEGETATIONSDECKE. SBER.OEST.AKAD.WISS., MATH.-NATURW.KL., ABT.1, 169, 101-198.

1824 FRANZ, G. (1971) - MIKROBIOLOGISCHE CHARAKTERISIERUNG EINIGER NATUERLICHER UND KULTIVIERTER STANDORTE IN DREI VERSCHIEDENEN OEKOLOGISCHEN REGIONEN CHILES. PL.SOIL 34, 133-158.

1825 FRANZ, G. (1973) - DER EINFLUSS DES PH WERTES DER BOEDEN SOWIE DER TEMPERATURVERHAELTNISSE AM STANDORT AUF DIE BODENPILZFLORA. LANDW.FORSCH., SONDERH. 28/1, 270-281.

1826 FRANZ, G. (1974) - MIKROBIOLOGISCHE UNTERSUCHUNGEN AN BOEDEN AUS NEPAL. PEDOBIOLOGIA 14, 372-401.

1827 FRANZ, G. (1975) - TEMPERATURANSPRUECHE MIKROSKOPISCHER BODENPILZE AUS KLIMATISCH UND GEOGRAPHISCH VERSCHIEDENEN STANDORTEN. Z.PFLERNAEHR.BODENK., 1975 (1), 73-87.

1828 FRANZ, H. & LOUP, W. (1959) - BODENBIOLOGISCHE UNTERSUCHUNGEN AN WALDDUENGUNGSVERSUCHEN. ZENTBL.GES.FORSTW. 76, 129-162.

1829 FRAPPIER, F., FERRON, P. & PAIS, M. (1975) - CHIMIE DES CHAMPIGNONS ENTOMOPATHOGENES - LE BEAUVELLIDE, NOUVEAU CYCLODEPSIPEPTIDE ISOLE D'UN BEAUVERIA TENELLA. PHYTOCHEMISTRY 14, 2703-2705.

1830 FREDERIKS, J.C. (1971) - UEBER L(+)-FUSARINOLSAEURE, EIN NEUES STOFFWECHSELPRODUKT VON FUSARIEN. VERH.SCHWEIZ.NATURFORSCH.GES. 151, 84-87.

1831 FREEMAN, G.G. & MORRISON, R.I. (1948) - TRICHOTHECIN - AN ANTIFUNGAL METABOLIC PRODUCT OF TRICHOTHECIUM ROSEUM LINK. NATURE, LOND. 162, 30.

1832 FREI, P. (1963) - DIE AUFNAHME VON STRONTIUM DURCH ZEA MAYS IN MISCHKULTUR MIT BODENPILZEN. BER.SCHWEIZ.BOT.GES. 73, 21-57.

1833 FREY, D. (1959) - ISOLATION OF A NEW SPECIES OF ALEURISMA FROM SOIL IN AUSTRALIA AND NEW GUINEA. MYCOLOGIA 51, 641-646.

1834 FREY, D. & GRIFFIN, D.M. (1961) - CTENOMYCES SERRATUS. TRANS.BR.MYCOL.SOC. 44, 449-452.

1835 FREY, D.M. (1965) - ISOLATION OF KERATINOPHILIC AND OTHER FUNGI FROM SOILS COLLECTED IN AUSTRALIA AND NEW GUINEA. MYCOLOGIA 57, 202-215.

1836 FREY, D.M. & DURIE, B.E. (1956) - THE ISOLATION OF KERATINOPHILIC FUNGI, INCLUDING MICROSPORUM GYPSEUM FROM AUSTRALIAN SOIL. AUS.J.EXP.BIOL.MED. SCI. 24, 199-204.

1837 FRIIS, J. & OTTOLENGHI, P. (1969) - PIGMENT FORMATION BY THE BLACK YEAST PHIALOPHORA JEANSELMEI. ANTONIE VAN LEEUWENHOEK 35 (SUPPL. YEAST SYMP.), H13-H14.

1838 FRIIS, J. & OTTOLENGHI, P. (1969) - THE PIGMENTATION OF BOVINE SERUM ALBUMIN BY PHIALOPHORA JEANSELMEI. C.R.TRAV.LAB.CARLSBERG 37, 179-193.

1839 FROST, D.A. & MORRISON, G.A. (1973) - METABOLIC PRODUCTS OF PENICILLIUM HERQUEI. TETRAHEDRON LETTERS, 1973 (46), 4729-4732.

1840 FUCHS, A., JOBSEN, J.A. & WOUTS, W.M. (1965) - ARABANASES IN PHYTOPATHOGENIC FUNGI. NATURE, LOND. 206, 714-715.

1841 FUHS, G.W. (1961) - DER MIKROBIELLE ABBAU VON KOHLENWASSERSTOFFEN. ARCH. MIKROBIOL. 39, 374-422.

1842 FUJIMOTO, Y., MORITA, Y. & TATSUNO, T. (1972) - RECHERCHES TOXICOLOGIQUES SUR LES SUBSTANCES TOXIQUES DE FUSARIUM NIVALE. ETUDE CHIMIQUE DES TOXINS PRINCIPALES, NIVALENOL, FUSARENON-X ET NIVALENOL-4,15-DI-O-ACETATE. CHEM.PHARM.BULL., TOKYO 20, 1194-1203.

1843 FUKUDA, Y., INOUE, Y. & FURUYA, M. (1971) - DEVELOPMENTAL ANATOMY OF EXPERIMENTALLY INDUCED ASCOCARPS IN GELASINOSPORA RETICULISPORA. BOT.MAG., TOKYO 84, 339-348.

1844 FULTON, N.D. & BOLLENBACHER, K. (1968) - EFFECT OF SOME CARBON SOURCES ON PRODUCTION OF A CHLOROSIS-INDUCING AGENT BY ALTERNARIA TENUIS. MYCOLOGIA 60, 685-691.

1845 FULTON, N.D., BOLLENBACHER, K. & TEMPLETON, G.E. (1965) - A METABOLITE FROM ALTERNARIA TENUIS THAT INHIBITS CHLOROPHYLL PRODUCTION. PHYTOPATHOLOGY 55, 49-51.

1846 FUNDER, S. (1949) - PHYSIOLOGICAL VARIATION IN PROTEOLYTIC PROPERTIES OF MOLDS. PROC.12TH INT.DAIRY CONGR. STOCKH. 2, 463-471.

1847 FUNES, A. & BURGOS, J. (1973/74) - HIDROCABUROS Y ESTEROIDES EN HEMISPORA STELLATA. AN.FAC.VET.LEON 19, 437-450.

1848 FURTADO, J.S. (1971) - THE SEPTAL PORE AND OTHER ULTRASTRUCTURAL FEATURES OF THE PYRENOMYCETE SORDARIA FIMICOLA. MYCOLOGIA 63, 104-113.

1849 FURUYA, K., ENOKITA, R. & SHIRASAKA, M. (1967) - STUDIES ON THE ANTIBIOTICS FROM FUNGI. 2. A NEW GRISEOFULVIN PRODUCER, NIGROSPORA ORYZAE. ANN. SANKYO RES.LAB. 19, 91-95.

1850 FUSKA, J., NEMEC, P. & KUHR, I. (1972) - VERMICULINE, A NEW ANTIPROTOZOAL ANTIBIOTIC FROM PENICILLIUM VERMICULATUM. J.ANTIBIOT., TOKYO 4, 208-211.

1851 GABRIEL, B.P. (1968) - ENZYMATIC ACTIVITIES OF SOME ENTOMOPHTHOROUS FUNGI. J.INVERTEBR.PATH. 11, 70-81.

1852 GABRIEL, B.P. & PADUA, L.E. (1974) - THE USE OF COCONUT MILK (GATA) AND OTHER MEDIA IN THE CULTURE OF ENTOMOPHTHORA CORONATA. KALIKASAN 3, 107-112.

1853 GAD, A.M. & WALKER, T.K. (1954) - MYCOLOGICAL FORMATION OF FAT. 1. MEDIA CONDUCIVE TO FORMATION OF FAT FROM SUCROSE BY ASPERGILLUS NIDULANS, PENICILLIUM JAVANICUM AND PENICILLIUM SPINULOSUM. J.SCI.FD AGRIC. 5, 339-343.

1854 GAEUMANN, E. & BOEHNI, E. (1947) - UEBER ADAPTIVE ENZYME BEI PARASITISCHEN PILZEN. 1. HELV.CHIM.ACTA 30, 24-38.

1855 GAEUMANN, E., NAEF-ROTH, S. & KERN, H. (1960) - ZUR PHYTOTOXISCHEN WIRK-
     SAMKEIT DER ENNIATINE. PHYTOPATH.Z. 40, 45-51.

1856 GAFOOR, A. & HEALE, J.B. (1971) - NEAR-UV IRRADIATION AND MORPHOGENESIS IN
     VERTICILLIUM. MICROBIOS 3, 131-141.

1857 GAHREN, W.J., ELLERSTAD, G.A., MARTIN, G.O. & KUNSTMANN, M.P. (1972) -
     LL-D 253 ALPHA, -BETA AND -GAMMA, NOVEL CHROMANONES FROM THE FUNGUS
     PHOMA PIGMENTIVORA. J.ORG.CHEM. 37, 1636-1639.

1858 GALANOPOULOS, N. & TRIBE, H.T. (1974) - CONIDIAL SURVIVAL IN VERTICILLIUM
     DAHLIAE. TRANS.BR.MYCOL.SOC. 63, 85-91.

1859 GALBRAITH, J.C. & SMITH, J.E. (1969) - SPORULATION OF ASPERGILLUS NIGER IN
     SUBMERGED LIQUID CULTURES. J.GEN.MICROBIOL. 59, 31-45.

1860 GALBRAITH, J.C. & SMITH, J.E. (1969) - CHANGES IN ACTIVITY OF CERTAIN EN-
     ZYMES OF THE TRICARBOXYLIC ACID CYCLE AND THE GLYOXYLATE CYCLE DURING
     THE INITIATION OF CONIDIATION OF ASPERGILLUS NIGER. CAN.J.MICROBIOL. 15,
     1207-1212.

1861 GALBRAITH, J.C. & SMITH, J.E. (1969) - FILAMENTOUS GROWTH OF ASPERGILLUS
     NIGER IN SUBMERGED SHAKE CULTURE. TRANS.BR.MYCOL.SOC. 52, 237-246.

1862 GALGOCZY, J. (1975) - DERMATOPHYTES - CONIDIUM ONTOGENY AND CLASSIFICATION.
     ACTA MICROBIOL.ACAD.SCI.HUNG. 22, 105-136.

1863 GALINDO, A.J. & ZENTMYER, G.A. (1964) - MATING TYPES IN PHYTOPHTHORA CIN-
     NAMOMI. PHYTOPATHOLOGY 54, 238-239.

1864 GALLEGLY, M.E. (1970) - GENETICS OF PHYTOPHTHORA. PHYTOPATHOLOGY 60, 1135-
     1141.

1865 GALLEMAERTS, V. (1910) - DE LA ZONATION DES CULTURES DE CHAMPIGNONS EN
     BOITE DE PETRI. RECL INST.BOT.LEO ERRERA 8, 213-223.

1866 GALLI, A. (1946) - UEBER DIE BILDUNG DER ASCORBINSAEURE UND IHRE STELLUNG
     IM STOFFWECHSEL VON ASPERGILLUS NIGER. BER.SCHWEIZ.BOT.GES. 56, 113-175.

1867 GALPIN, M.F.J. & JENNINGS, D.H. (1975) - HISTOCHEMICAL STUDY OF THE HYPHAE
     AND THE DISTRIBUTION OF ADENOSINE TRIPHOSPHATASE IN DENDRYPHIELLA SALI-
     NA. TRANS.BR.MYCOL.SOC. 65, 477-483.

1868 GALPIN, M.F.J., JENNINGS, D.H. & THORNTON, J.D. (1977) - HYPHAL BRANCHING
     IN DENDRYPHIELLA SALINA. EFFECT OF VARIOUS COMPOUNDS AND THE FURTHER
     ELUCIDATION OF THE EFFECT OF SORBOSE AND THE ROLE OF CYCLIC AMP. TRANS.
     BR.MYCOL.SOC. 69, 175-182.

1869 GALUN, E. (1971) - MORPHOGENESIS IN TRICHODERMA - INDUCTION OF CONIDIATION
     BY NARROW-BEAM ILLUMINATION OF RESTRICTED AREAS OF THE FUNGAL COLONY.
     PL.CELL PHYSIOL. 12, 779-783.

1870 GALUN, E. (1971) - SCANNING ELECTRON MICROSCOPY OF INTACT TRICHODERMA COL-
     ONIES. J.BACT. 108, 938-940.

1871 GALUN, E. (1972) - MORPHOGENESIS OF TRICHODERMA. AUTORADIOGRAPHY OF INTACT
     COLONIES LABELED BY (3H)M-ACETYLGLUCOSAMINE AS A MARKER OF NEW CELL WALL
     BIOSYNTHESIS. ARCH.MIKROBIOL. 86, 305-314.

1872 GALUN, E. (1977) - MORPHOGENESIS OF TRICHODERMA. ABS.2ND INT.MYCOL.CONGR.,
     TAMPA, 1977.

1873 GAMBOGI, P. (1967) - DECADIMENTO DEGLI AGRUMI CAUSATO DA FUSARIUM LATERI-TIUM NEES (GIBBERELLA BACCATA (WALLR.) SACC.). AGRICOLTURA ITAL., PISA 67, 77-83.

1874 GAMBOGI, P. (1969) - MICROMICETI NUOVI O RARI PER L'ITALIA, ISOLATI DA TERRENO DI BOSCO DEL LITORALE TIRRENICO. GIOR.BOT.ITAL. 103, 33-46.

1875 GAMBOGI, P. & MAZZUCCHETTI, G. (1966) - MICROFUNGHI CARTICOLI. AGRICOLTURA ITAL., PISA 66, 172-180.

1876 GAMS, W. (1959) - DIE BODENPILZE IM ZENTRALALPINEN ROHHUMUS. DISS.UNIV. INNSBRUCK.

1877 GAMS, W. (1960) - STUDIUM ZELLULOLYTISCHER BODENPILZE MIT HILFE DER ZEL-LOPHANSTREIFEN-METHODE UND MIT CARBOXYMETHYLZELLULOSE. SYDOWIA 14, 295-307.

1878 GAMS, W. (1966) - ZWEI ARTEN VON CHAETOMIUM MIT UNREGELMAESSIG GEFORMTEN ASCOSPOREN. NOVA HEDWIGIA 12, 385-388.

1879 GAMS, W. (1968) - TWO NEW SPECIES OF WARDOMYCES. TRANS.BR.MYCOL.SOC. 51, 798-802.

1880 GAMS, W. (1968) - DIE SYSTEMATISCHE STELLUNG DER SCHIMMELPILZE FUSIDIUM BUXI UND VERTICILLIUM CANDELABRUM. ACTA BOT.NEERL. 17, 455-460.

1881 GAMS, W. (1970) - GLIEDERUNGSPRINZIPIEN IN DER GATTUNG MORTIERELLA. NOVA HEDWIGIA 18, 30-43, 1969.

1882 GAMS, W. (1971) - CEPHALOSPORIUM-ARTIGE SCHIMMELPILZE (HYPHOMYCETES). G. FISCHER, STUTTGART.

1883 GAMS, W. (1977) - A KEY TO THE SPECIES OF MORTIERELLA. PERSOONIA 9, 381-391.

1884 GAMS, W. ( ) - GENERIC CONCEPTS IN HYPHOMYCETES WITH SLIMY ONE-CELLED PHIALOCONIDIA. IN: TAXONOMY OF FUNGI; SUBRAMANIAN, C.V. (ED.), UNIV. MADRAS, MADRAS (IN PRESS SINCE 1973).

1885 GAMS, W. (1978) - CONNECTED AND DISCONNECTED CHAINS OF PHIALOCONIDIA AND SAGENOMELLA GEN.NOV. SEGREGATED FROM ACREMONIUM. PERSOONIA 10, 97-112.

1886 GAMS, W., CHIEN, CH.-Y. & DOMSCH, K.H. (1972) - ZYGOSPORE FORMATION BY THE HETEROTHALLIC MORTIERELLA ELONGATA AND A RELATED HOMOTHALLIC SPECIES, M. EPIGAMA SP.NOV. TRANS.BR.MYCOL.SOC. 58, 5-13.

1887 GAMS, W. & DOMSCH, K.H. (1970) - BEMERKUNGEN ZU EINIGEN SCHWER BESTIMMBA-REN BODENPILZEN. NOVA HEDWIGIA 18, 1-29 (1969).

1888 GAMS, W. & DOMSCH, K.H. (1969) - THE SPATIAL AND SEASONAL DISTRIBUTION OF MICROSCOPIC FUNGI IN ARABLE SOILS. TRANS.BR.MYCOL.SOC. 52, 301-308.

1889 GAMS, W., DOMSCH, K.H. & WEBER, E. (1969) - NACHWEIS SIGNIFIKANT VERSCHIE-DENER PILZPOPULATIONEN BEI GLEICHER BODENNUTZUNG. PL.SOIL 31, 439-450.

1890 GAMS, W. & GERLAGH, M. (1968) - BEITRAEGE ZUR SYSTEMATIK UND BIOLOGIE VON PLECTOSPHAERELLA CUCUMERIS UND DER ZUGEHOERIGEN KONIDIENFORM. PERSOONIA 5, 177-188.

1891 GAMS, W. & HOLUBOVA-JECHOVA, V. (1976) - CHLORIDIUM AND SOME OTHER PHIALI-DIC DEMATIACEOUS GENERA GROWING ON DECAYING WOOD. STUD.MYCOL., BAARN 13, 99 PP.

1892 GAMS, W. & MOUCHACCA, J. (   ) - CONTRIBUTIONS TO THE KNOWLEDGE OF THE HYPHOMYCETE GENUS CLADORRHINUM. REVUE MYCOL. (IN PREPERATION).

1893 GAMS, W. & WILLIAMS, S.T. (1963) - HETEROTHALLISM IN MORTIERELLA PARVISPORA LINNEMANN. 1. MORPHOLOGY AND DEVELOPMENT OF ZYGOSPORES AND SOME FACTORS INFLUENCING THEIR FORMATION. NOVA HEDWIGIA 5, 342-357.

1894 GANCEDO, J.M., GANCEDO, C. & ASENSIO, C. (1967) - WIDESPREAD OCCURRENCE OF GALACTOSE OXIDASE AND GLUCOSE OXIDASE IN FUNGI. ARCHS BIOCHEM.BIOPHYS. 119, 588-590.

1895 GANDER, J.E. (1974) - FUNGAL CELL WALL GLYCOPROTEINS AND PEPTIDO-POLYSACCHARIDES. A.REV.MICROBIOL. 28, 103-119.

1896 GANDHI, A.P., BARAT, G.K. & DAS, N.B. (1974) - STUDIES ON THE PRODUCTION OF FUNGAL AMYLASES. MYCOPATH.MYCOL.APPL. 52, 307-311.

1897 GANGAWANE, L.V. & DESHPANDE, K.B. (1972) - TWO NEW RECORDS OF PENICILLIA FROM RHIZOSPHERE OF GROUNDNUT. CURR.SCI. 41, 78.

1898 GARBER, E.D. & BERAHA, L. (1966) - GENETICS OF PHYTOPATHOGENIC FUNGI. PECTOLYTIC ENZYMES OF VIRULENT AND AVIRULENT STRAINS OF THREE PHYTOPATHOGENIC PENICILLIA. CAN.J.BOT. 44, 1645-1650.

1899 GARBER, E.D., BERAHA, L. & SHAEFFER, S.G. (1965) - GENETICS OF PHYTOPATHOGENIC FUNGI. 13. PECTOLYTIC AND CELLULOLYTIC ENZYMES OF THREE PHYTOPATHOGENIC PENICILLIA. BOT.GAZ. 126, 36-40.

1900 GARBER, E.D. & RIPPON, J.W. (1968) - PROTEINS AND ENZYMES AS TAXONOMIC TOOLS. IN: ADV.APPL.MICROBIOL.; UMBREIT, W.W. & PERLMAN, D. (ED.), ACADEMIC PRESS, NEW YORK, LONDON, 10, 137-154.

1901 GARCIA-BALLESTA, J.P. (1971) - PURIFICACION Y PROPIEDADES DE LA BETA-(1-3)-GLUCANASA DE RHIZOPUS ARRHIZUS. MICROBIOL.ESP. 24, 257-269.

1902 GARDNER, D.E. & HENDRIX, F.F. (1973) - CARBON DIOXIDE AND OXYGEN CONCENTRATIONS IN RELATION TO SURVIVAL AND SAPROPHYTIC GROWTH OF PYTHIUM IRREGULARE AND PYTHIUM VEXANS IN SOIL. CAN.J.BOT. 51, 1593-1598.

1903 GARG, A.K. (1966) - OCCURRENCE OF KERATINOPHILIC CHRYSOSPORIUM CORDA SPECIES IN INDIAN SOILS. MYCOPATH.MYCOL.APPL. 29, 189-192.

1904 GARREN, K.H. & PORTER, D.M. (1970) - QUIESCENT ENDOCARPIC FLORAL COMMUNITIES IN CURED MATURE PEANUTS FROM VIRGINIA AND PUERTO RICO. PHYTOPATHOLOGY 60, 1635-1638.

1905 GARRETT, M.K. & ROBINSON, P.M. (1969) - A STABLE INHIBITOR OF SPORE GERMINATION PRODUCED BY FUNGI. ARCH.MIKROBIOL. 67, 370-377.

1906 GARRETT, S.D. (1941) - SOIL CONDITIONS AND THE TAKE-ALL DISEASE OF WHEAT. 7. SURVIVAL OF OPHIOBOLUS GRAMINIS ON THE ROOTS OF DIFFERENT GRASSES. ANN.APPL.BIOL. 28, 325-332.

1907 GARRETT, S.D. (1958) - INOCULUM POTENTIAL AS A FACTOR LIMITING LETHAL ACTION BY TRICHODERMA VIRIDE ON ARMILLARIA MELLEA. TRANS.BR.MYCOL.SOC. 41, 157-164.

1908 GARRETT, S.D. (1962) - DECOMPOSITION OF CELLULOSE IN SOIL BY RHIZOCTONIA SOLANI. TRANS.BR.MYCOL.SOC. 45, 115-120.

1909 GARRETT, S.D. (1963) – A COMPARISON OF CELLULOSE-DECOMPOSING ABILITY IN
      FIVE FUNGI CAUSING CEREAL FOOT ROTS. TRANS.BR.MYCOL.SOC. 46, 572-576.

1910 GARRETT, S.D. (1966) – CELLULOSE-DECOMPOSING ABILITY OF SOME CEREAL FOOT-
      ROT FUNGI IN RELATION TO THEIR SAPROPHYTIC SURVIVAL. TRANS.BR.MYCOL.
      SOC. 49, 57-68.

1911 GARRETT, S.D. (1967) – EFFECT OF NITROGEN LEVEL ON SURVIVAL OF OPHIOBOLUS
      GRAMINIS IN PURE CULTURE ON CELLULOSE. TRANS.BR.MYCOL.SOC. 50, 519-524.

1912 GARRETT, S.D. (1971) – EFFECTS OF NITROGEN LEVEL ON SURVIVAL OF PHIALOPHO-
      RA RADICICOLA AND COCHLIOBOLUS SATIVUS IN PURE CULTURE ON CELLULOSE.
      TRANS.BR.MYCOL.SOC. 57, 121-128.

1913 GARRETT, S.D. (1975) – SOURCES OF VARIABILITY IN DETERMINATIONS OF THE ME-
      DIAN PERIOD OF SAPROPHYTIC SURVIVAL BY COCHLIOBOLUS SATIVUS. TRANS.BR.
      MYCOL.SOC. 64, 351-355.

1914 GARRIDO, J.M. & WALKER, T.K. (1956) – MYCOLOGICAL FORMATION OF FAT. 2. SYN-
      THESIS OF FAT FROM VARIOUS CARBOHYDRATES IN SURFACE CULTURES OF ASPER-
      GILLUS NIDULANS, PENICILLIUM JAVANICUM AND PENICILLIUM SPINULOSUM AND
      THE INFLUENCE OF THE NITROGEN SOURCE ON THE SYNTHESIS OF FAT FROM GLU-
      COSE. J.SCI.FD AGRIC. 7, 234-237.

1915 GARRISON, R.G., BOYD, K.S. & LANE, J.W. (1975) – ULTRASTRUCTURAL STUDIES
      ON THERMOMYCES LANUGINOSA AND CERTAIN OTHER CLOSELY RELATED THERMOPHIL-
      IC FUNGI. MYCOLOGIA 67, 961-971.

1916 GARRISON, R.G., BOYD, K.S. & MARIAT, F. (1975) – ULTRASTRUCTURAL STUDIES
      ON THE MYCELIUM-TO-YEAST TRANSFORMATION OF SPOROTHRIX SCHENCKII. J.BACT.
      124, 959-968.

1917 GARRISON, R.G., DODD, H.T. & HAMILTON, J.W. (1970) – THE UPTAKE OF LOW
      MOLECULAR WEIGHT SULFUR-CONTAINING COMPOUNDS BY HISTOPLASMA CAPSULATUM
      AND RELATED DIMORPHIC FUNGI. MYCOPATH.MYCOL.APPL. 40, 171-180.

1918 GARRISON, R.G. & LANE, J.W. (1971) – YEAST-LIKE TO MYCELIAL PHASE TRANS-
      FORMATION OF HISTOPLASMA CAPSULATUM AS OBSERVED BY SCANNING ELECTRON
      MICROSCOPY. MYCOPATH.MYCOL.APPL. 43, 185-193.

1919 GARRISON, R.G. & LANE, J.W. (1973) – SCANNING-BEAM ELECTRON MICROSCOPY OF
      THE CONIDIA OF THE BROWN AND ALBINO FILAMENTOUS VARIETIES OF HISTOPLAS-
      MA CAPSULATUM. MYCOPATH.MYCOL.APPL. 49, 185-191.

1920 GARRISON, R.G., MARIAT, F., BOYD, K.S. & TALLY, J.F. (1975) – ULTRASTRUC-
      TURAL AND ELECTRON CYTOCHEMICAL STUDIES OF ENTOMOPHTHORA CORONATA. ANNLS
      MICROBIOL. 126B, 149-173.

1921 GASCOIGNE, J.A. & GASCOIGNE, M.M. (1960) – BIOLOGICAL DEGRADATION OF CEL-
      LULOSE. BUTTERWORTHS & CO., LONDON.

1922 GASSNER, G. & NIEMANN, E. (1955) – SYNERGISTISCHE UND ANTAGONISTISCHE WIR-
      KUNG VON PILZEN UND BAKTERIEN AUF DIE SPORENKEIMUNG VERSCHIEDENER TIL-
      LETIA-ARTEN. PHYTOPATH.Z. 23, 395-418.

1923 GATENBECK, S. & HERMODSSON, S. (1965) – ENZYMATIC SYNTHESIS OF THE AROMA-
      TIC PRODUCT ALTERNARIOL. ACTA CHEM.SCAND. 19, 65-71.

1924 GATENBECK, S. & SIERANKIEWICZ, J. (1973) – MICROBIAL PRODUCTION OF TENUA-
      ZONIC ACID ANALOGUES. ANTIMICROB.AGENTS CHEMOTHER. 3, 308-309.

1925 GATES, J.E., MILLIKAN, D.F. & CIMANOWSKI, J. (1975) - ENDOGENOUS CONSTITU-
ENTS IN APPLE BARK TISSUE AFFECTING THE IN VITRO GROWTH OF PHYTOPHTHO-
RA CACTORUM. BULL.ACAD.POL.SCI., SER.SCI.BIOL. 23, 283-290.

1926 GAUDET-DUPONT, G. (1973) - MORPHOGENESES COMPAREES DU MUCOR PRAINII ET DU
STOLON DU RHIZOPUS ARRHIZUS. REVUE MYCOL. 37, 214-217.

1927 GAUGER, W.L. (1961) - THE GERMINATION OF ZYGOSPORES OF RHIZOPUS STOLONIFER.
AM.J.BOT. 48, 427-429.

1928 GAUGER, W. (1965) - THE GERMINATION OF ZYGOSPORES OF MUCOR HIEMALIS. MYCO-
LOGIA 57, 634-641.

1929 GAUGER, W.L. (1975) - FURTHER STUDIES ON SEXUALITY IN AZYGOSPORIC STRAINS
OF MUCOR HIEMALIS. TRANS.BR.MYCOL.SOC. 64, 113-118.

1930 GAYED, S.K. (1966) - BACILLUS PUMILIS AND ITS MYCOLYTIC ACTION AGAINST HEL-
MINTHOSPORIUM SATIVUM. PL.SOIL 24, 178-180.

1931 GAYED, S.K. (1972) - RHIZOPUS ARRHIZUS CAUSING POLE ROT OF FLUE-CURED TO-
BACCO IN ONTARIO. CAN.J.PL.SCI. 52, 103-106.

1932 GAYED, S.K. & NAGUIB, K. (1962) - THE EFFECT OF PH VALUE ON THE TOXICITY
OF CULTURE FILTRATES OF HELMINTHOSPORIUM SATIVUM AND ON ITS POSSIBLE
CORRELATION TO EXTRACELLULAR NITROGEN ACCUMULATION. MYCOPATH.MYCOL.APPL.
16, 83-89.

1933 GEHRIG, R.F. & KNIGHT, S.G. (1961) - FORMATION OF 2-HEPTANONE FROM CAPRY-
LIC ACID BY SPORES OF VARIOUS FILAMENTOUS FUNGI. NATURE, LOND. 192, 1185.

1934 GEIGER, W.B. & CONN, J.E. (1945) - THE MECHANISM OF THE ANTIBIOTIC ACTION
OF CLAVACIN AND PENICILLIC ACID. J.AM.CHEM.SOC. 67, 112-116.

1935 GEIGER-HUBER, M. & GALLI, H. (1945) - UEBER DEN NACHWEIS DER L-ASCORBIN-
SAEURE ALS STOFFWECHSELPRODUKT VON ASPERGILLUS NIGER. HELV.CHIM.ACTA 28,
248-250.

1936 GENTILE, A.C. (1954) - CARBOHYDRATE METABOLISM AND OXALIC ACID SYNTHESIS
BY BOTRYTIS CINEREA. PL.PHYSIOL., LANCASTER 29, 257-261.

1937 GEORG, L.K., AJELLO, L., FRIEDMAN, L. & BRINKMAN, SH.A. (1961/62) - A NEW
SPECIES OF MICROSPORUM PATHOGENIC TO MAN AND ANIMALS. SABOURAUDIA 1,
189-196.

1938 GEORG, L.K., KAPLAN, W., AJELLO, L., WILLIAMSON, W.M. & TILDEN, E.B. (1959)
- THE PARASITIC NATURE OF THE SOIL FUNGUS KERATINOMYCES AJELLOI. J.IN-
VEST.DERM. 32, 539-544.

1939 GEORG, L.K., WILLIAMSON, W.M., TILDEN, E.B. & GETTY, R.E. (1962) - MYCOTIC
PULMONARY DISEASE OF CAPTIVE GIANT TORTOISES TO BEAUVARIA BASSIANA AND
PAECILOMYCES FUMOSO-ROSEUS. SABOURAUDIA 2, 80-86.

1940 GERASIMOVA, N.M., LE, ZUI-LIN & BEKHTEREVA, M.N. (1975) - (STUDY OF LIPID
COMPOSITION OF CUNNINGHAMELLA ELEGANS GROWN ON N-ALKANES). MIKROBIOLO-
GIYA 44, 460-464.

1941 GERLACH, W. (1956) - BEITRAEGE ZUR KENNTNIS DER GATTUNG CYLINDROCARPON. 1.
CYLINDROCARPON RADICICOLA ALS KRANKHEITSERREGER AN ALPENVEILCHEN. PHY-
TOPATHOLOGY 26, 161-170.

1942 GERLACH, W. (1959) - BEITRAEGE YUR KENNTNIS DER GATTUNG CYLINDROCARPON. 3.
CYLINDROCARPON OLIDUM UND SEINE PHYTOPATHOLOGISCHE BEDEUTUNG. PHYTOPATH.
Z. 35, 333-346.

1943 GERLACH, W. (1961) - FUSARIUM REDOLENS, SEINE MORPHOLOGIE UND SYSTEMATI-
SCHE STELLUNG. EIN BEITRAG ZUR KENNTNIS DER ELEGANS-FUSARIEN. PHYTOPATH.
Z. 42, 150-160.

1944 GERLACH, W. (1968) - CALONECTRIA UNISEPTATA N.SP., DIE BISHER UNBEKANNTE
HAUPTFRUCHTFORM VON CYLINDROCLADIUM SCOPARIUM MORGAN. PHYTOPATH.Z. 61,
372-381.

1945 GERLACH, W. (1970) - SUGGESTIONS TO AN ACCEPTABLE MODERN FUSARIUM SYSTEM.
ANNLS ACAD.SCI.FENN.A, IV BIOLOGICA 168, 37-49.

1946 GERLACH, W. (1972) - FUSARIEN AUS TRINKWASSERLEITUNGEN. ANNLS AGRIC.FENN.
11, 298-302.

1947 GERLACH, W. (1977) - FUSARIUM SPECIES INCITING PLANT DISEASES IN THE TRO-
PICS. IN: PESTS AND WEEDS IN TROPICAL CROPS; KRANZ, J., SCHMUTTERER, H.
& KOCH, W. (ED.), P.PAREY, BERLIN, HAMBURG, 210-217.

1948 GERLACH, W. (   ) - ILLUSTRATED ATLAS TO THE SPECIES OF FUSARIUM. MITT.
BIOL.BUNDANST.LD-U.FORSTW. (IN PREPERATION).

1949 GERLACH, W. & ERSHAD, D. (1970) - BEITRAG ZUR KENNTNIS DER FUSARIUM- UND
CYLINDROCARPON-ARTEN IN IRAN. NOVA HEDWIGIA 20, 725-784.

1950 GERLACH, W. & NILSSON, L. (1963) - BEITRAEGE ZUR KENNTNIS DER GATTUNG CY-
LINDROCARPON. 5. NECTRIA RADICICOLA N.SP., DIE BISHER UNBEKANNTE HAUPT-
FRUCHTFORM VON CYLINDROCARPON RADICICOLA. PHYTOPATH.Z. 48, 251-257.

1951 GERLACH, W. & PAG, H. (1961) - FUSARIUM REDOLENS WR., SEINE PHYTOPATHOLO-
GISCHE BEDEUTUNG UND EINE AN DIANTHUS-ARTEN GEFAESSPARASITAERE FORM (F.
REDOLENS WR. F. DIANTHI GERLACH). PHYTOPATH.Z. 42, 348-361.

1952 GERLAGH, M. (1968) - INTRODUCTION OF OPHIOBOLUS GRAMINIS INTO NEW POLDERS
AND ITS DECLINE. NETH.J.PL.PATH. 74, SUPPL.2, 1-97.

1953 GERRETSEN, F.C. (1956) - BORON, AN ESSENTIAL ELEMENT FOR AZOTOBACTER AND
SOME OTHER MICROORGANISMS. SCR.VARIA PONT.ACAD.SCI. 14, 233-244.

1954 GERRETTSON-CORNELL, L. (1974) - A COMPARATIVE TEST OF ISOLATION OF PHYTO-
PHTHORA CINNAMOMI BETWEEN THE LUPIN BAITING AND A NEWLY DEVISED APPLE
TRAP. PHYTON, B.AIRES 32, 35-36.

1955 GERRETTSON-CORNELL, L. & TOWNSEND, S.R. (1974) - A STUDY OF A LUPIN BAI-
TING TECHNIQUE FOR ISOLATION OF PHYTOPHTHORA CINNAMOMI UNDER DIFFERENT
LIGHTING CONDITIONS. PHYTON, B.AIRES 32, 39-44.

1956 GERSONDE, M. & KERNER-GANG, W. (1968) - UNTERSUCHUNGEN AN MODERFAEULE-PIL-
ZEN AUS HOLZSTAEBEN NACH FREILANDVERSUCHEN. MATER.ORG. 3, 199-212.

1957 GESER, G. (1962) - UNTERSUCHUNGEN AN ASPERGILLUS NIGER VAN TIEGH. - UEBER
ZINKAUFNAHME UND AKTIVITAETSVERAENDERUNGEN EINIGER ENZYME BEI ZINKMAN-
GEL. ARCH.MIKROBIOL. 41, 408-440.

1958 GESSNER, R.V. & GOOS, R.D. (1973) - FUNGI FROM DECOMPOSING SPARTINA ALTER-
NIFLORA. CAN.J.BOT. 51, 51-55.

1959 GESSNER, R.V. & GOOS, R.D. (1973) - FUNGI FROM SPARTINA ALTERNIFLORA IN
RHODE ISLAND. MYCOLOGIA 65, 1296-1301.

1960 GEZUELE, E., MACKINNON, J.E. & CONTI-DIAZ, I.A. (1972) - THE FREQUENT ISO-
LATION OF PHIALOPHORA VERRUCOSA AND PHIALOPHORA PEDROSOI FROM NATURAL
SOURCES. SABOURAUDIA 10, 266-273.

1961   GHABBOUR, S.I. & MISHRIKY, A.G. (1967) - FUNGI ISOLATED FROM EARTHWORM
       CULTURES. REVUE ECOL.BIOL.SOL 4, 645-648.

1962   GHAFFAR, A. (1972) - SOME OBSERVATIONS ON THE PARASITISM OF CONIOTHYRIUM
       MINITANS ON THE SCLEROTIA OF SCLEROTINIA SCLEROTIORUM. PAKIST.J.BOT. 4,
       85-87.

1963   GHAFFAR, A. & ABBAS, S.Q. (1972) - FUNGI OF KARACHI. SUPPLEMENT 2. PAKIST.
       J.BOT. 4, 195-208.

1964   GHAFFAR, A. & FATIMA, K. (1970) - INHIBITION OF TRICHODERMA VIRIDE BY STA-
       CHYBOTRYS ATRA. SCI.INDUST. 7, 88-90.

1965   GHAFFAR, A. & GHIZALA PARVEEN (1969) - COLONIZATION OF COTTON ROOTS BY
       SOIL MICROORGANISMS. MYCOPATH.MYCOL.APPL. 38, 373-376.

1966   GHATAK, P.N. & ROY, T.C. (1939) - STUDIES IN THE SOIL FUNGI OF THE PADDY-
       FIELDS OF BENGAL. 1. FUNGI OF AN UNMANURED PADDY-FIELD OF THE CHINSU-
       RAH AGRICULTURAL FARM. J.INDIAN BOT.SOC. 18, 113-127.

1967   GHEORGHIU, P. & BOJOR, O. (1957) - ANTIBIOTIC PROPERTIES OF THE FUNGUS
       SCLEROTINIA SCLEROTIORUM. FARMACIA, BUC. 5, 228-231.

1968   GHIORSE, W. & EDWARDS, M.R. (1973) - ULTRASTRUCTURE OF ASPERGILLUS FUMIGA-
       TUS CONIDIA DEVELOPMENT AND MATURATION. PROTOPLASMA 76, 49-59.

1969   GHOSH, A.K. (1966) - VITAMIN REQUIREMENTS OF TWO PATHOGENIC ISOLATES OF
       COLLETOTRICHUM DEMATIUM. INDIAN PHYTOPATH. 19, 245-250.

1970   GHOSH, G.R. (1955) - COMPARATIVE PHYSIOLOGY OF SOME MEMBERS OF THE GYMNOAS-
       CACEAE. DISS.ABSTR. 15, 15.

1971   GHOSH, R.K. & THANGAMANI, A. (1973) - INFLUENCE OF INORGANIC NITRATE ON
       THE FORMATION OF EXTRACELLULAR PROTEASE AND RIBONUCLEASE BY PENICILLIUM
       JANTHINELLUM. CAN.J.MICROBIOL. 19, 1219-1223.

1972   GIBBS, J.G. (1938) - A TECHNIQUE FOR STUDYING THE LONGEVITY OF PHOMA LIN-
       GAM IN THE SOIL. PHYTOPATHOLOGY 28, 762-763.

1973   GIBBS, J.N. (1967) - A STUDY OF THE EPIPHYTIC GROWTH HABIT OF FOMES ANNO-
       SUS. ANN.BOT. 31, 755-774.

1974   GIBSON, I.A.S. (1953) - CROWN ROT, A SEEDLING DISEASE OF GROUNDNUTS CAUSED
       BY ASPERGILLUS NIGER. TRANS.BR.MYCOL.SOC. 36, 198-209.

1975   GIBSON, I.A.S. (1957) - SAPROPHYTIC FUNGI AS DESTROYERS OF GERMINATING
       PINE SEEDS. E.AFR.AGRIC.FOR.J. 22, 203-206.

1976   GIEBEL, J. (1973) - BIOCHEMICAL ASSOCIATION BETWEEN INFECTION OF HETERODE-
       RA ROSTOCHIENSIS AND DEVELOPMENT OF RHIZOCTONIA SOLANI ON POTATO. BULL.
       ACAD.POL.SCI., CL.5, SER.SCI.BIOL. 21, 465-470.

1977   GIERCZAK, M. (1964) - (STUDIES ON THE OCCURRENCE OF FUNGI OF THE CLASS
       ASCOMYCETES IN FOREST SOILS). PR.KOM.NAUK ROLN.LESN., POZNAN 17, 21-27.

1978   GIERCZAK, M. (1967) - (MICROFLORA OF FOREST NURSERY SOILS, AND PARASITIC
       DAMPING-OFF OF SEEDLING ROOTS). ACTA MYCOL., WARSZAWA 3, 3-47.

1979   GILBERT, W.J. & HICKEY, R.J. (1946) - PRODUCTION OF CONIDIA IN SUBMERGED
       CULTURES OF PENICILLIUM NOTATUM. J.BACT. 51, 731-733.

1980   GILES, D. & TURNER, W.B. (1969) - CHLORINE-CONTAINING METABOLITES OF PERI-
       CONIA MACROSPINOSA. J.CHEM.SOC.(C), 1969 (16), 2187-2189.

1981   GILGAN, M.W., SMALLEY, E.B. & STRONG, F.M. (1966) - ISOLATION AND PARTIAL
       CHARACTERIZATION OF A TOXIN FROM FUSARIUM TRICINCTUM ON MOLDY CORN.
       ARCHS BIOCHEM.BIOPHYS. 114, 1-3.

1982   GILL, H.S. & POWELL, D. (1967) - DIFFERENTIATION OF THREE SPECIES OF PHY-
       TOPHTHORA BY POLYACRYLAMIDE GEL ELECTROPHORESIS. PHYTOPATHOLOGY 57, 812,
       (ABS.).

1983   GILLIAM, M. & PREST, D.B. (1972) - FUNGI ISOLATED FROM THE INTESTINAL CON-
       TENTS OF FORAGING WORKER HONEY BEES, APIS MELLIFERA. J.INVERTEBR.PATH.
       20, 101-103.

1984   GILMAN, G.A. (1969) - AN EXAMINATION OF FUNGI ASSOCIATED WITH GROUND-NUT
       PODS. TROP.SCI. 11, 38-48.

1985   GILMAN, J.C. & ABBOTT, E.V. (1927) - A SUMMARY OF THE SOIL FUNGI. IOWA
       ST.J.SCI. 1, 225-344.

1986   GILPATRICK, J.D. (1969) - EFFECT OF SOIL AMENDMENTS UPON INOCULUM SURVIVAL
       AND FUNCTION IN PHYTOPHTHORA ROOT ROT OF AVOCADO. PHYTOPATHOLOGY 59,
       979-985.

1987   GILPATRICK, J.D. & HENRY, A.W. (1950) - THE EFFECT OF NUTRITIONAL FACTORS
       ON THE DEVELOPMENT OF OPHIOBOLUS GRAMINIS. PROC.CAN.PHYTOPATH.SOC. 17,
       14.

1988   GINDRAT, D. (1966) - RECHERCHES SUR LA PHYSIOLOGIE DE LA NUTRITION DE GAEU-
       MANNOMYCES GRAMINIS ET ETABLISSEMENT D'UN MILIEU SYNTHETIQUE MINIMUM.
       BER.SCHWEIZ.BOT.GES. 75, 183-218.

1989   GINDRAT, D. (1966) - ETUDE DE LA FORMATION DES PERITHECES DE GAEUMANNOMY-
       CES GRAMINIS EN MILIEU ARTIFICIEL ET MISE AU POINT D'UNE TECHNIQUE D'IM-
       MERSION DES CULTURES POUR LEUR FORMATION INDUITE. BER.SCHWEIZ.BOT.GES.
       76, 157-175.

1990   GINDRAT, D. (1976) - COMPONENTS IN UNBLEACHED COMMERCIAL CHITIN STIMULATE
       PYTHIUM ULTIMUM IN SUGAR BEET SPERMOSPHERE. PHYTOPATHOLOGY 66, 312-316.

1991   GINDRAT, D. (1977) - EFFETS DE CONCENTRATIONS ELEVEES DE SELS SUR LA CROIS-
       SANCE, LA SPORULATION ET LA PIGMENTATION DE TRICHODERMA SPP. CAN.J.MI-
       CROBIOL. 23, 607-616.

1992   GINGRICH, W.D. (1962) - KERATOMYCOSIS. J.AM.MED.ASS. 179, 602.

1993   GIOELLI, F. (1932) - FENOMENI DI ANTAGONISMO IN PENICILLIUM DIGITATUM E
       PENICILLIUM ITALICUM IN NATURA. RIV.PAT.VEG., PADOVA 22, 1-6.

1994   GIRGINKOC, H.R. (1951) - UNTERSUCHUNGEN UEBER DIE "ZWARTE HOUTVATENZIEKTE"
       DER FUTTER- UND ZUCKERRUEBE, VERURSACHT DURCH PYTHIUM IRREGULARE. MEDED.
       LANDBHOGESCH.WAGENINGEN 51, 1-61.

1995   GISI, U. (1975) - EINE NEUE METHODE ZUR QUANTITATIVEN DIREKTBEOBACHTUNG
       DER SPORANGIEN VON PHYTOPHTHORA CACTORUM (LEB. & COHN) SCHROET. IM BO-
       DEN. Z.PFLKRANKH.PFLSCHUTZ 82, 30-47.

1996   GISI, U. (1975) - UNTERSUCHUNGEN UEBER DIE BODENPHASE VON PHYTOPHTHORA
       CACTORUM MIT FLUORESZENZOPTISCHER DIREKTBEOBACHTUNG. Z.PFLKRANKH.
       PFLSCHUTZ 82, 355-377.

1997 GISI, U. & MEYER, D. (1973) - OEKOLOGISCHE UNTERSUCHUNGEN AN PHYTOPHTHORA CACTORUM (LEB. & COHN) SCHROET. IM BODEN MIT·DIREKTEN BEOBACHTUNGSMETHODEN. PHYTOPATH.Z. 76, 276-279.

1998 GJAERUM, H. (1966) - THE GENUS ARTHRINIUM IN NORWAY. NYTT MAG.BOT. 13, 5-14.

1999 GLEASON, F.H. (1971) - ALCOHOL DEHYDROGENASE IN MUCORALES. MYCOLOGIA 63, 906-910.

2000 GLEASON, F.H. & LONG, G.L. (1976) - ALCOHOL DEHYDROGENASE IN MUCORALES. 3. MYCOLOGIA 68, 426-428.

2001 GLICK, A.D. & KWON-CHUNG, K.J. (1973) - ULTRASTRUCTURAL COMPARISON OF COILS AND ASCOSPORES OF EMMONSIELLA CAPSULATA AND AJELLOMYCES DERMATITIDIS. MYCOLOGIA 65, 216-220.

2002 GLISTER, G.A. & WILLIAMS, T.I. (1944) - PRODUCTION OF GLIOTOXIN BY ASPERGILLUS FUMIGATUS MUT. HELVOLA YUILL. NATURE, LOND. 153, 651.

2003 GLITZ, G., ANGEL, L. & EICHLER, D.C. (1972) - CHARACTERIZATION OF A GUANYLIC ACID SPECIFIC RIBONUCLEASE FROM ASPERGILLUS FUMIGATUS. BIOCHEMISTRY 11, 1746-1754.

2004 GOCHENAUR, S.E. (1964) - THE SOIL MICROFUNGI OF WILLOW-COTTONWOOD FORESTS IN SOUTHERN WISCONSIN. DISS.UNIV.WISCONSIN.

2005 GOCHENAUR, S.E. (1970) - SOIL MYCOFLORA OF PERU. MYCOPATH.MYCOL.APPL. 42, 259-272.

2006 GOCHENAUR, S.E. (1975) - DISTRIBUTIONAL PATTERNS OF MESOPHILOUS AND THERMOPHILOUS MICROFUNGI IN TWO BAHAMIAN SOILS. MYCOPATHOLOGIA 57, 155-164.

2007 GOCHENAUR, S.E. & BACKUS, M.P. (1967) - MYCOECOLOGY OF WILLOW AND COTTONWOOD LOWLAND COMMUNITIES IN SOUTHERN WISCONSIN. 2. SOIL MICROFUNGI IN IN THE SANDBAR WILLOW STANDS. MYCOLOGIA 59, 893-901.

2008 GOCHENAUR, S.E. & WHITTINGHAM, W.F. (1967) - MYCOECOLOGY OF WILLOW AND COTTON-WOOD LOWLAND COMMUNITIES IN SOUTHERN WISCONSIN. 1. SOIL MICROFUNGI IN THE WILLOW-COTTONWOOD FORESTS. MYCOPATH.MYCOL.APPL. 33, 125-139.

2009 GOCHENAUR, S.E. & WOODWELL, G.M. (1974) - THE SOIL MICROFUNGI OF A CHRONICALLY IRRADIATED OAK-PINE FOREST. ECOLOGY 55, 1004-1016.

2010 GODDARD, H.N. (1913) - CAN FUNGI LIVING IN AGRICULTURAL SOIL ASSIMILATE FREE NITROGEN? BOT.GAZ. 56, 249-305.

2011 GODEAS, A.M. (1972) - MICROFLORA DEL SUELO DE LA ARGENTINIA. 1. ALGUNAS FORMAS ASCOSPORICAS DE LA REGION CHAQUENA. MYCOPATH.MYCOL.APPL. 46, 189-204.

2012 GODEAS, A.M. (1975) - MICOFLORA DEL SUELO DE LA ARGENTINA. 5. FORMAS ASCOSPORICAS ADICIONALES DE LA PCIA. DE BUENOS AIRES, PROVINCIA FITOGEOGRAFICA DEL ESPINAL, DISTRITO DE LOS TALARES. MYCOPATHOLOGIA 56, 81-96.

2013 GODFREY, B.E.S. (1974) - PHYLLOPLANE MYCOFLORA OF BRACKEN, PTERIDIUM AQUILINUM. TRANS.BR.MYCOL.SOC. 62, 305-311.

2014 GODIN, P. (1954) - ETUDE DU METABOLISME TERNAIRE DE PENICILLIUM BREVICOMPACTUM. MEM.INST.AGRON.LOUVAIN 8, 1-68.

2015   GODTFREDSEN, W.O. & LORCK, H.O.B. (1963) - ANTIBIOTIC AND THERAPEUTIC COM-
       POSITIONS THEREOF. U.S.PATENT 3072531, 1963.

2016   GODTFREDSEN, W.O. & VANGEDAL, S. (1964) - TRICHODERMIN, A NEW ANTIBIOTIC,
       RELATED TO TRICHOTHECIN. PROC.CHEM.SOC., 1964, 188-189.

2017   GODTFREDSEN, W.O. & VANGEDAL, S. (1965) - TRICHODERMIN, A NEW SESQUITER-
       PENE ANTIBIOTIC. ACTA CHEM.SCAND. 19, 1088-1120.

2018   GOETTE, H. (1974) - UNTERSUCHUNGEN ZUR CHARAKTERISIERUNG VON PYTHIUM-ARTEN
       DURCH ANALYSE IHRER PROTEIN- UND ENZYMSPEKTREN. DISS.UNIV.BONN.

2019   GOLD, E.W. & VERTCH, F.P. (1973) - STUDIES ON A PYROPHOSPHATASE AND GLU-
       COSE-6-PHOSPHATASE FROM ASPERGILLUS ORYZAE. BIOCHIM.BIOPHYS.ACTA 327,
       166.

2020   GOLDING, N.S. (1945) - THE GAS REQUIREMENTS OF MOLDS. 4. A PRELIMINARY IN-
       TERPRETATION OF THE GROWTH RATES OF FOUR COMMON MOLD CULTURES ON THE
       BASIS OF ABSORBED GASES. J.DAIRY SCI. 28, 737-750.

2021   GOLEBIOWSKA, J. (1948) - (CONTRIBUTION TO THE STUDY OF CELLULOSE DECOMPO-
       SITION BY SOIL MOULDS). ANNLS UNIV.MARIAE CURIE-SKLODOWSKA 2E, 223-248.

2022   GOLLIFER, D.E. & BOOTH, R.H. (1973) - STORAGE LOSSES OF TARO CORMS IN THE
       BRITISH SOLOMON ISLAND PROTECTORATE. ANN.APPL.BIOL. 73, 349-356.

2023   GOMOLYAKO, N.I. (1956) - (FUNGI OCCURRING ON SPRING WHEAT ROOTS). MYKRO-
       BIOL.ZH. 18 (3), 12-24.

2024   GONDO, M. (1962) - SOIL-ECOLOGICAL STUDIES ON THE SOIL PATHOGENS. 4. EFFECTS
       OF VARIOUS SOIL-FACTORS ON THE GROWTH OF CORTICIUM ROLFSII CURZI. 5.
       EFFECT OF VARIOUS SOIL-FACTORS ON THE GROWTH OF AGROBACTERIUM TUMEFA-
       CIENS (SMITH & TOWNSEND) CONN. BULL.FAC.AGRIC.KAGOSHIMA UNIV. 10, 23-31.

2025   GOODAY, G.W. (1968) - HORMONAL CONTROL OF SEXUAL REPRODUCTION IN MUCOR MU-
       CEDO. NEW PHYTOL. 67, 815-821.

2026   GOODAY, G.W. (1973) - DIFFERENTIATION IN THE MUCORALES. IN: MICROBIAL DIF-
       FERENTIATION; ASHWORTH, J.M. & SMITH, J.E. (ED.), SYMP.SOC.GEN.MICRO-
       BIOL., CAMBRIDGE, 23, 269-294.

2027   GOODAY, G.W., FAWCETT, P., GREEN, D. & SHAW, G. (1973) - THE FORMATION OF
       FUNGAL SPOROPOLLENIN IN THE ZYGOSPORE WALL OF MUCOR MUCEDO - A ROLE FOR
       THE SEXUAL CAROTENOGENESIS IN THE MUCORALES. J.GEN.MICROBIOL. 74, 233-
       239.

2028   GOODMAN, N.L. & LARSH, H.W. (1967) - ENVIRONMENTAL FACTORS AND GROWTH OF
       HISTOPLASMA CAPSULATUM IN SOIL. MYCOPATH.MYCOL.APPL. 33, 145-156.

2029   GOOL, A.P.VAN & SCHMIDT, E.L. (1973) - NITRIFICATION IN RELATION TO GROWTH
       IN ASPERGILLUS FLAVUS. SOIL BIOL.BIOCHEM. 5, 259-265.

2030   GOOS, R.D. (1960) - SOIL FUNGI FROM COSTA RICA AND PANAMA. MYCOLOGIA 52,
       877-883.

2031   GOOS, R.D. (1963) - FURTHER OBSERVATIONS ON SOIL FUNGI IN HONDURAS. MYCO-
       LOGIA 55, 142-150.

2032   GOOS, R.D. (1965) - GROWTH AND SURVIVAL OF HISTOPLASMA CAPSULATUM IN SOIL.
       CAN.J.MICROBIOL. 11, 979-985.

2033   GOOS, R.D., COX, E.A. & STOTZKY, G. (1961) - BOTRYODIPLODIA THEOBROMAE AND
       ITS ASSOCIATION WITH MUSA SPECIES. MYCOLOGIA 53, 262-277.

2034   GOOS, R.D. & PIROZYNSKI, K.A. (1975) - FUNGI OF BARRO COLORADO ISLAND -
       NEW AND INTERESTING HYPHOMYCETES. CAN.J.BOT. 53, 2927-2932.

2035   GOOS, R.D. & TIMONIN, M.I. (1962) - FUNGI FROM THE RHIZOSPHERE OF BANANA
       IN HONDURAS. CAN.J.BOT. 40, 1371-1377.

2036   GORAL, V.M. & LAPPA, N.V. (1972) - (THE EFFECT OF MEDIUM PH ON GROWTH AND
       VIRULENCE OF BEAUVERIA BASSIANA (BALS.) VUILL.). MYKROBIOL.ZH. 34 (4),
       454-457.

2037   GORDEE, R.S. & PORTER, C.L. (1961) - STRUCTURE, GERMINATION, AND PHYSIOLO-
       GY OF MICROSCLEROTIA OF VERTICILLIUM ALBO-ATRUM. MYCOLOGIA 53, 171-182.

2038   GORDON, W.L. (1944) - THE OCCURRENCE OF FUSARIUM SPECIES IN CANADA. 1. SPE-
       CIES OF FUSARIUM ISOLATED FROM FARM SAMPLES OF CEREAL SEED IN MANITOBA.
       CAN.J.RES., SECT.C, 22, 282-286.

2039   GORDON, W.L. (1952) - THE OCCURRENCE OF FUSARIUM SPECIES IN CANADA. 2. PRE-
       VALENCE AND TAXONOMY OF FUSARIUM SPECIES IN CEREAL SEED. CAN.J.BOT. 30,
       209-251.

2040   GORDON, W.L. (1954) - THE OCCURRENCE OF FUSARIUM SPP. IN CANADA. 3. TAXON-
       OMY OF FUSARIUM SPECIES IN THE SEED OF VEGETABLES, FORAGE, AND MISCEL-
       LANEOUS CROPS. CAN.J.BOT. 32, 576-590.

2041   GORDON, W.L. (1956) - THE OCCURRENCE OF FUSARIUM SPECIES IN CANADA. 5. TAX-
       ONOMY AND GEOGRAPHIC DISTRIBUTION OF FUSARIUM SPECIES IN SOIL. CAN.J.
       BOT. 34, 833-846.

2042   GORDON, W.L. (1956) - THE TAXONOMY AND HABITATS OF THE FUSARIUM SPECIES IN
       TRINIDAD, B.W.I. CAN.J.BOT. 34, 847-864.

2043   GORDON, W.L. (1959) - THE OCCURRENCE OF FUSARIUM SPP. IN CANADA. 6. TAX-
       ONOMY AND GEOGRAPHIC DISTRIBUTION OF FUSARIUM SPP. ON PLANTS, INSECTS
       AND FUNGI. CAN.J.BOT. 37, 257-290.

2044   GORDON, W.L. (1960) - IS NECTRIA HAEMATOCOCCA THE PERFECT STAGE OF FUSA-
       RIUM OXYSPORUM? NATURE, LOND. 186, 903.

2045   GORDON, W.L. (1960) - THE TAXONOMY AND HABITATS OF FUSARIUM SPECIES FROM
       TROPICAL AND TEMPERATE REGIONS. CAN.J.BOT. 38, 643-658.

2046   GORDON, W.L. (1965) - PATHOGENIC STRAINS OF FUSARIUM OXYSPORUM. CAN.J.BOT.
       43, 1309-1318.

2047   GORIN, P.A.J., HASKINS, R.H. & WESTLAKE, D.W.S. (1966) - NEW GALACTOBIOSYL
       GLUCOSE FORMED FROM LACTOSE BY CHAETOMIUM GLOBOSUM. CAN.J.CHEM. 44,
       2083-2086.

2048   GORIN, P.A.J. & SPENCER, J.F.T. (1967) - A NOVEL PENTOSYLMANNAN ARISING
       FROM THE YEAST TRICHOSPORON CUTANEUM. CAN.J.CHEM. 45, 1543-1549.

2049   GORIN, P.A.J. & SPENCER, J.F.T. (1968) - STRUCTURAL CHEMISTRY OF FUNGAL
       POLYSACCHARIDES. ADV.CARBOH.CHEM. 23, 367-414.

2050   GORLENKO, M.V. (1948) - THE TOXINS OF MOLDS. AM.REV.SOVIET MED. 5, 163-
       164.

2051   GORNIAK, H. & KACZKOWSKI, J. (1973) - THE INFLUENCE OF NITROGEN SOURCE ON
       THE BIOSYNTHESIS AND PROPERTIES OF GLUCOSE OXIDASE IN CULTURES OF PENI-
       CILLIUM NOTATUM. BULL.ACAD.POL.SCI., CL.2, SER.SCI.BIOL. 21, 571-576.

2052 GORSKI, F. (1949) - THE UTILIZATION OF RACEMIC MALIC ACID BY ASPERGILLUS
     AND PENICILLIUM SPECIES. BULL.ACAD.POL.SCI.LITT., CL.SCI.MATH.NAT.,
     SER.D, 1949, 1-14.

2053 GOTTLIEB, D. & VAN ETTEN, J.L. (1964) - BIOCHEMICAL CHANGES DURING THE
     GROWTH OF FUNGI. 1. NITROGEN COMPOUNDS AND CARBOHYDRATE CHANGES IN PE-
     NICILLIUM ATROVENETUM. J.BACT. 88, 114-121.

2054 GOTTLIEB, D. & VAN ETTEN, J.L. (1966) - CHANGES IN FUNGI WITH AGE. 1.
     CHEMICAL COMPOSITION OF RHIZOCTONIA SOLANI AND SCLEROTIUM BATATICOLA.
     J.BACT. 91, 161-168.

2055 GOTTLIEB, D. & TRIPATHI, R.K. (1968) - THE PHYSIOLOGY OF SWELLING PHASE OF
     SPORE GERMINATION IN PENICILLIUM ATROVENETUM. MYCOLOGIA 60, 571-590.

2056 GOTTLIEB, D. & WOOD, S.G. (1975) - THE DIFFERENCES AND SIMILARITIES IN THE
     STEROL PATHWAY IN STEROL SYNTHESIZING AND STEROL NONSYNTHESIZING FUNGI.
     PROC.AM.PHYTOPATH.SOC. 2, 56.

2057 GOTTLIEB, M. & BUTLER, K.D. (1939) - A PYTHIUM ROOT ROT OF CUCURBITS. PHY-
     TOPATHOLOGY 29, 624-628.

2058 GOUJON, M. (1966) - MISE EN EVIDENCE D'UN TYPE FONDAMENTAL D'HYPHE CHEZ
     LE CORTICIUM ROLFSII. C.R.HEBD.SEANC.ACAD.SCI., PARIS, SER.D, 263, 1695-
     1698.

2059 GOUJON, M. (1967) - ORIENTATION ET FONCTION DES TRANSFERTS DE PROTOPLASME
     CHEZ LE CORTICIUM ROLFSII. C.R.HEBD.SEANC.ACAD.SCI., PARIS, SER.D, 264,
     261-264.

2060 GOUJON, M. (1967) - MISE EN EVIDENCE DE TROIS PHASES DISTINCTES DANS LE
     DEVELOPPEMENT DU CORTICIUM ROLFSII EN CE QUI CONCERNE LA FORMATION DES
     SCLEROTES. C.R.HEBD.SEANC.ACAD.SCI., PARIS, SER.D, 264, 2989-2991.

2061 GOUJON, M. (1968) - MISE EN EVIDENCE DANS LE MYCELIUM DU CORTICIUM ROLFSII
     (SACC.) CURZI, D'UN FACTEUR MORPHOGENETIQUE RESPONSABLE DE L'APPARITION
     DES SCLEROTES. C.R.HEBD.SEANC.ACAD.SCI., PARIS, SER.D, 267, 409-411.

2062 GOUJON, M. (1969) - ETUDE COMPARATIVE DU CORTICIUM ROLFSII ET DU CORTICIUM
     COFFEICOLUM. CAH. O.R.S.T.O.M., SER.BIOL. 7, 69-87.

2063 GOUJON, M. (1970) - MECANISMES PHYSIOLOGIQUES DE LA FORMATION DES SCLERO-
     TES CHEZ LE CORTICIUM ROLFSII. PHYSIOLOG.VEG. 8, 349-360.

2064 GOURLEY, C.O. (1969) - MICROFUNGI OF CROWNS AND ROOTS OF APPARENTLY HEAL-
     THY DORMANT STRAWBERRY PLANTS. CAN.J.BOT. 47, 945-949.

2065 GOURLEY, C.O. & MACNAB, A.A. (1964) - VERTICILLIUM DAHLIAE AND GLIOCLADIUM
     ROSEUM ISOLATION FROM STRAWBERRIES IN NOVA SCOTIA. CAN.J.PL.SCI. 44,
     544-549.

2066 GRAHAM, J.H. & ZEIDERS, K.E. (1960) - PATHOGENICITY AND MORPHOLOGY OF SOME
     LEGUMINICOLOUS AND RELATED SPECIES OF STEMPHYLIUM. PHYTOPATHOLOGY 50,
     757-760.

2067 GRAVES, R.R. & HESSELTINE, C.W. (1966) - FUNGI IN FLOUR AND REFRIGERATED
     DOUGH PRODUCTS. MYCOPATH.MYCOL.APPL. 29, 277-290.

2068 GRAY, T.R.G. & BAXBY, P. (1968) - CHITIN DECOMPOSITION IN SOIL. 2. THE
     ECOLOGY OF CHITINOCLASTIC MICRO-ORGANISMS IN FOREST SOIL. TRANS.BR.MY-
     COL.SOC. 51, 293-309.

2069   GRAY, T.R.G. & BELL, T.F. (1963) - THE DECOMPOSITION OF CHITIN IN AN ACID
       SOIL. IN: SOIL ORGANISMS; DOEKSEN, J. & DRIFT, J.VAN DER (ED.), NORTH
       HOLLAND PUBL.CO., AMSTERDAM, 222-230.

2070   GRAY, W.D. (1971) - THE USE OF FUNGI AS FOOD AND ON FOOD PROCESSING. CRC
       PRESS, CLEVELAND, OHIO, 113 PP.

2071   GREATHOUSE, G.A. (1950) - MICROBIOLOGICAL DEGRADATION OF CELLULOSE. TEXT.
       RES.J. 20, 227-238.

2072   GREATHOUSE, G.A. & AMES, L.M. (1945) - FABRIC DETERIORATION BY THIRTEEN
       DESCRIBED AND THREE NEW SPECIES OF CHAETOMIUM. MYCOLOGIA 37, 138-155.

2073   GREEN, R.J. (1957) - THE VERTICAL DISTRIBUTION OF VERTICILLIUM ALBO-ATRUM
       IN MUCK SOILS AND ITS CONTROL. PHYTOPATHOLOGY 47, 522 (ABS.).

2074   GREEN, R.J. (1969) - SURVIVAL AND INOCULUM POTENTIAL OF CONIDIA AND MICRO-
       SCLEROTIA OF VERTICILLIUM ALBO-ATRUM IN SOIL. PHYTOPATHOLOGY 59, 874-
       876.

2075   GREEN, R.J. & PAPAVIZAS, G.C. (1968) - THE EFFECT OF CARBON SOURCE, CARBON
       TO NITROGEN RATIOS, AND ORGANIC AMENDMENTS ON SURVIVAL OF PROPAGULES OF
       VERTICILLIUM ALBO-ATRUM IN SOIL. PHYTOPATHOLOGY 58, 567-570.

2076   GREENAWAY, W. (1972) - EPIFLORA OF OAT SEED TREATED WITH ORGANO-MERCURY.
       TRANS.BR.MYCOL.SOC. 52, 321-327.

2077   GREENAWAY, W., CRIPPS, A. & WARD, S. (1974) - RESISTANCE TO ORGANO-MERCURY
       BY PENICILLIA ISOLATED FROM CEREAL SEED. TRANS.BR.MYCOL.SOC. 63,
       137-141.

2078   GREGORY, K.F., ALLEN, D.N., RIKER, A.J. & PETERSON, W.H. (1952) - ANTIBIOT-
       ICS AND ANTAGONISTIC MICROORGANISMS AS CONTROL AGENTS AGAINST DAMPING-
       OFF OF ALFALFA. PHYTOPATHOLOGY 42, 613-622.

2079   GREGORY, P.H. (1949) - STUDIES ON SCLEROTINIA AND BOTRYTIS. TRANS.BR.MYCOL.
       SOC. 32, 1-10.

2080   GREGORY, P.H. (1973) - MICROBIOLOGY OF THE ATMOSPHERE. LEONARD HILL, AYLES-
       BURY, 2ND ED., 377 PP.

2081   GREGORY, P.H. & LACEY, M.E. (1963) - MYCOLOGICAL EXAMINATION OF DUST FROM
       MOULDY HAY ASSOCIATED WITH FARMER'S LUNG DISEASE. J.GEN.MICROBIOL. 30,
       75-88.

2082   GREGORY, P.H. & LACEY, M.E. (1964) - THE DISCOVERY OF PITHOMYCES CHARTARUM
       IN BRITAIN. TRANS.BR.MYCOL.SOC. 47, 25-30.

2083   GREGORY, P.H. & STEDMAN, O.J. (1958) - SPORE DISPERSAL IN OPHIOBOLUS GRAMI-
       NIS AND OTHER FUNGI OF CEREAL FOOT ROTS. TRANS.BR.MYCOL.SOC. 41, 449-
       456.

2084   GREWAL, J.S. (1955) - EFFECT OF NITROGEN NUTRITION ON GROWTH AND SPORULA-
       TION OF ALTERNARIA TENUIS STRAIN B, CAUSING CORE ROT OF APPLES. LLOY-
       DIA 18, 74-81.

2085   GREWAL, J.S. (1955) - EFFECT OF TRACE ELEMENTS ON GROWTH AND SPORULATION
       OF ALTERNARIA TENUIS. LLOYDIA 19, 188-191.

2086   GRIBANOVSKI-SASSU, O. & FOPPEN, F.H. (1967) - THE CAROTENOIDS OF THE FUN-
        GUS EPICOCCUM NIGRUM. PHYTOCHEMISTRY 6, 907-909.

2087   GRIBANOVSKI-SASSU, O. & FOPPEN, F.H. (1968) - LIPID CONSTITUENTS OF SOME
        FUSARIUM SPECIES. ARCH.MIKROBIOL. 62, 251-256.

2088   GRIBANOVSKI-SASSU, O. & FOPPEN, F.H. (1968) - LIGHT AND TEMPERATURE EFFECT
        ON EPICOCCUM NIGRUM. PHYTOCHEMISTRY 7, 1605-1612.

2089   GRIEBLE, H.G., RIPPON, J.W., MALIWAN, N. & DAUN, V. (1975) - SCOPULARIOP-
        SOSIS AND HYPERSENSITIVITY PNEUMONITIS IN AN ADDICT. ANN.INTERN.MED.
        83, 326-329.

2090   GRIESBACH, E. & EISBEIN, K. (1975) - DIE BEDEUTUNG VON UNKRAEUTERN FUER
        DIE UEBERTRAGUNG VON RHIZOCTONIA SOLANI KUEHN. 3. DER EINFLUSS DER UN-
        KRAEUTER AUF DEN BEFALL DER KARTOFFELN. ZENTBL.BAKT.PARASITKDE, ABT.2,
        130, 745-760.

2091   GRIFFIN, D.M. (1960) - FUNGAL COLONIZATION OF STERILE HAIR IN CONTACT WITH
        SOIL. TRANS.BR.MYCOL.SOC. 43, 583-596.

2092   GRIFFIN, D.M. (1960) - THE REDISCOVERY OF GYMNOASCUS GYPSEUS, THE PERFECT
        STATE OF MICROSPORUM GYPSEUM, AND A NOTE ON TRICHOPHYTON TERRESTRE.
        TRANS.BR.MYCOL.SOC. 43, 637-642.

2093   GRIFFIN, D.M. (1963) - SOIL MOISTURE AND THE ECOLOGY OF SOIL FUNGI. BIOL.
        REV. 38, 141-166.

2094   GRIFFIN, D.M. (1963) - SOIL PHYSICAL FACTORS AND THE ECOLOGY OF FUNGI. 2.
        BEHAVIOUR OF PYTHIUM ULTIMUM AT SMALL SOIL WATER SUCTIONS. TRANS.BR.MY-
        COL.SOC. 46, 368-372.

2095   GRIFFIN, D.M. (1963) - SOIL PHYSICAL FACTORS AND THE ECOLOGY OF FUNGI. 3.
        ACTIVITY OF FUNGI IN RELATIVELY DRY SOIL. TRANS.BR.MYCOL.SOC. 46, 373-
        377.

2096   GRIFFIN, D.M. (1966) - SOIL PHYSICAL FACTORS AND THE ECOLOGY OF FUNGI. 4.
        INFLUENCE OF THE SOIL ATMOSPHERE. TRANS.BR.MYCOL.SOC. 49, 115-119.

2097   GRIFFIN, D.M. (1966) - FUNGI ATTACKING SEEDS IN DRY SEED-BEDS. PROC.LINN.
        SOC.N.SW., 1966, 84-89.

2098   GRIFFIN, D.M. (1966) - A STUDY OF DAMPING-OFF, ROOT DAMAGE AND RELATED
        PHENOMENA IN CONIFEROUS SEEDLINGS IN BRITISH FOREST NURSERIES. BULL.FOR.
        COMMN., LOND. 37, 212-227.

2099   GRIFFIN, D.M. & NAIR, N.G. (1968) - GROWTH OF SCLEROTIUM ROLFSII AT DIF-
        FERENT CONCENTRATION OF OXYGEN AND CARBON DIOXIDE. J.EXP.BOT. 19, 812-
        816.

2100   GRIFFIN, G.J. (1969) - FUSARIUM OXYSPORUM AND ASPERGILLUS FLAVUS SPORE
        GERMINATION IN THE RHIZOSPHERE OF PEANUT. PHYTOPATHOLOGY 59, 1214-1218.

2101   GRIFFIN, G.J. (1970) - EXOGENOUS CARBON AND NITROGEN REQUIREMENTS FOR CHLA-
        MYDOSPORE GERMINATION BY FUSARIUM SOLANI: DEPENDENCE ON SPORE DENSITY.
        CAN.J.MICROBIOL. 16, 1366-1368.

2102   GRIFFIN, G.J. (1973) - MODIFICATION OF THE EXOGENOUS CARBON AND NITROGEN
        REQUIREMENTS FOR CHLAMYDOSPORE GERMINATION OF FUSARIUM SOLANI BY CON-
        TACT WITH SOIL. CAN.J.MICROBIOL. 19, 999-1005.

2103   GRIFFIN, G.J., FORD, R.H. & GARREN, K.H. (1975) - RELATION OF ASPERGILLUS
        FLAVUS COLONY GROWTH ON THREE SELECTIVE MEDIA TO RECOVERY FROM NATURAL-
        LY INFESTED SOIL. PHYTOPATHOLOGY 65, 704-707.

2104 GRIFFIN, G.J. & GARREN, K.H. (1974) - POPULATION LEVELS OF ASPERGILLUS FLA-
      VUS AND THE ASPERGILLUS NIGER GROUP IN VIRGINIA PEANUT FIELD SOILS. PHY-
      TOPATHOLOGY 64, 322-325.

2105 GRIFFIN, G.J., HORA, T.S. & BAKER, R. (1975) - SOIL FUNGISTASIS. ELEVATION
      OF THE EXOGENOUS CARBON AND NITROGEN REQUIREMENTS FOR SPORE GERMINATION
      BY FUNGISTATIC VOLATILES IN SOILS. CAN.J.MICROBIOL. 21, 1468-1475.

2106 GRIFFIN, H.D. (1968) - THE GENUS CERATOCYSTIS IN ONTARIO. CAN.J.BOT. 46,
      689-718.

2107 GRIFFIN, H.L., SLONEKER, J.H. & INGLETT, G.E. (1974) - CELLULASE PRODUC-
      TION BY TRICHODERMA VIRIDE ON FEEDLOT WASTE. APPL.MICROBIOL. 27, 1061-
      1066.

2108 GRIFFITHS, D.A. (1970) - PARAMURAL BODIES IN HYPHAE OF VERTICILLIUM DAH-
      LIAE REVEALED BY FREEZE ETCHING. ARCH.MIKROBIOL. 73, 331-336.

2109 GRIFFITHS, D.A. (1971) - HYPHAL STRUCTURE IN FUSARIUM OXYSPORUM (SCHLECHT.)
      REVEALED BY FREEZE-ETCHING. ARCH.MIKROBIOL. 79, 93-101.

2110 GRIFFITHS, D.A. (1973) - FINE STRUCTURE OF THE CHLAMYDOSPORE WALL IN FUSA-
      RIUM OXYSPORUM. TRANS.BR.MYCOL.SOC. 61, 1-6.

2111 GRIFFITHS, D.A. (1973) - FINE STRUCTURE OF CHLAMYDOSPORE GERMINATION IN
      FUSARIUM OXYSPORUM. TRANS.BR.MYCOL.SOC. 61, 7-12.

2112 GRIFFITHS, D.A. (1974) - DEVELOPMENT AND STRUCTURE OF THE ALEURIOSPORES OF
      HUMICOLA GRISEA TRAAEN. CAN.J.MICROBIOL. 20, 55-58.

2113 GRIFFITHS, D.A. & CAMPBELL, W.P. (1971) - THE FINE STRUCTURE OF RESTING
      MYCELIUM OF VERTICILLIUM ALBO-ATRUM R. & B. CAN.J.MICROBIOL. 17, 1533-
      1535.

2114 GRIFFITHS, E. & JONES, D. (1963) - COLONIZATION OF CELLULOSE BY SOIL MICRO-
      ORGANISMS. TRANS.BR.MYCOL.SOC. 46, 285-294.

2115 GRIFFITHS, E. & SIDDIQI, M.A. (1958) - MICROBIAL ANTAGONISM OF FUSARIUM
      CULMORUM. NATURE, LOND. 182, 956.

2116 GRIFFITHS, E. & SIDDIQI, M.A. (1961) - SOME FACTORS AFFECTING OCCURRENCE
      OF FUSARIUM CULMORUM IN THE SOIL. TRANS.BR.MYCOL.SOC. 44, 343-353.

2117 GRIGORTSOVSKAYA, T.P. & BORODAI, N.I. (1972) - (TESTS OF THE TOXICITY OF
      FUNGAL CULTURES OF ASPERGILLUS NIGER V. TIEGH., ASPERGILLUS FUMIGATUS
      FRES., TRICHODERMA LIGNORUM (TODE) HARZ FOR BEES IN THE MARITIME AREA).
      MIKOL.FITOPAT. 6, 345-346.

2118 GRIMES, R.M., DUNCAN, C.W. & HOPPERT, C.A. (1957) - MULTIPLICITY OF CELLU-
      LOLYTIC ENZYMES OF MYROTHECIUM VERRUCARIA. ARCHS BIOCHEM.BIOPHYS. 68,
      412-424.

2119 GRIMES, M., O'CONNOR, M. & CUMMINS, H.A. (1932) - A STUDY OF SOME PHOMA
      SPECIES. TRANS.BR.MYCOL.SOC. 17, 97-111.

2120 GRIMMER, H. (1974) - MYKOTISCHES GRANULOM DURCH TRICHOPHYTON TERRESTRE.
      MYKOSEN 17, 333-338.

2121 GRINDLE, M. (1963) - HETEROKARYON COMPATIBILITY OF UNRELATED STRAINS IN
      THE ASPERGILLUS NIDULANS GROUP. HEREDITY 18, 191-204.

2122 GRINDLE, M. (1963) - HETEROKARYON COMPATIBILITY OF CLOSELY RELATED WILD
      ISOLATES OF ASPERGILLUS NIDULANS. HEREDITY 18, 397-405.

2123 GROB, E.C. & BUETLER, R. (1956) - UEBER DIE BIOSYNTHESE DES BETA-CAROTINS
      BEI MUCOR HIEMALIS WEHMER. DIE BETEILIGUNG DER ESSIGSAEURE AM AUFBAU
      DER CAROTINMOLEKEL, INSBESONDERE IN DEN STELLUNGEN 3,4,6 BZW. 3',4',6',
      UNTERSUCHT MIT HILFE VON 14C-MARKIERTER ESSIGSAEURE. HELV.CHIM.ACTA 39,
      1975-1980.

2124 GROGAN, R.G. & ABAWI, G.S. (1975) - INFLUENCE OF WATER POTENTIAL ON GROWTH
      AND SURVIVAL OF WHETZELINIA SCLEROTIORUM. PHYTOPATHOLOGY 65, 122-128.

2125 GROSKLAGS, J.H. & SWIFT, M.E. (1957) - THE PERFECT STAGE OF AN ANTIBIOTIC
      -PRODUCING CEPHALOSPORIUM. MYCOLOGIA 49, 305-317.

2126 GROSSBARD, E. (1952) - ANTIBIOTIC PRODUCTION BY FUNGI ON ORGANIC MANURES
      AND IN SOIL. J.GEN.MICROBIOL. 6, 295-310.

2127 GROSSMANN, F. (1968) - WIRKUNGSMECHANISMEN DER GRUENDUENGUNG GEGENUEBER
      BODENBUERTIGEN PFLANZENKRANKHEITEN. QUALITAS PL.MATER.VEG. 3, 239-256.

2128 GROSU, R. & HULEA, A. (1973) - MORPHOGENESIS, SPOROGENESIS, CULTURAL AND
      PHYSIOLOGICAL FEATURES OF MYROTHECIUM VERRUCARIA. REVUE ROUM. BIOL.,
      SER.BOT. 18, 219-225.

2129 GROUET, D. (1961) - LE PYTHIUM DE LA TULIPE - BIOLOGIE - TRAITEMENTS. PHY-
      TIATR.PHYTOPHARM. 10, 71-76.

2130 GROVE, J.F. (1970) - PHYTOTOXIC COMPOUNDS PRODUCED BY FUSARIUM EQUISETI.
      5. TRANSFORMATION PRODUCTS OF 4-BETA,15-DIACETOXY-3-ALPHA,7-ALPHA-DIHY-
      DROXY-12,13-EPOXYTRICHOTHEC-9-EN-8-ONE AND THE STRUCTURES OF NIVALENOL
      AND FUSARENONE. J.CHEM.SOC.(C), 1970, 375-378.

2131 GROVE, J.F. (1970) - PHYTOTOXIC COMPOUNDS PRODUCED BY FUSARIUM EQUISETI.
      6. 4-BETA,8-ALPHA,15-TRIACETOXY-12,13-EPOXYTRICHOTHEC-9-ENE-3-ALPHA,7-
      ALPHA-DIOL. J.CHEM.SOC.(C), 1970, 378-379.

2132 GROVE, J.F. (1972) - NEW METABOLIC PRODUCTS OF ASPERGILLUS FLAVUS. 1. AS-
      PERENTIN, ITS METHYL ETHERS, AND 5-HYDROXYASPERENTIN. J.CHEM.SOC.PER-
      KIN TRANS.I, 1972 (19), 2400-2406.

2133 GROVE, J.F. (1972) - NEW METABOLIC PRODUCTS OF ASPERGILLUS FLAVUS. 2. J.
      CHEM.SOC.PERKIN TRANS.I, 1972, 2406-2411.

2134 GROVE, J.F. (1974) - NEW METABOLIC PRODUCTS OF ASPERGILLUS FLAVUS. 4. 4-
      HYDROXYASPERENTIN AND 5-HYDROXYASPERENTIN 8-METHYL ETHER. J.CHEM.SOC.
      PERKIN TRANS.I, 1974 (22), 2704-2706.

2135 GROVE, J.F. & BRIAN, P.W. (1951) - IDENTITY OF FREQUENTIC ACID AND CITRO-
      MYCETIN. NATURE, LOND. 167, 995.

2136 GROVE, S.N. (1972) - APICAL VESICLES IN GERMINATING CONIDIA OF ASPERGILLUS
      PARASITICUS. MYCOLOGIA 64, 638-640.

2137 GROVE, S.N., BRACKER, C.E. & MORRE, D.J. (1970) - AN ULTRASTRUCTURAL BASIS
      FOR HYPHAL TIP GROWTH IN PYTHIUM ULTIMUM. AM.J.BOT. 57, 245-266.

2138 GROVE, S.N., MORRE, D.J. & BRACKER, C.E. (1966) - DICTYOSOMES IN VEGETA-
      TIVE HYPHAE OF PYTHIUM ULTIMUM. PROC.INDIAN ACAD.SCI., SECT.B, 76, 210-
      214.

2139 GROVE, S.N., OUJEZDSKY, K.B. & SZANISZLO, P.J. (1973) - BUDDING IN THE DI-MORPHIC FUNGUS PHIALOPHORA DERMATITIDIS. J.BACT. 115, 323-329.

2140 GROVER, R.K. & DUTT, S. (1973) - MORPHOLOGICAL AND PATHOLOGICAL VARIABIL-ITY IN PYTHIUM APHANIDERMATUM. INDIAN PHYTOPATH. 26, 237-244.

2141 GROVES, J.W. & LOVELAND, C.A. (1953) - THE CONNECTION BETWEEN BOTRYOTINIA FUCKELIANA AND BOTRYTIS CINEREA. MYCOLOGIA 45, 415-425.

2142 GROVES, J.W. & SKOLKO, A.J. (1944) - NOTES ON SEED-BORNE FUNGI. 1. STEM-PHYLIUM. CAN.J.RES., SECT.C, 22, 190-199.

2143 GROVES, J.W. & SKOLKO, A.J. (1945) - NOTES ON SEED-BORNE FUNGI. 3. CURVU-LARIA. CAN.J.RES., SECT.C, 23, 94-104.

2144 GROVES, J.W. & SKOLKO, A.J. (1946) - NOTES ON SEED-BORNE FUNGI. 4. ACRE-MONIELLA, CHLAMYDOMYCES, AND TRICHOCLADIUM. CAN.J.RES., SECT.C, 24, 74-80.

2145 GRUBE, D. & SCHWARTZ, W. (1965) - UEBER DIE ANGEBLICHEN BEZIEHUNGEN VON CTENOMYCES SERRATUS EIDAM ZU DERMATOMYZETEN. Z.ALLG.MIKROBIOL. 5, 104-111.

2146 GRUNER, B.J., DEANGELO, A.B. & SHAW, P.D. (1972) - THE ISOLATION AND SOME PROPERTIES OF AN ENZYME SYSTEM WHICH CATALYZES THE DEGRADATION OF BETA -NITROPROPIONIC ACID. ARCHS BIOCHEM.BIOPHYS. 148, 107-114.

2147 GSTIRNER, F. (1942) - UEBER DIE HERSTELLUNG VON CALCIUM GLUCONICUM. CHEMI-KERZTG 66, 31-33.

2148 GUBA, E.F. (1961) - MONOGRAPH OF MONOCHAETIA AND PESTALOTIA. HARVARD UNIV. PRESS, CAMBRIDGE, MASS.

2149 GUBA, E.F. & RACKEMANN, F.M. (1938) - SPECIES OF CLADOSPORIUM ON TOMATO AND THE ALLERGIC RESPONSE IN MAN AS AN AID TO THEIR IDENTIFICATION. MY-COLOGIA 30, 625-634.

2150 GUEGUEN, F. (1905) - GLIOMASTIX (TORULA) CHARTARUM. CONTRIBUTION A L'ETUDE DE LA FORMATION ENDOGENE DES CONIDIES. BULL.TRIMEST.SOC.MYCOL.FR. 21, 230-242.

2151 GUERILLOT-VINET, J., GUERILLOT-VINET, A., GUYOT, L., MONTEGUT, J. & ROUX, L. (1950) - ANTIBIOTIQUES - SUR UNE SUBSTANCE ANTIBIOTIQUE EXTRAITE DU MYCELIUM DE GIBBERELLA BACCATA (WALLR.) SACC. C.R.HEBD.SEANC.ACAD.SCI., PARIS, SER.D, 230, 424-426.

2152 GUGINO, J.L., POKORNY, F.A. & HENDRIX, F.F. (1973) - POPULATION DYNAMICS OF PYTHIUM IRREGULARE BUIS. IN CONTAINER-PLANT PRODUCTION AS INFLUENCED BY PHYSICAL STRUCTURE OF MEDIA. PL.SOIL 39, 591-602.

2153 GUGNANI, H.C. (1972) - FUNGI ISOLATED FROM LUNGS OF SMALL WILD ANIMALS IN INDIA. MYKOSEN 15, 479-482.

2154 GUGNANI, H.C., GUPTA, S. & TALWAR, R.S. (1977) - ROLE OF OPPORTUNISTIC FUN-GI ON OCULAR INFECTIONS IN NIGERIA. ABS.2ND INT.MYCOL.CONGR., TAMPA, 1977.

2155 GUGNANI, H.C., RANDHAWA, H.S. & SHRIVASTAV, J.B. (1971) - ISOLATION OF DER-MATOPHYTES AND OTHER KERATINOPHILIC FUNGI FROM APPARENTLY HEALTHY SKIN COATS OF DOMESTIC ANIMALS. INDIAN J.MED.RES. 59, 1699-1702.

2156 GUGNANI, H.C. & SHRIVASTAV, J.B. (1972) - OCCURRENCE OF PATHOGENIC FUNGI
      IN SOIL IN INDIA. INDIAN J.MED.RES. 60, 40-47.

2157 GUHA MOZUMDER, B.K., CAROSELLI, N.E. & ALBERT, L.S. (1970) - INFLUENCE OF
      WATER ACTIVITY, TEMPERATURE, AND THEIR INTERACTION ON GERMINATION OF
      VERTICILLIUM ALBO-ATRUM CONIDIA. PL.PHYSIOL., LANCASTER 46, 347-349.

2158 GUILLEMAT, J. (1960) - INTERACTIONS ENTRE LA SIMAZINE ET LA MYCOFLORE DU
      SOL. C.R.HEBD.SEANC.ACAD.SCI., PARIS, SER.D, 250, 1343-1344.

2159 GUILLEMAT, J. & BIGOT, C. (1960) - MICROFLORE FONGIQUE D'UN SOL DU PUY-DE
      -DOME ET DE LA RHIZOSPHERE DE L'AIL. ANNLS EPIPHYT. 11, 217-249.

2160 GUILLEMAT, J., CHARPENTIER, M., TARDIEUX, P. & POCHON, J. (1960) - INTER-
      ACTIONS ENTRE UNE CHLORO-AMINOTRIAZINE HERBICIDE ET LA MICROFLORE FON-
      GIQUE ET BACTERIENNE DU SOL. ANNLS EPIPHYT. 11, 261-296.

2161 GUILLEMAT, J. & MONTEGUT, J. (1956) - CONTRIBUTION A L'ETUDE DE LA MICRO-
      FLORE FONGIQUE DES SOLS CULTIVES. ANNLS EPIPHYT. 7, 472-540.

2162 GUILLEMAT, J. & MONTEGUT, J. (1957) - DEUXIEME CONTRIBUTION A L'ETUDE DE
      LA MICROFLORA FONGIQUE DES SOLS CULTIVES. ANNLS EPIPHYT. 8, 185-207.

2163 GUILLEMAT, J. & MONTEGUT, J. (1960) - ACTION DE LA FUMURE MINERALE SUR
      CERTAINS CHAMPIGNONS DU SOL. IN: ECOLOGY OF SOIL FUNGI; PARKINSON, D. &
      WAID, J.S. (ED.), LIVERPOOL UNIV.PRESS, 98-105.

2164 GUJARATI, S. (1968) - ECOLOGY OF SOIL FUNGI OF CULTIVATED FIELDS. PROC.
      NATN.ACAD.SCI., INDIA, SECT.B, 38, 66-79.

2165 GULYAS, F. (1967) - THE ROLE OF SOME SOIL FUNGI IN THE MICROBIOLOGICAL DE-
      COMPOSITION OF LIGNIN. AGROKEM.TALAJT. 16, 137-150.

2166 GUNASEKARAN, M. (1972) - PHYSIOLOGICAL STUDIES ON PHYMATOTRICHUM OMNIVORUM.
      1. PATHWAYS OF GLUCOSE CATABOLISM. ARCH.MIKROBIOL. 83, 328-331.

2167 GUNASEKARAN, M. (1973) - PHYSIOLOGICAL STUDIES ON PHYMATOTRICHUM OMNIVORUM.
      3. ENZYMES OF GLUCOSE CATABOLISM. MYCOPATH.MYCOL.APPL. 49, 339-345.

2168 GUNASEKARAN, M. (1973) - PHYSIOLOGICAL STUDIES ON PHYMATOTRICHUM OMNIVORUM.
      4. EFFECT OF PH AND THE INTERACTION OF TEMPERATURE, MINERALS AND CARBON
      SOURCE ON GROWTH IN VITRO. MYCOPATH.MYCOL.APPL. 50, 313-321.

2169 GUNASEKARAN, M., HESS, W.M. & WEBER, D.J. (1972) - THE FATTY ACID COMPOSI-
      TION OF CONIDIA OF ASPERGILLUS NIGER V.TIEGH. CAN.J.MICROBIOL. 18,
      1575-1576.

2170 GUNASEKARAN, M., HESS, W.M. & WEBER, D.J. (1974) - LIPIDS AND ULTRASTRUC-
      TURE OF PHYMATOTRICHUM OMNIVORUM. TRANS.BR.MYCOL.SOC. 63, 519-525.

2171 GUNASEKARAN, M. & WEBER, D.J. (1972) - TRYPTOPHAN STIMULATION OF GROWTH
      AND SPORULATION OF RHIZOPUS ARRHIZUS FISCHER. CAN.J.MICROBIOL. 18,
      1185-1190.

2172 GUNASEKARAN, M. & WEBER, D.J. (1972) - AUXIN PRODUCTION OF THREE PHYTOPA-
      THOGENIC FUNGI. MYCOLOGIA 64, 1180-1183.

2173 GUNASEKARAN, M. & WEBER, D.J. (1974) - PHYSIOLOGICAL STUDIES ON PHYMATO-
      TRICHUM OMNIVORUM 6. LIPID COMPOSITION OF MYCELIUM AND SCLEROTIA. MY-
      COPATH.MYCOL.APPL. 52, 261-266.

2174 GUNASEKARAN, M. & WEBER, D.J. (1975) - INFLUENCE OF VARIOUS CARBON SOURCES
      AND TEMPERATURE ON LIPID COMPOSITION OF RHIZOPUS ARRHIZUS. TRANS.BR.MY-
      COL.SOC. 65, 539-545.

COMPENDIUM OF SOIL FUNGI

2175 GUNASEKARAN, M., WEBER, D.J. & HESS, S.L. (1972) - TOTAL, POLAR AND NEUTRAL
      LIPIDS OF RHIZOPUS ARRHIZUS FISCHER. LIPIDS 7, 430-434.

2176 GUNNER, H.B. & ALEXANDER, M. (1964) - ANAEROBIC GROWTH OF FUSARIUM OXYSPO-
      RUM. J.BACT. 87, 1309-1316.

2177 GUPTA, J.K., DAS, N.B. & GUPTA, Y.P. (1972) - EFFECT OF CULTURAL CONDITIONS
      ON CELLULASE FORMATION BY TRICHODERMA VIRIDE. AGRIC.BIOL.CHEM., TOKYO
      36, 1961-1967.

2178 GUPTA, K.S., SHARMA, M.C. & CHAUDHARY, K.C.B. (1965) - NEW RECORDS OF PENI-
      CILLIA FROM INDIAN SOILS. SYDOWIA 19, 108-109.

2179 GUPTA, M.L. (1975) - STUDIES ON MICROFUNGI FROM DIFFERENT SOILS OF GORAKH-
      PUR WITH SPECIAL REFERENCE TO THE ECOLOGY AND TAXONOMY OF ASPERGILLI.
      DISS.UNIV.GORAKHPUR.

2180 GUPTA, M.N. (1962) - NON-ADAPTIVE SECRETION OF PECTIC ENZYMES BY RHIZOCTO-
      NIA SOLANI, ISOLATED FROM SWEDE SEEDLINGS, ON SYNTHETIC MEDIA. SCI.CULT.
      28, 482-483.

2181 GUPTA, R.K. & PRAMER, D. (1970) - AMINO ACID TRANSPORT BY THE FILAMENTOUS
      FUNGUS ARTHROBOTRYS CONOIDES. J.BACT. 103, 120-130.

2182 GUPTA, R.K. & PRAMER, D. (1970) - METABOLISM OF VALINE BY THE FILAMENTOUS
      FUNGUS ARTHROBOTRYS CONOIDES. J.BACT. 103, 131-139.

2183 GUPTA, S.C. (1960) - STUDIES IN PECTIC ENZYMES PARASITIC FUNGI. 3. SECRE-
      TION OF PECTIC ENZYMES BY PENICILLIUM EXPANSUM. PROC.INDIAN ACAD.SOC.
      SCI., SECT.B, 52, 103-109.

2184 GUPTA, S.C. & GUPTA, S.P. (1967) - STUDIES IN PECTIC ENZYMES OF PARASITIC
      FUNGI. 8. PRODUCTION OF PECTIC ENZYMES BY GIBBERELLA FUJIKUROI (SAW.)
      WOLLENW. PROC.NATN.ACAD.SCI., INDIA, SECT.B, 37, 241-247.

2185 GUPTA, S.C. & RAUTELA, G.S. (1964) - PECTIC ENZYMES OF PARASITIC FUNGI. 5.
      PECTIC ENZYMES PRODUCED BY PENICILLIUM EXPANSUM. INDIAN PHYTOPATH. 17,
      191-201.

2186 GUPTA, S.K. & BASU CHAUDHARY, K.C. (1966) - SOIL MICRO-FUNGI OF BLACK WAT-
      TLE FOREST AT YERCUD (SALEM SOUTH FOREST DIVISION) MADRAS STATE IN RE-
      LATION TO GUMMOSIS DISEASE. PROC.NATN.ACAD.SCI., INDIA, SECT.B, 320-
      326.

2187 GUPTA, V.K. (1974) - EFFECT OF FOLIAR APPLICATION OF SUBAMYCIN ON RHIZOS-
      PHERE AND RHIZOPLANE MYCOFLORA. INDIAN PHYTOPATH. 27, 267.

2188 GUSEINOV, V.A. & RUNOV, V.I. (1974) - STRAIN DIFFERENCES IN THE DNA STRUC-
      TURE OF THE FUNGI VERTICILLIUM DAHLIAE. DOKL.AKAD.NAUK SSSR, SER.BIO-
      KHIM. 212, 450-452 (ENGL.TRANSL.).

2189 GUSEINOV, V.A. & SAFIYAZOV, ZH. (1976) - (MORPHOLOGICAL CHARACTERISTICS OF
      MICROSCLEROTIAL AND MYCELIAL STRAINS OF VERTICILLIUM DAHLIAE KLEB.). MI-
      KOL.FITOPAT. 10, 169-171.

2190 GUSEVA, I.I., KOZLOVSKII, A.G. & BEZBORODOV, A.M. (1972) - SYNTHESIS OF
      2,3-DIHYDROXY-4-PHENYLQUINOLINE BY A PENICILLIUM CYCLOPIUM. PRIKL.BIO-
      KHIM.MIKROBIOL. 8, 219-221 (ENGL.TRANSL.).

2191   GUSTAFSSON, M. (1965) - ON SPECIES OF THE GENUS ENTOMOPHTHORA FRES. IN
       SWEDEN. 2. CULTIVATION AND PHYSIOLOGY. K.LANTBRHOEGSK.ANNLR 31, 405-
       457.

2192   GUTTER, Y. (1961) - ON THE PATHOGENICTY OF TRICHODERMA VIRIDE TO CITRUS
       FRUITS. BULL.RES.COUN., ISRAEL, SECT.D, 10, 157-164.

2193   GUTTER, Y. (1963) - CONTRIBUTIONS TO THE BIOLOGY OF TRICHODERMA VIRIDE PA-
       THOGENIC TO CITRUS FRUITS. ISRAEL J.BOT. 12, 27-40.

2194   GUTTORMSON, R., MAIN, P., ALLISON, A.J. & OVERTON, K.H. (1970) - STRUCTURE
       OF ROSEIN. 3. X-RAY ANALYSIS WITHOUT A HEAVY ATOM. CHEM.COMMUN., 1970,
       719-720.

2195   GUYOT, L., GUILLEMAT, J. & MONTEGUT, J. (1955) - DE L'EFFET BIOSTATIQUE
       SELECTIF EXERCE PAR CERTAINES PLANTES PHYTOTOXIQUES SUR LA MICROFLORE
       DU SOL. ANNLS EPIPHYT. II, 119-163.

2196   HAARD, K.K. (1968) - TAXONOMIC STUDIES ON THE GENUS ARTHROBOTRYS CORDA.
       MYCOLOGIA 60, 1140-1159.

2197   HAASIS, F.A. & NELSON, R.R. (1966) - MATING BEHAVIOUR WITHIN SEVEN SPECIES
       AND ONE VARIETY OF PHYTOPHTHORA. J.ELISHA MITCHELL SCIENT.SOC. 82, 86-
       87.

2198   HAASIS, F.A., NELSON, R.R. & MARX, D.H. (1964) - MORPHOLOGICAL AND PHYSIO-
       LOGICAL CHARACTERISTICS OF MATING TYPES OF PHYTOPHTHORA CINNAMOMI. PHY-
       TOPATHOLOGY 54, 1146-1151.

2199   HADLEY, G. & HARROLD, C.E. (1958) - THE SPORULATION OF PENICILLIUM IN SUB-
       MERGED LIQUID CULTURE. 1. THE EFFECT OF CALCIUM AND NUTRIENTS ON SPORU-
       LATION INTENSITY. J.EXP.BOT. 9, 408-417.

2200   HADLEY, G. & HARROLD, C.E. (1958) - THE SPORULATION OF PENICILLIUM IN SUB-
       MERGED LIQUID CULTURE. 2. THE INITIAL SPORULATION PHASE. J.EXP.BOT. 9,
       418-425.

2201   HADLOK, R. (1969) - SCHIMMELPILZE BEI FLEISCHERZEUGNISSEN. FLEISCHWIRT-
       SCHAFT 49, 455-460.

2202   HAEFLIGER, W. & HAUSER, D. (1973) - ISOLIERUNG UND STRUKTURAUFKLAERUNG VON
       11-DESACETOXY-WORTMANNIN. HELV.CHIM.ACTA 56, 2901-2904.

2203   HAERRI, E. (1959) - PHYSIOLOGISCHE UNTERSUCHUNGEN UEBER DIE GATTUNGEN THIE-
       LAVIA ZOPF UND THIELAVIOPSIS WENT. PHYTOPATH.Z. 36, 27-66.

2204   HAERRI, E., LOEFFLER, W., SIGG, H.P., STAEHELIN, H. & TAMM, CH. (1963) -
       UEBER DIE ISOLIERUNG NEUER STOFFWECHSELPRODUKTE AUS PENICILLIUM BREFEL-
       DIANUM DODGE. HELV.CHIM.ACTA 46, 1235-1243.

2205   HAERRI, E., LOEFFLER, W., SIGG, H.P., STAEHELIN, H., STOLL, CH., TAMM, CH.
       & WIESINGER, C. (1962) - UEBER DIE VERRUCARINE UND RORIDINE, EINE GRUP-
       PE VON CYTOSTATISCH HOCHWIRKSAMEN ANTIBIOTICA AUS MYROTHECIUM-ARTEN.
       HELV.CHIM.ACTA 45, 839-853.

2206   HAGEM, O. (1908) - UNTERSUCHUNGEN UEBER NORWEGISCHE MUCORINEEN. 1. VID.
       SELSK.SKRIFTER, MATH.-NATURV.KL., 1907 (7), 1-50.

2207   HAGLUND, W.A., DURBIN, R.D. & KING, T.H. (1959) - SYNTHETIC MEDIUM FOR THE
       GROWTH OF APHANOMYCES EUTEICHES. PHYTOPATHOLOGY 49, 540 (ABS.).

2208   HAGLUND, W.A. & KING, T.H. (1962) - SULFUR NUTRITION OF APHANOMYCES EUTEI-
       CHES. PHYTOPATHOLOGY 52, 315-317.

2209   HAHN, H. & BOPP, M. (1972) - FOERDERUNG VON PROTONEMAWACHSTUM UND KNOSPEN-
       BILDUNG BEI DEM LAUBMOOS FUNARIA HYGROMETRICA DURCH PILZE. Z.PHYSIOL.
       68, 19-20.

2210   HAID, F. (1965) - UNTERSUCHUNGEN ZUR MORPHOLOGIE, PHYSIOLOGIE UND BIOLO-
       GISCHEN AKTIVITAET VON ALTERNARIA TENUIS. DISS.UNIV.MUENCHEN.

2211   HAIDER, K. & DOMSCH, K.H. (1969) - ABBAU UND UMSETZUNG VON LIGNIFIZIERTEM
       PFLANZENMATERIAL DURCH MIKROSKOPISCHE BODENPILZE. ARCH.MIKROBIOL. 64,
       338-348.

2212   HAIDER, K., FILIP, Z. & MARTIN, J.P. (1970) - EINFLUSS VON MONTMORILLONIT
       AUF DIE BILDUNG VON BIOMASSE UND STOFFWECHSELZWISCHENPRODUKTE DURCH EI-
       NIGE MIKROORGANISMEN. ARCH.MIKROBIOL. 73, 201-215.

2213   HAIDER, K. & MARTIN, J.P. (1967) - SYNTHESIS AND TRANSFORMATION OF PHENO-
       LIC COMPOUNDS BY EPICOCCUM NIGRUM IN RELATION TO HUMIC ACID FORMATION.
       PROC.SOIL SCI.SOC.AM. 31, 766-772.

2214   HAIDER, K. & MARTIN, J.P. (1970) - HUMIC ACID-TYPE PHENOLIC POLYMERS FROM
       ASPERGILLUS SYDOWI CULTURE MEDIUM, STACHYBOTRYS SPP. CELLS AND AUTOXI-
       DIZED PHENOL MIXTURES. SOIL BIOL.BIOCHEM. 2, 145-156.

2215   HAIRSTONE, M.A. (1967) - FINE STRUCTURE OF THE FILAMENTOUS ASCOMYCETE MO-
       NOSPORIUM APIOSPERMUM. CYTOLOGIA 32, 19-23.

2216   HALIM, A.F., NARCISO, J.A. & COLLINS, R.P. (1975) - ODOROUS CONSTITUENTS
       OF PENICILLIUM DECUMBENS. MYCOLOGIA 67, 1158-1165.

2217   HALL, I.M. & BELL, J.V. (1960) - THE EFFECT OF TEMPERATURE ON SOME ENTO-
       MOPHTHORACEOUS FUNGI. J.INSECT PATH. 2, 247-253.

2218   HALL, I.M. & BELL, J.V. (1961) - FURTHER STUDIES ON THE EFFECT OF TEMPERA-
       TURE ON THE GROWTH OF SOME ENTOMOPHTHORACEOUS FUNGI. J.INSECT PATH. 3,
       289-296.

2219   HALL, R. (1969) - VERTICILLIUM ALBO-ATRUM AND V. DAHLIAE DISTINGUISHED BY
       ACRYLAMIDE GEL-ELECTROPHORESIS OF PROTEINS. CAN.J.BOT. 47, 2100-2111.

2220   HALL, R. (1971) - EFFECT OF CARBON-NITROGEN RATIOS ON PRODUCTION OF PERI-
       THECIA BY SORDARIA FIMICOLA. CAN.J.MICROBIOL. 17, 132-134.

2221   HALL, R. & LY, H. (1972) - DEVELOPMENT AND QUANTITATIVE MEASUREMENT OF MI-
       CROSCLEROTIA OF VERTICILLIUM DAHLIAE. CAN.J.BOT. 50, 2097-2102.

2222   HALL, R., ZENTMYER, G.A. & ERWIN, D.C. (1969) - APPROACH TO TAXONOMY OF
       PHYTOPHTHORA THROUGH ACRYLAMIDE GEL-ELECTROPHORESIS OF PROTEINS. PHY-
       TOPATHOLOGY 59, 770-774.

2223   HALL, R.A. (1976) - A BIOASSAY OF THE PATHOGENICITY OF VERTICILLIUM LECA-
       NII CONIDIOSPORES ON THE APHID MACROSIPHONIELLA SANBORNI. J.INVERTEBR.
       PATH. 27, 41-48.

2224   HALLIWELL, G. (1966) - SOLUBILIZATION OF NATIVE AND DERIVED FORMS OF CEL-
       LULOSE BY CELL-FREE MICROBIAL ENZYMES. BIOCHEM.J. 100, 315-320.

2225   HALLIWELL, G. & GRIFFIN, M. (1973) - THE NATURE AND MODE OF ACTION OF THE
       CELLULOLYTIC COMPONENT C1 OF TRICHODERMA KONINGII ON NATIVE CELLULOSE.
       BIOCHEM.J. 135, 587-594.

2226 HALLIWELL, G. & RIAZ, M. (1971) - INTERACTIONS BETWEEN COMPONENTS OF THE
       CELLULASE COMPLEX OF TRICHODERMA KONINGII ON NATIVE SUBSTRATES. ARCH.
       MIKROBIOL. 78, 295-309.

2227 HALLOIN, J.M. (1975) - POSTHARVEST INFECTION OF COTTONSEED BY RHIZOPUS
       ARRHIZUS, ASPERGILLUS NIGER AND ASPERGILLUS FLAVUS. PHYTOPATHOLOGY 65,
       1229-1232.

2228 HALLOIN, J.M. & HAGEDORN, D.J. (1975) - EFFECTS OF TENTOXIN ON ENZYMIC AC-
       TIVITIES IN CUCUMBER AND CABBAGE COTYLEDONS. MYCOPATHOLOGIA 55, 159-162.

2229 HALPIN, J.E., HANSON, E.W. & DICKSON, J.C. (1954) - STUDIES ON THE PATHO-
       GENICITY OF SEVEN SPECIES OF PYTHIUM ON ALFALFA, SWEETCLOVER, AND LADI-
       NO CLOVER SEEDLINGS. PHYTOPATHOLOGY 44, 572-574.

2230 HALSALL, D.M. (1976) - ZOOSPORE CHEMOTAXIS IN AUSTRALIAN ISOLATES OF PHY-
       TOPHTHORA SPECIES. CAN.J.MICROBIOL. 22, 409-422.

2231 HALUK, J.P. & METCHE, M. (1970) - TRANSFORMATION MICROBIOLOGIQUE DE LA
       QUERCETINE PAR ASPERGILLUS NIGER. BULL.SOC.CHIM.BIOL. 52, 667-677.

2232 HAMASAKI, T., HATSUDA, Y., TERASHIMA, N. & RENBUTSU, M. (1967) - STUDIES
       ON THE METABOLITES OF ASPERGILLUS VERSICOLOR (VUILLEMIN) TIRABOSCHI. 5.
       ISOLATION AND STRUCTURES OF THREE NEW METABOLITES, VERSICOLORINS-A, -B
       AND -C. AGRIC.BIOL.CHEM., TOKYO 31, 11-17.

2233 HAMASAKI, T., KUWANO, H., ISONO, K., HATSUDA, Y., FUKUYAMA, K., TSUKIHARA,
       T. & KATSUBE, Y. (1975) - A NEW METABOLITE, PARASITICOLIDE-A, FROM AS-
       PERGILLUS PARASITICUS. AGRIC.BIOL.CHEM., TOKYO 39, 749-751.

2234 HAMASAKI, T., MATSUI, K., ISONO, K. & HATSUDA, Y. (1973) - A NEW METABO-
       LITE FROM ASPERGILLUS VERSICOLOR. AGRIC.BIOL.CHEM., TOKYO 37, 1769-1770.

2235 HAMASAKI, T., NAGAYAMA, K. & HATSUDA, Y. (1976) - STRUCTURE OF A NEW ME-
       TABOLITE FROM ASPERGILLUS CHEVALIERI. AGRIC.BIOL.CHEM., TOKYO 40, 203-
       205.

2236 HAMASAKI, T., RENBUTSU, M. & HATSUDA, Y. (1967) - A RED PIGMENT FROM AS-
       PERGILLUS VERSICOLOR (VUILLEMIN) TIRABOSCHI. AGRIC.BIOL.CHEM., TOKYO
       31, 1513-1614.

2237 HAMASAKI, T., SATO, Y. & HATSUDA, Y. (1975) - SYDONIC ACID, A NEW METABO-
       LITE FROM ASPERGILLUS SYDOWII. TETRAHEDRON LETTERS, 1975 (9), 659-660.

2238 HAMEED, K.M. & COUCH, H.B. (1972) - EFFECTS OF PENICILLIUM SIMPLICISSIMUM
       ON GROWTH, CHEMICAL COMPOSITION, AND ROOT EXUDATION OF AXENICALLY GROWN
       MARIGOLDS. PHYTOPATHOLOGY 62, 669 (ABS.).

2239 HAMILTON, I.R. & JOHNSTON, R.A. (1961) - STUDIES ON CUCUMBER SOFTENING UN-
       DER COMMERCIAL SALT-STOCK CONDITIONS IN ONTARIO. 2. PECTOLYTIC MICROOR-
       GANISMS ISOLATED. APPL.MICROBIOL. 9, 128-134.

2240 HAMMILL, T.M. (1970) - PAECILOMYCES CLAVISPORIS SP.NOV., TRICHODERMA SA-
       TURNISPORUM SP.NOV., AND OTHER NOTEWORTHY SOIL FUNGI FROM GEORGIA. MY-
       COLOGIA 62, 107-122.

2241 HAMMILL, T.M. (1971) - FINE STRUCTURE OF ANNELLOPHORES. 1. SCOPULARIOPSIS
       BREVICAULIS AND SCOPULARIOPSIS KONINGII. AM.J.BOT. 58, 88-97.

2242 HAMMILL, T.M. (1972) - ELECTRON MICROSCOPY OF PHIALOCONIDIOGENESIS IN ME-
       TARRHIZIUM ANISOPLIAE. AM.J.BOT. 59, 317-326.

2243 HAMMILL, T.M. (1972) - FINE STRUCTURAL OBSERVATIONS OF CONIDIOPHORES AND
      OF SYMPODIAL CONIDIOGENESIS IN PSEUDOBOTRYTIS TERRESTRIS AND TRITIRA-
      CHIUM ROSEUM. AM.J.BOT. 59, 666.

2244 HAMMILL, T.M. (1972) - ELECTRON MICROSCOPY OF CONIDIOGENESIS IN CHLORIDIUM
      CHLAMYDOSPORIS. MYCOLOGIA 64, 1054-1065.

2245 HAMMIL, T.M. (1972) - FINE STRUCTURES OF ANNELLOPHORES. 2. DORATOMYCES NA-
      NUS. TRANS.BR.MYCOL.SOC. 59, 249-253.

2246 HAMMILL, T.M. (1977) - TRANSMISSION ELECTRON MICROSCOPY OF ANNELLIDES AND
      CONIDIOGENESIS IN THE SYNNEMATAL HYPHOMYCETE TRICHURUS SPIRALIS. CAN.J.
      BOT. 55, 233-244.

2247 HAMPEL, M. (1970) - PHOMA EUPYRENA SACC. SS.WR. UND PLECTOSPHAERELLA CUCU-
      MERIS KLEB., ZWEI WENIG BEKANNTE KEIMLINGSPATHOGENE. Z.PFLKRANKH.PFLPATH.
      PFLSCHUTZ 77, 225-227.

2248 HAN, Y.W., CHEEKE, P.R., ANDERSON, A.W. & LEKPRAYOON, C. (1976) - GROWTH
      OF AUREOBASIDIUM PULLULANS ON STRAW HYDROLYSATE. APPL.ENVIRON.MICROBIOL.
      32, 799-802.

2249 HANADA, K., HIROSE, A. & NINOMIYA, E. (1974) - ISOLATION, IDENTIFICATION
      AND CULTURE CONDITION OF A DEXTRANASE-PRODUCING MOLD. STUDIES ON THE
      DEXTRANASE PRODUCED BY ASPERGILLUS USTUS. 1. J.AGRIC.CHEM.SOC.JAPAN 48,
      17-22.

2250 HANCOCK, J.G., MILLAR, R.L. & LORBEER, J.W. (1964) - PECTOLYTIC AND CELLU-
      LOLYTIC ENZYMES PRODUCED BY BOTRYTIS ALLII, B. CINEREA, AND B. SQUAMOSA
      IN VITRO AND IN VIVO. PHYTOPATHOLOGY 54, 928-931.

2251 HANEDA, K., WATANABE, S. & TAKEDA, I. (1971) - SYNTHESIS OF L-3,4-DIHYDR-
      OXYPHENYLALANINE FROM L-TYROSINE BY MICROORGANISMS. APPL.MICROBIOL. 22,
      721-722.

2252 HANLIN, R.T. (1961) - STUDIES IN THE GENUS NECTRIA. 2. MORPHOLOGY OF NEC-
      TRIA GLIOCLADIOIDES. AM.J.BOT. 48, 900-908.

2253 HANLIN, R.T. (1969) - FUNGI IN DEVELOPING PEANUT FRUITS. MYCOPATH.MYCOL.
      APPL. 38, 93-100.

2254 HANLIN, R.T. (1971) - MORPHOLOGY OF NECTRIA HAEMATOCOCCA. AM.J.BOT. 58,
      105-116.

2255 HANLIN, R.T. (1972) - SPECIES OF SORDARIA FROM PEANUT AND PECAN FRUITS.
      BULL.GA.ACAD.SCI. 30, 129-141.

2256 HANLIN, R.T. (1973) - CONIDIUM DEVELOPMENT IN ASPERGILLUS CLAVATUS. J.ELI-
      SHA MITCHELL SCIENT.SOC. 89, 215-217.

2257 HANLIN, R.T. (1976) - PHIALIDE AND CONIDIUM DEVELOPMENT IN ASPERGILLUS CLA-
      VATUS. AM.J.BOT. 63, 144-155.

2258 HANLIN, R.T. & BLANCHARD, R.O. (1974) - FUNGI ASSOCIATED WITH DEVELOPING
      PECAN FRUITS. BULL.GA ACAD.SCI. 32, 68-75.

2259 HANSEN, H.N. (1938) - THE DUAL PHENOMENON IN IMPERFECT FUNGI. MYCOLOGIA
      30, 442-455.

2260 HANSEN, J.D. & CURL, E.A. (1964) - INTERACTIONS OF SCLEROTIUM ROLFSII AND
      OTHER MICROORGANISMS ISOLATED FROM STOLON TISSUE OF TRIFOLIUM REPENS.
      PHYTOPATHOLOGY 54, 1127-1132.

2261 HANSON, J.R., HITCHCOCK, P.B. & NYFELER, R. (1975) - CYCLONEROTRIOL (6-(3-
      HYDROXY-2,3-DIMETHYLCYCLOPENTYL)-2-METHYLHEPT-2-ENE-1,6-DIOL), A NEW
      SESQUITERPENOID METABOLITE OF FUSARIUM CULMORUM. J.CHEM.SOC.PERKIN TRANS.
      I, 1975, 1586.

2262 HANTSCHKE, D. (1961/62) - UNTERSUCHUNGEN UEBER WELKEKRANKHEITEN DER EDEL-
      NELKE IN DEUTSCHLAND UND IHRE ERREGER. PHYTOPATH.Z. 43, 113-168.

2263 HARA, S., FENNELL, D.I. & HESSELTINE, C.W. (1973) - STUDIES ON THE MYCOLO-
      GICAL CHARACTERS OF AFLATOXIN-PRODUCING STRAINS BELONGING TO THE ASPER-
      GILLUS FLAVUS GROUP. REP.RES.INST.BREWING 145, 8-12.

2264 HARADA, T., NISHIKAWA, T. & HATANO, H. (1976) - ANTIGENIC SIMILARITY BE-
      TWEEN CERATOCYSTIS SPECIES AND SPOROTHRIX SCHENCKII AS OBSERVED BY IM-
      MUNOFLUORESCENCE. SABOURAUDIA 14, 211-215.

2265 HARCOURT, R.A. & THOMPSON, F.G. (1969) - MYCOTIC ABORTION AND MYCOTIC PNEU-
      MONIA IN A COW. VET.REC. 85, 199-200.

2266 HARDER, P. & TROLL, J. (1973) - ANTAGONISM OF TRICHODERMA SP. TO SCLEROTIA
      OF TYPHULA INCARNATA. PL.DIS.REPTR 57, 924-926.

2267 HARDING, H. (1975) - EFFECT OF D-AMINO ACIDS ON CONIDIUM SIZE AND NUMBERS
      OF PSEUDOSEPTA PER CONIDIUM IN ISOLATES OF BIPOLARIS SOROKINIANA. CAN.
      J.BOT. 53, 600-603.

2268 HARDING, H. (1975) - EFFECT OF PH AND SUCROSE CONCENTRATION ON CONIDIUM
      SIZE AND SEPTATION IN FOUR BIPOLARIS SPECIES. CAN.J.BOT. 53, 1457-1464.

2269 HARGREAVES, A.J. & FOX, R.A. (1977) - SURVIVAL OF FUSARIUM AVENACEUM IN
      SOIL. TRANS.BR.MYCOL.SOC. 69, 425-428.

2270 HARHASH, A.W. (1968) - STUDIES ON THE GLUTAMIC ACID DECARBOXYLASE IN FU-
      SARIUM MONILIFORME. BULL.FAC.SCI.EGYPT UNIV. 41, 57-65.

2271 HARHASH, A.W. (1968) - STUDIES ON AMYLASE IN FUSARIUM MONILIFORME. BULL.
      FAC.SCI.EGYPT UNIV. 41, 67-77.

2272 HARLEY, J.L. & WAID, J.S. (1955) - THE EFFECT OF LIGHT UPON THE ROOTS OF
      BEECH AND ITS SURFACE POPULATION. PL.SOIL 7, 96-112.

2273 HARMAN, G.E. (1972) - DETERIORATION OF STORED PEA SEED BY ASPERGILLUS RU-
      BER. EXTRACTION AND PROPERTIES OF A TOXIN. PHYTOPATHOLOGY 62, 206-208.

2274 HARMAN, G.E., KHAN, A.A. & DRURY, R.E. (1971) - MORPHACTIN INFLUENCES SEX-
      UAL AND ASEXUAL REPRODUCTION IN FUNGI. CAN.J.MICROBIOL. 17, 1477-1479.

2275 HARMAN, G.E. & NASH, G. (1972) - DETERIORATION OF STORED PEA SEED BY AS-
      PERGILLUS RUBER. EVIDENCE FOR INVOLVEMENT OF A TOXIN. PHYTOPATHOLOGY
      62, 209-212.

2276 HARMAN, G.E. & PFLEGER, F.L. (1974) - PATHOGENICITY AND INFECTION SITES OF
      ASPERGILLUS SPECIES IN STORED SEEDS. PHYTOPATHOLOGY 64, 1339-1344.

2277 HARNISH, W.N. (1965) - EFFECT OF LIGHT PRODUCTION OF OOSPORES AND SPORAN-
      GIA IN SPECIES OF PHYTOPHTHORA. MYCOLOGIA 57, 85-89.

2278 HARNISH, W.N. & MERZ, W.G. (1964) - THE EFFECT OF BETA-SITOSTEROL ON
      OOSPORE PRODUCTION BY SPECIES OF PHYTOPHTHORA. PHYTOPATHOLOGY 54, 747
      (ABS.).

2279   HARPER, J.E. & WEBSTER, J. (1964) - AN EXPERIMENTAL ANALYSIS OF COPROPHI-
       LOUS FUNGUS SUCCESSION. TRANS.BR.MYCOL.SOC. 47, 511-530.

2280   HARRIS, R.F., CHESTERS, G. & ALLEN, O.N. (1966) - SOIL AGGREGATE STABILI-
       ZATION BY THE INDIGENOUS MICROFLORA AS AFFECTED BY TEMPERATURE. PROC.
       SOIL SCI.SOC.AM. 30, 205-210.

2281   HARRIS, R.V. (1970) - EFFECT OF RHIZOPUS FERMENTATION ON THE LIPID COMPO-
       SITION OF CASSAVA FLOUR. J.SCI.FD AGRIC. 21, 626-627.

2282   HARRISON, A.F. (1971) - THE INHIBITORY EFFECT OF OAK LEAF LITTER TANNINS
       ON THE GROWTH OF FUNGI IN RELATION TO LITTER DECOMPOSITION. SOIL BIOL.
       BIOCHEM. 3, 167-172.

2283   HARRISON, J.A.C. (1971) - ASSOCIATION BETWEEN THE POTATO CYST-NEMATODE,
       HETERODERA ROSTOCHIENSIS WOLL., AND VERTICILLIUM DAHLIAE KLEB. IN THE
       EARLY-DYING DISEASE OF POTATOES. ANN.APPL.BIOL. 67, 185-193.

2284   HARRISON, J.A.C. & ISAAC, I. (1969) - SURVIVAL OF THE CAUSAL AGENTS OF
       "EARLY-DYING DISEASE" (VERTICILLIUM WILT) OF POTATOES. ANN.APPL.BIOL.
       63, 277-288.

2285   HART, J.H. (1965) - ROOT ROT OF OAK ASSOCIATED WITH CYLINDROCARPON RADICI-
       COLA. PHYTOPATHOLOGY 55, 1154-1155.

2286   HARTMAN, R.E. & KEEN, N.T. (1973) - ENZYMES CATALYZING ANAPLEROTIC CARBON
       DIOXIDE FIXATION IN VERTICILLIUM ALBO-ATRUM. PHYTOPATHOLOGY 63, 947-953.

2287   HARTMAN, R.E. & KEEN, N.T. (1974) - THE PYRUVATE CARBOXYLASE OF VERTICIL-
       LIUM ALBO-ATRUM. J.GEN.MICROBIOL. 81, 15-19.

2288   HARTMAN, R.E. & KEEN, N.T. (1974) - THE PHOSPHOENOLPYRUVATE CARBOXYKINASE
       OF VERTICILLIUM ALBO-ATRUM. J.GEN.MICROBIOL. 81, 21-26.

2289   HARTMAN, R.E., KEEN, N.T. & LONG, M. (1972) - CARBON DIOXIDE FIXATION BY
       VERTICILLIUM ALBO-ATRUM. J.GEN.MICROBIOL. 73, 29-34.

2290   HARTMANN, G.C. (1966) - THE CYTOLOGY OF ALTERNARIA TENUIS. MYCOLOGIA 58,
       694-701.

2291   HARVAIS, G. & PEKKALA, D. (1975) - VITAMIN PRODUCTION BY A FUNGUS SYMBIOT-
       IC WITH ORCHIDS. CAN.J.BOT. 53, 156-163.

2292   HARVAIS, G. & RAITSAKAS, A. (1975) - ON THE PHYSIOLOGY OF A FUNGUS SYMBIOT-
       IC WITH ORCHIDS. CAN.J.BOT. 53, 144-155.

2293   HARVEY, R. (1967) - AIR-SPORA STUDIES AT CARDIFF. 1. CLADOSPORIUM. TRANS.
       BR.MYCOL.SOC. 50, 479-495.

2294   HARVEY, R. (1970) - SPORE PRODUCTIVITY IN CLADOSPORIUM. MYCOPATH.MYCOL.
       APPL. 41, 251-256.

2295   HARVEY, R., HODGKISS, I.J. & LEWIS, P.N. (1969) - AIR-SPORA STUDIES AT CAR-
       DIFF. 2. CHAETOMIUM. TRANS.BR.MYCOL.SOC. 53, 269-278.

2296   HARWIG, J. & CHEN, Y.-K. (1974) - SOME CONDITIONS FAVORING PRODUCTION OF
       OCHRATOXIN-A AND CITRININ BY PENICILLIUM VIRIDICATUM IN WHEAT AND BAR-
       LEY. CAN.J.PL.SCI. 54, 17-22.

2297   HASANY, S.M., YOUSUF, M. & SHAHID HUSAIN, S. (1968) - STUDIES ON STORED
       GRAIN FUNGI. 1. FUNGI FROM WHEAT AND RICE FROM KARACHI. PAKIST.J.SCIENT.
       IND.RES. 11, 288-293.

2298 HASEGAWA, S., KIRKWOOD, S. & NORDIN, J.H. (1966) - ALPHA-1,3-GLUCANASE
      FROM A FUNGAL SOURCE. CHEM.IND., 1966, 1033.

2299 HASEGAWA, S., NORDIN, J.H. & KIRKWOOD, S. (1969) - ENZYMES THAT HYDROLYZE
      FUNGAL CELL WALL POLYSACCHARIDES. 1. PURIFICATION AND PROPERTIES OF AN
      ENDO-ALPHA-D-(1,3)-GLUCANASE FROM TRICHODERMA VIRIDE. J.BIOL.CHEM. 244,
      5460-5470.

2300 HASHIMOTO, T., KISHI, T. & YOSHIDA, N. (1964) - DEMONSTRATION OF MICROPO-
      RES IN FUNGAL CROSSWALL. NATURE, LOND. 202, 1353.

2301 HASHIMOTO, T., MORGAN, J. & CONTI, S.F. (1973) - MORPHOGENESIS AND ULTRA-
      STRUCTURE OF GEOTRICHUM CANDIDUM SEPTA. J.BACT. 116, 447-455.

2302 HASHIOKA, Y. (1973) - SCANNING ELECTRONMICROSCOPY ON THE MYCOPARASITES,
      TRICHODERMA, GLIOCLADIUM AND ACREMONIUM. REP.TOTTORI MYCOL.INST. 10,
      473-484.

2303 HASHIOKA, Y., ISHIKAWA, H., KOMATSU, M. & ARITA, I. (1961) - TRICHODERMA
      VIRIDE, AS AN ANTAGONIST OF THE WOOD-INHABITING HYMENOMYCETES. 2. A
      METABOLIC PRODUCT OF TRICHODERMA FUNGISTATIC TO THE HYMENOMYCETES. REP.
      TOTTORI MYCOL.INST. 1, 9-18.

2304 HASHIOKA, Y., OSAMU HORINO & KAMEI, T. (1966) - ELECTRONMICROGRAPHS OF TRI-
      CHODERMA AND PACHYBASIUM. REP.TOTTORI MYCOL.INST. 5, 18-24.

2305 HASHMI, M.H. (1973) - CONIDIUM ONTOGENY IN HYPHOMYCETES - ARTHRINIUM PHAEO-
      SPERMUM (CORDA) M.B.ELLIS AND DICTYOARTHRINIUM SACCHARI (STEVENSON) DA-
      MON. PAKIST.J.BOT. 5, 119-124.

2306 HASHMI, M.H., KENDRICK, B. & MORGAN-JONES, G. (1972) - CONIDIUM ONTOGENY
      IN HYPHOMYCETES. THE GENERA TORULOMYCES DELITSCH AND MONOCILLIUM SAKSE-
      NA. CAN.J.BOT. 50, 1461-1464.

2307 HASHMI, M.H., KENDRICK, B. & MORGAN-JONES, G. (1972) - MITOSIS IN THREE
      HYPHOMYCETES. CAN.J.BOT. 50, 2575-2578.

2308 HASHMI, M.H. & MORGAN-JONES, G. (1973) - CONIDIUM ONTOGENY IN HYPHOMYCE-
      TES. THE MERISTEM ARTHROSPORES OF WALLEMIA SEBI. CAN.J.BOT. 51, 1669-
      1671.

2309 HASHMI, M.H., MORGAN-JONES, G. & KENDRICK, B. (1973) - CONIDIUM ONTOGENY
      IN HYPHOMYCETES. THE BLASTOCONIDIA OF CLADOSPORIUM HERBARUM AND TORULA
      HERBARUM. CAN.J.BOT. 51, 1089-1091.

2310 HASIJA, S.K. (1970) - PHYSIOLOGICAL STUDIES OF ALTERNARIA CITRI AND A. TE-
      NUIS. MYCOLOGIA 62, 289-295.

2311 HASKINS, R.H. & KNAPP, C. (1969) - CEPHALOSPORIUM SP. (PRL 2070) AND THE
      PRODUCTION OF CEPHALOCHROMIN. CAN.J.MICROBIOL. 15, 435-437.

2312 HASKINS, R.H., TULLOCH, A.P. & MICETICH, R.G. (1964) - STEROIDS AND THE
      STIMULATION OF SEXUAL REPRODUCTION OF A SPECIES OF PYTHIUM. CAN.J.MI-
      CROBIOL. 10, 187-195.

2313 HASSALL, C.H. & JONES, D.W. (1962) - THE BIOSYNTHESIS OF PHENOLS. 4. A NEW
      METABOLIC PRODUCT OF ASPERGILLUS TERREUS THOM. J.CHEM.SOC., 1962, 4189-
      4191.

2314 HASSALL, C.H. & TODD, A.R. (1947) - THE STRUCTURE OF CLAVATOL, A METABOLIC
      PRODUCT OF ASPERGILLUS CLAVATUS. J.CHEM.SOC., 1947, 611-613.

2315 HASSELBRING, T.S., TANSEY, M.R. & JACK, M.A. (1975) - FUNGI ASSOCIATED WITH
       GROWING STALAGTITES. MYCOLOGIA 67, 171-172.

2316 HASTIE, A.C. (1962) - GENETIC RECOMBINATION IN THE HOP-WILT FUNGUS VERTI-
       CILLIUM ALBO-ATRUM. J.GEN.MICROBIOL. 27, 373-382.

2317 HASTIE, A.C. (1964) - THE PARASEXUAL CYCLE IN VERTICILLIUM ALBO-ATRUM. GE-
       NET.RES. 5, 305-315.

2318 HASTIE, A.C. (1973) - HYBRIDIZATION OF VERTICILLIUM ALBO-ATRUM AND VERTI-
       CILLIUM DAHLIAE. TRANS.BR.MYCOL.SOC. 60, 511-523.

2319 HATCHER, H.J. & SCHMIDT, E.L. (1971) - NITRIFICATION OF ASPARTATE BY ASPER-
       GILLUS FLAVUS. APPL.MICROBIOL. 21, 181-186.

2320 HATFIELD, W.C., WALKER, J.C. & OWEN, J.H. (1948) - ANTIBIOTIC SUBSTANCES
       IN ONION IN RELATION TO DISEASE RESISTANCE. J.AGRIC.RES. 77, 115-135.

2321 HATSUDA, Y., HAMASAKI, T., ISHIDA, M. & KIYAMA, Y. (1971) - 6,8-0-DIME-
       THYLVERSICOLORIN-A, A NEW METABOLITE FROM ASPERGILLUS VERSICOLOR. AGRIC.
       BIOL.CHEM., TOKYO 35, 444.

2322 HATSUDA, Y., HAMASAKI, T., ISHIDA, M., MATSUI, K. & HARA, S. (1972) - DI-
       HYDROSTERIGMATOCYSTIN AND DIHYDRODEMETHYLSTERIGMATOCYSTIN, NEW METABO-
       LITES FROM ASPERGILLUS VERSICOLOR. AGRIC.BIOL.CHEM., TOKYO 36, 521-522.

2323 HATSUDA, Y., HAMASAKI, T., ISHIDA, M. & YOSHIKAWA, S. (1969) - THE STRUC-
       TURE OF A NEW METABOLITE FROM ASPERGILLUS VERSICOLOR. AGRIC.BIOL.CHEM.,
       TOKYO 33, 131-133.

2324 HATSUDA, Y. & KUYAMA, SH. (1955) - METABOLIC PRODUCTS OF ASPERGILLUS VER-
       SICOLOR. 4. THE ANTIBIOTIC PROPERTIES OF VERSICOLORIN AND SOME HYDROXY-
       XANTHENONES. AGRIC.BIOL.CHEM., TOKYO 29, 11-14.

2325 HAUSER, D., LOOSLI, H.R. & NIKLAUS, P. (1972) - ISOLIERUNG VON 11ALPHA,11
       ALPHA-DIHYDROXYCHAETOCIN AUS VERTICILLIUM TENERUM. HELV.CHIM.ACTA 55,
       2182-2187.

2326 HAVENS, P.L. (1976) - COMPARATIVE ZONE ELECTROPHORESIS AND MATING EXPERI-
       MENTS IN THE TAXONOMY OF MUCOR HIEMALIS. MYCOTAXON 4, 218-232.

2327 HAWARE, M.P. & SHARMA, N.D. (1973) - A NEW GLUME BLOTCH OF RICE (ORYZA SA-
       TIVA). PL.DIS.REPTR 57, 436-437.

2328 HAWES, C.R. & BECKETT, A. (1977) - CONIDIUM ONTOGENY IN THIELAVIOPSIS BA-
       SICOLA. TRANS.BR.MYCOL.SOC. 68, 304-307.

2329 HAWKER, L.E. (1951) - MORPHOLOGICAL AND PHYSIOLOGICAL STUDIES ON SORDARIA
       DESTRUENS, SORDARIA FIMICOLA AND MELANOSPORA ZAMIAE. TRANS.BR.MYCOL.SOC.
       34, 174-186.

2330 HAWKER, L.E. (1962) - A PAIR OF COMPATIBLE STRAINS OF ABSIDIA GLAUCA WHICH
       HAS BECOME HETEROGAMOUS IN CULTURE. NATURE, LOND. 193, 294-295.

2331 HAWKER, L.E. (1963) - FINE STRUCTURE OF PYTHIUM DEBARYANUM AND ITS PROB-
       ABLE SIGNIFICANCE. NATURE, LOND. 197, 618-619.

2332 HAWKER, L.E. (1966) - GERMINATION - MORPHOLOGICAL AND ANATOMICAL CHANGES.
       IN: THE FUNGUS SPORE; MADELIN, M.F. (ED.), BUTTERWORTHS, LONDON, 151-
       163.

2333 HAWKER, L.E. & ABBOTT, P.MC V. (1963) - AN ELECTRON MICROSCOPE STUDY OF
      MATURATION AND GERMINATION OF SPORANGIOSPORES OF TWO SPECIES OF RHIZO-
      PUS. J.GEN.MICROBIOL. 32, 295-298.

2334 HAWKER, L.E., ABBOTT, P.MC V. & GOODAY, M.A. (1968) - INTERNAL CHANGES IN
      HYPHAE OF RHIZOPUS SEXUALIS (SMITH) CALLEN AND MUCOR HIEMALIS WEHM.
      ASSOCIATED WITH ZYGOSPORE FORMATION. ANN.BOT. 32, 137-151.

2335 HAWKER, L.E., HARRISON, R.W., NICHOLLS, V.D. & HAM, A.M. (1957) - STUDIES
      ON VESICULAR-ARBUSCULAR ENDOPHYTES. 1. A STRAIN OF PYTHIUM ULTIMUM IN
      ROOTS OF ALLIUM URSINUM AND OTHER PLANTS. TRANS.BR.MYCOL.SOC. 40, 375-
      390.

2336 HAWKINS, J.H., WIGGELL, P. & WILCOX, H.J. (1963) - A ROOT ROT OF CHRYSAN-
      THEMUMS. PL.PATH. 12, 21-22.

2337 HAWKSWORTH, D.L. (1975) - FARROWIA, A NEW GENUS OF THE CHAETOMIACEAE. PER-
      SOONIA 8, 167-185.

2338 HAWKSWORTH, D.L. (1976) - THE NATURAL HISTORY OF SLAPTON LEY NATURE RESERVE.
      10. FUNGI. FLD STUD. 4, 391-439.

2339 HAWKSWORTH, D.L. & BOOTH, C. (1974) - A REVISION OF THE GENUS ZOPFIA RA-
      BENH. MYCOL.PAP. 135, 38 PP.

2340 HAWKSWORTH, D.L. & WELLS, H. (1973) - ORNAMENTATION ON THE TERMINAL HAIRS
      IN CHAETOMIUM KUNZE EX FR. AND SOME ALLIED GENERA. MYCOL.PAP. 134, 1-24.

2341 HAWN, E.J. & VANTERPOOL, T.C. (1953) - PRELIMINARY STUDIES ON THE SEXUAL
      STAGE OF RHIZOCTONIA SOLANI KUEHN. CAN.J.BOT. 31, 699-710.

2342 HAY, G.W., WESTLAKE, D.W.S. & SIMPSON, F.J. (1961) - DEGRADATION OF RUTIN
      BY ASPERGILLUS FLAVUS. PURIFICATION AND CHARACTERIZATION OF RUTINASE.
      CAN.J.MICROBIOL. 7, 921-932.

2343 HAYES, A.J. (1965) - STUDIES ON THE DECOMPOSITION OF CONIFEROUS LEAF LIT-
      TER. 2. CHANGES IN EXTERNAL FEATURES AND SUCCESSION OF MICROFUNGI. J.
      SOIL SCI. 16, 242-257.

2344 HAYES, A.J. (1965) - SOME MICROFUNGI FROM SCOTS PINE LITTER. TRANS.BR.MY-
      COL.SOC. 48, 179-185.

2345 HAYES, A.J. (1967) - BIOLOGY OF FOREST SOILS - MYCOLOGY OF SCOTS PINE LIT-
      TER. REP.FOREST RES., 1967, 147-148.

2346 HAYES, A.W., DAVIS, N.D. & DIENER, U.L. (1966) - EFFECT OF AERATION ON
      GROWTH AND AFLATOXIN PRODUCTION BY ASPERGILLUS FLAVUS IN SUBMERGED CUL-
      TURE. APPL.MICROBIOL. 14, 1019-1021.

2347 HAYES, W.A. & BLACKBURN, F. (1966) - STUDIES ON THE NUTRITION OF ARTHRO-
      BOTRYS OLIGOSPORA AND A. ROBUSTA. 2. THE PREDACEOUS PHASE. ANN.APPL.
      BIOL. 58, 51-60.

2348 HEAL, O.W. (1963) - SOIL FUNGI AS FOOD FOR AMOEBAE. IN: SOIL ORGANISMS;
      DOEKSEN, J. & DRIFT, J. VAN DER (ED.), NORTH HOLLAND PUBL.CO., AMSTER-
      DAM, 289-297.

2349 HEALE, J.B. (1966) - HETEROKARYON SYNTHESIS AND MORPHOGENESIS IN VERTICIL-
      LIUM. J.GEN.MICROBIOL. 45, 419-427.

2350 HEALE, J.B. & GUPTA, D.P. (1970) - THE UTILIZATION OF CELLOBIOSE BY VERTI-
      CILLIUM ALBO-ATRUM. J.GEN.MICROBIOL. 63, 175-181.

2351   HEALE, J.B. & GUPTA, D.P. (1972) - MECHANISM OF VASCULAR WILTING INDUCED
       BY VERTICILLIUM ALBO-ATRUM. TRANS.BR.MYCOL.SOC. 58, 19-28.

2352   HEALE, J.B. & ISAAC, I. (1963) - WILT OF LUCERNE CAUSED BY SPECIES OF VER-
       TICILLIUM. 4. PATHOGENICITY OF VERTICILLIUM ALBO-ATRUM AND V. DAHLIAE
       TO LUCERNE AND OTHER CROPS. ANN.APPL.BIOL. 52, 439-451.

2353   HEALE, J.B. & ISAAC, I. (1965) - ENVIRONMENTAL FACTORS IN THE PRODUCTION
       OF DARK RESTING STRUCTURES IN VERTICILLIUM ALBO-ATRUM, V. DAHLIAE AND
       V. TRICORPUS. TRANS.MYCOL.SOC.JAPAN 48, 39-50.

2354   HEATH, L.A.F. & EGGINS, H.O.W. (1965) - EFFECTS OF LIGHT, TEMPERATURE AND
       NUTRIENTS ON THE PRODUCTION OF CONIDIA AND SCLEROTIA BY FORMS OF ASPER-
       GILLUS JAPONICUS. EXPERIENTIA 21, 385-386.

2355   HEATH, M.C. & HIGGINS, V.J. (1972) - DEGRADATION OF PHASEOLLIN AND PISATIN
       BY STEMPHYLIUM BOTRYOSUM. PHYTOPATHOLOGY 62, 763.

2356   HEATH, M.C. & HIGGINS, V.J. (1973) - IN VITRO AND IN VIVO CONVERSION OF
       PHASEOLLIN AND PISATIN BY AN ALFALFA PATHOGEN STEMPHYLIUM BOTRYOSUM.
       PHYSIOL.PL.PATH. 3, 107-120.

2357   HEDDEN, P., MACMILLAN, J. & GRINSTED, M.J. (1973) - FUNGAL PRODUCTS. 8.
       NEW KAURENOLIDES FROM GIBBERELLA FUJIKUROI. J.CHEM.SOC.PERKIN TRANS.I,
       1973 (22), 2773-2778.

2358   HEDGER, J.N. (1975) - THE ECOLOGY OF THERMOPHILIC FUNGI IN INDONESIA. IN:
       BIODEGRADATION ET HUMIFICATION; KILBERTUS, G., REISINGER, O., MOURAY,
       A. & CANCELA DA FONSECA J.A. (ED.), 1ST INT.COLLOQU., NANCY, 59-65.

2359   HEDGER, J.N. & HUDSON, H.J. (1970) - THIELAVIA THERMOPHILA AND SPOROTRI-
       CHUM THERMOPHILE. TRANS.BR.MYCOL.SOC. 54, 497-500.

2360   HEDGER, J.N. & HUDSON, H.J. (1974) - NUTRITIONAL STUDIES OF THERMOMYCES
       LANUGINOSUS FROM WHEAT STRAW COMPOST. TRANS.BR.MYCOL.SOC. 62, 129-143.

2361   HEIMANN, M. (1957) - DIE WELKEKRANKHEIT VON LIMONIUM TATARICUM (STATICE-
       STERBEN). GARTENBAUWISSENSCHAFT 22, 278-287.

2362   HEINEN, W. (1962) - UEBER DEN ENZYMATISCHEN CUTIN-ABBAU. 3. DIE ENZYMA-
       TISCHE AUSRUESTUNG VON PENICILLIUM SPINULOSUM ZUM ABBAU DER CUTICULAR-
       BESTANDTEILE. ARCH.MIKROBIOL. 41, 268-281.

2363   HEINEN, W. & BRAND, J.VAN DEN (1961) - UEBER DEN ENZYMATISCHEN CUTIN-AB-
       BAU. 2. EIGENSCHAFTEN EINES CUTINOLYTISCHEN ENZYMS AUS PENICILLIUM SPI-
       NULOSUM. ACTA BOT.NEERL. 10, 171-189.

2364   HEJTMANEK, M. (1960) - VARIABILITY IN ASSIMILATION PROPERTIES OF DERMATO-
       PHYTES. 2. THE GROWTH OF KERATINOMYCES AJELLOI ON MEDIA WITH VARIED
       NITROGEN SOURCE. ACTA UNIV.PALACK.OLOMUC 20, 5-20.

2365   HEJTMANEK, M. (1961) - VARIABILITY IN ASSIMILATION PROPERTIES OF DERMATO-
       PHYTES. 4. THE GROWTH OF KERATINOMYCES AJELLOI ON MEDIA OF VARIED CAR-
       BON SOURCE. ACTA UNIV.PALACK.OLOMUC, FAC.MED. 25, 5-16.

2366   HEJTMANEK, M., HEJTMANKOVA, N. & KUNERT, J. (1973) - (ON THE OCCURRENCE OF
       GEOPHILIC DERMATOPHYTES IN ASIA). CESKA MYKOL. 27, 159-161.

2367   HEJTMANKOVA, N., LENHART, K. & KOMENDA, S. (1974) - DISTRIBUTION OF NUCLEI
       IN MACROCONIDIA OF DERMATOPHYTES. FOLIA MICROBIOL. 19, 88-93.

2368 HEJTMANKOVA-UHROVA, N. & HEJTMANEK, M. (1965) - UEBER DIE INDUKTION DER SEXUELLEN VERMEHRUNG UND DIE GENOTYPISCHE DETERMINATION DER WUCHSFORM BEI MICROSPORUM GYPSEUM. MYCOPATH.MYCOL.APPL. 25, 183-194.

2369 HEJTMANKOVA-UHROVA, N. & HEJTMANEK, M. (1967) - SOMATIC KARYOKINESIS IN NANNIZZIA INCURVATA. NATURWISSENSCHAFTEN 54, 206.

2370 HEJTMANKOVA-UHROVA, N. & HEJTMANEK, M. (1968) - SOMATISCHE KARYOKINESE BEI NANNIZZIA INCURVATA. ZENTBL.BAKT.PARASITKDE, ABT.2, 122, 185-196.

2371 HELLMERS, E. (1965) - TORVESKIMMEL (OSTRACODERMA EPIGAEUM (LINK) HENNEBERT) OG DENS PERFEKTE STADIUM TORVE-BAEGERSVAMP (PEZIZA ATROVINOSA COOKE & GERARD). HORTICULTURA, ODENSE 19, 71-80.

2372 HEMMES, D.E. & WONG, L.D.S. (1975) - ULTRASTRUCTURE OF CHLAMYDOSPORES OF PHYTOPHTHORA CINNAMOMI. CAN.J.BOT. 53, 2945-2957.

2373 HEMPEL, H. & GOODMAN, N.L. (1975) - RAPID CONVERSION OF HISTOPLASMA CAP-SULATUM, BLASTOMYCES DERMATITIDIS AND SPOROTHRIX SCHENCKII IN TISSUE CULTURE. J.CLIN.MICROBIOL. 1, 420-424.

2374 HENDERSHOT, W.F., HESSELTINE, C.W., PRIDHAM, T.G., BENEDICT, R.G. & JACK-SON, R.W. (1962) - RAMULOSIN. INHIBITORY EFFECT AGAINST PLANT SEEDS AND VARIOUS FUNGI. ARCHS BIOCHEM.BIOPHYS. 96, 166-170.

2375 HENDERSON, M.E.K. (1961) - ISOLATION, IDENTIFICATION, AND GROWTH OF SOME SOIL HYPHOMYCETES AND YEAST-LIKE FUNGI WHICH UTILIZE AROMATIC COMPOUNDS RELATED TO LIGNIN. J.GEN.MICROBIOL. 26, 149-154.

2376 HENDERSON, M.E.K. (1961) - THE METABOLISM OF AROMATIC COMPOUNDS RELATED TO LIGNIN BY SOME HYPHOMYCETES AND YEAST-LIKE FUNGI OF SOIL. J.GEN.MICRO-BIOL. 26, 155-165.

2377 HENDERSON, M.E.K. (1963) - FUNGAL METABOLISM OF CERTAIN AROMATIC COMPOUNDS RELATED TO LIGNIN. PURE APPL.CHEM. 7, 589-602.

2378 HENDERSON, M.E.K. & DUFF, R.B. (1963) - THE RELEASE OF METALLIC AND SILI-CATE IONS FROM MINERALS, ROCKS AND SOILS BY FUNGAL ACTIVITY. J.SOIL SCI. 14, 236-246.

2379 HENDEY, N.I. (1964) - SOME OBSERVATION ON CLADOSPORIUM RESINAE AS A FUEL CONTAMINANT AND ITS POSSIBLE ROLE IN THE CORROSION OF ALUMINIUM ALLOY FUEL TANKS. TRANS.BR.MYCOL.SOC. 47, 467-475.

2380 HENDRIX, F.F. & CAMPBELL, W.A. (1968) - PYTHIACEOUS FUNGI ISOLATED FROM SOUTHERN FOREST NURSERY SOILS AND THEIR PATHOGENICITY TO PINE SEED-LINGS. FOREST SCI. 14, 292-297.

2381 HENDRIX, F.F. & CAMPBELL, W.A. (1970) - DISTRIBUTION OF PHYTOPHTHORA AND PYTHIUM SPECIES IN SOILS IN THE CONTINENTAL UNITED STATES. CAN.J.BOT. 48, 377-384.

2382 HENDRIX, F.F. & CAMPBELL, W.A. (1973) - PYTHIUMS AS PLANT PATHOGENS. A. REV.PHYTOPATH. 11, 77-98.

2383 HENDRIX, F.F. & CAMPBELL, W.A. (1974) - TAXONOMIC VALUE OF REPRODUCTIVE CELL SIZE IN THE GENUS PYTHIUM. MYCOLOGIA 66, 681-684.

2384 HENDRIX, F.F. & CAMPBELL, W.A. (1974) - TAXONOMY OF PYTHIUM SYLVATICUM AND RELATED FUNGI. MYCOLOGIA 66, 1049-1053.

2385 HENDRIX, F.F., CAMPBELL, W.A. & CHIEN, C.Y. (1971) - SOME PHYCOMYCETES IN-DIGENOUS TO SOILS OF OLD GROWTH FORESTS. MYCOLOGIA 63, 283-289.

2386   HENDRIX, F.F., CAMPBELL, W.A. & MONCRIEF, J.B. (1970) - PYTHIUM SPECIES
       ASSOCIATED WITH GOLF TURFGRASSES IN THE SOUTH AND SOUTHEAST. PL.DIS.
       REPTR 54, 419-421.

2387   HENDRIX, F.F. & KUHLMANN, E.G. (1965) - FACTORS AFFECTING DIRECT RECOVERY
       OF PHYTOPHTHORA CINNAMOMI FROM SOIL. PHYTOPATHOLOGY 55, 1183-1187.

2388   HENDRIX, J.W. (1965) - INFLUENCE OF STEROLS ON GROWTH AND REPRODUCTION OF
       PYTHIUM AND PHYTOPHTHORA SPP. PHYTOPATHOLOGY 55, 790-797.

2389   HENDRIX, J.W. (1975) - DIFFERENTIAL UPTAKE AND METABOLISM OF SITOSTEROL
       AND CHOLESTEROL BY ACHLYA, PYTHIUM AND PHYTOPHTHORA SPECIES. CAN.J.MI-
       CROBIOL. 21, 735-737.

2390   HENIS, Y. & CHET, I. (1967) - MODE OF ACTION OF AMMONIA ON SCLEROTIUM ROLF-
       SII. PHYTOPATHOLOGY 57, 425-427.

2391   HENIS, Y. & CHET, I. (1968) - THE EFFECT OF NITROGENOUS AMENDMENTS ON THE
       GERMINABILITY OF SCLEROTIA OF SCLEROTIUM ROLFSII AND ON THEIR ACCOMPANY-
       ING MICROFLORA. PHYTOPATHOLOGY 58, 209-211.

2392   HENIS, Y., CHET, I. & AVIZOHAR-HERSHENZON, Z. (1965) - NUTRITIONAL AND
       MECHANICAL FACTORS INVOLVED IN MYCELIAL GROWTH AND PRODUCTION OF SCLE-
       ROTIA BY SCLEROTIUM ROLFSII IN ARTIFICIAL MEDIUM AND AMENDED SOIL. PHY-
       TOPATHOLOGY 55, 87-91.

2393   HENIS, Y. & INBAR, M. (1968) - EFFECT OF BACILLUS SUBTILIS ON GROWTH AND
       SCLEROTIUM FORMATION BY RHIZOCTONIA SOLANI. PHYTOPATHOLOGY 58, 933-938.

2394   HENIS, Y., OKON, Y. & CHET, I. (1973) - THE RELATIONSHIP BETWEEN EARLY HY-
       PHAL BRANCHING AND FORMATION OF SCLEROTIA IN SCLEROTIUM ROLFSII. J.GEN.
       MICROBIOL. 79, 147-150.

2395   HENIS, Y., SNEH, B. & KATAN, J. (1967) - EFFECT OF ORGANIC AMENDMENTS ON
       RHIZOCTONIA AND ACCOMPANYING MICROFLORA IN SOIL. CAN.J.MICROBIOL. 13,
       643-650.

2396   HENNEBERT, G.L. (1962) - WARDOMYCES AND ASTEROMYCES. CAN.J.BOT. 40, 1203-
       1216.

2397   HENNEBERT, G.L. (1963) - BOTRYTIS ON ALLIUM. MEDED.LANDBHOGESCH.OPZOEKSTNS
       GENT 28, 851-876.

2398   HENNEBERT, G.L. (1968) - ECHINOBOTRYUM, WARDOMYCES, AND MAMMARIA. TRANS.
       BR.MYCOL.SOC. 51, 749-762.

2399   HENNEBERT, G.L. (1971) - PLEOMORPHISM IN FUNGI IMPERFECTI. IN: TAXONOMY OF
       FUNGI IMPERFECTI; KENDRICK, B. (ED.), UNIV.TORONTO PRESS, 202-223.

2400   HENNEBERT, G.L. (1973) - BOTRYTIS AND BOTRYTIS-LIKE GENERA. PERSOONIA 7,
       183-204.

2401   HENNEBERT, G.L. & GILLES, G.L. (1958) - EPIDEMIOLOGIE DE BOTRYTIS CINEREA
       PERS. SUR LES FRAISIERS. MEDED.LANDBHOGESCH.OPZOEKSTNS GENT 23, 864-888.

2402   HENNEBERT, G.L. & GROVES, J.W. (1963) - THREE NEW SPECIES OF BOTRYOTINIA
       ON RANUNCULACEAE. CAN.J.BOT. 41, 341-370.

2403   HENNEBERT, G.L. & KORF, R.P. (1975) - THE PEAT MOULD, CHROMELOSPORIUM OL-
       LARE, CONIDIAL STATE OF PEZIZA OSTRACODERMA, AND ITS MISAPPLIED NAMES,
       BOTRYTIS CRYSTALLINA, BOTRYTIS SPECTABILIS, OSTRACODERMA EPIGAEUM AND
       PEZIZA ATROVINOSA. MYCOLOGIA 67, 214-240.

2404 HENNEBERT, G.L. & WERESUB, L.K. (1977) - TERMS FOR STATES AND FORMS OF FUN-
      GI, THEIR NAMES AND TYPES. MYCOTAXON 6, 207-211.

2405 HENRICI, A.T. (1939) - AN ENDOTOXIN FROM ASPERGILLUS FUMIGATUS. J.IMMUN.
      36, 319-338.

2406 HENRIKSSON, L.E. & HENRIKSSON, E. (1974) - OCCURRENCE OF FUNGI ON THE VOL-
      CANIC ISLAND OF SURTSEY, ICELAND. ACTA BOT.ISL. 3, 82-88.

2407 HENRY, A.W. & MCKENZIE, A.R. (1959) - NOTE ON THE COMPARATIVE ACTIVITY OF
      MONOSPOROUS AND MYCELIAL ISOLATES OF OPHIOBOLUS GRAMINIS SACC. FROM THE
      SAME SOURCE AS WHEAT PATHOGENS IN NATURAL AND STERILIZED SOIL. CAN.J.
      PL.SCI. 39, 405-407.

2408 HENSON, L. & VALLEAU, W.D. (1940) - THE PRODUCTION OF APOTHECIA OF SCLERO-
      TINIA SCLEROTIORUM AND S. TRIFOLIORUM IN CULTURE. PHYTOPATHOLOGY 30,
      869-873.

2409 HENSSEN, A. (1957) - UEBER DIE BEDEUTUNG DER THERMOPHILEN MIKROORGANISMEN
      FUER DIE ZERSETZUNG DES STALLMISTES. ARCH.MIKROBIOL. 27, 63-81.

2410 HEPPLE, S. (1960) - THE MOVEMENT OF FUNGAL SPORES IN SOIL. TRANS.BR.MYCOL.
      SOC. 43, 73-79.

2411 HERING, T.F. (1965) - SUCCESSION OF FUNGI IN THE LITTER OF A LAKE DISTRICT
      OAKWOOD. TRANS.BR.MYCOL.SOC. 48, 391-408.

2412 HERMANIDES-NIJHOF, E.J. (1977) - AUREOBASIDIUM AND ALLIED GENERA. STUD.MY-
      COL., BAARN 15, 141-177.

2413 HERR, L.J. (1957) - NUTRITIONAL STUDIES OF AN ISOLATE OF PHYTOPHTHORA CAC-
      TORUM INCITING A ROOT ROT OF SOYBEANS IN OHIO. PHYTOPATHOLOGY 47, 16
      (ABS.).

2414 HERR, L.J. (1973) - DISK-PLATE METHOD FOR SELECTIVE ISOLATION OF RHIZOCTO-
      NIA SOLANI FROM SOIL. CAN.J.MICROBIOL. 19, 1269-1273.

2415 HERR, L.J. (1976) - IN FIELD SURVIVAL OF RHIZOCTONIA SOLANI IN SOIL AND
      DISEASED SUGARBEETS. CAN.J.MICROBIOL. 22, 983-988.

2416 HERRERA, T. & ULLOA, M. (1972) - ESTUDIO DE CANDIDA KRUSEI Y TRICHOSPORON
      CUTANEUM AISLADOS DEL POZOL. REVTA LAT.-AM.MICROBIOL. 13, 255-261.

2417 HERZOG, W. (1961) - DAS UEBERDAUERN UND DER SAPROPHYTISMUS DES WURZELTOE-
      TERS RHIZOCTONIA SOLANI IM BODEN. PHYTOPATH.Z. 40, 379-415.

2418 HERZOG, W. & WARTENBERG, H. (1958) - UNTERSUCHUNGEN UEBER DIE LEBENSDAUER
      DER SKLEROTIEN VON RHIZOCTONIA SOLANI IM BODEN. PHYTOPATH.Z. 33, 291-
      315.

2419 HERZOG, W. & WARTENBERG, H. (1960) - DER KONSERVIERUNGSEFFEKT ANTIBIOTI-
      SCHER MIKROORGANISMEN AN DEN SKLEROTIEN VON RHIZOCTONIA SOLANI. BER.DT.
      BOT.GES. 73, 346-348.

2420 HESS, W.M., MUELLER, E. & AUE, R. (1967) - GERM PORES OF CHAETOMIUM ASCO-
      SPORES. NATURWISSENSCHAFTEN 54, 521-522.

2421 HESS, W.M., SASSEN, M.M.A. & REMSEN, C.C. (1968) - SURFACE CHARACTERISTICS
      OF PENICILLIUM CONIDIA. MYCOLOGIA 60, 290-303.

2422   HESS, W.M. & STOCKS, D.L. (1969) - SURFACE CHARACTERISTICS OF ASPERGILLUS
       CONIDIA. MYCOLOGIA 61, 560-571.

2423   HESS, W.M. & WEBER, D.J. (1973) - ULTRASTRUCTURE OF DORMANT AND GERMINATED
       SPORANGIOSPORES OF RHIZOPUS ARRHIZUS. PROTOPLASMA 77, 15-33.

2424   HESSELTINE, C.W. (1943) - HAPLOSPORANGIUM BISPORALE. MYCOLOGIA 35, 255-
       256.

2425   HESSELTINE, C.W. (1969) - MYCOTOXINS. MYCOPATH.MYCOL.APPL. 39, 371-383.

2426   HESSELTINE, C.W. & ANDERSON, P. (1956) - THE GENUS THAMNIDIUM AND A STUDY
       OF THE FORMATION OF ITS ZYGOSPORES. AM.J.BOT. 43, 696-703.

2427   HESSELTINE, C.W., BENJAMIN, C.R., BRADLE, B. & HENDERSHOT, W.F. (1963) -
       RAMULOSIN FERMENTATION. AM.J.BOT. 50, 209-213.

2428   HESSELTINE, C.W., BENJAMIN, C.R. & MEHROTRA, B.S. (1959) - THE GENUS ZY-
       GORHYNCHUS. MYCOLOGIA 51, 173-194.

2429   HESSELTINE, C.W. & ELLIS, J.J. (1964) - THE GENUS ABSIDIA. GONGRONELLA AND
       CYLINDRICAL-SPORED SPECIES OF ABSIDIA. MYCOLOGIA 56, 568-601.

2430   HESSELTINE, C.W., SHOTWELL, O.L., SMITH, M., ELLIS, J.J., VANDERGRAFT, E.
       & SHANNON, G. (1968) - PRODUCTION OF VARIOUS AFLATOXINS BY STRAINS OF
       THE ASPERGILLUS FLAVUS SERIES. IN: TOXIC MICRO-ORGANISMS; HERZBERG, M.
       (ED.), PROC. 1ST. U.S.-JAPAN CONF. HONOLULU, 202-219.

2431   HESSELTINE, C.W., SORENSON, W.G. & SMITH, M. (1970) - TAXONOMIC STUDIES OF
       THE AFLATOXIN-PRODUCING STRAINS IN THE ASPERGILLUS FLAVUS GROUP. MYCO-
       LOGIA 62, 123-132.

2432   HESSELTINE, C.W., VANDEGRAFT, E.E., FENNELL, D.I., SMITH, M.L. & SHOTWELL,
       O.L. (1972) - ASPERGILLI AS OCHRATOXIN PRODUCERS. MYCOLOGIA 64, 539-550.

2433   HETHERINGTON, A.C. & RAISTRICK, H. (1931) - STUDIES IN THE BIOCHEMISTRY OF
       MICRO-ORGANISMS. 11. ON CITROMYCETIN, A NEW YELLOW COLOURING MATTER
       PRODUCED FROM GLUCOSE BY SPECIES OF CITROMYCES. PHIL.TRANS.R.SOC., B,
       220, 209-245.

2434   HETHERINGTON, A.C. & RAISTRICK, H. (1931) - STUDIES IN THE BIOCHEMISTRY OF
       MICRO-ORGANISMS. 14. ON THE PRODUCTION AND CHEMICAL CONSTITUTION OF A
       NEW YELLOW COLOURING MATTER, CITRININ, PRODUCED FROM GLUCOSE BY PENICIL-
       LIUM CITRINUM. PHIL.TRANS.R.SOC., B, 220, 269-295.

2435   HEUVEL, J.VAN DEN (1969) - EFFECTS OF AUREOBASIDIUM PULLULANS ON NUMBERS
       OF LESIONS ON DWARF BEAN LEAVES CAUSED BY ALTERNARIA ZINNIAE. NETH.J.
       PL.PATH. 75, 300-307.

2436   HEUVEL, J.VAN DEN, VAN ETTEN, H.D., SERUM, J.W., COFFEN, D.L. & WILLIAMS,
       T.H. (1974) - IDENTIFICATION OF 1ALPHA-HYDROXY PHASEOLLONE, A PHASEOL-
       LIN METABOLITE PRODUCED BY FUSARIUM SOLANI. PHYTOCHEMISTRY 13, 1129-
       1131.

2437   HEWETT, P.D. (1967) - A SURVEY OF SEED-BORNE FUNGI OF WHEAT. 2. THE INCI-
       DENCE OF COMMON SPECIES OF FUSARIUM. TRANS.BR.MYCOL.SOC. 50, 175-182.

2438   HEYNINGEN, S.VAN (1972) - AN ALKALINE PROTEASE FROM ACREMONIUM KILIENSE.
       THE ENZYME PROTEIN AND ITS PROPERTIES IN SOLUTIONS OF UREA AND SODIUM
       DODECYLSULPHATE. EUR.J.BIOCHEM. 27, 436-442.

2439 HEYNINGEN, S.VAN (1972) - AN ALKALINE PROTEASE FROM ACREMONIUM KILIENSE. SPECIFICITY, KINETICS, AND EFFECT OF PH. EUR.J.BIOCHEM. 28, 432-437.

2440 HEYNINGEN, S.VAN & SECHER, D.S. (1971) - A NEW ALKALINE PROTEASE FROM ACRE-MONIUM KILIENSE. BIOCHEM.J. 125, 1159-1160.

2441 HICKMAN, C.J. (1944) - PHYCOMYCETES OCCURRING IN GREAT BRITAIN. 1. PYTHIUM MAMILLATUM MEURS. TRANS.BR.MYCOL.SOC. 27, 49-51.

2442 HICKMAN, C.J. (1944) - PHYCOMYCETES OCCURRING IN GREAT BRITAIN. 3. PYTHIUM APHANIDERMATUM (EDSON) FITZPATRICK. TRANS.BR.MYCOL.SOC. 27, 63-67.

2443 HIDA, T. (1935) - UEBER DEN EINFLUSS DES NATRIUMFLUORIDS UND DER ANORGANI-SCHEN STICKSTOFFQUELLEN AUF DEN STOFFWECHSEL VON ASPERGILLUS NIGER, MIT BESONDERER BERUECKSICHTIGUNG DER BILDUNG VON BRENZTRAUBENSAEURE UND DI-METHYLBRENZTRAUBENSAEURE. J.SHANGHAI SCI.INST., SECT.4, 1, 199-221.

2444 HIDEKO, I., OKUYAMA, H., IKEZAWA, H. & TEJIMA, S. (1975) - STUDIES ON LI-PASE FROM MUCOR JAVANICUS. 1. PURIFICATION AND PROPERTIES. BIOCHIM.BIO-PHYS.ACTA 388, 413-422.

2445 HIGGINS, B.B. (1927) - PHYSIOLOGY AND PARASITISM OF SCLEROTIUM ROLFSII SACC. PHYTOPATHOLOGY 17, 417-448.

2446 HIGGINS, V.A. (1975) - INDUCED CONVERSION OF THE PHYTOALEXIN MAACKIAIN TO DIHYDROMAACKIAIN BY THE ALFALFA PATHOGEN STEMPHYLIUM BOTRYOSUM. PHYSIOL. PL.PATH. 6, 5-18.

2447 HIGGINS, V.J., STOESSL, A. & HEATH, M.C. (1974) - CONVERSION OF PHASEOLLIN TO PHASEOLLIN ISOFLAVAN BY STEMPHYLIUM BOTRYOSUM. PHYTOPATHOLOGY 64, 105-107.

2448 HIKINO, H., NABETANI, S. & TAKEMOTO, T. (1973) - STRUCTURE AND BIOSYNTHE-SIS OF CHRYSOGINE, A METABOLITE OF PENICILLIUM CHRYSOGENUM. YAKUGAKU ZASSHI 93, 619-623.

2449 HILL, P. (1972) - THE PRODUCTION OF PENICILLINS IN SOILS AND SEEDS BY PE-NICILLIUM CHRYSOGENUM AND THE ROLE OF PENICILLIN BETA-LACTAMASE IN THE ECOLOGY OF SOIL BACILLUS. J.GEN.MICROBIOL. 70, 243-252.

2450 HILL, P. & MARTIN, S.M. (1966) - CELLULAR PROTEOLYTIC ENZYMES OF PENICIL-LIUM CYANEOFULVUM. CAN.J.MICROBIOL. 12, 243-248.

2451 HILL, S.T. (1974) - CONIDIUM ONTOGENY IN THE XEROPHILIC FUNGUS WALLEMIA SEBI. J.STORED PROD.RES. 10, 209-215.

2452 HILL, T.F. & LYDA, S.D. (1976) - GAS EXCHANGES BY PHYMATOTRICHUM OMNIVORUM IN A CLOSED, AXENIC SYSTEM. MYCOPATHOLOGIA 59, 143-148.

2453 HILL, T.W. (1975) - ULTRASTRUCTURE OF ASCOSPOROGENESIS IN NANNIZZIA GYP-SEA. J.BACT. 122, 743-748.

2454 HINDORF, H. (1973) - COLLETOTRICHUM-POPULATION AUF COFFEA ARABICA IN KE-NIA. 1. EINE METHODE ZUR SYSTEMATISCHEN TRENNUNG VON PILZPOPULATIONEN. PHYTOPATH.Z. 77, 97-116.

2455 HINDORF, H. (1973) - COLLETOTRICHUM-POPULATION AUF COFFEA ARABICA L. IN KENIA. 2. QUALITATIVE UND QUANTITATIVE UNTERSCHIEDE IN DER COLLETOTRI-CHUM-POPULATION. PHYTOPATH.Z. 77, 216-234.

2456 HINDORF, H. (1975) - COLLETOTRICHUM OCCURRING ON COFFEA ARABICA. A REVIEW. J.COFFEE RES. 5, 43-56.

2457 HINDS, T.E. (1972) - INSECT TRANSMISSION OF CERATOCYSTIS SPECIES ASSOCIA-
      TED WITH ASPEN CANKERS. PHYTOPATHOLOGY 62, 221-225.

2458 HINE, R.B. (1960) - THE OCCURRENCE OF AMINO-ACIDS IN FOUR SPECIES OF PY-
      THIUM. MYCOLOGIA 52, 378-380.

2459 HINE, R.B. (1962) - EFFECT OF STREPTOMYCIN AND PIMARICIN ON GROWTH AND
      RESPIRATION OF PYTHIUM SPECIES. MYCOLOGIA 54, 640-646.

2460 HINE, R.B., ALABAN, C. & KLEMMER, H. (1964) - INFLUENCE OF SOIL TEMPERA-
      TURE ON ROOT AND HEART ROT OF PINEAPPLE CAUSED BY PHYTOPHTHORA CINNAMO-
      MI AND PHYTOPHTHORA PARASITICA. PHYTOPATHOLOGY 54, 1287-1289.

2461 HINE, R.B. & LUNA, L.V. (1963) - A TECHNIQUE FOR ISOLATING PYTHIUM APHANI-
      DERMATUM FROM SOIL. PHYTOPATHOLOGY 53, 727-728.

2462 HIRAOKA, N., FUKUMOTO, J. & TSURU, D. (1972) - STUDIES ON MOLD DEXTRANASES.
      3. PURIFICATION AND SOME ENZYMATIC PROPERTIES OF ASPERGILLUS CARNEUS
      DEXTRANASE. J.BIOCHEM. 71, 57-64.

2463 HIRAYAMA, S. & KOBAYASI, S. (1969) - STUDIES ON THE FUNGAL DETERIORATION
      OF TEXTILE MATERIALS. 1. ON A SPECIES OF DIHETEROSPORA. MATSUSAKA, MIE,
      JAPAN 6, 60-67.

2464 HIRAYAMA, S. & UDAGAWA, S. (1958) - TAXONOMIC STUDIES OF FUNGI ON STORED
      RICE GRAINS. 2. ASPERGILLUS GROUP. BULL.FAC.AGRIC.MIE UNIV. 16, 7-28.

2465 HIROTA, A., SUZUKI, A., AIZAWA, A. & TAMURA, S. (1973) - STRUCTURE OF
      CYL-2, A NOVEL CYCLOTETRAPEPTIDE FROM CYLINDROCLADIUM SCOPARIUM. AGRIC.
      BIOL.CHEM., TOKYO 37, 955-956.

2466 HIROTA, A., SUZUKI, A. & TAMURA, S. (1973) - CHARACTERIZATION OF FOUR AMI-
      NO ACIDS CONSTITUTING CYL-2, A METABOLITE FROM CYLINDROCLADIUM SCOPA-
      RIUM. AGRIC.BIOL.CHEM., TOKYO 37, 1185-1189.

2467 HIRTE, W. (1961) - VERGLEICHENDE MIKROBIOLOGISCHE UNTERSUCHUNGEN AN RIE-
      SELMUEDEN UND GESUNDEN BOEDEN DER BERLINER RIESELFELDER. 1. DIE MIKRO-
      ORGANISMENTAETIGKEIT (MIKROORGANISMENZAHL UND BIOCHEMISCHE AKTIVITAET).
      2. QUALITATIVE UNTERSUCHUNGEN. ZENTBL.BAKT.PARASITKDE, ABT.2, 114,
      367-387, 490-519.

2468 HITE, R.E. (1973) - THE EFFECT OF IRRADIATION ON THE GROWTH AND ASEXUAL
      REPRODUCTION OF BOTRYTIS CINEREA. PL.DIS.REPTR 57, 131-135.

2469 HITE, R.E. (1973) - SUBSTANCES FROM BOTRYTIS CINEREA ASSOCIATED WITH SPOR-
      ULATION AND EXPOSURE TO NEAR-ULTRAVIOLET RADIATION. PL.DIS.REPTR 57,
      760-764.

2470 HO, H.H. & FOSTER, B. (1972) - STARCH UTILIZATION BY PHYTOPHTHORA SPP.
      MYCOPATH.MYCOL.APPL. 46, 335-349.

2471 HO, H.H. & ZENTMYER, G.A. (1977) - MORPHOLOGY OF PHYTOPHTHORA CINNAMOMI.
      MYCOLOGIA 69, 701-713.

2472 HO, N.S.-M., YANG, B.-Y. & DEVOL, C.E. (1974) - STUDIES ON THE MUCORALES
      ISOLATED FROM YANG-MING-SHAN HUMUS. TAIWANIA 19, 75-87.

2473 HOCH, H.C., HAGEDORN, D.J., PINNOW, D.L. & MITCHELL, J.E. (1975) - ROLE OF
      PYTHIUM SPP. AS INCITANTS OF BEAN ROOT AND HYPOCOTYL ROT IN WISCONSIN.
      PL.DIS.REPTR 59, 443-447.

2474 HOCH, H.C. & MITCHELL, J.E. (1972) - A CONTINUOUS FLOW SYSTEM FOR INDUCING
      AND OBSERVING ASEXUAL SPORE FORMATION IN APHANOMYCES EUTEICHES. CAN.J.
      BOT. 50, 681-682.

2475 HOCK, W.K. & SISLER, H.D. (1969) - METABOLISM OF CHLORONEB BY RHIZOCTONIA
      SOLANI AND OTHER FUNGI. J.AGRIC.FD CHEM. 17, 123-128.

2476 HOCKENHULL, D.J.D., WALKER, A.D., WILKIN, G.D. & WINDER, F.G. (1952) -
      OXIDATION OF PHENYLACETIC ACID BY PENICILLIUM CHRYSOGENUM. BIOCHEM.J.
      50, 605-609.

2477 HOCKENHULL, D.J.D., WILKIN, G.D. & WINDER, F.G. (1951) - PRODUCTION OF KE-
      TOGLUTARATE BY PENICILLIUM CHRYSOGENUM. NATURE, LOND. 168, 1043.

2478 HODDINOTT, J. & OLSEN, O.A. (1972) - A STUDY OF THE CARBOHYDRATES IN THE
      CELL WALLS OF SOME SPECIES OF THE ENTOMOPHTHORALES. CAN.J.BOT. 50,
      1675-1679.

2479 HODGE, P. (1966) - NATURAL ACETYLENES. 14. THE BIOLOGICAL OXIDATION OF
      DEHYDRO-MATRICARIANOL. J.CHEM.SOC.(C), 1966, 1617-1621.

2480 HODGES, C.F. (1972) - INTERACTION OF CULTURE AGE AND TEMPERATURE ON GER-
      MINATION AND GROWTH OF CURVULARIA GENICULATA AND ON VIRULENCE. CAN.J.
      BOT. 50, 2093-2096.

2481 HODGES, C.F. (1975) - COMPARATIVE TOTAL AND PROPORTIONAL RATE OF GERMINA-
      TION OF BIPOLARIS SOROKINIANA AND CURVULARIA GENICULATA CONIDIA AS IN-
      FLUENCED BY CULTURE AGE AND TEMPERATURE. MYCOPATHOLOGIA 57, 9-14.

2482 HODGES, C.S. (1962) - FUNGI ISOLATED FROM SOUTHERN FOREST TREE NURSERY
      SOILS. MYCOLOGIA 54, 221-229.

2483 HODGES, F.A., ZUST, J.R., SMITH, H.R., NELSON, A.A., AMBRECHT, B.H. &
      CAMPBELL, A.D. (1964) - MYCOTOXINS - AFLATOXIN ISOLATED FROM PENICIL-
      LIUM PUBERULUM. SCIENCE, N.Y. 145, 1439.

2484 HODGES, P., RONALDSON, J.W., TAYLOR, A. & WHITE, E.P. (1963) - SPORIDESMIN
      AND SPORIDESMIN-B. CHEM.IND., 1963, 42-43.

2485 HODGKISS, I.J. (1970) - VIABILITY OF DISCHARGED AND RESIDUAL SPORES OF
      SOME COPROPHILOYS PYRENOMYCES. TRANS.BR.MYCOL.SOC. 55, 332-335.

2486 HODGKISS, I.J. & HARVEY, R. (1971) - EFFECTS OF TEMPERATURE ON SPORE DIS-
      CHARGE RHYTHMS IN PYRENOMYCETES. TRANS.BR.MYCOL.SOC. 56, 225-234.

2487 HODGKISS, I.J. & HARVEY, R. (1972) - EFFECT OF CARBON DIOXIDE ON THE GROWTH
      AND SPORULATION OF CERTAIN COPROPHILOUS PYRENOMYCETES. TRANS.BR.MYCOL.
      SOC. 59, 409-418.

2488 HODKINSON, M. & DALTON, S.A. (1973) - INTERACTIONS BETWEEN DDT AND RIVER
      FUNGI. 2. INFLUENCE OF CULTURE CONDITIONS ON THE COMPATIBILITY OF FUNGI
      AND P,P-DDT. BULL.ENVIRON.CONTAM.TOXICOL. 10, 356-359.

2489 HOEHNEL, F.VON (1924) - STUDIEN UEBER HYPHOMYCETEN. ZENTBL.BAKT.PARASITKDE,
      ABT.2, 60, 1-26.

2490 HOERTER, R. & HUNSTEGER, F. (1962) - MORTIERELLA-MYKOSE BEI VOEGELN. DT.
      TIERAERZTL.WSCHR. 69, 49-51.

2491 HOES, J.A. (1962) - DYNAMICS OF THE MYCOFLORA OF SUBTERRANEAN PARTS OF
      WINTER WHEAT IN THE DRYLAND AREA OF WASHINGTON. PHYTOPATHOLOGY 52, 736
      (ABS.).

2492 HOES, J.A. (1964) - DYNAMICS OF THE MYCOFLORA OF SUBTERRANEAN PARTS OF
      WINTER WHEAT IN THE DRYLAND AREA OF WASHINGTON. DISS.UNIV.ST.WASH.

2493 HOES, J.A. (1971) - DEVELOPMENT OF CHLAMYDOSPORES IN VERTICILLIUM NIGRES-
      CENS AND V. NUBILUM. CAN.J.BOT. 49, 1863-1866.

2494 HOES, J.A. & HUANG, H.C. (1975) - SCLEROTINIA SCLEROTIORUM - VIABILITY AND
      SEPARATION OF SCLEROTIA FROM SOIL. PHYTOPATHOLOGY 65, 1431-1432.

2495 HOFFMANN, G.M. (1966) - UNTERSUCHUNGEN UEBER DIE HETEROKARYOSEBILDUNG UND
      DEN PARASEXUALCYCLUS BEI FUSARIUN OXYSPORUM. 1. ANASTOMOSENBILDUNG IM
      MYCEL UND KERNVERHAELTNISSE BEI DER CONIDIENENTWICKLUNG. ARCH.MIKROBIOL.
      53, 336-347.

2496 HOFFMANN, G.M. (1968) - KERNVERHAELTNISSE BEI PFLANZENPATHOGENEN IMPERFEK-
      TEN PILZEN, INSBESONDERE ARTEN DER GATTUNG FUSARIUM. ZENTBL.BAKT.PARA-
      SITKDE, ABT.2, 122, 405-419.

2497 HOFMANN, E. (1934) - UNTERSUCHUNGEN UEBER GLYKOSIDE UND DISACCHARIDE SPAL-
      TENDE ENZYME VON SCHIMMELPILZEN. BIOCHEM.Z. 273, 198-206.

2498 HOFMANN, T. & SHAW, R. (1964) - PROTEOLYTIC ENZYMES OF PENICILLIUM JANTHI-
      NELLUM. 1. PURIFICATION AND PROPERTIES OF A TRYPSINOGEN-ACTIVATING EN-
      ZYME (PEPTIDASE-A). BIOCHIM.BIOPHYS.ACTA 92, 543-557.

2499 HOGG, B. (1966) - MICRO-FUNGI ON LEAVES OF FAGUS SYLVATICA. 2. DURATION OF
      SURVIVAL, SPORE VIABILITY AND CELLULOLYTIC ACTIVITY. TRANS.BR.MYCOL.
      SOC. 49, 193-204.

2500 HOGG, B.M. & HUDSON, H.J. (1966) - MICRO-FUNGI ON LEAVES OF FAGUS SYLVATI-
      CA. 1. THE MICRO-FUNGAL SUCCESSION. TRANS.BR.MYCOL.SOC. 49, 185-192.

2501 HOITINK, H.A.J. & SCHMITTHENNER, A.F. (1974) - RELATIVE PREVALENCE AND VIR-
      ULENCE OF PHYTOPHTHORA SPECIES INVOLVED IN RHODODENDRON ROOT ROT. PHY-
      TOPATHOLOGY 64, 1371-1374.

2502 HOLDING, A.J., FRANKLIN, D.A. & WATLING, R. (1965) - THE MIKROFLORA OF PEAT
      -PODZOL TRANSITIONS. J.SOIL SCI. 16, 44-59.

2503 HOLKER, J.S.E. & KAGAL, S.A. (1968) - 5-METHOXYSTERIGMATOCYSTIN, A METABO-
      LITE FROM A MUTANT STRAIN OF ASPERGILLUS VERSICOLOR. CHEM.COMMUN., 1968,
      1574-1575.

2504 HOLKER, J.S.E. & YOUNG, K. (1975) - BIOSYNTHESIS OF METABOLITES OF PERI-
      CONIA MACROSPINOSA FROM (1-13C)-, (2-13C)-, AND (1,2-13C)-ACETATE. CHEM.
      COMMUN., 1975, 525-526.

2505 HOLLAND, A.A. & CHOO, Y.SEN (1970) - IMMUNOELECTROPHORETIC CHARACTERISTICS
      OF OPHIOBOLUS GRAMINIS SACC. AS AN AID IN CLASSIFICATION AND DETERMINA-
      TION. ANTONIE VAN LEEUWENHOEK 36, 541-548.

2506 HOLLIGAN, P.M. & JENNINGS, D.H. (1972) - CARBOHYDRATE METABOLISM IN THE
      FUNGUS DENDRYPHIELLA SALINA. 1. CHANGES IN THE LEVELS OF SOLUBLE CARBO-
      HYDRATES DURING GROWTH. NEW PHYTOL. 71, 569-582.

2507 HOLLIGAN, P.M. & JENNINGS, D.H. (1972) - CARBOHYDRATE METABOLISM IN THE
      FUNGUS DENDRYPHIELLA SALINA. 2. THE INFLUENCE OF DIFFERENT CARBON AND
      NITROGEN SOURCES ON THE ACCUMULATION OF MANNITOL AND ARABITOL. NEW PHY-
      TOL. 71, 583-594.

2508 HOLLIGAN, P.M. & LEWIS, D.H. (1973) - THE SOLUBLE CARBOHYDRATES OF ASPER-
      GILLUS CLAVATUS. J.GEN.MICROBIOL. 75, 155-159.

2509 HOLLINGS, M. & STONE, O.M. (1969) - VIRUSES IN FUNGI. SCI.PROGR. 57, 371-391.

2510 HOLLINGS, M. & STONE, O.M. (1971) - VIRUSES THAT INFECT FUNGI. A.REV.PHYTOPATH. 9, 93-118.

2511 HOLLIS, J.P. (1948) - OXYGEN AND CARBON DIOXIDE RELATION OF FUSARIUM OXYSPORUM SCHLECHT. AND FUSARIUM EUMARTII CARP. PHYTOPATHOLOGY 38, 761-775.

2512 HOLMWOOD, G.M. & ROBERTS, J.C. (1971) - STUDIES IN MYCOLOGICAL CHEMISTRY. 29. TOTAL SYNTHESIS OF (+,-)-O-METHYLAVERSIN ((+,-)-TRI-O-METHYLVERSICOLORIN-B). THE STRUCTURE OF AVERSIN. J.CHEM.SOC.(C), 1971 (23), 3899-3902.

2513 HOLT, G. & MACDONALD, K.D. (1968) - ISOLATION OF STRAINS WITH INCREASED PENICILLIUM YIELD AFTER HYBRIDIZATION IN ASPERGILLUS NIDULANS. NATURE, LOND. 219, 636-637.

2514 HOLT, G. & MACDONALD, K.D. (1968) - PENICILLIN PRODUCTION AND ITS MODE OF INHERITANCE IN ASPERGILLUS NIDULANS. ANTONIE VAN LEEUWENHOEK 34, 409-416.

2515 HOLUBOVA-JECHOVA, V. (1970) - THE INTERNAL ROTS OF BRAZIL NUTS. CESKA MYKOL. 24, 207-214.

2516 HOLUBOVA-JECHOVA, V. (1971) - POLYPHENOLOXIDASE ENZYMES FROM WOOD-INHABITING HYPHOMYCETES. CESKA MYKOL. 25, 23-32.

2517 HOLUBOVA-JECHOVA, V. (1974) - THE CORRECT GENERIC AND SPECIFIC NAME FOR ACREMONIELLA ATRA. FOLIA GEOBOT.PHYTOTAX., PRAHA 9, 315-316.

2518 HOLZAPFEL, C.W. (1968) - THE ISOLATION AND STRUCTURE OF CYCLOPIAZONIC ACID, A TOXIC METABOLITE OF PENICILLIUM CYCLOPIUM WESTLING. TETRAHEDRON 24, 2101-2119.

2519 HOLZAPFEL, C.W., HUTCHISON, R.D. & WILKINS, D.C. (1970) - THE ISOLATION AND STRUCTURE OF TWO NEW INDOLE DERIVATIVES FROM PENICILLIUM CYCLOPIUM WESTLING. TETRAHEDRON 26, 5239-5246.

2520 HOLZAPFEL, C.W. & STEYN, P.S. (1968) - THE ISOLATION AND STRUCTURE OF A NEW DITERPENE LACTONE FROM TRICHOTHECIUM ROSEUM LINK. TETRAHEDRON 24, 3321-3328.

2521 HOLZAPFEL, C.W. & WILKINS, D.C. (1971) - ON THE BIOSYNTHESIS OF CYCLOPIAZONIC ACID. PHYTOCHEMISTRY 10, 351-358.

2522 HOOG, G.S.DE (1972) - THE GENERA BEAUVERIA, ISARIA, TRITIRACHIUM AND ACRODONTIUM GEN.NOV. STUD.MYCOL., BAARN 1, 1-41.

2523 HOOG, G.S.DE (1974) - THE GENERA BLASTOBOTRYS, SPOROTHRIX, CALCARISPORIUM AND CALCARISPORIELLA GEN.NOV. STUD.MYCOL., BAARN 7, 1-84.

2524 HOOG, G.S.DE (1977) - RHINOCLADIELLA AND ALLIED GENERA. STUD.MYCOL., BAARN 15, 1-140.

2525 HOOG, G.S.DE & ARX, J.A.VON (1973) - REVISION OF SCOLECOBASIDIUM AND PLEUROPHRAGMIUM. KAVAKA 1, 55-60.

2526 HOOG, G.S.DE & HERMANIDES-NIJHOF, E.J. (1977) - SURVEY OF THE BLACK YEASTS AND ALLIED FUNGI. STUD.MYCOL., BAARN 15, 178-221.

2527   HOOPER, G.R., WOOD, H.A., MYERS, R. & BOZARTH, R.F. (1972) - VIRUS-LIKE
        PARTICLES IN PENICILLIUM BREVI-COMPACTUM AND P. STOLONIFERUM HYPHAE AND
        SPORES. PHYTOPATHOLOGY 62, 823-825.

2528   HOPKINSON, S.M. & PRIDHAM, J.B. (1967) - ENZYMIC GLUCOSYLATION OF PHENOLS.
        BIOCHEM.J. 105, 655-662.

2529   HORA, TR.S. & IYENGAR, M.R.S. (1960) - NITRIFICATION BY SOIL FUNGI. ARCH.
        MIKROBIOL. 35, 252-257.

2530   HORAK, E. (1960) - DIE PILZVEGETATION IM GLETSCHERVORFELD (2290-2350 M)
        DES ROTMOOSFERNERS IN DEN OETZTALER ALPEN. NOVA HEDWIGIA 2, 487-504.

2531   HORIE, Y. (1972) - MATERIALS FOR THE FUNGUS FLORA OF JAPAN. 11. TRANS.MY-
        COL.SOC.JAPAN 13, 118-124.

2532   HORIE, Y., YAMAZAKI, M. & UDAGAWA, S. (1977) - (SOIL MYCOFLORAE IN GROUND-
        NUT FIELDS AND THEIR ASSOCIATIONS ON HARVESTED PODS AND KERNELS). TRANS.
        MYCOL.SOC.JAPAN 18, 203-210.

2533   HORIKOSHI, K. & IIDA, S. (1964) - STUDIES OF THE SPORE COATS OF FUNGI. 1.
        ISOLATION AND COMPOSITION OF THE SPORE COATS OF ASPERGILLUS ORYZAE.
        BIOCHIM.BIOPHYS.ACTA 83, 197-203.

2534   HORIKOSHI, K., IIDA, S. & IKEDA, Y. (1965) - MANNITOL AND MANNITOL DEHYDRO-
        GENASES IN CONIDIA OF ASPERGILLUS ORYZAE. J.BACT. 89, 326-330.

2535   HORISBERGER, M., LEWIS, B.A. & SMITH, F. (1972) - STRUCTURE OF A (1-3)-AL-
        PHA-D-GLUCAN (PSEUDONIGERAN) OF ASPERGILLUS NIGER NRRL 326 CELL WALL.
        CARBOHYD.RES. 23, 183-188.

2536   HORNBY, D. (1969) - METHODS OF INVESTIGATING POPULATIONS OF THE TAKE-ALL
        FUNGUS (OPHIOBOLUS GRAMINIS) IN SOIL. ANN.APPL.BIOL. 64, 503-513.

2537   HORNBY, D. (1975) - INOCULUM OF THE TAKE-ALL FUNGUS - NATURE, MEASUREMENT,
        DISTRIBUTION AND SURVIVAL. BULL.OEPP/EPPO 5, 319-333.

2538   HORNOK, L. (1975) - OCCURRENCE OF FUSARIUM SPECIES IN HUNGARY. ACTA PHYTO-
        PATH.ACAD.SCI.HUNG. 10, 347-357.

2539   HORNOK, L. & JAGICZA, A. (1973) - FLUORESCENT ANTIBODY STAINING OF FUSARI-
        UM CULMORUM. ACTA PHYTOPATH.ACAD.SCI.HUNG. 8, 357-363.

2540   HORTA, P. (1912) - CONTRIBUICOES PARA O ESTUDO DAS DERMATOMICOZES NO BRA-
        ZIL. 1. MICROSPORON FLAVESCENS, N.SP. AJENTE DUMA NOVA TINHA MICROSPORIA.
        MEM.INST.OSWALD CRUZ 3, 301-308.

2541   HORVATH, S.L. (1966) - EXAMINATIONS ON KERATINOPHILIC FUNGI. PRELIMINARY
        STUDIES. ANNLS UNIV.SCIENT.BPEST ROLANDO EOETVOES, SECT.BIOL. 8, 107-119.

2542   HOSFORD, R.M. (1975) - PHOMA GLOMERATA, A NEW PATHOGEN OF WHEAT AND TRI-
        TICALES, CULTIVAR RESISTANCE RELATED TO WET PERIOD. PHYTOPATHOLOGY 65,
        1236-1239.

2543   HOSFORD, R.M., SOLANGI, G.R.M. & KIESLING, R.L. (1975) - INHERITANCE IN
        COCHLIOBOLUS SATIVUS. PHYTOPATHOLOGY 65, 699-703.

2544   HOTSON, J.W. (1912) - CULTURE STUDIES OF FUNGI PRODUCING BULBILS AND SIM-
        ILAR PROPAGATIVE BODIES. PROC.AM.ACAD.ARTS SCI. 48, 227-306.

2545   HOTSON, J.W. (1917) - NOTES ON BULBIFEROUS FUNGI WITH A KEY TO DESCRIBED
        SPECIES. BOT.GAZ. 64, 265-284.

2546   HOU, C.T., CIEGLER, A. & HESSELTINE, C.W. (1971) - TREMORGENIC TOXINS FROM
        PENICILLIA. 3. TREMORTIN PRODUCTION BY PENICILLIUM SPECIES ON VARIOUS
        AGRICULTURAL COMMODITIES. APPL.MICROBIOL. 21, 1101-1103.

2547   HOU, C.T., CIEGLER, A. & HESSELTINE, C.W. (1972) - NEW MYCOTOXIN, TRICHO-
        TOXIN-A, FROM TRICHODERMA VIRIDE ISOLATED FROM SOUTHERN LEAF BLIGHT-IN-
        FECTED CORN. APPL.MICROBIOL. 23, 183-185.

2548   HOUIN, R., ROUGET-CAMPANA, Y., LE FICHOUX, Y., LANCASTER, F., BAZIN, J.-
        C., DENIAU, M. & BOLOGNINI, J. (1972) - ISOLEMENT DE TRICHOPHYTON MEN-
        TAGROPHYTES, NANNIZIA PERSICOLOR ET TRICHOPHYTON TERRESTRE DU PELAGE DE
        RONGEURS. ANNLS PARASIT.HUM.COMP. 47, 421-429.

2549   HOWARD, B.H. & RAISTRICK, H. (1950) - STUDIES IN THE BIOCHEMISTRY OF MI-
        CRO-ORGANISMS. 81. THE COLOURING MATTERS OF PENICILLIUM ISLANDICUM SOPP.
        2. CHRYSOPHANIC ACID, 4,5-DIHYDROXY-2-METHYLANTHRAQUINONE. BIOCHEM.J.
        46, 49-53.

2550   HOWARD, B.H. & RAISTRICK, H. (1954) - STUDIES IN THE BIOCHEMISTRY OF MICRO-
        ORGANISMS. 91. THE COLOURING MATTERS OF PENICILLIUM ISLANDICUM SOPP. 3.
        SKYRIN AND FLAVOSKYRIN. BIOCHEM.J. 56, 56-65.

2551   HOWARD, D.H. & ORR, G.F. (1963) - COMPARISON OF STRAINS OF SPOROTRICHUM
        SCHENCKII ISOLATED FROM NATURE. J.BACT. 85, 816-821.

2552   HOWELL, A. (1939) - STUDIES ON HISTOPLASMA CAPSULATUM AND SIMILAR FORM
        SPECIES. 1. MORPHOLOGY AND DEVELOPMENT. MYCOLOGIA 31, 191-216.

2553   HOWELL, C.R. (1970) - DIFFERENTIAL ENZYME SYNTHESIS BY HAPLOID AND DIPLOID
        FORMS OF VERTICILLIUM ALBO-ATRUM. PHYTOPATHOLOGY 60, 488-490.

2554   HOWELL, C.R., STIPANOVIC, R.D. & BELL, A.A. (1972) - DIHYDROSANGUINARINE,
        A PRODUCT OF SANGUINARINE DETOXIFICATION BY VERTICILLIUM DAHLIAE. PES-
        TIC.BIOCHEM.PHYSIOL. 2, 364-370.

2555   HOWELL, D.M.B. & FERGUS, C.L. (1964) - THE COMPONENT FATTY ACIDS FOUND IN
        SCLEROTIA OF SCLEROTIUM ROLFSII. CAN.J.MICROBIOL. 10, 616-618.

2556   HRUSHOVETZ, S.B. (1957) - EFFECT OF AMINO ACIDS ON THE VIRULENCE OF HELMIN-
        THOSPORIUM SATIVUM TO WHEAT SEEDLINGS. PHYTOPATHOLOGY 47, 261-264.

2557   HSIEH, D.P.H., LIN, M.T. & YAO, R.C. (1973) - CONVERSION OF STERIGMATOCYS-
        TIN TO AFLATOXIN-B1 BY ASPERGILLUS PARASITICUS. BIOCHEM.BIOPHYS.RES.
        COMMUNS 52, 992-997.

2558   HSU, D.-S. & HENDRIX, F.F. (1972) - INFLUENCE OF TEMPERATURE ON OOSPORE
        FORMATION OF FOUR HETEROTHALLIC PYTHIUM SPP. MYCOLOGIA 64, 447-451.

2559   HSU, S.C. & LOCKWOOD, J.L. (1971) - RESPONSES OF FUNGAL HYPHAE TO SOIL FUN-
        GISTASIS. PHYTOPATHOLOGY 61, 1355-1362.

2560   HSU, Y.C., HISER, J.L. & VOLZ, P.A. (1974) - NUCLEAR BEHAVIOUR IN VEGETA-
        TIVE HYPHAE OF TRICHOPHYTON TERRESTRE. MYCOPATH.MYCOL.APPL. 53, 69-75.

2561   HSU, Y.-C. & VOLZ, P.A. (1975) - ULTRASTRUCTURAL FEATURES OF MEIOSIS IN
        CHAETOMIUM GLOBOSUM. MYCOPATHOLOGIA 55, 25-27.

2562   HSU.Y.C. & VOLZ, P.A. (1975) - PENETRATION OF TRICHOPHYTON TERRESTRE IN
        HUMAN HAIR. MYCOPATHOLOGIA 55, 179-183.

2563 HSU, Y.C., YU, S.A. & VOLZ, P.A. (1972) - THE MEIOTIC CONFIGURATION OF
      CHAETOMIUM GLOBOSUM. MYCOPATH.MYCOL.APPL. 50, 145-150.

2564 HSU, Y.C., YU, S.A. & VOLZ, P.A. (1973) - THE MITOTIC CONFIGURATION OF
      CHAETOMIUM GLOBOSUM. MYCOPATH.MYCOL.APPL. 51, 243-249.

2565 HUANG, H.C. (1977) - IMPORTANCE OF CONIOTHYRIUM MINITANS IN SURVIVAL OF
      SCLEROTIA OF SCLEROTINIA SCLEROTIORUM IN WILTED SUNFLOWER. CAN.J.BOT.
      55, 289-295.

2566 HUANG, H.C. & HOES, J.A. (1976) - PENETRATION AND INFECTION OF SCLEROTINIA
      SCLEROTIORUM BY CONIOTHYRIUM MINITANS. CAN.J.BOT. 54, 406-410.

2567 HUANG, H.C. & PATRICK, Z.A. (1971) - VARIABILITY OF THIELAVIOPSIS BASICOLA
      IN CULTURE. CAN.J.BOT. 49, 1041-1047.

2568 HUANG, H.C. & PATRICK, Z.A. (1972) - NUCLEAR DISTRIBUTION AND BEHAVIOUR IN
      THIELAVIOPSIS BASICOLA. CAN.J.BOT. 50, 2423-2429.

2569 HUANG, H.C. & PATRICK, Z.A. (1974) - KARYOLOGY OF CONIDIOGENESIS AND ENDO-
      CONIDIUM GERMINATION IN THIELAVIOPSIS BASICOLA. CAN.J.BOT. 52, 2263-
      2267.

2570 HUANG, H.C. & TINLINE, R.D. (1974) - SOMATIC MITOSIS IN HAPLOID AND DI-
      PLOID STRAINS OF COCHLIOBOLUS SATIVUS. CAN.J.BOT. 52, 1561-1568.

2571 HUANG, H.C., TINLINE, R.D. & FOWKE, L.C. (1975) - ULTRASTRUCTURE OF SOMA-
      TIC MITOSIS IN A DIPLOID STRAIN OF THE PLANT PATHOGENIC FUNGUS COCHLIO-
      BOLUS SATIVUS. CAN.J.BOT. 53, 403-414.

2572 HUANG, L.H. & HANLIN, R.T. (1975) - FUNGI OCCURRING IN FRESHLY HARVESTED
      AND IN-MARKET PECANS. MYCOLOGIA 67, 689-700.

2573 HUANG, L.H. & SCHMITT, J.A. (1975) - SOIL MICROFUNGI OF CENTRAL AND SOUTH-
      ERN OHIO. MYCOTAXON 3, 55-80.

2574 HUBALEK, Z. (1974) - DISPERSAL OF FUNGI OF THE FAMILY CHAETOMIACEAE BY
      FREE-LIVING BIRDS. 1. A SURVEY OF RECORDS. CESKA MYKOL. 28, 65-79.

2575 HUBALEK, Z. (1974) - THE DISTRIBUTION PATTERNS OF FUNGI IN FREE-LIVING
      BIRDS. ACTA SCI.NATN.ACAD.SCI.BOHEMOSL.BRNO 8, 1-51.

2576 HUBALEK, Z. (1975) - DISPERSAL OF FUNGI OF THE FAMILY CHAETOMIACEAE BY
      FREE-LIVING BIRDS. 2. ECOLOGICAL ASPECTS. CESKA MYCOL. 29, 46-58.

2577 HUBALEK, Z., BALAT, F., TOUSKOVA, I. & VLK, J. (1973) - MYCOFLORA OF BIRDS
      NESTS IN NEST-BOXES. MYCOPATH.MYCOL.APPL. 49, 1-12.

2578 HUBER, D.M. & ANDERSEN, A.L. (1966) - NECROSIS OF HYPHAE OF FUSARIUM SOLA-
      NI F. PHASEOLI AND RHIZOCTONIA SOLANI INDUCED BY A SOIL-BORNE BACTERIUM.
      PHYTOPATHOLOGY 56, 1416-1417.

2579 HUBER, D.M. & FINLEY, A.M. (1959) - GLIOCLADIUM, A CAUSAL AGENT IN THE BEAN
      ROOT ROT COMPLEX IN IDAHO. PL.DIS.REPTR 43, 626-628.

2580 HUBER, D.M. & MCKAY, H.C. (1968) - EFFECT OF TEMPERATURE, CROP, AND DEPTH
      OF BURIAL ON THE SURVIVAL OF TYPHULA IDAHOENSIS SCLEROTIA. PHYTOPATHOL-
      OGY 58, 961-962.

2581 HUBER, G.A. (1930) - THE ASPERGILLI AND THEIR RELATION TO DECAY IN APPLES.
      J.AGRIC.RES. 41, 801-817.

2582   HUBER, J. (1958) - UNTERSUCHUNGEN ZUR PHYSIOLOGIE INSEKTENTOETENDER PILZE.
        ARCH.MIKROBIOL. 29, 257-276.

2583   HUDSON, H.J. (1962) - SUCCESSION OF MICRO-FUNGI ON AGEING LEAVES OF SAC-
        CHARUM OFFICINARUM. TRANS.BR.MYCOL.SOC. 45, 395-423.

2584   HUDSON, H.J. (1963) - THE PERFECT STATE OF NIGROSPORA ORYZAE. TRANS.BR.
        MYCOL.SOC. 46, 355-360.

2585   HUDSON, H.J. (1963) - PYRENOMYCETES OF SUGAR CANE AND OTHER GRASSES IN JA-
        MAICA. 2. CONIDIA OF APIOSPORA MONTAGNEI. TRANS.BR.MYCOL.SOC. 46, 19-23.

2586   HUDSON, H.J. (1968) - THE ECOLOGY OF FUNGI ON PLANT REMAINS ABOVE SOIL.
        NEW PHYTOL. 67, 837-874.

2587   HUDSON, H.J. (1969) - ASPERGILLI IN THE AIR-SPORA AT CAMBRIDGE. TRANS.BR.
        MYCOL.SOC. 52, 153-159.

2588   HUDSON, H.J. (1973) - THERMOPHILOUS AND THERMOTOLERANT FUNGI IN THE AIR-
        SPORA AT CAMBRIDGE. TRANS.BR.MYCOL.SOC. 60, 596-598.

2589   HUDSON, H.J., MCKENZIE, E.H.C. & TOMMERUP, I.C. (1976) - CONIDIAL STATES
        OF APIOSPORA SACC. TRANS.BR.MYCOL.SOC. 66, 359-362.

2590   HUDSON, H.J. & WEBSTER, J. (1958) - SUCCESSION OF FUNGI ON DECAYING STEMS
        OF AGROPYRON REPENS. TRANS.BR.MYCOL.SOC. 41, 165-177.

2591   HUGHES, G.C. (1975) - STUDIES OF FUNGI IN OCEANS AND ESTUARIES SINCE 1961.
        1. A.REV.OCEANOGR.MAR.BIOL. 13, 69-180.

2592   HUGHES, G.C. & BISALPUTRA, A.-A. (1970) - ULTRASTRUCTURE OF HYPHOMYCETES.
        CONIDIUM ONTOGENY IN PEZIZA OSTRACODERMA. CAN.J.BOT. 48, 361-366.

2593   HUGHES, S.J. (1946) - AN UNDESCRIBED SPECIES OF CHAETOMIUM WITH FOUR-SPOR-
        ED ASCI. TRANS.BR.MYCOL.SOC. 29, 70-73.

2594   HUGHES, S.J. (1951) - STACHYLIDIUM, GONYTRICHUM, MESOBOTRYS, CHAETOPSIS
        AND CHAETOPSELLA. TRANS.BR.MYCOL.SOC. 34, 551-576.

2595   HUGHES, S.J. (1951) - STUDIES IN MICROFUNGI. 5. ACROTHECA. MYCOL.PAP. 38,
        1-8.

2596   HUGHES, S.J. (1951) - STUDIES ON MICROFUNGI. 11. SOME HYPHOMYCETES WHICH
        PRODUCE PHIALIDES. MYCOL.PAP. 45, 1-36.

2597   HUGHES, S.J. (1952) - TRICHOCLADIUM. TRANS.BR.MYCOL.SOC. 35, 152-158.

2598   HUGHES, S.J. (1952) - FOUR SPECIES OF SEPTONEMA. NATURALIST, HULL, 7-12.

2599   HUGHES, S.J. (1953) - CONIDIOPHORES, CONIDIA, AND CLASSIFICATION. CAN.J.
        BOT. 31, 577-659.

2600   HUGHES, S.J. (1953) - FUNGI FROM THE GOLD COAST. 2. MYCOL.PAP. 50, 1-104.

2601   HUGHES, S.J. (1957) - MICROFUNGI. 3. MAMMARIA. SYDOWIA, BEIH. 1, 359-363.

2602   HUGHES, S.J. (1958) - REVISIONES HYPHOMYCETUM ALIQUOT CUM APPENDICE DE NO-
        MINIBUS REJICIENDIS. CAN.J.BOT. 36, 727-836.

2603   HUGHES, S.J. & DICKINSON, C.H. (1968) - NEW ZEALAND FUNGI. 11. GLIOMASTIX
        GUEGUEN. N.Z.JL BOT. 6, 105-114.

2604 HUISMAN, O.C. & ASHWORTH, L.J. (1972) - SEPARATION OF MICROSCLEROTIA OF
     VERTICILLIUM ALBO-ATRUM FROM SOIL RESIDUES BY DENSITY FLOTATION. PHYTO-
     PATHOLOGY 62, 766-767.

2605 HUISMAN, O.C. & ASHWORTH, L.J. (1974) - QUANTITATIVE ASSESSMENT OF VERTI-
     CILLIUM ALBO-ATRUM IN FIELD SOILS. PROCEDURAL AND SUBSTRATE IMPROVE-
     MENTS. PHYTOPATHOLOGY 64, 1043-1044.

2606 HUISMAN, O.C. & ASHWORTH, L.J. (1974) - VERTICILLIUM ALBO-ATRUM QUANTITA-
     TIVE ISOLATION OF MICROSCLEROTIA FROM FIELD SOILS. PHYTOPATHOLOGY 64,
     1159-1163.

2607 HUISMAN, O.C. & ASHWORTH, L.J. (1976) - INFLUENCE OF CROP ROTATION ON SUR-
     VIVAL OF VERTICILLIUM ALBO-ATRUM IN SOILS. PHYTOPATHOLOGY 66, 978-981.

2608 HULME, M.A. & STRANKS, D.W. (1971) - REGULATION OF CELLULASE PRODUCTION BY
     MYROTHECIUM VERRUCARIA GROWN ON NON-CELLULOSIC SUBSTRATES. J.GEN.MICRO-
     BIOL. 69, 145-155.

2609 HUMPHERSON-JONES, F.M. & COOKE, R.C. (1977) - INDUCTION OF SCLEROTIUM FOR-
     MATION BY ACID STALING COMPOUNDS IN SCLEROTINIA SCLEROTIORUM AND SCLE-
     ROTIUM ROLFSII. TRANS.BR.MYCOL.SOC. 68, 413-420.

2610 HUMPHERSON-JONES, F.M. & COOKE, R.C. (1977) - CHANGES IN SCLEROTIUM FOR-
     MATION OF SCLEROTINIA SCLEROTIORUM IN CULTURE. TRANS.BR.MYCOL.SOC. 68,
     459-461.

2611 HUMPHREYS JONES, D.R. & WAID, J.S. (1963) - INFLUENCE OF FUNGAL ISOLATES
     ON GERMINATION AND GROWTH OF PERENNIAL RYEGRASS. PL.SOIL 19, 139-150.

2612 HUNT, J. (1956) - TAXONOMY OF THE GENUS CERATOCYSTIS. LLOYDIA 19, 1-58.

2613 HUNTER, B.B. & BARNETT, H.L. (1971) - FACTORS AFFECTING PRODUCTION OF MI-
     CROSCLEROTIA BY SPECIES OF CYLINDROCLADIUM. PHYTOPATHOLOGY 61, 897 (ABS.).

2614 HUNTER, B.B. & BARNETT, H.L. (1976) - PRODUCTION OF MICROSCLEROTIA BY SPE-
     CIES OF CYLINDROCLADIUM. PHYTOPATHOLOGY 66, 777-780.

2615 HUNTER, B.B. & FEELO, B.E. (1975) - CYLINDROCLADIUM MICROSCLEROTIA. PROC.
     AM.PHYTOPATH.SOC. 2, 124.

2616 HUNTER, B.B. & SYLVESTER, M.A. (1975) - GERANIUM LEAF TISSUE AS A BAIT FOR
     SPECIES OF CYLINDROCLADIUM IN THE SOIL. PROC.AM.PHYTOPATH.SOC. 2, 27-28.

2617 HUNTER, B.B. & ZUMPETTA, G.M. (1975) - DIFFERENTIATING SPECIES OF CYLINDRO-
     CLADIUM BY ACRYLAMIDE GEL ELECTROPHORESIS. PROC.AM.PHYTOPATH.SOC. 2, 56.

2618 HUNTER, W.E. & BUTLER, E.E. (1975) - SYNCEPHALIS CALIFORNICA, A MYCOPARA-
     SITE INDUCING GIANT HYPHAL SWELLINGS IN SPECIES OF MUCORALES. MYCOLOGIA
     67, 863-872.

2619 HUPPERT, M. (1968) - RECENT DEVELOPMENTS IN COCCIDIOIDOMYCOSIS. REV.MED.VET.
     MYCOL. 6, 279-294.

2620 HURPIN, B. & VAGO, C. (1958) - LES MALADIES DU HANNETON COMMUN (MELOLONTHA
     MELOLONTHA L.) (CO. SCARABAEIDAE). ENTOMOPHAGA 3, 285-330.

2621 HUSAIN, S.S., HASANY, S.M. & AHMED, S.I. (1967) - SOME NEW RECORDS OF FUN-
     GI FROM WEST PAKISTAN. PAKIST.J.SCIENT.IND.RES. 10, 259-264.

2622 HUSAIN, S.S. & MCKEEN, W.E. (1963) - RHIZOCTONIA FRAGARIAE SP.NOV. IN RE-
     LATION TO STRAWBERRY DEGENERATION IN SOUTHWESTERN ONTARIO. PHYTOPATHOL-
     OGY 53, 532-540.

2623 HUSAIN, S.S. & QAMAR, F. (1972) - STUDIES ON THE NUTRITION OF FUNGI. 7. RE-
     SPONSE OF EIGHT FUSARIUM SPECIES TO RAFFINOSE CARBON AND GLYCINE NITRO-
     GEN IN CZAPEK'S LIQUID MEDIUM. FOLIA BIOL. 20, 389-393.

2624 HUSAIN, S.S. & ZAMIR, K. (1971) - STUDIES ON THE NUTRITION OF FUNGI. 6.
     EFFECT OF DIFFERENT COMBINATIONS OF MONO-, DI- AND TRISACCHARIDES ON
     THE GROWTH OF SOME FUNGI. PAKIST.J.BOT.3, 79-82.

2625 HUSSEY, C., ORSI, B.A., SCOTT, J. & SPENCER, B. (1965) - MECHANISM OF CHO-
     LINE SULPHATE UTILIZATION IN FUNGI. NATURE, LOND. 207, 632-634.

2626 HUTCHINSON, S.A. & COWAN, M.E. (1972) - IDENTIFICATION AND BIOLOGICAL EF-
     FECTS OF VOLATILE METABOLITES FROM CULTURES OF TRICHODERMA HARZIANUM.
     TRANS.BR.MYCOL.SOC. 59, 71-77.

2627 HWANG, S.C. & KO, W.H. (1975) - SURVIVAL POTENTIAL OF CHLAMYDOSPORES, SPO-
     RANGIA AND ZOOSPORES OF PHYTOPHTHORA CINNAMOMI IN SOIL. PROC.AM.PHYTO-
     PATH.SOC. 2, 115.

2628 HWANG, S.C., KO, W.H. & ARAGAKI, M. (1975) - A SIMPLIFIED METHOD FOR SPO-
     RANGIAL PRODUCTION BY PHYTOPHTHORA CINNAMOMI. MYCOLOGIA 67, 1233-1234.

2629 HYDE, H.A. & WILLIAMS, D.A. (1952) - THE INCIDENCE OF CLADOSPORIUM HERBA-
     RUM IN THE OUTDOOR AIR AT CARDIFF, 1949-50. TRANS.BR.MYCOL.SOC. 36, 260-
     266.

2630 HYDE, M.B. & GALLEYMORE, H.B. (1951) - THE SUBEPIDERMAL FUNGI OF CEREAL
     GRAINS. 2. THE NATURE, IDENTITY, AND ORIGIN OF THE MYCELIUM IN WHEAT.
     ANN.APPL.BIOL. 38, 348-356.

2631 IBBOTSON, R. & PUGH, G.J.F. (1975) - USE OF THE FLUORESCENT ANTIBODY TECH-
     NIQUE FOR THE EVALUATION OF ARTHRODERMA UNCINATUM IN SOIL. MYCOPATHOLO-
     GIA 56, 119-123.

2632 ICHINOE, M. (1967) - JAPANESE HYPHOMYCETE NOTES. 1. TRANS.MYCOL.SOC.JAPAN
     8, 64-72.

2633 ICHINOE, M. (1968) - JAPANESE HYPHOMYCETE NOTES. 2. TRANS.MYCOL.SOC.JAPAN
     9, 57-64.

2634 ICHINOE, M. (1972) - ISOLATION OF FOUR SPECIES OF PERICONIA IN JAPAN. BULL.
     NATN.INST.HYG.SCI., TOKYO 90, 140-143.

2635 IGAUE, I., KAMIHARAKO, T., KITO, S. & KURASAWA, F. (1969) - FUNGAL ENZYMES
     ACTIVE IN DEGRADING GENTOBIOSE. 2. SOME PROPERTIES OF BETA-GLUCOSIDASE
     OF ASPERGILLUS JAPONICUS AND ITS HYDROLYTIC AND TRANSFER ACTIONS ON
     GENTOBIOSE. J.AGRIC.CHEM.SOC.JAPAN 43, 232-239.

2636 IGAUE, I., KITO, S., HARUO, H. & KURASAWA, F. (1969) - FUNGAL ENZYMES AC-
     TIVE IN DEGRADING GENTOBIOSE. 1. PURIFICATION AND SOME PROPERTIES OF
     BETA-GLUCOSIDASE OF ASPERGILLUS JAPONICUS. J.AGRIC.CHEM.SOC.JAPAN 43,
     224-231.

2637 IIBUCHI, S., MINODA, Y. & YAMADA, K. (1972) - HYDROLYZING PATHWAY, SUB-
     STRATE SPECIFICITY AND INHIBITION OF TANNIN ACYL HYDROLASE OF ASPERGIL-
     LUS ORYZAE NO.7. AGRIC.BIOL.CHEM., TOKYO 36, 1553-1562.

2638 IIZUKA, H. (1953) - STUDY ON THE MORPHOLOGY AND CLASSIFICATION OF THE VIO-
     LET-BLACK ASPERGILLI. 1. J.AGRIC.CHEM.SOC.JAPAN 27, 801-809.

2639   ILAG, L.L. (1972) - PERIODICITY OF ETHYLENE PRODUCTION IN FUNGI. PHILIPP.
       AGRICST 56, 9-15.

2640   ILAG, L.L. (1976) - THE COTTONY LEAK DISEASE IN THE PHILIPPINES. PL.DIS.
       REPTR 60, 12-13.

2641   ILAG, L.L. & CURTIS, R.W. (1968) - PRODUCTION OF ETHYLENE BY FUNGI.
       SCIENCE, N.Y. 1357-1358.

2642   ILYINA, T.V. & BEZBORODOVA, S.I. (1972) - (PURIFICATION OF RNASE FROM PENI-
       CILLIUM BREVI-COMPACTUM). PRIKL.BIOKHIM.MIKROBIOL. 8, 226-231.

2643   IMADA, A., NAKAHAMA, K., IGARASI, S. & ISONO, M. (1973) - A BACTERIOLYTIC
       ENZYME FROM CHAETOMIUM GLOBOSUM, A MARINE-ISOLATE. ARCH.MIKROBIOL. 91,
       41-54.

2644   INDIRA, P.U. (1968) - HUMAN PATHOGENIC FUNGI FROM SOIL. PROC.INDIAN ACAD.
       SCI., SECT.B, 67, 68-76.

2645   INGESTAD, T. & NILSSON, H. (1964) - THE EFFECTS OF SOIL FUMIGATION, SU-
       CROSE APPLICATION, AND INOCULATION OF SUGAR FUNGI ON THE GROWTH OF FOR-
       EST-TREE SEEDLINGS. PL.SOIL 20, 74-84.

2646   INGLE, M.R. & HASTIE, A.C. (1974) - ENVIRONMENTAL FACTORS AFFECTING THE
       FORMATION OF DIPLOIDS IN VERTICILLIUM ALBO-ATRUM. TRANS.BR.MYCOL.SOC.
       62, 313-321.

2647   INGOLD, C.T. (1942) - AQUATIC HYPHOMYCETES OF DECAYING ALDER LEAVES. TRANS.
       BR.MYCOL.SOC. 25, 339-417.

2648   INGOLD, C.T. (1971) - FUNGAL SPORES, THEIR LIBERATION AND DISPERSAL. CLA-
       RENDON PRESS, OXFORD, 302 PP.

2649   INGOLD, C.T. (1975) - GUIDE TO AQUATIC HYPHOMYCETES. SCIENT.PUBL.FRESHWA-
       TER BIOL.ASSOC. 30, 96 PP.

2650   INGOLD, C.T. & DANN, V. (1968) - SPORE-SIZE AND DISCHARGE IN CONIDIOBOLUS.
       TRANS.BR.MYCOL.SOC. 51, 589-591.

2651   INGOLD, C.T. & DRING, V.J. (1957) - AN ANALYSIS OF SPORE DISCHARGE IN SOR-
       DARIA. ANN.BOT. 21, 465-477.

2652   INGOLD, C.T. & MARSHALL, B. (1963) - FURTHER OBSERVATIONS ON LIGHT AND
       SPORE DISCHARGE IN CERTAIN PYRENOMYCETES. ANN.BOT. 27, 481-491.

2653   INGOLD, C.T. & ZOBERI, M.H. (1963) - THE ASEXUAL APPARATUS OF MUCORALES IN
       RELATION TO SPORE LIBERATION. TRANS.BR.MYCOL.SOC. 46, 115-134.

2654   INGRAM, R. (1968) - VERTICILLIUM DAHLIAE VAR. LONGISPORUM, A STABLE DI-
       PLOID. TRANS.BR.MYCOL.SOC. 51, 339-341.

2655   INOUE, N. (1953) - PECTASE OF PENICILLIUM CHRYSOGENUM Q 176. 1. ESPECIALLY
       ON THE CLARIFYING ACTION IN FRUIT JUICE. A.REP.NATN INST.NUTRITION, JA-
       PAN, 1953, 64-65.

2656   INOUE, Y. & FURUYA, M. (1970) - PERITHECIAL FORMATION IN GELASINOSPORA RE-
       TICULISPORA. 1. EFFECTS OF LIGHT AT TWO DIFFERENT GROWTH STATES. DEVEL-
       OPM.GROWTH DIFFER. 12, 141-150.

2657   INOUE, Y. & FURUYA, M. (1974) - PERITHECIAL FORMATION IN GELASINOSPORA RE-
       TICULISPORA. 2. PROMOTIVE EFFECTS OF NEAR-ULTRAVIOLET AND BLUE LIGHT
       AFTER DARK INCUBATION. PL.CELL PHYSIOL. 15, 195-204.

2658 INOUE, Y. & FURUYA, M. (1974) - PERITHECIAL FORMATION IN GELASINOSPORA RE-
     TICULISPORA. 3. INHIBITORY EFFECTS OF NEAR-UV AND BLUE LIGHT DURING THE
     INDUCTIVE DARK PERIOD. PL.CELL PHYSIOL. 15, 469-475.

2659 INOUE, Y. & FURUYA, M. (1975) - PERITHECIAL FORMATION IN GELASINOSPORA RE-
     TICULISPORA. 4. ACTION SPECTRA FOR THE PHOTOINDUCTION. PL.PHYSIOL.,
     LANCASTER 55, 1098-1101.

2660 INOUE, Y. & FURUYA, M. (1975) - PERITHECIAL FORMATION IN GELASINOSPORA RE-
     TICULISPORA. 5. MICROSCOPICALLY VERSUS PHOTOBIOLOGICALLY RECOGNIZABLE
     DIFFERENTIATION OF HYPHAE. BOT.MAG., TOKYO 88, 31-40.

2661 INUI, T., TAKEDA, Y. & IIZUKA, H. (1965) - TAXONOMICAL STUDIES ON THE GE-
     NUS RHIZOPUS. J.GEN.APPL.MICROBIOL., TOKYO 11, SUPPL., 121 PP.

2662 IOACHIMESCU, M. (1973) - INFLUENTA TEMPERATURII ASUPRA CRESTERII SI DEZ-
     VOLTARII CIUPERCILOR IZOLATE DE PF LEMNUL DIN MINA. STUDII CERC.BIOL.,
     SER.BOT. 25, 167-170.

2663 IOANNOU, N., SCHNEIDER, R.W. & GROGAN, R.G. (1977) - EFFECT OF FLOODING ON
     THE SOIL GAS COMPOSITION AND THE PRODUCTION OF MICROSCLEROTIA BY VERTI-
     CILLIUM DAHLIAE IN THE FIELD. PHYTOPATHOLOGY 67, 651-656.

2664 IONITA, I. (1972) - SPECII DE CIUPERCI IZOLATE DE PE LEMNUL DIN MINA. STU-
     DII CERC.BIOL., SER.BOT. 24, 29-33.

2665 IONITA, I. (1973) - OBSERVATIONS ON THE DEGRADATION OF CELLULOSE FIBRES BY
     THE FUNGUS PAPULARIA ARUNDINIS. REVUE ROUM.BIOL., SER.BOT. 18, 125-127.

2666 IONITA, I. (1973) - CONTRIBUTIONS TO THE STUDY OF THE BIODETERIORATION OF
     THE WORKS OF ART AND HISTORICAL MONUMENTS. 4. FUNGI INVOLVED IN THE DE-
     TERIORATION OF MURAL PAINTING FROM THE MONASTERIES OF MOLDAVIA. REVUE
     ROUM.BIOL., SER.BOT. 18, 179-189.

2667 ISAAC, I. (1949) - A COMPARATIVE STUDY OF PATHOGENIC ISOLATES OF VERTICIL-
     LIUM. TRANS.BR.MYCOL.SOC. 32, 137-157.

2668 ISAAC, I. (1953) - A FURTHER COMPARATIVE STUDY OF PATHOGENIC ISOLATES OF
     VERTICILLIUM, V. NUBILIUM AND V. TRICORPUS SP.NOV. TRANS.BR.MYCOL.SOC.
     36, 180-195.

2669 ISAAC, I. (1953) - STUDIES ON THE INTERACTIONS BETWEEN SPECIES OF VERTI-
     CILLIUM. ANN.APPL.BIOL. 40, 623-629.

2670 ISAAC, I. (1953) - THE SPREAD OF DISEASES CAUSED BY SPECIES OF VERTICIL-
     LIUM. ANN.APPL.BIOL. 40, 630-638.

2671 ISAAC, I. (1954) - GLIOCLADIUM ROSEUM AND ITS SYNONYMS. TRANS.BR.MYCOL.
     SOC. 37, 193-208.

2672 ISAAC, I. (1956) - SOME SOIL FACTORS AFFECTING VERTICILLIUM WILT OF ANTIR-
     RHINUM. ANN.APPL.BIOL. 44, 105-112.

2673 ISAAC, I. (1967) - SPECIATION IN VERTICILLIUM. A.REV.PHYTOPATH. 5, 201-
     222.

2674 ISAAC, I. & ABRAHAM, G.H. (1959) - SALTATION AND ZONATION FORMATION IN VER-
     TICILLIUM LATERITIUM. CAN.J.BOT. 37, 801-814.

2675 ISAAC, I. & MACGARVIE, Q. (1966) - DORMANCY AND GERMINATION OF RESTING
     STRUCTURES OF VERTICILLIUM SPP. TRANS.BR.MYCOL.SOC. 49, 669-678.

2676   ISAAC, P.K. (1964) - METABOLIC SPECIALIZATION IN THE MYCELIUM OF RHIZOCTO-
       NIA SOLANI. CAN.J.MICROBIOL. 10, 621-622.

2677   ISAAC, P.K. & GUPTA, S.K. (1964) - A VIRUS-LIKE INFECTION OF ALTERNARIA
       TENUIS. ABS. 10TH INT.BOT.CONGR., EDINBURGH, 390-391.

2678   ISARLISHVILI, S.YA. & LABAKHUA, L.V. (1962) - (STUDY OF FUNGI-ANTAGONISTS
       IN THE CONTROL OF DISEASES OF FARM CROPS IN GEORGIA). TRANS.1ST ALL-
       UNION CONF.STUDY APPLIC.ANTIBIOTICS PL.CULTURE, 162-165.

2679   ISHAQUE, M. & TALUKDAR, M.J. (1967) - SURVEY OF FUNGAL FLORA OF EAST PA-
       KISTAN. AGRICULTURE PAKIST. 18, 17-26.

2680   ISHIDA, M., HAMASAKI, T. & HATSUDA, Y. (1972) - A NEW METABOLITE FROM AS-
       PERGILLUS NIDULANS. AGRIC.BIOL.CHEM., TOKYO 36, 1847-1848.

2681   ISHIDA, M., HAMASAKI, T., HATSUDA, Y., FUKUYAMA, K., TSUKIHARA, T. & KAT-
       SUBE, Y. (1975) - EMERICELLIN, A NEW METABOLITE FROM ASPERGILLUS NIDU-
       LANS. AGRIC.BIOL.CHEM., TOKYO 39, 291-292.

2682   ISHIDA, M., HAMASAKI, T., HATSUDA, Y., FUKUYAMA, K., TSUKIHARA, T. & KAT-
       SUBE, Y. (1976) - EPISHAMIXANTHONE, A NEW METABOLITE FROM ASPERGILLUS
       RUGULOSUS. AGRIC.BIOL.CHEM., TOKYO 40, 1051-1052.

2683   ISHII, K., SAKAI, K., UENO, Y., TSUNODA, H. & ENOMOTO, M. (1971) - SOLA-
       NIOL, A TOXIC METABOLITE OF FUSARIUM SOLANI. APPL.MICROBIOL. 22, 718-
       720.

2684   ISHII, K., SAWANO, M., UENO, Y. & TSUNODA, H. (1974) - DISTRIBUTION OF
       ZEARALENONE-PRODUCING FUSARIUM SPECIES IN JAPAN. APPL.MICROBIOL. 27,
       625-628.

2685   ISHII, S. (1976) - ENZYMATIC MACERATION OF PLANT TISSUES BY ENDO-PECTIN-
       LYASE AND ENDO-POLYGALACTURONASE FROM ASPERGILLUS JAPONICUS. PHYTOPATHOL-
       OGY 66, 281-289.

2686   ISHII, S. & YOKOTSUKA, T. (1972) - PURIFICATION AND PROPERTIES OF ENDO-PO-
       LYGALACTURONASE FROM ASPERGILLUS JAPONICUS. AGRIC.BIOL.CHEM., TOKYO 36,
       1885-1893.

2687   ISHITANI, C. & SAKAGUCHI, K. (1956) - HEREDITARY VARIATION AND RECOMBINA-
       TION IN KOJI-MOLDS (ASPERGILLUS ORYZAE AND A. SOJAE). 5. HETEROKARYOSIS.
       J.GEN.APPL.MICROBIOL., TOKYO 2, 345-400.

2688   ISHIYAMA, T., FURUTA, T., TAKAI, M. & OKIMOTO, Y. (1975) - L-THREO-BETA-
       HYDROXYASPARTIC ACID AS AN ANTIBIOTIC AMINO ACID. J.ANTIBIOT., TOKYO
       28, 821-823.

2689   ISOGAI, A., HORII, T., SUZUKI, A., MURAKOSHI, S., IKEDA, K., SATO, S. &
       TAMURA, S. (1975) - ISOLATION AND IDENTIFICATION OF NIGRAGILLIN AS AN
       INSECTICIDAL METABOLITE PRODUCED BY A ASPERGILLUS NIGER. AGRIC.BIOL.
       CHEM., TOKYO 39, 739-740.

2690   ISRAEL, O.P. & MD.SHAH ALI (1964) - EFFECT OF CARBOHYDRATES ON THE GROWTH
       OF RHIZOCTONIA SOLANI. BIOLOGIA PL.PRAHA 6, 84-87.

2691   ITO, K. & TANAKA, T. (1973) - FORMATION OF AMINE BY PATHOGENIC FUNGI. FOR-
       MATION OF TYRAMINE FROM N-ACETYLTYRAMINE BY PATHOGENIC FUNGI. BULL.
       PHARM.RES.INST.JAPAN 100, 1-11.

2692   IVANOV, V.T., LAVRINOVICH, I.A., PORTNOVA, S.L., SPASSOV, S.L., MESHCHERYA-
       KOVA, E.A., SENYAVINA, L.B. & OVCHINNIKOV, YU.A. (1975) - (STUDY OF
       CONFORMATIONAL STATES OF CYCLOPEPTIDE SYSTEMS. 13. SPATIAL STRUCTURE OF
       SPORIDESMOLIDES I-IV.). BIOORG.KHIM. 1, 33-41.

2693 IVANOVA, G.S., VALIUKAITE, R. & BEŻBORODOV, A.M. (1972) - (ISOLATION AND
      PROPERTIES OF INTRACELLULAR RIBONUCLEASE FROM ASPERGILLUS CLAVATUS
      1816). MIKROBIOLOGIYA 41, 626-632.

2694 IVARSON, K.C. (1973) - FUNGAL FLORA AND RATE OF DECOMPOSITION OF LEAF LIT-
      TER AT LOW TEMPERATURES. CAN.J.SOIL SCI. 53, 79-84.

2695 IVARSON, K.C. (1974) - COMPARATIVE SURVIVAL AND DECOMPOSING ABILITY OF
      FOUR FUNGI ISOLATED FROM LEAF LITTER AT LOW TEMPERATURES. CAN.J.SOIL
      SCI. 54, 245-253.

2696 IWAI, M., TSUJISAKA, Y., OKAMOTO, Y. & FUKUMOTO, J. (1973) - LIPID RE-
      QUIREMENT FOR THE LIPASE PRODUCTION BY GEOTRICHUM CANDIDUM. AGRIC.BIOL.
      CHEM., TOKYO 37, 929-931.

2697 IYENGAR, M.R.S. & STARKEY, R.L. (1953) - SYNERGISM AND ANTAGONISM OF AUXIN
      BY ANTIBIOTICS. SCIENCE, N.Y. 118, 357-358.

2698 JAARSVELD, A. (1942) - DER EINFLUSS VERSCHIEDENER BODENPILZE AUF DIE VI-
      RULENZ VON RHIZOCTONIA SOLANI. PHYTOPATH.Z. 14, 1-75.

2699 JACK, M.A. & TANSEY, M.R. (1977) - GROWTH, SPORULATION, AND GERMINATION OF
      SPORES OF THERMOPHILIC FUNGI INCUBATED IN SUN-HEATED SOIL. MYCOLOGIA
      69, 109-117.

2700 JACKSON, C.R. (1965) - PEANUT KERNEL INFECTION AND GROWTH IN VITRO BY FOUR
      FUNGI AT VARIOUS TEMPERATURES. PHYTOPATHOLOGY 55, 46-48.

2701 JACKSON, C.R. & BELL, D.K. (1969) - DISEASES OF PEANUTS CAUSED BY FUNGI.
      BULL.GA AGRIC.EXP.STN 56, 5-137.

2702 JACKSON, R.B. (1973) - THE METABOLISM OF ALLYLALCOHOL IN TRICHODERMA VI-
      RIDE. J.GEN.APPL.MICROBIOL., TOKYO 19, 41-54.

2703 JACKSON, R.M. (1957) - FUNGISTASIS AS A FACTOR IN THE RHIZOSPHERE PHENOME-
      NON. NATURE, LOND. 180, 96-97.

2704 JACKSON, R.M. (1960) - SOIL FUNGISTASIS AND THE RHIZOSPHERE. IN: ECOLOGY
      OF SOIL FUNGI; PARKINSON D. & WAID, J.S. (ED.), LIVERPOOL UNIV.PRESS,
      168-176.

2705 JACKSON, R.M. (1965) - STUDIES OF FUNGI IN PASTURE SOILS. 2. FUNGI ASSO-
      CIATED WITH PLANT DEBRIS AND FUNGAL HYPHAE IN SOIL. N.Z.JL AGRIC.RES.
      8, 865-877.

2706 JACKSON, R.M. (1965) - STUDIES OF FUNGI IN PASTURE SOILS. 3. PHYSIOLOGICAL
      STUDIES ON SOME FUNGAL ISOLATES FROM ROOT SURFACE AND FROM ORGANIC DE-
      BRIS. N.Z.JL AGRIC.RES. 8, 878-888.

2707 JACKSON, R.S. (1972) - REPEATED GERMINATION OF SCLEROTIA OF BOTRYTIS CON-
      VOLUTA TO PRODUCE SUCCESSIVE CROPS OF CONIDIA. CAN.J.BOT. 50, 985-989.

2708 JAFFE, L.F. (1966) - ON AUTOTROPISM IN BOTRYTIS. MEASUREMENT TECHNIQUE AND
      CONTROL BY CO2. PL.PHYSIOL., LANCASTER 41, 303-306.

2709 JAGATAP, A.P. (1973) - STUDIES OF THE ENTOMOGENOUS FUNGUS METARRHIZIUM
      ANISOPLIAE AFFECTING PYRILLA SP. ON SUGAR CANE. 3. PATHOLOGIC HISTOL-
      OGY. MAHARASHTRA VIDNYAN MANDIR PATRIKA 8, 25-30.

2710   JAIN, J.P. & GUPTA, B.M. (1974) - EFFECT OF CARBON, NITROGEN AND THEIR
       RATIO FOR THE GROWTH AND SPORULATION OF HELMINTHOSPORIUM SPICIFERUM.
       INDIAN PHYTOPATH. 27, 190-193.

2711   JALALUDDIN, M. (1969) - MICRO-ORGANIC COLONIZATION OF FOREST SOIL AFTER
       BURNING. PL.SOIL 30, 150-152.

2712   JALALUDDIN, M. (1975) - STUDY OF MICRO-ORGANISMS FROM ROOT REGIONS OF
       RICE. PL.SOIL 43, 337-346.

2713   JAMALAINEN, E.A. (1974) - RESISTANCE IN WINTER CEREALS AND GRASSES TO LOW
       -TEMPERATURE PARASITIC FUNGI. A.REV.PHYTOPATH. 12, 281-302.

2714   JAMES, A.W. & CASIDA, L.E. (1964) - ACCUMULATION OF PHOSPHORUS COMPOUNDS
       BY MUCOR RACEMOSUS. J.BACT. 87, 150-155.

2715   JAMES, A.W. & NOWAKOWSKI, R.J. (1968) - THE EFFECT OF CARBON SOURCE ON
       TRAP FORMATION BY ARTHROBOTRYS CONOIDES. CAN.J.MICROBIOL. 14, 1260-1261.

2716   JAMES, N., WILSON, J. & STARK, E. (1946) - THE MICROFLORA OF STORED WHEAT.
       CAN.J.RES., SECT.C, 24, 224-233.

2717   JANISCH, E. (1938) - EINE NEUE PILZKRANKHEIT BEI NONNENRAUPEN. ARB.PHYSIOL.
       ANGEW.ENT., BERL. 5, 1-20.

2718   JANKE, A. (1949) - DER ABBAU DER ZELLULOSE DURCH MIKROORGANISMEN. OEST.
       BOT.Z. 46, 399-443.

2719   JANKE, A. & HOLZER, H. (1929) - UEBER DIE SCHIMMELPILZFLORA DES ERDBODENS.
       ZENTBL.BAKT.PARASITKDE, ABT.2, 79, 50-74.

2720   JANKE, D. (1949) - ZUR KLINIK UND MYKOLOGIE DER CEPHALOSPORIOSE. EIN BEI-
       TRAG ZUR KENNTNIS SELTENER MYKOSEN. ARCH.DERMAT.SYPH. 188, 357-373.

2721   JANKOVITCH-BRMBOLITCH, A. (1965) - (SOME DERMATOPHYTES, FUNGI AND PREDA-
       TORS ISOLATED FROM THE SOIL IN THE GARDEN OF THE PASTEUR INSTITUTE OF
       TUNIS). ARCHS INST.PASTEUR TUNIS. 42, 141-147.

2722   JAROWAJA, N. (1970) - (THE GENUS ARTHROBOTRYS CORDA). ACTA MYCOL., WARSZA-
       WA 6, 337-406.

2723   JARVIS, B. & MOSS, M.O. (1973) - BIOASSAY METHODS FOR MYCOTOXINS. IN: THE
       MICROBIOLOGY SAFETY OF FOOD; HOBBS, B.C. & CHRISTIAN, J.H. (ED.), ACA-
       DEMIC PRESS, LONDON, U.K., 293-305.

2724   JARVIS, W.R. (1972) - PHOTOTROPISM IN BOTRYTIS CINEREA. TRANS.BR.MYCOL.
       SOC. 58, 526-527.

2725   JARVIS, W.R. (1977) - BOTRYOTINIA AND BOTRYTIS SPECIES. TAXONOMY, PHYSIOL-
       OGY, AND PATHOGENICITY. RES.STN, CAN.DEP.AGRIC., HARROW, MONOGR. 15,
       195 PP.

2726   JASEVOLI, G. (1924) - CONTRIBUTO ALLA CONOSCENZA DEGLI IFOMICETI DEL TER-
       RENO AGRARIO. BOLL.ORTO BOT.R.UNIV.NAPOLI 7, 217-233.

2727   JAURIHAR, S.S. & MEHTA, P.P. (1972) - INFLUENCE OF PHOSPHOROUS AND SULPHUR
       ON THE GROWTH AND SPORULATION OF FUSARIUM MONILIFORME. INDIAN PHYTO-
       PATH. 25, 541-546.

2728   JAWORSKI, E.G., WANG, L.C. & CARPENTER, W.D. (1965) - BIOSYNTHESIS OF CHI-
       TIN IN CELL-FREE EXTRACTS OF VENTURIA INAEQUALIS. PHYTOPATHOLOGY 55,
       1309-1312.

2729 JAYACHANDRAN, S. & RAMABADRAN, R. (1970) - PRODUCTION OF AMYLASE BY THER-
      MOASCUS AURANTIACUS MIEHE. J.INDIAN EXPL BIOL. 8, 344.

2730 JAYARAMAN, K.N. & PRASAD, N.N. (1971) - PRODUCTION OF ORGANIC ACIDS BY
      CERTAIN SOIL ASPERGILLI. CURR.SCI. 40, 198-199.

2731 JAYARAMAN, K.N. & PRASAD, N.N. (1972) - PRODUCTION OF PHOSPHATASE BY SOIL
      ASPERGILLI. MADRAS AGRIC.J.59, 640-641.

2732 JAYARAMAN, S. & SHANMUGASUNDARAM, E.R.B. (1972) - ISOLATION AND PURIFICA-
      TION OF A TOXIC PIGMENT FROM THE CULTURE FILTRATE OF ASPERGILLUS FLA-
      VIPES. INDIAN J.EXPL BIOL. 10, 399-400.

2733 JEFFERSON, W.E. (1967) - THE ISOLATION AND CHARACTERIZATION OF ASPERENONE,
      A NEW PHENYLPOLYENE FROM ASPERGILLUS NIGER. BIOCHEMISTRY 6, 3479-3484.

2734 JEFFERSON, W.E. & SISCO, G. (1961) - THE INFLUENCE OF EXOGENOUS STEROIDS
      ON THE GROWTH OF ASPERGILLUS NIGER AND TORULA UTILIS. J.GEN.PHYSIOL.
      44, 1029-1045.

2735 JEFFERYS, E.G. (1948) - A TECHNIQUE FOR RAPID DEMONSTRATION OF THE PRODUC-
      TION OF ANTIFUNGAL SUBSTANCES BY FUNGI OR OTHER MICROORGANISMS. TRANS.
      BR.MYCOL.SOC. 31, 246-248.

2736 JEFFERYS, E.G., BRIAN, P.W., HEMMING, H.G. & LOWE, B. (1953) - ANTIBIOTIC
      PRODUCTION BY THE MICROFUNGI OF ACID HEATH SOILS. J.GEN.MICROBIOL. 9,
      314-341.

2737 JENNINGS, D.H. (1977) - OSMOREGULATION IN DENDRYPHIELLA SALINA. ABS.2ND
      INT.MYCOL.CONGR., TAMPA, 1977, P.325.

2738 JENNINGS, D.H. & AUSTIN, S. (1973) - THE STIMULATORY EFFECT OF THE NON-
      METABOLIZED SUGAR 3-O-METHYL GLUCOSE ON THE CONVERSION OF MANNITOL AND
      ARABITOL TO POLYSACCHARIDE AND OTHER INSOLUBLE COMPOUNDS IN THE FUNGUS
      DENDRYPHIELLA SALINA. J.GEN.MICROBIOL. 75, 287-294.

2739 JENSEN, A. (1965) - VERTICILLIUM-ARTER I DANMARK. HORTICULTURA 19, 91-97.

2740 JENSEN, C.N. (1912) - FUNGOUS FLORA OF THE SOIL. BULL.CORNELL UNIV.AGRIC.
      EXP.STN 315, 414-501.

2741 JENSEN, H.L. (1931) - THE FUNGUS FLORA OF THE SOIL. SOIL SCI. 31, 123-158.

2742 JENSEN, H.L. (1957) - DECOMPOSITION OF CHLORO-ORGANIC ACIDS BY FUNGI. NA-
      TURE, LOND. 180, 1416.

2743 JENSEN, H.L. (1959) - (BIOLOGICAL DECOMPOSITION OF HERBICIDES IN THE SOIL.
      1. MONOCHLOROACETATE, TRICHLOROACETATE AND DICHLOROPROPIONATE). TIDS-
      SKR.PLAVL 63, 470-499.

2744 JENSEN, R.G. (1974) - CHARACTERISTICS OF THE LIPASE FROM THE MOLD, GEOTRI-
      CHUM CANDIDUM. A REVIEW. LIPIDS 9, 149-157.

2745 JENSEN, V. (1963) - STUDIES ON THE MICROFLORA OF DANISH BEECH FOREST SOILS.
      5. THE MICROFUNGI. ZENTBL.BAKT.PARASITKDE, ABT.2, 117, 167-179.

2746 JEREBZOFF, S. & LAMBERT, E. (1967) - DETECTION PAR LA METHODE DU SPECTRE
      DE VARIANCE DE DEUX RHYTHMES REGISSANT SIMULTANEMENT LA SPORULATION DE
      MYROTHECIUM VERRUCARIA (ALB. & SCHW.) DITM. EX FRIES. C.R.HEBD.SEANC.
      ACAD.SCI., PARIS, SER.D, 264, 322-325.

2747 JERMYN, M.A. (1953) - FUNGAL CELLULASES. 3. STACHYBOTRYS ATRA. GROWTH AND ENZYME PRODUCTION ON NON-CELLULOSIC SUBSTRATES. AUST.J.BIOL.SCI. 6, 48-69.

2748 JERMYN, M.A. (1955) - FUNGAL CELLULASES. 4. PRODUCTION AND PURIFICATION OF AN EXTRACELLULAR BETA-GLUCOSIDASE OF STACHYBOTRYS ATRA. AUST.J.BIOL.SCI. 8, 541-562.

2749 JERMYN, M.A. (1966) - FUNGAL CELLULASES. 17. THE BEHAVIOUR OF T-BUTYL ALCOHOL, PINACOL AND METHANOL AS ACCEPTORS FOR THE BETA-GLUCOSIDASE OF STACHYBOTRYS ATRA. AUST.J.BIOL.SCI. 19, 927-933.

2750 JERMYN, M.A. (1966) - FUNGAL CELLULASES. 19. POLYHYDROXYLIC ACCEPTORS FOR THE BETA-GLUCOSIDASE OF STACHYBOTRYS ATRA. AUST.J.BIOL.SCI. 19, 1153-1165.

2751 JERMYN, M.A. & DREW, P.G. (1967) - THE AVAILABILITY OF CERTAIN SUBSTANCES AS RESPIRATORY SUBSTRATES FOR STACHYBOTRYS ATRA. ENZYMOLOGIA 32, 85-96.

2752 JERMYN, M.A. & TOMKINS, R.G. (1950) - THE CHROMATOGRAPHIC EXAMINATION OF THE PRODUCTS OF THE ACTION OF PECTINASE ON PECTIN. BIOCHEM.J. 47, 437-442.

2753 JEZIORSKA, Z. (1974) - (THE INFLUENCE OF FUNGI ISOLATED FROM THE RHIZOSPHERE OF CHOSEN SPECIES). PAM.PULAWSKI 60, 187-200.

2754 JEZIORSKA, Z. (1974) - (WAYS OF AFFECTING THIELAVIOPSIS BASICOLA BY SOME ANTAGONISTIC FUNGI). PAM.PULAWSKI 60, 201-214.

2755 JHA, K.K. & OLIVE, L.S. (1975) - GENETICS OF SORDARIA FIMICOLA. 8. NITRO-SOGUANIDINE MUTAGENESIS AND ISOLATION OF PROTOPERITHECIAL MUTANTS. MYCOLOGIA 67, 45-55.

2756 JINKS, J.L., CATEN, C.E., SIMCHEN, G. & CROFT, J.H. (1966) - HETEROKARYON INCOMPATIBILITY AND VARIATION IN WILD POPULATIONS OF ASPERGILLUS NIDULANS. HEREDITY 21, 227-239.

2757 JODICE, R., FERRARA, R., CERUTI SCURTI, J., FIUSSELLO, N., OBERT, F. & CORTELLEZZI, G.C. (1974/75) - MICETI TERMOFILI. 1. CONTRIBUTO SULL'ISOLAMENTO, SUL METABOLISMO E SULLA CAPACITA DI DEGRADAZIONE DI MATERIALI ORGANICI. ALLIONIA 20, 53-74.

2758 JOENSSON, A.G. (1967) - PILOT-PLANT PRODUCTION OF PROTEASE BY ALTERNARIA TENUISSIMA. APPL.MICROBIOL. 15, 319-324.

2759 JOENSSON, A.G. & MARTIN, S.M. (1964) - PROTEASE PRODUCTION BY ASPERGILLUS FUMIGATUS. AGRIC.BIOL.CHEM., TOKYO 28, 734-739.

2760 JOENSSON, A.G. & MARTIN, S.M. (1965) - PROTEASE PRODUCTION BY ALTERNARIA TENUISSIMA. AGRIC.BIOL.CHEM., TOKYO 29, 787-791.

2761 JOFFE, A.Z. (1962) - BIOLOGICAL PROPERTIES OF SOME TOXIC FUNGI ISOLATED FROM OVERWINTERED CEREALS. MYCOPATH.MYCOL.APPL. 16, 201-221.

2762 JOFFE, A.Z. (1963) - THE MYCOFLORA OF A CONTINUOUSLY CROPPED SOIL IN ISRAEL, WITH SPECIAL REFERENCE TO EFFECTS OF MANURING AND FERTILIZING. MYCOLOGIA 55, 271-282.

2763 JOFFE, A.Z. (1966) - QUANTITATIVE RELATIONS BETWEEN SOME SPECIES OF FUSARIUM AND TRICHODERMA IN A CITRUS GROVE IN ISRAEL. SOIL SCI. 102, 240-243.

2764   JOFFE, A.Z. (1967) - THE MYCOFLORA OF A LIGHT SOIL IN A CITRUS FERTILIZER
       TRIAL IN ISRAEL. MYCOPATH.MYCOL.APPL. 32, 209-230.

2765   JOFFE, A.Z. (1968) - MYCOFLORA OF SURFACE-STERILIZED GROUNDNUT KERNELS.
       PL.DIS.REPTR 52, 608-611.

2766   JOFFE, A.Z. (1969) - RELATIONSHIPS BETWEEN ASPERGILLUS FLAVUS, ASPERGILLUS
       NIGER AND SOME OTHER FUNGI IN THE MYCOFLORA OF GROUNDNUT KERNELS. PL.
       SOIL 31, 57-64.

2767   JOFFE, A.Z. (1969) - AFLATOXIN PRODUCED BY 1626 ISOLATES OF ASPERGILLUS
       FLAVUS FROM GROUNDNUT KERNELS AND SOILS IN ISRAEL. NATURE, LOND. 221,
       492.

2768   JOFFE, A.Z. (1969) - THE MYCOFLORA OF GROUNDNUT RHIZOSPHERE, SOIL AND GEO-
       CARPOSPHERE ON LIGHT, MEDIUM AND HEAVY SOILS AND ITS RELATIONS TO AS-
       PERGILLUS FLAVUS. MYCOPATH.MYCOL.APPL. 37, 150-160.

2769   JOFFE, A.Z. (1972) - FUSARIA ISOLATED FROM AVOCADO, BANANA AND CITRUS
       FRUIT IN ISRAEL AND THEIR PATHOGENICITY. PL.DIS.REPTR 56, 963-966.

2770   JOFFE, A.Z. (1974) - A MODERN SYSTEM OF FUSARIUM TAXONOMY. MYCOPATH.MYCOL.
       APPL. 53, 201-228.

2771   JOFFE, A.Z. (1974) - GROWTH AND TOXIGENICITY OF FUSARIA OF THE SPOROTRI-
       CHIELLA SECTION AS RELATED TO ENVIRONMENTAL FACTORS AND CULTURE SUB-
       STRATES. MYCOPATH.MYCOL.APPL. 54, 35-46.

2772   JOFFE, A.Z. & BORUT, SH.Y. (1966) - SOIL AND KERNEL MYCOFLORA OF GROUNDNUT
       FIELDS IN ISRAEL. MYCOLOGIA 58, 629-640.

2773   JOFFE, A.Z. & PALTI, J. (1970) - FUSARIUM JAVANICUM KOORDERS IN ISRAEL.
       MYCOPATH.MYCOL.APPL. 42, 305-314.

2774   JOFFE, A.Z. & PALTI, J. (1972) - FUSARIUM SPECIES OF THE MARTIELLA SECTION
       IN ISRAEL. PHYTOPATH.Z. 73, 123-148.

2775   JOFFE, A.Z. & PALTI, J. (1974) - RELATIONS BETWEEN HARMFUL EFFECTS ON
       PLANTS AND ON ANIMALS OF TOXINS PRODUCED BY SPECIES OF FUSARIUM. MYCO-
       PATH.MYCOL.APPL. 52, 209-218.

2776   JOFFE, A.Z., PALTI, J. & ARBEL-SHERMAN, R. (1973) - FUSARIUM MONILIFORME
       SHELD. IN ISRAEL (GIBBERELLA FUJIKUROI (SAW.) WOLLENW.). MYCOPATH.MY-
       COL.APPL. 50, 85-107.

2777   JOFFE, A.Z., YAFFE, Y. & PALTI, J. (1967) - YIELD LEVELS AND MICROFLORA OF
       THE SOIL IN SHAMOUTI ORANGE PLOTS GIVEN VARIOUS NUTRIENT TREATMENTS.
       SOIL SCI. 104, 263-267.

2778   JOFFE, A.Z. & YAGEN, B. (1977) - COMPARATIVE STUDY OF THE YIELD OF T-2
       TOXIN PRODUCED BY FUSARIUM POAE, F. SPOROTRICHIOIDES AND F. SPOROTRI-
       CHIOIDES VAR. TRICINCTUM STRAINS FROM DIFFERENT SOURCES. MYCOPATHOLO-
       GIA 60, 93-97.

2779   JOHANN, F. (1932) - UNTERSUCHUNGEN UEBER DIE MUCORINEAE DES WALDBODENS.
       ZENTBL.BAKT.PARASITKDE, ABT.2, 85, 305-338.

2780   JOHNSON, B. (1975) - THE ENZYMES OF AMMONIA ASSIMILATION IN TRICHOSPORON
       CUTANEUM. J.GEN.MICROBIOL. 89, 195-198.

2781   JOHNSON, B.T. & KNOWLES, CH.O. (1970) - MICROBIAL DEGRADATION OF THE ACARI-
       CIDE N-(4-CHLORO-O-TOLYL)-N,N-DIMETHYLFORMAMIDINE. BULL.ENVIRON.CONTAM.
       TOXICOL. 5, 158-163.

2782 JOHNSON, D.E., NELSON, G.E.N. & CIEGLER, A. (1968) - STARCH HYDROLYSIS BY CONIDIA OF ASPERGILLUS WENTII. APPL.MICROBIOL. 16, 1678-1683.

2783 JOHNSON, G.T. & DIXON, G.J. (1959) - OXYGEN-UPTAKE STUDIES ON GLUCOSE-GROWN AND FATTY ACID-EXPOSED FUNGUS CELLS. MYCOLOGIA 51, 647-655.

2784 JOHNSON, H.W. (1923) - SOME RELATIONSHIP BETWEEN H-ION, AND OH-ION, AND SALT CONCENTRATIONS AND THE GROWTH OF SEVEN SOIL MOLDS. BULL.IOWA ST. RES. 76, 307-344.

2785 JOHNSON, J.R., BRUCE, W.F. & DUTCHER, J.D. (1943) - GLIOTOXIN, THE ANTI-BIOTIC PRINCIPLE OF GLIOCLADIUM FIMBRIATUM. 1. PRODUCTION, PHYSICAL AND BIOLOGICAL PROPERTIES. J.AM.CHEM.SOC. 65, 2005-2009.

2786 JOHNSON, L.F. & OSBORNE, T.S. (1963) - SURVIVAL OF FUNGI IN SOIL EXPOSED TO GAMMA RADIATION. CAN.J.BOT. 42, 105-113.

2787 JOHNSON, T.W. (1971) - AQUATIC FUNGI OF ICELAND, PYTHIUM. MYCOLOGIA 63, 517-536.

2788 JOHNSON, T.W.JR. & HALPIN, J.E. (1954) - ENVIRONMENTAL EFFECTS ON CONIDIAL VARIATION IN SOME FUNGI IMPERFECTI. J.ELISHA MITCHELL SCIENT.SOC. 70, 314-326.

2789 JOHNSTON, C.L. & GREANEY, F.G. (1942) - STUDIES ON THE PATHOGENICITY OF FUSARIUM SPECIES ASSOCIATED WITH ROOT ROT OF WHEAT. PHYTOPATHOLOGY 32, 670-684.

2790 JOHNSTON, J.R. (1965) - THE COMPOSITION OF THE CELL WALL OF ASPERGILLUS NIGER. BIOCHEM.J. 96, 651-658.

2791 JOHRI, K., JOHRI, B.N. & SAKSENA, S.B. (1975) - COLONIZATION CAPACITY OF THE SOIL MICRO-ORGANISMS IN RELATION TO FUNGISTASIS. PL.SOIL 43, 347-354.

2792 JOLY, P. (1964) - LE GENRE ALTERNARIA, RECHERCHES PHYSIOLOGIQUES, BIOLO-GIQUES ET SYSTEMATIQUES. ENCYCL.MYCOL. 33, 250 PP., P.LECHEVALIER, PARIS.

2793 JOLY, P. (1964) - RECHERCHES SUR LA NATURE ET LE MODE DE FORMATION DES SPORES CHEZ TORULA. BULL.TRIMEST.SOC.MYCOL.FR. 80, 186-196.

2794 JOLY, P. (1965) - A PROPOS DU PULLULARIA PULLULANS. BULL.TRIMEST.SOC.MYCOL. FR. 81, 402-420.

2795 JOLY, P. (1967) - KEY FOR DETERMINATION OF THE MOST COMMON SPECIES OF THE GENUS ALTERNARIA (NEES) WILTSH. EMEND. JOLY. PL.DIS.REPTR 51, 296-298.

2796 JONES, A.S. & HODGES, C.S. (1974) - PERSISTENCE OF MIREX AND ITS EFFECTS ON SOIL MICROORGANISMS. J.AGRIC.FD CHEM. 22, 435-439.

2797 JONES, D. (1970) - ULTRASTRUCTURE AND COMPOSITION OF THE CELL WALLS OF SCLEROTINIA SCLEROTIORUM. TRANS.BR.MYCOL.SOC. 54, 351-360.

2798 JONES, D. (1971) - FROZEN ETCHED SPORES OF TRICHODERMA VIRIDE. TRANS.BR. MYCOL.SOC. 57, 348-350.

2799 JONES, D. (1974) - ULTRASTRUCTURE OF THE STIPE AND APOTHECIUM OF SCLEROTINIA SCLEROTIORUM. TRANS.BR.MYCOL.SOC. 63, 386-389.

2800 JONES, D., BACON, J.S.D., FARMER, V.C. & WEBLEY, D.M. (1968) - LYSIS OF
      CELL WALLS OF MUCOR RAMANNIANUS MOELLER BY A STREPTOMYCES SP. ANTONIE
      VAN LEEUWENHOEK 34, 173-182.

2801 JONES, D. & FARMER, V.C. (1967) - THE ECOLOGY AND PHYSIOLOGY OF SOIL FUNGI
      INVOLVED IN THE DEGRADATION OF LIGNIN AND RELATED AROMATIC COMPOUNDS.
      J.SOIL SCI. 18, 74-84.

2802 JONES, D., FARMER, V.C., BACON, J.S.D. & WILSON, M.J. (1972) - COMPARISON
      OF ULTRASTRUCTURE AND CHEMICAL COMPONENTS OF CELL WALLS OF CERTAIN PLANT
      PATHOGENIC FUNGI. TRANS.BR.MYCOL.SOC. 59, 11-23.

2803 JONES, D., GORDON, A.H. & BACON, J.S.D. (1974) - CO-OPERATIVE ACTION BY
      ENDO- AND EXO-BETA-(1-3)-GLUCANASES FROM PARASITIC FUNGI IN THE DEGRA-
      DATION OF CELL WALL GLUCANS OF SCLEROTINIA SCLEROTIORUM (LIB.) DE BARY.
      BIOCHEM.J. 140, 47-55.

2804 JONES, D. & JOHNSON, R.P.C. (1970) - ULTRASTRUCTURE OF FROZEN, FRACTURED
      AND ETCHED PYCNIDIOSPORES OF CONITHYRIUM MINITANS. TRANS.BR.MYCOL.SOC.
      55, 83-87.

2805 JONES, D., MCHARDY, W.J. & FARMER, V.C. (1977) - ELECTRON PROBE MICROANA-
      LYSIS OF CELL WALLS OF CUNNINGHAMELLA ECHINULATA. TRANS.BR.MYCOL.SOC.
      69, 71-75.

2806 JONES, D., MCHARDY, W.J. & WILSON, M.J. (1976) - ULTRASTRUCTURE AND CHEM-
      ICAL COMPOSITION OF SPINES IN MUCORALES. TRANS.BR.MYCOL.SOC. 66, 153-
      157.

2807 JONES, D. & WATSON, D. (1969) - PARASITISM AND LYSIS BY SOIL FUNGI OF
      SCLEROTINIA SCLEROTIORUM (LIB.) DE BARY, A PHYTOPATHOGENIC FUNGUS. NA-
      TURE, LOND. 224, 287-288.

2808 JONES, D.B. (1975) - OPPORTUNISTIC FUNGAL INFECTIONS IN OPHTHALMOLOGY.
      FUNGAL KERATITIS. IN: OPPORTUNISTIC FUNGAL INFECTIONS; CHICK, E.W.,
      BALOWS, A. & FURCOLOW, M.L. (ED.), C.C.THOMAS PUBL., U.S.A., 103-125.

2809 JONES, E.B.G. (1974) - AQUATIC FUNGI. FRESHWATER AND MARINE. IN: BIOLOGY
      OF PLANT LITTER DECOMPOSITION; DICKINSON, C.H. & PUGH, G.J.F. (ED.),
      ACADEMIC PRESS, LONDON, NEW YORK, 337-383.

2810 JONES, F.R. & DRECHSLER, C. (1925) - ROOT ROT OF PEAS IN THE UNITED STATES
      CAUSED BY APHANOMYCES EUTEICHES (N.SP.). J.AGRIC.RES. 30, 293-325.

2811 JONES, J.P. (1976) - ULTRASTRUCTURE OF CONIDIUM ONTOGENY IN PHOMA POMORUM,
      MICROSPHAEROPSIS OLIVACEUM AND CONIOTHYRIUM FUCKELII. CAN.J.BOT. 54,
      831-851.

2812 JONES, K.C., WEST, CH.A. & PHINNEY, B.O. (1968) - ISOLATION, IDENTIFICA-
      TION AND BIOLOGICAL PROPERTIES OF GIBBERELLIN-A-14 FROM GIBBERELLA FU-
      JIKUROI. PHYTOCHEMISTRY 7, 283-291.

2813 JONES, S.R. & HOFMANN, T. (1972) - PENICILLOCARBOXYPEPTIDASE-S, A NONSPE-
      CIFIC SH-DEPENDENT EXOPEPTIDASE. CAN.J.BIOCHEM. 50, 1297-1310.

2814 JONES, T.M. & BATEMAN, D.F. (1972) - GALACTOSIDASE PRODUCTION BY SCLERO-
      TIUM ROLFSII. PHYTOPATHOLOGY 62, 767-768 (ABS.).

2815 JONG, S.C. & DAVIS, E.E. (1976) - CONTRIBUTIONS TO THE KNOWLEDGE OF STA-
      CHYBOTRYS AND MEMNONIELLA IN CULTURE. MYCOTAXON 3, 409-485.

2816   JOOSTE, W.J. (1966) - THE EFFECT OF DIFFERENT CROP SEQUENCES ON THE RHI-
       ZOSPHERE FUNGI OF WHEAT. S.AFR.J.AGRIC.SCI. 9, 127-136.

2817   JORDAN, E.G. & ERB, K. (1976) - EFFECTS OF TEMPERATURE AND NITROGEN SOUR-
       CES ON THE PARASITISM OF DIMARGARIS VERTICILLATA ON MORTIERELLA ALPINA
       AND M. RAMANNIANA VAR. ANGULISPORA. MYCOLOGIA 68, 920-924.

2818   JORDAN, H.V., DAWSON, P.R., SKINNER, J.J. & HUNTER, J.H. (1934) - THE RE-
       LATION OF FERTILIZERS TO THE CONTROL OF COTTON ROOT ROT IN TEXAS. TECH.
       BULL.U.S.D.A. 426, 75 PP.

2819   JORDAN, V.W.L., SNEH, B. & EDDY, B.P. (1972) - INFLUENCE OF ORGANIC SOIL
       AMENDMENTS ON VERTICILLIUM DAHLIAE AND ON THE MICROBIAL COMPOSITION OF
       THE STRAWBERRY RHIZOSPHERE. ANN.APPL.BIOL. 70, 139-148.

2820   JORGENSEN, J. (1969) - SPECIES OF FUSARIUM AND HELMINTHOSPORIUM ON SEEDS
       OF BARLEY GROWN IN DENMARK DURING 1965-1967. ACTA AGRIC.SCAND. 19, 92-
       98.

2821   JORGENSEN, J. (1974) - OCCURRENCE AND IMPORTANCE OF SEED-BORNE INOCULUM OF
       COCHLIOBOLUS SATIVUS ON BARLEY SEED IN DENMARK. ACTA AGRIC.SCAND. 24,
       49-54.

2822   JORGENSEN, J.R. & HODGES, C.S. (1970) - MICROBIAL CHARACTERISTICS OF A
       FOREST SOIL AFTER 20 YEARS OF PRESCRIBED BURNING. MYCOLOGIA 62, 721-726.

2823   JORGENSON, E.C. (1970) - ANTAGONISTIC INTERACTION OF HETERODERA SCHACHTII
       SCHMIDT AND FUSARIUM OXYSPORUM (WOLL.) ON SUGARBEETS. J.NEMATOL. 2,
       393-398.

2824   JOUSSIER, D. & CATROUX, G. (1973) - ESSAI DE MISE AU POINT D'UNE TECHNIQUE
       DE DENOMBREMENT DE BEAUVERIA TENELLA PAR IMMUNOFLUORESCENCE. ANNLS PHY-
       TOPATH. 5, 303 (ABS.).

2825   JOUSSIER, D. & CATROUX, G. (1976) - MISE AU POINT D'UN MILIEU DE CULTURE
       POUR LE DENOMBREMENT DE BEAUVERIA TENELLA DANS LES SOLS. ENTOMOPHAGA
       21, 223-225.

2826   JUELICH, W. (1968) - UEBER COPROPHILE PILZE MITTELEUROPAS. 1. VERH.BOT.VER.
       BRANDENB. 105, 34-43.

2827   JUENGST, F.W. & ALEXANDER, M. (1976) - CONVERSION OF 1,1,1-TRICHLORO-2,2-
       BIS-(P-CHLOROPHENYL)-ETHANE (DDT) TO WATER-SOLUBLE PRODUCTS BY MICRO-
       ORGANISMS. J.AGRIC.FD CHEM. 24, 111-115.

2828   JUNIPER, A.J. (1957) - DUNG AS A SOURCE OF PREDACIOUS FUNGI. TRANS.BR.MY-
       COL.SOC. 40, 346-348.

2829   KACZKA, E.A., DULANEY, E.L., GITTERMAN, CH.O., WOODRUFF, H.B. & FOLKERS,
       K. (1964) - ISOLATION AND INHIBITORY EFFECTS ON KB CELL CULTURES OF
       3-DEOXYADENOSINE FROM ASPERGILLUS NIDULANS. BIOCHEM.BIOPHYS.RES.COMMUNS
       14, 452-455.

2830   KACZKA, E.A., GITTERMAN, C.O., DULANEY, E.L. & FOLKERS, K. (1962) - HADA-
       CIDIN, A NEW GROWTH-INHIBITORY SUBSTANCE IN HUMAN TUMOR SYSTEMS. BIO-
       CHEMISTRY 1, 340-343.

2831   KACZKA, E.A., SMITH, M.C. & FOLKERS, K. (1963) - ISOLATION AND STRUCTURAL
       STUDIES OF TENUAZONIC ACID. FEDN PROC.FEDN AM.SOCS EXP.BIOL. 22, 306.

2832   KADKOL, M.V. & GOPALKRISHNAN, K.S. (1972) - MICROBIOLOGICAL ASPECTS OF
       HERBARIN PRODUCTION. INDIAN J.EXPL BIOL. 10, 213-216.

2833   KAEAERIK, A. (1968) - COLONIZATION OF PINE AND SPRUCE POLES BY SOIL FUNGI
       AFTER TWELVE AND EIGHTEEN MONTHS. MATER.ORG. 3, 185-198.

2834   KAILIDIS, D.S. (1960) - SOME ASPECTS OF THE DAMPING-OFF OF BLACK PINE, PI-
       NUS NIGRA. DISS.ABSTR. 20, 3013-3014.

2835   KAISER NAGUIB, A., ELBAZ YOUNIS & ELESSAWY, A.A. (1972) - ON THE METABO-
       LISM OF ASPERGILLUS TERREUS ON AMMONIUM NITRATE AT DIFFERENT PH VALUES.
       CAN.J.BOT. 50, 2211-2219.

2836   KAISER, W.J. (1962) - INFLUENCES OF LIGHT ON THE PRODUCTION OF MICROSCLERO-
       TIA BY VERTICILLIUM ALBO-ATRUM. PHYTOPATHOLOGY 52, 362 (ABS.).

2837   KAISER, W.J. (1963) - EFFECT OF BIOTIN ON GROWTH AND SPORULATION OF VERTI-
       CILLIUM ALBO-ATRUM. PHYTOPATHOLOGY 53, 1139-1140 (ABS.).

2838   KAISER, W.J. (1964) - EFFECTS OF LIGHT ON GROWTH AND SPORULATION OF THE
       VERTICILLIUM WILT FUNGUS. PHYTOPATHOLOGY 54, 765-770.

2839   KAJI, A. & ICHIMI, T. (1969) - PRODUCTION AND PROPERTIES OF GALACTOSIDASES
       FROM CORTICIUM ROLFSII. APPL.MICROBIOL. 18, 1036-1040.

2840   KAJI, A. & ICHIMI, T. (1973) - ALPHA-L-RHAMNOSIDASE ACTIVITY IN CULTURE
       FILTRATE OF CORTICIUM ROLFSII. ENZYMATIC ACTIVITY AT LOW PH. AGRIC.BIOL.
       CHEM., TOKYO 37, 431-432.

2841   KAJI, A. & OHSAKI, T. (1971) - ENDO-POLYGALACTURONASE FROM CORTICIUM ROLF-
       SII. STABILITY AND ACTIVITY OF THE ENZYME AT LOW PH VALUES. J.AGRIC.
       CHEM.SOC.JAPAN 45, 520-527.

2842   KAJI, A. & TAGAWA, K. (1970) - PURIFICATION, CRYSTALLIZATION AND AMINO
       ACID COMPOSITION OF ALPHA-L-ARABINOFURANOSIDASE FROM ASPERGILLUS NIGER.
       BIOCHIM.BIOPHYS.ACTA 207, 456-464.

2843   KAJI, A., TAGAWA, K. & MOTOYAMA, K. (1965) - ENZYMES ACTING ON ARABAN. 7.
       PROPERTIES OF ARABANASE PRODUCED BY PLANT PATHOGENS. AGRIC.BIOL.CHEM.,
       TOKYO 39, 352-357.

2844   KAJI, A., TAGAWA, K. & YAMASHITA, M. (1966) - PECTIC ENZYMES. 22. PECTIC
       ENZYMES PRODUCED BY BOTRYTIS CINEREA AND RELATION BETWEEN ENZYME AC-
       TIONS AND MACERATION OF PLANT TISSUES. AGRIC.BIOL.CHEM., TOKYO 40, 209-
       212.

2845   KAKKAR, R.K. & MEHROTRA, B.R. (1971) - STUDIES ON IMPERFECT FUNGI. 2. THE
       ACTIVITIES OF THE HYDROGEN AND HYDROXYLONS. SYDOWIA 25, 89-99.

2846   KAKKAR, R.K. & MEHROTRA, B.R. (1971) - STUDIES ON IMPERFECT FUNGI. 3. IN-
       FLUENCE OF TEMPERATURE. SYDOWIA 26, 119-127.

2847   KALLIO, T. & SALONEN, A. (1972) - THE EFFECT OF GLIOCLADIUM DELIQUESCENS
       SOPP ON THE DECAYING CAPACITY OF SOME DECAY FUNGI. ANNLS AGRIC.FENN.
       11, 320-322.

2848   KAL'VISH, T.K. (1972) - (INTERACTION BETWEEN MICRO FLORA OF CATERPILLARS
       OF THE SIBERIAN SILKWORM AND ENTOMOGENOUS FUNGI). MIKOL.FITOPAT. 6,
       157-159.

2849   KAL'VISH, T.K. (1974) - (THE EFFECT OF TEMPERATURE AND RELATIVE AIR HUMI-
       DITY ON MUSCARDINE FUNGI). IZV.SIB.OTD.AKAD.NAUK SSSR, SER.BIOL.NAUK.
       1, 67-76.

180 COMPENDIUM OF SOIL FUNGI

2850 KALYANASUNDARAM, I. (1973) - GROWTH REQUIREMENTS OF SOME FUNGI CAUSING
MADUROMYCOSIS. ANTONIE VAN LEEUWENHOEK 39, 521-528.

2851 KAMAL & BHARGAVA, K.S. (1969) - STUDIES ON SOIL FUNGI FROM TEAK FORESTS OF
GORAKHPUR. 3. ADDITIONS TO OUR KNOWLEDGE OF INDIAN ASPERGILLI. INDIAN
PHYTOPATH. 22, 376-381.

2852 KAMAL & BHARGAVA, K.S. (1970) - STUDIES ON SOIL FUNGI FROM TEAK FORESTS OF
GORAKHPUR. 5. A CONTRIBUTION TO INDIAN TORULACEAE. INDIAN PHYTOPATH.
23, 558-561.

2853 KAMAL & BHARGAVA, K.S. (1970) - STUDIES ON SOIL FUNGI FROM TEAK FORESTS OF
GORAKHPUR. 6. A STUDY ON PENICILLIA FROM THREE TEAK STANDS OF DIFFERENT
AGES. PROC.NATN.ACAD.SCI., INDIA, SECT.B, 40, 191-194.

2854 KAMAL & BHARGAVA, K.S. (1971) - STUDIES ON SOIL FUNGI FROM TEAK FORESTS OF
GORAKHPUR. 7. GROUND VEGETATION AND FUNGAL FLORA OF THREE TEAK STANDS.
PROC.NATN.ACAD.SCI., INDIA, SECT.B, 41, 395-404.

2855 KAMAL & SINGH, C.S. (1970) - RHIZOSPHERE MYCOFLORA OF VIRUS INFECTED GRASS
(CYNODON DACTYLON LINN.). PORT.ACTA BIOL., SER.A, 11, 359-364.

2856 KAMAL & SINGH, C.S. (1970) - A STUDY ON RHIZOSPHERE MYCOPOPULATION OF SOME
PTERIDOPHYTES. ANNLS INST.PASTEUR, PARIS 118, 825-831.

2857 KAMAL & SINGH, C.S. (1970) - STUDIES ON SOIL FUNGI FROM TEAK FORESTS OF
GORAKHPUR. 8. A COMPARATIVE ACCOUNT OF FUNGI OF EARTHWORM CASTS, TER-
MITARIUM AND SURROUNDING SOIL FROM A TEAK STAND. ANNLS INST.PASTEUR,
PARIS 119, 249-259.

2858 KAMAL & SINGH, C.S. (1970) - ON RHIZOSPHERE FUNGAL FLORA OF SOME FERNS
FROM DARJEELING (INDIA). ANNLS INST.PASTEUR, PARIS 119, 360-368.

2859 KAMAL & SINGH, C.S. (1970) - SUCCESSION OF FUNGI ON DECAYING LEAVES OF
SOME PTERIDOPHYTES. ANNLS INST.PASTEUR, PARIS 119, 468-482.

2860 KAMAL & SINGH, C.S. (1970) - RHIZOSPHERE MYCOFLORA OF SOME BRYOPHYTES.
ANNLS INST.PASTEUR, PARIS 119, 752-755.

2861 KAMAL & SINGH, N.P. (1974) - ON MICROFUNGI FROM ROOT REGION OF TEN SUGAR
CANE VARIETIES. INDIAN PHYTOPATH. 27, 347-354.

2862 KAMAL & SRIVASTAVA, K.S. (1974) - RHIZOSPHERE MICROFUNGI OF SOME WEEDS.
TECHNOLOGY 11, 440-442.

2863 KAMAL, M. (1963) - A STUDY OF THE GROWTH BEHAVIOUR OF MICROSCLEROTIA OF
VERTICILLIUM DAHLIAE KLEB. CAUSING WILT OF COTTON. SCIENTIST PAKIST. 4,
48-52.

2864 KAMAT, M.N. & RAO, V.G. (1969) - THE GENUS CURVULARIA BOEDIJN FROM INDIA.
NOVA HEDWIGIA 18, 597-626.

2865 KAMEL, M.Y. & TAHANY, M.M. (1973) - PENICILLIUM NOTATUM CATALASE PURIFI-
CATION AND PROPERTIES. ACTA BIOL.MED.GERM. 30, 13-23.

2866 KAMINSKI, E., LIBBEY, L.M., STAWICKI, S. & WASOWICZ, E. (1972) - IDENTIFI-
CATION OF THE PREDOMINANT VOLATILE COMPOUNDS PRODUCED BY ASPERGILLUS
FLAVUS. APPL.MICROBIOL. 24, 721-726.

2867 KAMINSKI, E., STAWICKI, S. & WASOWICZ, E. (1974) - VOLATILE FLAVOR COM-
POUNDS PRODUCED BY MOLDS OF ASPERGILLUS, PENICILLIUM, AND FUNGI IMPER-
FECTI. APPL.MICROBIOL. 27, 1001-1004.

2868   KAMOEN, O. (1959) - PHYSIOLOGIE DER FRUCTIFICATIE. ONDERZOEKINGEN MET CHAE-
       TOMIUM GLOBOSUM. VERH.RIJKSSTN PLZIEKT., GENT 1, 40 PP.

2869   KAMOEN, O. (1964) - GROEI, SCLEROTENVORMING EN SPORULATIE VAN EEN BOTRYTIS
       CINEREA-ISOLATIE UIT VLASZAAD OP CULTUURBODEMS MET VERSCHILLENDE N-BRON-
       NEN EN VERSCHILLENDE BEGIN-PH. VERH.RIJKSSTN PLZIEKT., GENT 19, 1-64.

2870   KAMOEN, O. & JAMART, G. (1973) - EEN FYTOTOXISCH POLYSACCHARIDE AFGESCHEI-
       DEN DOOR BOTRYTIS CINEREA. MEDED.FAC.LANDBOUWWET.RIJKSUNIV.GENT 38,
       38, 1467-1476.

2871   KAMYSHKO, O.P. (1968) - (SOIL MYCOFLORA OF GYJUVAN DISTRICT OF THE BUHARA
       REGION). MIKOL.FITOPAT. 2, 367-378.

2872   KAMYSHKO, O.P. (1971) - (SOIL FUNGI AND ACTINOMYCETES-ANTAGONISTS OF VER-
       TICILLIUM COTTON WILT CAUSAL AGENT IN BUKHARA REGION). TRUDY VSES.NAUCH-
       NO-ISSLED.INST.ZASHCH.RAST. 29, 118-125.

2873   KAN, C.M.L. & COOENY, J.J. (1975) - PHOSPHOLIPIDS OF CLADOSPORIUM RESINAE
       CULTURED ON GLUCOSE AND ON N-ALKANES. CAN.J.MICROBIOL. 21, 1205-1210.

2874   KANE, B.E. & MULLINS, J.T. (1973) - THERMOPHILIC FUNGI IN A MUNICIPAL
       WASTE COMPOST SYSTEM. MYCOLOGIA 65, 1087-1100.

2875   KANE, J. & FISCHER, J.B. (1975) - THE EFFECT OF SODIUM CHLORIDE ON THE
       GROWTH AND MORPHOLOGY OF DERMATOPHYTES AND SOME OTHER KERATOLYTIC FUN-
       GI. CAN.J.MICROBIOL. 21, 742-749.

2876   KANEKO, Y. & SANADA, M. (1969) - STUDIES ON THE FLUORESCENT SUBSTANCES
       PRODUCED BY ASPERGILLUS FUNGI. 8. PURIFICATION AND ISOLATION OF ASPERO-
       PTERIN-B AND CHEMICAL PROPERTIES OF ASPEROPTERIN-B AND -A. J.FERMENT.
       TECHNOL., OSAKA 47, 8-19.

2877   KANETSUNA, F., CARBONELL, L.M. & GIL, F. (1972) - ESTUDIOS QUIMICOS Y UL-
       TRAESTRUCTURALES SOBRE PAREDES DE HISTOPLASMA CAPSULATUM. ACTA CIENT.
       VENEZ. 23 (SUPPL.1), 63-64.

2878   KANEVSKAYA, I.G. (1966) - (DECOMPOSITION OF METHYLCELLULOSE BY SOIL FUN-
       GI). MIKROBIOLOGIYA 35, 868-870.

2879   KANG, K.S. & FELBECK, G.T. (1965) - A COMPARISON OF THE ALKALINE EXTRACT
       OF TISSUE OF ASPERGILLUS NIGER WITH HUMIC ACIDS FROM THREE SOILS. SOIL
       SCI. 99, 175-181.

2880   KAPICA, L. & BLANK, F. (1962) - FORMATION OF AMMONIUM MAGNESIUM PHOSPHATE
       CRYSTALS IN CULTURES OF FUNGI GROWING ON KERATIN. MYCOPATH.MYCOL.APPL.
       18, 119-121.

2881   KAPLAN, M.A., HOOPER, I.R. & HEINEMANN, B. (1954) - ANTIBIOTIC-PRODUCING
       PROPERTIES OF ASPERGILLUS TERREUS. ANTIBIOTICS CHEMOTHER. 4, 746-749.

2882   KAPLAN, W., CHANDLER, F.W., AJELLO, L., GAUTHIER, R., HIGGINS, R. &
       CAYOUETTE, P. (1975) - EQUINE PHAEOHYPHOMYCOSIS CAUSED BY DRECHSLERA
       SPICIFERA. CAN.VET.J. 16, 205-208.

2883   KAPOOR, I.J. & SINGH, G.R. (1973) - UTILIZATION OF CARBOHYDRATES BY NINE
       ISOLATES OF COLLETOTRICHUM GLOEOSPORIOIDES FROM CITRUS. INDIAN PHYTO-
       PATH. 26, 279-283.

2884   KAPPEN, H. (1910) - UEBER DIE ZERSETZUNG DES CYANAMIDS DURCH PILZE. ZENTBL.
       BAKT.PARASITKDE, ABT.2, 26, 633-643.

2885 KAR, A.K. & MAITY, M.K. (1971) - THE PYRENOMYCETES OF WEST BENGAL (INDIA).
      4. NORW.J.BOT. 18, 81-85.

2886 KARHUVAARA, L. (1960) - ON THE PARASITES OF THE SCLEROTIA OF SOME FUNGI.
      ACTA AGRIC.SCAND. 10, 127-134.

2887 KARIMOV, K.M. (1972) - (ISOLATION OF THIELAVIOPSIS BASICOLA FROM SOIL).
      MIKOL.FITOPAT. 6, 366-367.

2888 KAROW, E.O., WOODRUFF, H.B. & FOSTER, J.W. (1944) - PENICILLIC ACID FROM
      ASPERGILLUS OCHRACEUS, PENICILLIUM THOMII, AND PENICILLIUM SUAVOLENS.
      ARCHS BIOCHEM. 5, 279-282.

2889 KATO, A., ANDO, K., KIMURA, T., TAMURA, G. & ARIMA, K. (1969) - ISOLATION
      AND CHARACTERIZATION OF PAECILOMYCEROL, A NEW STEROIDAL ANTIVIRAL ANTI-
      BIOTIC. STUDIES ON ANTIVIRAL AND ANTITUMOR ANTIBIOTICS. 21. J.ANTIBIOT.,
      TOKYO 22, 419-422.

2890 KATO, M. & IKEDA, Y. (1968) - ON THE DEOXYRIBONUCLEASES-K1 AND -K2, ISO-
      LATED FROM MYCELIA OF ASPERGILLUS ORYZAE. J.BIOCHEM. 64, 321-328.

2891 KATUMOTO, K., IZUMI, H. & YUKAWA, Y. (1974) - SCANNING ELECTRON MICROSCOPY
      OF MORPHOLOGICAL ASPECTS OF THE GRAY MOLD, BOTRYTIS CINEREA. BULL.FAC.
      AGRIC.YAMAGUTI UNIV. 25, 965-978.

2892 KAUFMAN, D.D. & BLAKE, J. (1970) - DEGRADATION OF ATRAZINE BY SOIL FUNGI.
      SOIL BIOL.BIOCHEM. 2, 73-80.

2893 KAUFMAN, D.D. & BLAKE, J. (1973) - MICROBIAL DEGRADATION OF SEVERAL ACET-
      AMIDE, ACYLANILIDE, CARBAMATE, TOLUIDINE AND UREA PESTICIDES. SOIL BIOL.
      BIOCHEM. 5, 297-308.

2894 KAUFMAN, D.D., KEARNEY, PH.C. & SHEETS, TH.J. (1963) - SIMAZINE DEGRADA-
      TION BY SOIL MICROORGANISMS. SCIENCE, N.Y. 142, 405-406.

2895 KAUFMAN, D.D. & WILLIAMS, L.E. (1964) - EFFECT OF MINERAL FERTILIZATION
      AND SOIL REACTION ON SOIL FUNGI. PHYTOPATHOLOGY 54, 134-139.

2896 KAUFMAN, L. & BRANDT, B. (1964) - FLUORESCENT-ANTIBODY STUDIES OF THE MY-
      CELIAL FORM OF HISTOPLASMA CAPSULATUM AND MORPHOLOGICALLY SIMILAR FUN-
      GI. J.BACT. 87, 120-126.

2897 KAUFMAN, S.M. (1971) - CURVULARIA GENICULATA ENDOCARDITIS FOLLOWING CAR-
      DIAC SURGERY. AM.J.CLIN.PATH. 56, 466-470.

2898 KAVANAGH, F. (1942) - THE INTERACTION BETWEEN THIAMINE AND FOUR FUNGI.
      BULL.TORREY BOT.CLUB 69, 669-691.

2899 KAVANAGH, F., TUNIN, D. & WILD, G. (1958) - ANTIBIOTICS FORMED BY SPECIES
      OF EMERICELLOPSIS. MYCOLOGIA 50, 370-372.

2900 KAWAI, G., TANIGUCHI, H. & NAKAMURA, M. (1973) - POLYFRUCTAN AND OLIGO-
      FRUCTANS SYNTHESIZED FROM SUCROSE BY CONIDIA OF ASPERGILLUS SYDOWI.
      AGRIC.BIOL.CHEM., TOKYO 37, 2111-2119.

2901 KAWAI, M. (1966) - STIMULATIVE EFFECT OF MORTIERELLA NANA LINNEMANN UPON
      THE FRUITBODY FORMATION OF PSILOCYBE PANAEOLIFORMIS MURRILL. TRANS.MY-
      COL.SOC.JAPAN 7, 325-334.

2902 KAWASAKI, CH. & ITO, Y. (1964) - HYDROLYSIS OF CHITIN BY FUNGAL ENZYME
      PREPARATIONS. J.FERMENT.TECHNOL., OSAKA 42, 212-215.

2903 KAWASAKI, N. & SAITO, K. (1973) - PURIFICATION AND SOME PROPERTIES OF LYSOPHOSPHOLIPASE FROM PENICILLIUM NOTATUM. BIOCHIM.BIOPHYS.ACTA 296, 426-430.

2904 KAWASE, Y., ICHITANI, T. & TAKAHASHI, M. (1970) - ECOLOGIC AND TAXONOMIC STUDIES ON PYTHIUM AS PATHOGENIC SOIL FUNGI. 9. EFFECT OF INORGANIC NITROGEN ON VERTICAL DISTRIBUTION AND PATHOGENICITY OF SEVERAL SOIL-BORNE PLANT PATHOGENS. BULL.UNIV.OSAKA PREF., SER.B, 22, 95-102.

2905 KAZANSKAYA, T.B., LE ZUI LIN & BEKHTEREVA, M.N. (1975) - COMPOSITION OF FREE INTRACELLULAR AMINO ACIDS IN CUNNINGHAMELLA ELEGANS DURING ITS GROWTH ON MEDIA WITH HYDROCARBONS. MICROBIOLOGY 44, 541-543 (ENGL. TRANSL. MIKROBIOLOGIYA 44, 605-608).

2906 KEARNY, P.C., KAUFMAN, D.D. & SHEETS, T.J. (1965) - METABOLITES OF SIMA-ZINE BY ASPERGILLUS FUMIGATUS. J.AGRIC.FD CHEM. 13, 369-372.

2907 KEDDIE, F., SHADOMY, J. & BARFATANI, M. (1963) - BRIEF REPORT ON THE ISO-LATION OF ARTHRODERMA TUBERCULATUM FROM A HUMAN SOURCE. MYCOPATH.MYCOL. APPL. 20, 129-132.

2908 KEDROVA, O.S., TARASOV, K.L. & ANTONOV, A.S. (1973) - (NUCLEOTIDE COMPOSI-TION OF DNA OF SOME SPECIES BELONGING TO ACREMONIUM LINK EX FR. GENUS AS CORRELATED WITH ITS SYSTEMATIC POSITION). MIKOL.FITOPAT. 7, 93-95.

2909 KEEN, N.T. & ERWIN, D.C. (1971) - ENDOPOLYGALACTURONASE - EVIDENCE AGAINST INVOLVEMENT IN VERTICILLIUM WILT OF COTTON. PHYTOPATHOLOGY 61, 198-203.

2910 KEEN, N.T. & LONG, M. (1972) - ISOLATION OF A PROTEIN-LIPOPOLYSACCHARIDE COMPLEX FROM VERTICILLIUM ALBO-ATRUM. PHYSIOL.PL.PATH. 2, 307-315.

2911 KEEN, N.T., LONG, M. & ERWIN, D.C. (1970) - POSSIBLE INVOLVEMENT OF A PA-THOGEN-PRODUCED PROTEIN-LIPOPOLYSACCHARIDE COMPLEX IN VERTICILLIUM WILT OF COTTON. PHYSIOL.PL.PATH. 2, 317-331.

2912 KEEN, N.T., LONG, M. & MALCA, I. (1970) - INDUCTION AND REPRESSION OF BE-TA-GALACTOSIDASE SYNTHESIS BY VERTICILLIUM ALBO-ATRUM. PHYSIOLOGIA PL. 23, 691-696.

2913 KEEN, N.T., WANG, M.C., BARTNICKI-GARCIA, S. & ZENTMYER, G.A. (1975) - PHYTOTOXICITY OF MYCOLAMINARANS - BETA-1,3-GLUCANS FROM PHYTOPHTHORA SPP. PHYSIOL.PL.PATH. 7, 91-97.

2914 KEEN, N.T., WANG, M.-C. & LONG, M. (1970) - INDUCTION OF WILT SYMPTOMS IN COTTON CUTTINGS BY LIPOPOLYSACCHARIDE BUT NOT BY ENDOPOLYGALACTURONASE. PHYTOPATHOLOGY 60, 1298 (ABS.).

2915 KEEN, N.T., WANG, M.C., LONG, M. & ERWIN, D.C. (1971) - DIMORPHISM IN VER-TICILLIUM ALBO-ATRUM AS AFFECTED BY INITIAL SPORE CONCENTRATION AND AN-TISPORULANT CHEMICALS. PHYTOPATHOLOGY 61, 1266-1269.

2916 KEGEL, W. (1906) - VARICOSPORIUM ELODEAE, EIN WASSERPILZ MIT AUFFALLENDER KONIDIENBILDUNG. BER.DT.BOT.GES. 24, 213-216.

2917 KEILICH, G., BAILEY, P. & LIESE, W. (1970) - ENZYMATIC DEGRADATION OF CEL-LULOSE, CELLULOSE DERIVATIVES AND HEMICELLULOSES IN RELATION TO THE FUN-GAL DECAY OF WOOD. WOOD SCI.TECHNOL. 4, 273-283.

2918 KELLER-SCHIERLEIN, W., ZAEHNER, H., PUENTER-STREIT, V. & BAER, H. (1965) - STOFFWECHSELPRODUKTE VON MIKROORGANISMEN. 47. DIE BILDUNG VON 2-ANHY-DROMEVALONSAEURELACTON DURCH VERSCHIEDENE PILZE. BIOCHEM.Z. 341, 378-

386.

2919 KELLEY, W.D. (1975) - PHYSIOLOGICAL DIFFERENCES AMONG ISOLATES OF PHY-
      TOPHTHORA CINNAMOMI. CAN.J.MICROBIOL. 21, 1548-1552.

2920 KELLEY, W.D. (1977) - INTERACTIONS OF PHYTOPHTHORA CINNAMOMI AND TRICHO-
      DERMA SPP. IN RELATION TO PROPAGULE PRODUCTION IN SOIL CULTURES AT 26 C.
      CAN.J.MICROBIOL. 23, 288-294.

2921 KENDRICK, B. (1971) - TAXONOMY OF FUNGI IMPERFECTI. UNIV.TORONTO PRESS,
      309 PP.

2922 KENDRICK, W.B. (1962) - SOIL FUNGI OF A COPPER SWAMP. CAN.J.MICROBIOL. 8,
      639-647.

2923 KENDRICK, W.B. (1963) - FUNGI ASSOCIATED WITH BREAKDOWN OF PINE LEAF LIT-
      TER IN THE ORGANIC HORIZON OF A PODZOL. MYCOPATH.MYCOL.APPL. 19, 241-
      245.

2924 KENDRICK, W.B. & BHATT, G.C. (1966) - TRICHOCLADIUM OPACUM. CAN.J.BOT. 44,
      1728-1730.

2925 KENDRICK, W.B. & BURGES, A. (1962) - BIOLOGICAL ASPECTS OF THE DECAY OF
      PINUS SYLVESTRIS LEAF LITTER. NOVA HEDWIGIA 4, 313-344.

2926 KENDRICK, W.B. & COLE, G.T. (1968) - CONIDIUM ONTOGENY IN HYPHOMYCETES.
      THE SYMPODULAE OF BEAUVERIA AND CURVULARIA. CAN.J.BOT. 46, 1297-1301.

2927 KENDRICK, W.B. & COLE, G.T. (1969) - CONIDIUM ONTOGENY IN HYPHOMYCETES.
      TRICHOTHECIUM ROSEUM AND ITS MERISTEM ARTHROSPORES. CAN.J.BOT. 47,
      345-350.

2928 KENNEDY, B.W. & ERWIN, D.C. (1961) - SOME FACTORS INFLUENCING SPORANGIUM
      FORMATION OF A PHYTOPHTHORA SPECIES ISOLATED FROM LUCERNE IN CERTAIN
      SALT SOLUTIONS. TRANS.BR.MYCOL.SOC. 44, 291-297.

2929 KENNETH, R. (1964) - CONIDIAL RELEASE IN SOME HELMINTHOSPORIA. NATURE,
      LOND. 202, 1025-1026.

2930 KENNETH, R. & ISAAC, P.K. (1964) - CEPHALOSPORIUM SPECIES PARASITIC ON HEL-
      MINTHOSPORIUM (SENSU LATO). CAN.J.PL.SCI. 44, 182-187.

2931 KENNETH, R., WALLIS, G., OLMERT, Y. & HALPERIN, J. (1971) - A LIST OF EN-
      TOMOGENOUS FUNGI OF ISRAEL. ISRAEL J.AGRIC.RES. 21, 63-66.

2932 KENT, J. & HEATLEY, N.G. (1945) - ANTIBIOTICS FROM MOULDS. NATURE, LOND.
      156, 295-296.

2933 KEOGH, R.G. & CHRISTENSEN, M.J. (1976) - INFLUENCE OF PASSAGE THROUGH LUM-
      BRICUS RUBELLUS HOFFMEISTER EARTHWORMS ON VIABILITY OF PITHOMYCES CHAR-
      TARUM. N.Z.JL AGRIC.RES. 19, 155-256.

2934 KERLING, L.C.P. (1964) - FUNGI IN THE PHYLLOSPHERE OF LEAVES OF RYE AND
      STRAWBERRY. MEDED.LANDBHOGESCH.OPZOEKSTNS GENT 29, 885-895.

2935 KERMARREC, A. & MAULEON, H. (1975) - QUELQUES ASPECTS DE LA PATHOGENIE
      D'ENTOMOPHTHORA CORONATA POUR LA FOURMIE-MANIOC DE LA GUADELOUPE, ACRO-
      MYRMEX OCTOSPINOSUS. ANNLS PARASIT.HUM.COMP. 50, 351-360.

2936 KERN, H. & NAEF-ROTH, S. (1965) - ZUR BILDUNG PHYTOTOXISCHER FARBSTOFFE
      DURCH FUSARIEN DER GRUPPE MARTIELLA. PHYTOPATH.Z. 53, 45-64.

2937 KERN, H. & NAEF-ROTH, S. (1971) - PHYTOLYSIN, EIN DURCH PFLANZENPATHOGENE
      PILZE GEBILDETER MAZERIERENDER FAKTOR. PHYTOPATH.Z. 71, 231-246.

2938 KERN, H., NAEF-ROTH, ST. & DEFAGO, G. (1971) - ZUR TOXINBILDUNG VON NEO-
      COSMOSPORA VASINFECTA UND NEOCOSMOSPORA AFRICANA. PHYTOPATH.Z. 72,
      327-334.

2939 KERNER-GANG, W. (1970) - UNTERSUCHUNGEN AN ISOLIERTEN MODERFAEULE-PILZEN.
      MATER.ORG. 5, 33-57.

2940 KERNER-GANG, W. (1974) - BEITRAG ZUR MODERFAEULEPRUEFUNG IM VERMICULIT-
      EINGRABE-VERFAHREN. MATER.ORG. 9, 269-282.

2941 KERNER-GANG, W. & SCHNEIDER, R. (1969) - VON OPTISCHEN GLAESERN ISOLIERTE
      SCHIMMELPILZE. MATER.ORG. 4, 291-296.

2942 KERR, A. (1956) - SOME INTERACTIONS BETWEEN PLANT ROOTS AND PATHOGENIC
      SOIL FUNGI. AUST.J.BIOL.SCI. 9, 45-52.

2943 KERR, A. & FLENTJE, N.T. (1957) - HOST INFECTION IN PELLICULARIA FILAMEN-
      TOSA CONTROLLED BY CHEMICAL STIMULI. NATURE, LOND. 179, 204-205.

2944 KESHAVAN, B.R. & DESHPANDE, K.B. (1974) - PRODUCTION OF PECTIC ENZYMES BY
      CURVULARIA LUNATA. J.BIOL.SCI. 16/17, 78-81.

2945 KESHWAL, R.L. & JOSHI, L.K. (1972) - STUDIES ON CERTAIN SOIL FUNGI ANTAGO-
      NISTIC TO PYTHIUM DEBARYANUM. INDIAN PHYTOPATH. 25, 566-569.

2946 KESSEL, M. & ROSENBERGER, R.F. (1968) - REGULATION AND TIMING OF DEOXYRI-
      BONUCLEIC ACID SYNTHESIS IN HYPHAE OF ASPERGILLUS NIDULANS. J.BACT. 95,
      2275-2281.

2947 KEVORKIAN, A.G. (1937) - STUDIES IN THE ENTOMOPHTHORACEAE. 1. OBSERVATIONS
      ON THE GENUS CONIDIOBOLUS. J.AGRIC.UNIV.PUERTO RICO 21, 191-200.

2948 KHALABUDA, T.V. (1948) - (RESULTS OF A STUDY OF SOIL FUNGI). MIKROBIOLOGI-
      YA 17, 257-268.

2949 KHALABUDA, T.V. (1958) - (DIE VERBREITESTEN RHIZOSPHAERENPILZE DES WINTER-
      WEIZENS IM SUEDEN DER UKRAINISCHEN SSR). MYKROBIOL.ZH. 20 (3), 10-17.

2950 KHALABUDA, T.V. (1973) - GRIBY RODA MORTIERELLA. IZVO NAUKA, MOSKVA, 208
      PP.

2951 KHALIFA, O. (1965) - BIOLOGICAL CONTROL OF FUSARIUM WILT OF PEAS BY ORGAN-
      IC SOIL AMENDMENTS. ANN.APPL.BIOL. 56, 129-137.

2952 KHAN, S.R. (1975) - WALL STRUCTURE AND GERMINATION OF SPORES IN CUNNINGHA-
      MELLA ECHINULATA. J.GEN.MICROBIOL. 90, 115-124.

2953 KHAN, S.R. & TALBOT, P.H.B. (1975) - MONOSPOROUS SPORANGIOLA IN MYCOTYPHA
      AND CUNNINGHAMELLA. TRANS.BR.MYCOL.SOC. 65, 29-39.

2954 KHANNA, K.K. & CHANDRA, S. (1975) - A NEW DISEASE OF APPLE FRUIT. PL.DIS.
      REPTR 59, 329-330.

2955 KHANNA, P.K. (1970) - SUCCESSION OF FUNGI ON DECAYING SHOOTS OF BOTHRIO-
      CHLOA PERTUSA A.CAMUS. BULL.INT.SOC.TROP.ECOL. 11, 201-208.

2956 KHARCHENKO, S.M. (1960) - (THE ANTIBIOTIC PROPERTIES IN THE MONOVERTICIL-
      LATA SECTION OF THE GENUS PENICILLIUM ISOLATED FROM THE RHIZOSPHERE OF
      AGRICULTURAL PLANTS IN THE UKRAINE. 2. THE ANTIBIOTIC PROPERTIES IN RE-
      LATION TO BACTERIA AND FUNGI). MYKROBIOL.ZH. 22 (5), 45-51.

2957 KHEW, K.L. & ZENTMYER, G.A. (1973) - CHEMOTACTIC RESPONSE OF ZOOSPORES OF
      FIVE SPECIES OF PHYTOPHTHORA. PHYTOPATHOLOGY 63, 1511-1516.

2958 KIDD, G.H. & WOLF, F.T. (1973) - DIMORPHISM IN A PATHOGENIC FUSARIUM. MY-
      COLOGIA 65, 1371-1375.

2959 KIDD, M.N. & BEAUMONT, A. (1924) - APPLE ROT FUNGI IN STORAGE. TRANS.BR.
      MYCOL.SOC. 10, 98-118.

2960 KIEFER, E. & CANCELA DA FONSECA, J.P. (1971) - INTERACTIONS BETWEEN MICRO-
      ARTHROPODS AND MICROSCOPIC FUNGI IN A FOREST SOIL. ZENTBL.BAKT.PARASIT-
      KDE, ABT.2, 126, 510-520.

2961 KIEWNICK, L. (1963) - UNTERSUCHUNGEN UEBER DEN EINFLUSS DER SAMEN- UND
      BODENMIKROFLORA AUF DIE LEBENSDAUER DER SPELZFRUECHTE DES FLUGHAFERS
      (AVENA FATUA). 1. VORKOMMEN, ARTZUSAMMENSETZUNG UND EIGENSCHAFTEN DER
      MIKROORGANISMEN AN FLUGHAFERFRUECHTEN. WEED RES. 3, 322-332.

2962 KIEWNICK, L. (1964) - UNTERSUCHUNGEN UEBER DEN EINFLUSS DER SAMEN- UND
      BODENMIKROFLORA AUF DIE LEBENSDAUER DER SPELZFRUECHTE DES FLUGHAFERS
      (AVENA FATUA). 2. ZUM EINFLUSS DER MIKROFLORA AUF DIE LEBENSDAUER DER
      SAMEN IM BODEN. WEED RES. 4, 31-43.

2963 KIFFER, E. & MANGENOT, F. (1968) - ACTIVITES CELLULOLYTIQUES DE QUELQUES
      SOLS FORESTIERS. ANNLS INST.PASTEUR, PARIS 115, 582-595.

2964 KIFFER, E., MANGENOT, F. & REISINGER, O. (1969) - SUR LA POSITION TAXONO-
      MIQUE DE QUELQUES HYPHOMYCETES ISOLES DES SOLS DE LA R.C.P. 40. REVUE
      ECOL.BIOL.SOL 6, 181-194.

2965 KIFFER, E., MANGENOT, F. & REISINGER, O. (1971) - MORPHOLOGIE ULTRASTRUC-
      TURALE ET CRITERES TAXINOMIQUES CHEZ LES DEUTEROMYCETES. 4. DORATOMYCES
      PURPUREOFUSCUS (FRES.) MORTON & SMITH. REVUE ECOL.BIOL.SOL 8, 397-408.

2966 KIFFER, E. & REISINGER, O. (1970) - CONTRIBUTION A L'ETUDE DE LA MICRO-
      FLORE FONGIQUE DU CONGO. 1. CHAMPIGNONS OBSERVES SUR DEBRIS VEGETAUX ET
      SUR PIEGES DE CELLULOSE. REVUE ECOL.BIOL.SOL 7, 11-31.

2967 KIFFER, E. & REISINGER, O. (1971) - CONTRIBUTION A L' ETUDE DE LA MICRO-
      FLORE FONGIQUE DU CONGO. 2. SUCCESSION DE CHAMPIGNONS SUR PIEGES DE
      CELLULOSE ET SUR DEBRIS VEGETAUX. REVUE ECOL.BIOL.SOL 8, 227-234.

2968 KIKUCHI, Y., TAGUCHI, R., SAKANO, Y. & KOBAYASHI, T. (1973) - COMPARISON
      OF EXTRACELLULAR POLYSACCHARIDE PRODUCED BY PULLULARIA PULLULANS WITH
      POLYSACCHARIDES IN THE CELLS AND CELL WALL. AGRIC.BIOL.CHEM., TOKYO 37,
      1751-1753.

2969 KILBERTUS, G. (1968) - DECOMPOSITION D'UNE MOUSSE PSEUDOSCLEROPODIUM PURUM
      (HEDW.) FLEISCH. DANS LA NATURE. BULL.EC.NATN.SUPER.AGRON., NANCY 1,
      20-32.

2970 KILBERTUS, G. (1969) - SUCCESSION DE CHAMPIGNONS SUR FEUILLES DE BRACHYPO-
      DIUM PINNATUM P.B. REVUE ECOL.BIOL.SOL 6, 155-180.

2971 KILBERTUS, G. (1970) - DECOMPOSITION DES VEGETAUX. 1. OBSERVATION DE LA
      SURFACE DES FEUILLES DE BRACHYPODIUM PINNATUM P.B. AU MICROSCOPE ELEC-
      TRONIQUE A BALAYAGE. BULL.EC.NATN.SUPER.AGRON., NANCY 12, 59-61.

2972 KILLIAN, C. (1936) - ETUDE SUR LA BIOLOGIE DES SOLS DES HAUTS PLATEAUX AL-
      GERIENS. ANNLS AGRON. 6, 595-614.

2973 KILLIAN, C. & FEHER, D. (1935) - RECHERCHES SUR PHENOMENES MICROBIOLOGI-
QUES DES SOLS SAHARIENS. ANNLS INST.PASTEUR, PARIS 55, 573-622.

2974 KILLIAN, C. & FEHER, D. (1939) - MICROFLORE DU SOL DESERTIQUE. P.LECHEVA-
LIER, PARIS.

2975 KILPATRICK, R.A., HANSON, E.W. & DICKSON, J.G. (1954) - ROOT AND CROWN
ROTS OF RED CLOVER IN WISCONSIN AND THE RELATIVE PREVALENCE OF ASSOCI-
ATED FUNGI. PHYTOPATHOLOGY 44, 252-259.

2976 KILPATRICK, R.A., HANSON, E.W. & DICKSON, J.G. (1954) - RELATIVE PATHOGEN-
ICITY OF FUNGI ASSOCIATED WITH ROOT ROTS OF RED CLOVER IN WISCONSIN.
PHYTOPATHOLOGY 44, 292-297.

2977 KIM, H.S. (1975) - ETIOLOGY, ECOLOGY AND RESISTANCE OF PYTHIUM FRUIT ROT
OF TOMATO. PROC.AM.PHYTOPATH.SOC. 2, 99.

2978 KIM, H.S., GEDDES, W.F. & DEVAY, J.E. (1957) - STUDIES ON THE SYNTHESIS OF
ALPHA-AMYLASE AND FREE AMINO ACIDS BY MUTANTS OF ASPERGILLUS ORYZAE.
MYCOLOGIA 49, 453-462.

2979 KIMBROUGH, J.W. (1965) - STUDIES IN THE PSEUDOASCOBOLEAE. CAN.J.BOT. 44,
685-704.

2980 KIMBROUGH, J.W. & KORF, R.P. (1967) - A SYNOPSIS OF THE GENERA AND SPECIES
OF THE TRIBE THELEBOLEAE (=PSEUDOASCOBOLEAE). AM.J.BOT. 54, 9-23.

2981 KIMMIG, J. & MEYER-ROHN, J. (1962) - EXPERIMENTELLE UNTERSUCHUNGEN UND
KLINISCHE ERFAHRUNGEN MIT DEM NEUEN ANTIBIOTIKUM FUCIDIN. MEDSCHE WELT
34, 1742-1746.

2982 KIMURA, K., YAGI, K., KATSUKI, H. & TAKAHASHI, M. (1956) - THE SPORULATING
SUBSTANCE OF PYTHIUM ULTIMUM. NIPPON SHOKUBUTSU BYORI GAKKAIHO 21, 171-
174.

2983 KING, C.J., EATON, E.D. & HOPE, C. (1934) - CATALASE ACTIVITY IN RELATION
TO AGE AND VIABILITY OF SCLEROTIA OF THE COTTON ROOT-ROT FUNGUS. J.
AGRIC.RES. 49, 897-902.

2984 KING, C.J. & HOPE, C. (1932) - DISTRIBUTION OF THE COTTON ROOT-ROT FUNGUS
IN SOIL AND IN PLANT TISSUES IN RELATION TO CONTROL BY DISINFECTANTS.
J.AGRIC.RES. 45, 725-740.

2985 KING, C.J., HOPE, C. & EATON, E.D. (1934) - SOME MICROBIOLOGICAL ACTIVI-
TIES AFFECTED IN MANURIAL CONTROL OF COTTON ROOT ROT. J.AGRIC.RES. 49,
1093-1107.

2986 KING, C.J. & LOOMIS, H.F. (1929) - FURTHER STUDIES OF COTTON ROT IN ARIZO-
NA, WITH A DESCRIPTION OF A SCLEROTIUM STAGE OF THE FUNGUS. J.AGRIC.RES.
39, 641-676.

2987 KING, D.S. (1976) - SYSTEMATICS OF CONIDIOBOLUS (ENTOMOPHTHORALES) USING
NUMERICAL TAXONOMY. 1. BIOLOGY AND CLUSTER ANALYSIS. CAN.J.BOT. 54, 45-
65.

2988 KING, D.S. (1976) - SYSTEMATICS OF CONIDIOBOLUS (ENTOMOPHTHORALES) USING
NUMERICAL TAXONOMY. 2. TAXONOMIC CONSIDERATIONS. CAN.J.BOT. 54, 1284-
1296.

2989 KING, D.S. (1977) - SYSTEMATICS OF CONIDIOBOLUS (ENTOMOPHTHORALES) USING
NUMERICAL TAXONOMY. 3. DESCRIPTIONS OF RECOGNIZED SPECIES. CAN.J.BOT.
55, 718-729.

2990 KING, D.S. & JONG, S.C. (1976) - INDUCTION OF ARTHROCONIDIA IN TRICHOSPO-
      RON. MYCOPATHOLOGIA 59, 61-63.

2991 KING, D.S. & JONG, S.C. (1977) - A CONTRIBUTION TO THE GENUS TRICHOSPORON.
      MYCOTAXON 6, 391-417.

2992 KING, M.K. & ISAAC, P.K. (1964) - THE UPTAKE OF GLUCOSE-6-T AND GLYCINE-
      2-T BY RHIZOCTONIA SOLANI. CAN.J.BOT. 42, 815-821.

2993 KING, T.H. & BISSONNETTE, H.L. (1954) - PHYSIOLOGIC SPECIALIZATION IN APHA-
      NOMYCES EUTEICHES. PHYTOPATHOLOGY 44, 495 (ABS.).

2994 KING, T.H., KROG, N.E. & SCHROEDER, H.W. (1956) - THE EFFECT OF COPPER ON
      GROWTH REQUIREMENTS OF CONIOTHYRIUM FUCKELII. PHYTOPATHOLOGY 42, 468
      (ABS.).

2995 KING, T.J., ROBERTS, J.C. & THOMPSON, D.J. (1973) - STUDIES IN MYCOLOGICAL
      CHEMISTRY. 30. ISOLATION AND STRUCTURE OF PURPURIDE, A METABOLITE OF
      PENICILLIUM PURPUROGENUM. J.CHEM.SOC.PERKIN TRANS.I, 1973, 78-80.

2996 KINGHORN, J.R. & PATEMAN, J.A. (1974) - THE EFFECT OF THE CARBON SOURCE ON
      AMMONIUM REGULATION IN ASPERGILLUS NIDULANS. MOLEC.GEN.GENET. 128, 95-
      98.

2997 KINGSLAND, G.C. (1972) - FACTORS INFLUENCING SURVIVAL AND GERMINATION OF
      HELMINTHOSPORIUM SOROKINIANUM IN SOUTH CAROLINA. PHYTOPATHOLOGY 62,
      804-805 (ABS.).

2998 KINGSLAND, G. & CROSS, C. (1972) - INFLUENCE OF CELL-FREE SOIL EXTRACTS ON
      GERMINATION OF CONIDIA OF TWO HELMINTHOSPORIUM SPP. PHYTOPATHOLOGY 62,
      805 (ABS.).

2999 KINOSITA, R. & SHIKATA, T. (1965) - ON TOXIC MOLDY RICE. IN: MYCOTOXINS IN
      FOODSTUFFS; WOGAN, G.N. (ED.), MASSACHUSETTS INST. TECHNOL. PRESS, CAM-
      BRIDGE, MASS., 111-132.

3000 KIRBY, H.W. & GRAND, L.F. (1975) - SUSCEPTIBILITY OF PINUS STROBUS AND LU-
      PINUS SPP. TO PHYTOPHTHORA CINNAMOMI. PHYTOPATHOLOGY 65, 693-695.

3001 KIRCHOFF, W.F. (1959) - FACTORS AFFECTING THE PRODUCTION OF PROTEOLYTIC
      ENZYMES BY SPECIES OF THE MUCORALES. DISS.ABSTR. 20, 1547.

3002 KIRILENKO, T.S. (1965) - (SPECIES OF THE GENUS FUSARIUM IN BARLEY AND OAT
      RHIZOSPHERE IN DISTRICTS OF THE POLESS'E OF THE UKRAINIAN SSR). MYKRO-
      BIOL.ZH. 27 (2), 23-29.

3003 KIRILENKO, T.S. (1965) - (ASPERGILLUS FUNGI FOUND IN BARLEY AND OAT RHIZO-
      SPHERE IN THE POLESS'E DISTRICT OF THE UKRAINIAN SSR). MYKROBIOL.ZH. 27
      (4), 22-27.

3004 KIRILENKO, T.S. (1965) - (FUNGI OF THE ORDER MUCORALES IN THE RHIZOSPHERE
      OF BARLEY AND OATS IN THE POLESS'E DISTRICT OF THE UKRAINIAN SSR). MY-
      KROBIOL.ZH. 27 (5), 16-23.

3005 KIRILENKO, T.S. (1966) - (INFLUENCE OF FUNGI OF THE ORDER MUCORALES ON THE
      GROWTH OF BARLEY AND OAT SEEDLINGS). MYKROBIOL.ZH. 28 (3), 48-54.

3006 KIRILENKO, T.S. (1968) - (FUNGUS SPECIES ON THE BARLEY AND OAT ROOTS).
      MYKROBIOL.ZH. 30 (3), 204-210.

3007 KIRIYAMA, N., YAMAMOTO, Y. & TSUDA, Y. (1971) - STUDIES ON THE METABOLITE
OF TRICHOTHECIUM ROSEUM LINK. STRUCTURE OF ROSEIN-III. YAKUGAKU ZASSHI
(J.PHARMACEUT.SOC.JAPAN) 91, 1078-1087.

3008 KIRK, P.W.JR. (1967) - A COMPARISON OF SALINE TOLERANCE AND SPORULATION IN
MARINE AND CLINICAL ISOLATES OF ALLESCHERIA BOYDII SHEAR. MYCOPATH.MY-
COL.APPL. 33, 65-75.

3009 KIRKSEY, J.W. & COLE, R.J. (1973) - NEW TOXIN FROM ASPERGILLUS FLAVUS.
APPL.MICROBIOL. 26, 827-828.

3010 KIRSANOVA, R.V. & USENKO, L.I. (1974) - (GENETICS AND BREEDING OF THE EN-
TOMOPATHOGENIC FUNGUS BEAUVERIA BASSIANA. 4. VARIABILITY OF VIRULENCE
INDUCED BY UV-LIGHT). GENETIKA 10, 97-102.

3011 KIRST, G. (1971) - UNTERSUCHUNGEN ZUR HEMMUNG DER ZYGOSPORENBILDUNG BEI
MUCOR HIEMALIS. DISS.UNIV.TUEBINGEN.

3012 KISH, L.P., ALLEN, G.E., KIMBROUGH, J.W. & KUITERT, L.C. (1974) - A SURVEY
OF FUNGI ASSOCIATED WITH THE LOVEBUG, PLECIA NEARCTICA, IN FLORIDA.
FLA ENTOMOL. 57, 281-284.

3013 KISHIDA, T. & YOSHIMURA, S. (1966) - STUDIES ON PROTEINASES FROM GLIOCLA-
DIUM ROSEUM. 1. CRYSTALLIZATION AND SOME PROPERTIES. AGRIC.BIOL.CHEM.,
TOKYO 30, 1183-1190.

3014 KISHIMOTO, R.A. & BAKER, G.E. (1969) - PATHOGENIC AND POTENTIALLY PATHOGEN-
IC FUNGI ISOLATED FROM BEACH SANDS AND SELECTED SOILS OF OAHU, HAWAII.
MYCOLOGIA 61, 537-548.

3015 KISS, J., NAEF-ROTH, S., HARDEGGER, E., BOLLER, A., LOHSE, F., GAEUMANN,
E. & PLATTNER, P.A. (1960) - UEBER DIE ISOLIERUNG VON CULMOMARASMIN,
EINEM PEPTIDARTIGEN WELKSTOFF AUS DEM KULTURFILTRAT VON FUSARIUN CULMO-
RUM. HELV.CHIM.ACTA 43, 2096-2101.

3016 KITANO, K., KINTAKA, K., KATAMOTO, K., NARA, K. & NAKAO, Y. (1975) - OC-
CURRENCE OF 6-AMINOPENICILLIC ACID IN CULTURE BROTHS OF STRAINS BELONG-
ING TO THE GENERA THERMOASCUS, GYMNOASCUS, POLYPAECILUM AND MALBRAN-
CHEA. J.FERMENT.TECHNOL., OSAKA 53, 339-346.

3017 KITANO, K., KINTAKA, K., SUZUKI, S., KATAMOTO, K., NARA, K. & NAKAO, Y.
(1974) - PRODUCTION OF CEPHALOSPORIN ANTIBIOTICS FROM N-PARAFFINS BY
STRAINS BELONGING TO THE GENUS PAECILOMYCES. J.FERMENT.TECHNOL., OSAKA
52, 785-787.

3018 KIYOMOTO, R.K. & BRUEHL, G.W. (1976) - SEXUAL INCOMPATIBILITY AND VIRULENCE
IN TYPHULA IDAHOENSIS. PHYTOPATHOLOGY 66, 1001-1006.

3019 KJAER, D., KJAER, A., PEDERSEN, C., BU'LOCK, J.D. & SMITH, J.R. (1971) -
BIKAVERIN AND NORBIKAVERIN, BENZOXANTHENTRIONE PIGMENTS OF GIBBERELLA
FUJIKUROI. J.CHEM.SOC.(C), 1971, 2792-2797.

3020 KJOELLER, A. (1967) - MICROFUNGI ISOLATED FROM TROPICAL SOILS WITH NOTES
ON TRICHODERMA VIRIDE AND DELACROXIA CORONATA. BOT.TIDSSKR. 62, 323-336.

3021 KJOELLER, A. & ODUM, S. (1971) - EVIDENCE FOR LONGEVITY OF SEEDS AND MICRO-
ORGANISMS IN PERMAFROST. ARCTIC 24, 230-233.

3022 KLAPPER, B.F., JAMESON, D.M. & MAYER, R.M. (1973) - THE PURIFICATION AND
PROPERTIES OF AN EXTRACELLULAR PROTEASE FROM ASPERGILLUS ORYZAE NRRL
2160. BIOCHIM.BIOPHYS.ACTA 304, 505-512.

3023 KLAUSEMEIER, R.E. & JONES, W.A. (1961) - MICROBIAL DEGRADATION OF PLASTI-
      CIZERS. DEVS IND.MICROBIOL. 2, 47-53.

3024 KLEBAHN, H. (1930) - VERGILBENDE JUNGE TREIBGURKEN, EIN DARAUF GEFUNDENES
      CEPHALOSPORIUM UND DESSEN SCHLAUCHFRUECHTE. PHYTOPATH.Z. 1, 31-44.

3025 KLEGER, B. & KAUFMAN, L. (1973) - DETECTION AND IDENTIFICATION OF DIAGNOS-
      TIC HISTOPLASMA CAPSULATUM PRECIPITATES BY COUNTERELECTROPHORESIS. APPL.
      MICROBIOL. 26, 231-238.

3026 KLEIN, R. (1944) - DEVELOPMENTAL STUDIES IN THE FUNGI. 1. THE FOOT-CELL IN
      ASPERGILLUS CLAVATUS. TRANS.BR.MYCOL.SOC. 27, 121-130.

3027 KLEMMER, H.W. & LENNEY, J.F. (1965) - LIPIDS STIMULATING SEXUAL REPRODUC-
      TION AND GROWTH IN PYTHIACEOUS FUNGI. PHYTOPATHOLOGY 55, 320-323.

3028 KLEMMER, H.W. & NAKANO, R.Y. (1962) - TECHNIQUES IN ISOLATION OF PYTHIA-
      CEOUS FUNGI FROM SOIL AND DISEASED PINEAPPLE TISSUE. PHYTOPATHOLOGY 52,
      955-956.

3029 KLEMMER, H.W. & NAKANO, R.Y. (1964) - DISTRIBUTION AND PATHOGENICITY OF
      PHYTOPHTHORA AND PYTHIUM IN PINEAPPLE SOILS OF HAWAII. PL.DIS.REPTR 48,
      848-852.

3030 KLEMMER, H.W., RIKER, A.J. & ALLEN, O.M. (1955) - INHIBITION OF CROWN GALL
      BY SELECTED ANTIBIOTICS. PHYTOPATHOLOGY 45, 618-625.

3031 KLIEJUNAS, J.T. & KO, W.H. (1975) - CONTINUOUS VERSUS LIMITED GROWTH OF
      FUNGI. MYCOLOGIA 67, 362-366.

3032 KLIEJUNAS, J.T. & KO, W.H. (1976) - ASSOCIATION OF PHYTOPHTHORA CINNAMOMI
      WITH OHIA DECLINE ON THE ISLAND OF HAWAII. PHYTOPATHOLOGY 66, 116-121.

3033 KLIEJUNAS, J.T. & KO, W.H. (1976) - DISPERSAL OF PHYTOPHTHORA CINNAMOMI ON
      THE ISLAND OF HAWAII. PHYTOPATHOLOGY 66, 457-460.

3034 KLIMOV, A.N. & EFIMOVA, T.P. (1965) - (AMINO ACID METABOLISM AND GRISEO-
      FULVIN FORMATION BY PENICILLIUM NIGRICANS). PRIKL.BIOKHIM.MIKROBIOL. 1,
      433-439.

3035 KLIMOV, A.N. & EFIMOVA, T.P. (1966) - (FATTY ACID METABOLISM IN GRISEO-
      FULVIN-PRODUCING PENICILLIUM NIGRICANS). PRIKL.BIOKHIM.MIKROBIOL. 2,
      511-518.

3036 KLINGNER, A.E., HILDEBRAND, D.C. & WILHELM, S. (1971) - OCCURRENCE OF ER-
      WINIA CAROTOVORA IN THE RHIZOSPHERE OF COTTON PLANTS WHICH ESCAPE VER-
      TICILLIUM WILT. PL.SOIL 34, 215-218.

3037 KLINK, J.W. & BARKER, K.R. (1968) - EFFECT OF APHELENCHUS AVENAE ON THE
      SURVIVAL AND PATHOGENIC ACTIVITY OF ROOT-ROTTING FUNGI. PHYTOPATHOLOGY
      58, 228-232.

3038 KLITE, P.D., KELLEY, H.B. & DIERCKS, F.H. (1965) - A NEW SOIL SAMPLING
      TECHNIQUE FOR PATHOGENIC FUNGI. AM.J.EPIDEMIOL. 31, 124-130.

3039 KLOCHKO, M.D. (1970) - (INFLUENCE OF VARIOUS CONCENTRATIONS OF STARCH AND
      SOYBEAN FLOUR ON GROWTH AND SPORE FORMATION OF THE ENTOMOPATHOGENIC
      FUNGUS BEAUVERIA TENELLA). MIKOL.FITOPAT. 4, 538-541.

3040 KLOCHKO, M.D. (1973) - (CARBON AND NITROGEN NUTRITION OF BEAUVERIA TENELLA
      (DEL.) SIEM., A CAUSAL AGENT OF MYCOSIS IN THE POTATO LADY BEETLE).
      MIKOL.FITOPAT. 7, 48-49.

3041   KLOPOTEK, A.VON (1962) - UEBER DAS VORKOMMEN UND VERHALTEN VON SCHIMMEL-
       PILZEN BEI DER KOMPOSTIERUNG STAEDTISCHER ABFALLSTOFFE. ANTONIE VAN
       LEEUWENHOEK 28, 141-160.

3042   KLOPOTEK, A.VON (1967) - MYKOLOGISCHE UNTERSUCHUNGEN VERSCHIEDENER BOEDEN
       AN KLIMATISCH UNTERSCHIEDLICHEN STANDORTEN. IN: PROGRESS IN SOIL BIOL-
       OGY; GRAFF, O. & SATCHELL, J.E. (ED.), PROC.COLL. ON DYNAMICS OF SOIL
       COMMUNITIES, VIEWEG & SOHN, BRAUNSCHWEIG, NORTH HOLLAND PUBL.COMP.,
       AMSTERDAM, 171-177.

3043   KLOPOTEK, A.VON (1974) - REVISION DER THERMOPHILEN SPOROTRICHUM-ARTEN -
       CHRYSOSPORIUM THERMOPHILUM (APINIS) COMB.NOV. UND CHRYSOSPORIUM FERGU-
       SII SPEC.NOV. = STATUS CONIDIALIS VON CORYNASCUS THERMOPHILUS (FERGUS
       & SINDEN) COMB.NOV. ARCH.MIKROBIOL. 98, 365-369.

3044   KLOPOTEK, A.VON (1976) - THIELAVIA HETEROTHALLICA SPEC.NOV., DIE PERFEKTE
       FORM VON CHRYSOSPORIUM THERMOPHILUM. ARCH.MICROBIOL. 107, 223-224.

3045   KLOTZ, L.J., STOLZY, L.H. & DEWOLFE, T.A. (1963) - OXYGEN REQUIREMENT OF
       THREE ROOT-ROTTING FUNGI IN A LIQUID MEDIUM. PHYTOPATHOLOGY 53, 302-305.

3046   KLOTZ, L.J., STOLZY, L.H., DEWOLFE, T.A. & SZUSZKIEWICZ, T.E. (1965) -
       RATE OF OXYGEN SUPPLY AND DISTRIBUTION OF WOOD-ROTTING FUNGI IN SOILS.
       SOIL SCI. 99, 200-204.

3047   KLUGE, E. (1966) - PATHOGENITAET GEGENUEBER KIEFERNSAEMLINGEN UND TOXIN-
       BILDUNG BEI CYLINDROCARPON RADICICOLA. PHYTOPATH.Z. 55, 368-388.

3048   KLUYVER, A.J. & ZIJP, J.C.M.VAN (1951) - THE PRODUCTION OF HOMOGENTISIC
       ACID OUT OF PHENYLACETIC ACID BY ASPERGILLUS NIGER. ANTONIE VAN LEEU-
       WENHOEK 17, 315-324.

3049   KNIGHT, S.G. (1966) - PRODUCTION OF A RENNIN-LIKE ENZYME BY MOLDS. CAN.J.
       MICROBIOL. 12, 420-422.

3050   KNOESEL, D. & KIEWNICK, L. (1964) - BEITRAG ZUR WIRKUNG VON CYANAMID-
       FLUESSIG AUF BODENMIKROORGANISMEN. ZENTBL.BAKT.PARASITKDE, ABT.2, 118,
       386-396.

3051   KNOESEL, D. & RESZ, A. (1973) - PILZE AUS MUELLKOMPOST. STAEDTEHYGIENE 6,
       6 PP.

3052   KNUDSON, L. (1913) - TANNIC ACID FERMENTATION. 1. J.BIOL.CHEM. 14, 159-
       184.

3053   KNUDTSON, W.U. & ROBERSTAD, G.W. (1970) - THE ISOLATION OF KERATINOPHILIC
       FUNGI FROM SOIL AND WILD ANIMALS IN SOUTH DAKOTA. MYCOPATH.MYCOL.APPL.
       40, 309-323.

3054   KNUDTSON, W.U., WOHLGEMUTH, K. & BURY, R.J. (1973) - BOVINE CEREBRAL MU-
       CORMYCOSIS. REPORT OF A CASE. SABOURAUDIA 11, 156-158.

3055   KNYPL, J.S. (1963) - A FUNGISTATIC ACTION OF COUMARIN. NATURE, LOND. 200,
       800-802.

3056   KO, W.-H. & HORA, F.K. (1971) - A SELECTIVE MEDIUM FOR THE QUANTITATIVE
       DETERMINATION OF RHIZOCTONIA SOLANI IN SOIL. PHYTOPATHOLOGY 61, 707-710.

3057   KO, W.-H. & LOCKWOOD, J.L. (1968) - ACCUMULATION AND CONCENTRATION OF
       CHLORINATED HYDROCARBON PESTICIDES BY MICRO-ORGANISMS IN SOIL. CAN.J.
       MICROBIOL. 14, 1075-1078.

3058 KO, W.-H. & LOCKWOOD, J.L. (1970) - MECHANISMS OF LYSIS OF FUNGAL MYCELIA IN SOIL. PHYTOPATHOLOGY 60, 148-154.

3059 KOBAYASHI, H. & SUZUKI, H. (1973) - STUDIES ON THE DECOMPOSITION OF RAF-FINOSE BY ALPHA-GALACTOSIDASE OF MOLD. 2. FORMATION OF MOLD PELLET AND ITS ENZYME ACTIVITY. REP.FERMENT.RES.INST.CHIBA 43, 1-8.

3060 KOBAYASHI, N. & AKAI, S. (1974) - STUDIES ON THE ENCYSTMENT OF ZOOSPORES OF PYTHIUM APHANIDERMATUM. TRANS.MYCOL.SOC.JAPAN 15, 358-369.

3061 KOBAYASHI, N., IITAKA, Y., SANKAWA, U., OGIHARA, Y. & SHIBATA, S. (1968) - THE CRYSTAL AND MOLECULAR STRUCTURE OF A BROMINATION PRODUCT OF (+)TE-TRAHYDRORUGULOSIN. TETRAHEDRON LETTERS, 1968 (58), 6135-6138.

3062 KOBAYASI, Y., HIRATSUKA, N., KORF, R.P., TUBAKI, K., AOSHIMA, K., SONEDA, M. & SUGIYAMA, J. (1967) - MYCOLOGICAL STUDIES OF THE ALASKAN ARCTIC. A.REP.INST.FERMENT., OSAKA 3, 1-138.

3063 KOBAYASI, Y., MATSUSHIMA, T., TAKADA, M. & HAGIWARA, H. (1977) - REPORTS OF THE JAPANESE MYCOLOGICAL EXPEDITION TO MTS. RUWENZORI, CENTRAL AF-RICA. TRANS.MYCOL.SOC.JAPAN 18, 64-94.

3064 KOBAYASI, Y., TUBAKI, K. & SONEDA, M. (1968) - ENUMERATION OF THE HIGHER FUNGI, MOULDS AND YEASTS OF SPITSBERGEN. BULL.NATN.SCI.MUS.TOKYO 11, 33-76.

3065 KOCH, L.W. (1931) - SPURBLIGHT OF RASPBERRIES IN ONTARIO CAUSED BY DIDY-MELLA APPLANATA. PHYTOPATHOLOGY 21, 247-287.

3066 KOCHGAWAY, S.P. & DARADHIYAR, D. (1973) - SURFACE MYCOFLORA OF SWEET PO-TATOES IN SANTHAL PARGANAS. PROC.INDIAN SCI.CONGR.ASSOC. 60, 349 (ABS.).

3067 KOCOR, M., NESPIAK, A. & SIEWINSKI, A. (1961) - MYROTHECIUM RORIDUM META-BOLITES. 1. MYROTHECIN. BULL.ACAD.POL.SCI., SER.SCI.CHIM. 9, 207-211.

3068 KODAIRA, Y. (1961) - TOXIC SUBSTANCES TO INSECTS, PRODUCED BY ASPERGILLUS OCHRACEUS AND OOSPORA DESTRUCTOR. AGRIC.BIOL.CHEM., TOKYO 25, 261-262.

3069 KOEHLER, B. (1938) - FUNGUS GROWTH IN SHELLED CORN AS AFFECTED BY MOISTURE. J.AGRIC.RES. 56, 291-307.

3070 KOEHLER, B. (1957) - PERICARP INJURIES IN SEED CORN. BULL.ILL.AGRIC.EXP. STN 617, 72 PP.

3071 KOEHLER, B. (1959) - CORN EAR ROTS IN ILLINOIS. BULL.ILL.AGRIC.EXP.STN 639, 87 PP.

3072 KOEHLER, B. (1960) - CORNSTALK ROTS IN ILLINOIS. BULL.ILL.AGRIC.EXP.STN 658, 90 PP.

3073 KOEHLER, B. & WOODWORTH, C.M. (1938) - CORN SEEDLING VIRESCENCE CAUSED BY ASPERGILLUS FLAVUS AND ASPERGILLUS TAMARII. PHYTOPATHOLOGY 28, 811-823.

3074 KOENIG, E. (1961) - UNTERSUCHUNGEN UEBER DEN CHEMOTROPISMUS EINIGER PILZE GEGENUEBER SCHWER LOESLICHEN PHOSPHATEN. ARCH.MIKROBIOL. 40, 395-402.

3075 KOHAMA, T., FUJIMOTO, M., KUNINAKO, A. & YOSHINO, H. (1974) - STRUCTURE OF MALONOGALACTAN, AN ACID POLYSACCHARIDE OF PENICILLIUM CITRINUM. AGRIC. BIOL.CHEM., TOKYO 38, 127-134.

3076 KOHLMEYER, J. (1956) - UEBER DEN CELLULOSEABBAU DURCH EINIGE PHYTOPATHO-GENE PILZE. PHYTOPATH.Z. 27, 147-182.

3077 KOHLMEYER, J. (1971) - ANNOTATED CHECK-LIST OF NEW ENGLAND MARINE FUNGI.
      TRANS.BR.MYCOL.SOC. 57, 473-492.

3078 KOHLMEYER, J. & KOHLMEYER, E. (1968) - ICONES FUNGORUM MARIS. J.CRAMER,
      LEHRE.

3079 KOIDSUMI, K. (1957) - ANTIFUNGAL ACTION OF CUTICULAR LIPIDS. J.INSECT PHY-
      SIOL. 1, 40-51.

3080 KOIKE, H. (1965) - INFLUENCE OF CERTAIN NITROGENOUS SUBSTANCES ON THE
      LONGEVITY AND MORPHOLOGY OF PYTHIUM CULTURES IN VITRO. PHYTOPATHOLOGY
      55, 1064 (ABS.).

3081 KOK, L.T. & NORRIS, D.M. (1972) - SYMBIONTIC INTERRELATIONSHIP BETWEEN
      MICROBES AND AMBROSIA BEETLES. 6. AMINO ACID COMPOSITION OF ECTOSYM-
      BIOTIC FUNGI OF XYLEBORUS FERRUGINEUS. ANN.ENT.SOC.AM. 65, 598-602.

3082 KOK, L.T. & NORRIS, D.M. (1973) - COMPARATIVE STEROL COMPOSITIONS OF ADULT
      FEMALE XYLEBORUS FERRUGINEUS AND ITS MUTUALISTIC FUNGAL ECTOSYMBIONTS.
      COMP.BIOCHEM.PHYSIOL. 44, 499-505.

3083 KOMADA, H. (1972) - METHOD FOR THE SELECTIVE ISOLATION OF FUSARIUM OXY-
      SPORUM FROM NATURAL SOIL. BULL.TOKAI-KINKI NATN.AGRIC.EXP.STN 23, 144-
      178.

3084 KOMADA, H. (1975) - DEVELOPMENT OF A SELECTIVE MEDIUM FOR QUANTITATIVE
      ISOLATION OF FUSARIUM OXYSPORUM FROM NATURAL SOIL. REV.PL.PROT.RES. 8,
      114-125.

3085 KOMATSU, M. (1969) - NOTES ON THE HYPHOMYCETOUS FUNGI ISOLATED FROM SAW-
      DUST-RICEBRAN MEDIA OF PHOLIOTA NAMEKO. REP.TOTTORI MYCOL.INST. 7, 78-
      89.

3086 KOMATSU, M. (1976) - STUDIES ON HYPOCREA, TRICHODERMA AND ALLIED FUNGI
      ANTAGONISTIC TO SHIITAKE, LENTINUS EDODES. REP.TOTTORI MYCOL.INST. 13,
      1-113.

3087 KOMATSU, M. & HASHIOKA, Y. (1964) - TRICHODERMA VIRIDE, AS AN ANTAGONIST
      OF THE WOOD-INHABITING HYMENOMYCETES. 5. LETHAL EFFECT OF THE DIFFERENT
      TRICHODERMA FORMS ON LENTINUS EDODES INSIDE LOG-WOOD. REP.TOTTORI MY-
      COL.INST., JAPAN 4, 11-18.

3088 KOMMEDAHL, T. & SIGGEIRSSON, E.I. (1973) - PREVALENCE OF FUSARIUM SPECIES
      IN ROOTS AND SOIL OF GRASSLAND IN ICELAND. BULL.RES.INST.NERI AS,
      HVERAGERDI, ICELAND 14, 1-27.

3089 KOMMEDAHL, T., WINDELS, C.E. & LANG, D.S. (1975) - COMPARISON OF FUSARIUM
      POPULATIONS IN GRASSLANDS OF MINNESOTA AND ICELAND. MYCOLOGIA 67, 38-44.

3090 KONDAKOVA, E.I. (1976) - (FUNGI DEVELOPING IN THE CYSTS OF NEMATODES GEN.
      HETERODERA SCHMIDT). MIKOL.FITOPAT. 10, 172-175.

3091 KONNO, N., AMEMURA, A., KOKUMAI, K. & TERUI, G. (1963) - COMPONENTS OF THE
      CELLULASE SYSTEM FROM PENICILLIUM VARIABILE. J.FERMENT.TECHNOL., OSAKA
      41, 385-390.

3092 KOOIMAN, P. (1957) - SOME PROPERTIES OF CELLULASE OF MYROTHECIUM VERRUCA-
      RIA AND SOME OTHER FUNGI. 2. ENZYMOLOGIA 18, 371-384.

3093 KOOIMAN, P., ROELOFSEN, P.A. & SWEERIS, S. (1953) - SOME PROPERTIES OF
      CELLULASE FROM MYROTHECIUM VERRUCARIA. ENZYMOLOGIA 16, 237-246.

3094   KORF, R.P. & DUMONT, K.P. (1972) - WHETZELINIA, A NEW GENERIC NAME FOR
       SCLEROTINIA SCLEROTIORUM AND S. TUBEROSA. MYCOLOGIA 64, 248-251.

3095   KORNIENKO, V.Y. (1970) - (MYCOFLORA OF WINTER WHEAT ROOT ROT UNDER CONDI-
       TIONS OF IRRIGATION). UKR.BOT.ZH. 27 (6), 783-785.

3096   KOROBEINIKOVA, A.V. (1960) - (THE EFFECT OF NUTRITION, TEMPERATURE, HUMI-
       DITY, AND PH ON THE DEVELOPMENT OF SOME SPECIES OF THE GENUS FUSARIUM).
       TRUDY INST.BIOL.URAL.FIL., SVERDLOVSK, 1960, 71-81.

3097   KOROLEVA, V.P. (1967) - (TOXIC FUNGI DAMAGING GRAIN DURING GERMINATION).
       MIKOL.FITOPAT. 1, 82-84.

3098   KORPINEN, E.-L., KURKINEN, M., NUMMI, M. & ENARI, T.M. (1974) - STUDIES OF
       STACHYBOTRYS ALTERNANS. 3. CHROMATOGRAPHIE SEPARATION AND TISSUE CUL-
       TURE TOXICITY TEST OF STACHYBOTRYS TOXINS. ACTA PATH.MICROBIOL.SCAND.,
       SECT.B, 82, 7-11.

3099   KORPINEN, E.-L. & UOTI, J. (1974) - STUDIES ON STACHYBOTRYS ALTERNANS. 2.
       OCCURRENCE, MORPHOLOGY AND TOXIGENICITY. ACTA PATH.MICROBIOL.SCAND.,
       SECT.B, 82, 1-6.

3100   KOSARIC, N., YU, K., ZAJIC, J.E. & ROZANIS, J. (1973) - DEXTRANASE PRODUC-
       TION FROM PENICILLIUM FUNICULOSUM. BIOTECHNOL.BIOENG. 15, 729-741.

3101   KOSASIH, B.D. & WILLETTS, H.J. (1975) - ONTOGENETIC AND HISTOCHEMICAL STUD-
       IES OF THE APOTHECIUM OF SCLEROTINIA SCLEROTIORUM. ANN.BOT. 39, 185-191.

3102   KOSASIH, B.D. & WILLETTS, H.J. (1975) - TYPES OF ABNORMAL APOTHECIA PRO-
       DUCED BY SCLEROTINIA SCLEROTIORUM. MYCOLOGIA 67, 89-97.

3103   KOSHI, G., VICTOR, N. & CHACKO, J. (1972) - CAUSAL AGENTS IN MYCETOMA OF
       THE FOOT IN SOUTHERN INDIA. SABOURAUDIA 10, 14-18.

3104   KOSIR, M. (1975) - ERNAEHRUNG UND ENTWICKLUNG VON PYGMEPHORUS MESEMBRINAE
       UND PYGMEPHORUS QUADRATUS (PYGMEPHORIDAE, TARSONEMINI, ACARI) UND BEMER-
       KUNGEN UEBER DREI WEITERE ARTEN. PEDOBIOLOGIA 15, 313-329.

3105   KOSKE, R.E. & DUNCAN, I.W. (1974) - TEMPERATURE EFFECTS ON GROWTH, SPORU-
       LATION, AND GERMINATION OF SOME 'AQUATIC' HYPHOMYCETES. CAN.J.BOT. 52,
       1387-1391.

3106   KOSUGE, T. & DUTRA, F.C. (1963) - FIXATION OF C14 O2 BY GERMINATING CONID-
       IA OF BOTRYTIS CINEREA. PHYTOPATHOLOGY 53, 880.

3107   KOTSONIS, F.N., ELLISON, R.A. & SMALLEY, E.B. (1975) - ISOLATION OF ACETYL
       T-2 TOXIN FROM FUSARIUM POAE. APPL.MICROBIOL. 30, 493-495.

3108   KOUYEAS, H. (1964) - NOTES ON SPECIES OF PYTHIUM. ANNLS INST.PHYTOPATH. BE-
       NAKI, N.S. 6, 117-128.

3109   KOUYEAS, V. (1964) - AN APPROACH TO THE STUDY OF MOISTURE RELATIONS OF SOIL
       FUNGI. PL.SOIL 20, 351-363.

3110   KOUYEAS, V. & BALIS, C. (1968) - INFLUENCE OF MOISTURE ON THE RESTORATION
       OF MYCOSTASIS IN AIR DRIED SOILS. ANNLS INST.PHYTOPATH.BENAKI 3, 123-
       144.

3111   KOUYEAS, V. & KOUYEAS, H. (1963) - NOTES ON SPECIES OF PYTHIUM. ANNLS INST.
       PHYTOPATH.BENAKI, N.S. 5, 207-237.

3112   KOVAL, E.Z., ZAICHENKO, A.M. & HORBYK, L.T. (1969) - (EFFECT OF STORAGE
       UNDER LABORATORY CONDITIONS ON THE ABILITY OF SOME STRAINS OF MICRO-
       SCOPIC FUNGI TO OXIDIZE HYDROCARBONS). MYKROBIOL.ZH. 31 (5), 532-534.

3113   KOVALEVA, S.E. (1971) - (MYCOFLORA DECOMPOSING PLANT RESIDUES OF SOME AGRI-
       CULTURAL CROPS). MIKOL.FITOPAT. 5, 329-335.

3114   KOVAL'TSKOVA, S.V., ZAKHAROV, I.A. & LEVITIN, M.M. (1970) - (RESISTANCE OF
       A YEAST-LIKE FUNGUS PULLULARIA PULLULANS (DE BARY) BERKH. TO THE LETHAL
       AND MUTAGENIC ACTION OF UV AND X-RAYS). TSITOLOGIYA 12, 233-237.

3115   KOWALSKI, D.T. (1966) - THE MORPHOLOGY AND CYTOLOGY OF PREUSSIA FUNICULA-
       TA. AM.J.BOT. 53, 1036-1041.

3116   KRAFT, J.M. & BURKE, D.W. (1971) - PYTHIUM ULTIMUM AS A ROOT PATHOGEN OF
       BEANS AND PEAS IN WASHINGTON. PL.DIS.REPTR 55, 1056-1060.

3117   KRAFT, J.M. & ERWIN, D.C. (1965) - EFFECT OF NITROGEN SOURCES ON GROWTH OF
       PYTHIUM APHANIDERMATUM AND PYTHIUM ULTIMUM IN SYNTHETIC MEDIA. PHYTOPA-
       THOLOGY 55, 1065 (ABS.).

3118   KRAFT, J.M. & ERWIN, D.C. (1967) - EFFECTS OF NITROGEN SOURCES ON GROWTH
       OF PYTHIUM APHANIDERMATUM AND PYTHIUM ULTIMUM. PHYTOPATHOLOGY 57, 374-
       376.

3119   KRAFT, M.M. (1951) - MUCORINEES DE LA TOURBIERE DES TENASSES-BLONAY. BULL.
       SOC.VAUD.SCI.NAT. 65, 19-32.

3120   KRANZ, J. (1962) - VERGLEICHENDE UNTERSUCHUNGEN AN PHOMA-ISOLIERUNGEN VON
       DER KARTOFFEL. SYDOWIA 16, 1-40.

3121   KRAPIVINA, I.G. (1962) - (CHANGES PRODUCED BY MOULD FUNGI IN WOOD). VEST.
       MOSK.UNIV., SER.BIOL. 17 (5), 47-51.

3122   KRASIL'NIKOV, N.A., KHODZHIBALVA, S.M. & MIRCHINK, T.G. (1966) - (FORMA-
       TION OF TOXINS BY THE FUNGUS VERTICILLIUM DAHLIAE, THE CAUSATIVE ORGAN-
       ISM OF COTTON WILT). AGROKHIMIYA, 1965 (10), 128-134.

3123   KRAUSE, F.P. & LANGE, W. (1965) - VIGOROUS MOLD GROWTH IN SOILS AFTER AD-
       DITION OF WATER-INSOLUBLE FATTY SUBSTANCES. APPL.MICROBIOL. 13, 160-166.

3124   KREGER, D.R. (1954) - OBSERVATIONS ON CELL WALLS OF YEASTS AND SOME OTHER
       FUNGI BY X-RAY DIFFRACTION AND SOLUBILITY TESTS. BIOCHIM.BIOPHYS.ACTA
       13, 1-9.

3125   KREGER-VAN RIJ, N.J.W. & VEENHUIS, M. (1971) - SEPTAL PORES IN TRICHOSPO-
       RON CUTANEUM. SABOURAUDIA 9, 36-38.

3126   KREGER-VAN RIJ, N.J.W. & VEENHUIS, M. (1972) - SOME FEATURES OF VEGETATIVE
       AND SEXUAL REPRODUCTION IN ENDOMYCES SPECIES. CAN.J.BOT. 50, 1691-1695.

3127   KREHL-NIEFFER, R.M. (1950/51) - VERBREITUNG UND PHYSIOLOGIE MIKROSKOPI-
       SCHER BODENPILZE. ARCH.MIKROBIOL. 15, 389-402.

3128   KREJZOVA, R. (1972) - EXPERIMENTAL INFECTIONS OF SEVERAL SPECIES OF APHIDS
       BY SPECIMENS OF THE GENUS ENTOMOPHTHORA. VEST.CS.SPOL.ZOOL. 36, 17-22.

3129   KREJZOVA, R. (1975) - MORPHOLOGY AND TAXONOMY OF THE SPECIES CONIDIOBOLUS
       CORONATUS. CESKA MYKOL. 29, 174-178.

3130   KREMPL-LAMPRECHT, L. (1961) - THE COLONIZATION OF THE AUTOLYSIS PRODUCTS
       OF PURE DRY ROT FUNGUS BY SUCCESSION FUNGI OF THE GENUS SCOPULARIOPSIS.
       ARCH.MIKROBIOL. 38, 384-407.

3131   KREUTZER, W.A. (1972) - FUSARIUM SPP. AS COLONISTS AND POTENTIAL PATHOGENS
       IN ROOT ZONES OF GRASSLAND PLANTS. PHYTOPATHOLOGY 62, 1066-1070.

3132   KRITZMAN, G., OKON, Y., CHET, I. & HENIS, Y. (1976) - METABOLISM OF L-
       THREONINE AND ITS RELATIONSHIP TO SCLEROTIUM FORMATION IN SCLEROTIUM
       ROLFSII. J.GEN.MICROBIOL. 95, 78-86.

3133   KROEBER, H. & STAHL, M. (1974) - WURZELFAEULE AN GAERTNERISCH WICHTIGEN
       KAKTEEN DURCH PYTHIUM IRREGULARE BUISMAN. PHYTOPATH.Z. 81, 38-48.

3134   KROGH, P. & HASSELAGER, E. (1968) - STUDIES ON FUNGAL NEPHROTOXICITY.
       ARSSKR.K.VET.-LANDBOHOEJSK. 198/2, 14.

3135   KRUEGER, W. (1975) - UEBER DIE BILDUNG VON SKLEROTIEN DES RAPSKREBSERRE-
       GERS (SCLEROTINIA SCLEROTIORUM) IM BODEN. MITT.BIOL.BUNDANST.LD-U.FORSTW.
       163, 32-40.

3136   KRUG, J.C. (1971) - SOME NEW RECORDS OF ASCOMYCETES FROM SCOTLAND. TRANS.
       BOT.SOC.EDINB. 41, 197-199.

3137   KRUPKA, L.R. & RACLE, F.A. (1967) - DEGRADATION OF SALICYLATE BY ASPERGIL-
       LUS NIGER. NATURE, LOND. 216, 486-487.

3138   KRZEMIENIEWSKA, H. & BADURA, L. (1954) - (SOME OBSERVATIONS ON THE MYCO-
       FLORA OF BEECH WOODS). ACTA SOC.BOT.POL. 23, 545-587.

3139   KUBECZKA, K.-H. (1968) - VERGLEICHENDE UNTERSUCHUNGEN ZUR BIOGENESE
       FLUECHTIGER PRODUKTE DES SEKUNDAERSTOFFWECHSELS. 2. UNTERSUCHUNGEN AN
       SCHIMMELPILZEN. ARCH.MIKROBIOL. 60, 139-159.

3140   KUBIAK, M., BALAZY, S. & DYMALSKI, E. (1969) - INVESTIGATION INTO MICRO-
       ORGANISMS OF PINE CHIPS STORED IN CONICAL PILES. DREVARSKY VYSKUM 1, 11-
       23.

3141   KUBIKOVA, J. (1963) - THE SURFACE MYCOFLORA OF ASH ROOTS. TRANS.BR.MYCOL.
       SOC. 46, 107-114.

3142   KUBIKOVA, J. (1965) - MYCOFLORA SYNUSIAS ON THE ROOTS OF WOODY PLANTS.
       ROZPR.CSL.AKAD.VED MPV 75, 8.

3143   KUBLANOVSKAYA, G.M. & DZHALILOVA, V.M. (1958) - (METHOD OF BIOLOGICAL CON-
       TROL OF FUSARIUM WILT IN SUGAR MELON). SAD OGOROD, MOSKVA 96, 41-42.

3144   KUBLITSKAYA, M.A. & RYABTSEVA, N.A. (1968) - (THE ASCOUS STAGE OF THE FUN-
       GUS BOTRYTIS CINEREA PERS. EX FR. ON GRAPEVINE). MIKOL.FITOPAT. 2, 41-
       42.

3145   KUBLITSKAYA, M.A. & RYABTSEVA, N.A. (1972) - (EFFECT OF TEMPERATURE ON
       FORMATION OF SCLEROTIA IN BOTRYTIS CINEREA). MIKOL.FITOPAT. 6, 446-448.

3146   KUBOTA, T., TOKOROYAMA, T., KAMIKAWA, T. & SATOMURA, Y. (1966) - STRUC-
       TURES OF SCLERIN AND SCLEROLIDE, METABOLITES OF SCLEROTINIA LIBERTIA-
       ANA. TETRAHEDRON LETTERS, 1966, 5205-5210.

3147   KUCERA, M. (1971) - TOXINS OF THE ENTOMOPHAGOUS FUNGUS BEAUVERIA BASSIANA.
       2. EFFECT OF NITROGEN SOURCES ON FORMATION OF THE TOXIC PROTEASE IN SUB-
       MERGED CULTURE. J.INVERTEBR.PATH. 17, 211-215.

3148   KUCERA, M. & SAMSINAKOVA, A. (1968) - TOXINS OF THE ENTOMOPHAGOUS FUNGUS
       BEAUVERIA BASSIANA. J.INVERTEBR.PATH. 12, 316-320.

3149 KUEHN, H.H. (1958) - A PRELIMINARY SURVEY OF THE GYMNOASCACEAE. 1. MYCOLO-
      GIA 50, 417-439.

3150 KUEHN, H.H. (1956) - OBSERVATIONS ON GYMNOASCACEAE. 3. DEVELOPMENTAL MOR-
      PHOLOGY OF GYMNOASCUS REESSII, A NEW SPECIES OF GYMNOASCUS AND EIDAMEL-
      LA REFLEXA. MYCOLOGIA 48, 805-820.

3151 KUEHN, H.H. (1960) - OBSERVATIONS ON GYMNOASCACEAE. 8. A NEW SPECIES OF
      ARTHRODERMA. MYCOPATH.MYCOL.APPL. 13, 189-197.

3152 KUEHN, H.H. (1961) - NUTRITIONAL REQUIREMENTS OF ARTHRODERMA TUBERCULATUM.
      MYCOPATH.MYCOL.APPL. 14, 123-128.

3153 KUEHN, H.H. & GUNDERSON, M.F. (1963) - PSYCHROPHILIC AND MESOPHILIC FUNGI
      IN FROZEN FOOD PRODUCTS. APPL.MICROBIOL. 11, 352-356.

3154 KUEHN, H.H. & ORR, G.F. (1962) - A NUTRITIONAL STUDY OF EIGHT STRAINS OF
      GYMNOASCUS REESSII. MYCOPATH.MYCOL.APPL. 16, 351-361.

3155 KUEHN, H.H. & ORR, G.F. (1964) - ARACHNIOTUS RUBER. TRANS.BR.MYCOL.SOC.
      47, 552-558.

3156 KUERBIS, W.P. (1937) - MYKOLOGISCHE UNTERSUCHUNGEN UEBER DEN WURZELBEREICH
      DER ESCHE. FLORA, JENA 131, 129-175.

3157 KUESTER, E. & LOCCI, R. (1964) - STUDIES ON PEAT AND PEAT MICROORGANISMS.
      2. OCCURRENCE OF THERMOPHILIC FUNGI IN PEAT. ARCH.MIKROBIOL. 48, 319-
      324.

3158 KUHLMAN, E.G. (1964) - SURVIVAL AND PATHOGENICITY OF PHYTOPHTHORA CINNA-
      MOMI IN SEVERAL WESTERN OREGON SOILS. FOREST SCI. 10, 151-158.

3159 KUHLMAN, E.G. (1969) - MUCORALES ISOLATED FROM PINE ROOT BARK AND WOOD.
      CAN.J.BOT. 47, 1719-1723.

3160 KUHLMAN, E.G. (1972) - VARIATION IN ZYGOSPORE FORMATION AMONG SPECIES OF
      MORTIERELLA. MYCOLOGIA 64, 325-341.

3161 KUHLMAN, E.G. (1975) - ZYGOSPORE FORMATION IN MORTIERELLA ALPINA AND MOR-
      TIERELLA SPINOSA. MYCOLOGIA 67, 678-681.

3162 KUHLMAN, E.G. & HENDRIX, F.F. (1965) - DIRECT RECOVERY OF PHYTOPHTHORA
      CINNAMOMI FROM FIELD SOIL. PHYTOPATHOLOGY 55, 500 (ABS.).

3163 KUHN, R. & TIEDEMANN, H. (1954) - ENZYMATISCHE SPALTUNG VON N-ACETYL-BETA
      -D-GLUCOSAMINIDEN. CHEM.BER. 87, 1141-1147.

3164 KULIK, M. (1968) - A COMPILATION OF DESCRIPTIONS OF NEW PENICILLIUM SPE-
      CIES. AGRIC.HANDB.U.S.DEP.AGRIC. 351, 80 PP.

3165 KULIK, M.M. & BROOKS, A.G. (1970) - ELECTROPHORETIC STUDIES OF SOLUBLE PRO-
      TEINS FROM ASPERGILLUS SPP. MYCOLOGIA 62, 365-376.

3166 KULIK, M.M. & HANLIN, R.T. (1968) - OSMOPHILIC STRAINS OF SOME ASPERGILLUS
      SPECIES. MYCOLOGIA 60, 961-964.

3167 KULIK, M.M. & HOLADAY, C.E. (1966) - AFLATOXIN - A METABOLIC PRODUCT OF
      SEVERAL FUNGI. MYCOPATH.MYCOL.APPL. 30, 137-140.

3168 KULIK, M.M. & VINCENT, P.G. (1973) - PYROLYSIS-GAS-LIQUID CHROMATOGRAPHY
      OF FUNGI. OBSERVATIONS ON VARIABILITY AMONG NINE PENICILLIUM SPECIES OF
      THE SECTION ASYMMETRICA, SUBSECTION FASCICULATA. MYCOPATH.MYCOL.APPL.
      51, 1-18.

3169 KULKARNI, N.B. & AHMED, L. (1967) - STUDIES ON THE BASIDIAL FORMATION BY
      SCLEROTIUM ROLFSII SACC. - BASIDIAL FORMATION ON ARTIFICIALLY INOCULATED
      HOST (POTATO). SCI.CULT. 33, 73-75.

3170 KUMAGAI, T. & ODA, Y. (1969) - AN ACTION SPECTRUM FOR PHOTOINDUCED SPORU-
      LATION IN THE FUNGUS TRICHODERMA VIRIDE. PL.CELL PHYSIOL. 10, 387-392.

3171 KUMAR, S.R. (1973) - MARINE LIGNICOLOUS FUNGI FROM INDIA. KAVAKA 1, 73-85.

3172 KUMARI, D.L., GOVINDASWAMY, C.V. & VIDHYASEKARAN, P. (1973) - ISOLATION OF
      SEED-BORNE FUNGI FROM CASTOR SEEDS. MADRAS AGRIC.J. 60, 77-80.

3173 KUNDU, A.K. & DAS, S. (1970) - PRODUCTION OF AMYLASE IN LIQUID CULTURE BY
      A STRAIN OF ASPERGILLUS ORYZAE. APPL.MICROBIOL. 19, 598-603.

3174 KUNERT, J. (1965) - (NEUE KERATINOPHILE PILZE IN DER CSSR). CESKA MYKOL.
      19, 226-229.

3175 KUNERT, J. (1970) - ZU DEN BEDINGUNGEN DES KERATINABBAUES DURCH MICROSPO-
      RUM GYPSEUM IM FLUESSIGEN MEDIUM. 2. ZUSAMMENSETZUNG UND PH DES MEDIUMS.
      DERM.MSCHR. 156, 1035-1041.

3176 KUNERT, J. (1972) - KERATIN DECOMPOSITION BY DERMATOPHYTES. EVIDENCE OF
      THE SULPHITOLYSIS OF THE PROTEIN. EXPERIENTIA 28, 1025-1026.

3177 KUNERT, J. (1973) - KERATIN DECOMPOSITION BY DERMATOPHYTES. 1. SULFITE
      PRODUCTION AS A POSSIBLE WAY OF SUBSTRATE DENATURATION. Z.ALLG.MIKRO-
      BIOL. 13, 489-498.

3178 KUNERT, J. (1975) - FORMATION OF SULPHATE, SULPHITE AND S-SULPHOCYSTEINE
      BY THE FUNGUS MICROSPORUM GYPSEUM DURING GROWTH ON CYSTINE. FOLIA MI-
      CROBIOL. 20, 142-151.

3179 KUNERT, J. (1976) - KERATIN DECOMPOSITION BY DERMATOPHYTES. 2. PRESENCE OF
      S-SULFOCYSTEINE AND CYSTEIC ACID IN SOLUBLE DECOMPOSITION PRODUCTS. Z.
      ALLG.MIKROBIOL. 16, 97-105.

3180 KUNINAKA, A., KIBI, M., YOSHINO, H. & SAKAGUCHI, K. (1961) - STUDIES ON
      5-PHOSPHODIESTERASES IN MICROORGANISMS. 2. PROPERTIES AND APPLICATION
      OF PENICILLIUM CITRINUM 5-PHOSPHODIESTERASE. AGRIC.BIOL.CHEM., TOKYO
      25, 693-701.

3181 KURATA, H., SAKABE, F., UDAGAWA, SH., ICHINOE, M., SUZUKI, M. & TAKAHASHI,
      N. (1968) - A MYCOLOGICAL EXAMINATION FOR THE PRESENCE OF MYCOTOXIN-
      PRODUCERS ON THE 1954-1967'S STORED RICE GRAINS. BULL.NATN.INST.HYG.SCI.,
      TOKYO 86, 183-188.

3182 KURES, L., SCHWERTZ, A. & PERCEBOIS, G. (1975) - SENSIBILITE DE QUELQUES
      SOUCHES DE SCOPULARIOPSIS BREVICAULIS A DIVERS ANTIFONGIQUES ET ANTI-
      SEPTIQUES. BULL.SOC.FR.MYCOL.MED. 4, 167-168.

3183 KUROSAWA, Y. (1955) - ON THE DISCOLORATION PHENOMENA OF THE CONIDIA OF AS-
      PERGILLUS ORYZAE AND RELATED SPECIES. NAGAOA 5, 41-60.

3184 KURSANOV, L. & SHKLYAR, T.N. (1938) - (A COMPARATIVE STUDY OF THE FUNGUS
      FLORA OF SOILS FROM MOSCOW AND BATUM). BULL.SOC.NAT.MOSCOU, SECT.BIOL.,
      N.S. 47, 223-232.

3185 KUSAKARI, S. & UEYAMA, A. (1975) - DEGRADATION OF THE MYCELIA OF PYTHIUM
      APHANIDERMATUM BY LYTIC ACTINOMYCETES IN SOIL. TRANS.MYCOL.SOC.JAPAN
      16, 55-62.

3186 KUZNETSOV, V.D., NOVIKOVA, N.D. & BARTOSHEVICH, J.E. (1968) - (CULTIVATION,
      NATURAL VARIATION AND PRESERVATION OF THE FUSIDIN PRODUCER, THE FUNGUS
      FUSIDIUM COCCINEUM). MIKOL.FITOPAT. 2, 58-65.

3187 KVASHNINA, E.S. (1976) - (PHYSIOLOGICAL AND ECOLOGICAL CHARACTERISTICS OF
      FUSARIUM SPECIES SECT. SPOROTRICHIELLA). MIKOL.FITOPAT. 10, 275-281.

3188 KWON-CHUNG, K.J. (1969) - COCCIDIOIDES IMMITIS - CYTOLOGICAL STUDY ON THE
      FORMATION OF THE ARTHROSPORES. CAN.J.GENET.CYTOL. 11, 43-53.

3189 KWON-CHUNG, K.J. (1969) - STUDIES ON THE SEXUALITY OF NANNIZZIA. 2. MOR-
      PHOGENESIS OF GAMETANGIA IN N. INCURVATA. MYCOLOGIA 61, 593-605.

3190 KWON-CHUNG, K.J. (1972) - SEXUAL STAGE OF HISTOPLASMA CAPSULATUM. SCIENCE,
      N.Y. 175, 326.

3191 KWON-CHUNG, K.J. (1972) - EMMONSIELLA CAPSULATA. PERFECT STATE OF HISTO-
      PLASMA CAPSULATUM. SCIENCE, N.Y. 177, 368-369.

3192 KWON-CHUNG, K.J. (1973) - STUDIES ON EMMONSIELLA CAPSULATA. 1. HETEROTHAL-
      LISM AND DEVELOPMENT OF THE ASCOCARP. MYCOLOGIA 65, 109-121.

3193 KWON-CHUNG, K.J. (1975) - PERFECT STATE (EMMONSIELLA CAPSULATA) OF THE
      FUNGUS CAUSING LARGE-FORM AFRICAN HISTOPLASMOSIS. MYCOLOGIA 67, 980-990.

3194 KWON-CHUNG, K.J,, SCHWARTZ, J.S. & RYBAK, B.J. (1975) - A PULMONARY FUNGUS
      BALL PRODUCED BY CLADOSPORIUM CLADOSPORIOIDES. AM.J.CLIN.PATH. 64, 564-
      568.

3195 KWON-CHUNG, K.J., WEEKS, R.J. & LARSH, H.W. (1974) - STUDIES ON EMMONSIEL-
      LA CAPSULATA (HISTOPLASMA CAPSULATUM). AM.J.EPIDEMIOL. 99, 44-49.

3196 KWONG-CHUNG, K.J., YOUNG, R.C. & ORLANDO, M. (1975) - PULMONARY MUCORMY-
      COSIS CAUSED BY CUNNINGHAMELLA ELEGANS IN A PATIENT WITH CHRONIC MYELO-
      GENOUS LEUKEMIA. AM.J.CLIN.PATH. 64, 544-548.

3197 LAANE, M.M. (1967) - THE NUCLEAR DIVISION IN PENICILLIUM EXPANSUM. CAN.J.
      GENET.CYTOL. 9, 342-351.

3198 LAANE, M.M. (1969) - FURTHER CYTOLOGICAL STUDIES IN THE GENUS PENICILLIUM
      LINK. HEREDITAS 62, 153-184.

3199 LAANE, M.M. (1974) - NUCLEAR BEHAVIOUR DURING VEGETATIVE STAGE AND ZYGO-
      SPORE FORMATION IN ABSIDIA GLAUCA. NORW.J.BOT. 21, 125-135.

3200 LAATSCH, W., HOOPS, L. & BIENECK, O. (1952) - UEBER HUMINSAEUREN DES PIL-
      ZES SPICARIA ELEGANS. Z.PFLERNAEHR.DUENG.BODENK. 58, 258-268.

3201 LABORDA, F., GARCIA ACHA, I., URUBURU, F. & VILLANUEVA, J.R. (1974) -
      STRUCTURE OF CONIDIAL WALLS OF FUSARIUM CULMORUM. TRANS.BR.MYCOL.SOC.
      62, 557-566.

3202 LABOUREUR, P. & LANGLOIS, C. (1968) - URATE OXYDASE D'ASPERGILLUS FLAVUS.
      1. OBTENTION, PURIFICATION, PROPRIETES. BULL.SOC.CHIM.BIOL. 50, 811-825.

3203 LACEY, J. (1971) - THE MICROBIOLOGY OF MOIST BARLEY STORAGE IN UNSEALED
      SILOS. ANN.APPL.BIOL. 69, 187-212.

3204   LACEY, J. (1975) - AIRBORNE SPORES IN PASTURES. TRANS.BR.MYCOL.SOC. 64,
        265-281.

3205   LACEY, M.E. & GREGORY, P.H. (1962) - OCCURRENCE' IN BRITAIN OF THE FUNGUS
        CAUSING FACIAL ECZEMA IN SHEEP. NATURE, LOND. 193, 85.

3206   LACICOWA, B. (1966) - CLADOSPORIUM MACROCARPUM FROM CEREAL SEEDS. ACTA
        MYCOL., WARSZAWA 2, 169-173.

3207   LACICOWA, B. (1968) - (STUDIES ON THE MICROFLORA OF THE SEED OF SPRING
        BARLEY CULTIVATED IN THE LUBLIN VOIVODESHIP). ANNLS UNIV.MARIAE CURIE
        SKLODOWSKA, SECT.E, 22, 207-219.

3208   LAEMMLEN, F.F. & HALL, D.H. (1973) - INTERDEPENDENCE OF A MITE, SITEROPTES
        RENIFORMES, AND A FUNGUS, NIGROSPORA ORYZAE, IN THE NIGROSPORA LINT ROT
        OF COTTON. PHYTOPATHOLOGY 63, 308-315.

3209   LAFLAMME, G. & LORTIE, M. (1973) - MICRO-ORGANISMES DANS LES TISSUS COLO-
        RES ET CARIES DU PEUPLIER FAUX-TREMBLE. CAN.J.FOR.RES. 3, 155-160.

3210   LAGERBERG, T., LUNDBERG, G. & MELIN, E. (1928) - BIOLOGICAL AND PRACTICAL
        RESEARCHES INTO BLUEING IN PINE AND SPRUCE. SV.SKOGSV.FOEREN.TIDSKR.
        25, 145-272.

3211   LAHOZ, R., BALLESTEROS, A.M. & GONZALES, I.J. (1971) - CHEMICAL AND PHY-
        SIOLOGICAL CHANGES IN FILAMENTOUS FUNGI DURING AUTOLYSIS. 10. CHANGES
        IN THE CONCENTRATION OF POLYOL IN AUTOLYSING CULTURES OF SEVERAL FUNGI.
        MYCOPATH.MYCOL.APPL. 43, 223-228.

3212   LAI, M., SEMENIUK, G. & HESSELTINE, C.W. (1970) - CONDITIONS FOR PRODUC-
        TION OF OCHRATOXIN-A BY ASPERGILLUS SPECIES IN A SYNTHETIC MEDIUM. APPL.
        MICROBIOL. 19, 542-544.

3213   LAI, P. & BRUEHL, G.W. (1968) - ANTAGONISM AMONG CEPHALOSPORIUM GRAMINEUM,
        TRICHODERMA SPP. AND FUSARIUM CULMORUM. PHYTOPATHOLOGY 58, 562-566.

3214   LAINE, R.A. GRIFFIN, P.F.S., SWEELEY, C.C. & BRENNAN, P.J. (1972) - MONO-
        GLUCOSYLOXYOCTADECENOIC ACID - A GLYCOLIPID FROM ASPERGILLUS NIGER. BIO-
        CHEMISTRY 11, 2267-2270.

3215   LAKSHMANAN, M. & VANTERPOOL, T.C. (1967) - PHOMIC ACID, A TOXIC METABOLITE
        FROM PHOMA MEDICAGINIS. CAN.J.BOT. 45, 847-853.

3216   LAKSHMI-KUMARI, M., VIJAYALAKSHMI, K. & SUBBA RAO, N.S. (1972) - INTERAC-
        TION BETWEEN AZOTOBACTER SPECIES AND FUNGI. 1. IN VITRO STUDIES WITH
        FUSARIUM MONILIFORME SHELD. PHYTOPATH.Z. 75, 27-30.

3217   LAL, A. (1939) - INTERACTION OF SOIL MICRO-ORGANISMS WITH OPHIOBOLUS GRA-
        MINIS, THE FUNGUS CAUSING THE TAKE-ALL DISEASE OF WHEAT. ANN.APPL.BIOL.
        26, 247-261.

3218   LAL, B. & TANDON, R.N. (1969) - UTILIZATION AND SYNTHESIS OF OLIGOSACCHARI-
        DES BY SOME PATHOGENIC ISOLATES OF COLLETOTRICHUM GLOEOSPORIOIDES PENZ.
        PROC.NATN.INST.SCI., INDIA, SECT.B, 35, 460-470.

3219   LAL, S.P. & YADAV, A.S. (1964) - A PRELIMINARY LIST OF MICROFUNGI ASSOCI-
        ATED WITH THE DECAYING STEMS OF TRITICUM VULGARE AND ANDROPOGON SORGHUM.
        INDIAN PHYTOPATH. 17, 208-211.

3220   LALITHAKUMARI, D., GOVINDASWAMY, C.V. & VIDHYASEKARAN, P. (1972) - ISOLA-
        TION OF SEED-BORNE FUNGI FROM STORED GROUNDNUT SEEDS AND THEIR ROLE ON
        SEED SPOILAGE. MADRAS AGRIC.J. 59, 1-6.

3221   LAMB, B.C. (1967) - THE DIFFERENTIAL MATURATION OF ASCI AND ITS RELEVANCE
       TO RECOMBINATION STUDIES OF NEUROSPORA, SORDARIA AND SIMILAR ASCOMYCE-
       TES. GENET.RES. 10, 1-12.

3222   LANCASTER, M.C., JENKINS, F.P. & PHILIP, J.M. (1961) - TOXICITY ASSOCIATED
       WITH CERTAIN SAMPLES OF GROUNDNUTS. NATURE, LOND. 192, 1095-1096.

3223   LANDAU, J.W., SHECHTER, Y. & NEWCOMER, V.D. (1968) - BIOCHEMICAL TAXONOMY
       OF THE DERMATOPHYTES. 2. NUMERICAL ANALYSIS OF ELECTROPHORETIC PROTEIN
       PATTERNS. J.INVEST.DERM. 51, 170-176.

3224   LANDOLT, E. (1952) - UEBER WELKESTOFFBILDUNG BEI FUSARIUM CULMORUM. PHYTO-
       PATH.Z. 19, 126-128.

3225   LANG, W. & RAU, W. (1972) - UNTERSUCHUNGEN UEBER DIE LICHTABHAENGIGE CARO-
       TINOIDSYNTHESE. 9. ZUM INDUKTIONSMECHANISMUS DER CAROTINOIDBILDENDEN
       ENZYME BEI FUSARIUM AQUAEDUCTUUM. PLANTA 106, 345-354.

3226   LANZILOTTA, R.P. & PRAMER, D. (1970) - HERBICIDE TRANSFORMATION. 1. STUD-
       IES WITH WHOLE CELLS OF FUSARIUM SOLANI. APPL.MICROBIOL. 19, 301-306.

3227   LANZILOTTA, R.P. & PRAMER, D. (1970) - HERBICIDE TRANSFORMATION. 2. STUD-
       IES WITH AN ACYLAMIDASE OF FUSARIUM SOLANI. APPL.MICROBIOL. 19, 307-313.

3228   LARIONOV, YU.S. & CHULKINA, V.A. (1975) - (DEPTH OF SOWING OF SPRING WHEAT
       IN RELATION TO THE DEVELOPMENT OF COMMON ROOT-ROT). SEL'.KHOZ.BIOL. 10,
       784-786.

3229   LARSEN, A.D. & SYPHERD, P.S. (1974) - CYCLIC ADENOSINE 3,5-MONOPHOSPHATE
       AND MORPHOGENESIS IN MUCOR RACEMOSUS. J.BACT. 117, 432-438.

3230   LASHEN, E.S. & STARKEY, R.L. (1970) - DECOMPOSITION OF THIOUREAS BY PENI-
       CILLIUM SPECIES AND SOIL AND SEWAGE-SLUDGE MICROFLORA. J.GEN.MICROBIOL.
       64, 139-150.

3231   LASKIN, A.I. & LECHEVALIER, H.A.(EDS.) (1973) - HANDBOOK OF MICROBIOLOGY,
       VOL. 3. MICROBIAL PRODUCTS. CRC PRESS, CLEVELAND/OHIO.

3232   LASKIN, A.I. & LECHEVALIER, H.A.(EDS.) (1973) - HANDBOOK OF MICROBIOLOGY.
       VOL. 2. MICROBIAL COMPOSITION. CRC PRESS, CLEVELAND/OHIO.

3233   LATCH, G.C.M. (1965) - METARRHIZIUM ANISOPLIAE STRAINS IN NEW ZEALAND AND
       THEIR POSSIBLE USE FOR CONTROLLING PASTURE-INHABITING INSECTS. N.Z.JL
       AGRIC.RES. 8, 384-386.

3234   LATTER, P.M., CRAGG, J.B. & HEAL, O.W. (1967) - COMPARATIVE STUDIES ON THE
       MICROBIOLOGY OF FOUR MOORLAND SOILS IN THE NORTHERN PENNINES. J.ECOL.
       55, 445-464.

3235   LATTER, P.M. & HEAL, O.W. (1971) - A PRELIMINARY STUDY OF THE GROWTH OF
       FUNGI AND BACTERIA FROM TEMPERATE AND ANTARCTIC SOILS IN RELATION TO
       TEMPERATURE. SOIL BIOL.BIOCHEM. 3, 365-379.

3236   LAUBER, H.P. (1971) - VARIABILITAET UND KERNVERHAELTNISSE BEI BOTRYTIS CI-
       NEREA. SCHWEIZ.LANDW.FORSCH. 10, 1-64.

3237   LAUNDON, G.F. (1973) - RECORDS AND TAXONOMIC NOTES ON PLANT DISEASE FUNGI
       IN NEW ZEALAND. TRANS.BR.MYCOL.SOC. 60, 317-337.

3238   LAVANDIER, C. & TOUZE-SOULET, J.-M. (1969) - ETUDE PHYSIOLOGIQUE COMPAREE
       DE DEUX ORGANISMES MYCOPHAGES, L'UN PARASITE, HYPOMYCES CHLORINUS TUL.,
       L'AUTRE SAPROPHYTE, HYPOMYCES CHRYSOSPERMUS TUL.; UTILISATION, IN VI-
       TRO, DU GLUCOSE ET D'UNE SOURCE D'AZOTE (NANO 3), AU COURS DE LEUR
       DEVELOPPEMENT. C.R.HEBD.SEANC.ACAD.SCI., PARIS, SER.D, 269, 1635-1638.

3239 LAVERDE, S., MONCADA, L.H., RESTREPO, A. & VERA, C.L. (1973) — MYCOTIC KERATITIS. 5 CASES CAUSED BY UNUSUAL FUNGI. SABOURAUDIA 11, 119-123.

3240 LE, ZUI-LIN, KAZANSKAYA, T.B. & MEKHTEREVA, M.N. (1975) — (PRODUCTION AND DISTRIBUTION OF FREE AMINO ACIDS IN THE MYCELIUM OF CUNNINGHAMELLA ELEGANS GROWING ON MEDIA WITH GLUCOSE AND DODECANE). MIKROBIOLOGIYA 44, 67-71.

3241 LEACH, C.M. (1961) — THE EFFECT OF NEAR-ULTRAVIOLET IRRADIATION ON THE SPORULATION OF CERTAIN FUNGI. PHYTOPATHOLOGY 51, 65-66 (ABS.).

3242 LEACH, C.M. (1962) — SPORULATION OF DIVERSE SPECIES OF FUNGI UNDER NEAR-ULTRAVIOLET RADIATION. CAN.J.BOT. 40, 151-161.

3243 LEACH, C.M. (1963) — THE QUALITATIVE AND QUANTITATIVE RELATIONSHIP OF MONOCHROMATIC RADIATION TO SEXUAL AND ASEXUAL REPRODUCTION OF PLEOSPORA HERBARUM. MYCOLOGIA 55, 151-163.

3244 LEACH, C.M. (1965) — ULTRAVIOLET-ABSORBING SUBSTANCES ASSOCIATED WITH LIGHT-INDUCED SPORULATION IN FUNGI. CAN.J.BOT. 43, 185-200.

3245 LEACH, C.M. (1968) — AN ACTION SPECTRUM FOR LIGHT INHIBITION OF THE 'TERMINAL PHASE' OF PHOTOSPOROGENESIS IN THE FUNGUS STEMPHYLIUM BOTRYOSUM. MYCOLOGIA 60, 532-546.

3246 LEACH, C.M. (1971) — REGULATION OF PERITHECIUM DEVELOPMENT AND MATURATION IN PLEOSPORA HERBARUM BY LIGHT AND TEMPERATURE. TRANS.BR.MYCOL.SOC. 57, 295-315.

3247 LEACH, C.M. (1975) — INFLUENCE OF RELATIVE HUMIDITY AND RED-INFRARED RADIATION ON VIOLENT SPORE RELEASE BY DRECHSLERA TURCICA AND OTHER FUNGI. PHYTOPATHOLOGY 65, 1303-1312.

3248 LEACH, L.D. & DAVEY, A.E. (1935) — TOXICITY OF LOW CONCENTRATIONS OF AMMONIA TO MYCELIUM AND SCLEROTIA OF SCLEROTIUM ROLFSII. PHYTOPATHOLOGY 25, 957-959.

3249 LEACH, L.D. & DAVEY, A.E. (1938) — DETERMINING THE SCLEROTIAL POPULATION OF SCLEROTIUM ROLFSII BY SOIL ANALYSIS AND PREDICTING LOSSES OF SUGAR BEETS ON THE BASIS OF THESE ANALYSES. J.AGRIC.RES. 56, 619-631.

3250 LEAICH, L.L. & PAPA, K.E. (1974) — AFLATOXINS IN MUTANTS OF ASPERGILLUS FLAVUS. MYCOPATH.MYCOL.APPL. 52, 223-230.

3251 LEAL, J.A., FRIEND, J. & HOLLIDAY, P. (1964) — A FACTOR CONTROLLING SEXUAL REPRODUCTION IN PHYTOPHTHORA. NATURE, LOND. 203, 545-546.

3252 LEAL, J.A., GALLEGLY, M.E. & LILLY, V.G. (1971) — THE VALUE OF 21 AMINO ACIDS AS NITROGEN SOURCES FOR PHYTOPHTHORA CACTORUM AND P. HEVEAE. CAN. J.MICROBIOL. 17, 1319-1325.

3253 LEAL, J.A. & GOMEZ-MIRANDA, B. (1967) — EFFECT OF AMINO ACIDS ON THE SEXUAL REPRODUCTION OF SPECIES OF PHYTOPHTHORA AND PYTHIUM. TRANS.BR.MYCOL. SOC. 50, 77-84.

3254 LEAL, J.A. & RUPEREZ, P. (1978) — EXTRACELLULAR POLYSACCHARIDE PRODUCTION BY ASPERGILLUS NIDULANS. TRANS.BR.MYCOL.SOC. 70, 115-120.

3255   LEAL, J.A. & VILLANUEVA, J.R. (1962) - (DIGESTION OF UREDOSPORES BY VERTI-
       CILLIUM HEMILEIAE). MICROBIOLOGIA ESP. 15, 269-275.

3256   LEARY, J.V. (1972) - HETEROKARYOSIS OF FUSARIUM OXYSPORUM SCHLECHT. CAUS-
       ING CROWN ROT OF TOMATO. PHYTOPATHOLOGY 62, 771 (ABS.).

3257   LEATHERDALE, D. (1970) - THE ARTHROPOD HOSTS OF ENTOMOGENOUS FUNGI IN BRI-
       TAIN. ENTOMOPHAGA 15, 419-435.

3258   LE BARS, J. & ESCOULA, L. (1973) - MYCOFLORE DES FOURRAGE SECS. 1. INVEN-
       TAIRE ET FREQUENCE DES ESPECES. ANNLS RECH.VET. 4, 273-282.

3259   LECLERG, E.L. & SMITH, F.B. (1928) - FUNGI IN SOME COLORADO SOILS. SOIL
       SCI. 25, 433-441.

3260   LEDINGHAM, G.A. & ADAMS, G.A. (1942) - BIOLOGICAL DECOMPOSITION OF CHEMI-
       CAL LIGNIN. 2. STUDIES ON THE DECOMPOSITION OF CALCIUM LIGNOSULPHONATE
       BY WOOD-DESTROYING AND SOIL FUNGI. CAN.J.RES., SECT.C, 20, 13-27.

3261   LEDINGHAM, R.J. (1961) - CROP ROTATIONS AND COMMON ROOT ROT IN WHEAT. CAN.
       J.PL.SCI. 41, 479-486.

3262   LEDINGHAM, R.J. (1970) - SURVIVAL OF COCHLIOBOLUS SATIVUS CONIDIA IN PURE
       CULTURE AND IN NATURAL SOIL AT DIFFERENT RELATIVE HUMIDITIES. CAN.J.BOT.
       48, 1893-1896.

3263   LEDINGHAM, R.J. & CHINN, S.H.T. (1955) - A FLOTATION METHOD FOR OBTAINING
       SPORES OF HELMINTHOSPORIUM SATIVUM FROM SOIL. CAN.J.BOT. 33, 298-303.

3264   LEE, B.K.H. & BAKER, G.E. (1972) - AN ECOLOGICAL STUDY OF THE SOIL MICRO-
       FUNGI IN A HAWAIIAN MANGROVE SWAMP. PACIF.SCI. 26, 1-10.

3265   LEE, B.K.H. & BAKER, G.E. (1972) - ENVIRONMENT AND THE DISTRIBUTION OF MI-
       CROFUNGI IN A HAWAIIAN MANGROVE SWAMP. PACIF.SCI. 26, 11-19.

3266   LEE, J.D., DART, R.K. & STRETTON, R.J. (1977) - COMPUTERIZED CLASSIFICA-
       TION OF ASPERGILLUS. TRANS.BR.MYCOL.SOC. 69, 137-141.

3267   LEE, J.-Y. (1972) - SOIL MYCOFLORA IN LARCH FOREST IN SUGADAIRA. BULL.SU-
       GADAIRA BIOL.LAB. 5, 35-71.

3268   LEE, L.S., BENNETT, J.W., GOLDBLATT, L.A. & LUNDIN, R.E. (1970) - NORSO-
       LORINIC ACID FROM A MUTANT STRAIN OF ASPERGILLUS PARASITICUS. J.AM.OIL
       CHEM.SOC. 48, 93-94.

3269   LEE, Y.C. & SCOCCA, J.R. (1972) - A COMMON STRUCTURAL UNIT IN ASPARAGINE-
       OLIGOSACCHARIDES OF SEVERAL GLYCOPROTEINS FROM DIFFERENT SOURCES. J.BIOL.
       CHEM. 247, 5753-5758.

3270   LEE, Y.C. & WACEK, V. (1970) - GALACTOSIDASES FROM ASPERGILLUS NIGER. ARCHS
       BIOCHEM.BIOPHYS. 138, 254-271.

3271   LEELAVATHY, K.M. (1969) - RHIZOSPHERE FUNGAL FLORA OF THREE GRASSES GROWN
       IN STEAM STERILIZED AND UNSTERILIZED SOIL. INDIAN.J.MICROBIOL. 9, 1-10.

3272   LEELAVATHY, K.M. (1969) - EFFECT OF SOME COMMON RHIZOSPHERE FUNGI ON ROOT
       GROWTH OF SEEDLINGS. PL.SOIL 30, 335-338.

3273   LEELAVATHY, K.M. (1969) - EFFECT OF RHIZOSPHERE FUNGI ON SEED GERMINATION.
       PL.SOIL 30, 473-476.

3274   LEFEBVRE, C.L., JOHNSON, A.G. & SHERWIN, H.S. (1949) - AN UNDESCRIBED SPE-
       CIES OF PERICONIA. MYCOLOGIA 41, 416-419.

3275   LE GAL, M. (1960) - LES DISCOMYCETES DE L'HERBIER CROUAN. ANNLS SCI.NAT.
       BOT., SER.12, 1, 441-467.

3276   LEGGE, B.J. (1952) - USE OF GLASS FIBRE MATERIAL IN SOIL MYCOLOGY. NATURE,
       LOND. 169, 759-760.

3277   LE GRAND-PERNOT, F. (1972) - INFLUENCE DE LA LUMIERE SUR LA PRODUCTION PERI-
       THECIALE CHEZ GLOMERELLA CINGULATA. FRUITS 27, 339-348.

3278   LEHMAN, H. (1965) - UNTERSUCHUNGEN ZUR TYPHULA-FAEULE DES GETREIDES. 2.
       ZUR PATHOLOGIE DURCH TYPHULA INCARNATA ERKRANKTER WIRTSPFLANZEN. PHYTO-
       PATH.Z. 54, 209-239.

3279   LEHMANN, H. (1964) - SYSTEMATISCHE STELLUNG UND NOMENKLATUR DES ERREGERS
       DER TYPHULA-FAEULE (TYPHULA INCARNATA LASCH EX FR.). MBER.DT.AKAD.WISS.,
       BERLIN 6, 926-930.

3280   LEHMANN, H. (1965) - UNTERSUCHUNGEN UEBER DIE TYPHULA-FAEULE DES GETREI-
       DES. 1. ZUR PHYSIOLOGIE VON TYPHULA INCARNATA LASCH EX FR. PHYTOPATH.Z.
       53, 255-288.

3281   LEIGHTON, T.J. & STOCK, J.J. (1970) - BIOCHEMICAL CHANGES DURING FUNGAL
       SPORULATION AND SPORE GERMINATION. J.BACT. 101, 931-940.

3282   LEISTNER, L. & MINTZLAFF, H.-J. (1973) - MYKOTOXINE IN FLEISCHWAREN. Z.LE-
       BENSMITTELUNTERS.FORSCH. 151, 241-244.

3283   LEMAIRE, J.M. PONCHET, J. & JOUAN, B. (1966) - CONTRIBUTION A L'ETUDE DES
       FACTEURS PHYSIQUES ET MICROBIOLOGIQUES QUI INDUISENT LA FRUCTIFICATION
       D'OPHIOBOLUS GRAMINIS = LINOCARPON CARICETI. ANNLS EPIPHYT. 17, 61-73.

3284   LEMENSE, E.H., CORMAN, J. & VAN LANEN, J.M. (1947) - PRODUCTION OF MOLD
       AMYLASES IN SUBMERGED CULTURE. J.BACT. 54, 149-159.

3285   LENDNER, A. (1897) - DES INFLUENCES COMBINEES DE LA LUMIERE ET DU SUBSTRA-
       TUM SUR LE DEVELOPPEMENT DES CHAMPIGNONS. ANNLS SCI.NAT., BOT., SER.8,
       3, 1-64.

3286   LENHART, K. (1973) - HETEROKARYOSIS IN MICROSPORUM GYPSEUM. MYCOPATH.MY-
       COL.APPL. 49, 109-120.

3287   LENHART, K. & HEJTMANKOVA, N. (1972) - PARASEXUAL CYCLE IN DERMATOPHYTES.
       EXPERIENTIA 28, 711.

3288   LENHART, K., HEJTMANKOVA, N. & KOMENDA, S. (1973) - HETEROKARYOTIC CONSTI-
       TUTION AND NUCLEAR DISTRIBUTION IN MACROCONIDIA OF MICROSPORUM GYPSEUM.
       ACTA UNIV.PALACKI OLOMUC, FAC.MED. 65, 99-117.

3289   LENHART, K., HEJTMANKOVA, N., LENHARTOVA, E. & KOMENDA, S. (1974) - DI-
       PLOIDS IN MICROSPORUM GYPSEUM. MYCOPATH.MYCOL.APPL. 54, 253-266.

3290   LEONARD, K.J. & SUGGS, E.G. (1974) - SETOSPHAERIA PROLATA, THE ASCIGEROUS
       STATE OF EXSEROHILUM PROLATUM. MYCOLOGIA 66, 281-297.

3291   LEONIAN, L.H. & LILLY, V.G. (1938) - STUDIES ON THE NUTRITION OF FUNGI. 1.
       THIAMIN, ITS CONSTITUENTS, AND THE SOURCE OF NITROGEN. PHYTOPATHOLOGY
       28, 531-548.

3292   LEOPOLD, H., SAMSINAKOVA, A. & MISIKOVA, S. (1973) - DER ENZYMATISCHE CHA-
       RAKTER DER DURCH DEN ENTOMOPHAGEN PILZ BEAUVERIA BASSIANA SEZERNIERTEN
       TOXISCHEN STOFFE UND DIE STIMULATION IHRER BILDUNG. ZENTBL.BAKT.PARA-
       SITKDE, ABT.2, 128, 31-41.

3293   LEOPOLD, J. & SAMSINAKOVA, A. (1970) – QUANTITATIVE ESTIMATION OF CHITIN-
       ASE AND SEVERAL OTHER ENZYMES IN THE FUNGUS BEAUVERIA BASSIANA. J.INVER-
       TEBR.PATH. 15, 34-42.

3294   LEPIDI, A.A. (1966) – ANCORA SULLA PRESENZA DI ALCUNI LIEVITI E DI ALCUNI
       FUNGHI A MICELIO NELLA PASTA-LEGNO E SULLA LORO ATTIVITA CELLULOSOLITI-
       CA. AGRICOLTURA ITAL., PISA 66, 45-60.

3295   LEPIDI, A.A., NUTI, M.P., BERTOLDI, M.DE & SANTULLI, M. (1972) – CLASSIFI-
       CATION OF THE GENUS HUMICOLA TRAAEN. 2. THE DNA BASE COMPOSITION OF SOME
       STRAINS WITHIN THE GENUS. MYCOPATH.MYCOL.APPL. 47, 153-159.

3296   LESLIE, R. & PARBERY, D.G. (1972) – GROWTH OF VERTICILLIUM LECANII ON ME-
       DIUM CONTAINING SODIUM FLUORIDE. TRANS.BR.MYCOL.SOC. 58, 351-352.

3297   LETHAM, D.B. (1975) – STIMULATION BY LIGHT OF APOTHECIAL INITIAL DEVELOP-
       MENT OF SCLEROTINIA SCLEROTIORUM. TRANS.BR.MYCOL.SOC. 65, 333-335.

3298   LE TOURNEAU, D. (1957) – THE PRODUCTION OF OLIGOSACCHARIDES BY VERTICIL-
       LIUM ALBO-ATRUM. PHYTOPATHOLOGY 47, 527 (ABS.).

3299   LE TOURNEAU, D. (1966) – TREHALOSE AND ACYCLIC POLYOLS IN SCLEROTIA OF
       SCLEROTINIA SCLEROTIORUM. MYCOLOGIA 58, 934-942.

3300   LE TOURNEAU, D. (1974) – ALCOHOL-SOLUBLE SUGARS AND SUGAR ALCOHOLS PRODUCED
       FROM GLUCOSE BY VERTICILLIUM SPP. TRANS.BR.MYCOL.SOC. 62, 619-622.

3301   LE TOURNEAU, D., KEITH, R.S. & HAMMOND, D.L. (1976) – DEGRADATION OF SOME
       PHENOLS IN LIQUID MEDIA BY VERTICILLIUM DAHLIAE. TRANS.BR.MYCOL.SOC.
       66, 327-328.

3302   LEVI, C.P., TRENK, H.L. & MOHR, H.K. (1974) – STUDY OF THE OCCURRENCE OF
       OCHRATOXIN-A IN GREEN COFFEE BEANS. J.ASS.OFF.AGRIC.CHEM. 57, 866-870.

3303   LEVI, M.P. & COWLING, E.B. (1969) – ROLE OF NITROGEN IN WOOD DETERIORATION.
       7. PHYSIOLOGICAL ADAPTATION OF WOOD-DESTROYING AND OTHER OTHER FUNGI TO
       SUBSTRATES DEFICIENT IN NITROGEN. PHYTOPATHOLOGY 59, 460-468.

3304   LEVISOHN, I. (1957) – ANTAGONISTIC EFFECTS OF ALTERNARIA TENUIS ON CERTAIN
       ROOT-FUNGI OF FOREST TREES. NATURE, LOND. 179, 1143-1144.

3305   LEVITIN, M.M., KIRSANOVA, R.V. & YURCHENKO, L.V. (1971) – (GENETICS AND
       SELECTION OF BEAUVERIA BASSIANA (BALS.) VUILL., AN ENTOMOPATHOGENIC
       FUNGUS. 1. LETHAL AND MUTAGENIC EFFECTS OF ULTRAVIOLET AND X-RAYS). GE-
       NETIKA 7, 104-111.

3306   LEVITIN, M.M. & ZHURAVLEV, A.P. (1971) – (IDENTITY SPECIES OF KABATIELLA
       LINI (LAFF.) KARAK. AND PULLULARIA PULLULANS (DE BY.) BERKH.). MIKOL.
       FITOPAT. 5, 115-120.

3307   LEVKINA, L.M. & PILIPOVICH, A.I. (1971) – (CELLULASE ACTIVITY IN SPECIES
       OF THE GENUS CLADOSPORIUM). TRUDY VSES.NAUCHNO-ISSLED.INST.ZASHCH.RAST.
       29 (2), 140-148.

3308   LEVKINA, L.M. & REBRIKOVA, N.L. (1976) – (PHYSIOLOGICAL CHARACTERISTICS OF
       CLADOSPORIUM RESINAE (LINDAU) DE VRIES). MIKOL.FITOPAT. 10, 374-379.

3309   LEWIS, D.L., PARIS, D.F. & BAUGHAM, G.L. (1975) – TRANSFORMATION OF MALA-
       THION BY A FUNGUS, ASPERGILLUS ORYZAE, ISOLATED FROM A FRESHWATER POND.
       BULL.ENVIRON.CONTAM.TOXICOL. 13, 596-601.

3310 LEWIS, H. & JOHNSON, G.T. (1967) – GROWTH AND OXYGEN-UPTAKE RESPONSES OF CUNNINGHAMELLA ECHINULATA ON EVEN-CHAIN FATTY ACIDS. MYCOLOGIA 59, 878-887.

3311 LEWIS, J.A. (1976) – PRODUCTION OF VOLATILES FROM DECOMPOSING PLANT TISSUES AND EFFECT OF THESE VOLATILES ON RHIZOCTONIA SOLANI IN CULTURE. CAN.J.MICROBIOL. 22, 1300-1306.

3312 LEWIS, J.A. & PAPAVIZAS, G.C. (1969) – SURVIVAL OF ROOT-INFECTING FUNGI IN SOIL. 13. DECOMPOSITION OF FLAVONOID AND OTHER PHENOLICS IN SOIL AND THEIR EFFECTS ON FUSARIUM ROOT ROT OF BEAN. CAN.J.MICROBIOL. 15, 527-533.

3313 LEWIS, J.A. & PAPAVIZAS, G.C. (1971) – EFFECT OF SULFUR-CONTAINING VOLATILE COMPOUNDS AND VAPORS FROM CABBAGE DECOMPOSITION ON APHANOMYCES EUTEICHES. PHYTOPATHOLOGY 61, 208-214.

3314 LEWIS, J.A. & PAPAVIZAS, G.C. (1974) – EFFECT OF VOLATILES FROM DECOMPOSING PLANT TISSUES ON PIGMENTATION, GROWTH, AND SURVIVAL OF RHIZOCTONIA SOLANI. SOIL SCI. 118, 156-163.

3315 LEWIS, J.A. & STARKEY, R.L. (1969) – DECOMPOSITION OF PLANT TANNINS BY SOME SOIL MICROORGANISMS. SOIL SCI. 107, 235-241.

3316 LEWIS, L.A. (1969) – CORRELATED MEIOTIC AND MITOTIC MAPS IN ASPERGILLUS AMSTELODAMI. GENET.RES. 14, 185-193.

3317 LEWIS, U.J., RICKES, E.L MCCLELLAND, L. & BRINK, N.G. (1959) – PURIFICATION AND CHARACTERIZATION OF THE ANTIVIRAL AGENT HELENINE. J.AM.CHEM.SOC. 81, 4115.

3318 LEYENDECKER, P.J., JR. (1950) – EFFECTS OF CERTAIN CULTURAL PRACTICES ON VERTICILLIUM WILT OF COTTON IN NEW MEXICO. BULL.NEW MEX.AGRIC.EXP.STN 356, 1-28.

3319 LEYRITZ, M. & KAPICA, L. (1975) – YEAST-LIKE GROWTH OF MUCOR ALTERNANS (VAN TIEGHEM) IN TISSUE-CULTURE MEDIUM 199. CAN.J.MICROBIOL. 21, 75-78.

3320 LHOAS, P. (1971) – TRANSMISSION OF DOUBLE STRANDED RNA VIRUSES TO A STRAIN OF PENICILLIUM STOLONIFERUM THROUGH HETEROKARYOSIS. NATURE, LOND. 230, 248-249.

3321 LI, K.-H. & CHANG SHU-CHENG (1973) – THE PURIFICATION AND PROPERTIES OF NADP-MANNITOL DEHYDROGENASE OF GEOTRICHUM CANDIDUM. ACTA MICROBIOL.SIN. 13, 38-43.

3322 LI, L.H., FLORA, R.M. & KING, K.W. (1965) – INDIVIDUAL ROLES OF CELLULASE COMPONENTS DERIVED FROM TRICHODERMA VIRIDE. ARCHS BIOCHEM.BIOPHYS. 111, 439-447.

3323 LIESE, W. & PECHMANN, H.VON (1959) – UNTERSUCHUNGEN UEBER DEN EINFLUSS VON MODERFAEULEPILZEN AUF DIE HOLZFESTIGKEIT. FORSTWISS.ZENTBL. 78, 271-279.

3324 LIHNELL, D. (1939) – UEBER DIE MYKORRHIZEN UND DIE WURZELPILZE VON JUNIPERUS COMMUNIS. SYMB.BOT.UPSAL. 3 (3), 1-141.

3325 LIHNELL, D. (1944) – GROENMYKOS FOERORSAKED AV METARRHIZIUM ANISOPLIAE. 2. FYSIOLOGISKA UNDERSOEKNINGAR OEVER GROENMYKOSENS SVAMP. MEDDEL.STAT. VAEXTSKYDDSANST.STOCKH. 43, 59-90.

3326 LILLARD, H.S., HANLIN, R.T. & LILLARD, D.A. (1970) - AFLATOXIGENIC ISOLA-
      TES OF ASPERGILLUS FLAVUS FROM PECANS. APPL.MICROBIOL. 19, 128-130.

3327 LILLY, V.G. & BARNETT, H.L. (1947) - THE INFLUENCE OF PH AND CERTAIN GROWTH
      FACTORS ON MYCELIAL GROWTH AND PERITHECIAL FORMATION BY SORDARIA FIMI-
      COLA. AM.J.BOT. 34, 131-138.

3328 LILLY, V.G. & BARNETT, H.L. (1956) - THE UTILIZATION OF D- AND L-ARABINOSE
      BY FUNGI. AM.J.BOT. 43, 709-714.

3329 LILLY, V.G. & BARNETT, H.L. (1961) - ACETATE AS A CARBON SOURCE FOR FUNGI.
      PROC.W.VA ACAD.SCI. 33, 5-10.

3330 LILY, K. (1965) - ECOLOGICAL STUDIES ON SOIL FUNGI. 1. RECOLONIZATION OF
      STEAM-STERILIZED SOIL BY DIFFERENT MICROORGANISMS. J.INDIAN BOT.SOC. 44,
      276-289.

3331 LIM, G. (1969) - SOME OBSERVATIONS ON SOIL AND ROOT-SURFACE MYCOFLORA. PL.
      SOIL 31, 143-148.

3332 LIM, G. (1972) - FUSARIUM POPULATIONS OF INTENSIVELY CULTIVATED SOILS. TROP.
      AGRIC. 49, 77-80.

3333 LIM, G. (1972) - FUSARIUM IN PADDY SOILS OF WEST MALAYSIA. PL.SOIL 36, 47-
      51.

3334 LIM, G. & CHEW, C.H. (1970) - FUSARIUM IN SINGAPORE SOILS. PL.SOIL 33, 673-
      677.

3335 LIN, C.-F. (1973) - ISOLATION AND CULTURAL CONDITIONS OF MONASCUS SP. FOR
      THE PRODUCTION OF PIGMENT IN A SUBMERGED CULTURE. J.FERMENT.TECHNOL.,
      OSAKA 51, 407-414.

3336 LIN, F.K. & GOTTLIEB, D. (1974) - CELLULAR BASIS OF GROWTH RATE DIFFEREN-
      CES IN ISOLATES OF RHIZOCTONIA SOLANI - METABOLIC PROCESSES AND GROWTH
      RATES. PHYTOPATHOLOGY 64, 1220-1228.

3337 LIN, H.-T., IIDA, M. & IIZUKA, H. (1971) - FORMATION OF ORGANIC ACIDS AND
      ERGOSTEROL FROM N-ALKANES BY FUNGI ISOLATED FROM OIL FIELDS IN JAPAN.
      J.FERMENT.TECHNOL., OSAKA 49, 771-777.

3338 LIN, L.Z., KAZANSKAYA, T.B. & BEKHTEREVA, M.N. (1975) - FORMATION AND DIS-
      TRIBUTION OF FREE AMINO ACIDS IN THE MYCELIUM OF CUNNINGHAMELLA ELEGANS
      DURING GROWTH ON MEDIA WITH GLUCOSE OR DODECANE. MICROBIOLOGY 44, 55-58.
      (ENGL.TRANSL.MIKROBIOLOGIYA).

3339 LIN, M.T. & HSIEH, D.P.H. (1973) - AVERUFIN IN THE BIOSYNTHESIS OF AFLA-
      TOXIN-B1. J.AM.CHEM.SOC. 95, 1668-1669.

3340 LIN, M.T., HSIEH, D.P.H., YAO, R.C. & DONKERSLOOT, J.A. (1973) - CONVER-
      SION OF AVERUFIN INTO AFLATOXINS BY ASPERGILLUS PARASITICUS. BIOCHEM-
      ISTRY 12, 5167-5171.

3341 LIN, M.T., MAHAJAN, J.R., DIANESE, J.C. & TAKATSU, A. (1976) - HIGH PRO-
      DUCTION OF KOJIC ACID CRYSTALS BY ASPERGILLUS PARASITICUS UNBF A12 IN
      LIQUID MEDIUM. APPL.ENVIRONM.MICROBIOL. 32, 298-299.

3342 LINCOLN, S.D. & ADCOCK, J.L. (1968) - DISSEMINATED GEOTRICHOSIS IN A DOG.
      PATHOL.VET. 5, 282-289.

3343 LINDEBERG, G. & MALMGREN, H. (1952) - ENZYMATIC BREAKDOWN OF POLYMETAPHOS-
      PHATE. 6. INFLUENCE OF NUTRITIONAL FACTORS ON THE POLYMETAPHOSPHATASE
      PRODUCTION OF ASPERGILLUS NIGER. ACTA CHEM.SCAND. 6, 27-37.

208 COMPENDIUM OF SOIL FUNGI

3344 LINDERMAN, R.G. (1972) - ISOLATION OF CYLINDROCLADIUM FROM SOIL OR INFEC-
TED AZALEA STEMS WITH AZALEA LEAF TRAPS. PHYTOPATHOLOGY 62, 736-739.

3345 LINDERMAN, R.G. (1973) - FORMATION OF MICROSCLEROTIA OF CYLINDROCLADIUM
SPP. IN INFECTED AZALEA LEAVES, FLOWERS, AND ROOTS. PHYTOPATHOLOGY 63,
187-191.

3346 LINDERMAN, R.G. & GILBERT, R.G. (1969) - STIMULATION OF SCLEROTIUM ROLFSII
IN SOIL BY VOLATILE COMPONENTS OF ALFALFA HAY. PHYTOPATHOLOGY 59, 1366-
1372.

3347 LINDERMAN, R.G. & GILBERT, R.G. (1973) - INFLUENCE OF VOLATILE COMPOUNDS
FROM ALFALFA HAY ON MICROBIAL ACTIVITY IN SOIL IN RELATION TO GROWTH OF
SCLEROTIUM ROLFSII. PHYTOPATHOLOGY 63, 359-362.

3348 LINDERMAN, R.G. & GILBERT, R.G. (1973) - BEHAVIOUR OF SCLEROTIA OF SCLERO-
TIUM ROLFSII PRODUCED IN SOIL OR IN CULTURE REGARDING GERMINATION, STIM-
ULATION BY VOLATILES, FUNGISTASIS, AND SODIUM HYPOCHLORITE TREATMENT.
PHYTOPATHOLOGY 63, 500-504.

3349 LINDERMAN, R.G. & TOUSSOUN, T.A. (1967) - BEHAVIOUR OF CHLAMYDOSPORES AND
ENDOCONIDIA OF THIELAVIOPSIS BASICOLA. PHYTOPATHOLOGY 57, 729-731.

3350 LINDERMAN, R.G. & TOUSSOUN, T.A. (1968) - PATHOGENESIS OF THIELAVIOPSIS
BASICOLA IN NONSTERILE SOIL. PHYTOPATHOLOGY 58, 1578-1583.

3351 LINDQVIST, K. (1961) - KERATINOMYCES AJELLOI AND MICROSPORUM COOKEI IN
NORWEGIAN SOIL. ACTA PATH.MICROBIOL.SCAND. 51, 381-388.

3352 LINDSEY, B.I. & PUGH, G.J.F. (1976) - SUCCESSION OF MICROFUNGI ON ATTACHED
LEAVES OF HIPPOPHAE RHAMNOIDES. TRANS.BR.MYCOL.SOC. 67, 61-67.

3353 LINDSEY, B.I. & PUGH, G.J.F. (1976) - DISTRIBUTION OF MICROFUNGI OVER THE
SURFACES OF ATTACHED LEAVES OF HIPPOPHAE RHAMNOIDES. TRANS.BR.MYCOL.
SOC. 67, 427-433.

3354 LINEBACK, D.R., RUSSELL, I.J. & RASMUSSEN, C. (1969) - THE FORMS OF THE
GLUCOAMYLASE OF ASPERGILLUS NIGER. ARCHS BIOCHEM.BIOPHYS. 134, 539-553.

3355 LINGAPPA, B.T. & LINGAPPA, Y. (1969) - ROLE OF AUTO-INHIBITORS ON MYCELIAL
GROWTH AND DIMORPHISM OF GLOMERELLA CINGULATA. J.GEN.MICROBIOL. 56, 35-
45.

3356 LINGAPPA, B.T., LINGAPPA, Y. & BELL, E. (1973) - A SELF-INHIBITOR OF PRO-
TEIN SYNTHESIS IN THE CONIDIA OF GLOMERELLA CINGULATA. ARCH.MIKROBIOL.
94, 97-107.

3357 LINGAPPA, Y., SUSSMAN, A.S. & BERNSTEIN, I.A. (1963) - EFFECT OF LIGHT AND
MEDIA UPON GROWTH AND MELANIN FORMATION IN AUREOBASIDIUM PULLULANS (DE
BARY) ARN. (=PULLULARIA PULLULANS). MYCOPATH.MYCOL.APPL. 20, 109-128.

3358 LING-YONG, M. (1930) - ETUDE BIOLOGIQUE DES PHENOMENES DE LA SEXUALITE
CHEZ LES MUCORINEES. REVUF GEN.BOT. 42, 722-742.

3359 LINNEMANN, G. (1941) - DIE MUCORINEEN-GATTUNG MORTIERELLA COEMANS. G.FI-
SCHER, JENA (PFLFORSCHG, H.23).

3360 LINNEMANN, G. (1958) - UNTERSUCHUNGEN ZUR VERBREITUNG UND SYSTEMATIK DER
MORTIERELLEN. ARCH.MIKROBIOL. 30, 256-267.

3361 LINSKENS, H.F. & HAAGE, P. (1963) - CUTINASE-NACHWEIS IN PHYTOPATHOGENEN
      PILZEN. PHYTOPATH.Z. 48, 306-311.

3362 LISINA-KULIK, E.S. (1967) - (DIE PILZFLORA EINIGER BOEDEN IN DER REGION
      VON PERM). VEST.MOSK.UNIV., 1967 (3), 71-79.

3363 LISINA-KULIK, E.S. (1968) - (A REVIEW OF THE MYCOFLORA OF THE SOILS UNDER
      MEADOW GRASS, MOSCOW DISTRICT, ZEYA-BUREYA LOWLAND, TRANSBAIKALIA AND
      CENTRAL ASIA). MIKOL.FITOPAT. 2, 7-11.

3364 LISINA-KULIK, E.S. (1968) - (SOIL MYCOFLORA IN SOME CARST CAVES OF THE
      CAUCASUS, KRASNODAR REGION). MIKOL.FITOPAT. 2, 458-461.

3365 LISINA-KULIK, E.S. (1969) - (MYCOFLORA OF SOILS AND ROCKS OF SOME CARST
      CAVES IN SOUTHERN PRIMOR'E). MIKOL.FITOPAT. 3, 538-542.

3366 LISINA-KULIK, E.S. (1969) - (MYCOFLORA OF TUNDRA AND MARSHY TAIGA SOILS IN
      THE NORTH OF THE U.S.S.R.). NAUCH.DOKL.VYSSH.SHK.BIOL.NAUKI 12, 144-149.

3367 LISINA-KULIK, E.S. & BARSUKOVA, L.D. (1967) - (THE MYCOFLORA OF THE SOILS,
      WATER OF UNDERGROUND LAKES AND OF DIFFERENT TYPES OF ICE OF THE KUNGUR
      ICE CAVE). MIKOL.FITOPAT. 1, 140-146.

3368 LISINA-KULIK, E.S & MAKSIMOVA, P.A. (1967) - (SOME DATA ON THE MYCOFLORA
      IN THE PLANT RHIZOSPHERE AT THE SHORE OF THE WHITE SEA). NAUCH.DOKL.
      VYSSH.SHK.BIOL.NAUKI, 1967 (5), 84-87.

3369 LISKER, N. & JOFFE, A.Z. (1970) - RELATIONSHIP BETWEEN FUNGI OF THE ASPER-
      GILLUS GLAUCUS GROUP AND A. NIGER IN GROUNDNUT KERNELS. ISRAEL J.BOT.
      19, 620-623.

3370 LISKER, N., KATAN, J., CHET, I. & HENIS, Y. (1975) - RELEASE OF CELL-BOUND
      POLYGALACTURONASE AND CELLULASE FROM MYCELIUM OF RHIZOCTONIA SOLANI.
      CAN.J.MICROBIOL. 21, 521-526.

3371 LISKER, N., KATAN, J. & HENIS, Y. (1975) - SCANNING ELECTRON MICROSCOPY OF
      THE SEPTAL PORE APPARATUS OF RHIZOCTONIA SOLANI. CAN.J.BOT. 53, 1801-
      1804.

3372 LISKER, N., KATAN, J. & HENIS, Y. (1975) - SEQUENTIAL PRODUCTION OF POLY-
      GALACTURONASE, CELLULASE, AND PECTIN LYASE BY RHIZOCTONIA SOLANI. CAN.
      J.MICROBIOL. 21, 1298-1304.

3373 LITTLEFIELD, L.J., WILCOXSON, R.D. & SUDIA, T.W. (1965) - TRANSLOCATION OF
      PHOSPHORUS-32 IN RHIZOCTONIA SOLANI. PHYTOPATHOLOGY 55, 536-542.

3374 LITTRELL, R.H. (1965) - A MYROTHECIUM ROT OF GLOXINIAS. PL.DIS.REPTR 49,
      78-80.

3375 LITVINOV, M.A. (1967) - (ON THE PROBLEM OF THE SPECIFICITY OF THE FLORA OF
      RHIZOSPHERIC AND RADICAL MICROSCOPIC SOIL FUNGI INHABITING THE ROOTS
      SPHERE OF PLANTS. 1.). MIKOL.FITOPAT. 1, 201-214.

3376 LITVINOV, M.A. (1968) - (FUNGI MICROSCOPICI RHIZOSPHAERAE PLANTARUM STEP-
      PARUM SICCARUM KAZAKHSTANIAE CENTRALIS). NOV.SIST.NIZSH.RAST., 1968,
      131-140.

3377 LIU, CH.-H. & YANG, B.-Y. (1973) - STUDIES ON CERTAIN SPECIES OF TAIWAN
      MUCORALES. TAIWANIA 18, 73-82.

3378 LIU, SH. & VAUGHAN, E.K. (1965) - CONTROL OF PYTHIUM INFECTION IN TABLE
      BEET SEEDLINGS BY ANTAGONISTIC MICROORGANISMS. PHYTOPATHOLOGY 55, 986-
      989.

3379 LIU, S.-Y. & BOLLAG, J.-M. (1971) - CARBARYL DECOMPOSITION TO 1-NAPHTHYL-
      CARBAMATE BY ASPERGILLUS TERREUS. PESTIC.BIOCHEM.PHYSIOL. 1, 366-372.

3380 LIU, S.-Y. & BOLLAG, J.-M. (1971) - METABOLISM OF CARBARYL BY A SOIL FUN-
      GUS. J.AGRIC.FD CHEM. 19, 487-490.

3381 LIU, W.-H., BEPPU, T. & ARIMA, K. (1972) - CULTURAL CONDITIONS AND SOME
      PROPERTIES OF THE LIPASE OF HUMICOLA LANUGINOSA S-38. AGRIC.BIOL.CHEM.,
      TOKYO 36, 1919-1924.

3382 LIU UN RIGO, NAKANO, M., VEIGA, L.A. & FEINGOLD, D.S. (1976) - L-RHAMNOSE
      DEHYDROGENASE OF PULLULARIA PULLULANS. BIOCHIM.BIOPHYS.ACTA 445, 286-
      293.

3383 LIZAK, Y.V. (1975) - (EFFECT OF DIFFERENT SOURCES OF NITROGEN NUTRITION ON
      CELLULOLYTIC ACTIVITY OF DARK FUNGI). MYKROBIOL.ZH. 37, 693-699.

3384 LLANOS, C. & KJOELLER, A. (1976) - CHANGES IN THE FLORA OF SOIL FUNGI FOL-
      LOWING OIL WASTE APPLICATIONS. OIKOS 27, 377-382.

3385 LLANOS, C.M. & LOCKWOOD, J.L. (1960) - FACTORS AFFECTING ZOOSPORE PRODUC-
      TION BY APHANOMYCES EUTEICHES. PHYTOPATHOLOGY 50, 826-830.

3386 LLOYD, A.B. (1965) - LYSIS OF FUNGAL MYCELIUM BY SOIL. DISS.ABSTR. 26, 610.

3387 LLOYD, A.B. & LOCKWOOD, J.L. (1963) - EFFECT OF SOIL TEMPERATURE, HOST VAR-
      IETY, AND FUNGUS STRAIN ON THIELAVIOPSIS ROOT ROT OF PEAS. PHYTOPATHOL-
      OGY 53, 329-331.

3388 LLOYD, G.I., ANDERSON, J.G., SMITH, J.E. & MORRIS, E.O. (1972) - CONIDIA-
      TION AND ESTERASE SYNTHESIS IN ASPERGILLUS NIGER. TRANS.BR.MYCOL.SOC.
      59, 63-70.

3389 LLOYD, H.L. (1972) - ALTERNARIA LEAF SPOT OF TOBACCO. 2. INDEPENDENT SEGRE-
      GATION OF MORPHOLOGICAL AND VIRULENCE TRAITS IN CONIDIAL POPULATIONS OF
      ALTERNARIA TENUIS NEES. MYCOPATH.MYCOL.APPL. 47, 317-322.

3390 LLOYD, K.O. & BITOON, M.A. (1971) - ISOLATION AND PURIFICATION OF A PEPTI-
      DORHAMNOMANNAN FROM THE YEAST FORM OF SPOROTHRIX SCHENCKII. STRUCTURAL
      AND IMMUNOCHEMICAL STUDIES. J.IMMUN. 107, 663-671.

3391 LOBANOK, A.G. & SKLJAR, B.CH. (1968) - (CELLULOLYTIC ACTIVITY OF FUNGI
      ISOLATED FROM PEAT). VESTSI AKAD.NAVUK BSSR, BIYAL.NAVUK 3, 108-110.

3392 LOCCI, R. (1969) - INVESTIGATIONS ON FUNGAL FEATURES BY SCANNING ELECTRON
      MICROSCOPY. 1. THE LIFE CYCLE OF ASPERGILLUS AMSTELODAMI. RIV.PATOL.VEG.,
      PADOVA, SER.4, 5, 223-232.

3393 LOCCI, R., MERLINI, L. & NASINI, G. (1967) - MITORUBRINIC ACID AND RELATED
      COMPOUNDS FROM A STRAIN OF PENICILLIUM FUNICULOSUM THOM. GIORN.MICRO-
      BIOL. 15, 93-102.

3394 LOCCI, R. & QUARONI, S. (1970) - INVESTIGATIONS ON FUNGAL FEATURES BY SCAN-
      NING ELECTRON MICROSCOPY. 2. MORPHOLOGICAL CHARACTERISTICS OF THE PER-
      FECT STAGE OF ASPERGILLUS SPECIES. RIV.PATOL.VEG., PADOVA, SER.4, 6,
      141-192.

3395 LOCCI, R. & QUARONI, S. (1972) - INVESTIGATIONS ON FUNGAL FEATURES BY SCAN-
      NING ELECTRON MICROSCOPY. 5. FURTHER STUDIES ON ASCOSPORIC ASPERGILLUS
      SPECIES. RIV.PATOL.VEG., PADOVA, SER.4, 8, 253-320.

3396 LOCKWOOD, J.L. (1960) - LYSIS OF MYCELIUM OF PLANT-PATHOGENIC FUNGI BY NA-
      TURAL SOIL. PHYTOPATHOLOGY 50, 787-789.

3397 LOCKWOOD, L.B. & REEVES, M.D. (1945) - SOME FACTORS AFFECTING THE PRODUC-
      TION OF ITACONIC ACID BY ASPERGILLUS TERREUS. ARCHS BIOCHEM. 6, 455-469.

3398 LODDER, J. (1970) - THE YEASTS, A TAXONOMIC STUDY. 2ND ED., NORTH HOLLAND
      PUBL.CO., AMSTERDAM.

3399 LODHA, B.C. (1963) - NOTES ON TWO SPECIES OF TRICHURUS. J.INDIAN BOT.SOC.
      42, 135-142.

3400 LODHA, B.C. (1964) - STUDIES ON COPROPHILOUS FUNGI. 1. CHAETOMIUM. J.INDIAN
      BOT.SOC. 43, 121-140.

3401 LODHA, B.C. (1971) - STUDIES ON COPROPHILOUS FUNGI. 4. SOME CLEISTOTHECIAL
      ASCOMYCETES. J.INDIAN BOT.SOC. 50, 196-208.

3402 LOEHR, E. & OLSEN, J. (1969) - THE THERMOPHILIC FUNGUS HUMICOLA LANUGINO-
      SA. FRIESIA 9, 140-141.

3403 LOEWENBERG, J.R. (1977) - CELLULASE FORMATION AND SECRETION. ABS.2ND INT.
      MYCOL.CONGR., TAMPA, 1977.

3404 LOEWENBERG, J.R. & REESE, E.T. (1957) - MICROBIAL FRUCTOSANS AND FRUCTOSAN-
      ASES. CAN.J.MICROBIOL. 3, 643-650.

3405 LOGAN, C. & KHAN, A.A. (1969) - COMPARATIVE STUDIES OF PHOMA SPP. ASSOCIA-
      TED WITH POTATO GANGRENE IN NORTHERN IRELAND. TRANS.BR.MYCOL.SOC. 52,
      9-17.

3406 LOGAN, C. & O'NEILL, R. (1970) - PRODUCTION OF AN ANTIBIOTIC BY PHOMA EXI-
      GUA. TRANS.BR.MYCOL.SOC. 55, 67-75.

3407 LONES, G.W. & PEACOCK, C.L. (1960) - ROLE OF CARBON DIOXIDE IN THE DIMOR-
      PHISM OF COCCIDIOIDES IMMITIS. J.BACT. 79, 308-309.

3408 LOPATECKI, L.E. & PETERS, W. (1972) - A ROT OF PEARS IN COLD STORAGE CAUSED
      BY MUCOR PIRIFORMIS. CAN.J.PL.SCI. 52, 875-879.

3409 LOPEZ, A. & BURGOS, J. (1973/74) - ACILGLICOSAS DE HEMISPORA STELLATA.
      AN.FAC.VET.LEON. 19, 415-426.

3410 LOPEZ, A. & BURGOS, J. (1976) - LIPID COMPOSITION OF SPORENDONEMA EPIZOUM.
      PHYTOCHEMISTRY 15, 971-975.

3411 LOQUET, M. (1968) - A PROPOS DU GILMANIELLA HUMICOLA BARRON. BULL.SOC.LINN.
      NORMANDIE 10, 144-148.

3412 LORINCZI, F., DRAGAN-BULARDA, M., KISS, S. & RADULESCU, D. (1973) - (STUD-
      IES CONCERNING LEVANASE PRODUCTION OF SOME SOIL MICROMYCETES). STUDIA
      UNIV.BABES-BOLYAI, SER.BIOL. 18, 145-149.

3413 LOUB, W. (1956) - ORIENTIERENDE UNTERSUCHUNGEN UEBER DIE MIKROFLORA VER-
      SCHIEDENER BODENTYPEN IN OESTERREICH. 6TH INT.CONGR.SOIL SCI., PARIS,
      III, 87-93.

3414 LOUB, W. (1960) - DIE MIKROBIOLOGISCHE CHARAKTERISIERUNG VON BODENTYPEN.
      BODENKULTUR, AUSG.A, 11, 38-70.

3415 LOUB, W. (1963) - UNTERSUCHUNGEN ZUR MIKROBIOLOGIE AFRIKANISCHER BOEDEN.
      BODENKULTUR, AUSG.A, 14, 189-208.

3416 LOUB, W. (1965) - ZUR MIKROBIOLOGIE MITTEL- UND NORDEUROPAEISCHER PODSOLE. Z.PFLERNAEHR.DUENG.BODENK. 111, 157-167.

3417 LOUB, W. (1967) - UNTERSUCHUNGEN ZUR MIKROBIOLOGIE SPANISCHER BOEDEN. AN. EDAFOL.AGROBIOL. 26, 975-1008.

3418 LOUB, W. & HAYBACH, G. (1967) - JAHRESZYKLISCHE BEOBACHTUNGEN DER MIKRO-FLORA UND MIKROFAUNA VON BOEDEN IM SUEDLICHEN WIENERWALD. REVUE ECOL. BIOL.SOL 4, 59-80.

3419 LOWE, D.A. & JENNINGS, D.H. (1975) - CARBOHYDRATE METABOLISM IN THE FUNGUS DENDRYPHIELLA SALINA. 5. THE PATTERN OF LABEL IN ARABITOL AND POLYSAC-CHARIDE AFTER GROWTH IN THE PRESENCE OF SPECIFICALLY LABELLED CARBON SOURCES. NEW PHYTOL. 74, 67-79.

3420 LOWE, R.E. & KENNEL, E.W. (1972) - PATHOGENICITY OF THE FUNGUS ENTO-MOPHTHORA CORONATA IN CULEX PIPIENS QUINQUEFASCIATUS AND AEDES TAE-NIORHYNCHUS. MOSQUITO NEWS 32, 614-620.

3421 LUCAS, G.B. (1955) - THE CARDINAL TEMPERATURES AND PH RESPONSE OF THIELA-VIOPSIS BASICOLA. MYCOLOGIA 47, 793-798.

3422 LUCAS, G.B. (1971) - ALTERNARIA ALTERNATA (FR.) KEISSLER, THE CORRECT NAME FOR ALTERNARIA TENUIS AND A. LONGIPES. TOB.SCI. 15, 37-42.

3423 LUCAS, R.L. (1955) - A COMPARATIVE STUDY OF OPHIOBOLUS GRAMINIS AND FUSA-RIUM CULMORUM IN SAPROPHYTIC COLONIZATION OF WHEAT STRAW. ANN.APPL.BIOL. 43, 134-143.

3424 LUCAS, R.L. (1960) - TRANSPORT OF PHOSPHORUS BY FUNGAL MYCELIUM. NATURE, LOND. 188, 763-764.

3425 LUCET, A. & COSTANTIN, J. (1900) - RHIZOMUCOR PARASITICUS. ESPECE PATHO-GENE DE L'HOMME. REVUE GEN.BOT. 12, 81-98.

3426 LUCKNER, M. (1967) - ZUR BILDUNG VON CHINOLINALKALOIDEN IN PFLANZEN. 2. DIE FERMENTATIVE UMWANDLUNG DER PENICILLIUM-ALKALOIDE CYCLOPENIN UND CYCLOPENOL IN VIRIDICATIN UND VIRIDICATOL. EUR.J.BIOCHEM. 2, 74-78.

3427 LUDWIG, R.A. (1957) - TOXIN PRODUCTION BY HELMINTHOSPORIUM SATIVUM AND ITS ROLE IN PATHOGENICITY. PHYTOPATHOLOGY 47, 22.

3428 LUETHI, H. & HOCHSTRASSER, R. (1952) - UEBER ZWEI NEUE, GEGENWAERTIG HAEU-FIGER AUFTRETENDE PILZINFEKTIONEN IN DER SUESSMOSTEREI. FLUESSIGES OBST 19, 496-504.

3429 LUGAUSKAS, A.J. & GRYBAUSKIENE, V.J. (1970) - (THE PROTEOLYTIC ACTIVITY OF MICROMYCETES GROWING IN THE CLOVER ROOT ZONE AND ON THE ROOTS THEM-SELVES). TRUDY AKAD.NAUK LITOV.SSR, SER.C, 2, 25-31.

3430 LUIJK, A.VAN (1938) - ANTAGONISM BETWEEN VARIOUS MICROORGANISMS AND DIF-FERENT SPECIES OF THE GENUS PYTHIUM, PARASITIZING UPON GRASSES AND LU-CERNE. MEDED.PHYTOPATH.LAB.WILLIE COMMELIN SCHOLTEN 14, 43-83.

3431 LUKE, P. & VANI, M.A.M. (1972) - RHIZOSPHERE AND RHIZOPLANE MYCOFLORA OF NICOTIANA TABACUM L. MYSORE J.AGRIC.SCI. 6, 204-206.

3432 LULLA, B.S. & JOHAR, D.S. (1953) - PENICILLIUM NOTATUM AS A SOURCE OF FUN-GAL PECTINASE. CURR.SCI. 22, 79-80.

3433 LUMSDEN, R.D. (1969) - SCLEROTINIA SCLEROTIORUM INFECTION OF BEAN AND THE PRODUCTION OF CELLULASE. PHYTOPATHOLOGY 59, 653-657.

3434 LUMSDEN, R.D. (1970) - PHOSPHATIDASE OF SCLEROTINIA SCLEROTIORUM PRODUCED IN CULTURE AND IN INFECTED BEAN. PHYTOPATHOLOGY 60, 1106-1110.

3435 LUMSDEN, R.D. & AYERS, W.A. (1975) - INFLUENCE OF SOIL ENVIRONMENT ON THE GERMINABILITY OF CONSTITUTIVELY DORMANT OOSPORES OF PYTHIUM ULTIMUM. PHYTOPATHOLOGY 65, 1101-1107.

3436 LUMSDEN, R.D., AYERS, W.A. & DOW, R.L. (1975) - DIFFERENTIAL ISOLATION OF PYTHIUM SPECIES FROM SOIL BY MEANS OF SELECTIVE MEDIA, TEMPERATURE, AND PH. CAN.J.MICROBIOL. 21, 606-612.

3437 LUMSDEN, R.D. & BATEMAN, D.F. (1968) - PHOSPHATIDE-DEGRADING ENZYMES ASSO-CIATED WITH PATHOGENESIS IN PHASEOLUS VULGARIS INFECTED WITH THIELAVI-OPSIS BASICOLA. PHYTOPATHOLOGY 58, 219-227.

3438 LUMSDEN, R.D., PAPAVIZAS, G.C. & AYERS, W.A. (1970) - STUDIES ON THE MECH-ANISM OF ACTION OF BETA-METHYLASPARTIC ACID IN THE SUPPRESSION OF APHA-NOMYCES ROOT ROT OF PEA. CAN.J.BOT. 48, 631-637.

3439 LUND, N.A., ROBERTSON, A. & WHALLEY, W.B. (1953) - THE CHEMISTRY OF FUNGI. 21. ASPERXANTHONE AND A PRELIMINARY EXAMINATION OF ASPERGILLIN. J.CHEM. SOC., 1953, 2434-2439.

3440 LUNDEGARDH, H. (1923) - DIE BEDEUTUNG DES KOHLENSAEUREGEHALTS UND DER WAS-SERSTOFFIONENKONZENTRATION DES BODENS FUER DIE ENTSTEHUNG DER FUSARIO-SEN. BOT.NOTISER, 25-52.

3441 LUNDQVIST, N. (1972) - NORDIC SORDARIACEAE S.LAT. SYMB.BOT.UPSAL. 20 (1), 374 PP.

3442 LUNDSTROEM, H. (1972) - MICROSCOPIC STUDIES OF CAVITY FORMATION BY SOFT ROT FUNGI. STUDIA FOR.SUEC. 98, 1-18.

3443 LUNDSTROEM, H. (1973) - (STUDIES OF THE WOOD-DECAYING CAPACITY OF THE SOFT ROT FUNGI ALLESCHERIA TERRESTRIS, PHIALOPHORA (MARGARINOMYCES) LUTEO-VIRIDIS AND PHIALOPHORA RICHARDSIAE). RAPP.INST.VIRKESLAERA, SKOGS-HOEGSK., STOCKHOLM 87, 50 PP.

3444 LUNDSTROEM, H. (1974) - STUDIES ON THE PHYSIOLOGY OF THE THREE SOFT ROT FUNGI ALLESCHERIA TERRESTRIS, PHIALOPHORA (MARGARINOMYCES) LUTEO-VIRI-DIS AND PHIALOPHORA RICHARDSIAE. STUDIA FOREST SUEC. 115, 1-42.

3445 LUPPI-MOSCA, A.M. (1960) - SULLA MICOFLORA DEL TERRENO DI UN PASCOLO ALPI-NO IN VAL DI LANZO (ALPI GRAIE). ALLIONIA 6, 17-34.

3446 LUPPI-MOSCA, A.M. (1960) - INVESTIGACIONES SOBRE LA MICOFLORA DE TERRENOS ESPANOLES. AN.INST.BOT.A.J.CAVANILLES 18, 69-90.

3447 LUPPI-MOSCA, A.M. (1960) - SOBRE LA MICOFLORA DEL TERRENO DE UN BOSQUE DE PINUS NIGRA VAR. LARICIO. AN.INST.BOT.A.J.CAVANILLES 18, 91-108.

3448 LUPPI-MOSCA, A.M. (1961) - PRIMO CONTRIBUTO ALLA MICOLOGIA DELLA COPERTURA MORTA DEI BOSCHI DI LATIFOGLIE. ALLIONIA 7, 39-58.

3449 LUPPI-MOSCA, A.M. (1962) - FUNGHI SULLE FOGLIE MORTE DI BETULLA E CASTAG-NO. ALLIONIA 8, 19-25.

3450 LUPPI-MOSCA, A.M. (1964) - MICOFLORA DI UN TERRENO AGRARIO A POIRINO (TO-RINO). ALLIONIA 10, 7-16.

3451   LUPPI-MOSCA, A.M. (1972) - LA MICOFLORA DELLA RIZOSFERA NELLE TARTUFAIE.
       3. ANALISI MICOLOGICHE DI TERRENI TARTUFIFERI FRANCESI. ALLIONIA 18,
       33-40.

3452   LUPPI-MOSCA, A.M. (1973) - LA MICOFLORA DELLA RIZOSFERA NELLE TARTUFAIE.
       4. MICROFUNGHI DA RADICI DI PIOPPO MICORRIZATE DA TUBER MAGNATUM. AL-
       LIONIA 19, 29-32.

3453   LUPPI-MOSCA, A.M. & CAMPANINO, F. (1962) - ANALISI MICOLOGICHE DEL TERRENO
       DI GROTTE PIEMONTESI. ALLIONIA 8, 27-43.

3454   LUPPI-MOSCA, A.M., GRIBALDI, L. & SODANO, G.J. (1970) - LA MICOFLORA DELLA
       RIZOSFERA NELLE TARTUFAIE. 2. ANALISI MICOLOGICHE DI TERRENI TARTUFIFE-
       RI PIEMONTESI. ALLIONIA 16, 115-132.

3455   LUTTRELL, E.S. (1955) - A TAXONOMIC REVISION OF HELMINTHOSPORIUM SATIVUM
       AND RELATED SPECIES. AM.J.BOT. 42, 57-68.

3456   LUTTRELL, E.S. & ROGERSON, C.T. (1959) - HOMOTHALLISM IN AN UNDESCRIBED
       SPECIES OF COCHLIOBOLUS AND IN COCHLIOBOLUS KUSANOI. MYCOLOGIA 61, 195-
       202.

3457   L'VOVA, L.E. (1964) - (PHYSIOLOGICAL CHARCTERISTICS OF GRISEOFULVIN PRO-
       DUCERS, PENICILLIUM NIGRICANS AND PENICILLIUM URTICAE, CULTIVATED ON
       SYNTHETIC MEDIA). MATERIALY 2.KONF.MOLOD.UCHEN.LENINGR.INST.ANTIBIOT.,
       SB., 1964, 44-46.

3458   L'VOVA, L.E. (1966) - (COENZYME-A IN THE GROWTH CYCLE OF THE GRISEOFULVIN
       PRODUCER PENICILLIUM NIGRICANS). ANTIBIOTIKI 11, 419-422.

3459   LYDA, S.D. (1974) - STUDIES ON PHYMATOTRICHUM OMNIVORUM AND PHYMATOTRICHUM
       ROOT ROT. IN: THE RELATION OF SOIL MICROORGANISMS TO SOIL-BORNE PLANT
       PATHOGENS; G.C.PAPAVIZAS (ED.), SOUTH.COOP.SER.BULL. 183, VIRG.POLYTECH.
       INST.STATE UNIV., VIRGINIA, 69-73.

3460   LYDA, S.D. (1976) - OPTIMIZING MYCELIAL RESPIRATION OF PHYMATOTRICHUM OM-
       NIVORUM. MYCOLOGIA 68, 1011-1019.

3461   LYDA, S.D. & BURNETT, E. (1971) - INFLUENCE OF TEMPERATURE ON PHYMATOTRI-
       CHUM SCLEROTIAL FORMATION AND DISEASE DEVELOPMENT. PHYTOPATHOLOGY 61,
       728-730.

3462   LYDA, S.D. & BURNETT, E. (1971) - CHANGES IN CARBON DIOXIDE LEVELS DURING
       SCLEROTIAL FORMATION BY PHYMATOTRICHUM OMNIVORUM. PHYTOPATHOLOGY 61,
       858-861.

3463   LYDA, S.D. & BURNETT, E. (1975) - THE ROLE OF CO2 IN GROWTH AND SURVIVAL
       OF PHYMATOTRICHUM OMNIVORUM. IN: BIOLOGY AND CONTROL OF SOIL-BORNE PLANT
       PATHOGENS; BRUEHL, G.W. (ED.), ST.PAUL, MINNESOTA, 63-68.

3464   LYDA, S.D. & HILL, T.F. (1975) - GAS EXCHANGES BY PHYMATOTRICHUM OMNIVORUM
       IN AXENIC CLOSED SYSTEM. PROC.AM.PHYTOPATH.SOC. 2, 137-138.

3465   LYNCH, J.M. (1972) - IDENTIFICATION OF SUBSTRATES AND ISOLATION OF MICRO-
       ORGANISMS RESPONSIBLE FOR ETHYLENE PRODUCTION IN THE SOIL. NATURE, LOND.
       240, 45-46.

3466   LYNCH, J.M. (1973) - EXTRACELLULAR ETHYLENE FORMATION BY MUCOR HIEMALIS.
       J.GEN.MICROBIOL. 77, PAGE IV (ABS.).

3467   LYNCH, J.M. (1974) - MODE OF ETHYLENE FORMATION BY MUCOR HIEMALIS. J.GEN.
       MICROBIOL. 83, 407-411.

3468 LYNCH, J.M. & HARPER, S.H.T. (1974) - FORMATION OF ETHYLENE BY A SOIL FUN-
     GUS. J.GEN.MICROBIOL. 80, 187-195.

3469 LYNCH, J.M. & HARPER, S.H.T. (1974) - FUNGAL GROWTH RATE AND FORMATION OF
     ETHYLENE IN SOIL. J.GEN.MICROBIOL. 85, 91-96.

3470 LYNEN, F. & HOFFMANN-WALBECK, H.P. (1948) - ENZYME AUS SCHIMMELPILZEN. 1.
     UEBER EINIGE GAERUNGSFERMENTE AUS PENICILLIUM NOTATUM. LIEBIGS ANNLN
     CHEM. 559, 153-168.

3471 LYR, H. (1959) - DIE BILDUNG VON EKTOENZYMEN DURCH HOLZZERSTOERENDE UND
     HOLZBEWOHNENDE PILZE AUF VERSCHIEDENEN NAEHRBOEDEN. ARCH.MIKROBIOL. 33,
     266-282.

3472 LYR, H. (1959) - DIE BILDUNG VON EKTOENZYMEN DURCH HOLZZERSTOERENDE UND
     HOLZBEWOHNENDE PILZE AUF VERSCHIEDENEN NAEHRBOEDEN. 4. XYLAN UND GLU-
     COSE ALS C-QUELLEN. ARCH.MIKROBIOL. 34, 418-433.

3473 LYSEK, H. (1975) - OVICIDAL FUNGI IN THE SOIL OF FOUR COUNTRIES OF ASIA.
     ACTA UNIV.PALACKI OLOMUC, FAC.MED. 74, 41-46.

3474 LYTHGOE, J.N. (1961) - EFFECT OF LIGHT AND TEMPERATURE ON THAMNIDIUM ELE-
     GANS. TRANS.BR.MYCOL.SOC. 44, 199-213.

3475 MA, R.M. (1933) - A STUDY ON THE SOIL FUNGI OF THE PEKING DISTRICT. LIGNAN
     SCI.J. 12 (SUPPL.), 115-118.

3476 MAAG, G.W., DURRELL, L.W. & PAYNE, M. (1959) - A CHROMATOGRAPHIC STUDY OF
     THE FUNGUS EMERICELLOPSIS. BULL.TORREY BOT.CLUB 86, 120-125.

3477 MAAS, J.L. & POWELSON, R.L. (1972) - GROWTH AND SPORULATION OF BOTRYTIS
     CONVOLUTA WITH VARIOUS CARBON AND NITROGEN SOURCES. MYCOLOGIA 64, 897-
     903.

3478 MAAS, P.W.TH. (1965) - THE IDENTITY OF THE FOOTROT FUNGUS OF FLAX. NETH.J.
     PL.PATH. 71, 113-121.

3479 MAAS GEESTERANUS, R.A. (1969) - DE FUNGI VAN NEDERLAND. 2. PEZIZALES II.
     WET.MEDED.K.NED.NATUURHIST.VER. 80, 84 PP.

3480 MACAULEY, B.J. (1972) - QUANTITATIVE TECHNIQUES FOR ASSESSING COLONIZATION
     OF LEAF LITTER OF EUCALYPTUS REGNANS BY PENICILLIUM LAPIDOSUM. TRANS.
     BR.MYCOL.SOC. 59, 173-175.

3481 MACAULEY, B.J. & GRIFFIN, D.M. (1969) - EFFECTS OF CARBON DIOXIDE AND OXY-
     GEN ON THE ACTIVITY OF SOME SOIL FUNGI. TRANS.BR.MYCOL.SOC. 53, 53-62.

3482 MACAULEY, B.J. & GRIFFIN, D.M. (1969) - EFFECT OF CARBON DIOXIDE AND THE
     BICARBONATE ION ON THE GROWTH OF SOME SOIL FUNGI. TRANS.BR.MYCOL.SOC.
     53, 223-228.

3483 MACAULEY, B.J. & THROWER, L.B. (1966) - SUCCESSION OF FUNGI IN LEAF LITTER
     OF EUCALYPTUS REGNANS. TRANS.BR.MYCOL.SOC. 49, 509-520.

3484 MACDONALD, A.L., RETTIG, S.J. & TROTTER, J. (1974) - CRYSTAL AND MOLECULAR
     STRUCTURE OF 2-DEACYLUSNIC ACID. CAN.J.CHEM. 52, 723-733.

3485 MACDONALD, D.W., COVE, D.J. & CODDINGTON, A. (1974) - CYTOCHROME-C REDUCT-
     ASES FROM WILD-TYPE AND MUTANT STRAINS OF ASPERGILLUS NIDULANS. MOLEC.
     GEN.GENET. 128, 187-199.

3486 MACEK, J. (1973) - UNTERSUCHUNGEN ZUR AETIOLOGIE DER FROSCHAUGENKRANKHEIT
      AN APFELBLAETTERN IM ZUSAMMENHANG MIT DEM PILZ PHOMA GLOMERATA (CDA.)
      WOLLENW. & HOCHAPF. GARTENBAUWISSENSCHAFT 38, 151-158.

3487 MACFARLANE, C.S. (1939) - A ROT OF SCILLA BULBS CAUSED BY PENICILLIUM CY-
      CLOPIUM. TRANS.BOT.SOC.EDINB. 32, 542-547.

3488 MACGARVIE, Q. & ISAAC, I. (1966) - STRUCTURE AND BEHAVIOUR OF THE NUCLEI
      OF VERTICILLIUM SPECIES. TRANS.BR.MYCOL.SOC. 49, 687-693.

3489 MACH, F. (1956) - UNTERSUCHUNGEN UEBER DIE MOEGLICHKEITEN EINER BEKAEMP-
      FUNG PHYTOPATHOGENER PILZE MIT SAPROPHYTISCHER BODENPHASE (VERMEHRUNGS-
      PILZE) DURCH SUPERINFEKTION MIT ANTAGONISTISCH AKTIVEN STREPTOMYCES-
      STAEMMEN. ZENTBL.BAKT.PARASITKDE, ABT.2, 110, 1-25.

3490 MACHACEK, J.E. (1957) - PREVALENCE OF HELMINTHOSPORIUM SATIVUM, FUSARIUM
      CULMORUM AND CERTAIN OTHER FUNGI IN EXPERIMENTAL PLOTS SUBJECTED TO
      VARIOUS CULTURAL AND MANURIAL TREATMENTS. CAN.J.PL.SCI. 37, 353-365.

3491 MACHACEK, J.E. CHEREWICK, W.J., MEAD, H.W. & BROADFOOT, W.C. (1951) - A
      STUDY OF SOME SEED-BORNE DISEASES OF CEREALS IN CANADA. SCIENT.AGRIC.
      31, 193-206.

3492 MACHACEK, J.E. & WALLACE, H.A.H. (1952) - LONGEVITY OF SOME COMMON FUNGI
      IN CEREAL SEED. CAN.J.BOT. 30, 164-169.

3493 MACHIDA, Y. & NOZOE, S. (1972) - BIOSYNTHESIS OF TRICHOTHECIN AND RELATED
      COMPOUNDS. TETRAHEDRON 28, 5113-5117.

3494 MACIEJOWSKA, Z. (1962) - STUDIES ON SOIL MICROFLORA AND BIOLOGICAL CONTROL
      OF DAMPING-OFF OF APPLE. DISS.ABSTR. 24, 925.

3495 MACIEJOWSKA, Z. & WILLIAMS, E.B. (1961) - THE ISOLATION AND IDENTIFICATION
      OF SOIL FUNGI AND THEIR RELATION TO ROOT ROT OF APPLE. PROC.INDIAN ACAD.
      SCI., SECT.B, 70, 52-54.

3496 MACIEJOWSKA, Z. & WILLIAMS, E.B. (1963) - STUDIES ON MORPHOLOGICAL FORMS
      OF STAPHYLOTRICHUM COCCOSPORUM. MYCOLOGIA 55, 221-225.

3497 MACIEJOWSKA-POKACKA, Z. (1971) - (RESULTS OF ONE YEAR STUDIES ON THE IN-
      FLUENCE OF VARIOUS SOILS ON THE MYCOFLORA UNDER COCKSFOOT (DACTYLIS
      GLOMERATA L.). ACTA MYCOL., WARSZAWA 7, 31-40.

3498 MACIEJOWSKA-POKACKA, Z. (1971) - REACTION OF SOIL FUNGI AND OTHER MICRO-
      ORGANISMS TO VARIOUS LEVELS OF NITROGEN FERTILIZATION AND IRRIGATION OF
      COCKSFOOT (DACTYLIS GLOMERATA L.). ACTA MYCOL., WARSZAWA 7, 41-57.

3499 MACINTYRE, D. & ELLIOTT, C.G. (1974) - SELECTION FOR GROWTH-RATE DURING
      ASEXUAL AND SEXUAL PROPAGATION IN PHYTOPHTHORA CACTORUM. GENET.RES. 24,
      295-310.

3500 MACKENZIE, R.M. & COOK, R.P. (1951) - THE NITROGEN METABOLISM OF PENICIL-
      LIUM NOTATUM. BIOCHEM.J. 50, III.

3501 MACKINNON, J.E. (1939) - ASPERGILLUS TERREUS, PARASITO DEL HOMBRE. MYCO-
      PATH.MYCOL.APPL. 2, 127-129.

3502 MACKINNON, J.E. (1949) - ESTADISTICA SOBRE 1000 CASOS DE MICOSIS CUTANEAS
      EN EL URUGUAY Y DETERMINACION DE LAS ESPECIES CAUSANTES. AN.INST.
      HIGIENE MONTEVIDEO 3, 83-94.

3503   MACKINNON, J.E., CONTI-DIAZ, I.A., GEZUELE, E., CIVILA, E. & DA LUZ, S.
       (1969) - ISOLATION OF SPOROTHRIX SCHENCKII FROM NATURE AND CONSIDERA-
       TIONS ON ITS PATHOGENICITY AND ECOLOGY. SABOURAUDIA 7, 38-45.

3504   MACKINNON, J.E., GEZUELE, E., CONTI-DIAZ, I.A. & DE GIMENEZ, A.C. (1973) -
       PRODUCTION OF CAPSULE AND CONIDIA BY YEAST-LIKE CELLS OF PHIALOPHORA
       SPINIFERA AND PHIALOPHORA JEANSELMEI. SABOURAUDIA 11, 33-38.

3505   MACLEOD, D.M. (1954) - INVESTIGATIONS ON THE GENERA BEAUVERIA VUILL. AND
       TRITIRACHIUM LIMBER. CAN.J.BOT. 32, 818-890.

3506   MACMILLAN, A. (1956) - THE RELATION BETWEEN NITROGEN ASSIMILATION AND
       RESPIRATION IN SCOPULARIOPSIS BREVICAULIS. PHYSIOLOGIA PL. 9, 533-545.

3507   MACMILLAN, A. (1956) - THE ENTRY OF AMMONIA INTO FUNGAL CELLS. J.EXP.BOT.
       7, 113-126.

3508   MACMILLAN, J., VANSTONE, A.E. & YEBOAH, S.K. (1972) - FUNGAL PRODUCTS. 3.
       STRUCTURE OF WORTMANNIN AND SOME HYDROLYSIS PRODUCTS. J.CHEM.SOC.PERKIN
       TRANS.I, 1972 (22), 2898-2903.

3509   MADELIN, M.F. & DORABJEE, S. (1974) - CONIDIUM ONTOGENY IN WALLEMIA SEBI.
       TRANS.BR.MYCOL.SOC. 63, 121-130.

3510   MADUEWESI, J.N.C., SNEH, B. & LOCKWOOD, J.L. (1976) - IMPROVED SELECTIVE
       MEDIA FOR ESTIMATING POPULATIONS OF THIELAVIOPSIS BASICOLA IN SOIL ON
       DILUTION PLATES. PHYTOPATHOLOGY 66, 526-530.

3511   MAEKELAE, K. (1972) - LEAF SPOT FUNGI ON BARLEY IN FINLAND. SUOM.MAATAL.
       SEUR.JULK. 124 (3), 1-23.

3512   MAEKELAE, K. (1972) - SEED BORNE FUNGI ON CULTIVATED GRASSES IN FINLAND.
       SUOM.MAATAL.SEUR.JULK. 124 (2), 1-44.

3513   MAEKELAE, K. (1973) - SOME AQUATIC HYPHOMYCETES ON GRASSES IN FINLAND.
       KARSTENIA 13, 16-22.

3514   MAGDYCZ, W.P. & MANNING, W.J. (1973) - BOTRYTIS CINEREA PROTECTS BROAD
       BEANS AGAINST VISIBLE OZONE INJURY. PHYTOPATHOLOGY 63, 204.

3515   MAGGON, K.K., GOPAL, S. & VENKITASUBRAMANIAN, T.A. (1973) - EFFECT OF
       TRACE METALS ON AFLATOXIN PRODUCTION BY ASPERGILLUS FLAVUS. BIOCHEM.
       PHYSIOL.PFL. 164, 523-530.

3516   MAGGON, K.K. & VENKITASUBRAMANIAN, T.A. (1973) - METABOLISM OF AFLATOXINS
       -B1 AND -G1 BY ASPERGILLUS PARASITICUS. EXPERIENTIA 29, 1210-1211.

3517   MAHDI, M.T., SATOUR, M.M. & SHILTAWY, E. (1973) - FUNGI ASSOCIATED WITH
       FLAX SEEDS IN THE UAR. SEED SCI.TECHNOL. 1, 821-823.

3518   MAHESHWARI, R. (1968) - OCCURRENCE AND ISOLATION OF THERMOPHILIC FUNGI.
       CURR.SCI. 37, 277-279.

3519   MAHGOUB, E.S. (1971) - MADUROMYCETOMA CAUSED BY ASPERGILLUS NIDULANS. J.
       TROP.MED.HYG. 74 (3), 60-61.

3520   MAHGOUB, E.S. (1973) - MYCETOMAS CAUSED BY CURVULARIA LUNATA, MADURELLA
       GRISEA, ASPERGILLUS NIDULANS, AND NOCARDIA BRASILIENSIS IN SUDAN. SA-
       BOURAUDIA 11, 179-182.

3521   MAHGOUB, E.S. (1973) - CAN ASPERGILLUS FLAVUS CAUSE MADUROMYCETOMA? BULL.
       SOC.PATH.EXOT. 66, 390-395.

3522   MAHLEN, A. (1972) - PURIFICATION AND SOME PROPERTIES OF CITRATE SYNTHASE
        FROM PENICILLIUM SPICULISPORUM. EUR.J.BIOCHEM. 29, 60-66.

3523   MAHLEN, A. (1973) - PURIFICATION AND SOME PROPERTIES OF ATP CITRATE LYASE
        FROM PENICILLIUM SPICULISPORUM. EUR.J.BIOCHEM. 36, 342-346.

3524   MAHLEN, A. (1973) - PURIFICATION AND SOME PROPERTIES OF 2-DECYLHOMOCITRATE
        SYNTHASE FROM PENICILLIUM SPICULISPORUM. EUR.J.BIOCHEM. 38, 33-39.

3525   MAHMOOD, T. (1970) - GEOTRICHUM CANDIDUM, CAUSING SOUR ROT OF LEMON IN TUR-
        KEY. PL.DIS.REPTR 54, 881-882.

3526   MAHMOOD, T. (1971) - A QUALITATIVE AND QUANTITATIVE STUDY OF THE SOIL MY-
        COFLORA OF A BARLEY FIELD. ACTA BOT.NEERL. 20, 624-626.

3527   MAHMOODIAN, A. & STICKINGS, C.E. (1964) - STUDIES IN THE BIOCHEMISTRY OF
        MICROORGANISMS. 115. METABOLITES OF PENICILLIUM FREQUENTANS WESTLING -
        ISOLATION OF SULOCHRIN, ASTERRIC ACID, (+)-BISDECHLOROGEODIN AND TWO
        NEW SUBSTITUTED ANTHRAQUINONES, QUESTIN AND QUESTINOL. BIOCHEM.J. 92,
        369-378.

3528   MAHVI, T.A. (1970) - FACTORS GOVERNING THE EPIDEMIOLOGY OF HISTOPLASMA
        CAPSULATUM IN SOIL. MYCOPATH.MYCOL.APPL. 41, 167-176.

3529   MAINWARING, H.R. (1972) - THE FINE STRUCTURE OF ASCOSPORE WALL FORMATION
        IN SORDARIA FIMICOLA. ARCH.MIKROBIOL. 81, 126-135.

3530   MAJCHROWICZ, I. & DOMINIK, T. (1968) - THIRD CONTRIBUTION TO THE KNOWLEDGE
        OF KERATINOLYTIC AND KERATINOPHILIC SOIL FUNGI IN THE REGION OF SZCZE-
        CIN. EKOL.POL., SER.A, 16, 121-145.

3531   MAKKONEN, R. & POHJAKALLIO, O. (1960) - ON THE PARASITES ATTACKING THE
        SCLEROTIA OF SOME FUNGI PATHOGENIC TO HIGHER PLANTS AND ON THE RESIST-
        ANCE OF THESE SCLEROTIA TO THEIR PARASITES. ACTA AGRIC.SCAND. 10, 105-
        126.

3532   MAKSIMOVA, R.A. & GRUSHINA, V.A. (1974) - (THE INHIBITING EFFECT OF TRI-
        CHOTHECIN ON CONIDIAL GERMINATION OF TRICHOTHECIUM ROSEUM STRAINS, PRO-
        DUCING THE ANTIBIOTIC). MIKOL.FITOPAT. 8, 431-434.

3533   MAKSIMOVA, R.A. & HASSAN ALI, R. (1975) - (MORPHOLOGICAL AND BIOSYNTHETIC
        ACTIVITY OF TRICHOTHECIUM ROSEUM IN RELATION TO ITS POLYNUCLEATE CONID-
        IA). MIKROBIOLOGIYA 44, 666-671.

3534   MAKSIMOVA, R.A. & PALMOVA, N.P. (1969) - (A STUDY ON NUCLEI IN THE MYCE-
        LIUM AND CONIDIA OF TRICHOTHECIUM ROSEUM LINK). MIKROBIOLOGIYA 38, 674-
        678.

3535   MAKSIMOVA, R.A., PENNER, L.F. & MINAEVA, T.A. (1973) - (FORMATION OF CARO-
        TENOID PIGMENTS BY THE IMPERFECT FUNGUS, TRICHOTHECIUM ROSEUM LK. EX
        FR.). BIOL.NAUKI 16, 92-96.

3536   MAKSIMOVA, R.A. & POKH, L.I. (1974) - (FIBRINOLYTIC ACTIVITY OF TRICHOTHE-
        CIUM ROSEUM). MIKOL.FITOPAT. 8, 326-330.

3537   MALAJCZUK, N., MCCOMB, A.J. & PARKER, C.A. (1975) - AN IMMUNOFLUORESCENCE
        TECHNIQUE FOR DETECTING PHYTOPHTHORA CINNAMOMI. AUST.J.BOT. 23, 289-310.

3538   MALAN, C.E., AMBROSOLI, R. & ALESSANDRIA, G. (1969) - INTERVENTO DI COMMUNI
        IFOMICETI SAPROFITI NELLA UMIFICAZIONE DELLA COPERTURA MORTA DELLA FAG-
        GETA ALPINA. ALLIONIA 15, 133-153.

3539   MALAN, C.E. & LEONE, L. (1962) - IFOMICETI PECTOLITICI DEL SUOLO DI FRUT-
       TETO. ALLIONIA 8, 195-208.

3540   MALBRAN, E., ALBESI, E.J., DARO, H. & ZAPATER, R.C. (1973) - ENDOFTALMITIS
       POR PENICILLIUM LILACINUM. ARCHOS OFTAL.B.AIRES 48, 253-258.

3541   MALCOLM, A. & SHEPHERD, M.G. (1972) - PURIFICATION AND PROPERTIES OF PENI-
       CILLIUM GLUCOSE 6-PHOSPHATE DEHYDROGENASE. BIOCHEM.J. 128, 817-831.

3542   MALCOLMSON, J.F. (1958) - A CONSIDERATION OF THE SPECIES OF PHOMA WHICH
       PARASITIZE POTATOES. TRANS.BR.MYCOL.SOC. 41, 413-418.

3543   MALCOLMSON, J.F. & GRAY, E.G. (1968) - FACTORS AFFECTING THE OCCURRENCE OF
       GANGRENE (PHOMA EXIGUA) IN POTATOES. ANN.APPL.BIOL. 62, 77-87.

3544   MALIK, K.A. & EGGINS, H.O.W. (1970) - A PERFUSION TECHNIQUE FOR THE DETEC-
       TION OF FUNGAL INTERREACTION. 1. EFFECT OF GLIOCLADIUM ROSEUM ON SIX
       CELLULOLYTIC FUNGI. MYCOPATH.MYCOL.APPL. 41, 257-269.

3545   MALIK, K.A. & RAJOKA, M.I. (1973) - CELLULOLYTIC SOIL MYCOFLORA OF THE
       RICE GROWING AREAS OF THE PUNJAB. BIOLOGIA, LAHORE 19, 109-117.

3546   MALIK, K.A. & SANDHU, G.R. (1973) - SOME STUDIES ON THE FUNGI OF KALLAR
       GRASS (DIPLACHNE FUSCA) COMPOST. PAKIST.J.BOT. 5, 57-63.

3547   MALLA, D.S., DIEHL, J.F. & SALUNKHE, D.K. (1967) - IN VITRO SUSCEPTIBILITY
       OF STRAINS OF PENICILLIUM VIRIDICATUM AND ASPERGILLUS FLAVUS TO BETA-
       IRRADIATION. EXPERIENTIA 23, 492-493.

3548   MALLEA, M., MURRAY, I.G., SEGRETAIN, G., PHILPOT, C.M., CHARPIN, H.,
       GUEHO, E. & CHARPIN, J. (1972) - CENSUS OF ASPERGILLUS COLONIES IN THE
       AIR, COMPARISON BETWEEN LONDON, PARIS, LYON, MARSEILLES. ACTA ALLERGOL.
       27, 273-278.

3549   MALLIK, M.A.B. (1964) - RELATION BETWEEN SOIL FUNGI AND SEED PLANTS IN
       THREE SUCCESSIONAL FOREST COMMUNITIES IN OKLAHOMA. DISS.UNIV.OKLAHOMA.

3550   MALLIK, M.A.B. & RICE, E.L. (1966) - RELATION BETWEEN SOIL FUNGI AND SEED
       PLANTS IN THREE SUCCESSIONAL FOREST COMMUNITIES IN OKLAHOMA. BOT.GAZ.
       127, 120-127.

3551   MALLOCH, D. (1970) - NEW CONCEPTS IN THE MICROASCACEAE ILLUSTRATED BY TWO
       NEW SPECIES. MYCOLOGIA 62, 727-740.

3552   MALLOCH, D. & CAIN, R.F. (1972) - THE TRICHOCOMATACEAE. ASCOMYCETES WITH
       ASPERGILLUS, PAECILOMYCES, AND PENICILLIUM IMPERFECT STATES. CAN.J.BOT.
       50, 2613-2628.

3553   MALLOCH, D. & CAIN, R.F. (1973) - THE GENUS THIELAVIA. MYCOLOGIA 65, 1055-
       1077.

3554   MALLOCH, D. & CAIN, R.F. (1973) - THE TRICHOCOMACEAE (ASCOMYCETES), SYN-
       ONYMS IN RECENT PUBLICATIONS. CAN.J.BOT. 51, 1647-1648.

3555   MALONE, C. (1972) - THE NATURE OF THE ASCUS WALL, A PRELIMINARY STUDY.
       PROC.IOWA ACAD.SCI. 79, 70-71.

3556   MALONE, J.P. & MUSKETT, A.E. (1964) - SEED-BORNE FUNGI. DESCRIPTIONS OF 77
       FUNGUS SPECIES. PROC.INT.SEED TEST.ASS. 29/2, 179-384.

3557   MALPHETTES, C.B. & PERRIN, R. (1974) - LE DEPERISSEMENT DU HETRE EN FRANCE.
       EUR.J.FOR.PATH. 4, 249-251.

3558 MAMLUK, O.F. (1975) - BEITRAEGE ZUR TAXONOMIE DER IM MITTLEREN ORIENT AUF BAUMWOLLE AUFTRETENDEN VERTICILLIOSE. PHYTOPATH.Z. 84, 307-315.

3559 MANANDHAR, K.L. & APINIS, A.E. (1971) - TEMPERATURE RELATIONS IN MONASCUS. TRANS.BR.MYCOL.SOC. 57, 465-472.

3560 MANDELBROT, A.K. & ERB, K. (1972) - HOST SPECTRUM OF THE MYCOPARASITE DI-MARGARIS VERTICILLATA. MYCOLOGIA 64, 1124-1129.

3561 MANDELS, G.R. (1954) - METABOLISM OF SUCROSE AND RELATED OLIGOSACCHARIDES BY SPORES OF THE FUNGUS MYROTHECIUM VERRUCARIA. PL.PHYSIOL., LANCASTER 29, 18-26.

3562 MANDELS, G.R. (1955) - BIOTIN AND INTERRUPTED GROWTH OF MYROTHECIUM VERRU-CARIA. AM.J.BOT. 42, 921-929.

3563 MANDELS, G.R. & VITOLS, R. (1967) - CONSTITUTIVE AND INDUCED TREHALOSE TRANSPORT MECHANISMS IN SPORES OF THE FUNGUS MYROTHECIUM VERRUCARIA. J.BACT. 93, 159-167.

3564 MANDELS, G.R., VITOLS, R. & PARRISH, F.W. (1965) - TREHALOSE AS AN ENDOGEN-OUS RESERVE IN SPORES OF THE FUNGUS MYROTHECIUM VERRUCARIA. J.BACT. 90, 1589-1598.

3565 MANDELS, M. & REESE, E.T. (1957) - INDUCTION OF CELLULASE IN TRICHODERMA VIRIDE AS INFLUENCED BY CARBON SOURCES AND METALS. J.BACT. 73, 269-278.

3566 MANGALLAM, S., MENON, M.R., SUKAPURE, R.S. & GOPALKRISHNAN, K.S. (1967) - AMYLASE PRODUCTION BY SOME CEPHALOSPORIUM SPECIES. HINDUSTAN ANTIBIOT. BULL. 10, 194-199.

3567 MANGAN, A. (1967) - STUDIES ON WHEAT RHIZOSPHERE SOIL FUNGI. IR.J.AGRIC. RES. 6, 9-14.

3568 MANGENOT, F. (1952) - RECHERCHES METHODIQUES SUR LES CHAMPIGNONS DE CER-TAINS BOIS EN DECOMPOSITION. REVUE GEN.BOT. 59, 115 PP.

3569 MANGENOT, F. (1964) - UNE NOTE RECTIFICATIVE A PROPOS DE PHIALOPHORA. REVUE MYCOL. 29, 208.

3570 MANKA, K. (1970) - PARASITAERE SAEMLINGSKRANKHEITEN DER FORSTBAEUME UND DIE BODENPILZE. ZENTBL.BAKT.PARASITKDE, ABT.2, 124, 450-459.

3571 MANKA, K., BLONSKA, A. & WNEKOWSKI, S. (1961) - RESEARCHES ON THE COMPO-SITION OF THE MYCROFLORA OF SEVERAL KINDS OF SOILS AND ITS EFFECT ON THE DEVELOPMENT OF SOME PARASITIC SOIL FUNGI. PR.NAUK INST.OCHR.ROSL., POZNAN 3, 144-231.

3572 MANKA, K. & GIERCZAK, M. (1961) - (INVESTIGATIONS ON THE ROOT MYCOFLORA OF SCOTS PINE (PINUS SILVESTRIS L.)). PR.KOM.NAUK ROLN.LESN., POZNAN 9 (1), 46 PP.

3573 MANKA, K. & TRUSZKOWSKA, W. (1958) - (AN ATTEMPT AT A MYCOLOGICAL ANALYSIS OF ROOTS OF SPRUCE (PICEA EXCELSA)). ACTA SOC.BOT.POL. 27, 45-73.

3574 MANKAU, R. (1962) - SOIL FUNGISTASIS AND NEMATOPHAGOUS FUNGI. PHYTOPATHOL-OGY 52, 611-615.

3575 MANKAU, R. (1964) - ECOLOGICAL RELATIONSHIPS OF PREDACIOUS FUNGI ASSOCIA-TED WITH THE CITRUS NEMATODE. PHYTOPATHOLOGY 54, 1435 (ABS.).

3576 MANKAU, R. (1968) - ACREMONIUM SP. ATTACKING SOIL MITES AND COLLEMBOLA.
      J.INVERTEBR.PATH. 12, 463-464.

3577 MANKAU, R. (1969) - NEMATICIDAL ACTIVITY OF ASPERGILLUS NIGER CULTURE FIL-
      TRATES. PHYTOPATHOLOGY 59, 1170.

3578 MANKAU, R. & CLARKE, O.F. (1959) - NEMATODE-TRAPPING FUNGI IN SOUTHERN
      CALIFORNIA CITRUS SOILS. PL.DIS.REPTR 43, 968-969.

3579 MANKAU, R. & MANKAU, S.K. (1963) - THE ROLE OF MYCOPHAGOUS NEMATODES IN
      THE SOIL. 1. THE RELATIONSHIP OF APHELENCHUS AVENAE TO PHYTOPATHOGENIC
      SOIL FUNGI. IN: SOIL ORGANISMS; DOEKSEN, J. & DRIFT, J.VAN DER (ED.),
      NORTH HOLLAND PUBL.CO., AMSTERDAM, 271-280.

3580 MANKAU, S.K. & MANKAU, R. (1962) - MULTIPLICATION OF APHELENCHUS AVENAE ON
      PHYTOPATHOGENIC SOIL FUNGI. PHYTOPATHOLOGY 52, 741 (ABS.).

3581 MANNING, W.J. & CROSSAN, D.F. (1968) - IMMUNOFLUORESCENT STAINING AS A
      MEANS OF IDENTIFYING MYCELIUM OF RHIZOCTONIA SOLANI ON SLIDES USED IN
      SOIL ECOLOGICAL STUDIES. PHYTOPATHOLOGY 58, 886.

3582 MANNOZZI TORINI, L. (1932) - INFLUENCE DES PRODUITS D'EXCRETION DES CHAM-
      PIGNONS DU SOL SUR LE DEVELOPPEMENT DU BLE. BOLL.SOC.INT.MICROBIOL.,
      SEZ.ITAL. 4, 244-248.

3583 MANOHARACHARY, C. (1974) - A NOTE ON SOME INTERESTING FUNGI FROM HYDERABAD
      (INDIA). CURR.SCI. 43, 129-131.

3584 MANOHARACHARY, C. & VAIDYANATH, K. (1975) - MYCOFLORA OF PADDY GRAINS FROM
      HYDERABAD. GEOBIOS 2, 159.

3585 MANSFIELD, J.W., PORTER, E.A.A. & WIDDOWSON, D.A. (1973) - STRUCTURE OF A
      FUNGAL METABOLITE OF THE PHYTOALEXIN WYERONE ACID FROM VICIA FABA L.
      J.CHEM.SOC.PERKIN TRANS.I, 1973, 2557-2559.

3586 MANTOVANI, A. (1972) - HISTOPLASMOSIS IN EUROPE. ANNLS SOC.BELG.MED.TROP.
      52, 421-427.

3587 MANTOVANI, A. & MORGANTI, L. (1971) - HISTOPLASMOSIS IN ITALY. C.R.PROC.
      5TH I.S.H.A.M. CONGR., PARIS, 139-140.

3588 MANTUROVSKAYA, N.V. & SIZOVA, T.P. (1967) - (INTERACTION BETWEEN PINE SEED-
      LINGS AND SOIL-BORNE FUNGI). MIKOL.FITOPAT. 1, 500-503.

3589 MARASAS, W.F.O. & SCHUMANN, I.H. (1972) - THE GENUS PITHOMYCES IN SOUTH
      AFRICA. BOTHALIA 10, 509-515.

3590 MARASAS, W.F.O., WESTHUIZEN, G.C.A.VAN DER, WARMELO, K.T.VAN & PAPENDORF,
      M.C. (1966) - NEW AND INTERESTING RECORDS OF SOUTH AFRICAN FUNGI. 5.
      BOTHALIA 9, 229-243.

3591 MARCHANT, R. (1966) - WALL STRUCTURE AND SPORE GERMINATION IN FUSARIUM
      CULMORUM. ANN.BOT. 30, 821-830.

3592 MARCHANT, R. (1966) - FINE STRUCTURE AND SPORE GERMINATION IN FUSARIUM
      CULMORUM. ANN.BOT. 30, 441-445.

3593 MARCHANT, R. (1968) - AN ULTRASTRUCTURAL STUDY OF SEXUAL REPRODUCTION IN
      PYTHIUM ULTIMUM. NEW PHYTOL. 67, 167-171.

3594 MARCHANT, R. (1975) - AN ULTRASTRUCTURAL STUDY OF PHIALOSPORE FORMATION IN
      FUSARIUM CULMORUM GROWN IN CONTINUOUS CULTURE. CAN.J.BOT. 53, 1978-1987.

3595 MARCHANT, R. & SMITH, D.G. (1968) - A SEROLOGICAL INVESTIGATION OF HYPHAL
      GROWTH IN FUSARIUM CULMORUM. ARCH.MIKROBIOL. 63, 85-94.

3596 MARCHANT, R. & WHITE, M.F. (1967) - THE CARBON METABOLISM AND SWELLING OF
      FUSARIUM CULMORUM CONIDIA. J.GEN.MICROBIOL. 48, 65-77.

3597 MARCHELLI, R. & VINING, L.C. (1973) - BIOSYNTHESIS OF FLAVONOID AND TER-
      PHENYL METABOLITES BY THE FUNGUS ASPERGILLUS CANDIDUS. CHEM.COMMUN.,
      1973 (15), 555-556.

3598 MARCHELLI, R. & VINING, L.C. (1975) - TERPHENYLLIN, A NOVEL P-TERPHENYL
      METABOLITE FROM ASPERGILLUS CANDIDUS. J.ANTIBIOT., TOKYO 28, 328-331.

3599 MARCHISIO, V.F. (1972) - SU ALCUNI MICROMICETI AD ATTIVITA ANTIBIOTICA DI
      UN TERRENO AGRARIO. ALLIONIA 18, 97-102.

3600 MARCHISIO, V.F. (1977) - SULL'ATTIVITA ANTIBIOTICA DI DIHETEROSPORA CHLAMY-
      DOSPORIA E DI OIDIODENDRON TRUNCATUM. ALLIONIA 21, 67-71.

3601 MARCUS, S. (1947) - ANTIBACTERIAL ACTIVITIES OF GEODIN AND ERDIN. BIOCHEM.
      J. 41, 462-463.

3602 MARET, R. (1972) - CHIMIE ET MORPHOLOGIE SUBMICROSCOPIQUE DES PAROIS
      CELLULAIRES DE L'ASCOMYCETE CHAETOMIUM GLOBOSUM. ARCH.MIKROBIOL. 81,
      68-90.

3603 MARGARIS, N.S., MITRAKOS, K. & MARKOU, S. (1974) - CARBON SOURCES FOR AS-
      PERGILLUS NIGER. GROWTH UNDER DIFFERENT SHAKING PROGRAMMES. FOLIA MICRO-
      BIOL. 19, 394-396.

3604 MARIAT, F. (1960) - ACTION DE L'ANHYDRIDE CARBONIQUE SUR LA CROISSANCE DE
      SPOROTRICHUM SCHENCKII. C.R.HEBD.SEANC.ACAD.SCI., PARIS, SER.D, 250,
      3503-3505.

3605 MARIAT, F. (1971) - ADAPTATION DE CERATOCYSTIS A LA VIE PARASITAIRE CHEZ
      L'ANIMAL - ETUDE DE L'ACQUISITION D'UN POUVOIR PATHOGENE COMPARABLE A
      CELUI DE SPOROTHRIX SCHENCKII. SABOURAUDIA 9, 191-205.

3606 MARIAT, F. (1975) - OBSERVATIONS SUR L'ECOLOGIE DES SPOROTHRIX SCHENCKII
      ET DE CERATOCYSTIS STENOCERAS EN CORSE ET EN ALSACE, PROVINCES FRAN-
      CAISES INDEMNES DE SPOROTRICHOSE. SABOURAUDIA 13, 217-225.

3607 MARIAT, F. & DIEZ, E. (1971) - ADAPTATION DE CERATOCYSTIS STENOCERAS (RO-
      BAK) C. MOREAU A LA VIE PARASITAIRE CHEZ L'ANIMAL. ETUDE DE LA SOUCHE
      SAUVAGE ET DES MUTANTS PATHOGENES. COMPARAISON AVEC SPOROTHRIX SCHEN-
      CKII HEKTOEN & PERKINS. REVUE MYCOL. 36, 2-24.

3608 MARKS, G.C., FAGG, P.C. & KASSABY, F.Y. (1975) - THE DISTRIBUTION OF PHY-
      TOPHTHORA CINNAMOMI IN FORESTS OF EASTERN GIPPSLAND, VICTORIA. AUST.J.
      BOT. 23, 263-276.

3609 MARKS, G.C. & KASSABY, F.Y. (1974) - PATHOGENICITY OF PYTHIUM SPP. AND
      PHYTOPHTHORA DRECHSLERI TO EUCALYPTUS SPP. AUST.J.BOT. 22, 661-668.

3610 MARKS, G.C., KASSABY, F.Y. & FAGG, P.C. (1975) - VARIATION IN POPULATION
      LEVELS OF PHYTOPHTHORA CINNAMOMI IN EUCALYPTUS FOREST SOILS OF EASTERN
      VICTORIA. AUST.J.BOT. 23, 435-449.

3611 MARKS, G.C., KASSABY, F.Y. & REYNOLDS, S.T. (1972) - DIE-BACK IN THE MIXED
      HARDWOOD FORESTS OF EASTERN VICTORIA. A PRELIMINARY REPORT. AUST.J.BOT.
      20, 141-154.

3612 MARLOTH, R.H. (1931) - THE INFLUENCE OF HYDROGEN-ION CONCENTRATION AND OF SODIUM BICARBONATE AND RELATED SUBSTANCES ON PENICILLIUM ITALICUM AND P. DIGITATUM. PHYTOPATHOLOGY 21, 169-198.

3613 MARPLES, M.J. (1961) - SOME EXTRA-HUMAN RESERVOIRS OF PATHOGENIC FUNGI IN NEW ZEALAND. TRANS.R.SOC.TROP.MED.HYG. 55, 216-220.

3614 MARPLES, M.J. (1965) - THE DISTRIBUTION OF KERATINOPHILIC FUNGI IN SOILS FROM NEW ZEALAND AND FROM TWO POLYNESIAN ISLANDS. MYCOPATH.MYCOL.APPL. 25, 361-372.

3615 MARPLES, M.J. & SMITH, J.M.B. (1962) - TRICHOPHYTON TERRESTRE AS A RESIDENT IN HEDGEHOG SKIN. SABOURAUDIA 2, 100-107.

3616 MARSDEN, D.H. (1954) - STUDIES OF THE CREOSOTE FUNGUS, HORMODENDRUM RESINAE. MYCOLOGIA 46, 161-183.

3617 MARSH, P.B. & BOLLENBACHER, K. (1946) - THE VITAMIN REQUIREMENTS OF MEMNONIELLA AND STACHYBOTRYS. AM.J.BOT. 33, 245-249.

3618 MARSH, P.B., BOLLENBACHER, K., BUTLER, M.L. & RAPER, K.B. (1949) - THE FUNGI CONCERNED IN FIBER DETERIORATION. 2. THEIR ABILITY TO DECOMPOSE CELLULOSE. TEXT.RES.J. 19, 462-484.

3619 MARSH, P.B., TAYLOR, E.E. & BASSLER, L.M. (1959) - A GUIDE TO THE LITERATURE ON CERTAIN EFFECTS OF LIGHT ON FUNGI. REPRODUCTION, MORPHOLOGY, PIGMENTATION, AND PHOTOTROPIC PHENOMENA. PL.DIS.REPTR, SUPPL. 261, 251-312.

3620 MARSHALL, C.R. & WALKLEY, V.T. (1952) - SOME ASPECTS OF MICROBIOLOGY APPLIED TO COMMERCIAL APPLE JUICE PRODUCTION. 5. THERMAL DEATH RATES OF SPOILAGE ORGANISMS IN APPLE JUICE. FD RES. 17, 204-211.

3621 MARSHALL, J.J. (1973) - PURIFICATION AND SOME PROPERTIES OF RHIZOPUS ARRHIZUS BETA-1,3-GLUCANASE. TRANS.BIOCHEM.SOC., 1973 (1), 445.

3622 MARSHALL, K.C. & ALEXANDER, M. (1961) - FUNGI ACTIVE IN HETEROTROPHIC NITRIFICATION. CAN.J.MICROBIOL. 7, 955-957.

3623 MARTIN, G.W. (1925) - MORPHOLOGY OF CONIDIOBOLUS VILLOSUS. BOT.GAZ. 80, 311-318.

3624 MARTIN, J.F., LIRAS, P. & VILLANUEVA, J.R. (1974) - CHANGES IN COMPOSITION OF CONIDIA OF PENICILLIUM NOTATUM DURING GERMINATION. ARCH.MICROBIOL. 97, 39-50.

3625 MARTIN, J.F. & NICOLAS, G. (1970) - PHYSIOLOGY OF SPORE GERMINATION IN PENICILLIUM NOTATUM AND TRICHODERMA LIGNORUM. TRANS.BR.MYCOL.SOC. 55, 141-148.

3626 MARTIN, J.F., NICOLAS, G. & VILLANUEVA, J.R. (1973) - CHEMICAL CHANGES IN THE CELL WALLS OF CONIDIA OF PENICILLIUM NOTATUM DURING GERMINATION. CAN.J.MICROBIOL. 19, 789-796.

3627 MARTIN, J.F., URUBURU, F. & VILLANUEVA, J.R. (1973) - ULTRASTRUCTURAL CHANGES IN THE CONIDIA OF PENICILLIUM NOTATUM DURING GERMINATION. CAN.J.MICROBIOL. 19, 797-801.

3628 MARTIN, J.H.D. (1967) - RECORDS OF ENTOMOGENOUS FUNGI FROM QUEENSLAND, 1962-1965. QD J.AGRIC.ANIM.SCI. 24, 109-112.

3629 MARTIN, J.P. (1950) - EFFECTS OF FUMIGATION AND OTHER SOIL TREATMENTS IN
      THE GREENHOUSE ON THE FUNGUS POPULATION OF OLD CITRUS SOIL. SOIL SCI.
      69, 107-122.

3630 MARTIN, J.P. (1960) - FUNGI AND NEMATODES IN SOUTH AFRICAN CITRUS ORCHARD
      SOILS IN RELATION TO THE CITRUS REPLANT PROBLEM. PROC.SOIL SCI.SOC.AM.
      24, 469-472.

3631 MARTIN, J.P., BAINES, R.C. & ERVIN, J.O. (1957) - INFLUENCE OF SOIL FUMI-
      GATION FOR CITRUS REPLANTS ON THE FUNGUS POPULATION OF THE SOIL. PROC.
      SOIL SCI.SOC.AM. 21, 163-166.

3632 MARTIN, J.P. & ERVIN, J.O. (1958) - CHANGES IN FUNGUS POPULATION OF CALI-
      FORNIA OLD CITRUS ORCHARD SOILS WHEN CROPPED TO ORANGE SEEDLINGS IN THE
      GREENHOUSE. SOIL SCI. 86, 152-155.

3633 MARTIN, J.P., ERVIN, J.O. & SHEPHERD, R.A. (1959) - DECOMPOSITION AND AG-
      GREGATING EFFECT OF FUNGUS CELL MATERIAL IN SOIL. PROC.SOIL SCI.SOC.AM.
      23, 217-220.

3634 MARTIN, J.P. & HAIDER, K. (1969) - PHENOLIC POLYMERS OF STACHYBOTRYS ATRA,
      STACHYBOTRYS CHARTARUM AND EPICOCCUM NIGRUM IN RELATION TO HUMIC ACID
      FORMATION. SOIL SCI. 107, 260-270.

3635 MARTIN, J.P., KLOTZ, L.J., DEWOLFE, T.A. & ERVIN, J.O. (1956) - INFLUENCE
      OF SOME COMMON SOIL FUNGI ON GROWTH OF CITRUS SEEDLINGS. SOIL SCI. 81,
      259-267.

3636 MARTIN, J.P., RICHARDS, S.J. & HAIDER, K. (1967) - PROPERTIES AND DECOMPO-
      SITION AND BINDING ACTION IN SOIL OF HUMIC ACID SYNTHESIZED BY EPICOC-
      CUM NIGRUM. PROC.SOIL SCI.SOC.AM. 31, 657-662.

3637 MARTIN, P. (1958) - EINFLUSS DER KULTURFILTRATE VON MIKROORGANISMEN AUF
      DIE ABGABE VON SCOPOLETIN AUS DEN KEIMWURZELN DES HAFERS (AVENA SATIVA).
      ARCH.MIKROBIOL. 29, 154-168.

3638 MARTIN, P. (1964) - UNTERSUCHUNGEN UEBER EIN PHYTOPATHOGENES TOXIN VON PY-
      THIUM IRREGULARE. PHYTOPATH.Z. 50, 235-249.

3639 MARTIN, S.M. (1958) - PRODUCTION OF EXTRACELLULAR POLYSACCHARIDES BY MUCOR
      RACEMOSUS. CAN.J.MICROBIOL. 4, 317-319.

3640 MARTIN, S.M. & ADAMS, G.A. (1956) - A SURVEY OF FUNGAL POLYSACCHARIDES.
      CAN.J.MICROBIOL. 2, 715-721.

3641 MARTINELLI, S.D. (1972) - BIOCHEMICAL INVESTIGATIONS ON CONIDIATION OF AS-
      PERGILLUS NIDULANS IN SUBMERGED LIQUID CULTURE. BIOCHEM.J. 127, 16.

3642 MARTINELLI, S.D. (1976) - CONIDIATION OF ASPERGILLUS NIDULANS IN SUBMERGED
      CULTURE. TRANS.BR.MYCOL.SOC. 67, 121-128.

3643 MARTINELLI, S.D. & BAINBRIDGE, B.W. (1974) - PHENOLOXIDASES OF ASPERGILLUS
      NIDULANS. TRANS.BR.MYCOL.SOC. 63, 361-370.

3644 MARTINEZ, E.M. & CHRISTENSEN, C.M. (1973) - FUNGUS FLORA OF BLACK AND
      WHITE PEPPER (PIPER NIGRUM). REVTA LATINOAM.MICROBIOL. 15, 19-22.

3645 MARTINEZ, M.L., SCHIEBER, E., GOMEZ BRENES, R. & BRESSANI, R. (1970) -
      (PREVALENCE OF FUNGI IN CORN (ZEA MAYS L.) IN GUATEMALA). TURRIALBA 20,
      311-319.

3646   MARTIN-SCOTT, I. (1954) - ONYCHOMYCOSIS CAUSED BY SCOPULARIOPSIS BREVICAU-
       LIS. TRANS.BR.MYCOL.SOC. 37, 38-43.

3647   MARTINSON, C. & BAKER, R. (1962) - INCREASING RELATIVE FREQUENCY OF SPECI-
       FIC FUNGUS ISOLATIONS WITH SOIL MICROBIOLOGICAL SAMPLING TUBES. PHYTO-
       PATHOLOGY 52, 619-621.

3648   MARTINSON, C.A. (1967) - PASSIVE SURVIVAL OF ENDOCONIDIA AND CHLAMYDOSPORES
       OF THIELAVIOPSIS BASICOLA IN SOIL. PHYTOPATHOLOGY 57, 821 (ABS.).

3649   MARTINSON, C.A. & HORNER, C.E. (1962) - IMPORTANCE OF NONHOSTS IN MAIN-
       TAINING THE INOCULUM POTENTIAL OF VERTICILLIUM. PHYTOPATHOLOGY 52, 742
       (ABS.).

3650   MARTINSON, C.A. & HORNER, C.E. (1964) - COLONIZATION OF PLANT DEBRIS IN
       SOIL BY VERTICILLIUM DAHLIAE. PHYTOPATHOLOGY 54, 900 (ABS.).

3651   MARTINSON, F.D. (1971) - CHRONIC PHYCOMYCOSIS OF THE UPPER RESPIRATORY
       TRACT. AM.J.TROP.MED.HYG. 20, 449-455.

3652   MARTSENIUK, L.M. & MAZILKIN, I.A. (1972) - (FUNGI OCCURRING IN SOILS OF
       EAST SIBERIA). MIKOL.FITOPAT. 6, 448-450.

3653   MARUKAWA, S., FUNAKAWA, S. & SATOMURA, Y. (1975) - ROLE OF SCLERIN ON MOR-
       PHOGENESIS IN SCLEROTINIA SCLEROTIORUM (INCLUDING S. LIBERTIANA). AGRIC.
       BIOL.CHEM., TOKYO 39, 645-650.

3654   MARUMO, SH. (1959) - ISLANDITOXIN, A TOXIC METABOLITE PRODUCED BY PENICIL-
       LIUM ISLANDICUM SOPP. 3. STRUCTURE OF ISLANDITOXIN. BULL.AGRIC.CHEM.SOC.
       JAPAN 23, 428-437.

3655   MARVANOVA, L. & MARVAN, P. (1963) - (EINIGE HYPHOMYCETEN AUS DEN FLIESSEN-
       DEN GEWAESSERN DES HRUBY JESENIK). ACTA MUS.SILESIAE, SER.A, 12, 101-
       118.

3656   MARX, D.H. (1973) - GROWTH OF ECTOMYCORRHIZAL AND NONMYCORRHIZAL SHORTLEAF
       PINE SEEDLINGS IN SOIL WITH PHYTOPHTHORA CINNAMOMI. PHYTOPATHOLOGY 63,
       18-24.

3657   MARX, D.H. & HAASIS, F.A. (1965) - INDUCTION OF ASEPTIC SPORANGIAL FORMA-
       TION IN PHYTOPHTHORA CINNAMOMI BY METABOLIC DIFFUSATES OF SOIL MICRO-
       ORGANISMS. NATURE, LOND. 206, 673-674.

3658   MASAGO, H., YOSHIKAWA, M., FUKADA, M. & NAKANISHI, N. (1977) - SELECTIVE
       INHIBITION OF PYTHIUM SPP. ON A MEDIUM FOR DIRECT ISOLATION OF PHY-
       TOPHTHORA SPP. FROM SOILS AND PLANTS. PHYTOPATHOLOGY 67, 425-428.

3659   MASON, E.W. (1927) - ON SPECIES OF THE GENUS NIGROSPORA ZIMMERMANN RECORD-
       ED ON MONOCOTYLEDONS. TRANS.BR.MYCOL.SOC. 12, 152-165.

3660   MASON, E.W. (1933) - ANNOTATED ACCOUNT OF FUNGI RECEIVED AT THE IMPERIAL
       MYCOLOGICAL INSTITUTE. MYCOL.PAP. 3, 1-67.

3661   MASON, E.W. (1941) - ANNOTATED ACCOUNT OF FUNGI RECEIVED AT THE IMPERIAL
       MYCOLOGICAL INSTITUTE. LIST 2. MYCOL.PAP. 5, 101-144.

3662   MASON, E.W. & ELLIS, M.B. (1953) - BRITISH SPECIES OF PERICONIA. MYCOL.PAP.
       56, 1-127.

3663   MASON, P.J. & CROSSE, R. (1975) - CRYSTALLINE INCLUSIONS IN HYPHAE OF THE
       ASPERGILLUS GLAUCUS GROUP OF ASPERGILLI. TRANS.BR.MYCOL.SOC. 65, 129-
       134.

3664 MATANMI, B.A. & LIBBY, J.L. (1975) - SCANNING ELECTRON MICROSCOPY OF ENTO-
      MOPHTHORA VIRULENTA AND CONIDIOBOLUS CORONATUS (ENTOMOPHTHORALES - ENTO-
      MOPHTHORACEAE). J.INVERTEBR.PATH. 26, 165-170.

3665 MATANMI, B.A., LIBBY, J.L. & MAXWELL, D.P. (1974) - TWO PHYCOMYCETES IN-
      FECTING ROOT MAGGOT ADULTS IN WISCONSIN. ENVIRON.ENTOMOL. 3, 1030-1031.

3666 MATHISON, G.E. (1964) - THE MICROBIOLOGICAL DECOMPOSITION OF KERATIN.
      ANNLS SOC.BELGE MED.TROP. 44, 767-791.

3667 MATHRE, D.E. (1969) - PHYSIOLOGY OF THICK-WALLED SPORES OF SOIL-BORNE
      PLANT PATHOGENIC FUNGI. 1. RESPIRATION AND GERMINATION OF HELMINTHOSPO-
      RIUM SATIVUM AND H. PEDICELLATUM SPORES. CAN.J.BOT. 47, 1513-1520.

3668 MATHRE, D.E. & RAVENSCROFT, A.V. (1966) - PHYSIOLOGY OF GERMINATION OF
      CHLAMYDOSPORES AND ENDOCONIDIA OF THIELAVIOPSIS BASICOLA. PHYTOPATHOL-
      OGY 56, 337-342.

3669 MATHUR, S.B. (1962) - SOIL CONDITIONS IN RELATION TO SOME DISEASES OF
      CROPS. AGRA UNIV.J.RES. 11, 105-107.

3670 MATHUR, S.K., RAM NATH & MATHUR, S.B. (1973) - SEEDBORNE FUNGI OF PEARL
      MILLET (PENNISETUM TYPHOIDES) AND THEIR SIGNIFICANCE. SEED SCI.TECHNOL.
      1, 811-820.

3671 MATHUR, S.P. (1969) - MICROBIAL USE OF PODZOL BH FULVIC ACIDS. CAN.J.MICRO-
      BIOL. 15, 677-680.

3672 MATHUR, S.P. & PAUL, E.A. (1967) - MICROBIAL UTILIZATION OF SOIL HUMIC
      ACIDS. CAN.J.MICROBIOL. 13, 573-580.

3673 MATSUDA, T. (1949) - FOLIC ACID. 2. COMPARATIVE STUDIES FOR THE SYNTHESIS
      OF FOLIC ACID BY VARIOUS MOLDS. VITAMINS, JAP. 2, 121-124.

3674 MATSUMOTO, T.T., BUCKLEY, P.M., SOMMER, N.F. & SHALLA, T.A. (1969) - CHILL-
      ING-INDUCED ULTRASTRUCTURAL CHANGES IN RHIZOPUS STOLONIFER SPORANGIO-
      SPORES. PHYTOPATHOLOGY 59, 863-867.

3675 MATSUMOTO, T.T. & SOMMER, N.F. (1967) - SENSITIVITY OF RHIZOPUS STOLONIFER
      TO CHILLING. PHYTOPATHOLOGY 57, 881-884.

3676 MATSUMURA, F. & BOUSH, G.M. (1966) - MALATHION DEGRADATION BY TRICHODERMA
      VIRIDE AND PSEUDOMONAS SPECIES. SCIENCE, N.Y. 153, 1278-1280.

3677 MATSUMURA, F. & BOUSH, G.M. (1967) - DIELDRIN. DEGRADATION BY SOIL MICRO-
      ORGANISMS. SCIENCE, N.Y. 156, 959-961.

3678 MATSUMURA, F. & BOUSH, G.M. (1968) - DEGRADATION OF INSECTICIDES BY A SOIL
      FUNGUS, TRICHODERMA VIRIDE. J.ECON.ENT. 61, 610-612.

3679 MATSUSHIMA, T. (1971) - MICROFUNGI OF THE SOLOMON ISLANDS AND PAPUA-NEW
      GUINEA. NIPPON PRINTING AND PUBLISHING CO., OSAKA, 78 PP., 217 PLATES.

3680 MATSUSHIMA, T. (1975) - ICONES MICROFUNGORUM A MATSUSHIMA LECTORUM. KOBE,
      JAPAN, 209 PP. AND 415 PLATES.

3681 MATTA, K.L. & BAHL, O.P. (1972) - GLYCOSIDASES OF ASPERGILLUS NIGER. 4.
      PURIFICATION AND CHARACTERIZATION OF ALPHA-MANNOSIDASE. J.BIOL.CHEM.
      247, 1780-1787.

3682 MATTURI, S.T. & STENTON, H. (1958) - A TECHNIQUE FOR THE INVESTIGATION OF
      THE COMPETITIVE SAPROPHYTIC ABILITY OF SOIL FUNGI BY THE USE OF EASILY
      DECOMPOSED SUBSTRATES. NATURE, LOND. 182, 1248-1249.

3683   MATTURI, S.T. & STENTON, H. (1964) - DISTRIBUTION AND STATUS IN THE SOIL
       OF CYLINDROCARPON SPECIES. TRANS.BR.MYCOL.SOC. 47, 577-587.

3684   MATTURI, S.T. & STENTON, H. (1964) - THE BEHAVIOUR IN SOIL OF SPORES OF
       FOUR SPECIES OF CYLINDROCARPON. TRANS.BR.MYCOL.SOC. 47, 589-599.

3685   MAURER, C.L. & BAKER, R. (1965) - ECOLOGY OF PLANT PATHOGENS IN SOIL. 2.
       INFLUENCE OF GLUCOSE, CELLULOSE, AND INORGANIC NITROGEN AMENDMENTS ON
       DEVELOPMENT OF BEAN ROOT ROT. PHYTOPATHOLOGY 55, 69-72.

3686   MAXWELL, D.P. (1973) - OXALATE FORMATION IN WHETZELINIA SCLEROTIORUM BY
       OXALOACETATE ACETYLHYDROLASE. PHYSIOL.PL.PATH. 3, 279-288.

3687   MAXWELL, D.P. & BATEMAN, D.F. (1967) - GLUCOSE CATABOLISM IN SCLEROTIUM
       ROLFSII. PHYTOPATHOLOGY 58, 1630-1634.

3688   MAXWELL, D.P. & BATEMAN, D.F. (1968) - INFLUENCE OF CARBON SOURCE AND PH
       ON OXALATE ACCUMULATION IN CULTURE FILTRATES OF SCLEROTIUM ROLFSII.
       PHYTOPATHOLOGY 58, 1351-1355.

3689   MAXWELL, D.P. & BATEMAN, D.F. (1968) - OXALIC ACID BIOSYNTHESIS BY SCLERO-
       TIUM ROLFSII. PHYTOPATHOLOGY 58, 1635-1642.

3690   MAXWELL, D.P. & LUMSDEN, R.D. (1970) - OXALIC ACID PRODUCTION BY SCLEROTI-
       NIA SCLEROTIORUM IN INFECTED BEAN AND IN CULTURE. PHYTOPATHOLOGY 60,
       1395-1398.

3691   MAXWELL, D.P., MAXWELL, M.D., HOCH, H.C. & ARMENTROUT, V.M. (1973) - OCCUR-
       RENCE OF MICROBODIES IN PHYTOPATHOGENIC FUNGI. ABSTR. 2ND INT.CONGR.PL.
       PATH., P. 335.

3692   MAXWELL, D.P., WILLIAMS, P.H. & MAXWELL, M.D. (1972) - STUDIES ON THE POS-
       SIBLE RELATIONSHIPS OF MICROBODIES AND MULTIVESICULAR BODIES TO OXALATE,
       ENDOPOLYGALACTURONASE, AND CELLULASE (CX) PRODUCTION BY SCLEROTINIA
       SCLEROTIORUM. CAN.J.BOT. 50, 1743-1748.

3693   MAY, O.E., HERRICK, H.T., MOYER, A.J. & WELLS, P.A. (1934) - GLUCONIC ACID
       PRODUCTION BY SUBMERGED MOLD GROWTH UNDER INCREASED AIR PRESSURE. IND.
       ENGNG CHEM. 26, 575-578.

3694   MAY, O.E., HERRICK, H.T., THOM, C. & CHURCH, M.B. (1927) - THE PRODUCTION
       OF GLUCONIC ACID BY THE PENICILLIUM LUTEUM-PURPUROGENUM GROUP. 1. J.
       BIOL.CHEM. 75, 417-422.

3695   MAYORAL, B.M., KAPLAN, L. & PAPPELIS, A.J. (1964) - CARBOHYDRATE UTILIZA-
       TION BY CEPHALIOPHORA TROPICA. MYCOLOGIA 56, 626-630.

3696   MAYORGA, R., CAMEY, L., CACERES, A. & MARIAT, F. (1973) - EPIDEMIE DE
       SPOROTRICHOSE HUMAINE AU GUATEMALA. BULL.SOC.FR.MYCOL.MED. 2, 29-30.

3697   MCCLELLAN, W.D., BORTHWICK, H.A., BJORNSSON, I. & BARTON, H.M. (1955) -
       SOME RESPONSES OF FUNGI TO LIGHT. PHYTOPATHOLOGY 45, 465 (ABS.).

3698   MCCOLLOCH, L.P. (1944) - A STUDY OF THE APPLE ROT FUNGUS PHIALOPHORA MALO-
       RUM. MYCOLOGIA 36, 576-590.

3699   MCCONNELL, W.B., SPENCER, E.Y. & TREW, J.A. (1953) - PROTEOLYTIC ENZYMES
       OF MICROORGANISMS. 5. EXTRACELLULAR PEPTIDASES PRODUCED BY FUNGI GROWN
       IN SUBMERGED CULTURE. CAN.J.CHEM. 31, 697-704.

3700 MCCOY, E.C., GIRARD, A.E. & KORNFELD, J.M. (1972) - FINE STRUCTURE OF REST-
      ING AND GERMINATING PENICILLIUM CHRYSOGENUM CONIDIOSPORES. PROTOPLASMA
      73, 443-456.

3701 MCCULLY, E.K. & ROBINOW, C.F. (1973) - MITOSIS IN MUCOR HIEMALIS. A COM-
      PARATIVE LIGHT AND ELECTRON MICROSCOPICAL STUDY. ARCH.MIKROBIOL. 94,
      133-148.

3702 MCDONALD, D. (1970) - FUNGAL INFECTION OF GROUNDNUT FRUIT BEFORE HARVEST.
      TRANS.BR.MYCOL.SOC. 54, 453-460.

3703 MCDONALD, W.C. (1961) - A REVIEW OF THE TAXONOMY AND NOMENCLATURE OF SOME
      LOW-TEMPERATURE FORAGE PATHOGENS. CAN.PL.DIS.SURV. 41, 256-260.

3704 MCEVOY, J.J. (1974) - PHENYLALANINE HYDROXYLASE ACTIVITY IN A MUTANT OF
      GEOTRICHUM CANDIDUM. ANTONIE VAN LEEUWENHOEK 40, 409-416.

3705 MCFADDEN, A.G. & SUTTON, J.C. (1975) - RELATIONSHIPS OF POPULATIONS OF
      TRICHODERMA SPP. IN SOIL DISEASE IN MAIZE. CAN.J.PL.SCI. 55, 579-586.

3706 MCGINNIS, M.R. & AJELLO, L. (1974) - SCOLECOBASIDIUM TSHAWYTSCHAE. TRANS.
      BR.MYCOL.SOC. 63, 202-203.

3707 MCGINNIS, M.R., NILSON, A.D. & WARE, L.L. (1975) - MYCOTIC BIODETERIORA-
      TION ASSOCIATED WITH THE MOVEMENT AND STORAGE OF COMMERCIALLY HANDLED
      HOUSEHOLD GOODS. MYCOPATHOLOGIA 57, 41-45.

3708 MCGINNIS, M.R. & PADHYE, A.A. (1977) - EXOPHIALA JEANSELMEI, A NEW COMBI-
      NATION FOR PHIALOPHORA JEANSELMEI. MYCOTAXON 5, 341-352.

3709 MCHARGUE, J.S. & CALFEE, R.K. (1931) - EFFECT OF MANGANESE, COPPER, AND
      ZINC ON GROWTH AND METABOLISM OF ASPERGILLUS FLAVUS AND RHIZOPUS NIGRI-
      CANS. BOT.GAZ. 91, 183-193.

3710 MCILVEEN, W.D. & EDDINGTON, L.V. (1972) - ISOLATION OF THIELAVIOPSIS BASI-
      COLA FROM SOIL WITH UMBELLIFEROUS ROOT TISSUE AS BAITS. CAN.J.BOT. 50,
      1363-1366.

3711 MCINNES, A.G., SMITH, D.G., WAT, C.-K., VINING, L.C. & WRIGHT, J.L.C.
      (1974) - TENELLIN AND BASSIANIN, METABOLITES OF BEAUVERIA SPECIES -
      STRUCTURE ELUCIDATION WITH 15N- AND DOUBLY 13C-ENRICHED COMPOUNDS USING
      13C NUCLEAR MAGNETIC RESONANCE SPECTROSCOPY. J.CHEM.SOC.CHEM.COMMUN.,
      1974 (8), 281-282.

3712 MCINTOSH, D.L. (1964) - PHYTOPHTHORA SPECIES IN SOILS OF THE OKANAGAN AND
      SIMILKAMEEN VALLEYS OF BRITISH COLUMBIA. CAN.J.BOT. 42, 1411-1415.

3713 MCINTOSH, D.L. (1972) - EFFECTS OF SOIL WATER SUCTION, SOIL TEMPERATURE,
      CARBON AND NITROGEN AMENDMENTS, AND HOST ROOTLETS ON SURVIVAL IN SOIL
      OF ZOOSPORES OF PHYTOPHTHORA CACTORUM. CAN.J.BOT. 50, 269-272.

3714 MCINTOSH, D.L. (1975) - AN IMPROVED AGAR MEDIUM FOR ISOLATING PHYTOPHTHORA
      CACTORUM FROM SOIL. CAN.J.BOT. 53, 1444-1445.

3715 MCKEEN, C.D. & THORPE, H.J. (1971) - AN ADAPTATION OF A MOIST-CHAMBER
      METHOD FOR ISOLATING AND IDENTIFYING VERTICILLIUM SPP. CAN.J.MICROBIOL.
      17, 1139-1141.

3716 MCKEEN, C.D. & WENSLEY, R.N. (1961) - LONGEVITY OF FUSARIUM OXYSPORUM IN
      SOIL TUBE CULTURE. SCIENCE, N.Y. 134, 1528-1529.

3717 MCKEEN, W.E. (1975) - ELECTRON MICROSCOPY STUDIES OF A DEVELOPING PYTHIUM
      OOGONIUM. CAN.J.BOT. 53, 2354-2360.

3718 MCLEAN, D.M. (1958) - SOME EXPERIMENTS CONCERNED WITH THE FORMATION AND
      INHIBITION OF APOTHECIA OF SCLEROTINIA SCLEROTIORUM (LIB.) DE BY. PL.
      DIS.REPTR 42, 409-412.

3719 MCLENNAN, E.I. & DUCKER, S.C. (1954) - MICRO-FUNGAL POPULATION OF ACID
      SANDY PODSOLS. NATURE, LOND. 174, 1060-1061.

3720 MCLENNAN, E.I. & DUCKER, S.C. (1954) - THE ECOLOGY OF THE SOIL FUNGI OF AN
      AUSTRALIAN HEATHLAND. AUST.J.BOT. 2, 220-245.

3721 MCLENNAN, E.I. & DUCKER, S.C. (1954) - THE RELATIVE ABUNDANCE OF MORTIE-
      RELLA SPECIES IN ACID HEATH SOILS. AUST.J.BOT. 5, 36-43.

3722 MCMASTER, W.J., SCOTT, A.I. & TRIPPETT, S. (1960) - METABOLIC PRODUCTS OF
      PENICILLIUM PATULUM. J.CHEM.SOC., 1960, 4628-4631.

3723 MCMILLEN, S.H. (1960) - ANOTHER SOURCE OF MYCOTYPHA DICHOTOMA. MYCOLOGIA
      52, 653.

3724 MCPHEE, W.J. & COLOTELO, N. (1977) - FUNGAL EXUDATES. 1. CHARACTERISTICS
      OF HYPHAL EXUDATES IN FUSARIUM CULMORUM. CAN.J.BOT. 55, 358-365.

3725 MCQUADE, A.B. (1963) - MORPHOGENESIS AND NUTRITION IN THE MEMNONIELLA-
      STACHYBOTRYS GROUP OF FUNGI. J.GEN.MICROBIOL. 30, 429-435.

3726 MCROBBIE, D.I., PARKER, M.S., SMITH, J.E. & ANDERSON, J.G. (1972) - INFLU-
      ENCE OF TEMPERATURE, MEDIA AND PRESERVATIVE ON SPORE SWELLING OF ASPER-
      GILLUS NIGER AND TRICHODERMA VIRIDE. TRANS.BR.MYCOL.SOC. 59, 115-122.

3727 MCVEIGH, I. & HOUSTON, W.E. (1972) - FACTORS AFFECTING MYCELIAL TO YEAST
      PHASE CONVERSION AND GROWTH OF THE YEAST PHASE OF HISTOPLASMA CAPSULA-
      TUM. MYCOPATH.MYCOL.APPL. 47, 135-151.

3728 MEAGHER, J.W. & CHAMBERS, S.C. (1971) - PATHOGENIC EFFECTS OF HETERODERA
      AVENAE AND RHIZOCTONIA SOLANI AND THEIR INTERACTION ON WHEAT. AUST.J.
      AGRIC.RES. 22, 189-194.

3729 MEHROTRA, B.R. (1969) - SOME NEW REPORTS OF ASCOMYCETES FROM ALLAHABAD.
      SYDOWIA 23, 81-91.

3730 MEHROTRA, B.R., BAIJAL, U. & MEHROTRA, B.S. (1965) - SPECIES OF MUCOR FROM
      INDIA. 1. SYDOWIA 19, 238-243.

3731 MEHROTRA, B.R. & KAKKAR, R.K. (1969) - A NOTE ON AN INTERESTING ISOLATE OF
      THAMNIDIUM FROM INDIA. SYDOWIA 23, 198-199.

3732 MEHROTRA, B.R. & KAKKAR, R.K. (1972) - ECOLOGICAL STUDY OF SOIL FUNGI OF
      AN AGRICULTURAL FIELD IN ALLAHABAD. MYCOPATH.MYCOL.APPL. 47, 41-58.

3733 MEHROTRA, B.R. & KAKKAR, R.K. (1972) - RHIZOSPHERE SOIL FUNGI OF SOME VEG-
      ETABLE PLANTS. MYCOPATH.MYCOL.APPL. 46, 379-385.

3734 MEHROTRA, B.S. (1952) - INVERTASE ACTIVITY OF PENICILLIUM ITALICUM WEHMER.
      LLOYDIA 15, 185-187.

3735 MEHROTRA, B.S. & BAIJAL, U. (1963) - SPECIES OF MORTIERELLA FROM INDIA. 3.
      MYCOPATH.MYCOL.APPL. 20, 49-54.

3736 MEHROTRA, B.S. & KRISHNA NAND (1970) - MYCOLOGICAL FAT PRODUCTION IN IN-
      DIA. 3. EFFECT OF TEMPERATURES ON FAT FORMATION. SYDOWIA 24, 153-160.

3737 MEHROTRA, B.S., KUMAR, D. & AGNIHOTRI, V.P. (1963) - STUDIES ON ASPERGILLI
      AND PENICILLIA OF THE RHIZOSPHERE OF SOME CROP PLANTS. PROC.NATN.ACAD.
      SCI., INDIA, SECT.B, 33, 139-147.

3738 MEHROTRA, B.S. & MEHROTRA, B.R. (1964) - SPECIES OF MORTIERELLA FROM INDIA.
      4. ZENTBL.BAKT.PARASITKDE, ABT.2, 118, 178-185.

3739 MEHROTRA, B.S., SINGH, S.N. & BAIJAL, U. (1974) - THE SECTION SPHAEROSPO-
      RUS OF MUCOR. A REASSESSMENT. SYDOWIA 26, 41-62.

3740 MEHROTRA, B.S. & TANDON, G.D. (1969) - ADDITIONS TO PENICILLIA OF INDIA.
      1. PROC.NATN.ACAD.SCI., INDIA, SECT.B, 39, 115-120.

3741 MEIER, H. (1955) - UEBER DEN ZELLWANDABBAU DURCH HOLZVERMORSCHUNGSPILZE
      UND DIE SUBMIKROSKOPISCHE STRUKTUR VON FICHTENTRACHEIDEN UND BIRKENHOLZ-
      FASERN. HOLZ ROH-U.WERKST. 13, 323-338.

3742 MEINHOF, W. & GRABOWSKI, A. (1972) - GEOPHILE DERMATOPHYTEN UND ANDERE
      KERATINOPHILE BODENPILZE IN ERDPROBEN AUS EINER ALPENREGION. HAUTARZT
      23, 359-362.

3743 MEINHOF, W., THIANPRASIT, M. & RIETH, H. (1960) - NACHWEIS, ISOLIERUNG UND
      IDENTIFIZIERUNG KERATINVERWERTENDER HAUTPATHOGENER BODENPILZE. ARCH.KLIN.
      EXP.DERM. 212, 30-48.

3744 MEKHTIEVA, N.A. (1967) - (INTERRELATIONSHIP BETWEEN PREDATORY FUNGI AND
      OTHER SOIL MICROORGANISMS). DOKL.AKAD.NAUK AZERB.SSR, 23, 57-60.

3745 MEKHTIEVA, N.A. (1972) - (MAIN RESULTS AND PROSPECTS OF STUDYING PREDA-
      CIOUS FUNGI IN AZERBAIJAN). MIKOL.FITOPAT. 6, 477-482.

3746 MELENDEZ-HOWELL, L.M. (1970) - ANALYSE, PAR DECAPAGE, DU PORE GERMINATIF
      DES SPORES D'APIOSORDARIA VERRUCULOSA (JENSEN) V. ARX & GAMS EN MICRO-
      SCOPIE ELECTRONIQUE A BALAYAGE. ANNLS SCI.NAT.BOT., SER.12, 11, 153-168.

3747 MELENDEZ-HOWELL, L.M. & CAILLEUX, R. (1975) - SUR QUELQUES ASPECTS DU PORE
      GERMINATIF ASCOSPORAL DANS LE GENRE GELASINOSPORA DOWDING. BULL.TRIMEST.
      SOC.MYCOL.FR. 91, 105-116.

3748 MELERA, A. (1963) - ZUR KONSTITUTION VON HELVOLINSAEURE UND CEPHALOSPORIN
      -P1. EXPERIENTIA 19, 565-566.

3749 MELIN, E. & NANNFELDT, J.A. (1934) - RESEARCHES INTO THE BLUEING OF GROUND
      WOODPULP. SV.SKOGSV.FOEREN.TIDSKR. 32, 397-616.

3750 MELOUK, H.A. & HORNER, C.E. (1974) - VERTICILLIUM NIGRESCENS FROM PEPPER-
      MINT. PHYTOPATHOLOGY 64, 1267-1268.

3751 MELOUK, H.A. & HORNER, C.E. (1975) - CROSS PROTECTION IN MINTS BY VERTI-
      CILLIUM NIGRESCENS AGAINST V. DAHLIAE. PHYTOPATHOLOGY 65, 767-769.

3752 MEMMEN, K.F. (1974) - DER EINFLUSS VON CALCIUM, MAGNESIUM AND CHOLESTERIN
      AUF DAS WACHSTUM VON PYTHIUM PAROECANDRUM UND DESSEN PATHOGENITAET FUER
      ZUCKERRUEBEN. DISS.ETH, ZUERICH.

3753 MENDONCA-HAGLER, L.C., TRAVASSOS, L.R., LLOYD, K.O. & PHAFF, H.J. (1974) -
      DEOXYRIBONUCLEIC ACID BASE COMPOSITION AND HYBRIDIZATION STUDIES ON THE
      HUMAN PATHOGEN SPOROTHRIX SCHENCKII AND CERATOCYSTIS SPECIES. INFECT.
      IMMUN. 9, 934-938.

3754 MENGES, R.W. & GEORG, L.K. (1957) - SURVEY OF ANIMAL RINGWORM IN THE UNIT-
      ED STATES. PUBLIC HEALTH REPORTS (U.S.) 72, 503-509.

3755 MENZIES, J.D. (1962) - EFFECT OF ANAEROBIC FERMENTATION IN SOIL ON SURVIV-
      AL OF SCLEROTIA OF VERTICILLIUM DAHLIAE. PHYTOPATHOLOGY 52, 743 (ABS.).

3756 MENZIES, J.D. & GRIEBEL, G.E. (1967) - SURVIVAL AND SAPROPHYTIC GROWTH OF
      VERTICILLIUM DAHLIAE IN UNCROPPED SOIL. PHYTOPATHOLOGY 57, 703-709.

3757 MENZINGER, W. (1964) - UNTERSUCHUNGEN ZUR VARIABILITAET UND TAXONOMIE VON
      FORMEN UND ARTEN DER GATTUNG BOTRYTIS MICH. DISS.UNIV.MARBURG/LAHN.

3758 MENZINGER, W. (1965) - KARYOLOGISCHE UNTERSUCHUNGEN AN ARTEN UND FORMEN
      DER GATTUNG BOTRYTIS. ARCH.MIKROBIOL. 52, 178-196.

3759 MENZINGER, W. (1966) - ZUR VARIABILITAET UND TAXONOMIE VON ARTEN UND FOR-
      MEN DER GATTUNG BOTRYTIS. 1. UNTERSUCHUNGEN ZUR KULTURBEDINGTEN VARIA-
      BILITAET MOPHOLOGISCHER EIGENSCHAFTEN VON FORMEN DER GATTUNG BOTRYTIS.
      ZENTBL.BAKT.PARASITKDE, ABT.2, 120, 141-178.

3760 MENZINGER, W. (1966) - ZUR VARIABILITAET UND TAXONOMIE VON ARTEN UND FOR-
      MEN DER GATTUNG BOTRYTIS. 2. UNTERSUCHUNGEN ZUR VARIABILITAET DES KUL-
      TURTYPS UNTER KONSTANTEN KULTURBEDINGUNGEN. ZENTBL.BAKT.PARASITKDE, ABT.
      2, 120, 179-196.

3761 MERCER, E.J. & CARRIER, D.J.R. (1976) - ERGOSTEROL BIOSYNTHESIS IN MUCOR
      PUSILLUS. PHYTOCHEMISTRY 15, 283-286.

3762 MERDINGER, E. & MERDINGER, R.P. (1970) - UTILIZATION OF N-ALKANES BY PUL-
      LULARIA PULLULANS. APPL.MICROBIOL. 20, 651-652.

3763 MEREDITH, D.S. (1963) - VIOLENT SPORE RELEASE IN SOME FUNGI IMPERFECTI.
      ANN.BOT. 27, 39-47.

3764 MEREDITH, D.S. (1966) - DIURNAL PERIODICITY AND VIOLENT LIBERATION OF CO-
      NIDIA IN EPICOCCUM. PHYTOPATHOLOGY 56, 988-990.

3765 MERLINI, L., MONDELLI, R., NASINI, G. & HESSE, M. (1973) - STRUCTURE OF
      WORTMIN, A NEW METABOLITE FROM PENICILLIUM WORTMANNI. HELV.CHIM.ACTA
      56, 232-239.

3766 MERONUCK, R.A., STEELE, J.A., MIROCHA, C.J. & CHRISTENSEN, C.M. (1972) -
      TENUAZONIC ACID A TOXIN PRODUCED BY ALTERNARIA ALTERNATA. APPL.MICRO-
      BIOL. 23, 613-617.

3767 MERRILL, W. (1966) - DECAY OF WOOD AND WOOD FIBERBOARDS BY COMMON FUNGI
      IMPERFECTI. MATER.ORG., BEIH. 1, 69-76.

3768 MERRILL, W. & FRENCH, D.W. (1965) - WOOD FIBERBOARD STUDIES. 3. EFFECTS
      OF COMMON MOLDS ON THE CELL WALL STRUCTURE OF THE WOOD FIBERS. TAPPI
      48, 653-654.

3769 MERRILL, W. & FRENCH, D.W. (1966) - COLONIZATION OF WOOD BY SOIL FUNGI.
      PHYTOPATHOLOGY 56, 301-303.

3770 MERRILL, W., FRENCH, D.W. & HOSSFELD, R.L. (1965) - WOOD FIBERBOARD STUD-
      IES. 2. EFFECTS OF COMMON MOLDS ON PHYSICAL AND CHEMICAL PROPERTIES OF
      WOOD FIBERBOARD. TAPPI 48, 470-474.

3771 MERRIMAN, P.R., PRICE, R.D. & BAKER, K.F. (1974) - THE EFFECT OF INOCULA-
      TION OF SEED WITH ANTAGONISTS OF RHIZOCTONIA SOLANI ON THE GROWTH OF
      WHEAT. AUST.J.AGRIC.RES. 25, 213-218.

3772 MERRIMAN, P.R., PRICE, R.D., KOLLMORGEN, J.F., PIGGOTT, T. & RIDGE, E.H.
      (1974) - EFFECT OF SEED INOCULATION WITH BACILLUS SUBTILIS AND STREPTO-
      MYCES GRISEUS ON THE GROWTH OF CEREALS AND CARROTS. AUST.J.AGRIC.RES.
      25, 219-226.

3773 MERT, H.H. & DIZBAY, M. (1977) - THE EFFECT OF OSMOTIC PRESSURE AND SALIN-
      ITY OF THE MEDIUM ON THE GROWTH AND SPORULATION OF ASPERGILLUS NIGER
      AND PAECILOMYCES LILACINUM SPECIES. MYCOPATHOLOGIA 61, 125-127.

3774 MERTZ, D. & HENSON, W. (1967) - LIGHT STIMULATED BIOSYNTHESIS OF GIBBEREL-
      LINS IN FUSARIUM MONILIFORME. NATURE, LOND. 214, 844-846.

3775 MERWE, J.J.H.VAN DER & WYK, P.S.VAN (1973) - HOSTS OF PHYTOPHTHORA CINNA-
      MOMI IN THE WESTERN CAPE PROVINCE OF SOUTH AFRICA. PL.DIS.REPTR 57, 1005-
      1006.

3776 MERWE, K.J.VAN DER, STEYN, P.S. & FOURIE, L. (1965) - MYCOTOXINS. 2. THE
      CONSTITUTION OF OCHRATOXINS-A, -B, AND -C, METABOLITES OF ASPERGILLUS
      OCHRACEUS. J.CHEM.SOC., 1965, 7083-7088.

3777 MERWE, K.J.VAN DER, STEYN, P.S., FOURIE, L., SCOTT, B.DE & THERON, J.J.
      (1965) - OCHRATOXIN-A, A TOXIC METABOLITE PRODUCED BY ASPERGILLUS OCHRA-
      CEUS. NATURE, LOND. 205, 1112-1113.

3778 MERZ, W.G., BURRELL, R.G. & GALLEGLY, M.E. (1969) - A SEROLOGICAL COMPAR-
      ISON OF SIX HETEROTHALLIC SPECIES OF PHYTOPHTHORA. PHYTOPATHOLOGY 58,
      367-370.

3779 MESHCHERYAKOVA, R.I. (1970) - (FUNGI PYTHIUM FROM THE PURIFYING CONSTRUC-
      TIONS). MYKROBIOL.ZH. 32 (2), 210-215.

3780 MESLAND, D.A.M., HUISMAN, J.G. & ENDE, H.VAN DEN (1974) - VOLATILE SEXUAL
      HORMONES IN MUCOR MUCEDO. J.GEN.MICROBIOL. 80, 111-117.

3781 MESSIAEN, C.M. & LAFON, R. (1957) - LES CHAMPIGNONS NUISIBLES AUX SEMIS DE
      MAIS. ANNLS EPIPHYT. 8, 111-126.

3782 MEYER, C.E. (1966) - U-21,963, A NEW ANTIBIOTIC. 2. ISOLATION AND CHARAC-
      TERIZATION. APPL.MICROBIOL. 14, 511-512.

3783 MEYER, C.E. & REUSSER, F. (1967) - A POLYPEPTIDE ANTIBACTERIAL AGENT ISO-
      LATED FROM TRICHODERMA VIRIDE. EXPERIENTIA 23, 85-86.

3784 MEYER, D. (1974) - UNTERSUCHUNGEN UEBER DIE ENTWICKLUNG VON PHYTOPHTHORA
      CACTORUM IM BODEN. DISS.UNIV.BONN.

3785 MEYER, D. & SCHOENBECK, F. (1975) - UNTERSUCHUNGEN UEBER DIE ENTWICKLUNG
      VON PHYTOPHTHORA CACTORUM IM BODEN. Z.PFLKRANKH.PFLPATH.PFLSCHUTZ 82,
      337-354.

3786 MEYER, F.H. (1960) - VERGLEICH DES MIKROBIELLEN ABBAUS VON FICHTEN- UND
      BUCHENSTREU AUF VERSCHIEDENEN BODENTYPEN. ARCH.MIKROBIOL. 35, 340-360.

3787 MEYER, F.H. (1970) - ABBAU VON PILZMYCEL IM BODEN. Z.PFLERNAEHR.DUENG.BO-
      DENK. 127, 193-199.

3788 MEYER, J. (1958) - APPAREIL CONIDIEN DE TRICHOTHECIUM ROSEUM, CYLINDROCAR-
      PON CONGOENSIS ET ARTHROBOTRYS STILBACEA. BULL.TRIMEST.SOC.MYCOL.FR.
      74, 236-248.

3789 MEYER, J. (1959) - MOISISSURES DU SOL ET DES LITIERES DE LA REGION DE
      YANGAMBI (CONGO BELGE). PUBL.INST.NATN.ETUDE AGRON.CONGO, SER.SCIENT.
      75, 1-211.

3790 MEYER, J. (1963) - ECOLOGIE ET SOCIOLOGIE DES MICROCHAMPIGNONS DU SOL DE
      LA CUVETTE CENTRALE CONGOLAISE. PUBL.INST.NATN.ETUDE AGRON.CONGO, SER.
      SCIENT. 101, 9-137.

3791 MEYER, J.A. (1967) - RECHERCHES SUR LES FUSARIOSES. 2. ECOLOGIE ET PATHO-
      GENIE DU "FUSARIUM OXYSPORUM". ANNLS EPIPHYT. 18, 241-247.

3792 MEYER, J.A., GARBER, E.D. & SHAEFFER, S.G. (1964) - GENETICS OF PHYTOPATHO-
      GENIC FUNGI. 12. DETECTION OF ESTERASES AND PHOSPHATASES IN CULTURE
      FILTRATES OF FUSARIUM OXYSPORUM AND F. XYLARIOIDES BY STARCH-GEL ZONE
      ELECTROPHORESIS. BOT.GAZ. 125, 298-300.

3793 MEYER, W.L., TEMPLETON, G.E., GRABLE, C.I., JONES, R., KUYPER, L.F., LEWIS,
      R.B., SIGEL, C.W. & WOODHEAD, S.H. (1975) - USE OF 1H NUCLEAR MAGNETIC
      RESONANCE SPECTROSCOPY FOR SEQUENCE AND CONFIGURATION ANALYSIS OF CY-
      CLIC TETRAPEPTIDES. THE STRUCTURE OF TENTOXIN. J.AM.CHEM.SOC. 97, 3802-
      3809.

3794 MEYERS, S.P., AHAERN, D.G. & COOK, W.L. (1970) - MYCOLOGICAL STUDIES OF
      LAKE CHAMPLAIN. MYCOLOGIA 62, 504-515.

3795 MEYRATH, J. (1965) - INTERDEPENDENCE OF INOCULUM SIZE, METHOD OF CULTIVA-
      TION AND SUBSTRATE COMPOSITION IN AMYLASE PRODUCTION AND GROWTH OF AS-
      PERGILLUS ORYZAE. ZENTBL.BAKT.PARASITKDE, ABT.2, 119, 53-73.

3796 MICETICH, R.G. & MACDONALD, J.C. (1964) - METABOLITES OF ASPERGILLUS SCLE-
      ROTIORUM. J.CHEM.SOC., 1964, 1507-1510.

3797 MICHELL, A.J. & SCURFIELD, G. (1967) - COMPOSITION OF EXTRACTED FUNGAL
      CELL WALLS AS INDICATED BY INFRARED SPECTROSCOPY. ARCHS BIOCHEM.BIO-
      PHYS. 120, 628-637.

3798 MICKOVSKI, M. (1962) - THE FUNGUS FLORA UNDER PINUS MARITIMA AND ITS IN-
      FLUENCE ON THE PROCESS OF HUMUS FORMATION OVER THE SAME. ANNU.FAC.AGRIC.
      SKOPJE 15, 241-246.

3799 MICKOVSKI, M. & VERONA, O. (1967) - DECOMPOSIZIONE DI QUALCHE ERBICIDA
      TRIAZINICO DA PARTE DI ALCUNI FUNGHI DEL TERRENO. AGRICOLTURA ITAL.,
      PISA 67, 67-76.

3800 MIDDLETON, J.T. (1943) - THE TAXONOMY, HOST RANGE AND GEOGRAPHIC DISTRIBU-
      TION OF THE GENUS PYTHIUM. MEM.TORREY BOT.CLUB 20, 1-171.

3801 MIKOLA, P. & HINTIKKA, V. (1956) - THE DEVELOPMENT OF A MICROBIAL POPULA-
      TION IN THE DECOMPOSING FOREST LITTER. COMMUNICATIONES INST.FOR.FENN.
      MATSAETIET.TUTKIMUSLAIT.JULK. 46 (5), 1-15.

3802 MILDENHALL, J.P., PRATT, R.G., WILLIAMS, P.H. & MITCHELL, J.E. (1971) -
      PYTHIUM BROWN ROOT AND FORKING OF MUCK-GROWN CARROTS. PL.DIS.REPTR 55,
      536-540.

3803 MILHOLLAND, R.D. (1973) - A LEAF SPOT DISEASE OF HIGHBUSH BLUEBERRY CAUSED
      BY ALTERNARIA TENUISSIMA. PHYTOPATHOLOGY 63, 1395-1397.

3804 MILHOLLAND, R.D. (1975) - PATHOGENICITY AND HISTOPATHOLOGY OF PHYTOPHTHORA
      CINNAMOMI ON HIGHBUSH BLUEBERRY. PHYTOPATHOLOGY 65, 789-793.

3805 MIL'KO, A.A. (1965) - (NEW AND RARE EUROTIACEAE SPECIES ISOLATED FROM WA-
      TER). NOV.SIST.NIZSH.RAST. 122-125.

3806 MIL'KO, A.A. (1968) - (DE NOMENCLATURA MUCORALIUM NONNULLORUM CLAVIBUS
      DIAGNOSTICIS SPECIERUM CIRCINELLAE, THAMNIDII ET KICKXELLAE ADJECTIS).
      NOV.SIST.NIZSH.RAST., 1968, 79-88.

3807 MIL'KO, A.A. (1974) - OPREDELITEL' MUKORALNYKH GRIBOV. IZVO NAUKOVA DUMKA,
      KIEV, 302 PP.

3808 MIL'KO, A.A. & BELYAKOVA, L.A. (1967) - (THE GENUS CUNNINGHAMELLA AND THE
      TAXONOMY OF THE CUNNINGHAMELLACEAE). MIKROBIOLOGIYA 36, 684-690.

3809 MIL'KO, A.A. & BELYAKOVA, L.A. (1968) - (FUNGAL SPECIES OF VOLGA RIVER).
      MIKROBIOLOGIYA 37, 944-946.

3810 MIL'KO, A.A. & GABRYUSHINA, A.I. (1968) - (THE BEHAVIOUR OF SOME MORTIE-
      RELLA SPECIES TOWARDS CARBOHYDRATES AS CARBON SOURCES). IN: EKSPERI-
      MENTAL'NAYA MIKOLOGIYA; PIDOPLICHKO, N.M. (ED.), IZVO NAUKOVA DUMKA,
      KIEV, 185-190.

3811 MILLER, A.G. & BUDD, K. (1971) - CHLORIDE UPTAKE BY MYCELIUM OF NEOCOSMO-
      SPORA VASINFECTA AND ITS INHIBITION BY GLUCOSE. J.GEN.MICROBIOL. 66,
      243-245.

3812 MILLER, B.M. & PORTER, C.L. (1956/57) - NATURE OF ANTIBIOSIS MANIFESTED BY
      SELECTED SPECIES OF THE MUCORALES. ANTIBIOTICS ANN., 1956/57, 541-548.

3813 MILLER, C.W. & ANDERSON, N.A. (1961) - PROLIFERATION OF CONIDIOPHORES AND
      INTRAHYPHAL HYPHAE IN ASPERGILLUS NIGER. MYCOLOGIA 53, 433-436.

3814 MILLER, D.D. & GOLDING, N.S. (1949) - THE GAS REQUIREMENTS OF MOLDS. 5.
      THE MINIMUM OXYGEN REQUIREMENTS FOR NORMAL GROWTH AND FOR GERMINATION
      OF SIX MOLD CULTURES. J.DAIRY SCI. 32, 101-110.

3815 MILLER, F.A., RIGHTSEL, W.A., SLOAN, B.J., EHRLICH, J., FRENCH, J.C. &
      BARLZ, Q.R. (1963) - ANTIVIRAL ACTIVITY OF TENUAZONIC ACID. NATURE,
      LOND. 200, 1338-1339.

3816 MILLER, H.M. & SHEPHERD, M.G. (1972) - PURIFICATION AND PROPERTIES OF 6-
      PHOSPHOGLUCONATE DEHYDROGENASE FROM PENICILLIUM DUPONTI AND PENICILLIUM
      NOTATUM. CAN.J.MICROBIOL. 18, 1289-1298.

3817 MILLER, J.H., GIDDENS, J.E. & FOSTER, A.A. (1957) - A SURVEY OF THE FUNGI
      OF FOREST AND CULTIVATED SOILS OF GEORGIA. MYCOLOGIA 49, 779-808.

3818 MILLER, J.J. & REID, J. (1961) - STIMULATION BY LIGHT OF SPORULATION IN
      TRICHODERMA LIGNORUM. CAN.J.BOT. 39, 259-262.

3819 MILLER, M.W. (1968) - THE STRUCTURE OF TERREMUTIN. TETRAHEDRON 24, 4839-
      4851.

3820 MILLER, P.A., TROWN, P.W., FULMOR, W., MORTON, G.O. & KARLINER, J. (1968)
      - AN EPIDITHIAPIPERAZINEDIONE ANTIVIRAL AGENT FROM ASPERGILLUS TERREUS.
      BIOCHEM.BIOPHYS.RES.COMMUNS 33, 219-221.

3821 MILLER, R.M. & LIBERTA, A.E. (1977) - THE EFFECTS OF LIGHT AND TYROSINASE
      DURING SCLEROTIUM DEVELOPMENT IN SCLEROTIUM ROLFSII SACC. CAN.J.MICRO-
      BIOL. 23, 278-287.

3822 MILLER, SH.B. & BAXTER, L.W.JR. (1970) - SOME FACTORS INFLUENCING ASEXUAL
      SPORULATION IN A STRAIN OF GLOMERELLA CINGULATA PATHOGENIC TO CAMELLIAS.
      PHYTOPATHOLOGY 60, 743-744.

3823   MILLER, R.E. & BOOTHROYD, C.W. (1962) - SEASONAL POPULATION OF RHIZOSPHERE
       FUNGI ASSOCIATED WITH CORN ROOTS. PHYTOPATHOLOGY 52, 744.

3824   MILLER, T.C. & ESSLER, E.J. (1970) - REDUCTION OF STEROID-A RING DOUBLE
       BONDS BY PENICILLIUM DECUMBENS. BIOCHIM.BIOPHYS.ACTA 202, 354-360.

3825   MILLNER, P.D. (1975) - ASCOMYCETES OF PAKISTAN - CHAETOMIUM. BIOLOGIA,
       LAHORE 21, 39-73.

3826   MILLNER, P.D. (1977) - RADIAL GROWTH RESPONSES TO TEMPERATURE BY 58 CHAE-
       TOMIUM SPECIES, AND SOME TAXONOMIC RELATIONSHIPS. MYCOLOGIA 69, 492-
       502.

3827   MILLNER, P.D., MOTTA, J.J. & LENTZ, P.L. (1977) - ASCOSPORES, GERM PORES,
       ULTRASTRUCTURE AND THERMOPHILISM OF CHAETOMIUM. MYCOLOGIA 69, 720-733.

3828   MILLS, J., BARNES, T.G. & EGGINS, H.O.W. (1971) - TALAROMYCES EMERSONII -
       A POSSIBLE BIODETERIOGEN. INT.BIODETERIOR.BULL. 7, 105-108.

3829   MILLS, J. & EGGINS, H.O.W. (1974) - THE BIODETERIORATION OF CERTAIN PLAS-
       TICIZERS BY THERMOPHILIC FUNGI. INT.BIODETERIOR.BULL. 10, 39-44.

3830   MILLS, J.T. & SINHA, R.N. (1971) - INTERACTIONS BETWEEN A SPRINGTAIL, HY-
       POGASTRURA TULLBERGI, AND SOIL-BORNE FUNGI. J.ECON.ENT. 64, 396-401.

3831   MILLS, J.T. & VLITOS, A.J. (1965) - THE RHIZOSPHERE OF SUGARCANE. PRELIM-
       INARY ISOLATIONS OF FUNGI FROM AN UNCULTIVATED, HEAVY CLAY SOIL AND FROM
       SIMILAR SOIL IN WHICH SUGARCANE IS BEING CULTIVATED. PROC.INT.SOC.SUGAR
       CANE TECHNOL. 12, 125-136.

3832   MILLS, J.T. & VLITOS, A.J. (1967) - STUDIES ON THE RHIZOSPHERE OF SUGAR-
       CANE IN TRINIDAD. TROP.AGRIC., TRIN. 44, 151-157.

3833   MILTON, J.M. & ISAAC, I. (1967) - STUDIES ON A BIOTIN REQUIRING STRAIN OF
       VERTICILLIUM DAHLIAE. TRANS.BR.MYCOL.SOC. 50, 539-547.

3834   MILTON, J.M., ROGERS, W.G. & ISAAC, I. (1971) - APPLICATION OF ACRYLAMIDE
       GEL ELECTROPHORESIS OF SOLUBLE FUNGAL PROTEINS TO TAXONOMY OF VERTICIL-
       LIUM SPECIES. TRANS.BR.MYCOL.SOC. 56, 61-65.

3835   MINAMIKAWA, T., JAYASANKAR, N.P., BOHM, B.A., TAYLOR, I.E.P. & TOWERS,
       G.H.N. (1970) - AN INDUCIBLE HYDROLASE FROM ASPERGILLUS NIGER ACTING ON
       CARBON BONDS FOR PHLORIDZIN AND OTHER C-ACYLATED PHENOLS. BIOCHEM.J.
       116, 889-897.

3836   MING, Y.-N. & TA-FUH, Y. (1966) - IDENTIFICATION OF A FUSARIUM SPECIES,
       ISOLATED FROM CORNEAL ULCER. ACTA MICROBIOL.SIN. 12, 180-186.

3837   MINOURA, K. (1966) - TAXONOMIC STUDIES ON CLADOSPORIA. 4. MORPHOLOGICAL
       PROPERTIES. 2. J.FERMENT.TECHNOL., OSAKA 44, 137-149.

3838   MINOURA, K. (1968) - TAXONOMICAL STUDIES ON CLADOSPORIA. 6. VITAMIN RE-
       QUIREMENT. J.FERMENT.TECHNOL., OSAKA 46, 939-946.

3839   MINOURA, K. (1969) - NOTES ON SOME ASCOMYCETES OF EAST AFRICA. TRANS.MYCOL.
       SOC.JAPAN 10, 41-46.

3840   MINOURA, K., MORINAGA, T. & MUROI, T. (1975) - SOME ASCOMYCETES ISOLATED
       FROM SOIL OF NEPAL. 1. REP.TOTTORI MYCOL.INST. 12, 171-185.

3841   MINOURA, K., OCHI, K. & NEHIRA, T. (1973) - THERMOPHILIC FILAMENTOUS FUNGI
       IN JAPAN. 2. TRANS.MYCOL.SOC.JAPAN 14, 361-366.

3842 MINOURA, K. & OKAZAKI, G. (1968) - TAXONOMIC STUDIES ON CLADOSPORIA. 5.
      PHYSIOLOGICAL PROPERTIES. J.FERMENT.TECHNOL., OSAKA 46, 269-275.

3843 MINOURA, K., YOKOE, M., KIZIMA, T. & NEHIRA, T. (1973) - THERMOPHILIC FILA-
      MENTOUS FUNGI IN JAPAN. 1. TRANS.MYCOL.SOC.JAPAN 14, 352-361.

3844 MINTZLAFF, H.-J., CIEGLER, A. & LEISTNER, L. (1972) - POTENTIAL MYCOTOXIN
      PROBLEMS IN MOULD-FERMENTED SAUSAGE. Z.LEBENSMITTELUNTERS.FORSCH. 150,
      133-137.

3845 MIRCETICH, S.M. & KEIL, H.L. (1970) - PHYTOPHTHORA CINNAMOMI ROOT ROT AND
      STEM CANKER OF PEACH TREES. PHYTOPATHOLOGY 60, 1376-1382.

3846 MIRCETICH, S.M. & KRAFT, J.M. (1973) - EFFICIENCY OF VARIOUS SELECTIVE ME-
      DIA IN DETERMINING PYTHIUM POPULATION IN SOIL. MYCOPATH.MYCOL.APPL.
      50, 151-161.

3847 MIRCETICH, S.M. & ZENTMYER, G.A. (1966) - PRODUCTION OF OOSPORES AND CHLA-
      MYDOSPORES OF PHYTOPHTHORA CINNAMOMI IN ROOTS AND SOIL. PHYTOPATHOLOGY
      56, 1076-1078.

3848 MIRCETICH, S.M. & ZENTMYER, G.A. (1969) - EFFECT OF CARBON AND NITROGEN
      COMPOUNDS ON GERMINATION OF CHLAMYDOSPORES OF PHYTOPHTHORA CINNAMOMI IN
      SOIL. PHYTOPATHOLOGY 59, 1732-1735.

3849 MIRCHINK, T.G. (1957) - (ON FUNGI CAUSING TOXICITY OF TURF-PODZOL SOIL IN
      VARIOUS STAGES OF CULTIVATION). MIKROBIOLOGIYA 26, 78-86.

3850 MIRCHINK, T.G. (1971) - (FUNGAL FLORA OF PAMIR SOILS). VEST.MOSK.UNIV.,
      SER.BIOL.POCHV. 2, 73-79.

3851 MIRCHINK, T.G. & ASEEVA, I.V. (1959) - (FUNGI AS A TOXICITY FACTOR OF TURF-
      PODZOL SOIL AT DIFFERENT DEGREES OF CULTIVATION). NAUCH.DOKL.VYSSH.SHK.
      BIOL.NAUKI, 1959 (2), 206-211.

3852 MIRCHINK, T.G. & BELAYA, T.I. (1965) - (MYCOFLORA OF GUINEA TROPICAL SOILS
      AND ITS BIOLOGICAL PROPERTIES). MIKROBIOLOGIYA 34, 1049-1055.

3853 MIRCHINK, T.G. & GRESHNYKH, K.P. (1961) - (THE FORMATION OF TOXINS IN THE
      SOIL BY SOME SPECIES OF FUNGI OF THE GENUS PENICILLIUM). MIKROBIOLOGIYA
      30, 1045-1049.

3854 MIRCHINK, T.G., KASHKINA, G.B. & ABATUROV, YU.D. (1972) - (THE RESISTANCE
      OF FUNGI WITH DIFFERENT PIGMENTS TO GAMMA-RADIATION). MIKROBIOLOGIYA
      41, 83-86.

3855 MIRCHINK, T.G., KOPYSSKAYA, F.G. & GRESHNYKH, K.P. (1963) - (THE EFFECT OF
      TOXINS FROM SOIL FUNGI ON THE N AND AMINO ACID CONTENT IN PLANTS). MI-
      KROBIOLOGIYA 31, 669-676.

3856 MIRCHINK, T.G. & ZAPROMETOVA, K.M. (1970) - (REGULARITIES IN DISTRIBUTION
      OF DARK-COLORED FUNGI IN SOIL). VEST.MOSK.UNIV., SER.6, BIOL.POCHV. 25,
      99-105.

3857 MIROCHA, C.J., CHRISTENSEN, C.M. & NELSON, G.H. (1967) - ESTROGENIC META-
      BOLITE PRODUCED BY FUSARIUM GRAMINEARUM IN STORED CORN. APPL.MICROBIOL.
      15, 497-503.

3858 MIROCHA, C.J., CHRISTENSEN, C.M. & NELSON, G.H. (1969) - BIOSYNTHESIS OF
      THE FUNGAL ESTROGEN F-2 AND A NATURALLY OCCURRING DERIVATIVE (F-3) BY
      FUSARIUM MONILIFORME. APPL.MICROBIOL. 17, 482-483.

3859 MIROCHA, C.J., PALYUSIK, M., PATHRE, S. & SCHAUERHAMER, B. (1972) - MYCO-
      TOXINS FROM STACHYBOTRYS ALTERNANS GROWN ON OATS. PHYTOPATHOLOGY 62,
      778-779.

3860 MIRRINGTON, R.N., RITCHIE, E., SHOPPEE, C.W., STERNHELL, S. & TAYLOR, W.C.
      (1966) - SOME METABOLITES OF CYLINDROCARPON RADICICOLA. THE STRUCTURE
      OF RADICICOL (MONORDEN). AUST.J.CHEM. 19, 1265-1284.

3861 MIRZA, J.H. & NASIR, M.A. (1968) - ADDITIONS TO THE COPROPHILOUS FUNGI OF
      WEST PAKISTAN. 2. NOVA HEDWIGIA 16, 283-288.

3862 MISHRA, A.S. & VYAS, K.M. (1972) - PRODUCTION OF L-PROLINE BY SOIL MICRO-
      ORGANISMS. HINDUSTAN ANTIBIOT.BULL. 15, 30-33.

3863 MISHRA, R.R. (1966) - SEASONAL VARIATION IN FUNGAL FLORA OF GRASSLANDS OF
      VARANASI (INDIA). BULL.INT.SOC.TROP.ECOL. 7, 100-113.

3864 MISHRA, R.R. (1967) - NATURE OF RHIZOSPHERE FUNGAL FLORA OF CERTAIN PLANTS.
      PL.SOIL 27, 162-166.

3865 MISHRA, R.R. (1968) - FUNGAL POPULATION IN RELATION TO TEMPERATURE AND
      MOISTURE. PROC.NATN.ACAD.SCI., INDIA, SECT.B, 38, 211-224.

3866 MISHRA, R.R. & KAMAL (1972) - RHIZOSPHERE FUNGAL FLORA OF CERTAIN EUPHOR-
      BIACEOUS PLANTS. MYCOPATH.MYCOL.APPL. 46, 73-80.

3867 MISHRA, R.R. & KANAUJIA, R.S. (1973) - INVESTIGATIONS INTO RHIZOSPHERE
      MYCOFLORA. 13. EFFECT OF FOLIAR APPLICATION OF CERTAIN PLANT EXTRACTS
      ON PENNISETUM TYPHOIDES F.BURM STAPF & HUBB. ISRAEL J.AGRIC.RES. 22,
      3-9.

3868 MISHRA, R.R. & KANAUJIA, R.S. (1973) - STUDIES ON CERTAIN ECOLOGICAL AS-
      PECTS OF SOIL FUNGI. 2. DISTRIBUTION OF SOIL FUNGI IN RELATION TO COVER
      VEGETATION AND PHYSICO-CHEMICAL CHARACTERS OF THE SOIL. AN.EDAFOL.AGRO-
      BIOL. 32, 21-34.

3869 MISHRA, R.R. & SRIVASTAVA, V.B. (1969) - RHIZOSPHERE FUNGAL FLORA OF CER-
      TAIN LEGUMES. ANNLS INST.PASTEUR, PARIS 117, 717-723.

3870 MISHRA, R.R. & SRIVASTAVA, V.B. (1970) - VARIATION IN THE RHIZOSPHERE MI-
      CROFLORA OF CERTAIN CROP PLANTS. PROC.NATN.ACAD.SCI., INDIA, SECT.B,
      40, 195-202.

3871 MISHUSTIN, E.N., PUSHKINSKAYA, O.I. & TEPLYAKOVA, Z.F. (1961) - (THE ECO-
      LOGO-GEOGRAPHICAL DISTRIBUTION OF MICROSCOPIC SOIL FUNGI). TRUDY INST.
      POCHV., ALMA -ATA 12, 3-64.

3872 MISLIVEC, P.B. (1975) - THE EFFECT OF BOTRAN ON FASCICLE PRODUCTION BY
      SPECIES OF PENICILLIUM. MYCOLOGIA 67, 194-198.

3873 MISLIVEC, P.B., DIETER, C.T. & BRUCE, V.R. (1975) - EFFECT OF TEMPERATURE
      AND RELATIVE HUMIDITY ON SPORE GERMINATION OF MYCOTOXIC SPECIES OF AS-
      PERGILLUS AND PENICILLIUM. MYCOLOGIA 67, 1187-1189.

3874 MISLIVEC, P.B., HUNTER, J.H. & TUITE, J. (1968) - ASSAY FOR AFLATOXIN PRO-
      DUCTION BY THE GENERA ASPERGILLUS AND PENICILLIUM. APPL.MICROBIOL. 16,
      1053-1055.

3875 MISLIVEC, P.B. & TUITE, J. (1970) - SPECIES OF PENICILLIUM OCCURRING IN
      FRESHLY-HARVESTED AND IN STORED DENT CORN KERNELS. MYCOLOGIA 62, 67-74.

3876 MISLIVEC, P.B. & TUITE, J. (1970) - TEMPERATURE AND RELATIVE HUMIDITY RE-
QUIREMENTS OF SPECIES OF PENICILLIUM ISOLATED FROM YELLOW DENT CORN
KERNELS. MYCOLOGIA 62, 75-88.

3877 MISRA, A.P. & HAQUE, S.Q. (1960) - PERFECT STAGE OF SCLEROTIUM ROLFSII
SACC. NATURE, LOND. 186, 567.

3878 MITCHELL, A.D. (1969) - CELL-WALL PROTEINS OF ASPERGILLUS NIGER AND CHAE-
TOMIUM GLOBOSUM. J.GEN.MICROBIOL. 59, 103-109.

3879 MITCHELL, C.P. & DIX, N.J. (1975) - GROWTH AND GERMINATION OF TRICHODERMA
SPECIES UNDER THE INFLUENCE OF SOIL FUNGISTASIS. TRANS.BR.MYCOL.SOC.
64, 235-241.

3880 MITCHELL, D.J. & MITCHELL, J.E. (1973) - OXYGEN AND CARBON DIOXIDE CONCEN-
TRATION EFFECTS ON THE GROWTH AND REPRODUCTION OF APHANOMYCES EUTEICHES
AND CERTAIN OTHER SOIL-BORNE PLANT PATHOGENS. PHYTOPATHOLOGY 63, 1053-
1059.

3881 MITCHELL, D.J. & ZENTMYER, G.A. (1971) - EFFECTS OF OXYGEN AND CARBON DI-
OXIDE TENSIONS ON SPORANGIUM AND OOSPORE FORMATION BY PHYTOPHTHORA SPP.
PHYTOPATHOLOGY 61, 807-812.

3882 MITCHELL, D.T. (1970) - FUNGAL SUCCESSION ON DUNG OF SOUTH AFRICA OSTRICH
AND ANGORA GOAT. J.S.AFR.BOT. 36, 191-198.

3883 MITCHELL, J.E., BHALLA, H.S. & YANG, G.H. (1969) - AN APPROACH TO THE
STUDY OF THE POPULATION DYNAMICS OF APHANOMYCES EUTEICHES IN SOIL. PHY-
TOPATHOLOGY 59, 206-212.

3884 MITCHELL, J.E. & YANG, C.Y. (1966) - FACTORS AFFECTING GROWTH AND DEVELOP-
MENT OF APHANOMYCES EUTEICHES. PHYTOPATHOLOGY 56, 917-922.

3885 MITCHELL, R. & ALEXANDER, M. (1961) - THE MYCOLYTIC PHENOMENON AND BIOLOG-
ICAL CONTROL OF FUSARIUM IN SOIL. NATURE, LOND. 190, 109-110.

3886 MIURA, K. (1974) - STREAM SPORA OF JAPAN. TRANS.MYCOL.SOC.JAPAN 15, 289-
308.

3887 MIXON, A.C. & CURL, E.A. (1967) - INFLUENCE OF PLANT RESIDUES ON SCLERO-
TIUM ROLFSII AND INHIBITORY SOIL MICROORGANISMS. CROP SCI. 7, 641-644.

3888 MIYAKE, M. & SAITO, M. (1965) - LIVER INJURY AND LIVER TUMORS INDUCED BY
TOXINS OF PENICILLIUM ISLANDICUM SOPP GROWING ON YELLOWED RICE. IN:
MYCOTOXINS IN FOODSTUFFS; MATELES, R.I. & WOGAN, G.N. (ED.), MASS.INST.
TECHNOL. PRESS, CAMBRIDGE, MASS., 133-146.

3889 MIYAKE, S., YOSHIMURA, S. & YOSHIMURA, Y. (1958) - (PROTEASE OF SCOPULA-
RIOPSIS BREVICAULIS. 4. CRYSTALLIZATION OF PROTEASE-II BY THE USE OF
AMBERLITE IRC-50). HYOGO NOKA DAIGAKU KENKYU HOKOKU 3, 135-141.

3890 MIYAZAKI, T. & IRINO, T. (1970) - ACIDIC POLYSACCHARIDES FROM THE CELL
WALL OF ABSIDIA CYLINDROSPORA, MUCOR MUCEDO, AND RHIZOPUS NIGRICANS.
CHEM.PHARM.BULL., TOKYO 18, 1930-1931.

3891 MIYAZAKI, T. & IRINO, T. (1971) - STUDIES ON FUNGAL POLYSACCHARIDES. 9.
THE ACIDIC POLYSACCHARIDE FROM THE CELL WALL OF RHIZOPUS NIGRICANS.
CHEM.PHARM.BULL., TOKYO 19, 2545-2550.

3892 MIYAZAKI, T. & IRINO, T. (1972) - STUDIES ON FUNGAL POLYSACCHARIDES. 10.
EXTRACELLULAR HETEROGLYCANS OF ABSIDIA CYLINDROSPORA AND MUCOR MUCEDO.
CHEM.PHARM.BULL., TOKYO 20, 330-335.

3893 MIYAZAKI, T. & NADI, Y. (1974) - EXTRACELLULAR POLYSACCHARIDE OF CLADOSPO-
      RIUM HERBARUM. STUDIES ON FUNGAL POLYSACCHARIDE. 13. CHEM.PHARM.BULL.,
      TOKYO 22, 1360-1365.

3894 MIYAZAKI, T. & OIKAWA, N. (1976) - AN ENDO(1-6)-BETA-GLUCANASE FROM MUCOR
      HIEMALIS. CARBOH.RES. 48, 209.

3895 MIYOSHI, T. & HARADA, T. (1974) - UTILIZATION OF 2-BUTYNE-1,4-DIOL BY A
      STRAIN OF FUSARIUM MERISMOIDES. J.FERMENT.TECHNOL., OSAKA 52, 388-392.

3896 MIYOSHI, T., SATO, H. & HARADA, T. (1974) - FORMATION OF AETHYLENE DICARB-
      OXYLIC ACID AND ITS ESTERS WITH 2-BUTYNE-1,4-DIOL FROM 2-BUTYNE-1,4-
      DIOL BY FUSARIUM MERISMOIDES B11. AGRIC.BIOL.CHEM., TOKYO 38, 1355-1358.

3897 MIYOSHI, T., SATO, H. & HARADA, T. (1974) - NEW METABOLITES, 2,4,6-TRIKE-
      TO-SUBERIC ACID AND 2,4,6,8-TETRAKETO-SEBACIC ACID, FORMED FROM 2-BUTYNE
      -1,4-DIOL BY FUSARIUM MERISMOIDES B11. AGRIC.BIOL.CHEM., TOKYO, 38,
      1935-1939.

3898 MIYOSHI, T., SATO, H. & HARADA, T. (1974) - PURIFICATION AND CHARACTERIZA-
      TION OF 2-ALKYNE-1-OL DEHYDROGENASE INDUCED BY 2-BUTYNE-1,4-DIOL IN FU-
      SARIUM MERISMOIDES B11. BIOCHIM.BIOPHYS.ACTA 358, 231-239.

3899 MIZUNO, K., TSUJINO, M., TAKADA, M., HAYASHI, M., ATSUMI, K., ASANO, K. &
      MATSUDA, T. (1974) - STUDIES ON BREDININ. 1. ISOLATION, CHARACTERIZA-
      TION AND BIOLOGICAL PROPERTIES. J.ANTIBIOT., TOKYO 27, 775-782.

3900 MIZUSHIMA, S., IZAKI, K., TAKAHASHI, H. & SAKAGUCHI, K. (1956) - DETERMI-
      NATION OF D-GLUTAMIC AND D-ASPARTIC ACID CONTENT OF MALIGNANT TUMORS
      AND NORMAL TISSUES BY MEANS OF A NEW OXIDASE. GANN 47, 91-95.

3901 MOELLER, A. (1903) - UNTERSUCHUNGEN UEBER EIN- UND ZWEIJAEHRIGE KIEFERN IM
      MAERKISCHEN SANDBODEN. Z.FORST-U.JAGDW. 35, 321-338.

3902 MOHANTY, P.K. & ADDY, S.K. (1971) - PRODUCTION OF PECTOLYTIC AND CELLULO-
      LYTIC ENZYMES BY GLOMERELLA CINGULATA IN VITRO AND IN VIVO. INDIAN PHY-
      TOPATH. 24, 690-693.

3903 MOHYUDDIN, M., OSMAN, N. & SKOROPAD, W. (1972) - INACTIVATION OF CONIDIO-
      SPORES AND MYCELIA OF ASPERGILLUS FLAVUS BY GAMMA-RADIATION. RADIAT.BOT.
      12, 427-431.

3904 MOLINA, J.A.E. & ALEXANDER, M. (1971) - FORMATION OF NITRATE FROM 3-NITRO-
      PROPIONATE BY ASPERGILLUS FLAVUS. J.BACT. 105, 489-493.

3905 MOLINA, J.A.E. & ALEXANDER, M. (1972) - OXIDATION OF NITRITE AND HYDROXYL-
      AMINE BY ASPERGILLUS FLAVUS, PEROXIDASE AND CATALASE. ANTONIE VAN LEEU-
      WENHOEK 38, 505-512.

3906 MOLLER, W.J. & DEVAY, J.E. (1968) - INSECT TRANSMISSION OF CERATOCYSTIS
      FIMBRIATA IN DECIDUOUS FRUIT ORCHARDS. PHYTOPATHOLOGY 58, 1499-1508.

3907 MOLLER, W.J. & DEVAY, J.E. (1968) - CARROT AS A SPECIES-SELECTIVE ISOLA-
      TION MEDIUM FOR CERATOCYSTIS FIMBRIATA. PHYTOPATHOLOGY 58, 123-124.

3908 MOLLISON, J.E. (1953) - EFFECT OF PARTIAL STERILIZATION AND ACIDIFICATION
      OF SOIL ON THE FUNGAL POPULATION. TRANS.BR.MYCOL.SOC. 36, 215-228.

3909 MOLOT, P.M., CLERJEAU, M. & NOURRISSEAU, J.-G. (1973) - COMPORTEMENT DU
      PLANT DE FRAISIER CONTAMINE PAR LE PHYTOPHTHORA CACTORUM APRES REPIQUAGE
      SUR SOL DESINFECTE AU BROMURE DE METHYLE. REVUE ZOOL.AGRIC.PATHOL.VEGET.
      72, 133-136.

3910 MOLOT, P.M. & NOURRISSEAU, J.-G. (1973) - DETECTION PAR PIEGEAGE DES PHY-
      TOPHTHORA DANS LE SOL. ANNLS PHYTOPATH. 5, 308-309 (ABS.).

3911 MONOSON, H.L. (1968) - TRAPPING EFFECTIVENESS OF FIVE SPECIES OF NEMATO-
      PHAGOUS FUNGI CULTURES WITH MYCOPHAGOUS NEMATODES. MYCOLOGIA 60, 788-
      801.

3912 MONOKSON, A.M. (1960) - MOVEMENT OF RADIOISOTOPES IN RHIZOCTONIA SOLANI.
      PHYTOPATHOLOGY 50, 646 (ABS.).

3913 MONTEMARTINI CORTE, A. (1972) - ANALISI DELLA MICOFLORA DI RISAIA. ARCH.
      BOT.BIOGEOGR.ITAL. 48, 109-123.

3914 MOORE, E.J. (1937) - CARBON AND OXYGEN REQUIREMENTS OF THE COTTON ROOT-ROT
      ORGANISM PHYMATOTRICHUM OMNIVORUM, IN CULTURE. PHYTOPATHOLOGY 27, 918-
      930.

3915 MOORE, G.E. (1970) - ISOLATING ENTOMOGENOUS FUNGI AND BACTERIA, AND TESTS
      OF FUNGAL ISOLATES AGAINST THE SOUTHERN PINE BEETLE. J.ECON.ENT. 63,
      1702-1704.

3916 MOORE, G.E. (1973) - PATHOGENICITY OF THREE ENTOMOGENOUS FUNGI TO THE
      SOUTHERN PINE BEETLE AT VARIOUS TEMPERATURES AND HUMIDITIES. ENVIRON.
      ENTOMOL. 2, 54-57.

3917 MOORE, J.H., DAVIS, N.D. & DIENER.U.L. (1972) - MELLEIN AND 4-HYDROXYMEL-
      LEIN PRODUCTION BY ASPERGILLUS OCHRACEUS WILHELM. APPL.MICROBIOL. 23,
      1067-1072.

3918 MOORE, J.J. (1954) - SOME OBSERVATIONS ON THE MICROFLORA OF TWO PEAT PRO-
      FILES IN THE DUBLIN MOUNTAINS. PROC.R.SOC.DUBLIN 26, 379-395.

3919 MOORE, L.D. & COUCH, H.B. (1968) - INFLUENCE OF CALCIUM NUTRITION ON PEC-
      TOLYTIC AND CELLULOLYTIC ENZYME ACTIVITY OF EXTRACTS OF HIGHLAND BENT-
      GRASS FOLIAGE BLIGHTED BY PYTHIUM ULTIMUM. PHYTOPATHOLOGY 58, 833-838.

3920 MOORE-LANDECKER, E. & STOTZKY, G. (1972) - INHIBITION OF FUNGAL GROWTH AND
      SPORULATION BY VOLATILE METABOLITES FROM BACTERIA. CAN.J.MICROBIOL. 18,
      957-962.

3921 MOORE-LANDECKER, E. & STOTZKY, G. (1973) - MORPHOLOGICAL ABNORMALITIES OF
      FUNGI INDUCED BY VOLATILE MICROBIAL METABOLITES. MYCOLOGIA 65, 519-530.

3922 MOORE-LANDECKER, E. & STOTZKY, G. (1974) - EFFECTS OF CONCENTRATION OF
      VOLATILE METABOLITES FROM BACTERIA AND GERMINATING SEEDS ON FUNGI IN
      THE PRESENCE OF SELECTIVE ABSORBENTS. CAN.J.MICROBIOL. 20, 91-103.

3923 MOORE, P.M. & PEBERDY, J.F. (1975) - BIOSYNTHESIS OF CHITIN BY PARTICULATE
      FRACTIONS FROM CUNNINGHAMELLA ELEGANS. MICROBIOS 12, 29-39.

3924 MOORE, P.M. & PEBERDY, J.F. (1976) - EFFECT OF INOCULUM SIZE ON CONIDIAL
      GERMINATION IN ASPERGILLUS FLAVUS. TRANS.BR.MYCOL.SOC. 67, 495-497.

3925 MOORHOUSE, J. & BERTOLDI, M.DE (1975) - ELECTROPHORETIC CHARACTERISTICS OF
      ENZYMES AS A TAXONOMIC CRITERIUM IN THE GENUS HUMICOLA. MYCOTAXON 2,
      109-118.

3926 MORAVEC, Z. (1968) - REMARKS ON SOME COPROPHILOUS FUNGI IN NORWAY. CESKA
      MYKOL. 22, 301-309.

3927 MOREAU, C. (1953) - SORDARIA ET PLEURAGE. ENCYCL.MYCOL. 25, 330 PP.,
      P.LECHEVALIER, PARIS.

3928 MOREAU, C. (1963) - MORPHOLOGIE COMPAREE DE QUELQUES PHIALOPHORA ET VARIA-
      TIONS DU P. CINERESCENS (WR.) VAN BEYMA. REVUE MYCOL. 28, 260-276.

3929 MOREAU, C. (1968) - MOISISSURES TOXIQUES DANS L'ALIMENTATION. ENCYCL.MYCOL
      35, 374 PP., P.LECHEVALIER, PARIS.

3930 MOREAU, C. (1970) - LES MOISISSURES DES FARINES PANIFIABLES. ANNLS NUTR.
      ALIMENT. 24, 117-127.

3931 MOREAU, C. (1971) - PRESENCE DU MONASCUS PURPUREUS WENT DANS DU MAIS EN-
      SILE. REMARQUES SUR LA FORME IMPARFAITE BASIPETOSPORA. BULL.TRIMEST.
      SOC.MYCOL.FR. 87, 39-44.

3932 MOREAU, C. (1974) - QUELQUES MANIFESTATIONS DE MYCOTOXICOSES NOUVELLES OU
      PEU CONNUES EN FRANCE. REC.MED.VET. 150, 17-26.

3933 MOREAU, C. & MOREAU, M. (1963) - DEUX CURIOSITES MYCOLOGIQUES POLLUANT
      L'ATMOSPHERE D'INSTALLATIONS INDUSTRIELLES - ENTOMOPHTHORA CORONATA ET
      TILLETIOPSIS MINOR. BULL.TRIMEST.SOC.MYCOL.FR. 79, 242-248.

3934 MOREAU, C., MOREAU, M. & PELHATE, J. (1965) - COMPORTEMENT CULTURAL DE
      MOISISSURES DU BLE EN RELATION AVEC LEUR ECOLOGIE SUR GRAINS. C.R.HEBD.
      SEANC.ACAD.SCI., PARIS, SER.D, 260, 1229-1322.

3935 MOREAU, M. (1957) - LE DEPERISSEMENT DES OEILLETS. ENCYCL.MYCOL. 30, 308
      PP., P.LECHEVALIER, PARIS.

3936 MOREAU, M. (1962) - INFLUENCE DE LA TEMPERATURE SUR LE DEVELOPPEMENT DU
      PHIALOPHORA CINERESCENS (WR.) VAN BEYMA, AGENT DE LA VERTICILLIOSE DE
      L'OEILLET DES FLEURISTES. C.R.HEBD.SEANC.ACAD.SCI., PARIS, SER.D, 255,
      162-164.

3937 MOREAU, M. & AUZOLLE, F. (1964) - CONDITIONS THERMIQUES FAVORABLES A LA
      CROISSANCE LINEARE ET A LA GERMINATION DU PHIALOPHORA CINERESCENS.
      ANNLS SCI.NAT.BOT., SER.12, 5, 773-784.

3938 MOREAU, M. & CHOLLET, M.M. (1963) - QUELQUES FACTEURS MODIFIANT LA CROIS-
      SANCE PONDERALE ET LA SPORULATION DU PHIALOPHORA CINERESCENS (WR.) VAN
      BEYMA. BULL.TRIMEST.SOC.MYCOL.FR. 79, 382-391.

3939 MOREAU, M. & LEPICARD, D. (1971) - INFLUENCE DE LA TEMPERATURE SUR LA
      SPORULATION DU PHIALOPHORA CINERESCENS. BULL.TRIMEST.SOC.MYCOL.FR. 87,
      45-53.

3940 MOREAU, M. & MOREAU, C. (1960) - RECHERCHES SUR LA SPORULATION DE L'ASPER-
      GILLUS CLAVATUS. C.R.HEBD.SEANC.ACAD.SCI., PARIS, SER.D, 251, 1556-1557.

3941 MOREAU, M. & MOREAU, F. (1941) - PREMIERE CONTRIBUTION A L'ETUDE DE LA MI-
      CROFLORE DES DUNES. REVUE MYCOL. 6, 49-94.

3942 MOREAU, M. & MOREAU, F. (1948) - CONTRIBUTION A L'ETUDE DE LA MICROFLORE
      FONGIQUE DES EAUX DOUCES DE NORMANDIE. BULL.TRIMEST.SOC.MYCOL.FR. 64,
      223-237.

3943 MOREAU, M. & MOREAU, F. (1954) - SUR LE DEVELOPPEMENT DES PERITHECES DU
      CHAETOMIUM ELATUM. REVUE MYCOL. 19, 165-171.

3944 MOREAU, M. & TRIQUE, B. (1966) - RECHERCHE DES EXOENZYMES DANS LES FIL-
      TRATS DE CULTURES DE DEUX MOISISSURES DES GRAINS - L'ASPERGILLUS VER-
      SICOLOR (VUILL.) TIRABOSCHI ET LE PENICILLIUM CYCLOPIUM WESTL. C.R.HEBD.
      SEANC.ACAD.SCI., PARIS, SER.D, 263, 239-241.

3945 MORENZ, J. (1963) - GEOTRICHUM CANDIDUM LINK. TAXONOMIE, DIAGNOSE UND ME-DIZINISCHE BEDEUTUNG. MYKOL.SCHRREIHE, LEIPZIG 1, 79 PP.

3946 MORENZ, J. (1964) - TAXONOMISCHE UNTERSUCHUNGEN ZUR GATTUNG GEOTRICHUM. MYKOL.SCHRREIHE, LEIPZIG 2, 33-64.

3947 MORENZ, J. (1970) - GEOTRICHOSIS. HANDB.SPEZ.PATH.ANAT.HIST. 3, 919-952.

3948 MORGAN, D.J. (1971) - NUMERICAL TAXONOMIC STUDIES OF THE GENUS BOTRYTIS. 1. THE B. CINEREA COMPLEX. TRANS.BR.MYCOL.SOC. 56, 319-325.

3949 MORGAN, D.J. (1971) - NUMERICAL TAXONOMIC STUDIES OF THE GENUS BOTRYTIS. 2. OTHER BOTRYTIS TAXA. TRANS.BR.MYCOL.SOC. 56, 327-335.

3950 MORGAN, W.T., HENSLEY, C.F. & RIEHM, J.P. (1972) - PROTEINS OF THE THER-MOPHILIC FUNGUS HUMICOLA LANUGINOSA. J.BIOL.CHEM. 247, 6555-6565.

3951 MORISHITA, E., TAKEDA, T. & SHIBATA, S. (1968) - METABOLIC PRODUCTS OF FUNGI. 19. THE STRUCTURE OF AUROFUSARIN. CHEM.PHARM.BULL., TOKYO 16, 411-413.

3952 MORITA, T. & AOKI, H. (1974) - ISOSCLERONE, A NEW METABOLITE OF SCLEROTI-NIA SCLEROTIORUM. AGRIC.BIOL.CHEM., TOKYO 38, 1501-1505.

3953 MOROOKA, N., NAKANO, N., NAKAZAWA, S. & TSUNODA, H. (1971) - ON THE CHEM-ICAL PROPERTIES OF FUSARENON AND THE RELATED COMPOUND OBTAINED FROM TOX-IC METABOLITES OF FUSARIUM NIVALE. J.AGRIC.CHEM.SOC.JAPAN 45, 151-155.

3954 MOROZOVA, V.G. & BEZBORODOVA, S.I. (1972) - (EXTRACELLULAR ACID PHOSPHO-MONOESTERASE OF ASPERGILLUS CLAVATUS). MIKROBIOLOGIYA 41, 404-412.

3955 MORQUER, R. & ENJALBERT, L. (1957) - ETUDE MORPHOLOGIQUE ET PHYSIOLOGIQUE D'UN ASPERGILLUS NOUVELLEMENT ISOLE AU COURS D'UNE AFFECTION PULMONAIRE DE L'HOMME. C.R.HEBD.SEANC.ACAD.SCI., PARIS, SER.D, 244, 1405-1408.

3956 MORQUER, R. & KOMATSU, M. (1968) - TRICHODERMA AND GLIOCLADIUM FOUND ON BED-LOGS OF SHIITAKE MUSHROOM (LENTINUS EDODES) IN JAPAN. TRANS.MYCOL. SOC.JAPAN 8, 136-140.

3957 MORQUER, R. & TOUVET, A. (1974) - ACTION COMPAREE DE CHAMPIGNONS ANTAGO-NISTES SUR DIVERS HYMENOMYCETES PARASITES DES ARBRES RESINEUX. C.R.HEBD. SEANC.ACAD.SCI., PARIS, SER.D, 278, 709-713.

3958 MORQUER, R., VIALA, G., ROUCH, J., FAYRET, J. & BERGE, G. (1963) - CONTRI-BUTION A L'ETUDE MORPHOGENIQUE DU GENRE GLIOCLADIUM. BULL.TRIMEST.SOC. MYCOL.FR. 79, 137-241.

3959 MORRALL, R.A.A. (1974) - SOIL MICROFUNGI ASSOCIATED WITH ASPEN IN SAS-KATCHEWAN - SYNECOLOGY AND QUANTITATIVE ANALYSIS. CAN.J.BOT. 52, 1803-1817.

3960 MORRALL, R.A.A. (1977) - A PRELIMINARY STUDY OF THE INFLUENCE OF WATER POTENTIAL ON SCLEROTIUM GERMINATION IN SCLEROTINIA SCLEROTIORUM. CAN.J. BOT. 55, 8-11.

3961 MORRALL, R.A.A., DUCZEK, L.J. & SHEARD, J.W. (1972) - VARIATIONS AND COR-RELATIONS WITHIN AND BETWEEN MORPHOLOGY, PATHOGENICITY, AND PECTOLYTIC ENZYME ACTIVITY IN SCLEROTINIA FROM SASKATCHEWAN. CAN.J.BOT. 50, 767-786.

3962 MORRALL, R.A.A. & VANTERPOOL, T.C. (1968) - THE SOIL MICROFUNGI OF UPLAND
      BOREAL FOREST AT CANDLE LAKE, SASKATCHEWAN. MYCOLOGIA 60, 642-654.

3963 MORRIS, E.F. (1956) - TROPICAL FUNGI IMPERFECTI. MYCOLOGIA 48, 728-737.

3964 MORRISON, R.H. & FRENCH, D.W. (1969) - TAXONOMY OF CYLINDROCLADIUM FLORI-
      DANUM AND C. SCOPARIUM. MYCOLOGIA 61, 957-966.

3965 MORROW, M.B. (1932) - THE SOIL FUNGI OF A PINE FOREST. MYCOLOGIA 24, 398-
      402.

3966 MORTIMER, P.H., CAMPBELL, J., MENNA, M.E.DI & WHITE, E.P. (1971) - EXPERI-
      MENTAL MYROTHECIOTOXICOSIS AND POISONING IN RUMINANTS BY VERRUCARIN-A
      AND RORIDIN-A. RES.VET.SCI. 12, 508-515.

3967 MORTIMER, P.H. & TAYLOR, A. (1962) - THE EXPERIMENTAL INTOXICATION OF
      SHEEP WITH SPORIDESMIN, A METABOLIC PRODUCT OF PITHOMYCES CHARTARUM. 1.
      CLINICAL OBSERVATIONS AND FINDINGS AT POST-MORTEM EXAMINATION. RES.VET.
      SCI. 3, 147-160.

3968 MORTON, A.G. (1951) - FORMATION OF EXTRA-CELLULAR NITROGEN COMPOUNDS BY
      FUNGI. NATURE, LOND. 168, 333-334.

3969 MORTON, A.G. (1956) - NITRATE REDUCTION IN MOLD FUNGI. J.EXP.BOT. 7, 97-
      112.

3970 MORTON, A.G. & BROADBENT, D. (1955) - THE FORMATION OF EXTRACELLULAR NI-
      TROGEN COMPOUNDS BY FUNGI. J.GEN.MICROBIOL. 12, 248-258.

3971 MORTON, A.G., ENGLAND, D.J.F. & TOWLER, D.A. (1958) - THE PHYSIOLOGY OF
      SPORULATION IN PENICILLIUM GRISEOFULVUM DIERCKX. TRANS.BR.MYCOL.SOC.
      41, 39-51.

3972 MORTON, A.G. & MACMILLAN, A. (1954) - THE ASSIMILATION OF NITROGEN FROM
      AMMONIUM SALTS AND NITRATE BY FUNGI. J.EXP.BOT. 5, 232-252.

3973 MORTON, D.J. & STROUBE, W.H. (1955) - ANTAGONISTIC AND STIMULATORY EFFECTS
      OF SOIL MICROORGANISMS UPON SCLEROTIUM ROLFSII. PHYTOPATHOLOGY 45, 417-
      420.

3974 MORTON, F.J. & SMITH, G. (1963) - THE GENERA SCOPULARIOPSIS, MICROASCUS
      AND DORATOMYCES. MYCOL.PAP. 86, 1-96.

3975 MOSCA, A.M. (1956) - RICERCHE SULLA MICOFLORA DEL SUOLO IN UN PICEETO DEL
      PARCO NAZIONALE DEL GRAN PARADISO. ALLIONIA 3, 23-67.

3976 MOSCA, A.M. (1957) - RICERCHE SULLA MICOFLORA DEL TERRENO DI UNA VALLETTA
      NIVALE NEL PARCO NAZIONALE DEL GRAN PARADISO. ALLIONIA 3, 83-107.

3977 MOSES, V. (1954) - THE EFFECT OF AMMONIA ON THE OXIDATION OF GLUCOSE BY
      ZYGORHYNCHUS MOELLERI. BIOCHEM.J. 57, 547-556.

3978 MOSES, V. (1955) - GLUCOSE RESPIRATION IN ZYGORHYNCHUS MOELLERI, THE ENTRY
      OF GLUCOSE INTO THE CELLS. J.EXP.BOT. 6, 222-234.

3979 MOSES, V. (1957) - THE METABOLIC SIGNIFICANCE OF CITRIC ACID IN THE GROWTH
      OF THE FUNGUS ZYGORHYNCHUS MOELLERI. J.GEN.MICROBIOL. 16, 534-549.

3980 MOSES, V., HOLM-HANSEN, O. & CALVIN, M. (1959) - NONPHOTOSYNTHETIC FIXA-
      TION OF CARBON DIOXIDE BY THREE MICROORGANISMS. J.BACT. 77, 70-78.

3981 MOSES, V. & SYRETT, P.J. (1955) - THE ENDOGENOUS RESPIRATION OF MICROORGAN-
      ISMS. J.BACT. 70, 201-204.

3982 MOSKOVETS, V.S. (1957) - (THE FUNGAL MICROFLORA OF LUCERNE RHIZOSPHERE IN THE SOUTHERN UKRAINIAN SSR. 2. QUANTITATIVE AND QUALITATIVE COMPOSITION OF THE FUNGAL MICROFLORA IN THE RHIZOSPHERE OF LUCERNE). MYKROBIOL.ZH. 19 (3), 44-50.

3983 MOSKOVETS, V.S. (1957) - (THE FUNGAL MICROFLORA OF LUCERNE RHIZOSPHERE IN THE SOUTHERN UKRAINIAN SSR. 3. THE FUNGAL FLORA OR LUCERNE ROOTS). MY-KROBIOL.ZH. 19 (4), 16-21.

3984 MOSS, M.O., JACKSON, R.M. & ROGERS, D. (1975) - THE CHARACTERIZATION OF 6-(PENT-1-ENYL)-ALPHA-PYRONE FROM TRICHODERMA VIRIDE. PHYTOCHEMISTRY 14, 2706-2708.

3985 MOSS, M.O., ROBINSON, F.V. & WOOD, A.B. (1968) - RUBRATOXIN-B, A TOXIC ME-TABOLITE OF PENICILLIUM RUBRUM. CHEM.IND., 1968, 587-588.

3986 MOSS, M.O., WOOD, A.B. & ROBINSON, F.V. (1969) - THE STRUCTURE OF RUBRA-TOXIN-A, A TOXIC METABOLITE OF PENICILLIUM RUBRUM. TETRAHEDRON LETTERS, 1969 (5), 367-370.

3987 MOUBASHER, A.H. (1963) - SELECTIVE EFFECTS OF FUMIGATION WITH CARBON DI-SULPHIDE ON THE SOIL FUNGUS FLORA. TRANS.BR.MYCOL.SOC. 46, 338-344.

3988 MOUBASHER, A.H., ELNAGHY, M.A. & ABDEL-FATTAH, H.M. (1971) - CITRUS PLAN-TATION FUNGI IN UPPER EGYPT. TRANS.BR.MYCOL.SOC. 57, 289-294.

3989 MOUBASHER, A.H., ELNAGHY, M.A. & ABDEL-HAFEZ, S.I. (1972) - STUDIES ON THE FUNGUS FLORA OF THREE GRAINS IN EGYPT. MYCOPATH.MYCOL.APPL. 47, 261-274.

3990 MOUBASHER, A.H., ELNAGHY, M.A. & MEGALA, S.E. (1970) - FUNGI ISOLATED FROM SCLEROTIA OF SCLEROTIUM CEPIVORUM AND FROM SOIL AND THEIR EFFECTS UPON THE PATHOGEN. PL.SOIL 33, 305-312.

3991 MOUBASHER, A.H. & MAZEN, M.B. (1971) - SELECTIVE EFFECTS OF THREE FUMI-GANTS ON EGYPTIAN SOIL FUNGI. TRANS.BR.MYCOL.SOC. 57, 447-454.

3992 MOUBASHER, A.H. & MAZEN, M.B. (1972) - DEMATIACEOUS HYPHOMYCETES IN EGYPTIAN SOILS. TRANS.BR.MYCOL.SOC. 59, 527-530.

3993 MOUBASHER, A.H. & MOUSTAFA, A.F. (1970) - A SURVEY OF EGYPTIAN SOIL FUNGI WITH SPECIAL REFERENCE TO ASPERGILLUS, PENICILLIUM AND PENICILLIUM-RE-LATED GENERA. TRANS.BR.MYCOL.SOC. 54, 35-44.

3994 MOUCHACCA, J. (1972) - REMARQUES SUR LA TAXONOMIE DES ESPECES DE SCOLECO-BASIDIUM A CONIDIES PLURISEPTEES. REVUE MYCOL. 36, 298-305.

3995 MOUCHACCA, J. (1973) - LES THIELAVIA DES SOLS ARIDES - ESPECES NOUVELLES ET ANALYSE GENERIQUE. BULL.TRIMEST.SOC.MYCOL.FR. 89, 295-311.

3996 MOUCHACCA, J. & JOLY, P. (1969) - ESSAIS D'APPLICATION DE METHODES DE TRAITEMENT NUMERIQUE DES INFORMATIONS SYSTEMATIQUES. 3. ETUDE DE L'AC-TION DES VARIATIONS DU PH SUR LE DEVELOPPEMENT DE QUELQUES CHAMPIGNONS DES SOLS DESERTIQUES. BULL.TRIMEST.SOC.MYCOL.FR. 85, 503-526.

3997 MOUCHACCA, J. & JOLY, P. (1974) - ETUDE DE LA MYCOFLORE DES SOLS ARIDES DE L'EGYPTE. 1. LE GENRE PENICILLIUM. REVUE ECOL.BIOL.SOL 11, 67-88.

3998 MOUCHACCA, J., POLY, P. & JOLY, F. (1970) - ESSAIS D'APPLICATION DE METHO-DES DE TRAITEMENT NUMERIQUE DES INFORMATIONS SYSTEMATIQUES. 5. ETUDE DE L'ACTION DE FORTES CONCENTRATIONS DE NACL SUR LE DEVELOPPEMENT DE QUEL-QUES CHAMPIGNONS DES SOLS DESERTIQUES. BULL.TRIMEST.SOC.MYCOL.FR. 86, 883-910.

3999 MOUNTAIN, W.B. & MCKEEN, C.D. (1962) - INTERACTION OF VERTICILLIUM DAHLIAE
      AND PRATYLENCHUS PENETRANS IN TOMATO WILT. PHYTOPATHOLOGY 52, 744 (ABS.).

4000 MOUSTAFA, A.F. (1975) - OSMOPHILIC FUNGI IN THE SALT MARSHES OF KUWAIT.
      CAN.J.MICROBIOL. 21, 1573-1580.

4001 MOUSTAFA, A.F. & AL-MUSALLAM, A.A. (1975) - CONTRIBUTION TO THE FUNGAL FLO-
      RA OF KUWAIT. TRANS.BR.MYCOL.SOC. 65, 547-553.

4002 MOYER, A.J. & COGHILL, R.D. (1945) - THE LABORATORY SCALE PRODUCTION OF
      ITACONIC ACID BY ASPERGILLUS TERREUS. ARCHS BIOCHEM. 7, 167-183.

4003 MUELLER, E. (1950) - DIE SCHWEIZERISCHEN ARTEN DER GATTUNG LEPTOSPHAERIA
      UND IHRER VERWANDTEN. SYDOWIA 4, 185-319.

4004 MUELLER, E. (1977) - DIE SYSTEMATISCHE STELLUNG DES SCHNEESCHIMMELS. REVUE
      MYCOL. 41, 129-134.

4005 MUELLER, E. & ARX, J.A.VON (1955) - EINIGE BEITRAEGE ZUR SYSTEMATIK UND
      SYNONYMIE DER PILZE. PHYTOPATH.Z. 24, 353-372.

4006 MUELLER, E. & SEDLAR, L. (1977) - COMPATIBILITAETSVERHAELTNISSE IN CHAETO-
      MIUM. 3. BEZIEHUNGEN ZWISCHEN SELBSTCOMPATIBILITAET UND SELBSTINCOMPA-
      TIBILITAET. SYDOWIA 29, 252-271.

4007 MUELLER, G. & BEYER, R. (1965) - UEBER WECHSELBEZIEHUNGEN ZWISCHEN MIKRO-
      SKOPISCHEN BODENPILZEN UND FUNGIPHAGEN BODENTIEREN. ZENTBL.BAKT.PARASIT-
      KDE, ABT.2, 119, 133-147.

4008 MUELLER, G. & FOERSTER, I. (1963) - DER EINFLUSS MIKROSKOPISCHER BODENPIL-
      ZE AUF DIE NAEHRSTOFFFREISETZUNG AUS PRIMAEREN MINERALIEN, ALS BEITRAG
      ZUR BIOLOGISCHEN VERWITTERUNG. 1. ZENTBL.BAKT.PARASITKDE, ABT.2, 116,
      372-409.

4009 MUELLER, G. & FOERSTER, I. (1964) - DER EINFLUSS MIKROSKOPISCHER BODENPIL-
      ZE AUF DIE NAEHRSTOFFFREISETZUNG AUS PRIMAEREN MINERALIEN, ALS BEITRAG
      ZUR BIOLOGISCHEN VERWITTERUNG. 2. ZENTBL.BAKT.PARASITKDE, ABT.2, 118,
      594-621.

4010 MUELLER, G. & HEISIG, W. (1968) - DIE FREISETZUNG VON STICKSTOFF AUS UREA-
      FORM DURCH MIKROSKOPISCHE PILZE. ZENTBL.BAKT.PARASITKDE, ABT.2, 122,
      275-281.

4011 MUELLER, G. & HEISIG, W. (1970) - ZUR WIRKUNG VON UREAFORM AUF DIE MYZEL-
      BILDUNG BEI ZWEI PILZEN DER GATTUNG ASPERGILLUS. ZENTBL.BAKT.PARASITKDE,
      ABT.2, 124, 136-145.

4012 MUELLER, G.H., KAPLAN, W., AJELLO, L. & PADHYE, A.A. (1975) - PHAEOHYPHO-
      MYCOSIS CAUSED BY DRECHSLERA SPICIFERA IN A CAT. J.AM.VET.MED.ASS. 166,
      150-154.

4013 MUELLER, H. (1962) - UNTERSUCHUNGEN ZUR FRAGE WECHSELSEITIGER BEZIEHUNGEN
      ZWISCHEN KEIMENDEN SAMEN UND MIKROORGANISMEN IN SAMENNAEHE. ARCH.MIKRO-
      BIOL. 41, 351-382.

4014 MUELLER, H.E. (1975) - UEBER DAS VORKOMMEN VON NEURAMINIDASE BEI SPORO-
      THRIX SCHENCKII UND CERATOCYSTIS STENOCERAS UND IHRE BEDEUTUNG FUER DIE
      OEKOLOGIE UND DEN PATHOMECHANISMUS DIESER PILZE. ZENTBL.BAKT.PARASITKDE,
      ABT.1, 232, 365-372.

4015 MUELLER, H.J. (1964) - UNTERSUCHUNGEN UEBER BLATTFLECKENKRANKHEITEN DES HA-
      FERS. 2. PILZLICHE BLATTFLECKENERREGER DES HAFERS. PHYTOPATH.Z. 49, 266-
      290.

4016 MUELLER, H.M. (1965) - UNTERSUCHUNGEN ZUM SAEURESTOFFWECHSEL VON ASPERGIL-
      LUS NIGER. 1.DER EINFLUSS DES C/N VERHAELTNISSES DER AUSGANGS-NAEHRLOE-
      SUNG AUF DEN PH-WERT UND DIE OXALSAEUREANHAEUFUNG. ARCH.MIKROBIOL. 52,
      251-265.

4017 MUELLER, H.M. (1966) - UNTERSUCHUNGEN ZUM SAEURESTOFFWECHSEL VON ASPERGIL-
      LUS NIGER. 2. DER EINFLUSS DES C/N VERHAELTNISSES IN DER AUSGANGS-NAEHR-
      LOESUNG AUF DIE GLUCON-, CITRONEN- UND OXALSAEUREANHAEUFUNG BEI KON-
      TROLLIERTEM PH-WERT UND MITTLERER TEMPERATUR (30 C). ARCH.MIKROBIOL.
      53, 77-91.

4018 MUELLER, H.M. (1966) - UNTERSUCHUNGEN ZUM SAEURESTOFFWECHSEL VON ASPERGIL-
      LUS NIGER. 3. DER EINFLUSS DES C/N VERHAELTNISSES IN DER AUSGANGS-NAEHR-
      LOESUNG AUF DIE GLUCON-, CITRONEN- UND OXALSAEUREANHAEUFUNG BEI KON-
      TROLLIERTEM PH-WERT UND EXTREMEN TEMPERATUREN (43 UND 10 C). ARCH.MI-
      KROBIOL. 53, 277-287.

4019 MUELLER, H.M. (1975) - OXALATE ACCUMULATION FROM CITRATE BY ASPERGILLUS
      NIGER. ARCH.MIKROBIOL. 103, 185-189.

4020 MUELLER, J. (1972) - UNTERSUCHUNGEN UEBER DIE WECHSELWIRKUNGEN ZWISCHEN
      PRATYLENCHUS PENETRANS (COBB, 1917) CHITWOOD & OTEIFA, 1952 UND VERTI-
      CILLIUM ALBO-ATRUM REINKE & BERTHOLD. DISS.UNIV.HANNOVER.

4021 MUELLER-DOMBOIS, D. & PERERA, M. (1971) - ECOLOGICAL DIFFERENTIATION AND
      SOIL FUNGAL DISTRIBUTION IN THE MONTANE GRASSLANDS OF CEYLON. CEYLON
      J.SCI.BIOL.SCI. 9, 1-41.

4022 MUELLER-KOEGLER, E. (1938) - UNTERSUCHUNGEN UEBER DIE SCHWARZBEINIGKEIT DES
      GETREIDES UND DEN WIRTSPFLANZENKREIS IHRES ERREGERS. ARB.BIOL.REICHSANST.
      LD-U.FORSTW. 22, 271-319.

4023 MUELLER-KOEGLER, E. (1965) - PILZKRANKHEITEN BEI INSEKTEN. P.PAREY, BERLIN.

4024 MUELLER-KOEGLER, E. & HUGER, A. (1960) - WUNDINFEKTIONEN BEI RAUPEN VON MA-
      LACOSOMA NEUSTRIA DURCH PENICILLIUM BREVICOMPACTUM. Z.ANGEW.ENT. 45,
      421-429.

4025 MUELLER-KOEGLER, E. & SAMSINAKOVA, A. (1969) - KEIMUNGSPROZENTE UND KEI-
      MUNGSKURVEN DER KONIDIEN UND SUBMERS GEBILDETEN BLASTOSPOREN EINES STAM-
      MES VON BEAUVERIA BASSIANA (BALS.) VUILL. ENTOMOPHAGA 14, 369-382.

4026 MUELLER-KOEGLER, E. & SAMSINAKOVA, A. (1970) - ZUR MASSENKULTUR DES INSEK-
      TENPATHOGENEN PILZES BEAUVERIA BASSIANA. EXPERIENTIA 26, 1400.

4027 MUENZNER, R. (1969) - UEBER EINIGE DIE STRAHLENEMPFINDLICHKEIT VON SCHIM-
      MELPILZEN BEEINFLUSSENDE FAKTOREN. ARCH.MIKROBIOL. 64, 349-356.

4028 MUGHOGHO, L.K. (1968) - THE FUNGUS FLORA OF FUMIGATED SOILS. TRANS.BR.MYCOL.
      SOC. 51, 441-459.

4029 MUJUMDAR, S.B. & BHIDE, V.P. (1970) - EFFECT OF CARBON DIOXIDE CONCENTRA-
      TION ON FUNGI FROM RHIZOSPHERE AND NON-RHIZOPSHERE SOIL OF SUGAR CANE.
      J.UNIV.POONA 38, 137-141.

4030 MUKERJI, K.G. (1966) - ECOLOGICAL STUDIES ON THE MICROORGANIC POPULATION
      OF USAR SOILS. MYCOPATH.MYCOL.APPL. 29, 339-349.

4031   MUKERJI, K.G. (1968) - OBSERVATIONS ON THE MUTUAL RELATIONSHIPS AMONG SOIL
        MICROORGANISMS. J.GEN.APPL.MICROBIOL., TOKYO 14, 243-250.

4032   MULANAX, M. & HUBER, D. (1970) - MACERATING ENZYMES ASSOCIATED WITH TYPHU-
        LA IDAHOENSIS. PHYTOPATHOLOGY 60, 1536 (ABS.).

4033   MULANAX, M. & HUBER, D. (1972) - PROPOSED ROLES OF EXTRACELLULAR ENZYMES
        OF FUSARIUM NIVALE AND TYPHULA IDAHOENSIS INCITANTS OF SNOW MOLD OF WIN-
        TER WHEAT. PHYTOPATHOLOGY 62, 1105 (ABS.).

4034   MULDER, D. (1969) - THE PATHOGENICITY OF SEVERAL PYTHIUM SPECIES TO ROOT-
        LETS OF APPLE SEEDLINGS. NETH.J.PL.PATH. 75, 178-181.

4035   MULDER, E.G. (1938) - UEBER DIE BEDEUTUNG DES KUPFERS FUER DAS WACHSTUM
        VON MIKROORGANISMEN UND UEBER EINE MIKROBIOLOGISCHE METHODE ZUR BESTIM-
        MUNG DES PFLANZENVERFUEGBAREN BODENKUPFERS. ARCH.MIKROBIOL. 10, 72-86.

4036   MULDER, J.L. & PUGH, G.J.F. (1971) - FUNGAL BIOLOGICAL FLORA. 2. EPICOCCUM
        NIGRUM LINK. INT.BIODETERIOR.BULL. 7, 69-71.

4037   MULHEIRN, L.J. & CASPI, E. (1971) - MECHANISM OF SQUALENE CYCLIZATION. THE
        BIOSYNTHESIS OF FUSIDIC ACID. J.BIOL.CHEM. 246, 2494-2501.

4038   MULINGE, S.K. & CHESTERS, C.G.C. (1970) - ECOLOGY OF FUNGI ASSOCIATED WITH
        MOIST STORED BARLEY GRAIN. ANN.APPL.BIOL. 65, 277-284.

4039   MULLINS, J. & HARVEY, R. (1977) - SPORULATION AND SPORE LIBERATION IN AS-
        PERGILLUS FUMIGATUS. MYCOPATHOLOGIA 60, 175-177.

4040   MUMMA, R.O. & BRUSZEWSKI, T.E. (1970) - THE FATTY ACIDS OF ENTOMOPHTHORA
        CORONATA. LIPIDS 5, 915-920.

4041   MUMMA, R.O. & BRUSZEWSKI, T.E. (1973) - FUNGI PATHOGENIC TO INSECTS. 3.
        NEUTRAL AND POLAR LIPIDS OF ENTOMOPHTHORA CORONATA. LIPIDS 8, 745-752.

4042   MUNDEN, J.E., BUTTERWORTH, D., HANSCOMB, G. & VERRALL, M.S. (1970) - PRO-
        DUCTION OF CHLORFLAVONIN, AN ANTIFUGAL METABOLITE OF ASPERGILLUS CANDI-
        DUS. APPL.MICROBIOL. 19, 718-720.

4043   MUNJAL, R.L. (1960) - A COMMONLY OCCURRING LEAF SPOT DISEASE CAUSED BY MY-
        ROTHECIUM RORIDUM. INDIAN PHYTOPATH. 13, 150-155.

4044   MUNNECKE, D.E. & MOORE, B.J. (1969) - EFFECT OF STORAGE AT -18 C OF SOIL
        INFESTED WITH PYTHIUM OR FUSARIUM ON DAMPING-OFF OF SEEDLINGS. PHYTO-
        PATHOLOGY 59, 1517-1520.

4045   MUNTANJOLA-CVETKOVIC, M. & VUKIC, V.V. (1972) - INFLUENCE OF LIGHT ON
        HUELLE CELL AND ALEURIOSPORE FORMATION IN ASPERGILLUS. TRANS.BR.MYCOL.
        SOC. 58, 67-72.

4046   MURAKAMI, H. (1971) - TAXONOMIC STUDIES ON THE JAPANESE INDUSTRIAL STRAINS
        OF ASPERGILLUS. 17. CLASSIFICATION (ASPERGILLUS ORYZAE GROUP). REP.RES.
        INST.BREW., JAPAN 143, 5-14.

4047   MURAKAMI, H. (1971) - TAXONOMIC STUDIES ON THE JAPANESE INDUSTRIAL STRAINS
        OF ASPERGILLUS. 18. MOLDS OTHER THAN THE KOJI MOLD AND MYCOLOGICAL CHAR-
        ACTERS OF ASPERGILLUS STRAINS. REP.RES.INST.BREW., JAPAN 143, 16-29.

4048   MURAKAMI, H., MAKINO, M. & OGINO, Y. (1967) - TAXONOMIC STUDIES ON THE JAP-
        ANESE INDUSTRIAL STRAINS OF ASPERGILLUS. 7. MYCOLOGICAL CHARACTERS OF
        THE TYPE CULTURES, INDUSTRIAL AND NON-INDUSTRIAL STRAINS OF THE ASPER-
        GILLUS. REP.RES.INST.BREW., JAPAN 139, 16-23.

4049   MURAKAMI, H., SAGAWA, H. & TAKASE, S. (1968) - NON-PRODUCTIVITY OF AFLA-
       TOXIN BY JAPANESE INDUSTRIAL STRAINS OF THE' ASPERGILLUS. 3. COMMON CHAR-
       ACTERISTICS OF THE AFLATOXIN-PRODUCING STRAINS. J.GEN.APPL.MICROBIOL.,
       TOKYO 14, 252-262.

4050   MURAKAMI, H., SAGAWA, H. & TAKASE, S. (1968) - TAXONOMIC STUDIES ON THE
       JAPANESE INDUSTRIAL STRAINS OF ASPERGILLUS. 8. ON THE AFLATOXIN STRAINS.
       REP.RES.INST.BREW., JAPAN 140, 1-3.

4051   MURAKAMI, H., SUZUKI, A., NAGANAWA, M. & OHWAKI, K. (1965) - TAXONOMIC
       STUDIES ON THE JAPANESE INDUSTRIAL STRAINS OF ASPERGILLUS. 1. MORPHO-
       LOGICAL CHARACTERS OF THE YELLOW GREEN-SPORED ASPERGILLI. REP.RES.INST.
       BREW., JAPAN 137, 1-11.

4052   MURAKAMI, H., TAKASE, S. & KUWABARA, K. (1968) - NON-PRODUCTIVITY OF AFLA-
       TOXIN BY JAPANESE INDUSTRIAL STRAINS OF ASPERGILLUS. 2. PRODUCTION OF
       FLUORESCENT SUBSTANCES IN RICE KOJI, AND THEIR IDENTIFICATION BY ABSORP-
       TION SPECTRUM. J.GEN.APPL.MICROBIOL., TOKYO 14, 97-110.

4053   MURRAY, D.S., RIECK, W.L. & LYND, J.Q. (1970) - UTILIZATION OF METHYLTHIO-
       S-TRIAZINE FOR GROWTH OF SOIL FUNGI. APPL.MICROBIOL. 19, 11-13.

4054   MUSE, R.R., COUCH, H.B., MOORE, L.D. & MUSE, B.D. (1972) - PECTOLYTIC AND
       CELLULOLYTIC ENZYMES ASSOCIATED WITH HELMINTHOSPORIUM LEAF SPOT ON KEN-
       TUCKY BLUEGRASS. CAN.J.MICROBIOL. 18, 1091-1098.

4055   MUSKAT, J. (1955) - UNTERSUCHUNGEN UEBER SCHIMMELPILZE BAYRISCHER UND TU-
       NESISCHER BOEDEN. 1. FLORISTISCH-OEKOLOGISCHER TEIL. ARCH.MIKROBIOL.
       22, 1-20.

4056   MUSSEL, H.W. (1972) - TOXIC PROTEINS SECRETED BY COTTON ISOLATES OF VERTI-
       CILLIUM ALBO-ATRUM. IN: PHYTOTOXINS IN PLANT DISEASES; WOOD, R.K.S.,
       BALLIO, A. & GRANITI, A. (ED.), ACADEMIC PRESS, LONDON, NEW YORK, 443-
       445.

4057   MUSSEL, H.W. (1973) - ENDOPOLYGALACTURONASE - EVIDENCE FOR INVOLVEMENT IN
       VERTICILLIUM WILT OF COTTON. PHYTOPATHOLOGY 63, 62-70.

4058   MUSSEL, H.W. & STROUSE, B. (1971) - PROTEOLYTIC ENZYME PRODUCTION BY VER-
       TICILLIUM ALBO-ATRUM. PHYTOPATHOLOGY 61, 904 (ABS.).

4059   MUSTAFEE, T.P. & CHATTOPADHYAY, S.B. (1971) - EFFECT OF SOIL TEMPERATURE
       ON THE GROWTH OF MACROPHOMINA PHASEOLI AND SCLEROTIUM ROLFSII IN SOIL.
       INDIAN J.MICROBIOL. 11, 83-86.

4060   MYOKEI, R., SAKURAI, A., CHANG, CH.-F., KODAIRA, Y., TAKAHASHI, N. & TA-
       MURA, S. (1969) - ASPOCHRACIN, A NEW INSECTICIDAL METABOLITE OF ASPER-
       GILLUS OCHRACEUS. 1. ISOLATION, STRUCTURE AND BIOLOGICAL ACTIVITIES.
       AGRIC.BIOL.CHEM., TOKYO 33, 1491-1500.

4061   NADAKAVUKAREN, M.J. (1961) - THE EFFECT OF SOIL MOISTURE AND TEMPERATURE
       ON SURVIVAL OF VERTICILLIUM MICROSCLEROTIA. DISS.ABSTR. 21, 419.

4062   NADAKAVUKAREN, M.J. (1963) - FINE STRUCTURE OF MICROSCLEROTIA OF VERTICIL-
       LIUM ALBO-ATRUM R & B. CAN.J.MICROBIOL. 9, 411-413.

4063   NADAKAVUKAREN, M.J. & HORNER, C.E. (1959) - AN ALCOHOL AGAR MEDIUM SELEC-
       TIVE FOR DETERMINING VERTICILLIUM MICROSCLEROTIA IN SOIL. PHYTOPATHOL-
       OGY 49, 527-528.

4064 NADAKAVUKAREN M.J. & HORNER C.E. (1961) - INFLUENCE OF SOIL MOISTURE AND
      TEMPERATURE ON SURVIVAL OF VERTICILLIUM MICROSCLEROTIA. PHYTOPATHOLOGY
      51, 66 (ABS.).

4065 NAGANISHI, H. & HIRAHARA, S. (1970) - FORMATION OF ZYGOSPORES FROM THE
      MATINGS BETWEEN MUCOR STRAINS RESEMBLING MUCOR SUBTILISSIMUS OUDEMANS
      AND MUCOR HIEMALIS WEHMER. BULL.HIROSHIMA JOGAKUIN COLL. 20, 19-35.

4066 NAGANISHI, H., SESHITA, Y. & HIRAHARA, S. (1973) - A SUPPLEMENT TO 'THE
      FORMATION OF ZYGOSPORES FROM MATINGS BETWEEN MUCOR STRAINS RESEMBLING
      MUCOR SUBTILISSIMUS OUDEMANS AND MUCOR HIEMALIS WEHMER'. BULL.HIROSHI-
      MA JOGAKUIN COLL. 23, 181-191.

4067 NAGASAKI, S. (1968) - PHYSIOLOGICAL ASPECTS OF VARIOUS ENZYME ACTIVITIES
      IN RELATION TO THE CULTURE AGE OF ASPERGILLUS NIGER MYCELIA. J.GEN.APPL.
      MICROBIOL., TOKYO 14, 147-161.

4068 NAGORNAYA, N.M. (1971) - (ACTIVITY OF VERTICILLIUM DAHLIAE IN THE SOIL AND
      INFECTION OF COTTON WITH WILT). SEL'.KHOZ.BIOL. 6, 773-774.

4069 NAG RAJ, T.R. & GOVINDU, H.C. (1969) - FUNGI OF MYSORE. 4. SYDOWIA 23, 110-
      117.

4070 NAG RAJ, T.R. & KENDRICK, B. (1976) - A MONOGRAPH OF CHALARA AND ALLIED
      GENERA. WILFRID LAURIER UNIV.PRESS, WATERLOO, ONTARIO.

4071 NAGUIB, K. (1960) - GROWTH AND METABOLISM OF PENICILLIUM LILACINUM THOM
      WITH REFERENCE TO THE EFFECTS OF RIBOFLAVIN AND NICOTINIC ACID. ARCH.
      MIKROBIOL. 35, 296-302.

4072 NAGUIB, K., AL-SOHAILY, I.A. & AL-SULTAN, A.S. (1972) - ON MYCOLOGICAL FAT
      PRODUCTION FROM IRAQI DATE EXTRACT. THE DIBIS. MYCOPATH.MYCOL.APPL. 47,
      93-103.

4073 NAGUIB, K. & HANNA, H.A. (1974) - FAT FORMATION IN PREFORMED FUNGAL MATS
      OF PENICILLIUM NOTATUM. MYCOPATH.MYCOL.APPL. 54, 303-311.

4074 NAGUIB, M.I. (1968) - INTERACTION OF ASCORBIC ACID AND COLCHICINE WITH SU-
      CROSE UTILIZATION BY CUNNINGHAMELLA ELEGANS. FOLIA MICROBIOL. 13, 190-
      196.

4075 NAGUIB, M.I. (1968) - EFFECT OF VARIOUS NITROGEN SOURCES AND/OR COLCHICINE
      ON THE UTILIZATION OF L-ARABINOSE BY CUNNINGHAMELLA ELEGANS. ACTA BIOL.,
      SZEGED 19, 437-444.

4076 NAGUIB, M.I. & BAGNEID, M.O.S. (1974) - (EFFECT OF FEEDING WITH SUCROSE
      AND PHOSPHORUS, IN ALTERNATION OR TOGETHER, ON THE CARBOHYDRATE AND
      PHOSPHORUS METABOLISM OF PHOSPHORUS-STARVED MYCELIAL FELTS OF CUNNING-
      HAMELLA ELEGANS). BULL.FAC.SCI.CAIRO UNIV. 45, 97-108.

4077 NAIK, M., MODI, V.V. & PATEL, N.C. (1970) - STUDIES ON AFLATOXIN SYNTHESIS
      IN ASPERGILLUS FLAVUS. INDIAN J.EXPL BIOL. 8, 345-346.

4078 NAIKI, T. & UI, T. (1969) - ON THE SURVIVAL OF THE SCLEROTIA OF RHIZOCTO-
      NIA SOLANI KUEHN IN SOIL. MEM.FAC.AGRIC.HOKKAIDO UNIV. 6, 430-436.

4079 NAIKI, T. & UI, T. (1972) - LYTIC PHENOMENON OF THE HYPHAE OF RHIZOCTONIA
      IN SOIL. TRANS.MYCOL.SOC.JAPAN 13, 140-148.

4080 NAIKI, T. & UI, T. (1972) - THE MICROORGANISMS ASSOCIATED WITH THE SCLERO-
      TIA OF RHIZOCTONIA SOLANI KUEHN IN SOIL AND THEIR EFFECTS ON THE VIA-
      BILITY OF THE PATHOGENS. MEM.FAC.AGRIC.HOKKAIDO UNIV. 8, 252-265.

4081 NAIKI, T. & UI, T. (1974) - ULTRASTRUCTURES OF THE HYPHAL CELL WALLS AND
      THE SCLEROTIA OF RHIZOCTONIA SOLANI. TRANS.MYCOL.SOC.JAPAN 15, 113-120.

4082 NAIKI, T., UI, T. & SHIKATA, E. (1968) - FINE STRUCTURES OF THE HYPHAE OF
      RHIZOCTONIA SOLANI. TRANS.MYCOL.SOC.JAPAN 9, 57-62.

4083 NAIM, M.S. (1965) - DEVELOPMENT OF RHIZOSPHERE AND RHIZOPLANE MICROFLORA
      OF ARISTIDA COERULESCENS IN THE LIBYAN DESERT. ARCH.MIKROBIOL. 50, 321-
      325.

4084 NAIM, M.S. (1967) - CONTRIBUTION TO THE KNOWLEDGE OF SOIL FUNGI IN LIBYA.
      1. RHIZOSPHERE AND SOIL FUNGI OF ARTEMISIA HERBA ALBA IN TRIPOLI. MYCO-
      PATH.MYCOL.APPL. 31, 296-299.

4085 NAIM, M.S. (1967) - CONTRIBUTION TO THE KNOWLEDGE OF SOIL FUNGI IN LIBYA.
      2. FUNGUS FLORA UNDER CITRUS TREES IN LIBYA. MYCOPATH.MYCOL.APPL. 31,
      300-304.

4086 NAIR, N.G. (1962) - BEHAVIOUR OF BIPOLARIS SOROKINIANA IN THE RHIZOSPHERE
      OF WHEAT. PROC.INDIAN ACAD.SCI., SECT.B, 55, 290-295.

4087 NAIR, N.G. (1968) - SAPROPHYTIC ACTIVITY OF DRECHSLERA (=HELMINTHOSPORIUM)
      IN SOIL. PHYTOPATH.Z. 61, 331-341.

4088 NAITO, N. & TANI, T. (1959) - PRODUCTION OF PHENOLIC COMPOUNDS BY SCLERO-
      TINIA SCLEROTIORUM. KAGAWA DAIGAKU NOGAKUBU GAKUZYUTU HOKOKU 10, 121-
      124.

4089 NAITO, S. & KANEKO, Y. (1969) - TWO NEW PHENOLIC REDUCTONES FROM ASPERGIL-
      LUS TERREUS. TETRAHEDRON LETTERS, 1969 (53), 4675-4678.

4090 NAKADAI, T., NASUNO, S. & IGUCHI, N. (1973) - PURIFICATION AND PROPERTIES
      OF LEUCINE AMINOPEPTIDASE-III FROM ASPERGILLUS ORYZAE. AGRIC.BIOL.CHEM.,
      TOKYO 37, 775-782.

4091 NAKADAI, T., NASUNO, S. & IGUCHI, N. (1973) - PURIFICATION AND PROPERTIES
      OF ALKALINE PROTEINASE FROM ASPERGILLUS ORYZAE. AGRIC.BIOL.CHEM., TOKYO
      37, 2685-2694.

4092 NAKADAI, T., NASUNO, S. & IGUCHI, N. (1973) - PURIFICATION AND PROPERTIES
      OF NEUTRAL PROTEINASE-I FROM ASPERGILLUS ORYZAE. AGRIC.BIOL.CHEM., TO-
      KYO 37, 2695-2701.

4093 NAKADAI, T., NASUNO, S. & IGUCHI, N. (1973) - PURIFICATION AND PROPERTIES
      OF NEUTRAL PROTEINASE-II FROM ASPERGILLUS ORYZAE. AGRIC.BIOL.CHEM., TO-
      KYO 37, 2703-2708.

4094 NAKAHAMA, K., IMADA, A., IGARASI, S. & TUBAKI, K. (1973) - FORMATION OF L-
      ASPARAGINASE BY FUSARIUM SPECIES. J.GEN.MICROBIOL. 75, 269-273.

4095 NAKAMURA, S., NII, F., SHIMIZU, M. & WATANABE, I. (1971) - INHIBITION OF
      PHAGE GROWTH BY AN ANTIBIOTIC RUGULOSIN ISOLATED FROM MYROTHECIUM VER-
      RUCARIA. 1. PROPERTIES OF THE ANTI-PHAGE EFFECT. JAPAN.J.MICROBIOL. 15,
      113-120.

4096 NAKAMURA, S. & SHIMODA, CH. (1954) - (STUDIES ON AN ANTIBIOTIC SUBSTANCE
      ORYZACIDIN, PRODUCED BY ASPERGILLUS ORYZAE. 5. EXISTENCE OF BETA-NITRO-
      PROPIONIC ACID). J.AGRIC.CHEM.SOC.JAPAN 28, 909-913.

4097 NAKAMURA, S. & SHIRO, T. (1961) - STUDIES ON GROWTH INHIBITION OF HIOCHI-
      BACTERIA, SPECIFIC SAPROPHYTES OF SAKE. AGRIC.BIOL.CHEM., TOKYO 25, 573-
      579.

4098   NAKAMURA, T., GRANT, J.A., THRELKELD, R. & WIBLE, L. (1972) - PRIMARY
       CHROMOBLASTOMYCOSIS OF THE NASAL SEPTUM. AM.J.CLIN.PATH. 58, 365-370.

4099   NAKAMURA, Y. (1976) - PURIFICATION AND ISOLATION OF A BIOLOGICALLY ACTIVE
       PEPTIDO-RHAMNOGALACTAN FROM SPOROTHRIX SCHENCKII. J.DERMAT.TOKYO 3, 25-
       29.

4100   NAKANISHI, T. (1972) - MICROBIAL CONVERSION OF PENTACHLORONITROBENZENE IN
       SOIL. ANN.PHYTOPATH.SOC.JAPAN 38, 249-251.

4101   NAKASE, T. & KOMAGATA, K. (1968) - TAXONOMIC SIGNIFICANCE OF BASE COMPOSI-
       TION OF YEAST DNA. J.GEN.APPL.MICROBIOL., TOKYO 14, 345-357.

4102   NAKASHIMA, T. (1971) - NOTES ON THE ASSCOCIATED FUNGI AND THE MYCETANGIA
       OF THE AMBROSIA BEETLE, CROSSOTARSUS NIPONICUS BLANDFOR (COLEOPTERA,
       PLATYPODIDAE). APPL.ENT.ZOOL. 6, 131-137.

4103   NANDI, B. & SANTRA, S. (1974) - DIFFERENTIAL PHYTOTOXICITY OF METABOLIC
       BY-PRODUCTS OF NIGROSPORA ORYZAE IN DIFFERENT NITROGEN SOURCES ON SOME
       VARIETIES OF ORYZA SATIVA. INDIAN PHYTOPATH. 27, 49-52.

4104   NARASIMHACHARI, N., GOPALKRISHNAN, K.S., HASKINS, R.H. & VINING, L.C.
       (1963) - THE PRODUCTION OF THE ANTIBIOTIC ATROVENETIN BY A STRAIN OF
       PENICILLIUM HERQUEI BAINIER & SARTORY. CAN.J.MICROBIOL. 9, 134-136.

4105   NARASIMHACHARI, N. & VINING, L.C. (1972) - HERQUEICHRYSIN, A NEW PHENALE-
       NONE ANTIBIOTIC FROM PENICILLIUM HERQUEI. J.ANTIBIOT., TOKYO 25, 155-
       162.

4106   NARAYANAN, S.A. (1963) - SOME INTERESTING MICROFUNGI FROM FLOOD-AFFECTED
       SUBSTRATA IN POONA, INDIA. SYDOWIA 16, 205-211.

4107   NASH, C.H., DOUTHART, R.J., ELLIS, L.F., FRANK, R.M.VAN, BURNETT, J.P. &
       LEMKE, P.A. (1973) - ON THE MYCOPHAGE OF PENICILLIUM CHRYSOGENUM. CAN.
       J.MICROBIOL. 19, 97-103.

4108   NASH, S.M. & SNYDER, W.C. (1962) - QUANTITATIVE ESTIMATIONS BY PLATE COUNTS
       OF PROPAGULES OF THE BEAN ROOT FUSARIUM IN FIELD SOILS. PHYTOPATHOLOGY
       52, 567-572.

4109   NASUNO, S. (1972) - DIFFERENTIATION OF ASPERGILLUS SOJAE FROM ASPERGILLUS
       ORYZAE BY POLYACRYLAMIDE GEL DISC ELECTROPHORESIS. J.GEN.MICROBIOL. 71,
       29-33.

4110   NASUNO, S. (1974) - FURTHER EVIDENCE ON DIFFERENTIATION OF ASPERGILLUS SO-
       JAE FROM ASPERGILLUS ORYZAE BY ELECTROPHORETIC PATTERNS OF CELLULASE,
       PECTIN-LYASE, AND ACID PROTEINASE. CAN.J.MICROBIOL. 20, 413-416.

4111   NATH RAM, M., SETH, L. & RAYCHAUDHURI, S.P. (1966) - A NEW BLIGHT DISEASE
       OF BRINJAL (SOLANUM MELONGENA) CAUSED BY MYROTHECIUM RORIDUM. INDIAN
       PHYTOPATH. 19, 224-225.

4112   NATORI, S., SAKAKI, S., KURATA, H., UDAGAWA, S., ICHINOE, M., SAITO, M. &
       UMEDA, M. (1970) - CHEMICAL AND CYTOTOXIC SURVEY ON THE PRODUCTION OF
       OCHRATOXIN AND PENICILLIC ACID BY ASPERGILLUS OCHRACEUS WILHELM. CHEM.
       PHARM.BULL., TOKYO 18, 2259-2268.

4113   NATORI, S., SAKAKI, S., KURATA, H., UDAGAWA, S., ICHINOE, M., SAITO, M.,
       UMEDA, M. & OHTSUBO, K. (1970) - PRODUCTION OF RUBRATOXIN-B BY PENICIL-
       LIUM PURPUROGENUM STOLL. APPL.MICROBIOL. 19, 613-617.

4114   NAUMANN, G., GREEN, W.R. & ZIMMERMAN, L.E. (1967) - MYCOTIC KERATITIS. A
       HISTOPATHOLOGICAL STUDY OF 73 CASES. AM.J.OPHTHAL. 64, 668-682.

4115   NEAL, D.C. & WESTER, R.E. (1932) - EFFECTS OF ANAEROBIC CONDITIONS ON THE
       GROWTH OF THE COTTON-ROOT-ROT FUNGUS, PHYMATOTRICHUM OMNIVORUM. PHYTO-
       PATHOLOGY 22, 917-920.

4116   NEAL, D.C., WESTER, R.E. & GUNN, K.C. (1934) - MORPHOLOGY AND LIFE HISTORY
       OF THE COTTON ROOT-ROT FUNGUS IN TEXAS. J.AGRIC.RES. 49, 539-548.

4117   NEALSON, K.H. & GARBER, E.D. (1967) - AN ELECTROPHORETIC SURVEY OF ESTER-
       ASES, PHOSPHATASES, AND LEUCINE AMINOPEPTIDASES IN MYCELIAL EXTRACTS OF
       SPECIES OF ASPERGILLUS. MYCOLOGIA 59, 330-336.

4118   NEERGAARD, P. (1945) - DANISH SPECIES OF ALTERNARIA AND STEMPHYLIUM. COM-
       MUNS PHYTOPATH.LAB.J.E.OHLENS ENKE, COPENHAGEN, 560 PP.

4119   NEGRONI, P. & TEY, J.A. (1939) - ESTUDIO MICOLOGICO DEL PRIMER CASO ARGEN-
       TINO DE MICETOMA MADUROMICOSICO DE GRANOS NEGROS. REVTA INST.BACT., B.
       AIRES 9, 176-188.

4120   NEGRU, A. & VERONA, O. (1966) - CONTRIBUTIONS MYCOLOGIQUES POUR LA CON-
       NAISSANCE DE LA SPERMATOSPHERE DES GRAINES EN GERMINATION. MYCOPATH.
       MYCOL.APPL. 30, 305-313.

4121   NEGRUTSKII, S.F. (1963) - (ON THE USE OF ANTAGONISTIC FUNGI FOR COMBATING
       THE FUNGUS FOMES ANNOSUS). MIKROBIOLOGIYA 32, 632-635.

4122   NEILL, K.G. & RAISTRICK, H. (1957) - STUDIES IN THE BIOCHEMISTRY OF MICRO-
       ORGANISMS. 100. METABOLITES OF PENICILLIUM ATROVENETUM. 1. ATROVENETIN,
       A NEW CRYSTALLINE COLOURING MATTER. BIOCHEM.J. 65, 166-176.

4123   NELSON, E. (1969) - OCCURRENCE OF FUNGI ANTAGONISTIC TO PORIA WEIRII IN A
       DOUGLAS-FIR FOREST SOIL IN WESTERN OREGON. FOREST SCI. 15, 49-54.

4124   NELSON, G.E.N., JOHNSON, D.E. & CIEGLER, A. (1971) - PRODUCTION OF D-MAN-
       NITOL BY CONIDIA OF ASPERGILLUS CANDIDUS. APPL.MICROBIOL. 22, 484-485.

4125   NELSON, P.E., PENNYPACKER, B.W., TOUSSOUN, T.A. & HORST, R.K. (1975) - FU-
       SARIUM STUB DIEBACK OF CARNATION. PHYTOPATHOLOGY 65, 575-581.

4126   NELSON, P.E. & WILHELM, S. (1956) - AN UNDESCRIBED FUNGUS CAUSING A ROOT
       ROT OF STRAWBERRY. MYCOLOGIA 48, 547-551.

4127   NELSON, P.E. & WILHELM, S. (1958) - THERMAL DEATH RANGE OF VERTICILLIUM
       ALBO-ATRUM. PHYTOPATHOLOGY 48, 613-616.

4128   NELSON, R.R. (1964) - THE PERFECT STAGE OF CURVULARIA GENICULATA. MYCOLO-
       GIA 56, 777-779.

4129   NELSON, R.R. (1964) - THE PERFECT STAGE OF HELMINTHOSPORIUM SPICIFERUM.
       MYCOLOGIA 56, 198-201.

4130   NELSON, R.R. & HAASIS, F.A. (1964) - THE PERFECT STAGE OF CURVULARIA LUNA-
       TA. MYCOLOGIA 56, 316-317.

4131   NELSON, R.R., WEBSTER, R.K. & MACKENZIE, D.R. (1977) - THE OCCURRENCE OF
       DUAL COMPATIBILITY IN COCHLIOBOLUS SPICIFER. MYCOLOGIA 69, 173-178.

4132   NEMEC, S. (1969) - SPORULATION AND IDENTIFICATION OF FUNGI ISOLATED FROM
       ROOT ROT DISEASED STRAWBERRY PLANTS. PHYTOPATHOLOGY 59, 1552-1553.

4133 NEMEC, S. (1970) - FUNGI ASSOCIATED WITH STRAWBERRY ROOT ROT IN ILLINOIS.
      MYCOPATH.MYCOL.APPL. 41, 331-346.

4134 NEMEC, S. (1974) - PRODUCTION OF PECTINASES AND CELLULASE BY SIX PYTHIUM
      SPECIES ISOLATED FROM NECROTIC STRAWBERRY ROOTS. MYCOPATH.MYCOL.APPL.
      52, 283-290.

4135 NESBITT, H., MALAJCZUK, N. & GLENN, A.R. (1977) - BIOLOGICAL CONTROL OF
      PHYTOPHTHORA CINNAMOMI IN SOIL. FACTORS AFFECTING THE SURVIVAL OF P.
      CINNAMOMI IN SOIL. ABS.2ND INT.MYCOL.CONGR., TAMPA, 1977.

4136 NESPIAK, A. (1963) - (FUNGI ISOLATED FROM THE CULM BASES OF CEREALS IN
      LOWER SILESIA). ACTA AGROBOT. 14, 131-153.

4137 NESPIAK, A. (1970) - QUELQUES OBSERVATIONS SUR LES CHAMPIGNONS ISOLES DE
      L'INTERIEUR DES GROTTES POLONAISES DANS LES MONTAGNES TATRAS ET SUDE-
      TES. SCHWEIZ.Z.PILZK. 48, 107-110.

4138 NESPIAK, A., KOCOR, M. & SIEWINSKI, A. (1961) - ANTIBIOTIC PROPERTIES OF
      MYCELIUM AND METABOLITES OF MYROTHECIUM RORIDUM TODE. NATURE, LOND.
      192, 138-139.

4139 NESPIAK, A. & VOEROES, J. (1961) - FUNGISTATIC EFFECT OF HUNGARIAN SOIL
      FUNGI. AGROKEM.TALAJT. 10, 145-154.

4140 NETO, J.P.DA C. (1954) - OCORRENCIA E FORMA APOTECIAL DE SCLEROTINIA SCLE-
      ROTIORUM NO ESTADO DO RIO GRANDE DO SUL, BRASIL. REVTA AGRON.PORTO ALE-
      GRE 17, 109-112.

4141 NETTE, L.T. (1975) - (ORGANIC ACID SYNTHESIS BY THE FUNGUS CLADOSPORIUM
      RESINAE IN AN N-ALKANE-CONTAINING MEDIUM). PRIKL.BIOKHIM.MIKROBIOL. 11,
      52-56.

4142 NEUJAHR, H.Y. & GAAL, A. (1973) - PHENOL HYDROXYLASE FROM YEAST. PURIFICA-
      TION AND PROPERTIES OF THE ENZYME FROM TRICHOSPORON CUTANEUM. EUR.J.
      BIOCHEM. 35, 386-400.

4143 NEUJAHR, H.Y. & VARGA, J.M. (1970) - DEGRADATION OF PHENOLS BY INTACT
      CELLS AND CELL-FREE PREPARATIONS OF TRICHOSPORON CUTANEUM. EUR.J.BIO-
      CHEM. 13, 37-44.

4144 NEWHOOK, F.J. (1951) - MICROBIOLOGICAL CONTROL OF BOTRYTIS CINEREA PERS.
      1. THE ROLE OF PH CHANGES AND BACTERIAL ANTAGONISM. ANN.APPL.BIOL. 38,
      169-184.

4145 NEWHOOK, F.J. (1951) - MICROBIOLOGICAL CONTROL OF BOTRYTIS CINEREA PERS.
      2. ANTAGONISM BY FUNGI AND ACTINOMYCETES. ANN.APPL.BIOL. 38, 185-202.

4146 NEWTON, H.C. & SEQUEIRA, L. (1972) - ASCOSPORES AS THE PRIMARY INFECTIVE
      PROPAGULE OF SCLEROTINIA SCLEROTIORUM IN WISCONSIN. PL.DIS.REPTR 56,
      798-802.

4147 NEWTON, W. & MAYERS, N. (1935) - THE PHYSIOLOGY OF RHIZOCTONIA SOLANI. 3.
      THE SUSCEPTIBILITY OF DIFFERENT PLANTS AS DETERMINED BY SEEDLING INFEC-
      TION. 4. THE EFFECT OF A TOXIC SUBSTANCE PRODUCED BY RHIZOCTONIA SOLA-
      NI WHEN GROWN IN LIQUID CULTURE, ON THE GROWTH OF WHEAT, CARROTS, AND
      TURNIPS. SCIENT.AGRIC. 15, 393-401.

4148 NG, A.M.L., SMITH, J.E. & MCINTOSH, A.F. (1973) - CONIDIATION OF ASPERGIL-
      LUS NIGER IN CONTINUOUS CULTURE. ARCH.MIKROBIOL. 88, 119-126.

4149 NG, A.M.L., SMITH, J.E. & MCINTOSH, A.F. (1973) - CHANGES IN ACTIVITY OF
      TRICARBOXYLIC ACID CYCLE AND GLYOXYLATE CYCLE ENZYMES DURING SYNCHRO-
      NOUS DEVELOPMENT OF ASPERGILLUS NIGER. TRANS.BR.MYCOL.SOC. 61, 13-20.

4150 NG, A.M.L., SMITH, J.E. & MCINTOSH, A.F. (1974) - CHANGES IN CARBOHYDRATE
      COMPOSITION AND TREHALASE ACTIVITY DURING CONIDIATION OF ASPERGILLUS
      NIGER IN CONTINUOUS AND BATCH CULTURE. TRANS.BR.MYCOL.SOC. 63, 57-66.

4151 NGUYEN-DANG, T., MAYER, M. & PHILOGENE, E. (1970) - SUR LES AMINOACIDES
      CONTENUS DANS LE MILIEU DE CULTURE DU PHIALOPHORA CINERESCENS (WR.) V.
      BEYMA (MALADIE BLEUE DE L'OEILLET). C.R.HEBD.SEANC.ACAD.SCI., PARIS,
      SER.D, 271, 1650-1651.

4152 NICHOLLS, V.O. (1956) - FUNGI OF CHALK SOILS. TRANS.BR.MYCOL.SOC. 39, 233-
      236.

4153 NICHOLS, C.W., GARNSEY, S.M., RACKHAM, R.L., GOTAN, S.M. & MAHANNAH, C.N.
      (1964) - PYTHIACEOUS FUNGI AND PLANT-PARASITIC NEMATODES IN CALIFORNIA
      PEAR ORCHARDS. 1. OCCURRENCE AND PATHOGENICITY OF PYTHIACEOUS FUNGI IN
      ORCHARD SOILS. HILGARDIA 35, 577-602.

4154 NICHOLSON, P.B., BOCOCK, K.L. & HEAL, O.W. (1966) - STUDIES ON THE DECOM-
      POSITION OF THE FAECAL PELLETS OF A MILLIPEDE (GLOMERIS MARGINATA (VIL-
      LERS)). J.ECOL. 54, 755-766.

4155 NICOLLE, CH. & PINOY, E. (1906) - SUR UN CAS DE MYCETOME D'ORIGINE ASPER-
      GILLAIRE OBSERVE EN TUNISIE. ARCHS PARASIT. 10, 437-458.

4156 NICOT, J. (1948) - SUR QUELQUES PAPULASPORA DU SOL. BULL.TRIMEST.SOC.MYCOL.
      FR. 64, 209-222.

4157 NICOT, J. (1950) - CUNNINGHAMELLA ECHINULATA ET C. ELEGANS. BULL.TRIMEST.
      SOC.MYCOL.FR. 66, 21-30.

4158 NICOT, J. (1951) - REVUE SYSTEMATIQUE DU GENRE CYLINDROCARPON WOLLENWEBER.
      REVUE MYCOL. 16, 36-61.

4159 NICOT, J. (1953) - REMARQUES SUR LA MICROFLORE FONGIQUE DE QUELQUES SOLS
      DE GRANDE CULTURE EN AFRIQUE TROPICALE ET A MADAGASCAR. REVUE MYCOL. 18,
      SUPPL.COLON. 2, 88-93.

4160 NICOT, J. (1953) - UN HELMINTHOSPORIUM SAPROPHYTE DU SOL HELMINTHOSPORIUM
      SPICIFERUM (BAIN.) NOV.COM. OEST.BOT.Z. 100, 478-485.

4161 NICOT, J. (1957) - DEUX MUCORALES DU SOL. BULL.TRIMEST.SOC.MYCOL.FR. 73,
      83-93.

4162 NICOT, J. (1958) - QUELQUES MICROMYCETES DES SABLES LITORAUX. BULL.TRIMEST.
      SOC.MYCOL.FR. 74, 221-235.

4163 NICOT, J. (1958) - UNE MOISISSURE ARENICOLE DU LITTORAL ATLANTIQUE. DEN-
      DRYPHIELLA ARENARIA SP.NOV. REVUE MYCOL. 23, 87-99.

4164 NICOT, J. (1966) - MICROMYCETES SAPROPHYTES DE LA MABOKE. 1. PHIALOPHORA
      RICHARDSIAE (NANNF.) CONANT. CAH.MABOKE 4, 110-113.

4165 NICOT, J. (1968) - MICROMYCETES DE LA MABOKE. 3. PAECILOMYCES FUSIDIOIDES
      SP.NOV. CAH.MABOKE 6, 17-18.

4166 NICOT, J. & ADOLPHE, J.-P. (1964) - VEGETATION SAPROPHYTIQUE DU VERTICIL-
      LIUM PSALLIOTAE TRESCH., PARASITE DU CHAMPIGNON DE COUCHE, A LA SUR-
      FACE DES ROCHES CALCAIRES. C.R.HEBD.SEANC.ACAD.SCI., PARIS, SER.D, 258,
      1602-1605.

4167 NICOT, J. & CAILLAT, M. (1967) - ETUDE MORPHOLOGIQUE D'UNE SOUCHE AFRI-
      CAINE DE PHIALOPHORA RICHARDSIAE (NANNF.) CONANT. REVUE MYCOL. 32, 28-
      40.

4168 NICOT, J. & CHARPENTIE, J. (1971) - HERBIERS ET DOCUMENTS ORIGINAUX DE
      GABRIEL ARNAUD. 2. CHLORIDIELLA LEUCOPODA (BON.) ARN. ET IDRIELLA LUNA-
      TA. BULL.TRIMEST.SOC.MYCOL.FR. 87, 421-424.

4169 NICOT, J. & MARIAT, F. (1973) - CARACTERES MORPHOLOGIQUES ET POSITION SYS-
      TEMATIQUE DE SPOROTHRIX SCHENCKII, AGENT DE LA SPOROTRICHOSE HUMAINE.
      MYCOPATH.MYCOL.APPL. 49, 53-65.

4170 NICOT, J. & MEYER, J. (1957) - UN HYPHOMYCETE NOUVEAU DES SOLS TROPICAUX.
      STAPHYLOTRICHUM COCCOSPORUM NOV.GEN., NOV.SP. BULL.TRIMEST.SOC.MYCOL.
      FR. 72, 318-323.

4171 NICOT, J. & MOUCHACCA, J. (1972) - UNE NOUVELLE ESPECE DU GENRE IDRIELLA.
      REVUE MYCOL. 36, 185-193.

4172 NICOT, J. & ZAKARTCHENKO, V. (1966) - REMARQUES SUR LA MORPHOLOGIE ET LA
      BIOLOGIE DU CLADOSPORIUM RESINAE. REVUE MYCOL. 31, 48-74.

4173 NIELSEN, H.S.JR., CONANT, N.F.JR., WEINBERG, T. & REBACK, J.F. (1968) -
      REPORT OF A MYCETOMA DUE TO PHIALOPHORA JEANSELMEI AND UNDESCRIBED CHAR-
      ACTERISTICS OF THE FUNGUS. SABOURAUDIA 6, 330-333.

4174 NIELSEN, N. (1930) - FUNGI ISOLATED FROM THE SOIL AND FROM EXCREMENTS OF
      ARCTIC ANIMALS. MEDDEL.GROENLAND 74, 1-8.

4175 NIENHAUS, F. (1960) - DAS WIRTSSPEKTRUM VON PHYTOPHTHORA CACTORUM (LEB. &
      COHN) SCHROET. PHYTOPATH.Z. 38, 33-68.

4176 NIETHAMMER, A. (1929) - UEBER DIE VERSCHIEDENEN MOEGLICHKEITEN DER BEEIN-
      FLUSSUNG DES WACHSTUMS VON ASPERGILLUS NIGER DURCH ABGESTUFTE MENGEN
      VON ZINK- UND MANGANSALZEN. BEITR.BIOL.PFL. 17, 51-71.

4177 NIETHAMMER, A. (1935) - DIE MUCORINEEN DES ERDBODENS. VERBREITUNG, LEI-
      STUNGEN UND BESCHREIBUNG. Z.PFLKRANKH.PFLSCHUTZ 45, 241-280.

4178 NIETHAMMER, A. (1939) - VERBREITUNG UND WUCHSSTOFFBEDUERFNIS TYPISCHER BO-
      DENPILZE. ZENTBL.BAKT.PARASITKDE, ABT.2, 100, 294-301.

4179 NIETHAMMER, A. (1941) - WEITERE BEITRAEGE UEBER VERBREITUNG UND LEBEN MI-
      KROSKOPISCHER BODENPILZE. ARCH.MIKROBIOL. 12, 312-328.

4180 NIETHAMMER, A. (1942) - WEITERE BEITRAEGE UEBER MIKROSKOPISCHE BODENPILZE.
      ARCH.MIKROBIOL. 13, 60-73.

4181 NIETHAMMER, A. (1956) - BEMERKUNGEN UEBER VERBREITUNG UND LEBENSBEDINGUN-
      GEN VON ASPERGILLUS NIGER. GARTENBAUWISSENSCHAFT 3, 98-101.

4182 NIETHAMMER, A.E. (1963) - MIKROBIOLOGISCHE STUDIEN AN IRISCHEN BODENPRO-
      BEN. ZENTBL.BAKT.PARASITKDE, ABT.2, 116, 762-765.

4183 NIETHHAMMER, A. & JAEGER, B. (1967) - SYSTEMATIK SOWIE GEOGRAPHISCHE VER-
      BREITUNG MIKROSKOPISCHER BODENPILZE. ZENTBL.BAKT.PARASITKDE, ABT.2, 121,
      192-195.

4184 NIETHAMMER, A., KREHL-NIEFFER, R. & HITZLER, M. (1959) - MIKROSKOPISCHE
      BODENPILZE VERSCHIEDENER HERKUNFT UNTER VERSCHIEDENEN KULTURBEDINGUN-
      GEN. ZENTBL.BAKT.PARASITKDE, ABT.2, 112, 429-439.

4185 NIEUWENHUIS, M. & ENDE, H.VAN DEN (1975) - SEX SPECIFICITY OF HORMONE SYN-
      THESIS IN MUCOR MUCEDO. ARCH.MICROBIOL. 102,'167-169.

4186 NIGAM, S.S., RANGANATHAN, S.K., SEN GUPTA, S.R., SHUKLA, R.K. & TANDAN,
      R.N. (1960) - MICROBIAL DEGRADATION OF COTTON CELLULOSE IN SOIL. J.
      SCIENT.IND.RES.C, 19, 20-24.

4187 NILSSON, G.I. (1965) - PHIALOPHORA WILT OF CARNATION, DIANTHUS CARYOPHYL-
      LUS L. THE BEHAVIOUR OF THE PATHOGEN, PHIALOPHORA CINERESCENS, IN THE
      HOST AND IN THE SOIL. DISS.ABSTR. 25, 3201.

4188 NILSSON, S. (1958) - ON SOME SWEDISH FRESHWATER HYPHOMYCETES. SV.BOT.TID-
      SKR. 52, 291-318.

4189 NILSSON, S. (1960) - AQUATIC HYPHOMYCETES FROM NORTHERN SPAIN. SV.BOT.TID-
      SKR. 54, 530-532.

4190 NILSSON, S. (1964) - FRESHWATER HYPHOMYCETES. TAXONOMY, MORPHOLOGY, AND
      ECOLOGY. SYMB.BOT.UPSAL. 18 (2), 1-130.

4191 NILSSON, T. (1973) - STUDIES ON WOOD DEGRADATION AND CELLULOLYTIC ACTIVITY
      OF MICROFUNGI. STUDIA FOR.SUEC. 104, 5-40.

4192 NILSSON, T. (1974) - THE DEGRADATION OF CELLULOSE AND THE PRODUCTION OF
      CELLULASE, XYLANASE, MANNANASE AND AMYLASE PY WOOD-ATTACKING MICROFUN-
      GI. STUDIA FOR.SUEC. 114, 1-61.

4193 NILSSON, T. & HENNINGSSON, B. (1977) - ON THE OCCURRENCE OF PHIALOPHORA
      SPECIES IN PRESERVATIVE TREATED WOOD IN GROUND CONTACT. 9TH A.MEET.,
      INT.RES.GROUP WOOD PRESERV., NOORDWIJK AAN ZEE, 1977.

4194 NIRENBERG, H. (1976) - UNTERSUCHUNGEN UEBER DIE MORPHOLOGISCHE UND BIOLO-
      GISCHE DIFFERENZIERUNG IN DER FUSARIUM-SEKTION LISEOLA. MITT.BIOL.BUND-
      ANST.LD-U.FORSTW. 169, 117 PP.

4195 NISHI, A. (1961) - ROLE OF POLYPHOSPHATE AND PHOSPHOLIPID IN GERMINATING
      SPORES OF ASPERGILLUS NIGER. J.BACT. 81, 19-19.

4196 NISHIKAWA, T., HARADA, T., HARADA, S. & HATANO, H. (1975) - SEROLOGIC
      DIFFERENCES IN STRAINS OF SPOROTHRIX SCHENCKII. SABOURAUDIA 13, 285-290.

4197 NISIKADO, Y. & YAMAUTI, K. (1937) - ON NEOCOSMOSPORA VASINFECTA SMITH, A
      CAUSAL FUNGUS OF SEEDLING-WILT OF SILK-TREE, ALBIZZIA JULIBRISSIN
      DURRAZ. BER.OHARA INST.LANDW.BIOL. 7, 549-556.

4198 NITA, L. & BALINSCHI, I. (1966) - THE INFLUENCE OF SOME AGROTECHNICAL FAC-
      TORS UPON THE FUNGAL FLORA IN THE SOIL. SYMP.SOIL BIOL., CLUJ, RUM.NATN.
      SOC.SOIL SCI., 181-194.

4199 NITYANANDA, K., SIVASUBRAMANIAM, P. & AJELLO, L. (1964) - A CASE OF MYCO-
      TIC KERATITIS CAUSED BY CURVULARIA GENICULATA. ARCHS OPHTHAL. 71, 456-
      458.

4200 NOBLE, M. & RICHARDSON, M.J. (1968) - AN ANNOTATED LIST OF SEED-BORNE DIS-
      EASES. PHYTOPATH.PAP., 2ND ED., 8, 191 PP.

4201 NOBRE, G. & VIEGAS, M.P. (1972) - LIPOLYTIC ACTIVITY OF DERMATOPHYTES. MY-
      COPATH.MYCOL.APPL. 46, 319-323.

4202 NOGUCHI, I., BANNO, Y., WATANABE, T., NOZAWA, Y. & ITO, Y. (1975) - CARBO-
      HYDRATE COMPOSITION OF THE ISOLATED CELL WALLS OF DERMATOPHYTES. MYCO-
      PATHOLOGIA 55, 71-76.

4203 NOGUEIRA, M.L.B. & FURTADO, J.S. (1974) - ORIGIN OF THE CLEAVAGE MEMBRANE
      AND ASCOSPORE DELIMITATION IN SORDARIA FIMICOLA. REVUE MICROBIOL. 5,
      7-16.

4204 NOMA, Y. & NONOMURA, S. (1974) - CONVERSION OF (-)-CARVONE AND (+)-CARVONE
      BY A STRAIN OF ASPERGILLUS NIGER. AGRIC.BIOL.CHEM., TOKYO 38, 741-744.

4205 NOMBELA-CANO, C. & PEBERDY, J.F. (1971) - THE LIPID COMPOSITION OF FUSA-
      RIUM CULMORUM MYCELIUM. TRANS.BR.MYCOL.SOC. 57, 342-343.

4206 NONAKA, F., ARAKI, N. & SAKO, N. (1973) - PATHOGENICAL, MORPHOLOGICAL AND
      SEROLOGICAL COMPARISON OF CYLINDROCLADIUM SPP. AGRIC.BULL.SAGA UNIV.,
      JAPAN 35, 51-68.

4207 NORDBRING-HERTZ, B. (1972) - SCANNING ELECTRON MICROSCOPY OF THE NEMATODE
      -TRAPPING ORGANS IN ARTHROBOTRYS OLIGOSPORA. PHYSIOLOGIA PL. 26, 279-
      284.

4208 NORDBRING-HERTZ, B. (1973) - PEPTIDE-INDUCED MORPHOGENESIS IN THE NEMATODE
      -TRAPPING FUNGUS ARTHROBOTRYS OLIGOSPORA. PHYSIOLOGIA PL. 29, 223-233.

4209 NORDBRING-HERTZ, B. & BRINCK, C. (1974) - QUALITATIVE CHARACTERIZATION OF
      SOME PEPTIDES INDUCING MORPHOGENESIS IN THE NEMATODE-TRAPPING FUNGUS
      ARTHROBOTRYS OLIGOSPORA. PHYSIOLOGIA PL. 31, 59-63.

4210 NORDSTROEM, U.M. (1974) - BARK DEGRADATION BY ASPERGILLUS FUMIGATUS.
      GROWTH STUDIES. CAN.J.MICROBIOL. 20, 283-298.

4211 NORDWIG, A. & JALM, W.F. (1968) - A COLLAGENOLYTIC ENZYME FROM ASPERGILLUS
      ORYZAE - PURIFICATION AND PROPERTIES. EUR.J.BIOCHEM. 3, 519-529.

4212 NORMAN, A.G. (1930) - THE BIOLOGICAL DECOMPOSITION OF PLANT MATERIALS. 3.
      PHYSIOLOGICAL STUDIES ON SOME CELLULOSE-DECOMPOSING FUNGI. ANN.APPL.
      BIOL. 17, 575-613.

4213 NORMAN, A.G. (1931) - THE BIOLOGICAL DECOMPOSITION OF PLANT MATERIALS. 4.
      THE BIOCHEMICAL ACTIVITIES ON STRAW OF SOME CELLULOSE-DECOMPOSING FUN-
      GI. ANN.APPL.BIOL. 18, 244-259.

4214 NORSE, D. (1972) - FUNGI ISOLATED FROM SURFACE-STERILIZED TOBACCO LEAVES.
      TRANS.BR.MYCOL.SOC. 58, 515-518.

4215 NORSTADT, F.A. & MCCALLA, T.M. (1963) - PHYTOTOXIC SUBSTANCE FROM A SPE-
      CIES OF PENICILLIUM. SCIENCE, N.Y. 140, 410-411.

4216 NORSTADT, F.A. & MCCALLA, T.M. (1968) - MICROBIALLY INDUCED PHYTOTOXICITY
      IN STUBBLE-MULCHED SOIL. PROC.SOIL SCI.SOC.AM. 32, 241-245.

4217 NORSTADT, F.A. & MCCALLA, T.M. (1969) - PATULIN PRODUCTION BY PENICILLIUM
      URTICAE BAINIER IN BATCH CULTURE. APPL.MICROBIOL. 17, 193-196.

4218 NORSTADT, F.A. & MCCALLA, T.M. (1969) - MICROBIAL POPULATIONS IN STUBBLE-
      MULCHED SOIL. SOIL SCI. 107, 188-193.

4219 NORSTADT, F.A. & MCCALLA, T.M. (1971) - GROWTH AND PATULIN FORMATION BY
      PENICILLIUM URTICAE BAINIER IN PURE AND MIXED CULTURES. PL.SOIL 34, 97-
      108.

4220 NORTON, D.C. (1954) - ANTAGONISM IN SOIL BETWEEN MACROPHOMINA PHASEOLI AND
      SELECTED SOIL INHABITING ORGANISMS. PHYTOPATHOLOGY 44, 522-524.

4221   NOTTEBROCK, H., SCHOLER, H.J. & WALL, M. (1974) - TAXONOMY AND IDENTIFICA-
       TION OF MUCORMYCOSIS-CAUSING FUNGI. 1. SYNONYMITY OF ABSIDIA RAMOSA
       WITH A. CORYMBIFERA. SABOURAUDIA 12, 64-74.

4222   NOUR, M.A. (1956) - A PRELIMINARY SURVEY OF FUNGI IN SOME SUDAN SOILS.
       TRANS.BR.MYCOL.SOC. 39, 357-360.

4223   NOVAK, E.T. (1966) - CHAETOMIUM-ARTEN AUS UNGARN. ANNLS UNIV.SCIENT.BPEST.
       ROLANDO EOETVOES NOM., SECT.BIOL. 8, 210-222.

4224   NOVAK.E.T. (1970) - UNTERSUCHUNGEN DER CELLULOSEZERSETZUNG DURCH CHAETO-
       MIUM-ARTEN. ANNLS UNIV.SCIENT.BPEST.ROLANDO EOETVOES NOM., SECT.BIOL.
       12, 183-189.

4225   NOVAK, R.O. (1963) - THE SOIL MICROFUNGI OF A MAPLE-ELM-ASH FLOODPLAIN
       COMMUNITY IN AVON, WISCONSIN. DISS.UNIV.WISCONSIN.

4226   NOVAK, R.O. & WHITTINGHAM, W.F. (1968) - SOIL AND LITTER MICROFUNGI OF A
       MAPLE-ELM-ASH FLOODPLAIN COMMUNITY. MYCOLOGIA 60, 776-787.

4227   NOVIELLO, C. & GRIGORIU, A.C. (1967) - OSSERVAZIONI SU FUNGHI ISOLATI DA
       BANANE DI DIVERSA PROVENIENZA SBARCATE AL PORTO DI NAPOLI. ANNALI FAC.
       AGR.PORTICI 2, 471-488.

4228   NOVIKOVA, N.D. & LEBED, E.S. (1973) - (PRODUCTION OF PENICILLINS AND 6-AMI-
       NO-PENICILLIC ACID BY MORPHOLOGICAL VARIANTS OF PENICILLIUM CHRYSOGENUM
       THOM, STRAIN 194). MIKOL.FITOPAT. 7, 101-106.

4229   NOVOTNY, I.H. & TEWS, L.L. (1975) - LENTIC MOULDS OF SOUTHERN LAKE WINNE-
       BAGO. TRANS.BR.MYCOL.SOC. 65, 433-441.

4230   NOWAK, A. (1970) - (KERATINOLYTIC AND KERATINOPHILIC FUNGI ISOLATED FROM
       SOILS OF DOG, FOX, AND MINK BREEDING STATIONS IN THE REGION OF SZCZE-
       CIN). ZESZ.NAUK.WYZSZ.SZK.ROLN.SZCZEC. 32, 217-222.

4231   NOWAKOWSKA-WASCZUK, A. (1972) - FIXATION OF NITROGENS BY THE MUTANTS OF
       ASPERGILLUS TERREUS NRRL 1960. ACTA MICROBIOL.POL. 4, 75-82.

4232   NOZOE, S., GOI, M. & MORISAKI, N. (1970) - STRUCTURE OF CYCLONERODIOL.
       TETRAHEDRON LETTERS, 1970 (15), 1293-1296.

4233   NOZOE, S. & MACHIDA, Y. (1970) - ISOLATION AND STRUCTURE OF TRICHODIOL, A
       NEW SESQUITERPENOID. TETRAHEDRON LETTERS, 1970 (14), 1177-1179.

4234   NOZOE, S. & MACHIDA, Y. (1972) - THE STRUCTURES OF TRICHODIOL AND TRICHO-
       DIENE. TETRAHEDRON 28, 5105-5111.

4235   NUKINA, M., HATTORI, H. & MARUMO, S. (1975) - CIS-SATIVENEDIOL, A PLANT
       GROWTH PROMOTOR PRODUCED BY FUNGI. J.AM.CHEM.SOC. 97, 1542-1543.

4236   NUTI, M.P., BROOKS, J.B. & LEPIDI, A.A. (1975) - OCCURRENCE OF ALPHA-, BE-
       TA-, AND GAMMA-HYDROXYBUTYRATES IN SOME SOIL MICROFUNGI. TRANS.BR.MY-
       COL.SOC. 64, 79-87.

4237   NYESTE, L. (1960) - ISOLATION OF MOLD STRAINS OF HIGH POLYGALACTURONASE
       ACTIVITY. BUDAP.MUESZAKI EGYETEM MEZOEGAZDASAGI KEM.TECHNOL.TANSZEKENEK
       KOEZLEM., 51-57.

4238   NYESTE, L. & HOLLO, J. (1962) - UNTERSUCHUNGEN UEBER POLYGALAKTURONASE-EN-
       ZYME AUS SCHIMMELPILZEN. 1. ISOLIERUNG UND UNTERSUCHUNG VON SCHIMMEL-
       PILZSTAEMMEN MIT GROSSER POLYGALAKTURONASE-AKTIVITAET. NAHRUNG 6, 348-
       363.

4239 NYNS, E.J., AUQUIERE, J.P. & WIAUX, A.L. (1968) - TAXONOMIC VALUE OF THE PROPERTY OF FUNGI TO ASSIMILATE HYDROCARBONS. ANTONIE VAN LEEUWENHOEK 34, 441-457.

4240 NYVALL, R.F. (1976) - COLONIZATION OF SOYBEANS BY SPECIES OF FUSARIUM. MYCOLOGIA 68, 1002-1010.

4241 NYVALL, R.F. & KOMMEDAHL, T. (1966) - THICKENED HYPHAE AS A SURVIVAL MECHANISM IN FUSARIUM MONILIFORME. PHYTOPATHOLOGY 56, 893 (ABS.).

4242 NYVALL, R.F. & KOMMEDAHL, T. (1968) - INDIVIDUAL THICKENED HYPHAE AS SURVIVAL STRUCTURES OF FUSARIUM MONILIFORME IN CORN. PHYTOPATHOLOGY 58, 1704-1707.

4243 NYVALL, R.F. & KOMMEDAHL, T. (1970) - SAPROPHYTISM AND SURVIVAL OF FUSARIUM MONILIFORME IN CORN STALKS. PHYTOPATHOLOGY 60, 1233-1235.

4244 OBRIG, T.G. & GOTTLIEB, D. (1970) - IN VITRO PROTEIN SYNTHESIS AND AGING IN RHIZOCTONIA SOLANI. J.BACT. 101, 755-762.

4245 OENER, M. (1970) - SOIL MICROFUNGI OF TURKEY. MYCOPATH.MYCOL.APPL. 42, 81-87.

4246 OENER, M. (1974) - SEASONAL DISTRIBUTION OF SOME FUNGI IMPERFECTI IN THE SOILS OF WESTERN PART OF ANATOLIA. MYCOPATH.MYCOL.APPL. 52, 267-268.

4247 OFOSU-ASIEDU, A. & SMITH, R.S. (1973) - SOME FACTORS AFFECTING WOOD DEGRADATION BY THERMOPHILIC AND THERMOTOLERANT FUNGI. MYCOLOGIA 65, 87-98.

4248 OFOSU-ASIEDU, A. & SMITH, R.S. (1973) - DEGRADATION OF THREE SOFTWOODS BY THERMOPHILIC AND THERMOTOLERANT FUNGI. MYCOLOGIA 65, 240-244.

4249 OGARKOV, B.N., OGARKOV, G.R. & GOLUBYKH, E.T. (1975) - (BIOLOGICAL CHARACTERISTICS OF MUSCARDINE FUNGI ISOLATED IN EAST SIBERIA). MIKOL.FITOPAT. 9, 148-150.

4250 OGOSHI, A. (1972) - RHIZOCTONIA SOLANI. GROUPING OF RHIZOCTONIA SOLANI WITH HYPHAL ANASTOMOSIS. ANN.PHYTOPATH.SOC.JAPAN 38, 117-122.

4251 OGOSHI, A. (1973) - ON THE PERFECT STAGE OF ANASTOMOSIS GROUP AG-5 OF RHIZOCTONIA SOLANI. TRANS.MYCOL.SOC.JAPAN 14, 67-74.

4252 OGOSHI, A. (1976) - STUDIES ON THE GROUPING OF RHIZOCTONIA SOLANI KUEHN WITH HYPHAL ANASTOMOSIS AND ON THE PERFECT STAGES OF GROUPS. BULL.NATN. INST.AGRIC.SCI., TOKYO, SER.C, 30, 65 PP.

4253 OGURA, H. & AKAI, S. (1965) - STUDIES ON RHIZOCTONIA SOLANI (PELLICULARIA FILAMENTOSA). 4. THE ACTIVITY OF ANTAGONISTS TO RHIZOCTONIA SOLANI. ANN.PHYTOPATH.SOC.JAPAN 30, 219-224.

4254 OGURA, H., AKAI, S. & SATO, T. (1961) - STUDIES ON PELLICULARIA FILAMENTOSA. 2. ON THE FORMATION OF FREE AMINO ACIDS AND SUGARS IN P. FILAMENTOSA. ANN.PHYTOPATH.SOC.JAPAN 26, 31-36.

4255 OHMOMO, S., SUGITA, M. & ABE, M. (1973) - ISOLATION OF CYCLOPIAZONIC ACID, CYCLOPIAZONIC ACID IMINE AND BISSECODEHYDROCYCLOPIAZONIC ACID FROM THE CULTURES OF ASPERGILLUS VERSICOLOR. J.AGRIC.CHEM.SOC.JAPAN 47, 57-63.

4256 OHMOMO, S., SUGITA, M. & MATAZO, A. (1973) - ISOLATION OF CYCLOPIAZONIC ACID, CYCLOPIAZONIC ACID IMINE AND BISSECODEHYDROCYCLOPIAZONIC ACID FROM THE CULTURES OF ASPERGILLUS VERSICOLOR (VUILL.) TIRABOSCHI. J. AGRIC.CHEM.SOC.JAPAN 47, 57-63.

4257   OHTOMO, T., SUGIYAMA, J. & IIZUKA, H. (1975) - PHYSIOLOGY AND FINE STRUC-
       TURE IN CHLAMYDOSPORE OF THERMOMYCES LANUGINOSUS, A THERMOPHILIC HYPHO-
       MYCETE. TRANS.MYCOL.SOC.JAPAN 16, 289-300.

4258   OHTSUBO, K., KADEN, P. & MITTERMAYER, C. (1972) - POLYRIBOSOMAL BREAKDOWN
       IN MOUSE FIBROBLASTS (L-CELLS) BY FUSARENON-X, A TOXIC PRINCIPLE ISO-
       LATED FROM FUSARIUM NIVALE. BIOCHIM.BIOPHYS.ACTA 287, 520-525.

4259   OHTSURU, M. & HATA, T. (1973) - GENERAL CHARACTERISTICS OF THE INTRACELLU-
       LAR MYROSINASE FROM ASPERGILLUS NIGER. AGRIC.BIOL.CHEM., TOKYO 37,
       2543-2548.

4260   OHTSURU, M., TSURUO, I. & HATA, T. (1973) - THE PRODUCTION AND STABILITY
       OF INTRACELLULAR MYROSINASE FROM ASPERGILLUS NIGER. AGRIC.BIOL.CHEM.,
       TOKYO 37, 967-971.

4261   OJIMA, N., TAKENAKA, S. & SETO, S. (1973) - NEW BUTENOLIDES FROM ASPERGIL-
       LUS TERREUS. PHYTOCHEMISTRY 12, 2527-2529.

4262   OJIMA, N., TAKENAKA, S. & SETO, S. (1975) - STRUCTURES OF PULVINONE DERI-
       VATIVES FROM ASPERGILLUS TERREUS. PHYTOCHEMISTRY 14, 573-576.

4263   OKAFOR, N. (1966) - THERMOPHILIC MICROORGANISMS FROM ROTTING MAIZE. NA-
       TURE, LOND. 210, 220-221.

4264   OKAFOR, N. (1967) - DECOMPOSITION OF CHITIN BY MICROORGANISMS ISOLATED
       FROM A TEMPERATE AND A TROPICAL SOIL. NOVA HEDWIGIA 13, 209-226.

4265   OKAZAKI, H. & IIZUKA, H. (1971) - ON YEAST CELL LYTIC ACTIVITY AND BETA-1,
       3-GLUCANASE PRODUCED FROM THERMOPHILIC FUNGI. J.AGRIC.CHEM.SOC.JAPAN
       45, 461-470.

4266   OKON, Y., CHET, I. & HENIS, Y. (1973) - EFFECT OF LACTOSE, ETHANOL AND CY-
       CLOHEXIMIDE ON THE TRANSLOCATION PATTERN OF RADIOACTIVE COMPOUNDS AND
       ON SCLEROTIUM FORMATION IN SCLEROTIUM ROLFSII. J.GEN.MICROBIOL. 74,
       251-258.

4267   OKON, Y., CHET, I. & HENIS, Y. (1975) - THE EFFECT OF GLUCOSE AND LACTOSE
       ON BETA-D-GALACTOSIDASE ACTIVITY AND FORMATION OF SCLEROTIA IN SCLERO-
       TIUM ROLFSII. CAN.J.MICROBIOL. 21, 1123-1126.

4268   OKON, Y., CHET, I., KISLEV, N. & HENIS, Y. (1974) - EFFECT OF LACTOSE ON
       SOLUBLE-GLUCAN PRODUCTION AND ON THE ULTRASTRUCTURE OF SCLEROTIUM ROLF-
       SII GROWN IN SUBMERGED CULTURE. J.GEN.MICROBIOL. 81, 145-149.

4269   OKUDA, T., FUJIWARA, A. & FUJIWARA, M. (1977) - MATERIALS FOR THE FUNGUS
       FLORA OF JAPAN. 25. TRANS.MYCOL.SOC.JAPAN 18, 176-178.

4270   OLAH, G.M. & REISINGER, O. (1974) - ETUDE ULTRASTRUCTURALE ET CYTOCHIMIQUE
       DE L'APPAREIL SPORIFERE CHEZ PHIALOPHORA RICHARDSIAE. CAN.J.BOT. 52,
       2473-2480.

4271   OLCHOWECKI, A. & REID, J. (1974) - TAXONOMY OF THE GENUS CERATOCYSTIS IN
       MANITOBA. CAN.J.BOT. 52, 1675-1711.

4272   OLD, K.M. (1965) - FUNGISTATIC EFFECTS OF SOIL BACTERIA ON ROOT-ROTTING
       FUNGI WITH PARTICULAR REFERENCE TO HELMINTHOSPORIUM SATIVUM. PHYTO-
       PATHOLOGY 55, 901-905.

4273 OLD, K.M. (1967) - EFFECTS OF NATURAL SOIL ON SURVIVAL OF COCHLIOBOLUS SA-
      TIVUS. TRANS.BR.MYCOL.SOC. 50, 615-624.

4274 OLD, K.M. (1977) - GIANT SOIL AMOEBAE CAUSE PERFORATION OF CONIDIA OF COCH-
      LIOBOLUS SATIVUS. TRANS.BR.MYCOL.SOC. 68, 277-320.

4275 OLD, K.M. & NICOLSON, T.H. (1962) - USE OF NYLON MESH IN STUDIES OF SOIL
      FUNGI. PL.DIS.REPTR 46, 616.

4276 OLD, K.M. & PATRICK, Z.A. (1976) - PERFORATION AND LYSIS OF SPORES OF COCH-
      LIOBOLUS SATIVUS AND THIELAVIOPSIS BASICOLA IN NATURAL SOILS. CAN.J.BOT.
      54, 2798-2809.

4277 OLD, K.M. & ROBERTSON, W.M. (1970) - GROWTH OF BACTERIA WITHIN LYSING FUN-
      GAL CONIDIA IN SOIL. TRANS.BR.MYCOL.SOC. 54, 337-341.

4278 OLD, K.M. & ROBERTSON, W.M. (1970) - EFFECTS OF LYTIC ENZYMES AND NATURAL
      SOIL ON THE FINE STRUCTURE OF CONIDIA OF COCHLIOBOLUS SATIVUS. TRANS.
      BR.MYCOL.SOC. 54, 343-350.

4279 OLD, K.M. & SCHIPPERS, B. (1973) - ELECTRON MICROSCOPICAL STUDIES OF CHLA-
      MYDOSPORES OF FUSARIUM SOLANI F. CUCURBITAE FORMED IN NATURAL SOIL. SOIL
      BIOL.BIOCHEM. 5, 613-620.

4280 OLD, K.M. & WONG, J.N.F. (1976) - PERFORATION AND LYSIS OF FUNGAL SPORES IN
      NATURAL SOILS. SOIL BIOL.BIOCHEM. 8, 285-292.

4281 OLIVE, L.S. (1956) - GENETICS OF SORDARIA FIMICOLA. 1. ASCOSPORE COLOR MU-
      TANTS. AM.J.BOT. 43, 97-107.

4282 OLIVE, L.S. (1974) - SORDARIA. IN: HANDBOOK OF GENETICS; KING, R.C. (ED.),
      PLENUM PRESS, NEW YORK, LONDON, 553-562.

4283 OLIVER, P.T.P. (1972) - CONIDIOPHORE AND SPORE DEVELOPMENT IN ASPERGILLUS
      NIDULANS. J.GEN.MICROBIOL. 73, 45-54.

4284 OLOFSSON, J. (1968) - INFLUENCE OF HYDROGEN-ION CONCENTRATION ON GERMINA-
      TION OF NATURALLY PRODUCED OOSPORES OF APHANOMYCES EUTEICHES. PL.DIS.
      REPTR 52, 264-267.

4285 OLSEN, C.M., FLENTJE, N.T. & BAKER, K.F. (1967) - COMPARATIVE SURVIVAL OF
      MONOBASIDIAL CULTURES OF THANATEPHORUS CUCUMERIS IN SOIL. PHYTOPATHOL-
      OGY 57, 598-601.

4286 OLSEN, R.A. (1971) - METHOXYHYDROQUINONE, A GROWTH INHIBITOR OF OPHIOBOLUS
      GRAMINIS IN LEAVES OF OAT SEEDLINGS. PHYSIOLOGIA PL. 24, 34-39.

4287 OLSEN, R.A. (1971) - TRITERPENEGLYCOSIDES AS INHIBITORS OF FUNGAL GROWTH
      AND METABOLISM. 1. EFFECT ON GROWTH, ENDOGENOUS RESPIRATION AND LEAKAGE
      OF UV-ABSORBING MATERIAL FROM VARIOUS FUNGI. PHYSIOLOGIA PL. 24, 534-
      543.

4288 OLSON, B.H. (1963) - RESTRICTOCIN. U.S.PATENT 3104208.

4289 OLTHOF, TH.H.A. & ESTEY, R.H. (1963) - A NEMATOXIN PRODUCED BY THE NEMATO-
      PHAGOUS FUNGUS ARTHROBOTRYS OLIGOSPORA. NATURE, LOND. 197, 514-515.

4290 OLTHOF, TH.H.A. & ESTEY, R.H. (1965) - RELATION OF SOME ENVIRONMENTAL FAC-
      TORS TO GROWTH OF SEVERAL NEMATOPHAGOUS HYPHOMYCETES. CAN.J.MICROBIOL.
      11, 939-946.

4291   OLTHOF, TH.H.A. & ESTEY, R.H. (1966) - CARBON- AND NITROGEN-LEVELS OF A ME-
       DIUM IN RELATION TO GROWTH AND NEMATOPHAGOUS ACTIVITY OF ARTHROBOTRYS
       OLIGOSPORA FRESENIUS. NATURE, LOND. 209, 1158.

4292   OLUTIOLA, P.O. (1976) - SOME ENVIRONMENTAL AND NUTRITIONAL FACTORS AFFECT-
       ING GROWTH AND SPORULATION OF ASPERGILLUS FLAVUS. TRANS.BR.MYCOL.SOC.
       66, 131-136.

4293   OLUTIOLA, P.O. (1976) - CELLULASE ENZYMES IN CULTURE FILTRATES OF ASPERGIL-
       LUS FLAVUS. TRANS.BR.MYCOL.SOC. 67, 265-268.

4294   OLUTIOLA, P.O. (1978) - GROWTH, SPORULATION AND PRODUCTION OF PECTIC AND
       CELLULOLYTIC ENZYMES IN FUSARIUM OXYSPORUM. TRANS.BR.MYCOL.SOC. 70, 109-
       114.

4295   OMORI, A., SATO, S. & TAMIYA, N. (1972) - ISOLATION AND SOME PROPERTIES OF
       RIBONUCLEASE FROM FUSARIUM MONILIFORME. BIOCHIM.BIOPHYS.ACTA 268, 125.

4296   OMORI, K. & GOTTLIEB, D. (1965) - DEVELOPMENT OF RESPIRATORY ENZYME ACTIV-
       ITIES DURING SPORE GERMINATION. PHYTOPATHOLOGY 55, 1328-1336.

4297   OMVIK, AA. (1952) - EXPERIMENTS ON MANGANESE, ZINK AND CALCIUM AS CONSTIT-
       UENTS OF NUTRIENT SOLUTIONS FOR FUNGI. ARBOK UNIV.BERGEN, NATURV.REKKE
       8, 55 PP.

4298   OMVIK, A. (1970) - MORPHOLOGY AND NUTRITION OF CHLORIDIUM CHLAMYDOSPORIS
       (BISPOROMYCES CHLAMYDOSPORIS). MYCOLOGIA 62, 209-226.

4299   ONG, P.S. & GAUCHER, G.M. (1973) - PROTEASE PRODUCTION BY THERMOPHILIC
       FUNGI. CAN.J.MICROBIOL. 19, 129-133.

4300   ONUIGBO, W.I.B., GUGNANI, H., OKAFOR, B.C. & MISCH, K.A. (1975) - NASAL
       ENTOMOPHTHOROSIS IN AN IBO FROM NIGERIA. J.LARYNGOL.OTOL. 89, 657-661.

4301   ONUORAH, P.E. (1968) - THE INFLUENCE OF SUCROSE AND WHEAT ROOT EXUDATES ON
       THE GERMINATION AND GROWTH OF CONIDIA OF FUSARIUM CULMORUM (W.G. SM.)
       SACC. PL.SOIL 29, 27-32.

4302   OOKA, T., SHIMOJIMA, Y., AKIMOTO, T., TAKEDA, I., SENOH, S. & ABE, J.
       (1966) - A NEW ANTIBACTERIAL PEPTIDE, SUZUKACILLIN. AGRIC.BIOL.CHEM.,
       TOKYO 30, 700-702.

4303   OORSCHOT, C.A.N. VAN (1977) - THE GENUS MYCELIOPHTHORA. PERSOONIA 9, 404-
       408.

4304   ORAZOV, KH.N. & SIZOVA, T.P. (1966) - (ANTAGONISTIC PROPERTIES OF PENICIL-
       LIUM SPECIES ISOLATED FROM THE SOILS IN THE TURKMENIAN SSR). BYULL.MOSK.
       OBSHCH.ISPYT.PRIR., OTD.BIOL. 71, 118-130.

4305   ORDIN, A.P. (1961) - (THE MICROFLORA OF THE RHIZOSPHERE AND THE ROOTS OF
       CROP PLANTS). MIKROBIOLOGIYA 30, 679-683.

4306   ORDIN, A.P. (1964) - (ROLE OF MICROFLORA IN WHEAT SEED GRAIN GERMINATION
       DECREASE DURING STORAGE). MIKROBIOLOGIYA 33, 653-660.

4307   ORDIN, A.P. (1966) - (MICROFLORA OF WHEAT GRAIN WITH SPECIAL REFERENCE TO
       THE DATE OF GATHERING AND THE CULTIVATION AREA). MIKROBIOLOGIYA 35, 337-
       343.

4308   ORELLANA, R.G., FOY, C.D. & FLEMING, A.L. (1975) - EFFECT OF SOLUBLE ALU-
       MINUM ON GROWTH AND PATHOGENICITY OF VERTICILLIUM ALBO-ATRUM AND WHET-
       ZELINIA SCLEROTIORUM FROM SUNFLOWER. PHYTOPATHOLOGY 65, 202-205.

4309 ORIE, N.G.M., VRIES, G.A.DE & KIKSTRA, A. (1960) - GROWTH OF ASPERGILLUS
      IN THE HUMAN LUNG. AM.REV.RESP.DIS. 82, 649-662.

4310 ORLOWSKI, M. & SYPHERD, P.S. (1976) - CYCLIC GUANOSINE 3',5'-MONOPHOSPHATE
      IN THE DIMORPHIC FUNGUS MUCOR RACEMOSUS. J.BACT. 125, 1226-1228.

4311 ORMEROD, J.G. (1967) - THE NUTRITION OF THE HALOPHILIC MOULD SPORENDONEMA
      EPIZOUM. ARCH.MIKROBIOL. 56, 31-39.

4312 ORPURT, P.A. (1964) - THE MICROFUNGAL FLORA OF BAT CAVE SOILS FROM ELEU-
      THERA ISLAND, THE BAHAMAS. CAN.J.BOT. 42, 1629-1633.

4313 ORPURT, P.A. & CURTIS, J.T. (1957) - SOIL MICROFUNGI IN RELATION TO THE
      PRAIRIE CONTINUUM IN WISCONSIN. ECOLOGY 38, 628-637.

4314 ORR, G.F. & KUEHN, H.H. (1963) - THE GENUS CTENOMYCES EIDAM. MYCOPATH.MY-
      COL.APPL. 21, 321-333.

4315 ORR, G.F. & KUEHN, H.H. (1972) - NOTES ON GYMNOASCACEAE. 2. SOME GYMNOAS-
      CACEAE AND KERATINOPHILIC FUNGI FROM UTAH. MYCOLOGIA 64, 55-72.

4316 ORR, G.F., KUEHN, H.H. & PLUNKETT, O.A. (1963) - A NEW GENUS OF THE GYM-
      NOASCACEAE WITH SWOLLEN PERIDIAL SEPTA. CAN.J.BOT. 41, 1439-1456.

4317 ORR, G.F., KUEHN, H.H. & PLUNKETT, O.A. (1963) - THE GENUS GYMNOASCUS.
      MYCOPATH.MYCOL.APPL. 21, 1-18.

4318 ORTH, R. (1973) - EIN BEITRAG ZUR OEKOLOGIE UND PHYSIOLOGIE VON ASPERGIL-
      LUS VERSICOLOR (VUILLEMIN) TIRABOSCHI. DISS.RUPRECHT-KARL-UNIV., HEI-
      DELBERG.

4319 ORTIZ DE SERRA, M.I., SOWDEN, F.J. & SCHNITZER, M. (1973) - DISTRIBUTION
      OF NITROGEN IN FUNGAL HUMIC ACIDS. CAN.J.SOIL SCI. 53, 125-127.

4320 ORYNBAEV, S.O. & ERMEKOVA, B.D. (1973) - (EFFECT OF PH OF THE MEDIUM ON
      THE DEVELOPMENT OF HELMINTHOSPORIUM SATIVUM AND ALTERNARIA TENUIS).
      MIKOL.FITOPAT. 7, 539-541.

4321 OSO, B.A. (1974) - UTILIZATION OF LIPIDS AS SOLE CARBON SOURCES BY THERMO-
      PHILIC FUNGI. Z.ALLG.MIKROBIOL. 14, 713-717.

4322 OSTAZESKI, S.A. & GERDEMANN, J.W. (1957) - EFFECT OF METHODS OF SOIL IN-
      FESTATION ON THE PATHOGENICITY OF THREE FUNGI ASSOCIATED WITH RED CLO-
      VER ROOT ROT. PHYTOPATHOLOGY 47, 26 (ABS.).

4323 OTANI, Y. & KANZAWA, S. (1970) - NOTES ON COPROPHILOUS DISCOMYCETES IN JA-
      PAN. 2. TRANS.MYCOL.SOC.JAPAN 11, 43-48.

4324 OTCENASEK, M. & DVORAK, J. (1962) - THE ISOLATION OF TRICHOPHYTON TERRES-
      TRE AND OTHER KERATINOPHILIC FUNGI FROM SMALL MAMMALS OF SOUTH EASTERN
      MORAVIA. SABOURAUDIA 2, 111-113.

4325 OTCENASEK, M. & DVORAK, J. (1964) - THE ISOLATION OF CHRYSOSPORIUM KERATI-
      NOPHILUM AND SIMILAR FUNGI FROM CZECHOSLOVAKIAN SOIL. MYCOPATH.MYCOL.
      APPL. 23, 121-124.

4326 OTCENASEK, M. & DVORAK, J. (1975) - ECOLOGICAL CLASSIFICATION OF DERMATO-
      PHYTES. MYKOSEN 18, 425-434.

4327 OTCENASEK, M., DVORAK, J. & KUNERT, J. (1967) - GEOGRAPHIC DISTRIBUTION OF
      THE GEOPHILIC DERMATOPHYTES IN THE SOIL. MYCOPATH.MYCOL.APPL. 31, 151-
      162.

4328 OTROSINA, W.J. & MARX, D.H. (1975) - POPULATIONS OF PHYTOPHTHORA CINNAMOMI AND PYTHIUM SPP. UNDER SHORTLEAF AND LOBLOLLY PINES IN LITTLELEAF DISEASE SITES. PHYTOPATHOLOGY 65, 1224-1229.

4329 OTSUKA, H. & TAKE, T. (1970) - STUDIES ON THE UTILIZATION OF BARK. MEM.FAC. ED.NIIGATA UNIV. 12 (2), 57-68.

4330 OTTOW, J.C.G. & VON KLOPOTEK, A. (1969) - ENZYMATIC REDUCTION OF IRON OXIDE BY FUNGI. APPL.MICROBIOL. 18, 41-43.

4331 OUJEZDSKY, K.B., GROVE, N. & SZANISZLO, P.J. (1973) - MORPHOLOGICAL AND STRUCTURAL CHANGES DURING THE YEAST-TO-MOLD CONVERSION OF PHIALOPHORA DERMATITIDIS. J.BACT. 113, 468-477.

4332 OVERALL, B.T. (1952) - A TOXIN IN CULTURE FILTRATES OF SCLEROTINIA SCLEROTIORUM. AUST.J.SCI. 14, 197-198.

4333 OXFORD, A.E. & RAISTRICK, H. (1932) - STUDIES IN THE BIOCHEMISTRY OF MICRO-ORGANISMS. 25. 3,5-DIHYDROXYPHTHALIC ACID, A NEW PRODUCT OF THE METABOLISM OF GLUCOSE BY PENICILLIUM BREVICOMPACTUM AND RELATED SPECIES. BIOCHEM.J. 26, 1902-1906.

4334 OXFORD, A.E. & RAISTRICK, H. (1933) - STUDIES IN THE BIOCHEMISTRY OF MICRO-ORGANIMS. 30. THE MOLECULAR CONSTITUTION OF THE METABOLIC PRODUCTS OF PENICILLIUM BREVI-COMPACTUM AND RELATED SPECIES. BIOCHEM.J. 27, 634-653.

4335 OXFORD, A.E. & RAISTRICK, H. (1942) - ANTIBACTERIAL SUBSTANCES FROM MOULDS. 4. SPINULOSIN AND FUMIGATIN, METABOLIC PRODUCTS OF PENICILLIUM SPINULOSUM AND ASPERGILLUS FUMIGATUS. CHEM.IND. 1942 (61), 128-129.

4336 OXFORD, A.E., RAISTRICK, H. & SIMONART, P. (1939) - STUDIES IN THE BIOCHEMISTRY OF MICRO-ORGANISM. 60. GRISEOFULVIN, C17 H17 O6 CL, A METABOLIC PRODUCT OF PENICILLIUM GRISEO-FULVUM. BIOCHEM.J. 33, 240-248.

4337 OZAWA, J., TAKEDA, A. & HAYASHI, S. (1950) - FERMENTATION OF PECTIN. 8. RELATION BETWEEN THE DECOMPOSITION OF PECTIN AND MACERATION. NOGAKU KENKYU 38, 123-124, AND 39, 9-12.

4338 PACIONI, G. & FRIZZI, G. (1978) - PAECILOMYCES FARINOSUS, THE CONIDIAL STATE OF CORDYCEPS MEMORABILIS. CAN, J.BOT. 56, 391-394.

4339 PACKTER, N.M. & GLOVER, J. (1965) - BIOSYNTHESIS OF C14 FUMIGATIN IN ASPERGILLUS FUMIGATUS FRESENIUS. BIOCHIM.BIOPHYS.ACTA 100, 50-56.

4340 PACKTER, N.M. & STEWARD, M.W. (1967) - THE BIOSYNTHESIS OF PHENOLS IN FUNGI. BIOSYNTHESIS OF 3,4-DIMETHOXY-6-METHYLTOLUQUINOL AND GLIOROSEIN IN GLIOCLADIUM ROSEUM. BIOCHEM.J. 102, 122-132.

4341 PACKTER, N.M. & WARD, A.C. (1972) - BIOSYNTHESIS OF FATTY ACIDS AND PHENOLS BY STATIONARY-PHASE CULTURES OF ASPERGILLUS FUMIGATUS. BIOCHEM.J. 127, 14-15.

4342 PADHYE, A.A. & CARMICHAEL, J.W. (1970) - MATING REACTIONS OF PIGMENTED AND NON-PIGMENTED ISOLATES OF ARTHRODERMA UNCINATUM. SABOURAUDIA 8, 112-115.

4343 PADHYE, A.A. & CARMICHAEL, J.W. (1971) - THE GENUS ARTHRODERMA BERKELEY. CAN.J.BOT. 49, 1525-1540.

4344 PADHYE, A.A. & CARMICHAEL, J.W. (1972) - ARTHRODERMA INSINGULARE SP.NOV., ANOTHER GYMNOASCACEOUS STATE OF THE TRICHOPHYTON TERRESTRE COMPLEX. SABOURAUDIA 10, 47-51.

4345 PADHYE, A.A., MISRA, S.P. & THIRUMALACHAR, M.J. (1966) - OCCURRENCE OF
      SOIL INHABITING DERMATOPHYTES AND OTHER KERATINOPHILIC FUNGI FROM SOILS
      IN POONA. HINDUSTAN ANTIBIOT.BULL. 9, 90-93.

4346 PADHYE, A.A., PAWAR, V.H., SUKAPURE, R.S. & THIRUMALACHAR, M.J. (1967) -
      KERATINOPHILIC FUNGI FROM MARINE SOILS OF BOMBAY, INDIA. 1. HINDUSTAN
      ANTIBIOT.BULL. 10, 138-141.

4347 PADHYE, A.A., SEKHON, A.S. & CARMICHAEL, J.W. (1973) - ASCOCARP PRODUCTION
      BY NANNIZZIA AND ARTHRODERMA ON KERATINOUS AND NON-KERATINOUS MEDIA.
      SABOURAUDIA 11, 109-114.

4348 PADHYE, A.A. & THIRUMALACHAR, M.J. (1962) - ISOLATION OF KERATINOMYCES
      AJELLOI FROM SOIL IN INDIA. CURR.SCI. 31, 100-101.

4349 PADHYE, A.A. & THIRUMALACHAR, M.J. (1966) - MADUROMYCOSIS CAUSED BY PHIA-
      LOPHORA JEANSELMEI IN INDIA. HINDUSTAN ANTIBIOT.BULL. 9, 31-32.

4350 PADHYE, A.A. & THIRUMALACHAR, M.J. (1968) - DISTRIBUTION OF ALLESCHERIA
      BOYDII SHEAR, IN SOIL OF MAHARASHTRA STATE. HINDUSTAN ANTIBIOT.BULL.
      10, 200-201.

4351 PADY, S.M. & KAPICA, L. (1955) - FUNGI IN AIR OVER THE ATLANTIC OCEAN.
      MYCOLOGIA 47, 34-50.

4352 PADY.S.M., KRAMER, C.L. & CLARY, R. (1969) - PERIODICITY IN SPORE RELEASE
      IN CLADOSPORIUM. MYCOLOGIA 61, 87-98.

4353 PAGE, M.M. & COVE, D.J. (1972) - ALCOHOL AND AMINE CATABOLISM IN THE FUN-
      GUS ASPERGILLUS NIDULANS. BIOCHEM.J. 127, 17.

4354 PAGE, O.T. (1961) - INDUCED VARIATION IN FUSARIUM OXYSPORUM. CAN.J.BOT.
      39, 1509-1519.

4355 PAGE, R.M. & HUMBER, R.A. (1973) - PHOTOTROPISM IN CONIDIOBOLUS CORONATUS.
      MYCOLOGIA 65, 335-354.

4356 PAGE, W.J. & STOCK, J.J. (1971) - REGULATION AND SELF-INHIBITION OF MICRO-
      SPORUM GYPSEUM MACROCONIDIA GERMINATION. J.BACT. 108, 276-281.

4357 PAGE, W.J. & STOCK, J.J. (1972) - ISOLATION AND CHARACTERIZATION OF MICRO-
      SPORUM GYPSEUM LYSOSOMES - ROLE OF LYSOSOMES IN MACROCONIDIA GERMINA-
      TION. J.BACT. 110, 354-362.

4358 PAGE, W.J. & STOCK, J.J. (1974) - SEQUENTIAL ACTION OF CELL WALL HYDROL-
      ASES IN THE GERMINATION AND OUTGROWTH OF MICROSPORUM GYPSEUM MACROCONID-
      IA. CAN.J.MICROBIOL. 20, 483-489.

4359 PAGE, W.J. & STOCK, J.J. (1974) - PHOSPHATE-MEDIATED ALTERATION OF THE MI-
      CROSPORUM GYPSEUM GERMINATION PROTEASE SPECIFICITY FOR SUBSTRATE. EN-
      HANCED KERATINASE ACTIVITY. J.BACT. 117, 422-431.

4360 PAGE, W.J. & STOCK, J.J. (1974) - CHANGES IN MICROSPORUM GYPSEUM MYCELIAL
      WALL AND SPORE COAT GLYCOPROTEINS DURING SPORULATION AND SPORE GERMINA-
      TION. J.BACT. 119, 44-49.

4361 PAGE, W.M. (1951) - VIABILITY OF SPORES OF SOME COPROPHILOUS SPECIES OF
      SORDARIA AND CHAETOMIUM. TRANS.BR.MYCOL.SOC. 34, 539.

4362 PAINE, F.S. (1927) - STUDIES ON THE FUNGUS FLORA OF VIRGIN SOILS. MYCOLO-
      GIA 19, 248-266.

4363   PAINTER, H.A. (1954) - FACTORS AFFECTING THE GROWTH OF SOME FUNGI ASSO-
       CIATED WITH SEWAGE PURIFICATION. J.GEN.MICROBIOL. 10, 177-190.

4364   PAL, P.N. & GHOSH, B.L. (1965) - ISOLATION, PURIFICATION, AND PROPERTIES
       OF CELLULASES FROM ASPERGILLUS TERREUS AND PENICILLIUM VARIABILE. CAN.
       J.BIOCHEM. 43, 81-90.

4365   PAL'MOVA, N.P. & BEKKER, Z.E. (1966) - (TURF MYCOFLORA AND ITS PHYSIOLOGI-
       CAL PECULARITIES). BYULL.MOSK.OBSHCH.ISPYT.PRIR., OTD.BIOL. 71, 136-144.

4366   PAL'MOVA, N.P. & MAKSIMOVA, R.A. (1970) - (EFFECTS OF AMINO ACIDS ON THE
       GROWTH AND DEVELOPMENT OF VARIOUS STRAINS OF TRICHOTHECIUM ROSEUM
       LINK). VEST.MOSK.UNIV., SER.6, BIOL.POCHV. 25, 70-75.

4367   PAL'MOVA, N.P. & MAXIMOVA, R.A. (1970) - (A STUDY OF HETEROKARYOSIS AND
       ABILITY TO CONIDIA GERMINATION WITH RESPECT TO VARIABILITY OF TRICHO-
       THECIUM ROSEUM). MIKROBIOLOGIYA 39, 665-670.

4368   PALSSON, G. (1968) - GEOPHILIC DERMATOPHYTES IN THE SOIL IN SWEDEN. STUD-
       IES ON THEIR OCCURRENCE AND PATHOGENIC PROPERTIES. ACTA VET.SCAND.,
       SUPPL. 25, 1-89.

4369   PANASENKO, V.T. (1967) - ECOLOGY OF MICROFUNGI. BOT.REV. 33, 189-215.

4370   PANDEY, D.K. & GUPTA, S.C. (1966) - STUDIES ON PECTIC ENZYMES OF PARASITIC
       FUNGI. 6. FACTORS AFFECTING THE SECRETION OF PECTIC ENZYMES BY ALTER-
       NARIA TENUIS. BIOL.PL. 8, 131-141.

4371   PANWAR, K.S. (1970) - RHIZOSPHERE AND NON-RHIZOSPHERE MYCOFLORA OF SAND
       DUNES OF WESTERN RAJASTHAN, INDIA. SCI.CULT. 36, 661-662.

4372   PANWAR, K.S. (1970) - INFLUENCE OF AMINO ACIDS AND PH ON GROWTH OF CURVU-
       LARIA LUNATA. LABDEV J.SCI.TECHNOL., PART B, 8, 165-166.

4373   PANWAR, K.S. (1972) - UTILIZATION OF MONOSACCHARIDES BY FOUR SPECIES OF
       CURVULARIA. INDIAN PHYTOPATH. 25, 225-230.

4374   PANWAR, K.S. & BOHRA, A. (1973) - RECORDS OF MICROASCUS MANGINII AND SCO-
       PULARIOPSIS BRUMPTII FROM INDIA. CURR.SCI. 42, 585.

4375   PAPA, K.E. (1973) - THE PARASEXUAL CYCLE IN ASPERGILLUS FLAVUS. MYCOLOGIA
       65, 1201-1205.

4376   PAPA, K.E. (1976) - LINKAGE GROUPS IN ASPERGILLUS FLAVUS. MYCOLOGIA 68,
       159-165.

4377   PAPA, K.E., CAMPBELL, W.A. & HENDRIX, F.F. (1967) - SEXUALITY IN PYTHIUM
       SYLVATICUM - HETEROTHALLISM. MYCOLOGIA 59, 589-595.

4378   PAPACOSTEA, P. (1961) - (OCCURRENCE OF THE PENICILLIUM SPECIES IN AN AL-
       PINE PODZOL COVERED BY THE ASSOCIATION NARDETUM STRICTAE). LUCR.STIINT.
       CENT.EXP.INGRAS.BACT. 3, 73-82.

4379   PAPACOSTEA, P. & PREDA, C. (1961) - (CONTRIBUTION TO THE BETTER KNOWLEDGE
       OF MYCOCOENOSOS OF AN ALPINE SOIL IN THE BUCEGI MOUNTAINS COVERED BY
       THE ASSOCIATION NARDETUM STRICTAE). LUCR.STIINT.CENT.EXP.INGRAS.BACT.
       3, 83-98.

4380   PAPAVIZAS, G.C. (1963) - MICROBIAL ANTAGONISM IN BEAN RHIZOSPHERE AS AF-
       FECTED BY OAT STRAW AND SUPPLEMENTAL NITROGEN. PHYTOPATHOLOGY 53, 1430-
       1435.

4381 PAPAVIZAS, G.C. (1964) - NEW MEDIUM FOR THE ISOLATION OF THIELAVIOPSIS BA-
      SICOLA ON DILUTION PLATES FROM SOIL AND RHIZOSPHERE. PHYTOPATHOLOGY 54,
      1475-1481.

4382 PAPAVIZAS, G.C. (1965) - COMPARATIVE STUDIES OF SINGLE-BASIDIOSPORE ISO-
      LATES OF PELLICULARIA FILAMENTOSA AND PELLICULARIA PRATICOLA. MYCOLOGIA
      57, 91-103.

4383 PAPAVIZAS, G.C. (1966) - SUPPRESSION OF APHANOMYCES ROOT ROT OF PEAS BY
      CRUCIFEROUS SOIL AMENDMENTS. PHYTOPATHOLOGY 56, 1071-1075.

4384 PAPAVIZAS, G.C. (1967) - EVALUATION OF VARIOUS MEDIA AND ANTIMICROBIAL
      AGENTS FOR ISOLATION OF FUSARIUM FROM SOIL. PHYTOPATHOLOGY 57, 848-852.

4385 PAPAVIZAS, G.C. (1968) - SURVIVAL OF ROOT-INFECTING FUNGI IN SOIL. 6. EF-
      FECT OF AMENDMENTS ON BEAN ROOT ROT CAUSED BY THIELAVIOPSIS BASICOLA
      AND ON INOCULUM DENSITY OF THE CAUSAL ORGANISM. PHYTOPATHOLOGY 58, 421-
      428.

4386 PAPAVIZAS, G.C. (1969) - SURVIVAL OF ROOT-INFECTING FUNGI IN SOIL. 11.
      SURVIVAL OF RHIZOCTONIA SOLANI AS AFFECTED BY INOCULUM CONCENTRATION
      AND VARIOUS SOIL AMENDMENTS. PHYTOPATH.Z. 64, 101-111.

4387 PAPAVIZAS, G.C. (1970) - COLONIZATION AND GROWTH OF RHIZOCTONIA SOLANI IN
      SOIL. IN: RHIZOCTONIA SOLANI, BIOLOGY AND PATHOLOGY, SYMPOSIUM 1965;
      PARMETER, J.JR. (ED.), UNIV.CALIFORNIA PRESS, BERKELEY, 108-122.

4388 PAPAVIZAS, G.C. & ADAMS, P.B. (1969) - SURVIVAL OF ROOT-INFECTING FUNGI IN
      SOIL. 12. GERMINATION AND SURVIVAL OF ENDOCONIDIA AND CHLAMYDOSPORES OF
      THIELAVIOPSIS BASICOLA IN FALLOW SOIL AND IN SOIL ADJACENT TO GERMINAT-
      ING BEAN SEED. PHYTOPATHOLOGY 59, 371-378.

4389 PAPAVIZAS, G.C., ADAMS, P.B., LUMSDEN, R.D., LEWIS, J.A., DOW, R.L., AYERS,
      W.A. & KANTZES, J.G. (1975) - ECOLOGY AND EPIDEMIOLOGY OF RHIZOCTONIA
      SOLANI IN FIELD SOIL. PHYTOPATHOLOGY 65, 871-877.

4390 PAPAVIZAS, G.C. & AYERS, W.A. (1964) - EFFECT OF VARIOUS CARBON SOURCES ON
      GROWTH AND SEXUAL REPRODUCTION OF APHANOMYCES EUTEICHES. MYCOLOGIA 56,
      816-830.

4391 PAPAVIZAS, G.C. & AYERS, W.A. (1965) - VIRULENCE, HOST RANGE, AND PECTOLYT-
      IC ENZYMES OF SINGLE-BASIDIOSPORE ISOLATES OF RHIZOCTONIA PRATICOLA
      AND RHIZOCTONIA SOLANI. PHYTOPATHOLOGY 55, 111-116.

4392 PAPAVIZAS, G.C. & AYERS, W.A. (1966) - POLYGALACTURONATE TRANS-ELIMINASE
      PRODUCTION BY FUSARIUM OXYSPORUM AND FUSARIUM SOLANI. PHYTOPATHOLOGY
      56, 1269-1273.

4393 PAPAVIZAS, G.C. & AYERS, W.A. (1974) - APHANOMYCES SPECIES AND THEIR ROOT
      DISEASES IN PEA AND SUGARBEET. TECH.BULL.U.S.DEP.AGRIC., AGRIC.RES.SERV.
      NO.1485, 158 PP.

4394 PAPAVIZAS, G.C. & DAVEY, C.B. (1959) - INVESTIGATION ON THE CONTROL OF RHI-
      ZOCTONIA DISEASE OF SNAP BEANS BY GREEN ORGANIC SOIL AMENDMENTS. PHYTO-
      PATHOLOGY 49, 525.

4395 PAPAVIZAS, G.C. & DAVEY, C.B. (1959) - ISOLATION OF RHIZOCTONIA SOLANI
      FROM NATURALLY INFESTED AND ARTIFICIALLY INOCULATED SOILS. PL.DIS.REPTR
      43, 404-410.

4396   PAPAVIZAS, G.C. & DAVEY, C.B. (1960) - RHIZOCTONIA DISEASE OF BEAN AS AF-
       FECTED BY DECOMPOSING GREEN PLANT MATERIALS AND ASSOCIATED MICROFLORAS.
       PHYTOPATHOLOGY 50, 516-522.

4397   PAPAVIZAS, G.C. & DAVEY, C.B. (1960) - SAPROPHYTIC ACTIVITY AND SURVIVAL
       OF RHIZOCTONIA IN SOIL AS AFFECTED BY SOME ECOLOGICAL FACTORS. PHYTO-
       PATHOLOGY 50, 650 (ABS.).

4398   PAPAVIZAS, G.C. & DAVEY, C.B. (1960) - SOME FACTORS AFFECTING GROWTH OF
       APHANOMYCES EUTEICHES IN SYNTHETIC MEDIA. AM.J.BOT. 47, 758-765.

4399   PAPAVIZAS, G.C. & DAVEY, C.B. (1960) - SOME FACTORS AFFECTING SEXUAL REPRO-
       DUCTION OF APHANOMYCES EUTEICHES. AM.J.BOT. 47, 884-889.

4400   PAPAVIZAS, G.C. & DAVEY, C.B. (1961) - EXTENT AND NATURE OF THE RHIZOSPHERE
       OF LUPINUS. PL.SOIL 14, 215-236.

4401   PAPAVIZAS, G.C. & DAVEY, C.B. (1961) - SAPROPHYTIC BEHAVIOR OF RHIZOCTONIA
       IN SOIL. PHYTOPATHOLOGY 51, 693-699.

4402   PAPAVIZAS, G.C. & DAVEY, C.B. (1962) - ACTIVITY OF RHIZOCTONIA IN SOIL AS
       AFFECTED BY CARBON DIOXIDE. PHYTOPATHOLOGY 52, 759-766.

4403   PAPAVIZAS, G.C. & DAVEY, C.B. (1962) - ISOLATION AND PATHOGENICITY OF RHI-
       ZOCTONIA SAPROPHYTICALLY EXISTING IN SOIL. PHYTOPATHOLOGY 52, 834-839.

4404   PAPAVIZAS, G.C., DAVEY, C.B. & WOODARD, R.S. (1962) - COMPARATIVE EFFEC-
       TIVENESS OF SOME ORGANIC AMENDMENTS AND FUNGICIDES IN REDUCING ACTIVI-
       TY AND SURVIVAL OF RHIZOCTONIA SOLANI IN SOIL. CAN.J.MICROBIOL. 8, 915-
       922.

4405   PAPAVIZAS, G.C. & LEWIS, J.A. (1971) - SURVIVAL OF ENDOCONIDIA AND CHLAMY-
       DOSPORES OF THIELAVIOPSIS BASICOLA AS AFFECTED BY SOIL ENVIRONMENTAL
       FACTORS. PHYTOPATHOLOGY 61, 108-113.

4406   PAPAVIZAS, G.C. & LEWIS, J.A. (1971) - EFFECT OF AMENDMENTS AND FUNGICIDES
       ON APHANOMYCES ROOT ROT OF PEAS. PHYTOPATHOLOGY 61, 215-220.

4407   PAPENDORF, M.C. (1976) - THE SOIL MYCOFLORA OF AN ACACIA KARROO COMMUNITY
       IN THE WESTERN TRANSVAAL. BOTHALIA 12, 123-127.

4408   PAPENDORF, M.C. & JOOSTE, W.J. (1974) - THE MYCOFLORA OF WHEAT FIELD DE-
       BRIS. 1. BOTHALIA 11, 207-210.

4409   PAPENDORF, M.C. & JOOSTE, W.J. (1974) - NEW AND INTERESTING RECORDS OF
       SOUTH AFRICAN FUNGI. 8. BOTHALIA 11, 211-215.

4410   PARAMESWARAN, N. & LIESE, W. (1972) - WANDSTRUKTUREN DER PERITHECIUM-HAAR-
       HYPHEN VON CHAETOMIUM GLOBOSUM. ARCH.MIKROBIOL. 86, 225-229.

4411   PARBERY, D.G. (1967) - ISOLATION OF THE KEROSENE FUNGUS, CLADOSPORIUM RE-
       SINAE, FROM AUSTRALIAN SOILS. TRANS.BR.MYCOL.SOC. 50, 682-684.

4412   PARBERY, D.G. (1969) - AMORPHOTHECA RESINAE GEN.NOV., SP.NOV., THE PERFECT
       STATE OF CLADOSPORIUM RESINAE. AUST.J.BOT. 17, 331-357.

4413   PARBERY, D.G. (1969) - THE NATURAL OCCURRENCE OF CLADOSPORIUM RESINAE.
       TRANS.BR.MYCOL.SOC. 53, 15-23.

4414   PARBERY, D.G. (1969) - ISOLATION OF THE ASCAL STATE OF AMORPHOTHECA RESI-
       NAE DIRECT FROM SOIL. TRANS.BR.MYCOL.SOC. 53, 482-484.

4415   PARBERY, D.G. (1969) - THE SOIL AS A NATURAL SOURCE OF CLADOSPORIUM RESI-
       NAE. BIODETERIORATION OF MATERIALS, 1ST.INT.BIODETER.SYMP., SOUTHAMP-
       TON, ELSEVIER PUBL.CO., 371-380.

4416   PARBERY, D.G. (1971) - PHYSICAL FACTORS INFLUENCING GROWTH OF ARMORPHOTHE-
       CA RESINAE IN CULTURE. INT.BIODETER.BULL. 7, 5-9.

4417   PARBERY, D.G. (1972) - ECOLOGICAL AND GENETIC FACTORS CAUSING VARIATION IN
       CLADOSPORIUM RESINAE. BIODETER.MATER. 2, 19-26.

4418   PARBERY, D.G. & THISTLETHWAITE, P.J. (1973) - IMPROVED MINERAL SALTS SOLU-
       TION FOR THE GROWTH OF AMORPHOTHECA RESINAE. INT.BIODETER.BULL. 9, 11-
       16.

4419   PARIS, S., BIZZINI, B. & SEGRETAIN, G. (1975) - PURIFICATION D'UNE PRO-
       TEINE CARACTERISTIQUE DES SOUCHES PATHOGENES DE BEAUVERIA TENELLA.
       ANNLS MICROBIOL. 126A, 193-201.

4420   PARIS, S. & SEGRETAIN, G. (1975) - CARACTERES PHYSIOLOGIQUES DE BEAUVERIA
       TENELLA EN RAPPORT AVEC LA VIRULENCE DE SOUCHES DE CE CHAMPIGNON POUR
       LA LARVE DU HANNETON COMMUN (MELOLONTHA MELOLONTHA). ENTOMOPHAGA 20,
       135-138.

4421   PARK, D. (1955) - EXPERIMENTAL STUDIES ON THE ECOLOGY OF FUNGI IN SOIL.
       TRANS.BR.MYCOL.SOC. 38, 130-142.

4422   PARK, D. (1956) - ON THE ROLE OF AMENDMENTS IN THE BIOLOGY OF FUNGI IN
       SOIL. 6TH.INT.CONGR.SOIL SCI.PARIS III, 23-28.

4423   PARK, D. (1959) - SOME ASPECTS OF THE BIOLOGY OF FUSARIUM OXYSPORUM IN
       SOIL. ANN.BOT. 23, 35-49.

4424   PARK, D. (1961) - ISOLATION OF FUSARIUM OXYSPORUM FROM SOILS. TRANS.BR.
       MYCOL.SOC. 44, 119-122.

4425   PARK, D. (1961) - MORPHOGENESIS, FUNGISTASIS AND CULTURAL STALING IN FUSA-
       RIUM OXYSPORUM SNYDER & HANSEN. TRANS.BR.MYCOL.SOC. 44, 377-390.

4426   PARK, D. (1963) - THE PRESENCE OF FUSARIUM OXYSPORUM IN SOILS. TRANS.BR.
       MYCOL.SOC. 46, 444-448.

4427   PARK, D. (1963) - EVIDENCE FOR A COMMON FUNGAL GROWTH REGULATOR. TRANS.BR.
       MYCOL.SOC. 46, 541-548.

4428   PARK, D. (1964) - SOME PROPERTIES OF A STALING SUBSTANCE FROM FUSARIUM
       OXYSPORUM. TRANS.BR.MYCOL.SOC. 47, 541-546.

4429   PARK, D. (1972) - METHODS OF DETECTING FUNGI IN ORGANIC DETRITUS IN WATER.
       TRANS.BR.MYCOL.SOC. 58, 281-290.

4430   PARK, D. (1973) - GERMINATION OF THE THREE SPORE FORMS OF MAMMARIA ECHINO-
       BOTRYOIDES. TRANS.BR.MYCOL.SOC. 60, 351-354.

4431   PARK, D. (1974) - AQUATIC HYPHOMYCETES IN NON-AQUATIC HABITATS. TRANS.BR.
       MYCOL.SOC. 63, 183-187.

4432   PARK, D. (1974) - ACCUMULATION OF FUNGI BY CELLULOSE EXPOSED IN A RIVER.
       TRANS.BR.MYCOL.SOC. 63, 437-447.

4433   PARK, D. (1976) - NITROGEN LEVEL AND CELLULOSE DECOMPOSITION BY FUNGI.
       INT.BIODETER.BULL. 12, 95-99.

4434 PARK, D. (1976) - CARBON AND NITROGEN LEVELS AS FACTORS INFLUENCING FUNGAL
      DECOMPOSERS. IN: SYMP.BR.SOC.ECOL., 1975; ANDERSON, J.M. & MACFADYEN,
      A. (ED.), BLACKWELL, LONDON, 41-59.

4435 PARK, D. & ROBINSON, P.M. (1964) - ISOLATION AND BIOASSAY OF A FUNGAL MOR-
      PHOGEN. NATURE, LOND. 203, 988-989.

4436 PARK, D. & ROBINSON, P.M. (1969) - SPORULATION IN GEOTRICHUM CANDIDUM.
      TRANS.BR.MYCOL.SOC. 52, 213-222.

4437 PARK, D. & ROBINSON, P.M. (1970) - GERMINATION STUDIES WITH GEOTRICHUM
      CANDIDUM. TRANS.BR.MYCOL.SOC. 54, 83-92.

4438 PARK, J.Y. (1970) - ANTIFUNGAL EFFECT OF AN ECTOTROPHIC MYCORRHIZAL FUN-
      GUS, LACTARIUS SP., ASSOCIATED WITH BASSWOOD SEEDLINGS. CAN.J.MICROBIOL.
      16, 798-800.

4439 PARKER, A.D. (1973) - COPROPHILOUS ASCOMYCETES OF ILLINOIS. 1. PYRENOMYCE-
      TES. TRANS.ILL.ACAD.SCI. 66, 94-96.

4440 PARKER, E.J. (1974) - BEECH BARK DISEASE. FOREST REC., U.K. 96, 15 PP.

4441 PARKER, E.J. (1975) - SOME INVESTIGATIONS WITH BEECH BARK DISEASE NECTRIA
      IN SOUTHERN ENGLAND. EUR.J.FOREST PATH. 5, 118-124.

4442 PARKER, E.J. (1976) - PRODUCTION OF NECTRIA COCCINEA PERITHECIA IN CULTURE
      ON A NATURAL MEDIUM. TRANS.BR.MYCOL.SOC. 66, 519-520.

4443 PARKINSON, D. (1957) - NEW METHODS FOR THE QUALITATIVE AND QUANTITATIVE
      STUDY OF FUNGI IN THE RHIZOSPHERE. PEDOLOGIE, GEND, NO.SPEC., 146-154.

4444 PARKINSON, D. (1961) - DIE ENTWICKLUNG VON FUSARIEN IN DER WURZELREGION
      VON GETREIDE UND ANDEREN NUTZPFLANZEN. TAGBER.DT.AKAD.LANDWWISS.BERL.
      41, 7-14.

4445 PARKINSON, D. & BALASOORIYA, I. (1967) - STUDIES ON FUNGI IN A PINE-WOOD
      SOIL. 1. NATURE AND DISTRIBUTION OF FUNGI IN THE DIFFERENT SOIL HORI-
      ZONS. REVUE ECOL.BIOL.SOL 4, 463-478.

4446 PARKINSON, D. & CHESTERS, C.G.C. (1958) - OCCURRENCE OF FUSARIUM CULMORUM
      IN THE RHIZOSPHERE OF OATS. NATURE, LOND. 181, 1746-1747.

4447 PARKINSON, D. & CLARKE, J.H. (1964) - STUDIES ON FUNGI IN THE ROOT REGION.
      3. ROOT SURFACE FUNGI OF THREE SPECIES OF ALLIUM. PL.SOIL 20, 166-174.

4448 PARKINSON, D. & CROUCH, R. (1969) - STUDIES ON FUNGI IN A PINE-WOOD SOIL.
      5. ROOT MYCOFLORAS OF SEEDLINGS OF PINUS NIGRA VAR. LARICIO. REVUE
      ECOL.BIOL.SOL 6, 263-275.

4449 PARKINSON, D. & KENDRICK, W.B. (1960) - INVESTIGATIONS OF SOIL MICROHABI-
      TATS. IN: ECOLOGY OF SOIL FUNGI; PARKINSON, D. & WAID, J.S. (ED.), LIV-
      ERPOOL UNIV.PRESS, 22-28.

4450 PARKINSON, D. & PEARSON, R. (1965) - FACTORS AFFECTING THE STIMULATION OF
      FUNGAL DEVELOPMENT IN THE ROOT REGION. NATURE, LOND. 205, 205-206.

4451 PARKINSON, D., TAYLOR, G.S. & PEARSON, R. (1963) - STUDIES ON FUNGI IN THE
      ROOT REGION. 1. THE DEVELOPMENT OF FUNGI ON YOUNG ROOTS. PL.SOIL 19,
      332-349.

4452 PARKINSON, D. & THOMAS, A. (1965) - A COMPARISON OF METHODS FOR THE ISO-
      LATION OF FUNGI FROM RHIZOSPHERES. CAN.J.MICROBIOL. 11, 1001-1007.

4453 PARKINSON, D. & THOMAS, A. (1969) - STUDIES ON FUNGI IN THE ROOT REGION.
      8. QUALITATIVE STUDIES ON FUNGI IN THE RHIZOSPHERE OF DWARF BEAN PLANTS.
      PL.SOIL 31, 299-310.

4454 PARMETER, J.R., SHERWOOD, R.T. & PLATT, W.D. (1969) - ANASTOMOSIS GROUPING
      AMONG ISOLATES OF THANATEPHORUS CUCUMERIS. PHYTOPATHOLOGY 59, 1270-1278.

4455 PARMETER, J.R. & WHITNEY, H.S. (1970) - TAXONOMY AND NOMENCLATURE OF THE
      IMPERFECT STATE. IN: RHIZOCTONIA SOLANI, BIOLOGY AND PATHOLOGY, SYMPO-
      SIUM 1965; PARMETER, J.JR. (ED.), UNIV.CALIFORNIA PRESS, BERKELEY, 7-19.

4456 PARMETER, J.R., WHITNEY, H.S. & PLATT, W.D. (1967) - AFFINITIES OF SOME
      RHIZOCTONIA SPECIES THAT RESEMBLE MYCELIUM OF THANATEPHORUS CUCUMERIS.
      PHYTOPATHOLOGY 57, 218-223.

4457 PARR, J.F. & NORMAN, A.G. (1964) - GROWTH AND ACTIVITY OF SOIL MICROORGAN-
      ISMS IN GLASS MICRO-BEADS. 1. CARBON DIOXIDE EVOLUTION. SOIL SCI. 97,
      361-366.

4458 PARRISH, F.W., WILEY, B.J., SIMMONS, E.G. & LONG, L. (1966) - PRODUCTION
      OF AFLATOXIN AND KOJIC ACID BY SPECIES OF ASPERGILLUS AND PENICILLIUM.
      APPL.MICROBIOL. 14, 139.

4459 PASINETTI, A. (1955) - STUDIO CITOTOPOGRAFICO DELLE FOSFOESTERASI NEGLI
      EUMICETI. 1. LA FOSFATASI ALCALINICA IN PENICILLIUM DIGITATUM. ANNALI
      FITOPAT. 3, 3-34.

4460 PASS, T. & GRIFFIN, G.J. (1972) - EXOGENOUS CARBON AND NITROGEN REQUIRE-
      MENTS FOR CONIDIAL GERMINATION BY ASPERGILLUS FLAVUS. CAN.J.MICROBIOL.
      18, 1453-1470.

4461 PASS, T. & GRIFFIN, G.J. (1974) - INTERACTION OF PH AND TEMPERATURE WITH
      EXOGENOUS CARBON AND NITROGEN NUTRITION IN CONIDIAL GERMINATION BY AS-
      PERGILLUS FLAVUS. PHYTOPATHOLOGY 64, 1151-1152.

4462 PATEL, K.S. (1973) - OCCURRENCE OF BARRAGE PHENOMENON IN ASPERGILLUS NIDU-
      LANS. CURR.SCI. 42, 144.

4463 PATHAK, S.G. & ELANDER, R.P. (1971) - BIOCHEMICAL PROPERTIES OF HAPLOID
      AND DIPLOID STRAINS OF PENICILLIUM CHRYSOGENUM. APPL.MICROBIOL. 22,
      366-386.

4464 PATIL, K.C., MATSUMURA, F. & BOUSH, G.M. (1970) - DEGRADATION OF ENDRIN,
      ALDRIN, AND DDT BY SOIL MICROORGANISMS. APPL.MICROBIOL. 19, 714-717.

4465 PATIL, S.S. & DIMOND, A.E. (1967) - INHIBITION OF VERTICILLIUM POLYGALAC-
      TURONASE BY OXIDATION PRODUCTS OF POLYPHENOLS. PHYTOPATHOLOGY 57, 492-
      496.

4466 PATIL, S. & DIMOND, A.E. (1968) - EFFECT OF PHENOLS AND CYTOKININS ON PO-
      LYGALACTURONASE PRODUCTION BY VERTICILLIUM ALBO-ATRUM IN CULTURE. PHY-
      TOPATHOLOGY 58, 868-869.

4467 PATON, W.H.N. & BUDD, K. (1972) - ZINC UPTAKE IN NEOCOSMOSPORA VASINFECTA.
      J.GEN.MICROBIOL. 72, 173-184.

4468 PATRICK, Z.A. & SCHLIFER, M. (1970) - INDUCTION OF PIGMENTATION OF THIE-
      LAVIOPSIS BASICOLA AND OTHER FUNGI BY A BACTERIUM ISOLATED FROM SOIL.
      CAN.J.BOT. 48, 1879-1886.

4469 PATRICK, Z.A., TOUSSOUN, T.A. & THORPE, H.J. (1965) - GERMINATION OF CHLA-
      MYDOSPORES OF THIELAVIOPSIS BASICOLA. PHYTOPATHOLOGY 55, 466-467.

4470 PAUL, C. (1970) - EIN BEITRAG ZUR AUTOLYSE VON BODENPILZEN. ZENTBL.BAKT.
      PARASITKDE, ABT.2, 124, 673-683.

4471 PAUL, E.A. & MATHUR, S.P. (1967) - CLEAVAGE OF HUMIC ACIDS BY PENICILLIUM
      FREQUENTANS. PL.SOIL 27, 297-299.

4472 PAUL, W.R.C. (1929) - A COMPARATIVE MORPHOLOGICAL AND PHYSIOLOGICAL STUDY
      OF A NUMBER OF STRAINS OF BOTRYTIS CINEREA WITH SPECIAL REFERENCE TO
      THEIR VIRULENCE. TRANS.BR.MYCOL.SOC. 14, 118-135.

4473 PAULSON, G.A. & SCHOENEWEISS, D.F. (1971) - EPIDEMIOLOGY OF STEM BLIGHT OF
      VINCA MINOR INCITED BY PHOMA EXIGUA VAR. EXIGUA. PHYTOPATHOLOGY 61, 959-
      963.

4474 PAVLENKO, V.F. (1966) - (SPECIFIC COMPOSITION OF THE FUNGI OF SOME PEAT
      FIELDS, SOILS AND BROWN COALS OF ZHITOMIR REGION). MYKROBIOL.ZH. 28 (4),
      33-38.

4475 PAWAR, V.H., DESHMUKH, P.V. & THIRUMALACHAR, M.J. (1965) - NECROCITIN, A
      NEW CRYSTALLINE ANTIFUNGAL ANTIBIOTIC AND PLANT TOXIN. HINDUSTAN ANTI-
      BIOT.BULL. 8, 59-63.

4476 PAWAR, V.H., PADHYE, A.A. & THIRUMALACHAR, M.J. (1963) - ISOLATION OF MO-
      NOSPORIUM APIOSPERMUM FROM MARINE SOIL IN BOMBAY. HINDUSTAN ANTIBIOT.
      BULL. 6, 50-53.

4477 PAWAR, V.H. & THIRUMALACHAR, M.J. (1966) - STUDIES ON SOIL FUNGI FROM BOM-
      BAY. NOVA HEDWIGIA 12, 497-508.

4478 PAZNOKAS, J.L. & SYPHERD, P.S. (1975) - RESPIRATORY CAPACITY, CYCLIC ADE-
      NOSINE 3',5'-MONOPHOSPHATE, AND MORPHOGENESIS OF MUCOR RACEMOSUS. J.BACT.
      124, 134-139.

4479 PAZUR, J.H., BUDOVICH, T. & TIPTON, C.L. (1957) - THE ENZYMATIC SYNTHESIS
      AND DISPROPORTIONATION OF 3,0-ALPHA-D-GLUCOPYRANOSYL-D-GLUCOSE. J.AM.
      CHEM.SOC. 79, 625-628.

4480 PAZUR, J.H. & FRENCH, D. (1951) - THE TRANSGLUCOSIDASE OF ASPERGILLUS ORY-
      ZAE. J.AM.CHEM.SOC. 73, 3536.

4481 PAZUR, J.H. & KLEPPE, K. (1962) - THE HYDROLYSIS OF ALPHA-D-GLUCOSIDES BY
      AMYLOGLUCOSIDASE FROM ASPERGILLUS NIGER. J.BIOL.CHEM. 237, 1002-1006.

4482 PEACH, M. (1954) - AQUATIC PREDACIOUS FUNGI. 3. TRANS.BR.MYCOL.SOC. 37,
      240-247.

4483 PEARSON, R.C. & HALL, D.H. (1975) - FACTORS AFFECTING THE OCCURRENCE AND
      SEVERITY OF BLACKMOLD OF RIPE TOMATO FRUIT CAUSED BY ALTERNARIA ALTER-
      NATA. PHYTOPATHOLOGY 65, 1352-1359.

4484 PEBERDY, J.F. (1971) - PROTOPLASTS FROM MORTIERELLA VINACEA. TRANS.BR.MY-
      COL.SOC. 56, 67-72.

4485 PEBERDY, J.F. & TURNER, M. (1968) - THE ESTERASES OF MORTIERELLA RAMANNIA-
      NA IN RELATION TO TAXONOMY. J.GEN.MICROBIOL. 51, 303-312.

4486 PECHAK, D.G. & CRANG, R.E. (1977) - AN ANALYSIS OF AUREOBASIDIUM PULLULANS
      DEVELOPMENTAL STAGES BY MEANS OF SCANNING ELECTRON MICROSCOPY. MYCOLO-
      GIA 69, 783-792.

4487 PECHMANN, H.VON (1966) - DER EINFLUSS DER TEMPERATUR AUF DAS WACHSTUM VON
      BLAEUEPILZEN. IN: HOLZ UND ORGANISMEN; BECKER, G. & LIESE, W. (ED.),
      BEIH. MATER.ORG. 1, 237-250.

4488 PEDROSO, M.C., MARCANO, N.C. & FAVRAUD, L. (1972) - THE ISOLATION OF THE
      PERFECT FORM OF MICROSPORUM GYPSEUM, NANNIZZIA GYPSEA STOCKDALE, 1963,
      FROM BRASILIAN SOIL. MEMS INST.OSWALDO CRUZ 70, 585-589.

4489 PEERALLY, M.A. & COLHOUN, J. (1969) - THE EPIDEMIOLOGY OF ROOT ROT OF
      CHRYSANTHEMUMS CAUSED BY PHOMA SP. TRANS.BR.MYCOL.SOC. 52, 115-123.

4490 PEERS, F.G. (1967) - AFLATOXIN - A SUMMARY OF RECENT WORK. TROP.SCI. 9,
      186-203.

4491 PEGG, G.F. (1974) - VERTICILLIUM DISEASES. REV.PL.PATH. 53, 157-182.

4492 PELHATE, J. (1968) - INVENTAIRE DE LA MYCOFLORE DES BLES DE CONSERVATION.
      BULL.TRIMEST.SOC.MYCOL.FR. 84, 127-143.

4493 PELHATE, J. (1968) - RECHERCHE DES BESOINS EU EAU CHEZ QUELQUES MOISISSU-
      RES DES GRAINS. MYCOPATH.MYCOL.APPL. 36, 117-128.

4494 PELHATE, J. (1975) - MYCOFLORE DES MAIS-FOURRAGES ENSILES. REVUE MYCOL.
      39, 65-95.

4495 PELLETIER, G. & AUBE, C. (1970) - CONIDIAL SIZE AND CONTENTS IN VERTICIL-
      LIUM AS AFFECTED BY ENVIRONMENTAL FACTORS. CAN.J.MICROBIOL. 16, 231-236.

4496 PELLETIER, G. & HALL, R. (1971) - RELATIONSHIPS AMONG SPECIES OF VERTICIL-
      LIUM-PROTEIN COMPOSITION OF SPORES AND MYCELIUM. CAN.J.BOT. 49, 1293-
      1298.

4497 PELZ, B.F. & REHM, H.-J. (1972) - ISOLIERUNG, SUBSTRATASSIMILATION UND
      EINIGE PRODUKTE ALKANABBAUENDER SCHIMMELPILZE. ARCH.MIKROBIOL. 84, 20-
      28.

4498 PELZ, B.F. & REHM, H.J. (1972) - DEGRADATION OF N-ALKANES BY MOLDS. NATUR-
      WISSENSCHAFTEN 59, 513.

4499 PENGRA, R.M., COLE, M.A. & ALEXANDER, M. (1969) - CELL WALLS AND LYSIS OF
      MORTIERELLA PARVISPORA HYPHAE. J.BACT. 97, 1056-1061.

4500 PENSKAYA, L.V., ROMANOVA, I.B. & KRUGLAYA, O.V. (1975) - (ISOLATION OF AL-
      KALOID-LIKE SUBSTANCES FROM PENICILLIUM FUNGI). PRIKL.BIOKHIM.MIKROBIOL.
      11, 274-276.

4501 PENTLAND, G.D. (1965) - STIMULATION OF RHIZOMORPH DEVELOPMENT OF ARMILLA-
      RIA MELLEA BY AUREOBASIDIUM PULLULANS IN ARTIFICIAL CULTURE. CAN.J.MI-
      CROBIOL. 11, 345-350.

4502 PENTLAND, G.D. (1967) - ETHANOL PRODUCED BY AUREOBASIDIUM PULLULANS AND
      ITS EFFECT ON THE GROWTH OF ARMILLARIA MELLEA. CAN.J.MICROBIOL. 13,
      1631-1639.

4503 PENTZ, H.-D.V. (1954) - UEBER DEN EINFLUSS EINIGER PHYSIOLOGISCHER FAKTO-
      REN AUF DIE HEMMSTOFFABSONDERUNG BEI PENICILLIUM LINK UND TRICHODERMA
      TODE. ZENTBL.BAKT.PARASITKDE, ABT.2, 107, 506-522.

4504 PERCEBOIS, G. & VADOT, J. (1972) - UN CAS D'AFFECTION HUMAINE A MICROSPO-
      RUM GYPSEUM (NANNIZZIA GYPSEA - STOCKDALE 1963). ANNLS MED.NANCY 11,
      1359-1365.

4505   PERCIVAL, J.C. & THORNTON, R.H. (1958) - RELATIONSHIP BETWEEN THE PRESENCE
        OF FUNGAL SPORES AND A TEST FOR HEPATOTOXIC GRASS. NATURE, LOND. 182,
        1095-1096.

4506   PERESSE, M. & MOREAU, M. (1969) - SUSCEPTIBILITE DE DIVERSES CARYOPHYLLA-
        CEES A LA VERTICILLIOSE. C.R.HEBD.SEANC.ACAD.AGRIC.FR. 55, 1277-1280.

4507   PERISIC, M. & STOJANOVIC, D. (1967) - A STUDY OF THE BIOLOGY OF STEMPHY-
        LIUM BOTRYOSUM WALLR. - PLEOSPORA HERBARUM (PERS.) RABENH. - THE CAUSE
        OF BROWN SPOTS ON ALFALFA LEAVES. ZASTITA BILJA 18, 37-44.

4508   PERLMAN, D. (1948) - ON THE NUTRITION OF MEMNONIELLA ECHINATA AND STACHY-
        BOTRYS ATRA. AM.J.BOT. 35, 36-41.

4509   PERLMAN, D. (1950) - OBSERVATIONS ON THE PRODUCTION OF ETHANOL BY FUNGI
        AND YEASTS. AM.J.BOT. 37, 237-241.

4510   PERLMAN, D. (1951) - ON THE EFFECTS OF BIOLOGICALLY ACTIVE AGENTS ON FUNGI
        AT DIFFERENT STAGES OF GROWTH. AM.J.BOT. 38, 652-658.

4511   PERO, R.W., HARVAN, D. & BLOIS, M.C. (1973) - ISOLATION OF THE TOXIN, AL-
        TENUISOL, FROM THE FUNGUS, ALTERNARIA TENUIS AUCT. TETRAHEDRON LETTERS,
        1973 (12), 945-948.

4512   PERO, R.W. & MAIN, C.E. (1970) - CHLOROSIS OF TOBACCO INDUCED BY ALTERNA-
        RIOL MONOMETHYL ETHER PRODUCED BY ALTERNARIA TENUIS. PHYTOPATHOLOGY 60,
        1570-1573.

4513   PERO, R.W., OWENS, R.G., DALE, S.W. & HARVAN, D. (1971) - ISOLATION AND
        IDENTIFICATION OF A NEW TOXIN, ALTENUENE, FROM THE FUNGUS ALTERNARIA
        TENUIS. BIOCHIM.BIOPHYS.ACTA 230, 170-179.

4514   PERO, R.W., POSNER, H., BLOIS, M., HARVAN, D. & SPALDING, J.W. (1973) -
        TOXICITY OF METABOLITES PRODUCED BY ALTERNARIA. ENVIRON.HLTH PERSPECT.
        4, 87-94.

4515   PERRIN, P.W. (1972) - CONIDIUM GERMINATION IN ARTHROBOTRYS. TRANS.BR.MYCOL.
        SOC. 58, 331-332.

4516   PESTINSKAYA, T.V. (1956) - (BIOLOGISCHE BESONDERHEITEN VON PYTHIUM DEBARY-
        ANUM UND MOEGLICHKEITEN SEINER UNTERDRUECKUNG IM BODEN). BOT.ZH.SSSR
        41, 571-575.

4517   PESTINSKAYA, T.V. (1959) - (CHANGE IN THE ANTAGONISTIC PROPERTIES OF FUNGI
        UNDER THE INFLUENCE OF TEMPERATURE). BOT.ZH.SSSR 44, 1007-1009.

4518   PETCH, T. (1907-1910) - ON LASIODIPLODIA. ANN.R.BOT.GDN, PERADENIYA 4, 445-
        465.

4519   PETCHER, T.J., WEBER, H.-P. & KIS, Z. (1972) - CRYSTAL STRUCTURE AND AB-
        SOLUTE CONFIGURATION OF WORTMANNIN AND OF WORTMANNIN-P-BROMOBENZOATE.
        CHEM.COMMUN., 1972 (19), 1061-1062.

4520   PETERS, I. & RIPPEL-BALDES, A. (1948) - UEBER DAS VORKOMMEN VERSCHIEDENER
        RASSEN VON ASPERGILLUS NIGER IM BODEN. ARCH.MIKROBIOL. 14, 203-211.

4521   PETERSEN, R.H. (1962) - AQUATIC HYPHOMYCETES FROM NORTH AMERICA. 1. ALEU-
        RIOSPOREAE. PART 1 AND KEY TO THE GENERA. MYCOLOGIA 54, 117-151.

4522   PETERSEN, R.H. (1963) - AQUATIC HYPHOMYCETES FROM NORTH AMERICA. 3. PHIA-
        LOSPORAE AND MISCELLANEOUS SPECIES. MYCOLOGIA 55, 570-581.

4523   PETERSON, E.A. (1958) - OBSERVATIONS ON FUNGI ASSOCIATED WITH PLANT ROOTS.
       CAN.J.MICROBIOL. 4, 257-265.

4524   PETERSON, E.A. & KATZNELSON, H. (1956) - THE EFFECT OF TRACE ELEMENTS ON
       GROWTH OF HELMINTHOSPORIUM SATIVUM AND SEVERAL RELATED SPECIES. CAN.J.
       MICROBIOL. 2, 441-446.

4525   PETERSON, E.A. & KATZNELSON, H. (1964) - OCCURRENCE OF NEMATODE-TRAPPING
       FUNGI IN THE RHIZOSPHERE. NATURE, LOND. 204, 1111-1112.

4526   PETERSON, R.H. (1962) - SPORE FORMATION IN TRICELLULA AND VOLUCRISPORA.
       BULL.TORREY BOT.CLUB 89, 287-293.

4527   PETHYBRIDGE, G.H. (1919) - NOTES ON SOME SAPROPHYTIC SPECIES OF FUNGI,
       ASSOCIATED WITH DISEASED POTATO PLANTS AND TUBERS. TRANS.BR.MYCOL.SOC.
       6, 104-120.

4528   PETTERSSON, G. (1963) - SEPERATION OF CELLULASES ON SEPHADEX G-100. BIO-
       CHIM.BIOPHYS.ACTA 77, 665-667.

4529   PETTERSSON, G. (1964) - ON THE BIOSYNTHESIS OF TOLUQUINONES FROM ASPERGIL-
       LUS FUMIGATUS. 1. THE BIOGENETIC ROLE OF ORSELLINIC ACID AND ORCINOL.
       ACTA CHEM.SCAND. 18, 1202-1207.

4530   PETTERSSON, G. (1964) - TWO NEW BENZOQUINONES FROM GLIOCLADIUM ROSEUM.
       ACTA CHEM.SCAND. 18, 2303-2308.

4531   PETTERSSON, G. (1965) - NEW PHENOLIC METABOLITES FROM GLIOCLADIUM ROSEUM.
       ACTA CHEM.SCAND. 19, 414-420.

4532   PETTERSSON, G. (1965) - BIOSYNTHESIS OF SPINULOSIN IN PENICILLIUM SPINULO-
       SUM. ACTA CHEM.SCAND. 19, 1016-1017.

4533   PETTERSSON, G. (1965) - BIOSYNTHESIS OF AURANTIOGLIOCLADIN. ACTA CHEM.SCAND.
       19, 1827-1837.

4534   PETTERSSON, G. (1965) - ORSELLINIC ACID DECARBOXYLASE ISOLATED FROM GLIO-
       CLADIUM ROSEUM. ACTA CHEM.SCAND. 19, 2013-2021.

4535   PETRAK, F. (1952) - UEBER DIE GATTUNGEN GAEUMANNOMYCES, HALOPHIOBOLUS UND
       LINOCARPON. SYDOWIA 6, 383-388.

4536   PETZOLDT, K. & BOEHM, K.H. (1966) - NACHWEIS VON KERATINVERWERTENDEN DER-
       MATOPHYTEN IM ERDBODEN. ARCH.EXP.VET.-MED. 20, 383-390.

4537   PEYRONEL, B. (1961) - FUNGHI DEL SUOLO DI UN BOSCO DI FAGGIO DELL'ASPRO-
       MONTE. ALLIONIA 7, 27-37.

4538   PEYRONEL, B. & DAL VESCO, G. (1955) - RICERCHE SULLA MICOFLORA DI UN TER-
       RENO AGRARIO PRESSO TORINO. ALLIONIA 2, 357-417.

4539   PHAFF, H.J. (1947) - THE PRODUCTION OF EXOCELLULAR PECTIC ENZYMES BY PENI-
       CILLIUM CHRYSOGENUM. 1. ON THE FORMATION AND ADAPTIVE NATURE OF POLY-
       GALACTURONASE AND PECTIN ESTERASE. ARCHS BIOCHEM. 13, 67-81.

4540   PHELPS, J.W. (1973) - MICROFUNGI IN TWO WISCONSIN SAND BLOWS. TRANS.BR.
       MYCOL.SOC. 61, 386-388.

4541   PHILIPS, E. & WALKER, T.K. (1958) - MYCOLOGICAL FORMATION OF FAT. 5. FAC-
       TORS WHICH INFLUENCE THE FORMATION OF FAT IN SURFACE CULTURES OF PENI-
       CILLIUM LILACINUM THOM. J.SCI.FD AGRIC. 9, 223-227.

4542   PHILLIPS, D.V. (1972) - A SOYBEAN DISEASE CAUSED BY NEOCOSMOSPORA VASINFEC-
       TA. PHYTOPATHOLOGY 62, 612-615.

4543   PHILLIPS, D.V., LEBEN, C. & ALLISON, C.C. (1967) - A MECHANISM FOR THE RE-
       DUCTION OF FUSARIUM WILT BY A CEPHALOSPORIUM SPECIES. PHYTOPATHOLOGY 57,
       916-919.

4544   PICCI, G. (1956) - L'UTILISATION DES METAPHOSPHATES PAR CERTAINS CHAMPIG-
       NONS DU SOL. 6TH INT.CONGR.SOIL SCI.PARIS III, 54, 331-332.

4545   PICCI, G. (1965) - INTORNO ALLA MICROFLORA PRESENTE SULLE OLIVE SANE E
       COLPITE DA CICLOCONIO. AGRICOLTURA ITAL., PISA 65, 1-11.

4546   PICCI, G. (1966) - SULLA MICOFLORA PRESENTE NELLE STRUTTURE IN LEGNO
       SOGGETTE ALL'AZIONE DELL'ACQUA DI MARE. RICERCA SCIENT. 36, 153-157.

4547   PICCI, G. & VERONA, P. (1956) - QUALCHE RICERCA BIOLOGICA SUI TERRENI DEL-
       LO STATO DI S.PAOLO DEL BRASILE. BOLL.IST.SIEROTER.MILANO 35, 157-179.

4548   PIDOPLICHKO, N.M. (1953) - GRIBNAYA FLORA GRUBYKH KORMOV. IZVO AKAD.NAUK
       UKR.SSR, KIEV.

4549   PIDOPLICHKO, N.M. (1972) - PENITSILLII. IZVO NAUKOVA DUMKA, KIEV, 150 PP.

4550   PIDOPLICHKO, N.M., BILAI, V.I. & DYMOVICH, V.A. (1964) - (ANTIBIOTIC PROP-
       ERTIES OF PENICILLIUM SPECIES IN RESPECT TO PHYTOPATHOGENIC BACTERIA).
       MYKROBIOL.ZH. 26 (1), 37-41.

4551   PIDOPLICHKO, N.M. & KIRILENKO, T.S. (1972) - (ON THE TAXONOMY OF THE GENUS
       TRICHOCLADIUM HARZ). MIKOL.FITOPAT. 6, 510-515.

4552   PIDOPLICHKO, N.M., KIRILENKO, T.S. & ZAKHARCHENKO, V.O. (1973) - (NEW SPE-
       CIES OF THE GENUS THIELAVIA OF THE UKRAINIAN FLORA). MYKROBIOL.ZH. 35,
       723-729.

4553   PIDOPLICHKO, N.M., MOSKOVETS, V.S. & ZHDANOVA, N.M. (1960) - (THE EFFECT
       ON THE SHOOTS OF SOME FUNGI FROM THE MAIZE RHIZOSPHERE). MYKROBIOL.ZH.
       22 (3), 15-20.

4554   PIDOPLICHKO, N.M., MOSKOVETS, V.S. & ZHDANOVA, N.M. (1962) - (OCCURRENCE
       OF FUNGI FROM THE GENUS PENICILLIUM IN THE MAIZE RHIZOSPHERE IN TEN
       STEPPE AND FOREST-STEPPE REGIONS OF THE UKRAINIAN SSR). MYKROBIOL.ZH.
       24 (3), 42-49.

4555   PIDOPLICHKO, N.M., MOSKOVETS, V.S. & ZHDANOVA, N.M. (1962) - (OCCURRENCE
       OF FUNGI OF THE GENUS ASPERGILLUS IN MAIZE RHIZOSPHERE SOIL IN TEN
       STEPPE AND FOREST-STEPPE REGIONS OF THE UKRAINIAN SSR). MYKROBIOL.ZH.
       24 (5), 3-8.

4556   PIDOPLICHKO, N.M., MOSKOVETS, V.S. & ZHDANOVA, N.M. (1962) - (OCCURRENCE
       OF FUNGI OF THE GENUS FUSARIUM IN MAIZE RHIZOSPHERE IN TEN REGIONS OF
       THE STEPPE AND FOREST-STEPPE ZONES OF THE UKRAINIAN SSR). MYKROBIOL.ZH.
       24 (6), 19-26.

4557   PIDOPLICHKO, N.M., MOSKOVETS, V.S. & ZHDANOVA, N.M. (1963) - (EFFECT OF
       CERTAIN FUNGI FROM THE MAIZE RHIZOSPHERE ON ITS SHOOTS. 2.). MYKROBIOL.
       ZH. 25 (6), 38-43.

4558   PIDOPLICHKO, V.N. (1970) - (MYCOFLORA OF WINTER WHEAT ROOT ROT UNDER CON-
       DITIONS OF SOUTH-EAST OF THE UKRAINIAN SSR). MYKROBIOL.ZH. 32 (2), 215-
       220.

4559 PIDOPLICHKO, V.N. & TOPOROVSKA, Y.S. (1969) - (INTRAROOT MYCOFLORA OF SUG-
      ARBEET). MYKROBIOL.ZH. 31 (5), 453-459.

4560 PIECZARKA, D.J. & ABAWI, G.S. (1975) - OCCURRENCE OF PYTHIUM SPP. IN BEAN
      ROOTS AND SOILS IN NEW YORK STATE. PROC.AM.PHYTOPATH.SOC. 2, 104.

4561 PIER, A.C., RHOADES, K.R. HAYES, T.L. & GALLAGHER, J. (1972) - SCANNING
      ELECTRON MICROSCOPY OF SELECTED DERMATOPHYTES OF VETERINARY IMPORTANCE.
      AM.J.VET.RES. 33, 607-613.

4562 PIERSON, CH.F. (1966) - EFFECTS OF TEMPERATURE ON THE GROWTH OF RHIZOPUS
      STOLONIFER ON PEACHES AND ON AGAR. PHYTOPATHOLOGY 56, 276-278.

4563 PILLAI, C.G.P., WEETE, J.D., CURL, E.A. & BLACK, H.S. (1975) - INFLUENCE
      OF LIGHT ON FORMATION AND LIPID COMPOSITION OF SCLEROTIUM ROLFSII SCLE-
      ROTIA. PROC.AM.PHYTOPATH.SOC. 2, 54.

4564 PINE, L. (1954) - STUDIES ON THE GROWTH OF HISTOPLASMA CAPSULATUM. 1.
      GROWTH OF THE YEAST PHASE IN LIQUID MEDIA. J.BACT. 68, 671-679.

4565 PINE, L. (1957) - STUDIES ON THE GROWTH OF HISTOPLASMA CAPSULATUM. 3. EF-
      FECT OF THIAMIN AND OTHER VITAMINS ON THE GROWTH OF THE YEAST AND MY-
      CELIAL PHASE OF HISTOPLASMA CAPSULATUM. J.BACT. 74, 239-245.

4566 PINE, L. (1970) - GROWTH OF HISTOPLASMA CAPSULATUM. 6. MAINTENANCE OF THE
      MYCELIAL PHASE. APPL.MICROBIOL. 19, 413-420.

4567 PINE, L. & PEACOCK, C.L. (1958) - STUDIES ON THE GROWTH OF HISTOPLASMA
      CAPSULATUM. 4. FACTORS INFLUENCING CONVERSION OF THE MYCELIAL PHASE TO
      THE YEAST PHASE. J.BACT. 75, 167-174.

4568 PINKERTON, M.E. (1936) - A COMPARATIVE STUDY OF CONIDIAL FORMATION IN CE-
      PHALOSPORIUM AND SOME RELATED HYPHOMYCETES. ANN.MO.BOT.GDN 23, 1-69.

4569 PIONTELLI, E. & CARETTA, G. (1974) - CONSIDERAZIONI ECOLOGICHE SU ALCUNI
      GEOMICETI ISOLATI, SU SUBSTRATI CHERATINICI, IN LOCALITA MONTAGNOSE
      DELLE ANDE DEL CILE. RIV.PAT.VEG. 10, 261-314.

4570 PISANO, M.A., OLENIACZ, W.S., MASON, R.T., FLEISCHMAN, A.I., VACCARO, S.E.
      & CATALANO, G.R. (1963) - ENZYME PRODUCTION BY SPECIES OF CEPHALOSPO-
      RIUM. APPL.MICROBIOL. 2, 111-115.

4571 PISKORZ, B. (1967) - INVESTIGATIONS ON THE ACTION OF LIGHT ON THE GROWTH
      AND DEVELOPMENT OF PENICILLIUM CLAVIFORME. ACTA SOC.BOT.POLON. 36, 677-
      697.

4572 PISKORZ, B. & FIEMA, J. (1972) - NUTRIENT SOLUTION REQUIREMENTS OF REPRE-
      SENTATIVES OF THE PENICILLIUM CLAVIGERUM SECTION. ACTA MYCOL., WARSZAWA
      8, 47-57.

4573 PISPEK, P.A. (1929) - EDAFSKE MUKORINEJE JUGOSLAVIJE. ACTA BOT.INST.BOT.
      BOT.UNIV.ZAGREB 4, 77-112.

4574 PISTOR, R. (1930) - BEITRAEGE ZUR KENNTNIS DER BIOLOGISCHEN TAETIGKEIT VON
      PILZEN IN WALDBOEDEN. ZENTBL.BAKT.PARASITKDE, ABT.2, 80, 169-200.

4575 PITT, D. (1964) - STUDIES ON SHARP EYESPOT DISEASE OF CEREALS. 2. VIABILI-
      TY OF SCLEROTIA. PERSISTENCE OF THE CAUSAL FUNGUS, RHIZOCTONIA SOLANI.
      ANN.APPL.BIOL. 54, 231-240.

4576 PITT, D. (1969) - CYTOCHEMICAL OBSERVATIONS ON THE LOCALIZATION OF SUL-
      PHYDRYL GROUPS IN BUDDING YEAST CELLS AND IN THE PHIALIDES OF PENICIL-
      LIUM NOTATUM WESTLING DURING CONIDIATION. J.GEN.MICROBIOL. 59, 257-262.

4577 PITT, D. (1970) - EFFECT OF SELENITE AND TELLURITE ON MORPHOGENESIS IN PE-
NICILLIUM NOTATUM. TRANS.BR.MYCOL.SOC. 55, 325-327.

4578 PITT, J.I. (1973) - AN APPRAISAL OF IDENTIFICATION METHODS FOR PENICILLIUM
SPECIES - NOVEL TAXONOMIC CRITERIA BASED ON TEMPERATURE AND WATER RELA-
TIONS. MYCOLOGIA 65, 1135-1157.

4579 PITT, J.I. (1974) - A SYNOPTIC KEY TO THE GENUS EUPENICILLIUM AND TO SCLERO-
TIGENIC PENICILLIUM SPECIES. CAN.J.BOT. 52, 2231-2236.

4580 PITT, J.I. & CHRISTIAN, J.H.B. (1970) - HEAT RESISTANCE OF XEROPHILIC FUN-
GI BASED ON MICROSCOPICAL ASSESSMENT OF SPORE SURVIVAL. APPL.MICROBIOL.
20, 682-686.

4581 PLAATS-NITERINK, A.J.VAN DER (1968) - THE OCCURRENCE OF PYTHIUM IN THE
NETHERLANDS. ACTA BOT.NEERL. 17, 320-329.

4582 PLAATS-NITERINK, A.J.VAN DER (1975) - SPECIES OF PYTHIUM IN THE NETHER-
LANDS. NETH.J.PL.PATH. 81, 22-37.

4583 PODLAHOVA, R. (1973) - UEBER EINIGE PYRENOMYCETEN AUF ALNUS VIRIDIS (CHAIX)
LAM. & DC. AUS SUEDBOEHMEN. CESKA MYCOL. 27, 84-97.

4584 POHJAKALLIO, O. & MAKKONEN, R. (1957) - ON THE RESISTANCE OF THE SCLEROTIA
OF SOME PHYTOPATHOLOGICAL FUNGI AGAINST THEIR PARASITES. ACTA CHEM.FENN.
30, 222.

4585 POISSON, J., CAHAGNIER, B. & GUILBOT, A. (1971) - SUR LA RADIOSENSIBILITE
DES CONIDIOSPORES DES MOISISSURES DOMINANTES DU MAIS. INCIDENCE SUR LA
RADURISATION DES GRAINS. MYCOPATH.MYCOL.APPL. 45, 193-209.

4586 POLACK, F.M., SIVERIO, C. & BRESKY, R.H. (1976) - CORNEAL CHROMOMYCOSIS.
DOUBLE INFECTION BY PHIALOPHORA VERRUCOSA (MEDLAR) AND CLADOSPORIUM
CLADOSPORIOIDES (FRESENIUS). ANN.OPHTHAL. 8, 139-144.

4587 POLLOCK, A.V. (1947) - PRODUCTION OF CITRININ BY FIVE SPECIES OF PENICIL-
LIUM. NATURE, LOND. 160, 331.

4588 POLLOCK, R.T. (1973) - ENVIRONMENTAL FACTORS AFFECTING THE PATTERN OF PERI-
THECIUM DEVELOPMENT IN SORDARIA FIMICOLA ON AGAR MEDIUM. BULL.TORREY
BOT.CLUB 100, 78-83.

4589 POLTORAK, V.A. & SILAEV, A.B. (1964) - (CHEMICAL AND PHYSICO-CHEMICAL PROP-
ERTIES OF JANTHINELLIN). ANTIBIOTIKI 9, 25-27.

4590 PONCHET, J. (1962) - ETUDE DES FACTEURS QUI CONDITIONNENT LE DEVELOPPEMENT
DU PIETIN-ECHAUDAGE, LINOCARPON CARICETI. ANNLS EPIPHYT. 13, 151-165.

4591 PONCHET, J. (1966) - ETUDE DES COMMUNAUTES MYCOPERICARPIQUES DU CARYOPSE
DE BLE. ANNLS EPIPHYT. 17, HORS SER.1, 1-112.

4592 PONCHET, J., PIONNAT, J.-C. & AUGE, G. (1972) - EFFETS DE LA LUMIERE SUR
LA SPORULATION IN VITRO DE L'EPICOCCUM NIGRUM. ANNLS PHYTOPATH. 4, 119-
132.

4593 PONNAPPA, K.M. (1971) - A HIGHLY VIRULENT STRAIN OF MYROTHECIUM RORIDUM ON
TRAPA BISPINOSA. INDIAN J.MYCOL.PL.PATH. 1, 90-94.

4594 PONS, J., GRATEAU, P., RIGAUD, A. & PASTUREL, A. (1975) - PHYCOMYCOSE FA-
CIALE. REVUE STOMATOL. 76, 461-468.

4595   PONTECORVO, G. (1953) - THE GENETICS OF ASPERGILLUS NIDULANS. ADV.GENET.
       5, 141-238.

4596   POOLE, N.J. & PRICE, P.C. (1971) - THE OCCURRENCE OF CHRYSOSPORIUM PANNO-
       RUM IN SOILS RECEIVING INCREMENTAL CELLULOSE. SOIL BIOL.BIOCHEM. 3, 161-
       166.

4597   POPE, S. (1944) - A NEW SPECIES OF METARRHIZIUM ACTIVE IN DECOMPOSING CEL-
       LULOSE. MYCOLOGIA 36, 343-350.

4598   PORE, R.S. & LARSH, H.W. (1967) - ALEURIOSPORE FORMATION IN FOUR RELATED
       ASPERGILLUS SPECIES. MYCOLOGIA 59, 318-325.

4599   PORE, R.S. & LARSH, H.W. (1967) - EXPERIMENTAL PATHOLOGY OF ASPERGILLUS
       TERREUS-FLAVIPES GROUP SPECIES. SABOURAUDIA 6, 89-93.

4600   PORE, R.S., PYLE, C., LARSH, H.W. & SKVARLA, J.J. (1969) - ASPERGILLUS
       CARNEUS ALEURIOSPORE CELL WALL ULTRASTRUCTURE. MYCOLOGIA 61, 418-422.

4601   PORE, R.S., TSAO, G.C. & PLUNKETT, O.A. (1965) - A NEW SPECIES OF ARTHRO-
       DERMA ESTABLISHED ACCORDING TO BIOLOGICAL SPECIES CONCEPTS. MYCOLOGIA
       57, 969-973.

4602   PORTER, D.M. & GARREN, K.H. (1970) - ENDOCARPIC MICROORGANISMS OF TWO TYPES
       OF WINDROW-DRIED PEANUT FRUIT (ARACHIS HYPOGAEA L.). APPL.MICROBIOL. 20,
       133-138.

4603   POSTHUMUS, A.C. (1973) - EXTRACTION, PURIFICATION AND IDENTIFICATION OF 3-
       INDOLEACETIC ACID (IAA) FROM CULTURE FILTRATES OF PYTHIUM SYLVATICUM.
       NETH.J.PL.PATH. 79, 282-284.

4604   POTGIETER, H.J. & ALEXANDER, M. (1966) - SUSCEPTIBILITY AND RESISTANCE OF
       SEVERAL FUNGI TO MICROBIAL LYSIS. J.BACT. 91, 1526-1533.

4605   POTLAICHUK, V.I. (1952) - (THE GENUS NIGROSPORA ZIMM., ITS SPECIES AND SYS-
       TEMATIC POSITION). MIKROBIOLOGIYA 21, 219-225.

4606   POUND, G.S. (1947) - VARIABILITY IN PHOMA LINGAM. J.AGRIC.RES. 75, 113-133.

4607   POUNDS, J.R. & LUCAS, G.B. (1972) - THERMOPHILIC FUNGI OF TOBACCO. BULL.N.
       C.AGRIC.EXP.STN 211, 3-24.

4608   POWELL, J.M. (1971) - FUNGI AND BACTERIA ASSOCIATED WITH CRONARTIUM COMAN-
       DRAE ON LODGEPOLE PINE IN ALBERTA. PHYTOPROTECTION 52, 45-51.

4609   POWELSON, R.L. (1966) - AVAILABILITY OF DIFFUSIBLE NUTRIENTS FOR GERMINA-
       TION AND GROWTH OF VERTICILLIUM DAHLIAE IN SOILS AMENDED WITH OAT AND
       ALFALFA RESIDUES. PHYTOPATHOLOGY 56, 895 (ABS.).

4610   PRAKASH, D. & KHAN, A.M. (1971) - FUNGAL POPULATION IN SUGAR CANE SOILS.
       1. J.INDIAN BOT.SOC. 50, 153-157.

4611   PRAKASH, R. & SAKSENA, R.K. (1952) - DECOMPOSITION OF PADDY AND BAJRA (PEN-
       NISETUM TYPHOIDEUM) STRAWS BY FUNGI COMMONLY FOUND IN ALLAHABAD SOILS.
       PROC.INDIAN ACAD.SCI., SECT.B, 36, 119-128.

4612   PRAMER, D. & SHIMPEI, K. (1963) - NEMIN AND THE NEMATODE-TRAPPING FUNGI.
       BACT.REV. 27, 282-292.

4613   PRAMER, D. & STOLL, N.R. (1959) - NEMIN - A MORPHOGENIC SUBSTANCE CAUSING
       TRAP FORMATION BY PREDACEOUS FUNGI. SCIENCE, N.Y. 129, 966-967.

4614 PRASAD, M. (1972) - COMPARATIVE STUDIES ON THE EFFECT OF VITAMINS ON SPOR-
      ULATION IN FUSARIUM OXYSPORUM SCHLECHT. EX FR. AND FUSARIUM MONILIFORME
      VAR. SUBGLUTINANS WR. & RG. MYCOPATH.MYCOL.APPL. 46, 367-372.

4615 PRASAD, S.S. & BILGRAMI, R.S. (1974) - INVESTIGATIONS ON DISEASES OF LIT-
      CHI. 2. INFLUENCE OF TEMPERATURE AND HUMIDITY ON THE DECAY OF FRUITS
      CAUSED BY NINE VIRULENT PATHOGENS. INDIAN PHYTOPATH. 26, 517-522.

4616 PRASERTPHON, S. (1963) - PATHOGENICITY OF DIFFERENT STRAINS OF ENTOMOPHTHO-
      RA CORONATA (COSTANTIN) KEVORKIAN FOR LARVAE OF THE GREATER WAX MOTH.
      J.INSECT PATH. 5, 174-181.

4617 PRASERTPHON, S. (1963) - CONIDIAL FORMATION IN ENTOMOPHTHORA CORONATA (CO-
      STANTIN) KEVORKIAN. J.INSECT PATH. 5, 318-335.

4618 PRATT, B.H. (1971) - ISOLATION OF BASIDIOMYCETES FROM AUSTRALIAN EUCALYPT
      FOREST AND ASSESSMENT OF THEIR ANTAGONISM TO PHYTOPHTHORA CINNAMOMI.
      TRANS.BR.MYCOL.SOC. 56, 243-250.

4619 PRATT, B.H. & HEATHER, W.A. (1972) - METHOD FOR RAPID DIFFERENTIATION OF
      PHYTOPHTHORA CINNAMOMI FROM OTHER PHYTOPHTHORA SPECIES ISOLATED FROM
      SOIL BY LUPIN BAITING. TRANS.BR.MYCOL.SOC. 59, 87-96.

4620 PRATT, B.H. & HEATHER, W.A. (1973) - THE ORIGIN AND DISTRIBUTION OF PHY-
      TOPHTHORA CINNAMOMI RANDS IN AUSTRALIAN NATIVE PLANT COMMUNITIES AND
      THE SIGNIFICANCE OF ITS ASSOCIATION WITH PARTICULAR PLANT SPECIES.
      AUST.J.BIOL.SCI. 26, 559-573.

4621 PRATT, B.H., HEATHER, W.A. & SHEPHERD, C.J. (1972) - TRANSCONTINENTAL OC-
      CURRENCE OF A1 AND A2 STRAINS OF PHYTOPHTHORA CINNAMOMI IN AUSTRALIA.
      AUST.J.BIOL.SCI. 25, 1099-1100.

4622 PRATT, B.H., HEATHER, W.A. & SHEPHERD, C.J. (1973) - RECOVERY OF PHYTO-
      PHTHORA CINNAMOMI FROM NATIVE VEGETATION IN A REMOTE AREA OF NEW SOUTH
      WALES. TRANS.BR.MYCOL.SOC. 60, 197-204.

4623 PRATT, B.H., SEDGLEY, J.H., HEATHER, W.A. & SHEPHERD, C.J. (1972) - OOSPORE
      PRODUCTION IN PHYTOPHTHORA CINNAMOMI IN THE PRESENCE OF TRICHODERMA KO-
      NINGII. AUST.J.BIOL.SCI. 25, 861-863.

4624 PRATT, R.G. & GREEN, R.J. (1971) - THE TAXONOMY AND HETEROTHALLISM OF PY-
      THIUM SYLVATICUM. CAN.J.BOT. 49, 273-279.

4625 PRATT, R.G. & GREEN, R.J.JR. (1973) - THE SEXUALITY AND POPULATION STRUC-
      TURE OF PYTHIUM SYLVATICUM. CAN.J.BOT. 51, 429-436.

4626 PRATT, R.G. & MITCHELL, J.E. (1973) - DIFFERENTIAL EFFECTS OF CHOLESTEROL
      IN MATING THALLI OF PYTHIUM SYLVATICUM AND PHYTOPHTHORA CAPSICI. CAN.
      J.BOT. 51, 595-599.

4627 PREECE, T.F. & COOPER, D.J. (1969) - THE PREPARATION AND USE OF A FLUORES-
      CENT ANTIBODY REAGENT FOR BOTRYTIS CINEREA GROWN ON GLASS SLIDES. TRANS.
      BR.MYCOL.SOC. 52, 99-104.

4628 PREMA KUMAR, R., SUBBA RAO, P.V. & VAIDYANATHAN, C.S. (1973) - M-HYDROXY-
      BENZOATE 4-HYDROXYLASE FROM ASPERGILLUS NIGER. PURIFICATION AND PROPER-
      TIES. INDIAN J.BIOCHEM.BIOPHYS. 10, 184-190.

4629 PRENTICE, N. (1962) - PARTIAL PURIFICATION OF A METABOLITE PRODUCED BY FU-
      SARIUM MONILIFORME WHICH INHIBITS UTILIZATION OF OXYGEN BY GERMINATING
      BARLEY. PHYSIOLOGIA PL. 15, 693-699.

4630   PRENTICE, N., DICKSON, A.D. & DICKSON, J.G. (1959) - PRODUCTION OF EMETIC
       MATERIAL BY SPECIES OF FUSARIUM. NATURE, LOND. 184, 1319.

4631   PREST, D.B., GILLIAM, M., TABER, S. & MILLS, J.P. (1974) - FUNGI ASSOCIA-
       TED WITH DISCOLORED HONEY BEE, ASPIS MELLIFERA, LARVAE AND PUPAE. J.IN-
       VERTEBR.PATH. 24, 253-255.

4632   PRESTON, N.C. (1943) - OBSERVATIONS ON THE GENUS MYROTHECIUM. 1. THE THREE
       CLASSIC SPECIES. TRANS.BR.MYCOL.SOC. 26, 158-168.

4633   PRESTON, N.C. (1961) - OBSERVATIONS ON THE GENUS MYROTHECIUM. 3. THE CYLIN-
       DRICAL-SPORED SPECIES OF MYROTHECIUM KNOWN IN BRITAIN. TRANS.BR.MYCOL.
       SOC. 44, 31-41.

4634   PRICE, D.W. (1976) - PASSAGE OF VERTICILLIUM ALBO-ATRUM PROPAGULES THROUGH
       THE ALIMENTARY CANAL OF THE BULB MITE. PHYTOPATHOLOGY 66, 46-50.

4635   PRICE, K. & COLHOUN, J. (1975) - A STUDY OF VARIABILITY OF ISOLATES OF
       SCLEROTINIA SCLEROTIORUM FROM DIFFERENT HOSTS. PHYTOPATH.Z. 83, 159-166.

4636   PRIESTLEY, H. (1914) - MICROSPORON SCORTEUM (N.SP.) FROM A CASE OF RING-
       WORM IN MAN. ANN.TROP.MED. 8, 113-118.

4637   PRILLWITZ, H.G. (1963) - EIN BISHER UNBEKANNTER CLADOSPORIUM-BESATZ AUF
       GETREIDEKOERNERN. NACHRBL.DT.PFLSCHUTZDIENST, BERL. 15, 83-85.

4638   PRINGLE, R.B. (1976) - COMPARATIVE BIOCHEMISTRY OF THE PHYTOPATHOGENIC
       FUNGUS HELMINTHOSPORIUM. 16. THE PRODUCTION OF VICTOXININE BY HELMIN-
       THOSPORIUM SATIVUM AND HELMINTHOSPORIUM VICTORIAE. CAN.J.BIOCHEM. 54,
       783-787.

4639   PRITCHARD, G.G. (1965) - THE PRODUCTION OF PYRUVIC AND ALPHA-OXOGLUTARIC
       ACIDS BY MUCOR SPECIES. J.EXP.BOT. 16, 487-497.

4640   PRUDLOV, B., USHAKOVA, V.I. & EGOROV, N.S. (1972) - (EFFECT OF VARIOUS
       CARBON COMPOUNDS ON THE PRODUCTION OF PROTEOLYTIC ENZYMES BY FUSARIUM
       GRAMINEARUM AND ALTERNARIA SP). MIKROBIOLOGIYA 41, 791-797.

4641   PRUDLOV, B., USHAKOVA, V.I. & EGOROV, N.S. (1973) - (EFFECT OF NITROGEN
       SOURCES IN THE MEDIUM ON THE PRODUCTION OF PROTEOLYTIC ENZYMES BY FUSA-
       RIUM GRAMINEARUM AND ALTERNARIA SP.). MIKROBIOLOGIYA 42, 203-207.

4642   PRUESS, L.M., EICHINGER, E.C. & PETERSON, W.H. (1933/34) - THE CHEMISTRY
       OF MOLD TISSUE. 3. COMPOSITION OF CERTAIN MOLDS WITH SPECIAL REFERENCE
       TO THE LIPID CONTENT. ZENTBL.BAKT.PARASITKDE, ABT.2, 89, 370-377.

4643   PUDELKO, Z. (1975) - (CHROMELOSPORIUM OLLARE, THE FUNGUS NOT NOTED IN
       GREENHOUSE CULTURES IN POLAND). ACTA MYCOL., WARSZAWA 11, 101-106.

4644   PUGH, G.J.F. (1958) - LEAF LITTER FUNGI FOUND ON CAREX PANICULATA. TRANS.
       BR.MYCOL.SOC. 41, 185-195.

4645   PUGH, G.J.F. (1960) - THE FUNGAL FLORA OF TIDAL MUD FLATS. IN: ECOLOGY OF
       SOIL FUNGI; PARKINSON, D. & WAID, J.S. (ED.), LIVERPOOL UNIV.PRESS,
       202-208.

4646   PUGH, G.J.F. (1962) - STUDIES ON FUNGI IN COASTAL SOILS. 2. FUNGAL ECOLOGY
       IN A DEVELOPING SALT MARSH. TRANS.BR.MYCOL.SOC. 45, 560-566.

4647   PUGH, G.J.F. (1964) - AN INVESTIGATION OF SOIL-BORNE CELLULOSE-DECOMPOSING
       FUNGI IN GREECE. ANNLS INST.PHYTOPATH.BENAKI, N.S. 7, 19-27.

4648   PUGH, G.J.F. (1963/64) - DISPERSAL OF ARTHRODERMA CURREYI BY BIRDS, AND
       ITS ROLE IN THE SOIL. SABOURAUDIA 3, 275-287.

4649   PUGH, G.J.F. (1965) - CELLULOLYTIC AND KERATINOPHILIC FUNGI RECORDED ON
       BIRDS. SABOURAUDIA 4, 85-91.

4650   PUGH, G.J.F. (1966) - ASSOCIATIONS BETWEEN BIRDS' NESTS, THEIR PH AND KE-
       RATINOPHILIC FUNGI. SABOURAUDIA 5, 49-53.

4651   PUGH, G.J.F. (1966) - CELLULOSE-DECOMPOSING FUNGI ISOLATED FROM SOILS NEAR
       MADRAS. J.INDIAN BOT.SOC. 45, 232-241.

4652   PUGH, G.J.F. (1966) - FUNGI ON BIRDS IN INDIA. J.INDIAN BOT.SOC. 45, 296-
       303.

4653   PUGH, G.J.F. (1972) - THE CONTAMINATION OF BIRDS' FEATHERS BY FUNGI. IBIS
       114, 172-177.

4654   PUGH, G.J.F., BLAKEMAN, J.P. & MORGAN-JONES, G. (1964) - THERMOMYCES VER-
       RUCOSUS SP.NOV. AND T. LANUGINOSUS. TRANS.BR.MYCOL.SOC. 47, 115-121.

4655   PUGH, G.J.F., BLAKEMAN, J.P., MORGAN-JONES, G. & EGGINS, H.O. (1963) -
       STUDIES ON FUNGI IN COASTAL SOILS. 4. CELLULOSE DECOMPOSING SPECIES IN
       SAND DUNES. TRANS.BR.MYCOL.SOC. 46, 565-571.

4656   PUGH, G.J.F. & BUCKLEY, N.G. (1971) - AUREOBASIDIUM PULLULANS, AN ENDO-
       PHYTE IN SYCAMORE AND OTHER TREES. TRANS.BR.MYCOL.SOC. 57, 227-231.

4657   PUGH, G.J.F. & DICKINSON, C.H. (1965) - STUDIES ON FUNGI IN COASTAL SOILS.
       6. GLIOCLADIUM ROSEUM. TRANS.BR.MYCOL.SOC. 48, 279-286.

4658   PUGH, G.J.F. & EMDEN, J.H.VAN (1969) - CELLULOSE-DECOMPOSING FUNGI IN POL-
       DER SOILS AND THEIR POSSIBLE INFLUENCE ON PATHOGENIC FUNGI. NETH.J.PL.
       PATH. 75, 287-295.

4659   PUGH, G.J.F. & EVANS, M.D. (1970) - KERATINOPHILIC FUNGI ASSOCIATED WITH
       BIRDS. 1. FUNGI ISOLATED FROM FEATHERS, NESTS AND SOILS. TRANS.BR.MY-
       COL.SOC. 54, 233-240.

4660   PUGH, G.J.F. & EVANS, M.D. (1970) - KERATINOPHILIC FUNGI ASSOCIATED WITH
       BIRDS. 2. PHYSIOLOGICAL STUDIES. TRANS.BR.MYCOL.SOC. 54, 241-250.

4661   PUGH, G.J.F. & HUGHES, G.C. (1975) - EPISTOLAE MYCOLOGICAE. 5. KERATINO-
       PHILIC FUNGI FROM BRITISH COLUMBIA COASTAL HABITATS. SYESIS 8, 297-300.

4662   PUGH, G.J.F. & MATHISON, G.E. (1962) - STUDIES ON FUNGI IN COASTAL SOILS.
       3. AN ECOLOGICAL SURVEY OF KERATINOPHILIC FUNGI. TRANS.BR.MYCOL.SOC.
       45, 567-572.

4663   PUGH, G.J.F. & MULDER, J.L. (1971) - MYCOFLORA ASSOCIATED WITH TYPHA LATI-
       FOLIA. TRANS.BR.MYCOL.SOC. 57, 273-292.

4664   PUGH, G.J.F. & NICOT, J. (1964) - STUDIES ON FUNGI IN COASTAL SOILS. 5.
       DENDRYPHIELLA SALINA (SUTHERLAND) COMB.NOV. TRANS.BR.MYCOL.SOC. 47,
       263-267.

4665   PUGH, G.J.F. & WILLIAMS, G.M. (1968) - FUNGI ASSOCIATED WITH SALSOLA KALI.
       TRANS.BR.MYCOL.SOC. 51, 389-396.

4666   PUHALLA, J.E. (1973) - DIFFERENCES IN SENSITIVITY OF VERTICILLIUM SPECIES
       TO ULTRAVIOLET IRRADIATION. PHYTOPATHOLOGY 63, 1488-1492.

4667 PUHALLA, J.E. & MAYFIELD, J.E. (1974) - THE MECHANISM OF HETEROKARYOTIC GROWTH IN VERTICILLIUM DAHLIAE. GENETICS 76, 411-422.

4668 PUNITHALINGAM, E. (1972) - CYTOLOGY OF FUSARIUM CULMORUM. TRANS.BR.MYCOL. SOC. 58, 225-230.

4669 PUNITHALINGAM, E. (1975) - CYTOLOGY OF SOME FUSARIUM SPECIES. NOVA HEDWIGIA 26, 275-304.

4670 PURCHASE, I.F.H. (1971) - THE ACUTE TOXICITY OF THE MYCOTOXIN CYCLOPIAZONIC ACID TO RATS. TOXIC.APPL.PHARMACOL. 18, 114-123.

4671 PURCHASE, I.F.H. (1974) - MYCOTOXINS. ELSEVIER SCIENT.PUBL.COMP., AMSTERDAM, OXFORD, NEW YORK, 443 PP.

4672 PURDY, L.H. (1955) - A BROADER CONCEPT OF THE SPECIES SCLEROTINIA SCLEROTIORUM, BASED ON VARIABILITY. PHYTOPATHOLOGY 45, 421-427.

4673 PURDY, L.H. (1956) - FACTORS AFFECTING APOTHECIAL PRODUCTION BY SCLEROTINIA SCLEROTIORUM. PHYTOPATHOLOGY 46, 409-410.

4674 PURDY, L.H. & GROGAN, R.C. (1954) - PHYSIOLOGICAL STUDIES OF SCLEROTINIA SCLEROTIORUM IN LIQUID AND AGAR CULTURE. PHYTOPATHOLOGY 44, 36-38.

4675 PURKAYASTHA, R.P. & SEN GUPTA, M. (1975) - STUDIES ON COLLETOTRICHUM GLOEOSPORIOIDES INCITING ANTHRACNOSE OF JUTE. INDIAN PHYTOPATH. 28, 454-458.

4676 PUSEY, D.F.G. & ROBERTS, J.C. (1963) - STUDIES IN MYCOLOGICAL CHEMISTRY. 13. AVERUFIN, A RED PIGMENT FROM ASPERGILLUS VERSICOLOR. J.CHEM.SOC., 1963, 3542-3547.

4677 PUSHKINSKAYA, O.I. (1972) - MICROFLORA OF SOLONETZ SOILS. IN: MICROFLORA OF SOILS IN THE NORTHERN AND CENTRAL USSR.; MISHUSTIN, E.N. (ED.), ISRAEL PROGR. SCIENT.TRANSL., JERUSALEM, 355-414.

4678 PYKE, T.R. (1962) - STUDIES ON THE CELLULAR COMPOSITION AND GERMINATION OF MICROSCLEROTIA OF VERTICILLIUM ALBO-ATRUM R. & B. DISS.ABSTR. 22, 38.

4679 PYKE, T.R. & DIETZ, A. (1966) - U-21,963, A NEW ANTIBIOTIC. 1. DISCOVERY AND BIOLOGICAL ACTIVITY. APPL.MICROBIOL. 14, 506-510.

4681 QUINN, R.M. & STROBEL, G.A. (1971) - ALPHA-KETOBUTYRATE DECARBOXYLASE ACTIVITY IN RHIZOCTONIA SOLANI. CAN.J.BOT. 49, 1059-1065.

4682 QURESHI, A.A. & PAGE, O.T. (1970) - OBSERVATIONS ON CHLAMYDOSPORE PRODUCTION BY FUSARIUM IN A TWO-SALT SOLUTION. CAN.J.MICROBIOL. 16, 29-32.

4683 QURESHI, A.A. & PAGE, O.T. (1972) - OBSERVATIONS ON MORPHOLOGICAL AND NUTRITIONAL ASPECTS OF PERITHECIAL FORMATION OF NECTRIA HAEMATOCOCCA AND HYPOMYCES SOLANI. CAN.J.BOT. 50, 2443-2448.

4684 RAADE, P.E. (1971) - CARBOHYDRATE UPTAKE AND METABOLISM OF OPHIOBOLUS GRAMINIS. PHYSIOLOGIA PL. 24, 209-213.

4685 RABACHE, M., NEUMANN, J. & LAVOLLAY, J. (1974) - PHENYLPOLYENES D'ASPERGILLUS NIGER. STRUCTURE ET PROPRIETES DE L'ASPERRUBROL. PHYTOCHEMISTRY 13, 637-642.

4686 RABIE, C.J., DEKLERK, W.A. & TERBLANCHE, M. (1964) - TOXICITY OF ASPERGILLUS AMSTELODAMI TO POULTRY AND RABBITS. S.AFR.J.AGRIC.SCI. 7, 341-346.

4687 RABIE, C.J., LUEBBEN, A. & STEYN, M. (1976) - PRODUCTION OF STERIGMATOCYS-
      TIN BY ASPERGILLUS VERSICOLOR AND BIPOLARIS SOROKINIANA ON SEMISYNTHET-
      IC LIQUID AND SOLID MEDIA. APPL.ENVIRONM.MICROBIOL. 32, 206-208.

4688 RABINOVICH, Z.D. (1956) - (SAPROPHYTIC AND PATHOGENIC FUNGAL MICROFLORA OF
      JUTE IN SOUTHERN UKRAINE). MIKROBIOLOGIYA 217-220.

4689 RADHA, K. & MENON, K.P.V. (1957) - THE GENUS RHIZOCTONIA IN RELATION TO
      SOIL MOISTURE. 1. STUDIES ON RHIZOCTONIA SOLANI AND RHIZOCTONIA BATATI-
      COLA. INDIAN COCON.J. 10, 29-36.

4690 RAGHEB, H.S. & FABIAN, F.W. (1955) - GROWTH AND PECTOLYTIC ACTIVITY OF
      SOME TOMATO MOLDS AT DIFFERENT PH LEVELS. FD RES. 20, 614-625.

4691 RAGHUVEER RAO, P. & DEV RAO (1964) - THE GENUS PERICONIA FROM INDIA. MY-
      COPATH.MYCOL.APPL. 22, 285-310.

4692 RAGOT, J. (1966) - (KERATINOLYTIC ACTION OF KERATINOMYCETES AJELLOI ON
      NON-DENATURED WOOL). C.R.HEBD.SEANC.ACAD.SCI., PARIS, SER.D, 262,
      412-415.

4693 RAGOT, J. (1966) - ACTIVITE PROTEOLYTIQUE DU KERATINOMYCÈS AJELLOI. C.R.
      HEBD.SEANC.ACAD.SCI., PARIS, SER.D, 263, 1895-1898.

4694 RAGOT, J. (1966) - ETUDE QUALITATIVE ET QUANTITATIVE DES EXIGENCES CAR-
      BONEES DU KERATINOMYCES AJELLOI. C.R.HEBD.SEANC.ACAD.SCI., PARIS, SER.
      D, 263, 1073-1076.

4695 RAGOT, J. (1966) - (INFLUENCE OF NITROGEN SOURCE ON GROWTH, SPORULATION,
      AND MORPHOLOGY OF KERATINOMYCES AJELLOI). C.R.SOC.BIOL.TOULOUSE 160,
      682-686.

4696 RAHMAN, R., TAYLOR, A., DAS, B.C. & VERPOORTE, J.A. (1976) - A NEW DEPSI-
      PEPTIDE FROM PITHOMYCES CHARTARUM. CAN.J.CHEM. 54, 1360-1364.

4697 RAI, J.N. & AGARWAL, S.C. (1974) - INCREASED OSMOTIC TOLERANCE OF SOME
      ASPERGILLI ISOLATED FROM USAR (ALKALINE) SOILS. A POSSIBLE INDICATION
      OF ECOLOGICAL SPECIALIZATION. MYCOPATH.MYCOL.APPL. 52, 299-305.

4698 RAI, J.N., AGARWAL, S.C. & TEWARI, J.P. (1971) - FUNGAL MICROFLORA OF
      "USAR" SOILS OF INDIA. J.INDIAN BOT.SOC. 50, 63-74.

4699 RAI, J.N. & SAXENA, V.C. (1975) - SCLEROTIAL MYCOFLORA AND ITS ROLE IN
      NATURAL BIOLOGICAL CONTROL OF WHITE-ROT DISEASE. PL.SOIL 43, 509-513.

4700 RAI, J.N., TEWARI, J.P. & MUKERJI, K.G. (1969) - MYCOFLORA OF MANGROVE MUD.
      MYCOPATH.MYCOL.APPL. 38, 17-31.

4701 RAI, J.N., TEWARI, J.P. & SINHA, A.K. (1967) - EFFECT OF ENVIRONMENTAL CON-
      DITIONS ON SCLEROTIA AND CLEISTOTHECIA PRODUCTION IN ASPERGILLUS. MYCO-
      PATH.MYCOL.APPL. 31, 209-224.

4702 RAI, R.A. & AGNIHOTRI, J.P. (1971) - INFLUENCE OF NUTRITION AND PH ON
      GROWTH AND SCLEROTIA FORMATION OF SCLEROTINIA SCLEROTIORUM (LIB.) DE
      BARY FROM GAILLARDIA PULCHELLA FOUGH. MYCOPATH.MYCOL.APPL. 43, 89-95.

4703 RAILLO, A. (1929) - BEITRAEGE ZUR KENNTNIS DER BODENPILZE. ZENTBL.BAKT.
      PARASITKDE, ABT.2, 78, 515-524.

4704 RAISTRICK, H. & RUDMAN, P. (1956) - STUDIES IN THE BIOCHEMISTRY OF MICRO-
      ORGANISMS. 97. FLAVIPIN, A CRYSTALLINE METABOLITE OF ASPERGILLUS FLAVI-
      PES (BAINIER & SARTORY) THOM & CHURCH AND ASPERGILLUS TERREUS THOM.
      BIOCHEM.J. 63, 395-406.

4705 RAISTRICK, H. & SMITH, G. (1935) - STUDIES IN THE BIOCHEMISTRY OF MICRO-
     ORGANISMS. 62. THE METABOLIC PRODUCTS OF ASPERGILLUS TERREUS THOM. A
     NEW MOULD METABOLIC PRODUCT "TERREIN". BIOCHEM.J. 29, 606-611.

4706 RAISTRICK, H., STICKINGS, C.E. & THOMAS, R. (1953) - STUDIES IN THE BIO-
     CHEMISTRY OF MICRO-ORGANISMS. 90. ALTERNARIOL AND ALTERNARIOL MONOME-
     THYL ETHER, METABOLIC PRODUCTS OF ALTERNARIA TENUIS. BIOCHEM.J. 55, 421-
     433.

4707 RAISTRICK, H. & STOESSL, A. (1958) - STUDIES IN THE BIOCHEMISTRY OF MICRO-
     ORGANISMS. 104. METABOLITES OF PENICILLIUM ATROVENETUM. BETA-NITROPRO-
     PIONIC ACID, A MAJOR METABOLITE. BIOCHEM.J. 68, 647-653.

4708 RAIZADA, B.B.S. (1962) - TAXONOMIC STUDIES ON SOME MEMBERS OF THE MUCORA-
     LES. NOVA HEDWIGIA 4, 421-432.

4709 RAJAN, K.M. & SINGH, R.S. (1973) - SOIL PHYSICAL FACTORS AND THE POPULA-
     TION OF PYTHIUM APHANIDERMATUM. INDIAN J.MYCOL.PL.PATH. 3, 44-49.

4710 RAJAN, K.M. & SINGH, R.S. (1974) - EFFECT OF FERTILIZERS ON POPULATION OF
     PYTHIUM APHANIDERMATUM, ASSOCIATED SOIL MICROFLORA AND SEEDLING STAND
     OF TOMATO. INDIAN PHYTOPATH. 27, 62-69.

4711 RALL, G. (1965) - SOIL FUNGI FROM THE ALPINE ZONE OF THE MEDICINE BOW MOUN-
     TAINS, WYOMING. MYCOLOGIA 57, 872-881.

4712 RAM, C.S.V. (1952) - SOIL BACTERIA AND CHLAMYDOSPORE FORMATION IN FUSARIUM
     SOLANI. NATURE, LOND. 170, 889.

4713 RAMACHANDRAN, K. & RADHA, V. (1955) - KETO-ACID FORMATION IN MOULD CUL-
     TURES. CURR.SCI. 24, 50.

4714 RAMACHANDRAN, K. & WALKER, T.K. (1951) - A BIOSYNTHESIS OF DIMETHYLPYRUVIC
     ACID. ARCHS BIOCHEM.BIOPHYS. 31, 224-233.

4715 RAMA RAJE URS, N.V. & GOVINDU, H.C. (1971) - METARRHIZIUM ANISOPLIAE
     METCHNIKOFF) SOROKIN, AND ITS HOST RANGE. MYCOPATH.MYCOL.APPL. 44, 317-
     320.

4716 RAMA RAO, P. (1970) - STUDIES ON SOIL FUNGI. 3. SEASONAL VARIATION AND
     DISTRIBUTION OF MICROFUNGI IN SOME SOILS OF ANDHRA PRADESH (INDIA).
     MYCOPATH.MYCOL.APPL. 40, 277-298.

4717 RAMANARAYANAN, M. & VAIDYANATHAN, C.S. (1973) - MANDELATE OXIDASE OF ASPER-
     GILLUS NIGER. 1. PROPERTIES OF PARTICULATE D(-)-MANDELATE OXIDASE. IN-
     DIAN J.BIOCHEM.BIOPHYS. 10, 254-256.

4718 RAMBELLI, A. & BARTOLI, A. (1972) - RECHERCHES SUR LA MICROFLORE FONGIQUE
     DES SOLS DE LAMTO (COTE D'IVOIRE). REVUE ECOL.BIOL.SOL 9, 41-54.

4719 RAMBELLI, A., PUPPI, G., BARTOLI, A. & ALBONETTI, S.G. (1973) - DEUXIEME
     CONTRIBUTION A LA CONNAISSANCE DE LA MICROFLORE FONGIQUE DANS LES SOLS
     DE LAMTO EN COTE D'IVOIRE. REVUE ECOL.BIOL.SOL 10, 13-18.

4720 RAMBO, G.W. & BEAN, G.A. (1974) - STEROLS AND FATTY ACIDS OF AFLATOXIN AND
     NON-AFLATOXIN PRODUCING ISOLATES OF ASPERGILLUS. PHYTOCHEMISTRY 13,
     195-198.

4721 RAMOS, S. & GARCIA ACHA, I. (1975) - A VEGETATIVE CYCLE OF PULLULARIA PUL-
     LULANS. TRANS.BR.MYCOL.SOC. 64, 129-135.

4722 RAMOS, S., GARCIA ACHA, I. & PEBERDY, J.F. (1975) - WALL STRUCTURE AND THE BUDDING PROCESS IN PULLULARIA PULLULANS. TRANS.BR.MYCOL.SOC. 64, 283-288.

4723 RAMSEY, G.B. (1925) - SCLEROTINIA SPECIES CAUSING DECAY OF VEGETABLE UNDER TRANSIT AND MARKET CONDITIONS. J.AGRIC.RES. 31, 597-632.

4724 RANDS, R.D. (1922) - STREEPKANKER VAN KANEEL, VEROORZAAKT DOOR PHYTOPHTHORA CINNAMOMI N.SP. MEDED.INST.PLZIEKT., BATAVIA 54, 1-53.

4725 RANGA RAO, V. (1971) - SEXUAL REPRODUCTION IN TWO SPECIES OF CHAETOMIUM. CURR.SCI. 40, 357-359.

4726 RANGA RAO, V. (1972) - STUDIES ON FUNGI IN THE ROOT ZONE OF FOUR CULTIVATED PLANTS. TRANS.MYCOL.SOC.JAPAN 13, 34-48.

4727 RANGA RAO, V. & MUKERJI, K.G. (1971) - FUNGI IN THE ROOT ZONE OF 4 CULTIVARS OF WHEAT. ANNLS INST.PASTEUR, PARIS 121, 533-544.

4728 RANGA RAO, V. & MUKERJI, K.G. (1972) - NUCLEAR BEHAVIOUR DURING THE DEVELOPMENT OF ASCUS IN CHAETOMIUM BOSTRYCHODES. TRANS.MYCOL.SOC.JAPAN 13, 105-112.

4729 RANGASWAMI, G. (1961) - PYTHIACEOUS FUNGI (A REVIEW). INDIAN COUNC.AGRIC. RES., NEW DELHI, 276 PP.

4730 RANGASWAMI, G. & CHANDRASEKARAN, A. (1963) - CELLULOLYTIC PROPERTIES OF FOUR SPECIES OF SOIL FUNGI. INDIAN J.MICROBIOL. 3, 35-40.

4731 RANGASWAMI, G. & ETHIRAJ, S. (1963) - STUDIES ON THE SURVIVAL OF PLANT PATHOGENS ADDED TO THE SOIL. 2. HELMINTHOSPORIUM SACCHARI, H. SATIVUM, AND H. TURCICUM. INDIAN PHYTOPATH. 16, 10-14.

4732 RANZONI, F.V. (1953) - THE AQUATIC HYPHOMYCETES OF CALIFORNIA. FARLOWIA 4, 353-398.

4733 RANZONI, F.V. (1968) - FUNGI ISOLATED IN CULTURE FROM SOILS OF THE SONORAN DESERT. MYCOLOGIA 60, 356-371.

4734 RAO, A.S. (1959) - A COMPARATIVE STUDY OF COMPETITIVE SAPROPHYTIC ABILITY IN TWELVE ROOT-INFECTING FUNGI BY AN AGAR PLATE METHOD. TRANS.BR.MYCOL. SOC. 42, 97-111.

4735 RAO, A.S. (1962) - FUNGAL POPULATION IN THE RHIZOSPHERE OF PEANUT (ARACHIS HYPOGAEA). PL.SOIL 17, 260-266.

4736 RAO, A.S. (1965) - FUNGAL FLORA OF TWO SOILS AT TIRUPATI. CURR.SCI. 34, 489-490.

4737 RAO, A.S. & RAYUDU, G.V.N. (1964) - NITROGEN NUTRITION OF RHIZOCTONIA SOLANI IN RELATION TO ITS OCCURRENCE ON ROOT SURFACES. CURR.SCI. 33, 186-187.

4738 RAO, A.V. & SETHUNATHAN, N. (1974) - DEGRADATION OF PARATHION BY PENICILLIUM WAKSMANI ZALESKI ISOLATED FROM FLOODED ACID SULPHATE SOIL. ARCH. MICROBIOL. 97, 203-208.

4739 RAO, P.L.N. & VENKATARAMAN, R. (1952) - NITROGEN METABOLISM OF PENICILLIUM CHRYSOGENUM - Q 176. EXPERIENTIA 8, 350-353.

4740 RAO, P.V. & SINGHAL, G.S. (1978) - CHARACTERIZATION OF LIGHT DEPENDENT,
      SYNCHRONOUS PYCNIDIAL PRODUCTION IN BOTRYODIPLODIA THEOBROMAE. TRANS.
      BR.MYCOL.SOC. 70, 121-129.

4741 RAO, V. & HOOG, G.S.DE (1975) - SOME NOTES ON TORULA. PERSOONIA 8, 199-206.

4742 RAO, V.G. (1969) - THE GENUS ALTERNARIA FROM INDIA. NOVA HEDWIGIA 17, 219-
      258.

4743 RAPER, K.B. & FENNELL, D.I. (1953) - HETEROCARYOSIS IN ASPERGILLUS. J.ELI-
      SHA MITCHELL SCIENT.SOC. 69, 1-29.

4744 RAPER, K.B. & FENNELL, D.I. (1965) - THE GENUS ASPERGILLUS. WILLIAMS &
      WILKINS CO., BALTIMORE.

4745 RAPER, K.B. & THOM, CH. (1948) - A MANUAL OF THE PENICILLIA. WILLIAMS &
      WILKINS CO., BALTIMORE. REPRINT HAFNER, NEW YORK, 1968.

4746 RASHBA, E.Y. & VARBANETS, L.D. (1970) - (SPLITTING OF SOME POLYSACCHARIDES
      BY DIFFERENT SPECIES OF FUSARIUM). MYKROBIOL.ZH. 32 (3), 392-394.

4747 RATHAIAH, Y. & PAVGI, M.S. (1973) - FUSARIUM SEMITECTUM MYCOPARASITIC ON
      CERCOSPORAE. PHYTOPATH.Z. 77, 278-281.

4748 RATTAN, P.S. (1974) - DECOMPOSITION OF CELLULOSE BY THREE PEA PATHOGENS IN
      PURE CULTURE. TRANS.BR.MYCOL.SOC. 62, 113-117.

4749 RATTIGAN, A. & AYRES, P.G. (1975) - GROWTH OF FIVE PHYTOPATHOGENIC FUNGI IN
      LIQUID MEDIA CONTAINING A URONIC ACID AS THE SOLE CARBOHYDRATE. TRANS.
      BR.MYCOL.SOC. 65, 315-317.

4750 RAU, W. (1967) - UNTERSUCHUNGEN UEBER DIE LICHTABHAENGIGE CAROTINOIDSYNTHE-
      SE. 1. DAS WIRKUNGSSPEKTRUM VON FUSARIUM AQUAEDUCTUUM. PLANTA 72, 14-28.

4751 RAU, W. & ZEHENDER, C. (1959) - DIE CAROTENOIDE VON FUSARIUM AQUAEDUCTUUM
      LAGH. ARCH.MIKROBIOL. 32, 423-428.

4752 RAVISE, A. & BOCCAS, B. (1969) - PREMIERE LISTE ANNOTEE DES PYTHIACEES PARA-
      SITES DES PLANTES CULTIVEES AU CONGO. CAH.MABOKE 7, 41-69.

4753 RAWLINGS, R.E. (1940) - OBSERVATIONS ON THE CULTURAL AND PATHOGENIC HABITS
      OF THIELAVIOPSIS BASICOLA (BERK. & BR.) FERRARIS. ANN.MO.BOT.GDN 27,
      561-598.

4754 RAWLINSON, C.J. & COLHOUN, J. (1969) - THE OCCURRENCE OF FUSARIUM NIVALE IN
      SOIL. PL.PATH. 18, 41-45.

4755 RAWLINSON, C.J., HORNBY, D., PEARSON, V. & CARPENTER, J.M. (1973) - VIRUS-
      LIKE PARTICLES IN THE TAKE-ALL FUNGUS, GAEUMANNOMYCES GRAMINIS. ANN.
      APPL.BIOL. 74, 197-209.

4756 RAYMOND, F.L., ETCHELLS, J.L., BELL, T.A. & MASLEY, P.M. (1959) - FILAMEN-
      TOUS FUNGI FROM BLOSSOMS, OVARIES, AND FRUIT OF PICKLING CUCUMBERS. MY-
      COLOGIA 51, 492-511.

4757 RAYNER, A.D.M. (1977) - FUNGAL COLONIZATION OF HARDWOOD STUMPS FROM NATURAL
      SOURCES. 1. NON-BASIDIOMYCETES. TRANS.BR.MYCOL.SOC. 69, 291-302.

4758 RAYSS, T. (1950) - NOUVELLE CONTRIBUTION A L'ETUDE DE LA MYCOFLORE DE PA-
      LESTINE. 5. PALEST.J.BOT. 5, 17-27.

4759 RAYSS, T. & BORUT, S. (1958) - CONTRIBUTION TO THE KNOWLEDGE OF SOIL FUNGI
      IN ISRAEL. MYCOPATH.MYCOL.APPL. 10, 142-174.

4760   REBER, H. (1967) - VERGLEICHENDE UNTERSUCHUNGEN ZUR TOXIZITAET UND SELEK-
       TIVITAET VON ENTSEUCHUNGSMITTELN FUER BODENORGANISMEN. Z.PFLKRANKH.
       PFLSCHUTZ 74, 414-426.

4761   REDAELLI, P. & CIFERRI, R. (1934) - STUDIO COMPARATIVO DI VENTUN CEPPI DI
       SPORENDONEMA EPIZOUM. ATTI IST.BOT.UNIV.LAB.CRITTOGAM.PAVIA, SER.4, 5,
       145-198.

4762   REDCHITS, T.I. (1972) - (RIBOFLAVIN FORMATION BY FUNGI OF THE GENUS ASPER-
       GILLUS GROWN ON MEDIA WITH HYDROCARBONS). MYKROBIOL.ZH. 34, 729-733.

4763   REDDY, B.D., KELLEY, D.C., MINOCHA, H.C. & ANTHONY, H.D. (1974) - PATHO-
       GENICITY OF ALTERNARIA ALTERNATA AND ITS ANTIBODY PRODUCTION IN EXPERI-
       MENTAL ANIMALS. MYCOPATH.MYCOL.APPL. 54, 385-390.

4764   REDDY, M.N. & RAO, A.S. (1975) - AMINO ACIDS IN MYCELIUM AND CULTURE FIL-
       TRATES OF RHIZOCTONIA SOLANI. TRANS.BR.MYCOL.SOC. 64, 527-528.

4765   REDDY, M.N. & RAO, A.S. (1975) - PHENOLICS ASSOCIATED WITH RHIZOCTONIA SO-
       LANI DURING PATHOGENESIS. PHYTOPATH.Z. 83, 103-109.

4766   REDDY, M.N., RAO, A.S. & RAO, K.N. (1975) - PRODUCTION OF PHENOLIC COM-
       POUNDS BY RHIZOCTONIA SOLANI. TRANS.BR.MYCOL.SOC. 64, 146-148.

4767   REDDY, M.N. & STAHMANN, M.A. (1972) - ISOZYME PATTERNS OF FUSARIUM SPECIES
       AND THEIR SIGNIFICANCE IN TAXONOMY. PHYTOPATH.Z. 74, 115-125.

4768   REDDY, S.M. (1969) - UTILIZATION OF MONOSACCHARIDES BY FIVE SPECIES OF
       HELMINTHOSPORIUM. PATH.MICROBIOL. 33, 185-190.

4769   REDHEAD, S.A. & MALLOCH, D.W. (1977) - THE ENDOMYCETACEAE - NEW CONCEPTS,
       NEW TAXA. CAN.J.BOT. 55, 1701-1711.

4770   REDMOND, D.R. & CUTTER, V.M. (1951) - AN EXAMPLE OF SYNERGISTIC GROWTH IN-
       HIBITION BETWEEN ROOT-INHABITING FUNGI. MYCOLOGIA 43, 723-726.

4771   REEN, L. (1971) - VIRULENCE OF PYTHIUM SPP. ON POTATO TUBER AND THEIR CA-
       PACITY TO PRODUCE PECTIC ENZYMES. INDIAN PHYTOPATH. 24, 88-100.

4772   REES, R.G. (1967) - KERATINOPHILIC FUNGI FROM QUEENSLAND. 2. ISOLATION
       FROM FEATHERS OF WILD BIRDS. SABOURAUDIA 6, 14-18.

4773   REES, R.G. (1967) - KERATINOPHILIC FUNGI FROM QUEENSLAND. 3. ISOLATION
       FROM FEATHERS OF DOMESTIC FOWLS. SABOURAUDIA 6, 19-28.

4774   REESE, E.T., CLAPP, R.C. & MANDELS, M. (1958) - A THIOGLUCOSIDASE IN FUN-
       GI. ARCHS BIOCHEM.BIOPHYS. 75, 228-242.

4775   REESE, E.T. & DOWNING, M.H. (1951) - ACTIVITY OF THE ASPERGILLI ON CELLU-
       LOSE, CELLULOSE DERIVATIVES, AND WOOL. MYCOLOGIA 43, 16-28.

4776   REESE, E.T. & MAGUIRE, A. (1971) - AUREOBASIDIUM PULLULANS AS A SOURCE OF
       SUCRASE. CAN.J.MICROBIOL. 17, 329-332.

4777   REESE, E.T., MAGUIRE, A, & PARRISH, F.W. (1973) - PRODUCTION OF BETA-XYLO-
       PYRANOSIDASES BY FUNGI. CAN.J.MICROBIOL. 19, 1065-1074.

4778   REESE, E.T. & MANDELS, M. (1959) - BETA-D-1,3-GLUCANASES IN FUNGI. CAN.J.
       MICROBIOL. 5, 173-185.

4779 REESE, E.T. & LEVINSON, H.S. (1952) - A COMPARATIVE STUDY OF THE BREAKDOWN OF CELLULOSE BY MICROORGANISMS. PHYSIOLOGIA PL. 5, 345-366.

4780 REESE, E.T., PARRISH, F.W. & MANDELS, M. (1961) - BETA-D-1,2-GLUCANASES IN FUNGI. CAN.J.MICROBIOL. 7, 309-317.

4781 REESE, E.T. & SHIBATA, Y. (1965) - BETA-MANNANASES OF FUNGI. CAN.J.MICRO-BIOL. 11, 167-183.

4782 REEVES, F. (1969) - ASCOSPOROGENESIS IN NEOCOSMOSPORA VASINFECTA. ABS.11TH INT.BOT.CONGR., SEATTLE, 178.

4783 REEVES, F.B. (1971) - THE STRUCTURE OF THE ASCUS APEX IN SORDARIA FIMICOLA. MYCOLOGIA 63, 204-212.

4784 REEVES, F.B. & HORN, C. (1976) - TRICHODERMA IN COLORADO. MYCOTAXON 3, 337-344.

4785 REEVES, R.J. (1975) - BEHAVIOUR OF PHYTOPHTHORA CINNAMOMI RANDS IN DIFFER-ENT SOILS AND WATER REGIMES. SOIL BIOL.BIOCHEM. 7, 19-24.

4786 REEVES, R.J. & JACKSON, R.M. (1972) - INDUCTION OF PHYTOPHTHORA CINNAMOMI OOSPORES IN SOIL BY TRICHODERMA VIRIDE. TRANS.BR.MYCOL.SOC. 59, 156-159.

4787 REEVES, R.J. & JACKSON, R.M. (1974) - STIMULATION OF SEXUAL REPRODUCTION IN PHYTOPHTHORA BY DAMAGE. J.GEN.MICROBIOL. 84, 303-310.

4788 REHM, H.J. & REHM, U. (1953) - UNTERSUCHUNGEN UEBER DIE BODENMIKROFLORA VON GATERSLEBEN UND UMGEBUNG (MITTELDEUTSCHES LOESSGEBIET). 1. KULTUR-PFLANZE 1, 111-121.

4789 REHM, H.-J. & SCHMIDT, I. (1970) - MYKOTOXINE IN LEBENSMITTELN. 3. BILDUNG VON OCHRATOXINEN IN VERSCHIEDENEN LEBENSMITTELN. ZENTBL.BAKT.PARASITKDE, ABT.2, 124, 364-368.

4790 REICHLE, R.E., SNYDER, W.C. & MATUO, T. (1964) - HYPOMYCES STATE OF FUSA-RIUM SOLANI F. PISI. NATURE, LOND. 203, 664-665.

4791 REINECKE, P. (1977) - UNTERSUCHUNGEN ZUM ERREGERSPEKTRUM DES FUSSKRANKHEITS-KOMPLEXES AN GETREIDE UNTER BESONDERER BERUECKSICHTIGUNG VON RHIZOCTO-NIA SOLANI. DISS.UNIV.GOETTINGEN.

4792 REINHARDT, D.J., HACKNEY, D. & MOSS, C.W. (1972) - USE OF GAS LIQUID CHRO-MATOGRAPHY FOR THE DIFFERENTIATION OF SPECIES OF GEOTRICHUM AND TRICHO-SPORON. BULL.GA.ACAD.SCI. 30, 57 (ABS.).

4793 REINKING, O.A. (1936) - CYLINDROCARPON ISOLATIONS FROM TROPICAL SOILS. ZENTBL.BAKT.PARASITKDE, ABT.2, 94, 137-142.

4794 REINKING, O.A. & MANNS, M.M. (1933) - PARASITIC AND OTHER FUSARIA COUNTED IN TROPICAL SOILS. Z.PARASITKDE 6, 23-75.

4795 REINKING, O.A. & MANNS, M.M. (1934) - PARASITIC AND OTHER FUSARIA COUNTED IN COLOMBIA SOILS. ZENTBL.BAKT.PARASITKDE, ABT.2, 89, 502-519.

4796 REINKING, O.A. & WOLLENWEBER, H.W. (1927) - TROPICAL FUSARIA. PHILIPP.J. SCI. 32, 103-253.

4797 REINMUTH, E. & SEIDEL, D. (1961) - DER EINFLUSS ORGANISCHER DUENGUNG AUF DEN BEFALL VON KEIMPFLANZEN DURCH PYTHIUM DEBARYANUM UND RHIZOCTONIA SOLANI. NATURWISSENSCHAFTEN 48, 227.

4798   REISINGER, O. (1968) - REMARQUES SUR LES GENRES DENDRYPHIELLA ET DENDRY-
        PHION. BULL.TRIMEST.SOC.MYCOL.FR. 84, 27-51.

4799   REISINGER, O. (1970) - ETUDE AUX MICROSCOPES ELECTRONIQUES A BALAYAGE ET A
        TRANSMISSION DE LA PAROI SPORALE ET DE SON ROLE DANS LA DISPERSION AC-
        TIVE DES CONIDIES CHEZ HELMINTHOSPORIUM SPICIFERUM. C.R.HEBD.SEANC.ACAD.
        SCI., PARIS, SER.D, 270, 3031-3032.

4800   REISINGER, O. (1972) - CONTRIBUTION A L'ETUDE ULTRASTRUCTURALE DE L'APPA-
        REIL SPORIFERE CHEZ QUELQUES HYPHOMYCETES A PAROI MELANISEE. GENESE, MO-
        DIFICATION ET DECOMPOSITION. DISS.UNIV.NANCY.

4801   REISINGER, O. & KILBERTUS, G. (1973) - BIODEGRADATION AND HUMIFICATION. 3.
        RELEASE OF GRANULES, EXPERIMENTAL MODEL IN THE PRESENCE OF BACTERIA.
        SOIL BIOL.BIOCHEM. 5, 187-192.

4802   REISINGER, O. & OLAH, G.M. (1974) - ETUDE ULTRASTRUCTURALE ET CYTOCHIMIQUE
        DE LA CONIDIOGENESE CHEZ BEAUVERIA BASSIANA. CAN.J.MICROBIOL. 20, 1387-
        1392.

4803   REISS, E. & NICKERSON, W.J. (1971) - CONTROL OF DIMORPHISM IN PHIALOPHORA
        VERRUCOSA. SABOURAUDIA 12, 202-213.

4804   REISS, E. & NICKERSON, W.J. (1974) - CHARACTERIZATION OF TWO MELANINS PRO-
        DUCED BY PHIALOPHORA VERRUCOSA. SABOURAUDIA 12, 193-201.

4805   REISS, J. (1969) - UNTERSUCHUNGEN UEBER DEN EINFLUSS VON COFFEIN, COLCHI-
        CIN, ACENAPHTHEN, CUMARIN UND 8-HYDROXYCHINOLIN AUF DIE KERNE DES PIL-
        ZES THAMNIDIUM ELEGANS LINK. CYTOLOGIA 34, 449-453.

4806   REISS, J. (1971) - INHIBITION OF FUNGAL SPORULATION BY AFLATOXIN. ARCH.
        MIKROBIOL. 76, 219-222.

4807   REISS, J. (1972) - CYTOLOGIE VON THAMNIDIUM ELEGANS LINK. CYTOCHEMISCHE
        UND PHASENKONTRASTMIKROSKOPISCHE UNTERSUCHUNGEN AN HYPHEN, SPORANGIEN
        UND SPORANGIOLEN. PROTOPLASMA 74, 71-84.

4808   REISS, J. (1972) - TOXICITY OF RUBRATOXIN-B TO FUNGI. J.GEN.MICROBIOL. 71,
        167-172.

4809   REISS, J. (1973) - TOXICITY OF MOLDS TO THE LARVAE OF TENEBRIO MOLITOR.
        J.INVERTEBR.PATH. 21, 112-113.

4810   REISS, J. (1974) - CYTOCHEMICAL DETECTION OF HYDROLASES IN FUNGUS CELLS.
        3. ARYL SULFATASE. J.HISTOCHEM.CYTOCHEM. 22, 183-188.

4811   REISS, J. (1976) - CYTOLOGY OF THAMNIDIUM ELEGANS LINK. 2. DISTRIBUTION
        AND BEHAVIOUR OF NUCLEI IN HYPHAE, SPORANGIOPHORES AND SPORANGIOSPORES.
        ARCH.MICROBIOL. 108, 133-139.

4812   REISS, J. (1977) - NUCLEI IN HYPHAE AND CONIDIA OF CLADOSPORIUM HERBARUM.
        TRANS.BR.MYCOL.SOC. 68, 130-134.

4813   REMACLE, J. (1963) - CONTRIBUTIONS A LA MICROBIOLOGIE DU SOL. 1. INTRODUC-
        TION GENERALE A L'ECOLOGIE DES MICROMYCETES DU SOL. 2. TECHNIQUES D'E-
        TUDE DES CHAMPIGNONS DU SOL. LEJEUNIA 19, 1-47.

4814   REMACLE, J. (1963/64) - ETUDE COMPAREE DE LA RHIZOSPHERE DE PLANTES TY-
        PIQUES DE DIVERS GROUPES ECOLOGIQUES. DISS.UNIV.LIEGE.

4815   REMACLE, J. (1965) - POPULATION MICROMYCETIQUE DE QUELQUES TYPES FORESTIERS
        DU PLATEAU DU SORT TILMAN (LIEGE, BELGIQUE). PL.SOIL 23, 285-294.

4816   REMACLE, J. (1966) - ETUDE MICROBIOLOGIQUE ET MICROMYCETIQUE DE PLANTES
       TYPIQUES DE DIVERS GROUPES ECOLOGIQUES. BULL.SOC.R.BOT.BELG. 99, 201-
       219.

4817   REMACLE, J. (1970) - LA MICROFLORE DES LITIERES. BULL.SOC.R.BOT.BELG. 103,
       83-96.

4818   REMAUT, J.L. (1962) - PIGMENT BIOSYNTHESIS WITH ASPERGILLUS VERSICOLOR AS
       A FUNCTION OF THE CONDITIONS OF THE MEDIUM. REVUE FERMENT.IND.ALIMENT.
       17, 77-81.

4819   REMSBERG, R.E. (1940) - STUDIES IN THE GENUS TYPHULA. MYCOLOGIA 32, 52-96.

4820   RENNERFELT, E. (1949) - THE EFFECT OF SOIL ORGANISMS ON THE DEVELOPMENT OF
       POLYPORUS ANNOSUS, THE ROOT ROT FUNGUS. OIKOS 1, 65-78.

4821   RESZ, A. (1968) - UNTERSUCHUNGEN UEBER DEN MIKROORGANISMENBESATZ VON BE-
       LUEFTETEM HEU. ZENTBL.BAKT.PARASITKDE, ABT.2, 122, 597-634.

4822   REUSSER, F. (1967) - BIOSYNTHESIS OF ANTIBIOTIC U-22,324, A CYCLIC POLY-
       PEPTIDE. J.BIOL.CHEM. 242, 243-247.

4823   REYNOLDS, D.R. (1970) - FUNGI ISOLATED FROM RICE PADDY SOIL AT CENTRAL EX-
       PERIMENT STATION, U.P. COLLEGE OF AGRICULTURE. PHILIPP.AGRICST 54, 55-
       59.

4824   REYNOLDS, E.S. (1950) - PULLULARIA AS A CAUSE OF DETERIORATION OF PAINT
       AND PLASTIC SURFACES IN SOUTH FLORIDA. MYCOLOGIA 42, 432-448.

4825   REYNOLDS, H.W. & HANSON, R.G. (1957) - RHIZOCTONIA DISEASE OF COTTON IN
       PRESENCE OR ABSENCE OF THE COTTON ROOTKNOT NEMATODE IN ARIZONA. PHYTO-
       PATHOLOGY 47, 256-261.

4826   RIBEIRO, O.K., ERWIN, D.C. & ZENTMYER, G.A. (1975) - AN IMPROVED SYNTHETIC
       MEDIUM FOR OOSPORE PRODUCTION AND GERMINATION OF SEVERAL PHYTOPHTHORA
       SPECIES. MYCOLOGIA 67, 1012-1019.

4827   RIBEIRO, O.K., ZENTMYER, G.A. & ERWIN, D.C. (1975) - COMPARATIVE EFFECTS
       OF MONOCHROMATIC RADIATION ON THE GERMINATION OF OOSPORES OF THREE PHY-
       TOPHTHORA SPP. PHYTOPATHOLOGY 65, 904-907.

4828   RIBEIRO, O.K., ZENTMYER, G.A. & ERWIN, D.C. (1976) - THE INFLUENCE OF QUAL-
       ITATIVE AND QUANTITATIVE RADIATION ON REPRODUCTION AND SPORE GERMINATION
       OF FOUR PHYTOPHTHORA SPECIES. MYCOLOGIA 68, 1162-1173.

4829   RICARD, J.L. (1977) - EXPERIENCE WITH IMMUNIZING COMMENSALS. NETH.J.PL.
       PATH. 83 (SUPPL.1), 443-448.

4830   RICCIARDI, R.P., HOLLOMON, D.W. & GOTTLIEB, D. (1974) - AGE DEPENDENT
       CHANGES IN FUNGI - RIBOSOMES AND PROTEIN SYNTHESES IN RHIZOCTONIA SOLA-
       NI MYCELIUM. ARCH.MICROBIOL. 95, 325-336.

4831   RICHARD, J.L., TIFFANY, L.H. & PIER, A.C. (1969) - TOXIGENIC FUNGI ASSOCI-
       ATED WITH STORED CORN. MYCOPATH.MYCOL.APPL. 38, 313-326.

4832   RICHARDS, M., BIRD, A.E. & MUNDEN, J.E. (1969) - CHLORFLAVONIN, A NEW AN-
       TIFUNGAL ANTIBIOTIC. J.ANTIBIOT., TOKYO 22, 388-389.

4833   RICHARDS, O.W. (1949) - SOME FUNGOUS CONTAMINANTS OF OPTICAL INSTRUMENTS.
       J.BACT. 58, 453-455.

4834   RICHMOND, D.V. & FISHER, D.J. (1972) - FATTY ACIDS AND HYDROCARBONS ON THE
       SURFACE AND IN THE WALLS OF FUNGUS SPORES. J.GEN.MICROBIOL. 71, XI.

4835   RICHTER, H. & SCHNEIDER, R. (1953) - UNTERSUCHUNGEN 'ZUR MORPHOLOGISCHEN
       UND BIOLOGISCHEN DIFFERENZIERUNG VON RHIZOCTONIA SOLANI. PHYTOPATH.Z.
       20, 167-226.

4836   RIDINGS, W.H., GALLEGLY, M.E. & LILLY, V.G. (1969) - THIAMINE REQUIREMENTS
       HELPFUL IN DISTINGUISHING ISOLATES OF PYTHIUM FROM THOSE OF PHYTOPHTHO-
       RA. PHYTOPATHOLOGY 59, 737-742.

4837   RIEDHART, J.M. & PORTER, C.L. (1958) - STUDIES OF A UNIQUE PIGMENT COMPLEX
       AND A PHOTOBIOLOGICAL REACTION IN PENICILLIUM HERQUEI. MYCOLOGIA 50,
       390-402.

4838   RIEDL, H. (1968) - CLADOSPORIUM HERBARUM UND CL. MURORUM. SYDOWIA 20, 331-
       338.

4839   RIETH, A. (1957) - VORKOMMEN VON PLICARIA FULVA SCHNEIDER. KULTURPFLANZE
       5, 186-189.

4840   RIETH, H. (1971) - SELTENE DERMATOPHYTISCHE ERREGER VON NAGELMYKOSEN - TRI-
       CHOPHYTON SCHOENLEINII, TRICHOPHYTON VERRUCOSUM, MICROSPORUM CANIS UND
       MICROSPORUM GYPSEUM. MYKOSEN 14, 143-144.

4841   RIFAI, M.A. (1968) - THE HYPHOMYCETE GENUS DACTYLARIA SACC. REINWARDTIA 7,
       357-374.

4842   RIFAI, M.A. (1969) - A REVISION OF THE GENUS TRICHODERMA. MYCOL.PAP. 116,
       1-56.

4843   RIFAI, M.A. & COOKE, R.C. (1966) - STUDIES ON SOME DIDYMOSPOROUS GENERA OF
       NEMATODE-TRAPPING HYPHOMYCETES. TRANS.BR.MYCOL.SOC. 49, 147-168.

4844   RIGGENBACH, A. (1956) - UNTERSUCHUNGEN UEBER DEN ESCHENKREBS. PHYTOPATH.Z.
       27, 1-40.

4845   RIGHELATO, R.C., TRINCI, A.P.J., PIRT, S.J. & PEAT, A. (1968) - THE INFLU-
       ENCE OF MAINTENANCE ENERGY AND GROWTH RATE ON THE METABOLIC ACTIVITY,
       MORPHOLOGY AND CONIDIATION OF PENICILLIUM CHRYSOGENUM. J.GEN.MICROBIOL.
       50, 399-412.

4846   RIKER, A.E. (1968) - FOR COCCIDIOIDOMYCOSIS - A POSSIBLE SOURCE OF INFEC-
       TIOUS SPORES AND OF THERAPEUTIC AGENTS. MYCOPATH.MYCOL.APPL. 34, 155-
       160.

4847   RIPPEL, A. (1940) - UEBER DIE VERBREITUNG VON ASPERGILLUS NIGER INSBESON-
       DERE IN DEUTSCHLAND. ARCH.MIKROBIOL. 11, 1-32.

4848   RIPPEL, A. & HEILMANN, F. (1930) - QUANTITATIVE UNTERSUCHUNGEN UEBER DIE
       WIRKUNG DER KOHLENSAEURE AUF HETEROTROPHEN. ARCH.MIKROBIOL. 1, 119-136.

4849   RIPPON, J.W. & VARADI, D.P. (1968) - THE ELASTASES OF PATHOGENIC FUNGI AND
       ACTINOMYCETES. J.INVEST.DERM. 50, 54-58.

4850   RISTANOVIC, B. & MILLER, C.E. (1969) - SALINITY TOLERANCES AND ECOLOGICAL
       ASPECTS OF SOME FUNGI COLLECTED FROM FRESH WATER, ESTUARINE AND MARINE
       HABITATS. MYCOPATH.MYCOL.APPL. 37, 273-280.

4851   RISTANOVIC, M. (1971) - (A CONTRIBUTION TO THE KNOWLEDGE OF MORPHOLOGY AND
       ECOLOGY OF PHYLLOSTICTA PRUNICOLA). ZAST.BILJA 22, 185-203.

4852 RISTANOVIC, M. & RISTANOVIC, B. (1970) - (SOME BIOCHEMICAL PROPERTIES OF
      PHYLLOSTICTA PRUNICOLA). ZAST.BILJA 21, 43-50.

4853 RITTER, R. (1955) - PHYSIOLOGISCHE UNTERSUCHUNGEN AN ZYGOMYCETEN. ARCH.MI-
      KROBIOL. 22, 248-284.

4854 RIVERA, R. & CANGIR, A. (1975) - TRICHOSPORON SEPSIS AND LEUKEMIA. CANCER
      36, 1106-1110.

4855 RIZVI, S.R.H. (1966) - A STUDY OF FUNGUS FLORA OF KARACHI CANTT. SOIL.
      PAKIST.J.SCIENT.IND.RES. 9, 277-279.

4856 ROANE, C.W. & FENNE, S.B. (1955) - SOME NEW PLANT DISEASE RECORDS FOR VIR-
      GINIA. PL.DIS.REPTR 39, 695-696.

4857 ROBAK, H. (1932) - FUNGAL INFECTION IN NORVEGIAN WOOD PULP. NYT MAG.NATUR-
      VID. 71, 185-330.

4858 ROBBERS, J.E., MARCELLO, M.G., CARLTON, W.W. & TUITE, J.F. (1973) - THE
      ISOLATION AND IDENTIFICATION OF BREVIANAMIDE-A FROM CORN CULTURES OF
      PENICILLIUM VIRIDICATUM. LLOYDIA 36, 440 (ABS.).

4859 ROBBINS, W.J., HERVEY, A., DAVIDSON, R.W., MA, R. & ROBBINS, W.C. (1945) -
      A SURVEY OF SOME WOOD-DESTROYING AND OTHER FUNGI FOR ANTIBACTERIAL AC-
      TIVITY. BULL.TORREY BOT.CLUB 72, 165-190.

4860 ROBBINS, W.J. & KAVANAGH, F. (1938) - VITAMIN-B1, OR ITS INTERMEDIATES AND
      GROWTH OF CERTAIN FUNGI. AM.J.BOT. 25, 229-236.

4861 ROBBINS, W.J. & MA, R. (1941) - BIOTIN AND THE GROWTH OF FUSARIUM AVENA-
      CEUM. BULL.TORREY BOT.CLUB 68, 446-462.

4862 ROBERG, M. (1928) - UEBER DIE WIRKUNG VON EISEN, ZINK UND KUPFER AUF ASPER-
      GILLEN. ZENTBL.BAKT.PARASITKDE, ABT.2, 74, 333-371.

4863 ROBERTS, D.W. (1965) - PRODUCTION, EXTRACTION, AND ASSAY OF TOXIC SUBSTAN-
      CES FROM THE ENTOMOGENOUS FUNGUS METARRHIZIUM ANISOPLIAE. DISS.ABSTR.
      25, 3807.

4864 ROBERTS, D.W. (1966) - TOXINS FROM THE ENTOMOGENOUS FUNGUS METARRHIZIUM
      ANISOPLIAE. 1. PRODUCTION IN SUBMERGED AND SURFACE CULTURES, AND IN
      INORGANIC AND ORGANIC NITROGEN MEDIA. J.INVERTEBR.PATH. 8, 212-221.

4865 ROBERTS, D.W. (1969) - TOXINS FROM THE ENTOMOGENOUS FUNGUS METARRHIZIUM
      ANISOPLIAE - ISOLATION OF DESTRUXINS FROM SUBMERGED CULTURES. J.INVER-
      TEBR.PATH. 14, 82-88.

4866 ROBERTS, D.W. (1973) - MEANS FOR INSECT REGULATION - FUNGI. ANN.N.Y.ACAD.
      SCI. 217, 76-84.

4867 ROBERTS, J.C. & ROFFEY, P. (1965) - MYCOLOGICAL CHEMISTRY. 17. AVERYTHRIN,
      AN ANTHRAQUINONOID PIGMENT FROM ASPERGILLUS VERSICOLOR. J.CHEM.SOC.,
      1965, 3666-3672.

4868 ROBERTS, J.C., & THOMPSON, D.J. (1971) - STUDIES IN MYCOLOGICAL CHEMISTRY.
      28. ISOLATION AND STRUCTURE OF DEOXYPURPUROGENONE, A MINOR PIGMENT OF
      PENICILLIUM PURPUROGENUM. J.CHEM.SOC.PERKIN TRANS.I, 1971, 3493-3495.

4869 ROBERTS, J.C. & WARREN, C.W.H. (1955) - STUDIES IN MYCOLOGICAL CHEMISTRY.
      4. PURPUROGENONE, A METABOLIC PRODUCT OF PENICILLIUM PURPUROGENUM STOLL.
      J.CHEM.SOC., 1955, 2992-2998.

4870 ROBERTS, J.M. (1952) - ANTIBIOTIC SUBSTANCES PRODUCED BY SPECIES OF CEPHA-
      LOSPORIUM, WITH A DESCRIPTION OF A NEW SPECIES. MYCOLOGIA 44, 292-306.

4871 ROBERTSON, G.I. (1973) - OCCURRENCE OF PYTHIUM SPP. IN NEW ZEALAND SOILS,
      SANDS, PUMICES, AND PEAT, AND ON ROOTS OF CONTAINER-GROWN PLANTS. N.Z.
      JL AGRIC.RES. 16, 357-366.

4872 ROBERTSON, G.I. (1973) - PATHOGENICITY OF PYTHIUM SPECIES TO SEEDS AND
      SEEDLING ROOTS. N.Z.JL AGRIC.RES. 16, 367-372.

4873 ROBERTSON, G.I. (1975) - A PAPER DISC TECHNIQUE FOR THE RECOVERY OF PYTHI-
      UM SPECIES FROM SOIL OR WATER. N.Z.JL AGRIC.RES. 18, 409-410.

4874 ROBINOW, C.F. (1957) - THE STRUCTURE AND BEHAVIOR OF THE NUCLEI IN SPORES
      AND GROWING HYPHAE OF MUCORALES. 1. MUCOR. CAN.J.MICROBIOL. 3, 771-789.

4875 ROBINOW, C.F. & CATEN, C.E. (1969) - MITOSIS IN ASPERGILLUS NIDULANS. J.
      CELL SCI. 5, 403-431.

4876 ROBINSON, J.H., ANTHONY, C. & DRABBLE, W.T. (1973) - THE ACIDIC AMINO-ACID
      PERMEASE OF ASPERGILLUS NIDULANS. J.GEN.MICROBIOL. 79, 53-63.

4877 ROBINSON, P.M. (1973) - CHEMOTROPISM IN FUNGI. TRANS.BR.MYCOL.SOC. 61,
      303-313.

4878 ROBINSON, P.M. & GARRETT, M.K. (1969) - IDENTIFICATION OF VOLATILE SPORO-
      STATIC FACTORS FROM CULTURES OF FUSARIUM OXYSPORUM. TRANS.BR.MYCOL.SOC.
      52, 293-299.

4879 ROBINSON, P.M. & GRIFFITH, P.J. (1977) - EFFECT OF RESTRICTED AERATION ON
      CHEMOTROPISM, MORPHOGENESIS AND POLARITY OF LATERAL BRANCH INDUCTION IN
      GEOTRICHUM CANDIDUM LINK EX PERS. TRANS.BR.MYCOL.SOC. 68, 311-314.

4880 ROBINSON, P.M. & PARK, D. (1966) - CITRININ - A FUNGISTATIC ANTIBIOTIC AND
      NARROWING FACTOR. NATURE, LOND. 211, 883-884.

4881 ROBINSON, P.M. & PARK, D. (1966) - VOLATILE INHIBITORS OF SPORE GERMINA-
      TION PRODUCED BY FUNGI. TRANS.BR.MYCOL.SOC. 49, 639-649.

4882 ROBINSON, P.M., PARK, D. & GARRET, M.K. (1968) - SPOROSTATIC PRODUCTS OF
      FUNGI. TRANS.BR.MYCOL.SOC. 51, 113-124.

4883 ROBINSON, P.M., PARK, D. & GRAHAM, T.A. (1968) - AUTOTROPISM IN FUNGAL
      SPORES. J.EXP.BOT. 19, 125-134.

4884 ROBINSON, P.M. & SMITH, J.M. (1976) - MORPHOGENESIS AND GROWTH KINETICS OF
      GEOTRICHUM CANDIDUM IN CONTINUOUS CULTURE. TRANS.BR.MYCOL.SOC. 66, 413-
      420.

4885 ROBINSON, R.K. & LUCAS, R.L. (1963) - THE USE OF ISOTOPICALLY LABELLED MY-
      CELIUM TO INVESTIGATE THE HOST RANGE AND RATE OF SPREAD OF OPHIOBOLUS
      GRAMINIS. NEW PHYTOL. 62, 50-52.

4886 ROBISON, B.M. (1970) - MICROFUNGI OF SUGAR CANE ROOTS AND SOIL IN JAMAICA.
      TROP.AGRIC. 47, 23-29.

4887 RODIG, O.R., ELLIS, L.C. & GLOVER, I.T. (1966) - THE BIOSYNTHESIS OF CITRI-
      NIN IN PENICILLIUM CITRINUM. 1. PRODUCTION AND DEGRADATION OF CITRININ.
      2. TRACER STUDIES ON THE FORMATION OF CITRININ. BIOCHEMISTRY 5, 2458-
      2462.

4888 RODRICKS, J.V. & EPPLEY, R.M. (1974) - STACHYBOTRYS AND STACHYBOTRYOTOXI-
      COSIS. IN: MYCOTOXINS; PURCHASE, I.F.H. (ED.), ELSEVIER SCIENT.PUBL.CO.,
      NEW YORK, 181-197.

4889 RODRICKS, J.V., HENERY-LOGAN, K.R., CAMPBELL, A.D., STOLOFF, L. & VERRETT,
      M.J. (1968) - ISOLATION OF A NEW TOXIN FROM CULTURES OF ASPERGILLUS FLA-
      VUS. NATURE, LOND. 217, 668.

4890 RODRIGUEZ-KABANA, R. (1969) - ENZYMATIC INTERACTIONS OF SCLEROTIUM ROLFSII
      AND TRICHODERMA VIRIDE IN MIXED SOIL CULTURE. PHYTOPATHOLOGY 59, 910-
      921.

4891 RODRIGUEZ-KABANA, R., BACKMAN, P.A. & WIGGINS, E.A. (1974) - DETERMINATION
      OF SCLEROTIAL POPULATIONS OF SCLEROTIUM ROLFSII IN SOIL BY A RAPID FLO-
      TATION-SIEVING TECHNIQUE. PHYTOPATHOLOGY 64, 610-615.

4892 RODRIGUEZ-KABANA, R. & CURL, E.A. (1968) - SACCHARASE ACTIVITY OF SCLERO-
      TIUM ROLFSII IN SOIL AND THE MECHANISM OF ANTAGONISTIC ACTION BY TRI-
      CHODERMA VIRIDE. PHYTOPATHOLOGY 58, 985-992.

4893 ROEED, H. (1969) - ET BIDRAG TIL OPPKLARING AV FORHOLDET MELLOM TYPHULA
      GRAMINUM KARST. OG TYPHULA INCARNATA LASCH EX FR. FRIESIA 9, 219-225.

4894 ROESCH, R. & LIESE, W. (1971) - UNTERSUCHUNGEN UEBER DIE ENZYME VON BLAEUE-
      PILZEN. 2. PHENOLOXIDASEN-AKTIVITAET. ARCH.MIKROBIOL. 76, 212-218.

4895 ROESCH, R., LIESE, W. & BERNDT, H. (1969) - UNTERSUCHUNGEN UEBER DIE ENZY-
      ME VON BLAEUEPILZEN. 1. CELLULASE-, POLYGALAKTURONASE-, PEKTINESTERASE-
      UND LACCASE-AKTIVITAET. ARCH.MIKROBIOL. 67, 28-50.

4896 ROGERS, A.L. (1971) - ISOLATION OF KERATINOPHILIC FUNGI FROM SOIL IN THE
      VICINITY OF BOGOTA, COLOMBIA. MYCOPATH.MYCOL.APPL. 44, 261-264.

4897 ROGERS, A.L. & BENEKE, E.S. (1964) - HUMAN PATHOGENIC FUNGI RECOVERED FROM
      BRASILIAN SOIL. MYCOPATH.MYCOL.APPL. 22, 15-20.

4898 ROGERS, C.H. (1939) - THE RELATION OF MOISTURE AND TEMPERATURE TO GROWTH
      OF THE COTTON ROOT ROT FUNGUS. J.AGRIC.RES. 58, 701-709.

4899 ROGERS, D.P. (1944) - THE GENERA TRECHISPORA AND GALZINIA (THELEPHORA-
      CEAE). MYCOLOGIA 36, 70-103.

4900 ROGERSON, C.T. (1970) - THE HYPOCREALIAN FUNGI (ASCOMYCETES, HYPOCREALES).
      MYCOLOGIA 62, 865-910.

4901 ROLINSON, G.N. & LUMB, M. (1953) - THE OXIDATION OF LARD OIL BY PENICIL-
      LIUM CHRYSOGENUM. J.GEN.MICROBIOL. 9, 385-393.

4902 ROLL-HANSEN, F. (1949) - INVESTIGATION OF FUSARIUM ON CULTIVATED PLANTS IN
      NORWAY. ANNLS AGRIC.COLL.NORWAY, 1959, 257-264.

4903 ROMANELLI, R.A., HOUSTON, C.W. & BARNETT, S.M. (1975) - STUDIES ON THERMO-
      PHILIC CELLULOLYTIC FUNGI. APPL.MICROBIOL. 30, 276-281.

4904 ROMANKOVA, A.G. (1936) - UEBER PARASITISMUS DES SCHIMMELPILZES PENICILLIUM
      RUGULOSUM AUF ASPERGILLUS NIGER. C.R.ACAD.SCI.USSR 1, 137-138.

4905 RONCADORI, R.W., LEHMAN, P.S. & MCCARTER, S.M. (1974) - EFFECT OF PYTHIUM
      IRREGULARE ON COTTON GROWTH AND YIELD, AND JOINT ACTION WITH OTHER SOIL
      -BORNE PATHOGENS. PHYTOPATHOLOGY 64, 1303-1306.

4906 RONCADORI, R.W. & MCCARTER, S.M. (1972) - EFFECT OF SOIL TREATMENT, SOIL
      TEMPERATURE, AND PLANT AGE ON PYTHIUM ROOT ROT OF COTTON. PHYTOPATHOL-
      OGY 62, 373-376.

4907   ROQUEBERT, M.-F. (1974) - MODALITES DE LA SPOROGENESE CHEZ DEUX PHIALIDES.
       ASPERGILLUS TAMARII ET STILBOTHAMNIUM NUDIPES. REVUE MYCOL. 38, 3-8.

4908   ROSATI, L., DESTOMBES, P., SEGRETAIN, G., NAZIMOFF, O. & ARCOUTEIL, A.
       (1962) - SUR UN NOUVEL AGENT DE MYCETOME ISOLE EN SOMALIA. BULL.SOC.
       PATH.EXOT. 54, 1265-1271.

4909   ROSEN, D., EDELMAN, M., GALUN, E. & DANON, D. (1974) - BIOGENESIS OF MITO-
       CHONDRIA IN TRICHODERMA VIRIDE - STRUCTURAL CHANGES IN MITOCHONDRIA AND
       OTHER SPORE CONSTITUENTS DURING CONIDIUM MATURATION AND GERMINATION.
       J.GEN.MICROBIOL. 83, 31-49.

4910   ROSENBERG, J.A. (1959) - CONSIDERAZIONI INTORNO AL GENERE ACTINOMUCOR.
       ATTI IST.BOT.UNIV.LAB.CRITTOGAM.PAVIA, SER.5, 16, 295-300.

4911   ROSENBERG, S.L. (1975) - TEMPERATURE AND PH OPTIMA FOR 21 SPECIES OF THER-
       MOPHILIC AND THERMOTOLERANT FUNGI. CAN.J.MICROBIOL. 21, 1535-1540.

4912   ROSETT, T., SANKHALA, R.H., STICKINGS, C.E., TAYLOR, M.E. & THOMAS, R.
       (1957) - STUDIES IN THE BIOCHEMISTRY OF MICRO-ORGANISMS. 103. METABO-
       LITES OF ALTERNARIA TENUIS, CULTURE FILTRATE PRODUCTS. BIOCHEM.J. 67,
       390-400.

4913   ROSS, A.J. & YASUTAKE, W.T. (1973) - SCOLECOBASIDIUM HUMICOLA, A FUNGAL
       PATHOGEN OF FISH. J.FISH RES.BOARD CAN. 30, 994-995.

4914   ROSS, D.J. (1960) - PHYSIOLOGICAL STUDIES OF SOME COMMON FUNGI FROM GRASS-
       LAND SOILS. N.Z.JL SCI. 3, 219-257.

4915   ROSS, E.W. & MARX, D.H. (1972) - SUSCEPTIBILITY OF SAND PINE TO PHY-
       TOPHTHORA CINNAMOMI. PHYTOPATHOLOGY 62, 1197-1200.

4916   ROSTRUP, O. (1916) - BIDRAG TIL DANMARKS SVAMPEFLORA. 1. DANSK BOT.ARK. 2
       (5), 1-56.

4917   ROSTRUP, O. (1935) - BIDRAG TIL DANMARKS SVAMPEFLORA. 2. DANSK BOT.ARK. 8
       (8), 1-60.

4918   ROTH, F.J., ORPURT, P.A. & AHEARN, D.G. (1964) - OCCURRENCE AND DISTRIBU-
       TION OF FUNGI IN A SUBTROPICAL MARINE ENVIRONMENT. CAN.J.BOT. 42, 375-
       383.

4919   ROTH, G. (1959) - UEBER DIE MIKROFLORA DER GERSTENSAMEN UND IHRE SELEKTIVE
       BEEINFLUSSUNG DURCH BEIZUNG. MITT.BIOL.BUNDESANST.LD-U.FORSTW. 97, 203-
       211.

4920   ROTH, J.N. (1962) - VARIATION IN, AND THE EFFECTS OF VITAMINS ON VERTICIL-
       LIUM ALBO-ATRUM. DISS.ABSTR. 23, 1864-1865.

4921   ROUCH, J. & NICOT, J. (1963) - OBSERVATIONS PRELIMINAIRES SUR LA MICRO-
       FLORE FONGIQUE DE CERTAINS SOLS DE VIGNOBLES DE LA REGION TOULOUSANE.
       C.R.HEBD.SEANC.ACAD.SCI., PARIS, SER.D, 256, 4713-4716.

4922   ROUTIEN, J.B. (1967) - A NEW SPECIES OF ANIXIOPSIS. MYCOLOGIA 59, 475-481.

4923   ROUTLEY, R. & ROUTLEY, V. (1974) - NOTE ON THE RECOVERY OF PHYTOPHTHORA
       CINNAMOMI FROM THE BUDAWANG RANGES. TRANS.BR.MYCOL.SOC. 63, 413-419.

4924   ROUXEL, F. & BOUHOT, D. (1971) - RECHERCHES SUR L'ECOLOGIE DES CHAMPIGNONS
       PARASITES DANS LE SOL. 4. NOUVELLES MISES AU POINT CONCERNANT L'ANALYSE
       SELECTIVE ET QUANTITATIVE DES FUSARIUM OXYSPORUM ET FUSARIUM SOLANI
       DANS LE SOL. ANNLS PHYTOPATH. 3, 171-188.

4925 ROVIRA, A.D. & CAMPBELL, R. (1975) - A SCANNING ELECTRON MICROSCOPE STUDY OF INTERACTIONS BETWEEN MICRO-ORGANISMS AND GAEUMANNOMYCES GRAMINIS (SYN. OPHIOBOLUS GRAMINIS) ON WHEAT ROOTS. MICROBIAL ECOL. 2, 177-185.

4926 ROWLEY, B.I. & PIRT, S.J. (1972) - MELANIN PRODUCTION BY ASPERGILLUS NIDULANS IN BATCH AND CHEMOSTAT CULTURES. J.GEN.MICROBIOL. 72, 553-563.

4927 ROY, A.D. & CAMERON, H.M. (1972) - RHINOPHYCOMYCOSIS ENTOMOPHTHORAE OCCURRING IN A CHIMPANZEE IN THE WILD IN EAST AFRICA. AM.J.TROP.MED.HYG. 21, 234-237.

4928 ROY, A.K. (1966) - STUDIES ON CHAETOMIUM BOSTRYCHODES ZOPF. INDIAN PHYTOPATH. 19, 113-114.

4929 ROY, A.K. & BARUAH, P.K. (1972) - NEW RECORDS OF FUNGI CAUSING DISCOLOURATION OF RICE GRAIN. SCI.CULT. 38, 405-406.

4930 ROY, A.K. & BILGRAMI, K.K. (1977) - CHOLESTEROL SYNTHESIS IN COLLETOTRICHUM DEMATIUM. CURR.SCI. 46, 203.

4931 ROY, I. (1972) - COPROPHILIC ASCOMYCOTA FROM SCOTLAND. 2. NOVA HEDWIGIA 23, 45-47.

4932 ROY, K., GHOSH, G.R. & DUTTA, S.K. (1972) - KERATOPHILIC FUNGI AND THE PREVALENCE OF DERMATOMYCOSES IN ORISSA, INDIA. SABOURAUDIA 10, 218-229.

4933 ROY, R.Y. & DWIVEDI, R.S. (1962) - A COMPARISON OF SOIL FUNGAL FLORA OF THREE DIFFERENT GRASSLANDS. PROC.NATN.ACAD.SCI., INDIA, SECT.B, 32, 421-428.

4934 ROYLE, D.J. & HICKMANN, C.J. (1964) - OBSERVATIONS ON PHYTOPHTHORA CINNAMOMI. CAN.J.BOT. 42, 311-318.

4935 RUBIDGE, T. (1974) - A NEW SELECTIVE MEDIUM FOR THE SCREENING OF AIRCRAFT FUELS FOR BIODETERIOGENIC FUNGI. INT.BIODETERIOR.BULL. 10, 53-55.

4936 RUDICK, M.J. & ELBEIN, A.D. (1973) - GLYCOPROTEIN ENZYMES SECRETED BY ASPERGILLUS FUMIGATUS. PURIFICATION AND PROPERTIES OF BETA-GLUCOSIDASE. J.BIOL.CHEM. 248, 6506-6513.

4937 RUDICK, M.J. & ELBEIN, A.D. (1974) - GLYCOPROTEIN ENZYMES SECRETED BY ASPERGILLUS FUMIGATUS. PURIFICATION AND PROPERTIES OF ALPHA-GLUCOSIDASE. ARCHS BIOCHEM.BIOPHYS. 161, 281-290.

4938 RUDNICKI, R., BORECKA, H. & PIENIAZEK, J. (1969) - ABSCISIC ACID IN PENICILLIUM ITALICUM. PLANTA 86, 195-196.

4939 RUELIUS, H.W. & GAUHE, A. (1950) - UEBER FUSARUBIN, EINEN NAPHTHOCHINONFARBSTOFF AUS FUSARIEN. LIEBIGS ANNLN CHEM. 569, 38-59.

4940 RUEMKER, R.V. (1951) - UEBER DIE OEKOLOGIE VON ASCOCHYTA PINODELLA UND FUSARIUM CULMORUM IN DER RHIZOSPHAERE ANFAELLIGER UND NICHT ANFAELLIGER PFLANZEN. PHYTOPATH.Z. 18, 55-100.

4941 RUESCH, M.E. & STAEHELIN, H. (1965) - UEBER EINIGE BIOLOGISCHE WIRKUNGEN DES CYTOSTATICUM VERRUCARIN-A. ARZNEIMITTELFORSCHUNG 15, 893-897.

4942 RUFFIN, P., ANDRIEU, S., BISERTE, G. & BIGUET, J. (1976) - SULPHITOLYSIS IN KERATINOLYSIS. BIOCHEMICAL PROOF. SABOURAUDIA 14, 181-184.

4943 RUOKOLA, A.-L. & SALONEN, A. (1967) - ON NEMATODE-DESTROYING FUNGI IN FIN-
      LAND. J.SCIENT.AGRIC.SOC.FINL. 39, 119-130.

4944 RUPPEL, E.G. (1974) - FACTORS AFFECTING CONIDIAL DIMENSIONS OF A DRECHS-
      LERA SPECIES. MYCOLOGIA 66, 803-807.

4945 RUSAN, M. & MANOLIU, A. (1970) - CONTRIBUTIONS TO THE BIOLOGY OF THE FUN-
      GUS TRICHOTHECIUM ROSEUM LINK. 2. BOLM SOC.BROTERIANA, SER.2A, 44, 171-
      183.

4946 RUSCOE, Q.W. (1971) - MYCOFLORA OF LIVING AND DEAD LEAVES OF NOTHOFAGUS
      TRUNCATA. TRANS.BR.MYCOL.SOC. 56, 463-474.

4947 RUSCOE, Q.W. (1971) - THE SOIL MYCOFLORA OF A HARD BEECH FOREST. N.Z.JL
      SCI. 14, 554-567.

4948 RUSCOE, Q.W. (1973) - CHANGES IN THE MYCOFLORAS OF PASTURE SOILS AFTER
      LONG-TERM IRRIGATION. N.J.JL SCI. 16, 9-20.

4949 RUSH-MUNRO, F.M., BLACK, H. & DINGLEY, J.M. (1971) - ONYCHOMYCOSIS CAUSED
      BY FUSARIUM OXYSPORUM. AUST.J.DERM. 12, 18-29.

4950 RUSHDI, M.K. & JEFFERS, W.J. (1952) - VARIATION IN RHIZOCTONIA SOLANI.
      PHYTOPATHOLOGY 42, 473-474 (ABS.).

4951 RUSSEL, R.C. (1958) - LONGEVITY STUDIES WITH WHEAT SEED AND CERTAIN SEED-
      BORNE FUNGI. CAN.J.PL.SCI. 38, 29-33.

4952 RUSSEL, S. (1974) - CELLULOLYTIC ACTIVITY OF VERTICILLIUM ALBO-ATRUM. ACTA
      MICROBIOL.POL. 6, 97-103.

4953 RUSSEL, S. (1975) - CHARACTERISTICS OF VERTICILLIUM ALBO-ATRUM CELLULASE.
      PHYTOPATH.Z. 84, 222-232.

4954 RUSSELL, T.A. (1931) - OBSERVATIONS ON FOOT-ROT DISEASES OF CEREALS. TRANS.
      BR.MYCOL.SOC. 16, 253-269.

4955 RUTHERFORD, T.R. (1965) - A SURVEY OF LIGNICOLOUS FUNGI IN THE AREA ABOUT
      BLACKBURG, VIRGINIA. DISS.POLYTECHNIC VIRGINIA.

4956 RYAN, G.F., GREENBLATT, G. & AL-DELAIMY, K.A. (1961) - SEEDLING ALBINISM
      INDUCED BY AN EXTRACT OF ALTERNARIA TENUIS. SCIENCE, N.Y. 134, 833-834.

4957 RYNEARSON, T.K. & PETERSON, J.L. (1965) - SELECTIVE ISOLATION OF PARAFFINO-
      LYTIC FUNGI USING A DIRECT SOIL-BAITING METHOD. MYCOLOGIA 51, 761-765.

4958 SAAD, S. & HAGEDORN, D.J. (1970) - GROWTH AND NUTRITION OF AN ALTERNARIA
      PATHOGENIC TO SNAPBEANS. PHYTOPATHOLOGY 60, 903-906.

4959 SAAD, S.M., HALLOIN, J.M. & HAGEDORN, D.J. (1970) - PRODUCTION, PURIFICA-
      TION AND BIOASSAY OF TENTOXIN. PHYTOPATHOLOGY 60, 415-418.

4960 SAALTINK, G.J. (1965) - PENICILLIUM CORYMBIFERUM ALS PARASIET VAN BOL IRIS.
      MEDED.LANDBHOGESCH.OPZOEKSTNTS GENT 30, 1652-1659.

4961 SABET, K.A. & ISLAM DIN KHAN (1969) - COMPETITIVE SAPROPHYTIC ABILITY AND
      INOCULUM POTENTIAL OF COTTON ROOT-INFECTING FUNGI IN FIVE SOILS. COTT.
      GROW.REV. 46, 119-133.

4962 SABET, Y.S. (1935) - A PRELIMINARY STUDY OF THE EGYPTIAN SOIL FUNGI. BULL.
      FAC.SCI.EGYPT.UNIV. 5, 1-29.

4963   SACCARDO, P.A. (1911) - NOTAE MYCOLOGICAE. ANNLS MYCOL. 9, 247-257.

4964   SACHIDANANDA, J. & RAMAKRISHNAN, K. (1971) - NEMATOPHAGOUS FUNGI OF AGRI-
       CULTURAL SOILS. MYCOPATH.MYCOL.APPL. 43, 235-241.

4965   SADASIVAM, K.V. (1974) - CYANIDE-TOLERANT MICROORGANISMS IN THE RHIZOSPHERE
       OF TAPIOCA. SOIL BIOL.BIOCHEM. 6, 203.

4966   SADASIVAN, T.S. (1939) - SUCCESSION OF FUNGI DECOMPOSING WHEAT STRAW IN
       DIFFERENT SOILS, WITH SPECIAL REFERENCE TO FUSARIUM CULMORUM. ANN.APPL.
       BIOL. 26, 497-508.

4967   SAEZ, H. (1975) - PIGEMENTATION ET THERMOTOLERANCE DE DEUX ECHANTILLONS DE
       SOUCHES DE TRICHOPHYTON TERRESTRE. BULL.TRIMEST.SOC.MYCOL.FR. 91, 423-
       427.

4968   SAFE, S. & BREWER, D. (1973) - LIPID COMPOSITION OF CHAETOMIUM COCHLIODES.
       EFFECT OF MEDIA. LIPIDS 8, 311-314.

4969   SAFE, S. & TAYLOR, A. (1972) - SPORIDESMIN. 13. OVINE ILL-THRIFT IN NOVA
       SCOTIA. 3. THE CHARACTERISATION OF CHETOMIN, A TOXIC METABOLITE OF CHAE-
       TOMIUM COCHLIODES AND CHAETOMIUM GLOBOSUM. J.CHEM.SOC.PERKIN TRANS.I,
       1972 (4), 472-479.

4970   SAFIAYZOV, Z. (1971) - (SOME CYTOPHYSIOLOGICAL CHARACTERISTICS ON THE CAU-
       SAL AGENT OF COTTON WILT). SEL'.KHOZ.BIOL. 6, 403-406.

4971   SAGARA, N. (1973) - PROTEOPHILOUS FUNGI AND FIREPLACE FUNGI. TRANS.MYCOL.
       SOC.JAPAN 14, 41-46.

4972   SAGARA, N. (1975) - AMMONIA FUNGI - A CHEMOECOLOGICAL GROUPING OF TERRES-
       TRIAL FUNGI. CONTR.BIOL.LAB.KYOTO UNIV. 24, 205-276.

4973   SAGROMSKY, H. (1956) - ZUR LICHTINDUZIERTEN RINGBILDUNG BEI PILZEN. 3.
       BIOL.ZENTBL. 75, 385-397.

4974   SAHAI, D. (1967) - A NEW DISEASE OF POTATO TUBERS CAUSED BY GILMANIELLA
       HUMICOLA BARRON. CURR.SCI. 36, 645-646.

4975   SAHARAN, G.S. & GUPTA, V.K. (1973) - INFLUENCE OF ASPERGILLI ON SOYBEAN
       SEEDS IN STORAGE. PHYTOPATH.Z. 78, 141-146.

4976   SAHNI, V.P. (1965) - DEUTEROMYCETES FROM JABALPUR. 1. MYCOPATH.MYCOL.APPL.
       27, 342-356.

4977   SAHNI, V.P. (1966) - DEUTEROMYCETES FROM JABALPUR. 2. MYCOPATH.MYCOL.APPL.
       29, 226-244.

4978   SAID, H. & HARHASH, A.W. (1966) - THE EFFECT OF VARIOUS INORGANIC NITROGEN
       SOURCES ON THE CARBON DIOXIDE OUTPUT AND KETO-ACID PRODUCTION BY MATS
       OF FUSARIUM OXYSPORUM. ACTA BIOL.MED.GER. 17, 127-134.

4979   SAID, H. & HARHASH, A.W. (1966) - COMPARATIVE STUDY OF THE EFFECT OF NI-
       TRATE AND AMINO ACID-NITROGEN ON THE RESPIRATION, KETO-ACID PRODUCTION,
       AND NITROGEN METABOLISM OF FUSARIUM OXYSPORUM. ACTA BIOL.MED.GER. 17,
       135-144.

4980   SAITO, I. (1973) - INITIATION AND DEVELOPMENT OF APOTHECIAL STIPE PRIMOR-
       DIA IN SCLEROTIA OF SCLEROTINIA SCLEROTIORUM. TRANS.MYCOL.SOC.JAPAN 14,
       343-351.

4981   SAITO, I. (1974) - ULTRASTRUCTURAL ASPECTS OF THE MATURATION OF SCLEROTIA
       OF SCLEROTINIA SCLEROTIORUM. TRANS.MYCOL.SOC.JAPAN 15, 384-400.

4982   SAITO, I. (1974) - UTILIZATION OF BETA-GLUCANS IN GERMINATING SCLEROTIA OF
       SCLEROTINIA SCLEROTIORUM. ANN.PHYTOPATH.SOC.JAPAN 40, 372-374.

4983   SAITO, I. (1977) - GENESIS OF SCLEROTIAL MEDULLA AND ITS DEVELOPMENT TO
       APOTHECIAL STIPES IN SCLEROTINIA SCLEROTIORUM. ABS.2ND INT.MYCOL.CONGR.,
       TAMPA, 1977.

4984   SAITO, K. (1960) - MICROBIAL DECOMPOSITION OF FIR LITTER. SCI.REP.TOHOKU
       UNIV., SER.4, 26, 133-138.

4985   SAITO, M., ENOMOTO, M. & TATSUNO, T. (1969) - RADIOMIMETIC BIOLOGICAL
       PROPERTIES OF THE NEW SCIRPENE METABOLITES OF FUSARIUM NIVALE. GANN
       (JAP.J.CANCER RES.) 60, 599-603.

4986   SAITO, M., ISHIKO, T., ENOMOTO, M., OHTSUBO, K., UMEDA, M., KURATA, H.,
       UDAGAWA, S., TANIGUCHI, S. & SEKITA, S. (1974) - SCREENING TEST USING
       HELA CELLS AND MICE FOR DETECTION OF MYCOTOXIN-PRODUCING FUNGI ISOLATED
       FROM FOODSTUFFS. JAPAN.J.EXP.MED. 44, 63-82.

4987   SAITO, T. (1952) - THE SOIL FUNGI OF A SALT MARSH AND ITS NEIGHBOURHOOD.
       ECOL.REV., SENDAI 13, 111-119.

4988   SAITO, T. (1955) - THE GERMINATION OF FUNGUS SPORES IN RELATION TO EXTER-
       NAL CONDITIONS. ECOL.REV., SENDAI 14, 75-80.

4989   SAITO, T. (1956) - MICROBIOLOGICAL DECOMPOSITION OF BEECH LITTER. ECOL.REV.,
       SENDAI 14, 141-147.

4990   SAITO, T. (1966) - SEQUENTIAL PATTERN OF DECOMPOSITION OF BEECH LITTER
       WITH SPECIAL REFERENCE TO MICROBIAL SUCCESSION. ECOL.REV., SENDAI 16,
       245-264.

4991   SAKAGUCHI, K., KURANE, R. & MURATA, M. (1975) - ASSIMILATION OF FORMALDE-
       HYDE AND OTHER C1-COMPOUNDS BY GLIOCLADIUM DELIQUESCENS AND PAECILOMY-
       CES VARIOTI. AGRIC.BIOL.CHEM., TOKYO 39, 1695-1702.

4992   SAKANO, Y., HIGUCHI, M. & KOBAYASHI, T. (1972) - PULLULAN 4-GLUCANOHYDRO-
       LASE FROM ASPERGILLUS NIGER. ARCHS BIOCHEM.BIOPHYS. 153, 180-187.

4993   SAKANO, Y., HIGUCHI, M., MASUDA, N. & KOBAYASHI, T. (1973) - PRODUCTION OF
       PULLULAN 4-GLUCANOHYDROLASE BY ASPERGILLUS NIGER. J.FERMENT.TECHNOL.,
       OSAKA 51, 726-733.

4994   SAKANO, Y., MASUDA, N. & KOBAYASHI, T. (1971) - HYDROLYSIS OF PULLULAN BY
       A NOVEL ENZYME FROM ASPERGILLUS NIGER. AGRIC.BIOL.CHEM., TOKYO 35, 971-
       973.

4995   SAKSENA, R.K., KRISHNA NAND & SARBHOY, A.K. (1967) - ECOLOGY OF THE SOIL
       FUNGI OF UTTAR PRADESH. 2. SOILS OF THE HIMALAYAN FORESTS AND THEIR
       MICROFUNGI. PROC.NATN.INST.SCI., INDIA, SECT.B, BIOL.SCI. 33, 144-153.

4996   SAKSENA, R.K., KRISHNA NAND & SARBHOY, A.K. (1967) - ECOLOGY OF THE SOIL
       FUNGI OF UTTAR PRADESH. 4. BUNDELKHUND AND GANGETIC TRACT SOILS. PROC.
       NATN.INST.SCI., INDIA, SECT.B, BIOL.SCI. 33, 298-306.

4997   SAKSENA, R.K. & SARBHOY, A.K. (1963) - ECOLOGY OF THE SOIL FUNGI OF UTTAR
       PRADESH. 1. FUNGI IN DIFFERENT SOILS AT ALLAHABAD. PROC.NATN.INST.SCI.,
       INDIA, SECT.B, BIOL.SCI. 29, 207-224.

4998   SAKSENA, R.K., SARBHOY, A.K. & KRISHNA NAND (1967) - ECOLOGY OF THE SOIL
       FUNGI OF UTTAR PRADESH. 3. SOILS OF THE SUB-HIMALAYAN TRACT AND THEIR
       MICROFUNGI. PROC.NATN.INST.SCI., INDIA, SECT.B, BIOL.SCI. 33, 154-161.

4999   SAKSENA, R.K. & SINHA, U. (1973) - CONIDIATION OF ASPERGILLUS NIDULANS IN
       SUBMERGED LIQUID CULTURE. J.GEN.APPL.MICROBIOL., TOKYO 19, 141-146.

5000   SAKSENA, S.B. (1955) - ECOLOGICAL FACTORS GOVERNING THE DISTRIBUTION OF
       SOIL MICROFUNGI IN SOME FOREST SOILS OF SAGAR. J.INDIAN BOT.SOC. 34,
       262-298.

5001   SAKSENA, S.B. (1960) - EFFECT OF CARBON DISULPHIDE FUMIGATION ON TRICHO-
       DERMA VIRIDE AND OTHER SOIL FUNGI. TRANS.BR.MYCOL.SOC. 43, 111-116.

5002   SAKSENA, S.B. & LILY, K. (1967) - STUDIES ON THE INTERACTION BETWEEN SOIL
       MICROORGANISMS WITH SPECIAL REFERENCE TO PENICILLIUM NIGRICANS. J.INDIAN
       BOT.SOC. 46, 185-192.

5003   SAKURAI, Y. & SHIOBA, H. (1970) - MULTIPLE FORMS OF ACID PHOSPHATASE PRO-
       DUCED BY ASPERGILLUS ORYZAE. J.GEN.MICROBIOL. 16, 335-339.

5004   SALA, F.J. & BURGOS, J. (1972) - SIMPLE METHOD FOR MASS PRODUCTION AND
       COLLECTION OF CONIDIA FROM HEMISPORA STELLATA. APPL.MICROBIOL. 24, 504-
       505.

5005   SALA, T. & FRANCISCO, J. (1973) - PURIFICATION AND PROPERTIES OF CYTO-
       CHROME-C (550, HEMISPORA STELLATA). ARCH.MIKROBIOL. 88, 11-24.

5006   SALAMA, A.M., YOUNIS, A.E. & ATTABY, H.S. (1973) - STUDIES ON FAST AND
       TA AND CLADOSPORIUM HERBARUM AS AFFECTED BY CULTURAL CONDITIONS. ACTA
       BIOL.HUNG. 24, 43-50.

5007   SALAMA, A.M., YOUNIS, A.E. & ATTABY, H.S. (1973) - STUDIES ON FAST AND
       SLOW GROWTH IN FUNGI. 2. COMPARATIVE GROWTH OF CUNNINGHAMELLA ECHINULA-
       TA AND CLADOSPORIUM HERBARUM IN THE LIGHT OF THEIR CARBOHYDRATE AND NI-
       TROGEN METABOLISM. ACTA BIOL.HUNG. 24, 51-57.

5008   SALAMA, A.M., YOUNIS, A.E. & ATTABY, H.S. (1973) - STUDIES ON FAST AND
       SLOW GROWTH IN FUNGI. 3. HORMONAL PICTURE IN MEDIA AND MATS OF CUNNING-
       HAMELLA ECHINULATA AND CLADOSPORIUM HERBARUM. ACTA BIOL.HUNG. 24, 59-
       64.

5009   SALEEM, A., HUSSAIN, T., TANVEER, M., YACOOB, M. & EHSAN-UL-HAQUE (1975) -
       FUNGAL FLORA OF PAKISTAN COTTON. PAKIST.J.BOT. 7, 183-191.

5010   SALEH, A.M. (1960) - EFFECT OF AGE OF THE MYCELIAL MATS OF FUSARIUM CULMO-
       RUM ON THEIR GROWTH, RESPIRATION AND NITROGEN METABOLISM. ARCH.MIKROBIOL.
       36, 116-123.

5011   SALKIN, I.F. & STONE, W.B. (1974) - SUBCUTANEOUS MYCOTIC INFECTION OF A
       WHITE-TAILED DEER. J.WILDLIFE DIS. 10, 34-38.

5012   SALLAM, L.A.R., EL-KADY, I.A. & EL-REFAI, A.H. (1974) - SOME CULTURE CON-
       DITIONS INFLUENCING THE 17-ALPHA-HYDROXYLATION OF PROGESTERONE WITH TRI-
       CHOTHECIUM ROSEUM. MICROBIOL.ESP. 27, 299-308.

5013   SALLANS, B.J. (1965) - ROOT ROTS OF CEREALS. 3. BOT.REV. 31, 505-536.

5014   SALMANOVA, L.S. & ZHDANOVA, L.A. (1975) - (EFFECT OF PH ON THE ENZYMIC AC-
       TIVITY OF THE FUNGI TRICHOTHECIUM ROSEUM AND ASPERGILLUS NIGER, HYDRO-
       LYZING NONSTARCH POLYSACCHARIDES). PRIKL.BIOKHIM.MIKROBIOL. 11, 214-218.

5015 SALONEN, A. (1968) - ON KERATINOPHILIC SOIL FUNGI IN FINLAND. ACTA AGRIC.
      SCAND. 18, 159-167.

5016 SALONEN, A. & RUOKOLA, A.-L. (1969) - MYCOFLORA OF THE FINNISH 'SAUNA'
      (BATH-HOUSE). MYCOPATH.MYCOL.APPL. 38, 327-336.

5017 SAMSINAKOVA, A. (1966) - GROWTH AND SPORULATION OF SUBMERSED CULTURES OF
      THE FUNGUS BEAUVERIA BASSIANA IN VARIOUS MEDIA. J.INVERTEBR.PATH. 8,
      395-400.

5018 SAMSINAKOVA, A., KALALOVA, S., DANIEL, M., DUSBABEK, F., HONZAKOVA, E. &
      CERNY, V. (1974) - ENTOMOGENOUS FUNGI ASSOCIATED WITH THE TICK IXODES
      RICINUS. FOLIA PARASITOL. 21, 39-48.

5019 SAMSINAKOVA, A. & MISIKOVA, S. (1973) - ENZYME ACTIVITIES IN CERTAIN ENTO-
      MOPHAGOUS REPRESENTATIVES OF DEUTEROMYCETES (MONILIALES) IN RELATION-
      SHIP TO THEIR VIRULENCE. CESKA MYKOL. 27, 55-60.

5020 SAMSINAKOVA, A., MISIKOVA, S. & LEOPOLD, J. (1971) - ACTION OF ENZYMATIC
      SYSTEMS OF BEAUVERIA BASSIANA ON THE CUTICLE OF THE GREATER WAX MOTH
      LARVAE (GALLERIA MELLONELLA). J.INVERTEBR.PATH. 18, 322-330.

5021 SAMSINAKOVA, A. & SAMSINAK, K. (1970) - MILBEN (ACARI) ALS VERBREITER DES
      PILZES BEAUVERIA BASSIANA (BALS.) VUILL. Z.PARASITKDE 34, 351-355.

5022 SAMSON, R.A. (1969) - REVISION OF THE GENUS CUNNINGHAMELLA (FUNGI, MUCORA-
      LES). PROC.K.NED.AKAD.WET., SER.C, 72, 322-335.

5023 SAMSON, R.A. (1972) - NOTES ON PSEUDOGYMNOASCUS, GYMNOASCUS AND RELATED
      GENERA. ACTA BOT.NEERL. 21, P. 517.

5024 SAMSON, R.A. (1974) - PAECILOMYCES AND SOME ALLIED HYPHOMYCETES. STUD.MY-
      COL., BAARN 6, 119 PP.

5025 SAMSON, R.A., CRISMAN, M.J. & TANSEY, M.R. (1977) - OBSERVATIONS ON THE
      THERMOPHILOUS ASCOMYCETES THIELAVIA TERRESTRIS. TRANS.BR.MYCOL.SOC. 69,
      417-423.

5026 SAMSON, R.A. & EVANS, H.C. (1977) - NOTES ON ENTOMOGENOUS FUNGI FROM GHA-
      NA. 4. THE GENERA PAECILOMYCES AND NOMURAEA. PROC.K.NED.AKAD.WET., SER.
      C, 80, 128-134.

5027 SAMSON, R.A., HADLOK, R. & STOLK, A.C. (1977).- A TAXONOMIC STUDY OF THE
      PENICILLIUM CHRYSOGENUM SERIES. ANTONIE VAN LEEUWENHOEK 43, 169-175.

5028 SAMSON, R.A. & MOUCHACCA, J. (1975) - ADDITIONAL NOTES ON SPECIES OF ASPER-
      GILLUS, EUROTIUM AND EMERICELLA FROM EGYPTIAN DESERT SOIL. ANTONIE VAN
      LEEUWENHOEK 41, 343-351.

5029 SAMSON, R.A., STOLK, A.C. & HADLOK, R. (1976) - REVISION OF THE SUBSECTION
      FASCICULATA OF PENICILLIUM AND SOME ALLIED SPECIES. STUD.MYCOL., BAARN.
      12, 1-47.

5030 SAMSON, R.A. & TARIQ MAHMOOD (1970) - THE GENUS ACROPHIALOPHORA (FUNGI,
      MONILIALES). ACTA BOT.NEERL. 19, 804-808.

5031 SAMUEL, G. & GREANEY, F.J. (1937) - SOME OBSERVATIONS ON THE OCCURRENCE OF
      FUSARIUM CULMORUM ON WHEAT. TRANS.BR.MYCOL.SOC. 21, 114-117.

5032 SAMUELS, G.J. (1976) - A REVISION OF THE FUNGI FORMERLY CLASSIFIED AS NEC-
      TRIA SUBGENUS HYPHONECTRIA. MEM.NEW YORK BOT.GDN 26, 126 PP.

5033   SAMUELS, G.J. (1977) - NECTRIA CONSORS AND ITS VOLUTELLA CONIDIAL STATE.
        MYCOLOGIA 69, 255-262.

5034   SANCHOLLE, M. & MONTANT, C. (1972) - ANALYSE DES CONSTITUANTS DE LA FRAC-
        TION LIPIDIQUE ISOLEE DU MYCELIUM DU TRICHOTHECIUM ROSEUM AU COURS DES
        PREMIERS STADES DE LA CROISSANCE. CAN.J.BOT. 50, 247-251.

5035   SANDERSON, F.R. (1970) - FUSARIUM DISEASES OF CEREALS. 7. THE EFFECT OF
        LIGHT ON SPORULATION OF F. NIVALE IN CULTURE. TRANS.BR.MYCOL.SOC. 55,
        131-135.

5036   SANDERSON, K.E. & SRB, A.M. (1965) - HETEROKARYOSIS AND PARASEXUALITY IN
        THE FUNGUS ASCOCHYTA IMPERFECTA. AM.J.BOT. 52, 72-81.

5037   SANDISON, A.T., GENTLES, J.C., DAVIDSON, C.M. & BRANKO, M. (1967) - ASPER-
        GILLOMA OF PARANASAL SINUSES AND ORBIT IN NORTHERN SUDANESE. SABOURAU-
        DIA 6, 57-69.

5038   SANFORD, G.B. (1952) - PERSISTENCE OF RHIZOCTONIA SOLANI IN SOIL. CAN.J.
        BOT. 30, 652-664.

5039   SANFORD, G.B. & BROADFOOT, W.C. (1931) - STUDIES OF THE EFFECTS OF OTHER
        SOIL-INHABITING MICRO-ORGANISMS ON THE VIRULENCE OF OPHIOBOLUS GRAMINIS.
        SCIENT.AGRIC. 11, 512-528.

5040   SANFORD, G.B. & SKOROPAD, W.P. (1955) - DISTRIBUTION OF NUCLEI IN HYPHAL
        CELLS OF RHIZOCTONIA SOLANI. CAN.J.MICROBIOL. 1, 412-415.

5041   SANKHALA, R.H. (1968) - METABOLIC PRODUCTS OF PENICILLIUM RESTRICTUM. IN-
        DIAN J.EXP.BIOL. 6, 57-58.

5042   SANSING, G.A., DAVIS, N.D. & DIENER, U.L. (1973) - EFFECT OF TIME AND TEM-
        PERATURE ON OCHRATOXIN-A PRODUCTION BY ASPERGILLUS OCHRACEUS. CAN.J.
        MICROBIOL. 19, 1259-1263.

5043   SANSING, G.A., DETROY, R.W., FREER, S.N. & HESSELTINE, C.W. (1973) - VIRUS
        PARTICLES FROM CONIDIA OF PENICILLIUM SPECIES. APPL.MICROBIOL. 26, 914-
        918.

5044   SANSOME, E.R. (1947) - SPONTANEOUS VARIATION IN PENICILLIUM NOTATUM STRAIN
        N.R.R.L. 1249 B 21. TRANS.BR.MYCOL.SOC. 31, 66-79.

5045   SANTRA, S. & NANDI, B. (1973) - ROLE OF TEMPERATURE SHOCK TREATMENT ON
        SPORE GERMINATION OF NIGROSPORA ORYZAE (B. & BR.) PETCH IN CULTURE.
        SCI.CULT. 39, 53-55.

5046   SANYAL, M. & THAMMAYYA, A. (1975) - HISTOPLASMA CAPSULATUM IN THE SOIL OF
        THE GANGETIC PLAIN IN INDIA. INDIAN J.MED.RES. 63, 1020-1028.

5047   SAPPA, F. (1955) - LA MICOFLORA DEL TERRENO QUASI ELEMENTO STRUTTURALE DEL-
        LE COMMUNITA VEGETALI. 1. SAGGI METODOLOGICI SUL CALLUNETO DI S.FRAN-
        CESCO AL CAMPO (TORINO). ALLIONIA 2, 293-345.

5048   SAPPA, F. & MOSCA, A.M. (1954) - RICERCHE SULLA MICOFLORA DEI TERRENI FORES-
        TALI SOMALI. ALLIONIA 2, 145-193.

5049   SAPPA, F. & MOSCA, A.M. (1954) - RICERCHE SULLA MICOFLORA DEI TERRENI DEL-
        LA SAVANNA SPINOSA SOMALA. ALLIONIA 2, 195-238.

5050   SARASIN, A. (1953) - UNTERSUCHUNGEN UEBER DIE LACTOFLAVINBILDUNG DURCH AS-
        PERGILLUS NIGER. BER.SCHWEIZ.BOT.GES. 63, 287-317.

5051   SARASWATHI-DEVI, L. (1958) - BIOASSEY - THE ASPERGILLUS NIGER TECHNIQUE FOR
       HEAVY METALS. MEM.INDIAN BOT.SOC. 1, 82-86.

5052   SARASWATHI-DEVI, L. (1958) - ESSENTIALITY OF TRACE ELEMENTS TO SOME SOIL
       FUNGI. J.INDIAN BOT.SOC. 37, 509-516.

5053   SARBHOY, A.K. (1962) - NUTRITIONAL STUDIES ON SIX MEMBERS OF THE MUCORA-
       LES. 1. UTILIZATION OF CARBOHYDRATES. PHYTON, B.AIRES 19, 59-64.

5054   SARBHOY, A.K. (1963) - NUTRITIONAL STUDIES ON SOME MEMBERS OF THE MUCORA-
       LES. 3. UTILIZATION OF MIXTURES OF DIFFERENT AMINO ACIDS. LLOYDIA 26,
       236-242.

5055   SARBHOY, A.K. (1963) - NUTRITIONAL STUDIES OF SOME MEMBERS OF MUCORALES.
       4. SUGARS, AMINO- AND ORGANIC ACIDS OF THE MYCELIUM. MYCOPATH.MYCOL.
       APPL. 19, 37-43.

5056   SARBHOY, A.K. (1965) - NUTRITIONAL STUDIES ON SOME MEMBERS OF THE MUCORA-
       LES. 5. UTILIZATION OF DIFFERENT NITROGEN COMPOUNDS. PATHOL.MICROBIOL.
       28, 816-829.

5057   SARBHOY, A.K. (1965) - NUTRITIONAL STUDIES OF SOME MEMBERS OF MUCORALES.
       6. UTILIZATION OF DIFFERENT SULPHUR COMPOUNDS. 7. EFFECT OF ENVIRONMEN-
       TAL FACTORS, TEMPERATURE AND HYDROGEN-ION CONCENTRATION. MYCOPATH.MYCOL.
       APPL. 27, 115-128.

5058   SARBHOY, A.K. (1967) - SPECIES OF MUCORALES RECORDED FOR INDIA. MYCOL.PAP.
       108, 1-13.

5059   SASAKI, Y. & SASAKI, H. (1971) - A TAXONOMIC STUDY ON CELLULOSE DECOMPOS-
       ING FUNGI. MEM.FAC.AGRIC.HOKKAIDO UNIV. 8, 30-39.

5060   SASAKI, Y. & YOSHIDA, T. (1971) - MICROBIOLOGICAL STUDIES ON RIVER POLLU-
       TION. 1. ON MOLDS IN SLIME OF PAPER MILLS. MEM.FAC.AGRIC.HOKKAIDO UNIV.
       8, 59-70.

5061   SASAKI, Y. & YOSHIDA, T. (1971) - A NOTE ON THE WOOD-ROTTING FUNGI. MEM.
       FAC.AGRIC.HOKKAIDO UNIV. 8, 71-76.

5062   SASSA, T., AOKI, H., NAMIKI, M. & MUNAKATA, K. (1968) - PLANT GROWTH PROMOT-
       ING METABOLITES OF SCLEROTINIA SCLEROTIORUM. AGRIC.BIOL.CHEM., TOKYO
       32, 1432-1439.

5063   SATCHUTHANANTHAVALE, V. & COOKE, R.C. (1967) - VITAMIN REQUIREMENTS OF
       SOME NEMATODE-TRAPPING FUNGI. TRANS.BR.MYCOL.SOC. 50, 221-228.

5064   SATCHUTHANANTHAVALE, V. & COOKE, R.C. (1967) - NITROGEN NUTRITION OF SOME
       NEMATODE-TRAPPING FUNGI. TRANS.BR.MYCOL.SOC. 50, 423-428.

5065   SATCHUTHANANTHAVALE, V. & COOKE, R.C. (1967) - CARBOHYDRATE NUTRITION OF
       SOME NEMATODE-TRAPPING FUNGI. NATURE, LOND. 214, 321-322.

5066   SATOUR, M.M. (1967) - RAPE SEED EXTRACT AGAR - A NEW MEDIUM FOR PRODUCTION
       AND DETECTION OF OOSPORES OF HETEROTHALLIC SPECIES OF PHYTOPHTHORA. MY-
       COLOGIA 59, 161-166.

5067   SATYANARAYANA, T., JOHRI, B.N. & SAKSENA, S.B. (1977) - SEASONAL VARIATION
       IN MYCOFLORA OF NESTING MATERIALS OF BIRDS WITH SPECIAL REFERENCE TO
       THERMOPHILIC FUNGI. TRANS.BR.MYCOL.SOC. 68, 307-309.

5068   SAUNDERS, P.R., SIU, R.G.H. & GENEST, R.N. (1948) - A CELLULOLYTIC ENZYME
       PREPARATION FROM MYROTHECIUM VERRUCARIA. J.BIOL.CHEM. 174, 697-703.

5069   SAUR, R. & SCHOENBECK, F. (1975) - UNTERSUCHUNGEN UEBER DEN EINFLUSS SYS-
       TEMISCHER FUNGIZIDE AUF DEN BEFALL DER GERSTE MIT HELMINTHOSPORIUM SA-
       TIVUM. Z.PFLKRANKH.PFLSCHUTZ 82, 173-175.

5070   SAUVE, R.J. & MITCHELL, D.J. (1977) - AN EVALUATION OF METHODS FOR OBTAIN-
       ING MYCELIUM-FREE OOSPORES OF PYTHIUM APHANIDERMATUM AND P. MYRIOTYLUM.
       CAN.J.MICROBIOL. 23, 643-648.

5071   SAVAGE, E.J., CLAYTON, C.W., HUNTER, J.H., BRENNEMAN, J.A., LAVIOLA, C. &
       GALLEGLY, M.E. (1968) - HOMOTHALLISM, HETEROTHALLISM, AND INTERSPECIFIC
       HYBRIDIZATION IN THE GENUS PHYTOPHTHORA. PHYTOPATHOLOGY 58, 1004-1021.

5072   SAVORY, J.G. (1954) - BREAKDOWN OF TIMBER BY ASCOMYCETES AND FUNGI IMPER-
       FECTI. ANN.APPL.BIOL. 41, 336-347.

5073   SAVORY, J.G. & PINION, L.C. (1958) - CHEMICAL ASPECTS OF DECAY OF BEECH
       WOOD BY CHAETOMIUM GLOBOSUM. HOLZFORSCHUNG 12, 99-103.

5074   SAWYER, R.T., DESKINS, D.C. & VOLZ, P.A. (1975) - PHOSPHOGLYCERIDES OF
       TRICHOPHYTON TERRESTRE AND ONE PHENOTYPE SELECTED FROM THE APOLLO 16
       MICROBIAL ECOLOGY EVALUATION DEVICE. APPL.MICROBIOL. 29, 658-662.

5075   SAYED, M.Q. (1961) - THE EFFECT OF NUTRITION, PH, AND NEMATODES ON DAMPING-
       OFF DISEASE OF PEA, TOMATO AND CUCUMBER. DISS.ABSTR. 21, 1701-1702.

5076   SCALES, F.M. (1915) - SOME FILAMENTOUS FUNGI TESTED FOR CELLULOSE DESTROY-
       ING POWER. BOT.GAZ. 60, 149-153.

5077   SCHABORT, C., WILKENS, D.C., HOLZAPFEL, C.W., POTGIETER, D.J.J. & NEITZ,
       W. (1971) - BETA-CYCLOPIAZONATE OXIDOCYCLASE FROM PENICILLIUM CYCLOPIUM.
       1. ASSAY METHODS, ISOLATION AND PURIFICATION. BIOCHIM.BIOPHYS.ACTA 250,
       311-328.

5078   SCHADE, W. (1965) - UNTERSUCHUNGEN UEBER DEN EINFLUSS VON AMINOSAEUREN AUF
       DIE CITRONENSAEUREBILDUNG DURCH ASPERGILLUS NIGER. 1. DIE WIRKUNG EINI-
       GER ORGANISCHER STICKSTOFFQUELLEN AUF DIE MYCELAKTIVITAET VON ASPERGIL-
       LUS NIGER IN EMERSKULTUR. ZENTBL.BAKT.PARASITKDE, ABT.2, 119, 37-52.

5079   SCHAEFER, CH. (1957) - UEBER DIE BILDUNG UND WIRKUNG EINES ZELLULOSESPAL-
       TENDEN FERMENTES AUS SCHIMMELPILZEN. BER.SCHWEIZ.BOT.GES. 67, 218-270.

5080   SCHAERFFENBERG, B. (1959) - ZUR BIOLOGIE UND OEKOLOGIE DES INSEKTENTOETEN-
       DEN PILZES METARRHIZIUM ANISOPLIAE. Z.ANGEW.ENT. 44, 262-271.

5081   SCHAERFFENBERG, B. (1964) - BEITRAEGE ZUR BIOLOGIE UND CHEMIE DER INSEKTEN-
       TOETENDEN BEAUVERIA-PILZE. 1. DIE BEAUVERIA-FORMEN. NOVA HEDWIGIA 8,
       151-159.

5082   SCHAERFFENBERG, B. & WINKLER, R. (1969) - BEITRAEGE ZUR BIOLOGIE UND CHE-
       MIE DER INSEKTENTOETENDEN BEAUVERIA-PILZE. 3. UNTERSUCHUNGEN UEBER DIE
       INSEKTIZIDE WIRKUNG TOXISCHER SUBSTANZEN AUS BEAUVERIA BASSIANA (BALS.)
       VUILL. NOVA HEDWIGIA 17, 203-218.

5083   SCHAPOSCHNIKOW, W. & MANTEIFEL, A. (1924) - UEBER DIE KOREMIENBILDUNG BEI
       EINIGEN PILZEN. ZENTBL.BAKT.PARASITKDE, ABT.2, 62, 295-300.

5084   SCHAREN, A.L. (1960) - GERMINATION OF OOSPORES OF APHANOMYCES EUTEICHES
       EMBEDDED IN PLANT DEBRIS. PHYTOPATHOLOGY 50, 274-277.

5085   SCHAUMANN, K. (1974) - EXPERIMENTELLE UNTERSUCHUNGEN ZUM EINFLUSS DES SALZ-
       GEHALTES UND DER TEMPERATUR AUF DAS MYCELWACHSTUM HOEHERER PILZE AUS DEM
       MEER- UND BRACKWASSER. VEROEFF.INST.MEERESFORSCH.BREMERH., SUPPL.5, 443-
       474.

5086   SCHAUMANN, K. (1974) - EXPERIMENTELLE UNTERSUCHUNGEN ZUR PRODUKTION UND AK-
       TIVITAET CELLULOLYTISCHER ENZYME BEI HOEHEREN PILZEN AUS DEM MEER- UND
       BRACKWASSER. MAR.BIOL. 28, 221-235.

5087   SCHEER, H.A.T.VAN DER (1969) - THE OCCURRENCE OF CROWN ROT CAUSED BY PHY-
       TOPHTHORA CACTORUM IN THE APPLE ROOTSTOCK MM104. NETH.J.PL.PATH. 75,
       369-370.

5088   SCHEER, H.A.T.VAN DER (1973) - SUSCEPTIBILITY OF STRAWBERRY TO ISOLATES OF
       PHYTOPHTHORA CACTORUM AND PHYTOPHTHORA CITRICOLA. MEDED.FAC.LANDBWET.
       RIJKSUNIV.GENT 38, 1407-1415.

5089   SCHENK, S., KENDRICK, W.B. & PRAMER, D. (1977) - A NEW NEMATODE-TRAPPING
       HYPHOMYCETE AND A REEVALUATION OF DACTYLARIA AND ARTHROBOTRYS. CAN.J.
       BOT. 55, 977-985.

5090   SCHENK, S. & PRAMER, D. (1976) - NEMATODES AS NUTRIENTS FOR SOIL FUNGI.
       NEMATOLOGICA 22, 312-318.

5091   SCHENK, S. & STOTZKY, G. (1974) - EFFECT OF VOLATILE COMPOUNDS RELEASED
       FROM GERMINATING SEEDS ON GROWTH OF MICROORGANISMS. AM.J.BOT. 61, 25
       (ABS.).

5092   SCHINDLER, A.F., ABADIE, A.N., GECAN, J.S., MISLIVEC, P.B. & BRICKEY, P.M.
       (1974) - MYCOTOXINS PRODUCED BY FUNGI ISOLATED FROM INSHELL PECANS.
       J.FD SCI. 39, 213-214.

5093   SCHINDLER, A.F., PALMER, J.G. & EISENBERG, W.V. (1967) - AFLATOXIN PRODUC-
       TION BY ASPERGILLUS FLAVUS AS RELATED TO VARIOUS TEMPERATURES. APPL.MI-
       CROBIOL. 15, 1006-1009.

5094   SCHIPPER, M.A.A. (1969) - ZYGOSPORIC STAGES IN HETEROTHALLIC MUCOR. ANTONIE
       VAN LEEUWENHOEK 35, 189-208.

5095   SCHIPPER, M.A.A. (1970) - TWO SPECIES OF MUCOR WITH OVAL- AND SPHERICAL-
       SPORED STRAINS. ANTONIE VAN LEEUWENHOEK 36, 475-488.

5096   SCHIPPER, M.A.A. (1971) - INDUCTION OF ZYGOSPORE PRODUCTION IN MUCOR SAXI-
       MONTENSIS, AN AGAMIC STRAIN OF ZYGORHYNCHUS MOELLERI. TRANS.BR.MYCOL.
       SOC. 56, 157-158.

5097   SCHIPPER, M.A.A. (1973) - A STUDY ON VARIABILITY IN MUCOR HIEMALIS AND RE-
       LATED SPECIES. STUD.MYCOL., BAARN 4, 40 PP.

5098   SCHIPPER, M.A.A. (1975) - ON MUCOR MUCEDO, MUCOR FLAVUS AND RELATED SPE-
       CIES. STUD.MYCOL., BAARN 10, 33 PP.

5099   SCHIPPER, M.A.A. (1976) - ON MUCOR CIRCINELLOIDES, MUCOR RACEMOSUS AND RE-
       LATED SPECIES. STUD.MYCOL., BAARN 12, 40 PP.

5100   SCHIPPER, M.A.A. (1976) - INDUCED AZYGOSPORE FORMATION IN MUCOR (RHIZOMU-
       COR) PUSILLUS BY ABSIDIA CORYMBIFERA. ANTONIE VAN LEEUWENHOEK 42, 141-
       144.

5101   SCHIPPER, M.A.A. (1978) - 1. ON CERTAIN SPECIES OF MUCOR WITH A KEY TO ALL
       ACCEPTED SPECIES. 2. ON THE GENERA RHIZOMUCOR AND PARASITELLA. STUD.MY-
       COL., BAARN 17, 71 PP.

5102   SCHIPPER, M.A.A., SAMSON, R.A. & STALPERS, J.A. (1975) - ZYGOSPORE ORNAMEN-
       TATION IN THE GENERA MUCOR AND ZYGORRHYNCHUS. PERSOONIA 8, 321-328.

5103 SCHIPPERS, B. (1970) - SURVIVAL OF ENDOCONIDIA OF THIELAVIOPSIS BASICOLA
      IN SOIL. NETH.J.PL.PATH. 76, 206-211.

5104 SCHIPPERS, B. & OLD, K.M. (1974) - FACTORS AFFECTING CHLAMYDOSPORE FORMA-
      TION BY FUSARIUM SOLANI F. CUCURBITAE IN PURE CULTURE. SOIL BIOL.BIO-
      CHEM. 6, 153-160.

5105 SCHLOESSER, E. & GOTTLIEB, D. (1968) - THE EFFECT OF STEROLS ON THE META-
      BOLISM OF PYTHIUM SPECIES. ARCH.MIKROBIOL. 61, 246-253.

5106 SCHLOESSER, U.G. (1970) - UEBER FOERDERUNG UND ERHALTUNG DER SPORULATION
      IN EINER KULTURSAMMLUNG PARASITISCHER PILZE VON GRAMINEEN DURCH LANG-
      WELLIGES UV-LICHT. PHYTOPATH.Z. 68, 171-180.

5107 SCHMALFUSS, K. (1938) - DER ABBAU DES ZYANAMIDS. BODENK.PFLERNAEHR. 9/10,
      273-305.

5108 SCHMIDT, G.C., WALKER, H.W., ROEGNER, F.R. & FISCHER, C.G. (1966) - REQUIRE-
      MENTS FOR THE GROWTH OF ASPERGILLUS VERSICOLOR ON ATROPINE SULFATE.
      J.PHARM.SCI. 55, 914-919.

5109 SCHMITTHENNER, A.F. (1959) - THE EFFECT OF MEDIA CONCENTRATION ON SPORAN-
      GIA PRODUCTION IN PHYTOPHTHORA. PHYTOPATHOLOGY 49, 550 (ABS.).

5110 SCHMITTHENNER, A.F. (1962) - EFFECT OF CROP ROTATION ON PYTHIUM ULTIMUM
      AND OTHER PYTHIUM SPECIES IN THE SOIL. PHYTOPATHOLOGY 52, 27 (ABS.).

5111 SCHMITTHENNER, A.F. (1962) - ISOLATION OF PYTHIUM FROM SOIL PARTICLES.
      PHYTOPATHOLOGY 52, 1133-1138.

5112 SCHMITTHENNER, A.F. (1964) - PREVALENCE AND VIRULENCE OF PHYTOPHTHORA,
      APHANOMYCES, PYTHIUM, RHIZOCTONIA, AND FUSARIUM ISOLATED FROM DISEASED
      ALFALFA SEEDLINGS. PHYTOPATHOLOGY 54, 1012-1018.

5113 SCHMITTHENNER, A.F. (1970) - SIGNIFICANCE OF POPULATIONS OF PYTHIUM AND
      PHYTOPHTHORA IN SOILS. IN: ROOT DISEASES AND SOIL-BORNE PATHOGENS;
      TOUSSOUN, T.A. ET AL. (ED.), UNIV.CALIFORNIA PRESS, BERKELY, 25-27.

5114 SCHMITTHENNER, A.F. (1972) - EFFECT OF LIGHT AND CALCIUM ON GERMINATION OF
      OOSPORES OF PYTHIUM APHANIDERMATUM. PHYTOPATHOLOGY 62, 788.

5115 SCHNATHORST, W.C. (1962) - THE ORIGIN OF NEW MYCELIAL GROWTH IN MICRO-
      SCLEROTIAL MASSES OF VERTICILLIUM ALBO-ATRUM REINKE & BERTH. PHYTOPATH-
      OLOGY 52, 27 (ABS.).

5116 SCHNEIDER, G., SEMBDNER, G., FOCKE, I. & SCHREIBER, K. (1971) - MIKROBIEL-
      LE UMWANDLUNG VON GIBBERELLINEN - ENTACETYLIERUNG VON O(3,13)-DIACETYL-
      GIBBERELLINSAEURE. PHYTOCHEMISTRY 10, 3009-3014.

5117 SCHNEIDER, R. (1954) - PLICARIA FULVA N.SP., EIN BISHER NICHT BEKANNTER
      GEWAECHSHAUSBEWOHNER. ZENTBL.BAKT.PARASITKDE, ABT.2, 108, 147-153.

5118 SCHNEIDER, R. (1958) - UNTERSUCHUNGEN UEBER VARIABILITAET UND TAXONOMIE
      VON FUSARIUM AVENACEUM. PHYTOPATH.Z. 32, 95-126.

5119 SCHNEIDER, R. & BOEREMA, G.H. (1975) - NACHWEIS EINER SPEZIALISIERTEN FORM
      VON PHOMA CHRYSANTHEMICOLA (PHOMA CHRYSANTHEMICOLA HOLLOS F. SP. CHRYS-
      ANTHEMICOLA). PHYTOPATH.Z. 83, 239-243.

5120 SCHNEIDER, R. & CRUEGER, G. (1976) - EINE NEUE BLATTFLECKENKRANKHEIT AN
      GEWAECHSHAUSTOMATEN IN DER BUNDESREPUBLIK DEUTSCHLAND, VERURSACHT DURCH
      EINE SPEZIALISIERTE FORM VON STEMPHYLIUM BOTRYOSUM. PHYTOPATH.Z. 87,
      264-273.

5121   SCHNEIDER, R. & PLATE, H.-P. (1966) - NACHWEIS EINER PENICILLIUM-ZWIEBEL-
       FAEULE AN IRIS HOLLANDICA IN DEUTSCHLAND. NACHRBL.DT.PFLSCHUTZDIENST,
       BRAUNSCHWG 18, 138-140.

5122   SCHNEIDER, R. & PLATE, H.-P. (1970) - EINE FUER DEUTSCHLAND NEUE WURZEL-
       UND STENGELFAEULE AN CHRYSANTHEMUM INDICUM L. UND IHR ERREGER PHOMA
       CHRYSANTHEMICOLA HOLLOS. PHYTOPATH.Z. 67, 97-111.

5123   SCHNITZER, M. & NEYROUD, J.A. (1975) - FURTHER INVESTIGATIONS ON THE CHEM-
       ISTRY OF FUNGAL HUMIC ACIDS. SOIL BIOL.BIOCHEM. 7, 365-371.

5124   SCHNITZER, M., ORTIZ DE SERRA, M.I. & IVARSON, K. (1973) - THE CHEMISTRY
       OF FUNGAL HUMIC ACID-LIKE POLYMERS AND OF SOIL HUMIC ACIDS. PROC.SOIL
       SCI.SOC.AM. 37, 229-236.

5125   SCHOLER, H.J. (1970) - MUCORMYKOSEN BEI MENSCH UND TIER. TAXONOMIE DER ER-
       REGER. CHEMOTHERAPIE IM TIEREXPERIMENT UND IN DER KLINIK. HABILITATIONS-
       SCHR.UNIV.BASEL.

5126   SCHOLER, H.J. & MUELLER, E. (1966) - BEZIEHUNGEN ZWISCHEN BIOCHEMISCHEN
       LEISTUNGEN UND MORPHOLOGIE BEI PILZEN AUS DER FAMILIE DER MUCORACEEN.
       PATH.MICROBIOL. 29, 730-741.

5127   SCHOLER, H.J. & MUELLER, E. (1971) - TAXONOMY OF THE PATHOGENIC SPECIES OF
       RHIZOPUS. 7TH A.MEET.BR.SOC.MYCOPATH., EDINBURGH, 1971.

5128   SCHOL-SCHWARZ, M.B. (1959) - THE GENUS EPICOCCUM. TRANS.BR.MYCOL.SOC. 42,
       149-173.

5129   SCHOL-SCHWARZ, M.B. (1968) - RHINOCLADIELLA, ITS SYNONYM FONSECAEA AND ITS
       RELATION TO PHIALOPHORA. ANTONIE VAN LEEUWENHOEK 34, 119-152.

5130   SCHOL-SCHWARZ, M.B. (1970) - REVISION OF THE GENUS PHIALOPHORA (MONILIA-
       LES). PERSOONIA 6, 59-94.

5131   SCHOLTEN, G. (1964) - NECTRIA RADICICOLA EN THIELAVIOPSIS BASICOLA ALS
       PARASIETEN VAN CYCLAMEN PERSICUM. NETH.J.PL.PATH. 70, SUPPL. 2, 1-68.

5132   SCHOLZ, H.-D. & MEYER, L. (1965) - MORTIERELLA POLYCEPHALA ALS ERREGER EI-
       NER LUNGENMYKOSE BEIM RIND. BERL.MUENCH.TIERAERZTL.WSCHR. 78, 27-30.

5133   SCHOPFER, W.H. (1935) - ETUDE SUR LES FACTEURS DE CROISSANCE. ACTION DE LA
       VITAMINE CRISTALLISEE B1 ET DE L'EXTRAIT DE GERME DE BLE SUR RHIZOPUS
       ET D'AUTRES MUCORINEES. Z.VITAMINFORSCHG 4, 187-206.

5134   SCHOULTIES, C.L. & YANG, C.Y. (1972) - SPORULATION OF APHANOMYCES EUTEI-
       CHES. PHYTOPATHOLOGY 62, 788 (ABS.).

5135   SCHRANTZ, J.P. (1960) - RECHERCHES SUR LES PYRENOMYCETES DE L'ORDRE DES
       DIATRYPALES SENSU M.CHADEFAUD. BULL.TRIMEST.SOC.MYCOL.FR. 76, 305-407.

5136   SCHREIBER, L.R. & GREEN, R.J. (1962) - COMPARATIVE SURVIVAL OF MYCELIUM,
       CONIDIA AND MICROSCLEROTIA OF VERTICILLIUM ALBO-ATRUM IN MINERAL SOIL.
       PHYTOPATHOLOGY 52, 288-289.

5137   SCHREIBER, L.R. & GREEN, R.J. (1966) - ANASTOMOSIS IN VERTICILLIUM ALBO-
       ATRUM IN SOIL. PHYTOPATHOLOGY 56, 1110-1111.

5138 SCHREUDER, W.H.E. (1954) - SCHIMMELAANTASTING VAN CACAOBONEN. CACAO, CHO-
      COLADE, SUIKERWERKEN 22, 1-8.

5139 SCHROEDER, C. (1972) - UNTERSUCHUNGEN ZUM WIRT-PARASIT-VERHAELTNIS VON
      TULPE UND BOTRYTIS SPP. 2. SAEURE- UND ENZYMBILDUNG VON BOTRYTIS CINE-
      REA UND BOTRYTIS TULIPAE. Z.PFLKRANKH.PFLPATH.PFLSCHUTZ 79, 94-104.

5140 SCHROEDER, H.W. & CHRISTENSEN, J.J. (1963) - FACTORS AFFECTING RESISTANCE
      OF WHEAT TO SCAB CAUSED BY GIBBERELLA ZEAE. PHYTOPATHOLOGY 53, 831-838.

5141 SCHROEDER, H.W. & VERRETT, M.J. (1969) - PRODUCTION OF AFLATOXIN BY ASPER-
      GILLUS WENTII WEHMER. CAN.J.MICROBIOL. 15, 895-898.

5142 SCHUBERT, J., AJELLO, L. & HALL, J. (1957) - VARIATION IN COMPLEMENT FIXA-
      TION ANTIGENICITY OF DIFFERENT YEAST PHASE STRAINS OF HISTOPLASMA CAP-
      SULATUM. J.LAB.CLIN.MED. 50, 304-307.

5143 SCHUBERT, J., AJELLO, L., STANFORD, S. & GRANT, V. (1953) - VARIATION IN
      COMPLEMENT FIXATION ANTIGEN PRODUCTION BY DIFFERENT STRAINS OF HISTO-
      PLASMA CAPSULATUM GROWN ON TWO MEDIA. J.LAB.CLIN.MED. 41, 91-97.

5144 SCHUEEPP, H. & FREI, E. (1969) - SOIL FUNGISTASIS WITH RESPECT TO PH AND
      PROFILE. CAN.J.MICROBIOL. 15, 1273-1279.

5145 SCHUETT, P. (1971) - UNTERSUCHUNGEN UEBER DEN EINFLUSS VON CUTICULARWACH-
      SEN AUF DIE INFEKTIONSFAEHIGKEIT PATHOGENER PILZE. 1. LOPHODERMIUM PI-
      NASTRI UND BOTRYTIS CINEREA. EUR.J.FOREST PATH. 1, 32-50.

5146 SCHUETT, P. (1973) - DIE WIRKUNG GASFOERMIGER BLATTAUSSCHEIDUNGEN AUF SPO-
      RENKEIMUNG UND MYZELENTWICKLUNG VON BOTRYTIS CINEREA. EUR.J.FOREST
      PATH. 3, 187-192.

5147 SCHUMAIER, G., DE VOLT, H.M., LAFFER, N.C. & CREEK, R.D. (1963) - STACHY-
      BOTRYOTOXICOSIS OF CHICKS. POULTRY SCI. 42, 70-74.

5148 SCHWARTZ, A. (1963) - MIKROBIELLE KORROSION VON KUNSTSTOFFEN UND IHREN BE-
      STANDTEILEN. AKADEMIE VERLAG, BERLIN.

5149 SCHWARTZ, I. & EMMONS, C.W. (1968) - SUBCUTANEOUS CYSTIC GRANULOMA CAUSED
      BY A FUNGUS OF WOOD PULP (PHIALOPHORA RICHARDSIAE). AM.J.CLIN.PATH. 49,
      500-505.

5150 SCHWARZE, P. & FRANDSEN, N.O. (1958) - BEOBACHTUNGEN UEBER DEN TRYPTOPHAN-
      ABBAU DURCH PILZE. PLANTA 50, 353-358.

5151 SCHWEISFURTH, R. (1969) - MANGANOXIDIERENDE PILZE. ZENTBL.BAKT.PARASITKDE,
      ABT.1, 212, 486-491.

5152 SCHWENK, E., ALEXANDER, G.J., GOLD, A.M. & STEVENS, D.F. (1958) - BIOGEN-
      ESIS OF CITRININ. J.BIOL.CHEM. 233, 1211-1213.

5153 SCHWINN, F.J. (1959) - UNTERSUCHUNGEN ZUR SYSTEMATIK DER GATTUNG PHY-
      TOPHTHORA DE BARY. ARCH.MIKROBIOL. 33, 223-252.

5154 SCHWINN, F.J. (1961) - DER NACHWEIS VON PHYTOPHTHORA CACTORUM (LEB. &
      COHN) SCHROET. IM BODEN. MITT.BIOL.BUNDANST.LD-U.FORSTW. 104, 42-44.

5155 SCHWINN, F.J. (1962) - PHYTOPHTHORA CITRICOLA SAWADA, EINE VARIETAET VON
      PHYTOPHTORA CACTORUM (LEB. & COHN) SCHROET. PHYTOPATH.Z. 45, 217-236.

5156 SCOTT, A.I., PHILLIPS, G.T. & KIRCHEIS, U. (1971) - BIOSYNTHESIS OF POLY-
      KETIDES. THE SYNTHESIS OF 6-METHYLSALICYLIC ACID AND TRIACETIC ACID LAC-
      TONE IN PENICILLIUM PATULUM. BIOORG.CHEM. 1, 380-399.

5157 SCOTT, A.I., ZAMIR, L., PHILLIPS, G.T. & YALPANI, M. (1973) - THE BIOSYNTHESIS OF PATULIN. BIOORG.CHEM. 2, 124-139.

5158 SCOTT, D.B. (1965) - TOXIGENIC FUNGI ISOLATED FROM CEREAL AND LEGUMES PRODUCTS. MYCOPATH.MYCOL.APPL. 25, 213-222.

5159 SCOTT, D.B. (1968) - THE GENUS EUPENICILLIUM LUDWIG. REP.COUN.SCIENT.IND. RES.S.AFR. 272, 150 PP.

5160 SCOTT, D.B. & STOLK, A.C. (1967) - STUDIES ON THE GENUS EUPENICILLIUM LUDWIG. 2. PERFECT STATES OF SOME PENICILLIA. ANTONIE VAN LEEUWENHOEK 33, 297-314.

5161 SCOTT, P.M., HARWIG, J., CHEN, Y.-K. & KENNEDY, B. (1975) - CYTOCHALASINS-A AND -B FROM STRAINS OF PHOMA EXIGUA VAR. EXIGUA AND FORMATION OF CYTOCHALASIN-B IN POTATO GANGRENE. J.GEN.MICROBIOL. 87, 177-180.

5162 SCOTT, P.M., KENNEDY, B., HARWIG, J. & CHEN, Y-K. (1974) - FORMATION OF DIKETO-PIPERAZINES BY PENICILLIUM ITALICUM ISOLATED FROM ORANGES. APPL. MICROBIOL. 28, 892-894.

5163 SCOTT, P.M., KENNEDY, B. & WALBEEK, W.VAN (1971) - SIMPLIFIED PROCEDURE FOR THE PURIFICATION OF OCHRATOXIN-A FROM EXTRACTS OF PENICILLIUM VIRIDICATUM. J.ASSOC.ANAL.CHEM. 54, 1445-1447.

5164 SCOTT, P.M., KENNEDY, B. & WALBEEK, W.VAN (1972) - DESOXYPATULINIC ACID FROM A PATULIN-PRODUCING STRAIN OF PENICILLIUM PATULUM. EXPERIENTIA 28, 1252.

5165 SCOTT, P.M., WALBLEEK, W.VAN, KENNEDY, B. & ANYETI, D. (1972) - MYCOTOXINS (OCHRATOXIN-A, CITRININ, AND STERIGMATOCYSTIN) AND TOXIGENIC FUNGI IN GRAINS AND OTHER AGRICULTURAL PRODUCTS. J.AGRIC.FD CHEM. 20, 1103-1109.

5166 SCOTT, P.M., WALBEEK, W.VAN & MACLEAN, W.M. (1971) - CLADOSPORIN, A NEW ANTIFUNGAL METABOLITE FROM CLADOSPORIUM CLADOSPORIOIDES. J.ANTIBIOT., TOKYO 24, 747-755.

5167 SCOTT, P.R. (1969) - EFFECTS OF NITROGEN AND GLUCOSE ON SAPROPHYTIC SURVIVAL OF OPHIOBOLUS GRAMINIS IN BURIED STRAW. ANN.APPL.BIOL. 63, 27-36.

5168 SCOTT, P.R. (1970) - PHIALOPHORA RADICICOLA, AN AVIRULENT PARASITE OF WHEAT AND GRASS ROOTS. TRANS.BR.MYCOL.SOC. 55, 163-167.

5169 SCOTT, W.W. (1961) - A MONOGRAPH OF THE GENUS APHANOMYCES. TECH.BULL.VA AGRIC.EXP.STN 151, 95 PP.

5170 SEAVER, F.J. (1928) - THE NORTH AMERICAN CUP-FUNGI (OPERCULATES). REPRINT HAFNER PUBL. CO., NEW YORK (1961), 377 PP.

5171 SEDLAR, L., DREYFUSS, M. & MUELLER, E. (1972) - KOMPATIBILITAETSVERHAELTNISSE IN CHAETOMIUM. 1. VORKOMMEN VON HOMO- UND HETEROTHALLIE IN ARTEN UND STAEMMEN. ARCH.MIKROBIOL. 83, 172-178.

5172 SEDLAR, L., MUELLER, E. & DREYFUSS, M. (1973) - KOMPATIBILITAETSVERHAELTNISSE IN CHAETOMIUM. 2. INTERSPEZIFISCHE FERTILITAET. ARCH.MIKROBIOL. 92, 105-113.

5173 SEDMERA, P., VOKOUN, J., PODOJIL, M., VANEK, Z., FUSKA, NEMEC, P. & KUHR, I. (1973) - STRUCTURE OF VERMICULINE, A NEW NINE-MEMBERED LACTONE FROM PENICILLIUM VERMICULATUM. TETRAHEDRON LETTERS, 1973 (16), 1347-1348.

5174   SEEMUELLER, E. (1968) - UNTERSUCHUNGEN UEBER DIE MORPHOLOGISCHE UND BIOLO-
       GISCHE DIFFERENZIERUNG IN DER FUSARIUM-SEKTION SPOROTRICHIELLA. MITT.
       BIOL.BUNDANST.LD-U.FORSTW. 127, 1-93.

5175   SEGEL, I.H. & JOHNSON, M.J. (1963) - INTERMEDIATES IN INORGANIC SULFATE
       UTILIZATION BY PENICILLIUM CHRYSOGENUM. ARCHS BIOCHEM.BIOPHYS. 103,
       216-226.

5176   SEGRETAIN, G. & DESTOMBES, P. (1961) - DESCRIPTION D'UN NOUVEL AGENT DE
       MADUROMYCOSE, NEOTESTUDINA ROSATII, N.GEN., N.SP., ISOLE EN AFRIQUE.
       C.R.HEBD.SEANC.ACAD.SCI., PARIS, SER.D, 253, 2577-2579.

5177   SEGRETAIN, G. & MARIAT, F. (1968) - RECHERCHES SUR LA PRESENCE D'AGENTS DE
       MYCETOMAS DANS LE SOL ET SUR LES EPINEUX DE SENEGAL ET DE LA MAURITANIE.
       BULL.SOC.PATH.EXOT. 61, 194-202.

5178   SEGRETAIN, G., MARIAT, F. & DESTOMBES, P. (1977) - CHAMPIGNONS AGENTS DE
       MYCETOMES DE L'HOMME. IN: TRAVAUX DEDIES A G. VIENNOT-BOURGIN, SOC.
       FRANC.PHYTOPATH., PARIS, 347-360.

5179   SEICHERTOVA, O. & LEOPOLD, H. (1969) - DIE AKTIVIERUNG VON STAEMMEN DES
       ASPERGILLUS NIGER. 1. DIE BILDUNG VON MUTANTEN DURCH WIEDERHOLTE BE-
       STRAHLUNG DER STAEMME MITTELS UV-LICHT. ZENTBL.BAKT.PARASITKDE, ABT.2,
       123, 559-563.

5180   SEIDEL, D. (1961) - DURCH ORGANISCHE DUENGUNG VERAENDERTE BIOLOGISCHE BO-
       DENVERHAELTNISSE IN IHRER BEDEUTUNG FUER PHYTOPATHOGENE BODENPILZE.
       WISS.Z.UNIV.ROSTOCK, REIHE MATH.NATURW. 10, 19-23.

5181   SEIDEL, D. (1965) - UNTERSUCHUNGEN UEBER DIE KEIMHEMMUNG VON PILZSPOREN IM
       BODEN MIT HILFE DES AGARSCHEIBENTESTS. ZENTBL.BAKT.PARASITKDE, ABT.2,
       119, 74-87.

5182   SEIDEL, D. (1966) - DIE WIRKUNG EINER STALLMISTDUENGUNG AUF DAS UEBERLEBEN
       PHYTOPATHOGENER BODENPILZE IN WIRTSPFLANZENRESTEN. WISS.Z.UNIV.ROSTOCK,
       REIHE MATH.NATURW. 15, 205-208.

5183   SEIDEL, D. (1970) - PFLANZEN IN IHREN AUSWIRKUNGEN AUF PHYTOPATHOGENE BO-
       DENPILZE. 3. HELMINTHOSPORIUM SATIVUM P., K. & B. ZENTBL.BAKT.PARASIT-
       KDE, ABT.2, 124, 441-445.

5184   SEIKETOV, G.SH. (1954) - (DER EINFLUSS DES ANTAGONISTEN TRICHODERMA AUF
       DEN RHIZOCTONIA BEFALL DER KARTOFFEL). DOKL.AKAD.NAUK KAZAKH.SSR, PHYS-
       IOL.MED., SER.3, 61-75.

5185   SEIKETOV, G.SH. (1962) - (FUNGI ANTAGONISTS OF THE TRICHODERMA FAMILY AND
       THEIR USE IN SOME POTATO DISEASES IN KAZAKHSTAN). TRANS.1ST ALL-UNION
       CONF.STUDY APPL.ANTIBIOT.PL.CULTURE, 147-152.

5186   SEIKETOV, G.S. & NIKITINA, E.T. (1962) - (PARASITIC FEATURES OF THE FUNGI
       OF THE GENUS TRICHODERMA ISOLATED FROM THE KAZAKHSTAN SOILS). TRUDY
       INST.MIKROBIOL.VIRUS ALMA ATA, 1962, 42-47.

5187   SEITZ, L.M. & MOHR, H.E. (1976) - ANALYSIS OF ALTERNARIA METABOLITES BY
       HIGH-PRESSURE LIQUID CHROMATOGRAPHY. ANALYT.BIOCHEM. 70, 224-230.

5188   SEKHON, A.S. & CARMICHAEL, J.W. (1975) - CLASSIFICATION OF SOME GYMNO-
       ASCACEAE BY PYROLYSIS GAS LIQUID CHROMATOGRAPHY USING ADDED MARKER COM-
       POUNDS. SABOURAUDIA 13, 83-88.

5189   SEKHON, A.S. & PADHYE, A.A. (1976) - MATING BEHAVIOUR OF CTENOMYCES SER-
       RATUS. MYCOPATHOLOGIA 60, 33-37.

5190   SEKHON, A.S., PADHYE, A.A. & CARMICHAEL, J.W. (1973) - MATING REACTIONS IN
       ARTHRODERMA TUBERCULATUM. SABOURAUDIA 11, 283-286.

5191   SEKHON, A.S., PADHYE, A.A. & CARMICHAEL, J.W. (1974) - DISC-GEL ELECTRO-
       PHORESIS OF + AND - STRAINS AND OF GYMNOTHECIAL CULTURES OF ARTHRODER-
       MA TUBERCULATUM. SABOURAUDIA 12, 12-17.

5192   SEKITA, S., YOSHIHIRA, K. & NATORI, S. (1973) - STRUCTURES OF CHAETOGLO-
       BOSIN-A AND -B, CYTOTOXIC METABOLITES OF CHAETOMIUM GLOBOSUM. TETRAHE-
       DRON LETTERS, 1973 (23), 2109-2112.

5193   SEKITA, S. YOSHIHIRA, K., NATORI, S. & KUWANO, H. (1976) - STRUCTURES OF
       CHAETOGLOBOSINS-C, -D, -E AND -F, CYTOTOXIC INDOL-3-YL-(13)-CYTOCHALA-
       SANS FROM CHAETOMIUM GLOBOSUM. TETRAHEDRON LETTERS, 1976, 1351.

5194   SELBY, K. & MAITLAND, C.C. (1967) - COMPONENTS OF TRICHODERMA VIRIDE CEL-
       LULASE. ARCHS BIOCHEM.BIOPHYS. 118, 254-257.

5195   SELBY, K. & MAITLAND, C.C. (1967) - THE CELLULASE OF TRICHODERMA VIRIDE.
       SEPERATION OF THE COMPONENTS INVOLVED IN THE SOLUBILIZATION OF COTTON.
       BIOCHEM.J. 104, 716-724.

5196   SELBY, K., MAITLAND, C.C. & THOMPSON, K.V.A. (1963) - THE DEGRADATION OF
       COTTON CELLULOSE BY EXTRACELLULAR CELLULASE OF MYROTHECIUM VERRUCARIA.
       BIOCHEM.J. 88, 288-296.

5197   SELVARAJ, J.C. (1973) - LIBERATION OF ENDO-POLYGALCTURONASE FROM THE CO-
       NIDIA OF VERTICILLIUM DAHLIAE. INDIAN PHYTOPATH. 26, 744-746.

5198   SELVARAJ, J.C. (1974) - EFFECT OF CARBON NITROGEN RATIO ON THE GROWTH AND
       CULTURAL CHARACTERISTICS OF VERTICILLIUM SPP. INDIAN PHYTOPATH. 26, 746-
       748.

5199   SELVARAJ, J.C. (1975) - DIFFERENTIAL GROWTH RESPONSE OF THE ISOLATES OF
       VERTICILLIUM DAHLIAE AND V. ALBO-ATRUM TO THE NUTRITION OF CERTAIN AMI-
       NO ACIDS. INDIAN PHYTOPATH. 27, 117-119.

5200   SELVARAJ, J.C. & MEYER, J.A. (1974) - ELECTROPHORETIC PROTEIN AND ENZYME
       PATTERNS AND ANTIGENIC STRUCTURE IN VERTICILLIUM DAHLIAE AND V. ALBO-
       ATRUM. MYCOPATH.MYCOL.APPL. 54, 549-558.

5201   SEMENIUK, G. & CARMICHAEL, J.W. (1966) - SPOROTRICHUM THERMOPHILE IN NORTH
       AMERICA. CAN.J.BOT. 44, 105-108.

5202   SEMENIUK, G. & HENRY, A.W. (1960) - RELATIVE DECLINE OF OPHIOBOLUS GRAMI-
       NIS, HELMINTHOSPORIUM SATIVUM AND FUSARIUM CULMORUM IN THE SOIL. CAN.J.
       PL.SCI. 40, 288-294.

5203   SEN GUPTA, P.-K. & DAS, C.-R. (1971) - STUDIES ON SOME ISOLATES OF SCLE-
       ROTIUM ROLFSII SACC. ANNLS PHYTOPATH. 3, 263-266.

5204   SEN GUPTA, R., CHANDRAN, R.R. & DIVEKAR, P.V. (1966) - BOTRYODIPLODIN - A
       NEW ANTIBIOTIC FROM BOTRYODIPLODIA THEOBROMAE PAT. 1. PRODUCTION, ISO-
       LATION AND BIOLOGICAL PROPERTIES. INDIAN J.EXPL BIOL. 4, 152-153.

5205   SENSER, F., REHM, H.-J. & RAUTENBERG, E. (1967) - ZUR KENNTNIS FRUCHTSAFT-
       VERDERBENDER MIKROORGANISMEN. 2. SCHIMMELPILZARTEN IN VERSCHIEDENEN
       FRUCHTSAEFTEN. ZENTBL.BAKT.PARASITKDE, ABT.2, 121, 736-746.

5206   SEO, J.S. (1959) - A STUDY OF CELLULASE PRODUCTION BY CERTAIN FUNGI. DISS.
       ABSTR. 20, 460.

5207   SEO, S., SANKAWA, U., OGIHARA, Y., IITAKA, Y. & SHIBATA, S. (1973) - STUD-
       IES ON FUNGAL METABOLITES. 32. A RENEWED INVESTIGATION ON (-)-FLAVOSKY-
       RIN AND ITS ANALOGUES. TETRAHEDRON 29, 3721-3726.

5208   SEQUEIRA, L. (1962) - INFLUENCE OF ORGANIC AMENDMENTS ON SURVIVAL OF FU-
       SARIUM OXYSPORUM F. CUBENSE IN THE SOIL. PHYTOPATHOLOGY 52, 976-983.

5209   SEREBRYAKOV, E.P., SIMOLIN, A.V., KUCHEROV, V.F. & ROSYNOV, B.V. (1970) -
       NEW METABOLITES OF FUSARIUM MONILIFORME SHELD. TETRAHEDRON 26, 5215-
       5223.

5210   SERGEEVA, N.V. (1961) - (THE SPECIES COMPOSITION OF BACTERIA DECOMPOSING
       TRICALCIUM PHOSPHATE AND THEIR PHYSIOLOGICAL ACTIVITY). IZV.MOLDAV.FIL.
       AKAD.NAUK SSSR, 1961, 66-71.

5211   SERGEJEVA, K.S. (1961) - SPECIES NOVAE GENERIS CHAETOMIUM. 3. NOT.SYST.
       SECT.CRYPT.INST.BOT.KOMAROVII 14, 139-150.

5212   SESHADRI, K. & PAYAK, M.M. (1970) - NUCLEAR STRUCTURE AND BEHAVIOUR IN THE
       VEGETATIVE HYPHAE OF PYTHIUM APHANIDERMATUM. MYCOPATH.MYCOL.APPL. 40,
       145-153.

5213   SETH, H.K. (1967) - STUDIES ON THE GENUS CHAETOMIUM. 1. HETEROTHALLISM.
       MYCOLOGIA 59, 580-584.

5214   SETH, H.K. (1967) - CHAETOMIDIUM SUBFIMETI N.SP. FROM WALES. TRANS.BR.MY-
       COL.SOC. 50, 45-47.

5215   SETH, H.K. (1968) - COPROPHILIC ASCOMYCOTA FROM GERMANY. NOVA HEDWIGIA 16,
       495-499.

5216   SETH, H.K. (1970) - A MONOGRAPH OF THE GENUS CHAETOMIUM. NOVA HEDWIGIA,
       BEIH., 37, 134 PP.

5217   SETHI, K.K., RANDHAWA, H.S., KURUP, P.V. & AJELLO, L. (1967) - ISOLATION
       OF MICROSPORUM VANBREUSEGHEMII FROM SOIL IN INDIA. SABOURAUDIA 6, 81-82.

5218   SETLIFF, D.L. & WANG, C.J.K. (1970) - FLUORESCENT ANTIBODY STUDIES OF THE
       BLACK YEASTS. RECENT TRENDS YEAST RES. 1, 161-180.

5219   SEVILLA, M.J., ISUSI, P., GUTIERREZ, R., EGA, L. & URUBURU, F. (1977) -
       INFLUENCE OF CARBON AND NITROGEN SOURCES ON THE MORPHOLOGY OF PULLULA-
       RIA PULLULANS. TRANS.BR.MYCOL.SOC. 68, 300-303.

5220   SEWELL, G.W.F. (1959) - STUDIES OF FUNGI IN A CALLUNA HEATHLAND SOIL. 1.
       VERTICAL DISTRIBUTION IN SOIL AND ON ROOT SURFACES. TRANS.BR.MYCOL.SOC.
       42, 343-353.

5221   SEWELL, G.W.F. (1959) - STUDIES OF FUNGI IN A CALLUNA HEATHLAND SOIL. 2.
       BY THE COMPLEMENTARY USE OF SEVERAL ISOLATION METHODS. TRANS.BR.MYCOL.
       SOC. 42, 354-369.

5222   SEWELL, G.W.F. (1959) - THE ECOLOGY OF FUNGI IN CALLUNA-HEATHLAND SOILS.
       NEW PHYTOL. 58, 5-15.

5223   SEWELL, G.W.F. & BROWN, J.C. (1959) - ECOLOGY OF MUCOR RAMANNIANUS MOELLER.
       NATURE, LOND. 183, 1344-1345.

5224   SEWELL, G.W.F. & WILSON, J.F. (1966) - VERTICILLIUM WILT OF THE HOP. THE
       SURVIVAL OF V. ALBO-ATRUM IN SOIL. ANN.APPL.BIOL. 58, 241-249.

5225   SEWELL, G.W.F., WILSON, J.F. & DAKWA, J.T. (1974) - SEASONAL VARIATIONS IN
       THE ACTIVITY IN SOIL OF PHYTOPHTHORA CACTORUM, P. SYRINGAE AND P. CITRI-
       COLA IN RELATION TO COLLAR ROT DISEASE OF APPLE. ANN.APPL.BIOL. 76, 179-
       186.

5226   SHAMEEMULLAH, M., PARKINSON, D. & BURGES, A. (1971) - THE INFLUENCE OF SOIL
       MOISTURE TENSION ON THE FUNGAL POPULATION OF A PINEWOOD SOIL. CAN.J.MI-
       CROBIOL. 17, 975-986.

5227   SHAPOVALOV, M. (1927) - THE TWO MOST COMMON DECAYS OF COTTON BOLLS IN THE
       SOUTHWESTERN STATES. J.AGRIC.RES. 35, 307-312.

5228   SHARAPOV, V.M. (1974) - (NEW KERATINOPHILIC FUNGAL SPECIES AND NEW USSR
       RECORDS). NOV.SIST.NIZSHIKH RAST 11, 266-271.

5229   SHARAPOV, V.M. & KUZMINA, V.S. (1976) - (KERATINOPHILIC FUNGI IN BIRDS IN
       WEST SIBERIA). MIKOL.FITOPAT. 10, 380-384.

5230   SHARDA, D.P., WILSON, R.F., WILLIAMS, L.E. & SWIGER, L.A. (1971) - EFFECT
       OF FEEDING CORN INOCULATED WITH NIGROSPORA ORYZAE AND CLADOSPORIUM ON
       THE PERFORMANCE OF GROWING SWINE AND RATS. J.ANIM.SCI. 33, 1259-1262.

5231   SHARMA, K.R. & MUKERJI, K.G. (1972) - SUCCESSION OF FUNGI ON COTTON LEAVES.
       ANNLS INST.PASTEUR, PARIS 122, 425-454.

5232   SHARMA, K.R. & MUKERJI, K.G. (1973) - ASEXUAL COMPLEMENTATION AFFECTING
       PYCNIDIUM PRODUCTION IN PHOMA EXIGUA. MYCOLOGIA 65, 709-712.

5233   SHARMA, P.D. (1973) - SUCCESSION OF FUNGI ON DECAYING SETARIA GLAUCA
       BEAUV. A QUALITATIVE ANALYSIS OF THE MYCOFLORA. ANN.BOT. 37, 203-208.

5234   SHARMA, P.D. (1974) - EXPERIMENTAL STUDIES ON SOME MICROFUNGI FROM DECAY-
       ING SHOOTS OF SETARIA GLAUCA. TRANS.BR.MYCOL.SOC. 63, 397-400.

5235   SHARMA, R.D. & SINGH, R.S. (1973) - A TECHNIQUE FOR SELECTIVE ISOLATION OF
       FUSARIUM MONILIFORME FROM SOIL AND PLANT TISSUES. INDIAN J.MYCOL.PL.
       PATH. 3, 67-70.

5236   SHARP, E.L. (1959) - TWO PREVIOUSLY UNREPORTED FUNGI ON CEREALS IN MONTA-
       NA. PL.DIS.REPTR 43, 12-13.

5237   SHARP, R.F. (1975) - THE MICROBIAL COLONIZATION OF SOME WOODS OF SMALL DI-
       MENSIONS BURIED IN SOIL. CAN.J.MICROBIOL. 21, 784-793.

5238   SHARP, R.F. (1975) - SOME OBSERVATIONS ON THE PENETRATION SEQUENCES, EFFECT
       OF PH AND HUMUS FORMATION BY WOOD MICROFUNGI. MYCOPATHOLOGIA 55, 41-46.

5239   SHARP, R.F. & EGGINS, H.O.W. (1970) - THE ECOLOGY OF SOFT-ROT FUNGI. 1. IN-
       FLUENCE OF PH. INT.BIODETERIOR.BULL. 6, 53-64.

5240   SHARP, R.F. & MILLS, J. (1973) - HUMUS SUBSTANCES FROM SOME WOOD MICROFUN-
       GI. MATER.ORG. 8, 145-155.

5241   SHATLA, M.N. & SINCLAIR, J.B. (1963) - TOLERANCE TO PENTACHLORONITROBEN-
       ZENE AMONG COTTON ISOLATES OF RHIZOCTONIA SOLANI. PHYTOPATHOLOGY 53,
       1407-1411.

5242   SHATLA, M.N. & SINCLAIR, J.B. (1964) - NUCLEAR CONDITION AND DIVISION IN
       VEGETATIVE HYPHAE OF RHIZOCTONIA SOLANI. PHYTOPATHOLOGY 54, 907 (ABS.).

5243   SHATLA, M.N., YANG, C.Y. & MITCHELL, J.E. (1966) - CYTOLOGICAL AND FINE-
       STRUCTURE STUDIES OF APHANOMYCES EUTEICHES. PHYTOPATHOLOGY 56, 923-928.

5244   SHAW, D.E. & VALDER, P.G. (1953) - A STUDY OF THE MICROFLORA OF WHEAT GRAINS
       IN NEW SOUTH WALES. PROC.LINN.SOC.N.S.W. 77, 307-322.

5245   SHAW, P.D. & GOTTLIEB, D. (1966) - THE ORIGIN OF 3-NITROPROPIONIC ACID IN
       FUNGI. BIOGENESIS ANTIBIOT.SUBST., MATER.PANEL DISC.CONGR.ANTIBIOT.,
       PRAHA, 261-269, 1966.

5246   SHAW, R. (1968) - PROTEOLYTIC ENZYMES OF PENICILLIUM JANTHINELLUM. 2. PROP-
       ERTIES OF PEPTIDASE-B. BIOCHIM.BIOPHYS.ACTA 92, 558-567.

5247   SHCHERBINA, S.M. (1973) - (EFFECT OF DIFFERENT SOURCES OF NITROGEN NUTRI-
       TION ON BIOSYNTHESIS OF GROUP B VITAMINS IN FUSARIUM MONILIFORME). MY-
       KROBIOL.ZH. 35, 713-718.

5248   SHEAR, C.L. (1925) - THE LIFE HISTORY OF THE TEXAS ROOT ROT FUNGUS, OZO-
       NIUM OMNIVORUM SHEAR. J.AGRIC.RES. 30, 475-477.

5249   SHEARER, C.A. (1972) - FUNGI OF THE CHESAPEAKE BAY AND ITS TRIBUTARIES. 3.
       THE DISTRIBUTION OF WOOD-INHABITING ASCOMYCETES AND FUNGI IMPERFECTI OF
       THE PATUXENT RIVER. AM.J.BOT. 59, 961-969.

5250   SHEARER, C.A. & CRANE, J.L. (1971) - FUNGI OF THE CHESAPEAKE BAY AND ITS
       TRIBUTARIES. 1. PATUXENT RIVER. MYCOLOGIA 63, 237-260.

5251   SHECHTER, I. (1973) - BIOSYNTHESIS OF TRANS-FARNESYL TRIPHOSPHATE IN GIB-
       BERELLA FUJIKUROI. BIOCHIM.BIOPHYS.ACTA 316, 222-234.

5252   SHEKHOVTSOV, A.G. (1975) - (FUNGAL SPECIES NEW AND RARE FOR MYCOFLORA OF
       THE USSR). MYKROBIOL.ZH. 37, 232-234.

5253   SHEPHERD, A.M. (1956) - A SHORT SURVEY OF DANISH NEMATOPHAGOUS FUNGI.
       FRIESIA 5, 396-408.

5254   SHEPHERD, C.J. & PRATT, B.H. (1974) - TEMPERATURE - GROWTH RELATIONS AND
       GENETIC DIVERSITY OF A2 MATING-TYPE ISOLATES OF PHYTOPHTHORA CINNAMOMI
       IN AUSTRALIA. AUST.J.BOT. 22, 231-249.

5255   SHEPHERD, C.J., PRATT, B.H. & TAYLOR, P.A. (1974) - COMPARATIVE MORPHOLOGY
       AND BEHAVIOR OF A1 AND A2 ISOLATES OF PHYTOPHTHORA CINNAMOMI. AUST.J.
       BOT. 22, 461-470.

5256   SHERIDAN, J.E. (1971) - THE KEROSENE FUNGUS AMORPHOTHECA RESINAE PARBERY
       AS A NATURAL COMPONENT OF THE AIRSPORA AND ON BIRD FEATHERS. N.Z.JL SCI.
       14, 1094-1096.

5257   SHERIDAN, J.E. (1974) - ISOLATION AND GEOGRAPHIC DISTRIBUTION OF CLADOSPO-
       RIUM RESINAE IN SOIL AND AIR. N.Z.JL SCI. 17, 545-550.

5258   SHERIDAN, J.E. & NELSON, J. (1971) - THE SELECTIVE ISOLATION OF THE KERO-
       SENE FUNGUS FROM THE AIR. INT.BIODETERIOR.BULL. 7, 161-162.

5259   SHERIDAN, J.E., NELSON, J. & TAN, Y.L. (1972) - STUDIES ON THE KEROSENE
       FUNGUS CLADOSPORIUM RESINAE. 2. THE NATURAL HABITAT OF CLADOSPORIUM RE-
       SINAE. TUATARA 19, 70-96.

5260   SHERIDAN, J.E. & SHERIDAN, M. (1972) - PERIODICITY OF THE KEROSENE FUNGUS,
       AMORPHOTHECA RESINAE PARBERY, CONIDIAL STATE CLADOSPORIUM RESINAE (LIN-
       DAU) DE VRIES, IN THE ATMOSPHERE OVER WELLINGTON, NEW ZEALAND, IN 1971.
       SEARCH 3, 385-386.

5261   SHERIDAN, J.E. & SOTEROS, J.J. (1974) - A SURVEY OF FUNGI IN JET AIRCRAFT
       FUEL SYSTEMS IN NEW ZEALAND. INT.BIODETERIOR.BULL. 10, 105-107.

5262   SHERIDAN, J.E. & STEEL, J. (1971) - NATURE OF ASCAL STATE OF AMORPHOTHECA
       RESINAE IN MINERAL OIL. TRANS.BR.MYCOL.SOC. 56, 477-478.

5263   SHERIDAN, J.E., STEEL, J. & KNOX, M.D.E. (1971) - THE NATURAL OCCURRENCE
       OF THE KEROSENE FUNGUS AMORPHOTHECA RESINAE IN NEW ZEALAND SOILS. N.Z.
       JL SCI. 14, 147-160.

5264   SHERIDAN, J.E., TAN, Y.L. & NELSON, J. (1972) - STUDIES ON THE KEROSENE
       FUNGUS CLADOSPORIUM RESINAE. 3. MORPHOLOGY, TAXONOMY AND PHYSIOLOGY.
       TUATARA 19, 130-175.

5265   SHERIDAN, J.E. & TROUGHTON, J.H. (1973) - CONIDIOPHORES AND CONIDIA OF THE
       KEROSENE FUNGUS CLADOSPORIUM RESINAE IN THE LIGHT AND SCANNING ELECTRON
       MICROSCOPES. N.Z.JL BOT. 11, 145-152.

5266   SHERROD, L.L. & DOMSCH, K.H. (1970) - THE ROLE OF PHENOLS AND BETA-GLYCO-
       SIDASE IN THE PATHOGENICITY MECHANISM OF GLIOCLADIUM CATENULATUM TO
       ROOTS OF PEAS (PISUM SATIVUM L.). SOIL BIOL.BIOCHEM. 2, 19, 197-201.

5267   SHERWOOD, M. & CARROLL, G. (1974) - FUNGAL SUCCESSION ON NEEDLES AND YOUNG
       TWIGS OF OLD-GROWTH DOUGLAS FIR. MYCOLOGIA 66, 499-506.

5268   SHERWOOD, R.T. (1964) - PECTINTRANSELIMINASE AND POLYGALACTURONASE PRODUC-
       TION BY RHIZOCTONIA SOLANI AND OTHER FUNGI. PHYTOPATHOLOGY 54, 907 (ABS.)

5269   SHERWOOD, R.T. (1966) - PECTIC LYASE UND POLYGALACTURONASE PRODUCTION BY
       RHIZOCTONIA SOLANI AND OTHER FUNGI. PHYTOPATHOLOGY 56, 279-286.

5270   SHERWOOD, R.T. (1967) - ANASTOMOSIS IN RELATION TO MORPHOLOGY AND PHYSIOL-
       OGY OF RHIZOCTONIA SOLANI. PHYTOPATHOLOGY 57, 830-831 (ABS.).

5271   SHERWOOD, R.T. (1969) - MORPHOLOGY AND PHYSIOLOGY IN FOUR ANASTOMOSIS
       GROUPS OF THANATEPHORUS CUCUMERIS. PHYTOPATHOLOGY 59, 1924-1929.

5272   SHERWOOD, R.T. (1970) - PHYSIOLOGY OF RHIZOCTONIA SOLANI. IN: RHIZOCTONIA
       SOLANI, BIOLOGY AND PATHOLOGY, SYMPOSIUM 1965; PARMETER, J.JR. (ED.),
       UNIV.CALIFORNIA PRESS, BERKELEY, 69-92.

5273   SHERWOOD, R.T. & HAGEDORN, D.J. (1961) - EFFECT OF OXYGEN TENSION ON GROWTH
       OF APHANOMYCES EUTEICHES. PHYTOPATHOLOGY 51, 492-493.

5274   SHERWOOD, R.T. & HAGEDORN, D.J. (1962) - STUDIES ON THE BIOLOGY OF APHANO-
       MYCES EUTEICHES. PHYTOPATHOLOGY 52, 150-154.

5275   SHERWOOD, R.T. & LINDBERG, C.G. (1962) - PRODUCTION OF A PHYTOTOXIN BY
       RHIZOCTONIA SOLANI. PHYTOPATHOLOGY 52, 586-587.

5276   SHIBATA, S. (1973) - SOME RECENT STUDIES ON THE METABOLITES OF FUNGI AND
       LICHENS. PURE APPL.CHEM. 33, 109-128.

5277   SHIBATA, SH., MORISHITA, E. TAKEDA, T. & SAKATA, K. (1966) - STRUCTURE OF
       AUROFUSARIN. TETRAHEDRON LETTERS, 1966, 4855-4860.

5278   SHIBATA, SH., NATORI, S. & UDAGAWA, S. (1964) - LIST OF FUNGAL PRODUCTS.
       UNIV.TOKYO PRESS.

5279   SHIBATA, Y. & FUKIMBARA, T. (1973) - A BETA-1,6-GLUCANOHYDROLASE FROM GIB-
       BERELLA FUJIKUROI. J.FERMENT.TECHNOL., OSAKA 51, 216-226.

5280 SHIEH, T.R. & WARE, J.H. (1968) - SURVEY OF MICROORGANISMS FOR THE PRODUC-
TION OF EXTRACELLULAR PHYTASE. APPL.MICROBIOL. 16, 1348-1351.

5281 SHIGEURA, H.T. & GORDON, C.N. (1963) - THE BIOLOGICAL ACTIVITY OF TENUAZO-
NIC ACID. BIOCHEMISTRY 2, 1132-1137.

5282 SHIGO, A.L. (1958) - FUNGI ISOLATED FROM OAK-WILT TREES AND THEIR EFFECTS
ON CERATOCYSTIS FAGACEARUM. MYCOLOGIA 50, 757-769.

5283 SHIGO, A.L. (1971) - SUCCESSION OF MICROORGANISMS AND PATTERNS OF DISCOLOR-
ATION AND DECAY AFTER WOUNDING IN RED OAK AND WHITE OAK. PHYTOPATHOLOGY
62, 256-259.

5284 SHIGO, A.L. (1972) - THE BEECH BARK DISEASE TODAY IN THE NORTHEASTERN U.S.
J.FOR. 70, 286-289.

5285 SHIH, C.N. & MARTH, E.H. (1973) - AFLATOXIN PRODUCED BY ASPERGILLUS PARA-
SITICUS WHEN INCUBATED IN THE PRESENCE OF DIFFERENT GASES. J.MILK FD
TECHNOL. 36, 421-425.

5286 SHIH, C.N. & MARTH, E.H. (1974) - SOME CULTURAL CONDITIONS THAT CONTROL
BIOSYNTHESIS OF LIPID AND AFLATOXIN BY ASPERGILLUS PARASITICUS. APPL.
MICROBIOL. 27, 452-456.

5287 SHIH, C.N. & MARTH, E.H. (1975) - PRODUCTION OF ALFATOXIN AND ITS PARTI-
TION BETWEEN THE MEDIUM AND THE MYCELIUM OF ASPERGILLUS PARASITICUS
DURING INCUBATION UNDER VARIOUS CONDITIONS. Z.LEBENSMITTEL UNTERS.FORSCH.
158, 215-224.

5288 SHIKATA, S. (1964) - MULTIPLICITY OF THE CELLULOLYTIC SYSTEM OF TRICHODER-
MA VIRIDE. J.BIOCHEM., TOKYO 56, 1-5.

5289 SHIMADA, K., MATSUSHIMA, K., FUKUMOTO, J. & YAMAMOTO, T. (1969) - POLY-(L)-
MALIC ACID - A NEW PROTEASE INHIBITOR FROM PENICILLIUM CYCLOPIUM. BIO-
CHEM.BIOPHYS.RES.COMMUNS 35, 619-624.

5290 SHIMI, I.R., IMAM, G.M. & SAAD, A. (1966) - NEGAPILLIN, A NEW ANTIBIOTIC
ISOLATED FROM METABOLITES OF PENICILLIUM CHRYSOGENUM. J.ANTIBIOT., TO-
KYO, SER.A, 19, 19-22.

5291 SHIMI, I.R., NOUR EL DEIN, M.S. & IMAM, G.M. (1961) - BIOSYNTHESIS OF FAT
FROM SOME ORGANIC ACIDS IN SUBMERGED CULTURES OF PENICILLIUM SPINULO-
SUM. ARCH.MIKROBIOL. 39, 292-297.

5292 SHIPTON, P.J., COOK, R.J. & SITTON, J.W. (1973) - OCCURRENCE AND TRANSFER
OF A BIOLOGICAL FACTOR IN SOIL THAT SUPPRESSES TAKE-ALL OF WHEAT IN
EASTERN WASHINGTON. PHYTOPATHOLOGY 63, 511-517.

5293 SHIPTON, W.A. & CHAMBERS, S.C. (1966) - THE INTERNAL MICROFLORA OF WHEAT
GRAINS IN WESTERN AUSTRALIA. AUST.J.EXP.AGRIC.ANIM.HUSB. 6, 432-436.

5294 SHIRAISHI, M., FUKUTOMI, M. & AKAI, S. (1970) - ON THE MYCELIAL GROWTH AND
SPORULATION OF BOTRYTIS CINEREA AND THE CONIDIUM GERMINATION AND APPRES-
SORIUM FORMATION AS AFFECTED BY THE CONIDIAL AGE. EFFECTS OF TEMPERA-
TURE ON THE CONIDIUM GERMINATION AND APPRESSORIUM FORMATION OF BOTRYTIS
CINEREA. ANN.PHYTOPATH.SOC.JAPAN 36, 230-236.

5295 SHKLYAR, M.S. (1961) - (EINFLUSS VON STOFFWECHSELPRODUKTEN VON FUSARIUM
MONILIFORME AUF SAMENKEIMUNG UND PFLANZENWACHSTUM). TRUDY INST.MIKRO-
BIOL.AKAD.NAUK LATV. SSR 11, 318-326.

5296 SHKLYAR, M.S. & KHALIMOVA, L.A. (1962) - (ON THE TOXIC ACTION OF BACTERIA
OF THE GENUS PSEUDOMONAS ON PLANT SEED). UZBEK.BIOL.ZH. 6, 21-25.

5297   SHKURENKO, V.A. (1966) - (THERMOPHILIC SPECIES OF THE GENUS ASPERGILLUS IN
       VARIOUS SOILS OF THE UKRAINE). MYKROBIOL.ZH. 28 (5), 29-35.

5298   SHKURENKO, V.A. (1967) - (OCCURRENCE OF WARMTH-LOVING FUNGI OF THE ORDER
       MUCORALES IN SOME SOILS OF THE UKRAINIAN SSR). MYKROBIOL.ZH. 29 (1),
       10-12.

5299   SHMOTINA, G.E., KOKURINA, M.A. & GORLENKO, M.V. (1971) - (DNA NUCLEOTIDE
       COMPOSITION OF THE CAUSAL AGENT OF PLANT VERTICILLIUM WILT). MIKOL.FI-
       TOPAT. 5, 311-313.

5300   SHMYGUN, M.P., ZHDANOVA, N.N. & SVISHCHUK, A.A. (1975) - (ON BELONGING OF
       DARK PIGMENT OF OIDIODENDRON CEREALIS TO MELANINS). MYKROBIOL.ZH. 37,
       700-702.

5301   SHOEMAKER, P.B. & LORBEER, J.W. (1971) - THE ROLE OF DEW AND TEMPERATURE
       IN THE EPIDEMIOLOGY OF BOTRYTIS LEAF BLIGHT OF ONION. PHYTOPATHOLOGY
       61, 910 (ABS.).

5302   SHOEMAKER, R.A. (1955) - BIOLOGY, CYTOLOGY AND TAXONOMY OF COCHLIOBOLUS
       SATIVUS. CAN.J.BOT. 33, 562-576.

5303   SHOEMAKER, R.A. (1959) - NOMENCLATURE OF DRECHSLERA AND BIPOLARIS, GRASS
       PARASITES SEGREGATED FROM HELMINTHOSPORIUM. CAN.J.BOT. 37, 879-887.

5304   SHOEMAKER, R.A. (1962) - DRECHSLERA ITO. CAN.J.BOT. 40, 809-836.

5305   SHOEMAKER, R.A. & MUELLER, E. (1963) - GENERIC CORRELATIONS AND CONCEPTS.
       BROOMELLA AND PESTALOTIA. CAN.J.BOT. 41, 1235-1244.

5306   SHOPE, R.E. (1953) - AN ANTIVIRAL SUBSTANCE FROM PENICILLIUM FUNICULOSUM.
       1. EFFECT UPON INFECTION IN MICE WITH SWINE INFLUENZA VIRUS AND COLUM-
       BIA-SK ENCEPHALOMYELITIS VIRUS. J.EXP.MED. 97, 601-650.

5307   SHOPE, R.E. (1953) - AN ANTIVIRAL SUBSTANCE FROM PENICILLIUM FUNICOLOSUM.
       2. EFFECT OF HELENINE UPON INFECTION IN MICE WITH SEMLIKI FOREST VIRUS.
       J.EXP.MED. 97, 627-638.

5308   SHREEMALI, J.L. (1973) - THE EFFECT OF CARBON AND NITROGEN SOURCES ON THE
       GROWTH AND SPORULATION OF SIX DIFFERENT ISOLATES OF BOTRYODIPLODIA THEO-
       BROMAE. INDIAN PHYTOPATH. 26, 220-224.

5309   SHU-CHEN SUNG (1965) - CUP-PLATE ASSAY OF PROTEINASE, LIPASE, AND PHOSPHA-
       TASE OF MUCOR. BULL.INST.CHEM.ACAD.SINICA 10, 69-74.

5310   SHUKLA, D.S. (1972) - STUDIES ON THE GROWTH AND SPORULATION OF COLLETOTRI-
       CHUM GLOEOSPORIOIDES IN RELATION TO VITAMINS. INDIAN PHYTOPATH. 25, 300-
       302.

5311   SHUKLA, D.S. & SARKAR, S.K. (1972) - EFFECT OF VITAMINS ON THE GROWTH AND
       SPORULATION OF BOTRYODIPLODIA THEOBROMAE IN CULTURE. INDIAN PHYTOPATH.
       25, 40-43.

5312   SHUKLA, T.N. & BAIS, B.S. (1971) - EFFECT OF CERTAIN VITAMINS ON THE GROWTH
       AND SPORULATION OF CURVULARIA LUNATA (WAKKER) BOEDIJN. MYCOPATH.MYCOL.
       APPL. 45, 109-111.

5313   SIDDIQI, M.A. (1964) - FUNGUS FLORA OF COFFEA ARABICA IN NYASALAND. TRANS.
       BR.MYCOL.SOC. 47, 281-284.

5314 SIDDIQUI, M.R. & KHAN, I.D. (1973) - FUNGI AND FACTORS ASSOCIATED WITH THE
      DEVELOPMENT OF SORGHUM EAR-MOLDS. TRANS.MYCOL.SOC.JAPAN 14, 289-293.

5315 SIEGLE, H. (1961) - UEBER MISCHINFEKTIONEN MIT OPHIOBOLUS GRAMINIS AND DI-
      DYMELLA EXITIALIS. PHYTOPATH.Z. 42, 305-348.

5316 SIEPMANN, R. (1959) - EIN BEITRAG ZUR SAPROPHYTISCHEN PILZFLORA DES WATTES
      DER WESERMUENDUNG. VEROEFF.INST.MEERESFORSCH.BREMERHAVEN 6, 213-301.

5317 SIERANKIEWICZ, J. & GATENBECK, S. (1972) - A NEW DEPSIDONE FROM ASPERGIL-
      LUS NIDULANS. ACTA CHEM.SCAND. 26, 455-458.

5318 SIETSMA, J.H. & HASKINS, R.H. (1967) - FURTHER STUDIES ON STEROL STIMULA-
      TION OF SEXUAL REPRODUCTION IN PYTHIUM. CAN.J.MICROBIOL. 13, 361-367.

5319 SIETSMA, J.H. & WOUTERS, J.T.M. (1971) - CELL WALL COMPOSITION AND 'PROTO-
      PLAST' FORMATION OF GEOTRICHUM CANDIDUM. ARCH.MIKROBIOL. 79, 263-273.

5320 SIGG, H.P. & WEBER, H.P. (1968) - ISOLIERUNG UND STRUKTURAUFKLAERUNG VON
      OVALICIN. HELV.CHIM.ACTA 51, 1395-1408.

5321 SIGGEIRSSON, E.I. (1976) - SNAESVEPPUR (FUSARIUM NIVALE (FR.) CES.).
      RANNSOKNASTOFNUNIN NEDRI AS, HVERAGERDI, NO.14, 13 PP.

5322 SIGLER, L. & CARMICHAEL, J.W. (1976) - TAXONOMY OF MALBRANCHEA AND SOME
      OTHER HYPHOMYCETES WITH ARTHROCONIDIA. MYCOTAXON 4, 349-488.

5323 SIH, C.J. (1958) - THE CARBOHYDRATE METABOLISM AND CYTOCHROME OXIDASE OF
      PENICILLIUM CHRYSOGENUM. DISS.ABSTR. 18, 1944.

5324 SIKURA, A.N. & BEVZENKO, T.M. (1974) - (ACTIVITY OF SOME ENZYMES OF THE
      FUNGUS BEAUVERIA BASSIANA UNDER DEEP CULTIVATION CONDITIONS). MIKOL.FI-
      TOPAT. 8, 65-67.

5325 SILVA, R.L.DE & WOOD, R.K.S. (1964) - INFECTION OF PLANTS BY CORTICIUM SO-
      LANI AND C. PRATICOLA. EFFECT OF PLANT EXUDATES. TRANS.BR.MYCOL.SOC.
      47, 15-24.

5326 SILVERMAN, M.P. & MUNOZ, E.F. (1970) - FUNGAL ATTACK ON ROCK-SOLUBILIZA-
      TION AND ALTERED INFRARED SPECTRA. SCIENCE, N.Y. 169, 985-987.

5327 SILVERMAN, M.P. & MUNOZ, E.F. (1971) - FUNGAL LEACHING OF TITANIUM FROM
      ROCK. APPL.MICROBIOL. 22, 923-924.

5328 SIMMONDS, J.H. (1965) - A STUDY OF THE SPECIES OF COLLETOTRICHUM CAUSING
      RIPE FRUIT ROTS IN QUEENSLAND. QD J.AGRIC.ANIM.SCI. 22, 437-459.

5329 SIMMONDS, P.M. (1947) - THE INFLUENCE OF ANTIBIOSIS IN THE PATHOGENICITY
      OF HELMINTHOSPORIUM SATIVUM. SCIENT.AGRIC. 27, 625-632.

5330 SIMMONDS, P.M. & LEDINGHAM, R.J. (1937) - A STUDY OF THE FUNGUS FLORA WHEAT
      ROOTS. SCIENT.AGRIC. 18, 49-59.

5331 SIMMONDS, P.M., SALLANS, B.J. & LEDINGHAM, R.J. (1950) - THE OCCURRENCE OF
      HELMINTHOSPORIUM SATIVUM IN RELATION TO PRIMARY INFECTIONS IN COMMON
      ROOTROT OF WHEAT. SCIENT.AGRIC. 30, 407-417.

5332 SIMMONS, E.G. (1967) - TYPIFICATION OF ALTERNARIA, STEMPHYLIUM, AND ULOCLA-
      DIUM. MYCOLOGIA 59, 67-92.

5333 SIMMONS, E.G. (1969) - PERFECT STATES OF STEMPHYLIUM. MYCOLOGIA 61, 1-26.

5334 SIMONART, P. & CHOW, K.Y. (1951) - SEPARATION CHROMATOGRAPHIQUE DE L'AMY-
LASE ET DE LA PROTEINASE D'ASPERGILLUS TAMARII. ENZYMOLOGIA 14, 356-361.

5335 SIMONSON, L.G. & LIBERTA, A.E. (1975) - NEW SOURCES OF FUNGAL DEXTRANASE.
MYCOLOGIA 67, 845-862.

5336 SIMONSON, L.G., LIBERTA, A.E. & RICHARDSON, A. (1975) - CHARACTERIZATION
OF AN EXTRACELLULAR DEXTRANASE FROM FUSARIUM MONILIFORME. APPL.MICRO-
BIOL. 30, 855-861.

5337 SIMORDOVA, M. & HEJTMANEK, M. (1970) - DERMATOPHYTEN UND ANDERE KERATINO-
LYTISCHE PILZE IN OBERFLAECHEN- UND ABWAESSERN. MYKOSEN 13, 467-471.

5338 SIMORDOVA, M. & HEJTMANEK, M. (1971) - BEITRAG ZUM VORKOMMEN VON DERMATO-
PHYTEN UND KERATINOPHILEN PILZEN IM BODEN. ACTA UNIV.OLOMUC, FAC.MED.
59, 5-16.

5339 SIMPSON, M.E., MARSH, P.B., MEROLA, G.V., FERRETTI, R.J. & FILSINGER, E.C.
(1973) - FUNGI THAT INFECT COTTON-SEEDS BEFORE HARVEST. APPL.MICROBIOL.
26, 608-613.

5340 SIMPSON, T.J. (1976) - BIOSYNTHESIS OF DEOXYHERQUEINONE IN PENICILLIUM HER-
QUEI FROM 13C-ACETATE AND 13C-MALONATE. ASSEMBLY PATTERN OF ACETATE IN-
TO THE PHENALENONE RING SYSTEM. J.CHEM.SOC.CHEM.COMMUN., 1976, 258-260.

5341 SIMS, A.C. (1960) - EFFECT OF CULTURE SUBSTRATE ON THE VIRULENCE OF SINGLE-
BASIDIOSPORE ISOLATES OF PELLICULARIA FILAMENTOSA. PHYTOPATHOLOGY 50,
282-286.

5342 SINCLAIR, J.B. (1970) - RHIZOCTONIA SOLANI. SPECIAL METHODS OF STUDY. IN:
RHIZOCTONIA SOLANI, BIOLOGY AND PATHOLOGY, SYMPOSIUM 1965; PARMETER, J.
JR. (ED.), UNIV.CALIFORNIA PRESS, BERKELEY, 199-217.

5343 SINCLAIR, N.A. & HERRING, C.M. (1975) - ISOLATION OF PENICILLIUM CORYLOPHI-
LUM DIERCKX FROM ACID MINE WATER AND ITS OPTIMAL GROWTH ON HYDROCARBONS
AT ACID PH. MYCOPATHOLOGIA 57, 19-22.

5344 SING-FANG, F., TZU-CHENG, Y. & JING-CHU, Y. (1966) - IDENTIFICATION OF SOME
SPECIES OF GEOTRICHUM. ACTA MICROBIOL.SIN. 12, 64-73.

5345 SINGH, A.B. (1972) - EFFECT OF VIRUS INFECTION ON THE RHIZOSPHERE MYCOFLO-
RA OF PAPAYA PLANTS. PL.SOIL 36, 205-208.

5346 SINGH, B. (1941) - BULB ROT OF SCILLA NUTANS CAUSED BY PENICILLIUM CYCLO-
PIUM. TRANS.BR.MYCOL.SOC. 25, 194-199.

5347 SINGH, B., GUPTA, K.G. & BHATNAGAR, L. (1974) - GROWTH AND EXTRACELLULAR
LIPIDS OF CERTAIN PATHOGENIC FUNGI IN PRESENCE OF DIFFERENT CONCENTRA-
TIONS OF AMINO ACID. ZENTBL.BAKT.PARASITKDE, ABT.1, 226, 278-282.

5348 SINGH, B.P. & TANDON, R.N. (1971) - SULPHUR REQUIREMENTS OF CERTAIN ISO-
LATES OF ALTERNARIA TENUIS AUCT. MYCOPATH.MYCOL.APPL. 43, 97-101.

5349 SINGH, C.S. & KAMAL (1970) - A STUDY OF SOME MICRO-ORGANIC CONTENTS OF A
DWABA SOIL. SYDOWIA 24, 217-222.

5350 SINGH, I. & CHOHAN, J.S. (1973) - SEED MYCOFLORA OF GUAR (CYAMOPSIS TETRA-
GONALOBA) AND THEIR EFFECT ON GERMINATION AND GROWTH OF SEEDLINGS. IN-
DIAN J.MYCOL.PL.PATH. 3, 86-92.

5351 SINGH, J. (1957) - THE COMPONENT FATTY ACIDS OF ASPERGILLUS FLAVUS FAT.
J.SCIENT.IND.RES., NEW DELHI, SECT.C, 16, 113-115.

5352 SINGH, J., SHAH, S. & WALKER, T.K. (1956) - THE COMPONENT FATTY ACIDS OF
      PENICILLIUM LILACINUM FAT. BIOCHEM.J. 62, 222-224.

5353 SINGH, J. & SOOD, M.G. (1972) - INFLUENCE OF NITROGEN SOURCE ON THE SYN-
      THESIS OF FAT FROM SUCROSE BY ASPERGILLUS TERREUS, ASPERGILLUS OCHRACE-
      US, CLADOSPORIUM FULVUM, CLADOSPORIUM HERBARUM AND PENICILLIUM GLADIOLI.
      J.SCI.FD AGRIC. 23, 1113-1118.

5354 SINGH, J. & SOOD, M.G. (1973) - COMPONENT FATTY ACIDS OF ASPERGILLUS TER-
      REUS FAT. J.AM.OIL CHEM.SOC. 50, 485-486.

5355 SINGH, J. & WALKER, T.K. (1956) - INFLUENCE OF PH OF THE MEDIUM ON THE
      CHARACTERISTICS AND COMPOSITION OF ASPERGILLUS NIDULANS FAT. J.SCIENT.
      IND.RES., NEW DELHI, SECT.C, 15, 222-224.

5356 SINGH, K., SEHGAL, S.N. & VEZINA, C. (1965) - TRANSFORMATION OF REICH-
      STEIN'S COMPOUND 'S' AND OXIDATION OF CARBOHYDRATES BY SPORES OF SEP-
      TOMYXA AFFINIS. CAN.J.MICROBIOL. 11, 351-364.

5357 SINGH, K., SEHGAL, S.N. & VEZINA, C. (1968) - LARGE-SCALE TRANSFORMATION
      OF STEROIDS BY FUNGAL SPORES. APPL.MICROBIOL. 16, 393-400.

5358 SINGH, K., SINGH, R.P. & AGNIHOTRI, V.P. (1975) - TAXONOMY AND PATHOGEN-
      ICITY OF FUNGI CAUSING SUGARCANE WILT SYNDROME. INDIAN PHYTOPATH. 28,
      86-91.

5359 SINGH, K. & VEZINA, C. (1971) - AN EXTRACELLULAR PROTEOLYTIC ENZYME FROM
      SCOPULARIOPSIS BREVICAULIS. 1. PURIFICATION AND PROPERTIES. CAN.J.MI-
      CROBIOL. 17, 1029-1042.

5360 SINGH, K. & VEZINA, C. (1972) - AN EXTRACELLULAR PROTEOLYTIC ENZYME FROM
      SCOPULARIOPSIS BREVICAULIS. 2. HYDROLYSIS OF POLYAMINO ACIDS. CAN.J.MI-
      CROBIOL. 18, 1165-1167.

5361 SINGH, N. & WEBSTER, J. (1972) - EFFECT OF COPROPHILOUS SPECIES OF MUCOR
      AND BACTERIA ON SPORANGIAL PRODUCTION OF PILOBOLUS. TRANS.BR.MYCOL.SOC.
      59, 43-49.

5362 SINGH, N. & WEBSTER, J. (1973) - ANTAGONISM BETWEEN STILBELLA ERYTHROCE-
      PHALA AND OTHER COPROPHILOUS FUNGI. TRANS.BR.MYCOL.SOC. 61, 487-495.

5363 SINGH, P. (1976) - SOME FUNGI IN THE FOREST SOILS OF NEWFOUNDLAND. MYCOLO-
      GIA 68, 881-890.

5364 SINGH, P.N. (1974) - THE NUTRITION OF ALTERNARIA ALTERNATA ISOLATED FROM
      SOLANUM NIGRUM. LABDEV J.SCI.TECHNOL., PART B, LIFE SCI. 12, 109-112.

5365 SINGH, R. (1973) - THE FOOT CELL MORPHOLOGY OF GENUS ASPERGILLUS. MYCOPATH.
      MYCOL.APPL. 49, 209-215.

5366 SINGH, R.A. & SINGH, D. (1972) - MYCOFLORA FROM EXCRETA OF SOME WILD AND
      RARE ANIMALS. INDIAN PHYTOPATH. 25, 477-478.

5367 SINGH, R.K. & WOOD, R.K.S. (1954) - PRODUCTION AND PROPERTIES OF PECTIC
      ENZYMES SECRETED BY FUSARIUM MONILIFORME. INT.BOT.CONGR., PARIS, SECT.
      18, NO.20, 118-119.

5368 SINGH, R.K. & WOOD, R.K.S. (1956) - STUDIES IN THE PHYSIOLOGY OF PARASIT-
      ISM. 21. THE PRODUCTION AND PROPERTIES OF PECTIC ENZYMES SECRETED BY FU-
      SARIUM MONILIFORME. ANN.BOT. 20, 89-103.

5369 SINGH, R.N. (1970) - PENICILLIUM ROTS OF GLADIOLUS IN INDIA. PL.SOIL 33, 249-250.

5370 SINGH, R.S. (1964) - EFFECT OF TRICHODERMA VIRIDE ON THE GROWTH OF PYTHIUM SP. IN STERILIZED AND UNSTERILIZED SOIL. NATURWISSENSCHAFTEN 51, 173.

5371 SINGH, R.S. (1964) - THE DEVELOPMENT OF PYTHIUM AT DIFFERENT TEMPERATURES IN THE SOIL PLANTED WITH CORN. MYCOPATH.MYCOL.APPL. 22, 182-184.

5372 SINGH, R.S. & KHANNA, R.N. (1969) - EFFECT OF CERTAIN INORGANIC CHEMICALS ON GROWTH AND SPORE GERMINATION OF ALTERNARIA TENUIS AUCT., THE FUNGUS CAUSING CORE ROT OF MANDARIN ORANGES IN INDIA. MYCOPATH.MYCOL.APPL. 37, 89-96.

5373 SINGH, R.S. & NENE, Y.L. (1965) - MALACHITE GREEN IN SYNTHETIC MEDIUM FOR THE ISOLATION OF FUSARIUM SPECIES FROM PLANT TISSUES. NATURWISSENSCHAFTEN 52, 94.

5374 SINGH, R.S. & PANDE, K.R. (1965) - STIMULATION OF PYTHIUM APHANIDERMATUM IN SOIL AMENDED WITH CHITINOUS MATERIALS. INDIAN J.EXPL BIOL. 3, 146-147.

5375 SINGH, S.S. (1972) - CHAETOMIACEAE OF CHHATARPUR. INDIAN PHYTOPATH. 25, 602-603.

5376 SINGH, S.S. & CHANDA, R. (1969) - CHAETOMIACEAE OF CHHATARPUR. INDIAN PHYTOPATH. 22, 393-394.

5377 SINGH, U.P. (1972) - ANASTOMOSES AND NUCLEAR CONDITION IN CEPHALOSPORIUM COCCORUM PETCH. MYCOPATH.MYCOL.APPL. 48, 167-174.

5378 SINGLETON, V.L., BOHONOS, N. & ULLSTRUP, A.J. (1958) - DECUMBIN, A NEW COMPOUND FROM A SPECIES OF PENICILLIUM. NATURE, LOND. 181, 1072-1073.

5379 SINHA, R.N. (1964) - ECOLOGICAL RELATIONSHIPS OF STORED-PRODUCTS MITES AND SEED-BORNE FUNGI. ACAROLOGIA 6, 372-389.

5380 SINHA, R.N. (1966) - FEEDING AND REPRODUCTION OF SOME STORED-PRODUCT MITES ON SEED-BORNE FUNGI. J.ECON.ENT. 39, 1227-1232.

5381 SINHA, R.N. (1971) - FUNGUS AS FOOD FOR SOME STORED-PRODUCT INSECTS. J.ECON.ENT. 64, 3-6.

5382 SINHA, R.N. & HARASYMEK, L. (1974) - SURVIVAL AND REPRODUCTION OF STORED-PRODUCT MITES AND BEETLES ON FUNGAL AND BACTERIAL DIETS. ENVIRON.ENT. 3, 243-246.

5383 SINHA, R.N. & MILLS, J.T. (1968) - FEEDING AND REPRODUCTION OF THE GRAIN MITE AND THE MUSHROOM MITE ON SOME SPECIES OF PENICILLIUM. J.ECON.ENT. 61, 1548-1552.

5384 SINOHARA, H. (1970) - INDUCTION OF ENZYMES IN DORMANT SPORES OF ASPERGILLUS ORYZAE. J.BACT. 101, 1070-1072.

5385 SIPORIN, C. & COONEY, J.J. (1975) - EXTRACELLULAR LIPIDS OF CLADOSPORIUM (AMORPHOTHECA) RESINAE GROWN ON GLUCOSE OR ON N-ALKANES. APPL.MICROBIOL. 29, 604-609.

5386 SIU, R.G.H. (1951) - MICROBIAL DECOMPOSITION OF CELLULOSE. REINHOLD PUBL. CO., NEW YORK.

5387 SIU, R.G.H., DARBY, R.T., BURKHOLDER, P.R. & BARGHOORN, E.S. (1949) - SPECIFICITY OF MICROBIOLOGICAL ATTACK ON CELLULOSE DERIVATIVES. TEXT.RES.J. 19, 484-488.

5388 SIU, R.G.H. & SINDEN, J.W. (1951) - EFFECTS OF PH, TEMPERATURE, AND MIN-
      ERAL NUTRITION ON CELLULOLYTIC FUNGI. AM.J.BOT. 38, 284-290.

5389 SIVANESAN, A. & MANNERS, J.G. (1970) - FUNGI ASSOCIATED WITH SPARTINA TOWN-
      SENDII IN HEALTHY AND DIE-BACK SITES. TRANS.BR.MYCOL.SOC. 55, 191-204.

5390 SIVASITHAMPARAM, K. (1975) - PHIALOPHORA AND PHIALOPHORA-LIKE FUNGI OCCUR-
      RING IN THE ROOT REGION OF WHEAT. AUST.J.BOT. 23, 193-212.

5391 SIVASITHAMPARAM, K., STUKELY, M. & PARKER, C.A. (1975) - A VOLATILE FACTOR
      INDUCING TRANSMISSIBLE LYSIS IN GAEUMANNOMYCES GRAMINIS VAR. TRITICI.
      CAN.J.MICROBIOL. 21, 293-300.

5392 SIZOVA, T.P., BAGHDADI, V.KH. & GORLENKO, M.V. (1967) - (THE SOIL MYCOFLO-
      RA OF MUKHAFEZ OF DAMASCUS AND ES-SUVEIDA (SYRIA)). MIKOL.FITOPAT. 1,
      286-294.

5393 SIZOVA, T.P., TURCHINOV, G.A., SOROKINA, L.Y. & PROTOPOPYAN, M.G. (1976) -
      (MICROSCOPIC FUNGI OF HOLE MICROBIOTOPES OF THE GREAT GERBIL IN THE RE-
      GION BETWEEN THE URAL AND THE EMBA RIVERS). MIKOL.FITOPAT. 10, 264-266.

5394 SIZOVA, T.P. & VASIN, V.B. (1962) - (THE MICROFLORA OF THE OAK RHIZOSPHERE).
      BYULL.MOSKOV.OBSHCH.ISPYT.PRIR., OTD.BIOL. 66 (4), 102-115.

5395 SJOELAND, S. & GATENBECK, S. (1966) - THE ENZYME SYNTHESIZING THE AROMATIC
      PRODUCT ALTERNARIOL. ACTA CHEM.SCAND. 20, 1053-1059.

5396 SKADOW, K. (1969) - EIN BEITRAG ZUR VERTICILLIUM TAXONOMIE. ARCH.PFLSCHUTZ
      5, 155-166.

5397 SKADOW, K. (1969) - UNTERSUCHUNGEN UEBER DIE WELKEERREGER VERTICILLIUM AL-
      BO-ATRUM RKE. & BERTH. UND V. DAHLIAE KLEB. 1. UNKRAEUTER ALS WIRTS-
      PFLANZEN. ZENTBL.BAKT.PARASITKDE, ABT.2, 123, 715-735.

5398 SKADOW, K. (1969) - UNTERSUCHUNGEN UEBER DIE WELKEERREGER VERTICILLIUM AL-
      BO-ATRUM RKE. & BERTH. UND V. DAHLIAE KLEB. 2. UNKRAEUTER ALS INFEK-
      TIONSRESERVOIRE. ZENTBL.BAKT.PARASITKDE, ABT.2, 123, 736-765.

5399 SKINNER, F.A. (1953) - INHIBITION OF FUSARIUM CULMORUM BY STREPTOMYCES AL-
      BIDOFLAVUS. NATURE, LOND. 172, 1191.

5400 SKINNER, F.A. (1956) - INHIBITION OF THE GROWTH OF FUNGI BY STREPTOMYCES
      SPECIES IN RELATION TO NUTRIENT CONDITIONS. J.GEN.MICROBIOL. 14, 381-
      392.

5401 SKINNER, F.A. (1956) - THE EFFECT OF ADDING CLAYS TO MIXED CULTURES OF
      STREPTOMYCES ALBIDOFLAVUS AND FUSARIUM CULMORUM. J.GEN.MICROBIOL. 14,
      393-405.

5402 SKOLKO, A.J. & GROVES, J.W. (1948) - NOTES ON SEED-BORNE FUNGI. 5. CHAETO-
      MIUM SPECIES WITH DICHOTOMOUSLY BRANCHED HAIRS. CAN.J.RES., SECT.C, 26,
      269-280.

5403 SKOLKO, A.J. & GROVES, J.W. (1953) - NOTES ON SEED-BORNE FUNGI. 7. CHAETO-
      MIUM. CAN.J.BOT. 31, 779-809.

5404 SKOU, J.P. (1967) - DISEASES IN BUMBLE-BEES (BOMBUS LATR.). THE OCCURRENCE,
      DESCRIPTION AND PATHOGENICITY OF FIVE HYPHOMYCETES. ARSSKR.K.VET.-LAND-
      BOHOEJSK., COPENHAGEN, 134-153.

5405   SKOU, J.P. (1968) - STUDIES ON THE TAKE-ALL FUNGUS, GAEUMANNOMYCES GRAMI-
       NIS. 1. NOTES ON TAXONOMY, NOMENCLATURE, MORPHOLOGY AND IDENTIFICATION
       OF VARIETIES. ARSSKR.K.VET.-LANDBOHOEJSK., COPENHAGEN, 109-116.

5406   SKOU, J.P. (1969) - THE EFFECT OF TEMPERATURE ON THE GROWTH AND SURVIVAL
       OF AUREOBASIDIUM PULLULANS AND OF THE RADULASPORIC STAGE OF GUIGNARDIA
       FULVIDA AND SYDOWIA POLYSPORA. FRIESIA 9, 226-236.

5407   SKOWRONSKI, B.S. & GOTTLIEB, D. (1970) - AGE-DEPENDENT METABOLIC DIFFEREN-
       CES IN PERIPHERAL HYPHAE OF RHIZOCTONIA SOLANI. J.BACT. 104, 640-645.

5408   SKUJINS, J.J., POTGIETER, H.J. & ALEXANDER, M. (1965) - DISSOLUTION OF
       FUNGAL CELL WALLS BY A STREPTOMYCETE CHITINASE AND BETA-(1-3)-GLUCANASE.
       ARCHS BIOCHEM.BIOPHYS. 111, 358-364.

5409   SLAGG, C.M. & FELLOWS, H. (1947) - EFFECTS OF CERTAIN SOIL FUNGI AND THEIR
       BY-PRODUCTS ON OPHIOBOLUS GRAMINIS. J.AGRIC.RES. 75, 279-293.

5410   SLATER, G.P., HASKINS, R.H., HOGGE, L.R. & NESBITT, L.R. (1967) - METABOL-
       IC PRODUCTS FROM A TRICHODERMA VIRIDE. CAN.J.CHEM. 45, 92-96.

5411   SLATER, G.P., MACDONALD, J.C. & NAKASHIMA, R. (1970) - BIOSYNTHESIS OF
       ECHINULIN BY ASPERGILLUS AMSTELODAMI FROM CYCLO-L-ALANYL-L-TRYPTOPHYL-
       C14. BIOCHEMISTRY 9, 2886-2889.

5412   SLIFKIN, M.K. (1971) - CONIDIAL WALL STRUCTURE AND MORPHOLOGY OF ALTERNA-
       RIA SPP. J.ELISHA MITCHELL SCIENT.SOC. 87, 231-236.

5413   SLYKHUIS, J.R. (1947) - STUDIES ON FUSARIUM CULMORUM BLIGHT OF CRESTED
       WHEAT AND BROME GRASS SEEDLINGS. CAN.J.RES., SECT.C, 25, 155-180.

5414   SMALLEY, E.B. & HANSEN, H.N. (1957) - THE PERFECT STAGE OF GLIOCLADIUM RO-
       SEUM. MYCOLOGIA 49, 529-533.

5415   SMILEY, R.W. (1974) - TAKE-ALL OF WHEAT AS INFLUENCED BY ORGANIC AMEND-
       MENTS AND NITROGEN FERTILIZERS. PHYTOPATHOLOGY 64, 822-825.

5416   SMIRNOVA, N.V. (1976) - (SOIL MICROMYCETES IN THE RHIZOSPHERE AND ROOT AERA
       OF PLANTS FAM. LEGUMINOSAE IN REPETEKSKII RESERVATION). MIKOL.FITOPAT.
       10, 176-178.

5417   SMIT, J. & WIERINGA, K.T. (1953) - MICROBIOLOGICAL DECOMPOSITION OF LITTER.
       NATURE, LOND. 171, 794-795.

5418   SMITH, A.F. & PHILLIPS, D.V. (1975) - DEGRADATION OF ALACHLOR BY RHIZOCTO-
       NIA SOLANI. AGRON.J. 67, 347-349.

5419   SMITH, A.M. (1972) - DRYING AND WETTING SCLEROTIA PROMOTES BIOLOGICAL CON-
       TROL OF SCLEROTIUM ROLFSII SACC. SOIL BIOL.BIOCHEM. 4, 119-123.

5420   SMITH, A.M. (1972) - NUTRIENT LEAKAGE PROMOTES BIOLOGICAL CONTROL OF DRIED
       SCLEROTIA OF SCLEROTIUM ROLFSII SACC. SOIL BIOL.BIOCHEM. 4, 125-129.

5421   SMITH, A.M. (1972) - BIOLOGICAL CONTROL OF FUNGAL SCLEROTIA IN SOIL. SOIL
       BIOL.BIOCHEM. 4, 131-134.

5422   SMITH, A.M. & NOBLE, D. (1972) - EFFECTS OF OXYGEN AND CARBON DIOXIDE ON
       THE GROWTH OF TWO VARIETIES OF GAEUMANNOMYCES GRAMINIS. TRANS.BR.MYCOL.
       SOC. 58, 499-532.

5423   SMITH, D.F. & LYNCH, G.P. (1973) - ASPERGILLUS FUMIGATUS IN SAMPLES OF MOL-
       DY SILAGE. J.DAIRY SCI. 56, 828-829.

5424 SMITH, D.G. & MARCHANT, R. (1968) - CHLORAMPHENICOL INHIBITION OF PYTHIUM ULTIMUM AND RHODOTORULA GLUTINIS. ARCH.MIKROBIOL. 60, 262-274.

5425 SMITH, D.S.H., POOLE, N.J. & JOWETT, W.F.A. (1973) - TRANSFORMATION OF 23, 24-BISNORCHOL-4-EN-3-ONE-22-OL BY RHIZOPUS ARRHIZUS. PHYTOCHEMISTRY 12, 561-562.

5426 SMITH, E.F. (1899) - WILT DISEASE OF COTTON, WATERMELON, AND COWPEA. BULL. U.S.DEP.AGRIC., DIV.VEG.PHYSIOL.PATH. 17, 72 PP.

5427 SMITH, F.B. & BROWN, P.E. (1935) - THE DECOMPOSITION OF LIGNIN AND OTHER ORGANIC CONSTITUENTS BY CERTAIN SOIL FUNGI. J.AM.SOC.AGRON. 27, 109-119.

5428 SMITH, G. (1946) - NOTE ON THE OCCURRENCE OF SPECIES OF OIDIODENDRON ROBAK IN BRITAIN. TRANS.BR.MYCOL.SOC. 29, 232-233.

5429 SMITH, G. (1951) - SOME NEW SPECIES OF MOULDS AND SOME NEW BRITISH RECORDS. TRANS.BR.MYCOL.SOC. 34, 17-22.

5430 SMITH, G. (1954) - AN INTRODUCTION TO INDUSTRIAL MYCOLOGY. EDWARD ARNOLD LTD, LONDON, (6TH ED. 1969).

5431 SMITH, G. (1956) - SOME NEW SPECIES OF SOIL MOULDS. TRANS.BR.MYCOL.SOC. 39, 111-114.

5432 SMITH, G. (1957) - SOME NEW AND INTERESTING SPECIES OF MICRO-FUNGI. TRANS. BR.MYCOL.SOC. 40, 481-488.

5433 SMITH, G. (1961) - SOME NEW AND INTERESTING SPECIES OF MICRO-FUNGI. 2. TRANS.BR.MYCOL.SOC. 44, 42-50.

5434 SMITH, G. (1962) - SOME NEW AND INTERESTING SPECIES OF MICRO-FUNGI. 3. TRANS.BR.MYCOL.SOC. 45, 387-394.

5435 SMITH, G. (1965) - THREE NEW SPECIES OF PENICILLIUM, P. ASPEROSPORUM NOM. NOV., AND P. LAPIDOSUM RAPER & FENNELL EMEND. TRANS.BR.MYCOL.SOC. 48, 273-277.

5436 SMITH, H.C. (1965) - THE MORPHOLOGY OF VERTICILLIUM ALBO-ATRUM, V. DAHLIAE AND V. TRICORPUS. N.Z.JL AGRIC.RES. 8, 450-478.

5437 SMITH, H.C. & SUTTON, B.C. (1964) - LEPTOSPHAERIA MACULANS THE ASCOGENOUS STATE OF PHOMA LINGAM. TRANS.BR.MYCOL.SOC. 47, 159-165.

5438 SMITH, J.E. & ANDERSON, J.G. (1973) - DIFFERENTIATION IN THE ASPERGILLI. IN: MICROBIAL DIFFERENTIATION; ASHWORTH, J.M. & SMITH, J.E. (ED.), SYMP.SOC.GEN.MICROBIOL. 23, 295-337.

5439 SMITH, J.E. & PATEMAN, J.A.(ED.) (1977) - GENETICS AND PHYSIOLOGY OF ASPER-GILLUS. SYMP.BR.MYCOL.SOC. 1, 1977, ACADEMIC PRESS, LONDON, NEW YORK, SAN FRANCISCO, 552 PP.

5440 SMITH, J.G. (1959) - THE INFLUENCE OF ANTAGONISTIC FUNGI ON THIELAVIOPSIS BASICOLA (BERK. & BR.) FERRARIS. ACTA BOT.NEERL. 9, 59-118.

5441 SMITH, J.M.B. (1968) - ANIMAL MYCOSES IN NEW ZEALAND. MYCOPATH.MYCOL.APPL. 34, 323-336.

5442 SMITH, L.R. & ASHWORTH, L.J.JR. (1965) - A COMPARISON OF THE MODES OF AC-TION OF SOIL AMENDMENTS AND PENTACHLORONITROBENZENE AGAINST RHIZOCTO-NIA SOLANI. PHYTOPATHOLOGY 55, 1144-1146.

5443 SMITH, M.J., PATIK, C. & ROSINSKI, M.A. (1967) - A COMPARISON OF CELLULOSE PRODUCTION IN THE GENUS CERATOCYSTIS. MYCOLOGIA 59, 965-969.

5444 SMITH, P.G. & WALKER, J.C. (1941) - CERTAIN ENVIRONAL AND NUTRITIONAL FAC-TORS AFFECTING APHANOMYCES ROOT ROT OF GARDEN PEA. J.AGRIC.RES. 63, 1-20.

5445 SMITH, R.S. & OFOSU-ASIEDU, A. (1972) - DISTRIBUTION OF THERMOPHILIC AND THERMOTOLERANT FUNGI IN A SPRUCE-PINE CHIP PILE. CAN.J.FOR.RES. 2, 16-26.

5446 SMITH, S.N. & LYON, A.J.E. (1976) - THE UPTAKE OF PARAQUAT BY SOIL FUNGI. NEW PHYTOL. 76, 479-484.

5447 SMITH, S.N., LYON, A.J.E. & BIN SAHID, I. (1976) - THE BREAKDOWN OF PARA-QUAT AND DIQUAT BY SOIL FUNGI. NEW PHYTOL. 77, 735-740.

5448 SMITH, W.H. & PETERSON, J.L. (1966) - THE INFLUENCE OF THE CARBOHYDRATE FRACTION OF THE ROOT EXUDATE OF RED CLOVER, TRIFOLIUM PRATENSE L., ON FUSARIUM SPP. ISOLATED FROM THE CLOVER ROOT AND RHIZOSPHERE. PL.SOIL 25, 413-424.

5449 SMITH, W.L.JR. & BLOMQUIST, M. (1970) - THERMOLABILITY OF DORMANT AND GER-MINATED MONILINIA FRUCTICOLA AND RHIZOPUS STOLONIFER SPORES. PHYTOPA-THOLOGY 60, 866-868.

5450 SNEH, B. (1972) - AN AGAR MEDIUM FOR THE ISOLATION AND MACROSCOPIC RECOG-NITION OF PHYTOPHTHORA SPP. FROM SOIL ON DILUTION PLATES. CAN.J.MICRO-BIOL. 18, 1389-1392.

5451 SNEH, B. (1972) - USE OF CELLULASE AND HEMICELLULASE FOR THE SEPARATION OF PHYTOPHTHORA CACTORUM OOSPORES FROM MYCELIUM MATS. CAN.J.BOT. 50, 2685-2686.

5452 SNEH, B. (1974) - RECOVERY OF SPORANGIA OF PHYTOPHTHORA CACTORUM FROM SOIL. CAN.J.BOT. 52, 1777-1778.

5453 SNEH, B. & HENIS, Y. (1972) - PRODUCTION OF ANTIFUNGAL SUBSTANCES ACTIVE AGAINST RHIZOCTONIA SOLANI IN CHITIN-AMENDED SOIL. PHYTOPATHOLOGY 62, 595-599.

5454 SNEH, B., HUMBLE, S.J. & LOCKWOOD, J.L. (1977) - PARASITISM OF OOSPORES OF PHYTOPHTHORA MEGASPERMA VAR. SOJAE, P. CACTORUM, PYTHIUM SP., AND APHA-NOMYCES EUTEICHES IN SOIL BY OOMYCETES, CHYTRIDIOMYCETES, HYPHOMYCETES, ACTINOMYCETES, AND BACTERIA. PHYTOPATHOLOGY 67, 622-628.

5455 SNEH, B., KATAN, J. & HENIS, Y. (1971) - MODE OF INHIBITION OF RHIZOCTONIA SOLANI IN CHITIN-AMENDED SOIL. PHYTOPATHOLOGY 61, 1113-1117.

5456 SNEH, B., KATAN, J. & HENIS, Y. (1972) - COLONIZATION OF STEM SEGMENTS AND CHITIN PARTICLES BY RHIZOCTONIA SOLANI IN SOIL. PHYTOPATHOLOGY 62, 852-857.

5457 SNEH, B., KATAN, J., HENIS, Y. & WAHL, I. (1966) - METHODS FOR EVALUATING INOCULUM DENSITY OF RHIZOCTONIA IN NATURALLY INFECTED SOIL. PHYTOPATH-OLOGY 56, 74-78.

5458 SNEH, B. & MCINTOSH, D.L. (1974) - STUDIES ON THE BEHAVIOUR AND SURVIVAL OF PHYTOPHTHORA CACTORUM IN SOIL. CAN.J.BOT. 52, 795-802.

5459 SNYDER, W.C. & HANSEN, H.N. (1940) - THE SPECIES CONCEPT OF FUSARIUM. AM.
      J.BOT. 27, 64-67.

5460 SNYDER, W.C. & HANSEN, H.N. (1941) - THE SPECIES CONCEPT OF FUSARIUM. SEC-
      TION MARTIELLA. AM.J.BOT. 28, 738-742.

5461 SNYDER, W.C. & HANSEN, H.N. (1945) - THE SPECIES CONCEPT IN FUSARIUM WITH
      REFERENCE TO DISCOLOR AND OTHER SECTIONS. AM.J.BOT. 32, 657-666.

5462 SNYDER, W.C., SCHROTH, M.N. & CHRISTOU, TH. (1959) - EFFECT OF PLANT RES-
      IDUES ON ROOT ROT OF BEAN. PHYTOPATHOLOGY 49, 755-756.

5463 SOBERS, E.K. (1972) - MORPHOLOGY AND PATHOGENICITY OF CALONECTRIA FLORIDA-
      NA, CALONECTRIA KYOTENSIS, AND CALONECTRIA UNISEPTATA. PHYTOPATHOLOGY
      62, 485-487.

5464 SOBERS, E.K. & SEYMOUR, C.P. (1967) - CYLINDROCLADIUM FORIDANUM SP.N.
      ASSOCIATED WITH DECLINE OF PEACH TREES IN FLORIDA. PHYTOPATHOLOGY 57,
      389-393.

5465 SOEDERSTROEM, B.E. (1975) - VERTICAL DISTRIBUTION OF MICROFUNGI IN A SPRUCE
      FOREST SOIL IN THE SOUTH OF SWEDEN. TRANS.BR.MYCOL.SOC. 65, 419-425.

5466 SOERGEL, G. (1960) - ZUM PROBLEM DER TRENNUNG VON ARTEN BEI PILZEN, DARGE-
      STELLT AM BEISPIEL DER ASCOMYCETENGATTUNG CHAETOMIUM. ARCH.MIKROBIOL.
      36, 51-66.

5467 SOHI, H.S. & PUTTOO, B.L. (1972) - STUDIES ON THE FUNGAL FLORA OF ONION
      (ALLIUM CEPA) SEEDS. INDIAN J.HORT. 29, 231-234.

5468 SOLBERG, L. (1925) - SYGDOM PAA ERTER. HAVEDYRKNINGENS VENNERS MEDLEMSSKR.
      4, 6 PP.

5469 SOLOVEVA, A.I. & POLYARKOVA, L.V. (1940) - (WILT OF COTTON). TASHKENT
      AGRIC.PUB.DEPT.UZBEK., 1-63.

5470 SOMERVILLE, D.A. & MARPLES, M.J. (1967) - THE EFFECT OF SOIL ENRICHMENT ON
      THE ISOLATION OF KERATINOPHILIC FUNGI FROM SOIL SAMPLES. SABOURAUDIA 6,
      70-76.

5471 SOMKUTI, G.A. (1974) - SYNTHESIS OF CELLULASE BY MUCOR PUSILLUS AND MUCOR
      MIEHEI. J.GEN.MICROBIOL. 81, 1-6.

5472 SOMKUTI, G.A. & BABEL, F.J. (1967) - CONDITIONS INFLUENCING THE SYNTHESIS
      OF ACID PROTEASE BY MUCOR PUSILLUS. APPL.MICROBIOL. 15, 1309-1312.

5473 SOMKUTI, G.A. & BAPEL, F.J. (1968) - LIPASE ACTIVITY OF MUCOR PUSILLUS.
      APPL.MICROBIOL. 16, 617-619.

5474 SOMKUTI, G.A., BABEL, F.J. & SOMKUTI, A.C. (1969) - CELLULOLYSIS BY MUCOR
      PUSILLUS. APPL.MICROBIOL. 17, 888-892.

5475 SOERENSEN, H. (1953) - ENZYMATIC HYDROLYSIS OF XYLAN. NATURE, LOND. 172,
      305-306.

5476 SOERENSEN, R.H. (1964) - SURVIVAL CHARACTERISTICS OF MYCELIA AND SPHERULES
      OF COCCIDIOIDES IMMITIS IN A SIMULATED NATURAL ENVIRONMENT. AM.J.HYG.
      80, 275-285.

5477 SOMMER, N.F., BUCHANAN, J.R. & FORTLAGE, R.J. (1974) - PRODUCTION OF PATU-
      LIN BY PENICILLIUM EXPANSUM. APPL.MICROBIOL. 28, 589-593.

5478   SONI, N.K. & VYAS, K.M. (1973) – RESPIRATORY AND GROWTH RESPONSES OF FUSA-
       RIUM OXYSPORUM SACC. INDUCED BY VARIOUS SUBSTANCES. INDIAN J.EXPL BIOL.
       11, 217-219.

5479   SOOD, M.G. & SINGH, J. (1973) – THE COMPONENT FATTY ACIDS OF ASPERGILLUS
       OCHRACEUS FAT. J.SCI.FD AGRIC. 24, 1171-1174.

5480   SOPRUNOV, F.F. (1958) – PREDACEOUS HYPHOMYCETES AND THEIR APPLICATION IN
       THE CONTROL OF PATHOGENIC NEMATODES. ENGL.TRANSL.JERUSALEM, 1966, 292
       PP.

5481   SOPRUNOV, F.F. & GALIULINA, Z.A. (1951) – (PREDACIOUS HYPHOMYCETES FROM
       TURKMENISTAN SOIL). MIKROBIOLOGIYA 20, 489-499.

5482   SORENSEN, W.G., SNELLER, M.R. & LARSH, H.W. (1975) – QUALITATIVE AND QUAN-
       TITATIVE ASSAY OF TRICHOTHECIN – A MYCOTOXIN PRODUCED BY TRICHOTHECIUM
       ROSEUM. APPL.MICROBIOL. 29, 653-657.

5483   SORENSON, W.G., HESSELTINE, C.W. & SHOTWELL, O.L. (1967) – EFFECT OF TEM-
       PERATURE ON PRODUCTION OF AFLATOXIN ON RICE BY ASPERGILLUS FLAVUS. MY-
       COPATH.MYCOL.APPL. 33, 49-55.

5484   SPAAR, D. & VESPER, E. (1970) – UNTERSUCHUNGEN UEBER DIE ANWENDUNGSMOEG-
       LICHKEITEN MYKOSEROLOGISCHER DIAGNOSEMETHODEN IN DER PHYTOPATHOLOGIE.
       1. UEBER BEZIEHUNGEN ZWISCHEN TITERHOEHE UND SPEZIFITAET VON ANTISEREN.
       ZENTBL.BAKT.PARASITKDE, ABT.2, 125, 1-15.

5485   SPALDING, D.H. (1963) – PRODUCTION OF PECTINOLYTIC AND CELLULOLYTIC ENZY-
       MES BY RHIZOPUS STOLONIFER. PHYTOPATHOLOGY 53, 929-931.

5486   SPALDING, D.H. & ABDUL-BAKI, A.A. (1973) – IN VITRO AND IN VIVO PRODUCTION
       OF PECTIN LYASE BY PENICILLIUM EXPANSUM. PHYTOPATHOLOGY 63, 231-234.

5487   SPALDING, D.H., WELLS, J.M. & ALLISON, D.W. (1973) – CATABOLITE REPRESSION
       OF POLYGALACTURONASE, PECTIN LYASE, AND CELLULASE SYNTHESIS IN PENICIL-
       LIUM EXPANSUM. PHYTOPATHOLOGY 63, 840-843.

5488   SPALLA, C. (1963) – RICERCHE SULLA RIPRODUZIONE SESSUALE IN MUCORALES. 1.
       LA RIPRODUZIONE SESSUALE IN CUNNINGHAMELLA BLAKESLEEANA E IN C. ELE-
       GANS. RIV.PATOL.VEG.PAVIA, SER.3, 3, 107-128.

5489   SPALLA, C. (1963) – RICERCHE SULLA RIPRODUZIONE SESSUALE IN MUCORALES. 2.
       LA RIPRODUZIONE SESSUALE IN MUCOR HIEMALIS E IN M. RACEMOSUS. RIV.PATOL.
       VEG.PAVIA, SER.3, 3, 129-140.

5490   SPEK, J.VAN DER (1972) – ZIEKTEN VAN ZAADBIETEN. JVERSL.INST.PLZIEKTENK.
       ONDERZ. 1971, 40-42.

5491   SPEK, J.VAN DER (1973) – SEED TRANSMISSION OF VERTICILLIUM DAHLIAE. MEDED.
       FAC.LANDBOUWWET.RIJKSUNIV.GENT 38, 1427-1434.

5492   SPENCER, J.A. & COOPER, W.E. (1967) – PATHOGENESIS OF COTTON (GOSSYPIUM
       HIRSUTUM) BY PYTHIUM SPECIES – ZOOSPORE AND MYCELIUM ATTRACTION AND
       INFECTIVITY. PHYTOPATHOLOGY 57, 1332-1338.

5493   SPENCER, J.F.T. & GORIN, P.A.J. (1971) – SYSTEMATICS OF THE GENERA CERA-
       TOCYSTIS AND GRAPHIUM. PROTON MAGNETIC RESONANCE SPECTRA OF THE MANNO-
       SE-CONTAINING POLYSACCHARIDES AS AN AID IN CLASSIFICATION. MYCOLOGIA
       63, 387-402.

5494   SPIEGEL, S., HENIS, Z., CHET, I. & MESSER, G. (1975) – THE EFFECT OF HEAT
       SHOCK ON DIFFERENTIATION OF GERMINATING CONIDIA OF TRICHODERMA VIRIDE.
       CAN.J.BOT. 53, 2274-2281.

5495 SPIERS, A.G. (1974) - A PYTHIUM DISEASE OF WILLOW SEEDLINGS. J.Z.JL EXP. AGRIC. 2, 436-440.

5496 SPIRE, D. (1971) - VIRUS DES CHAMPIGNONS. PHYSIOLOG.VEG. 9, 555-567.

5497 SPRAGUE, R. (1948) - GLOEOSPORIUM DECAY IN GRAMINEAE. PHYTOPATHOLOGY 38, 131-136.

5498 SPRAGUE, R. (1950) - DISEASES OF CEREALS AND GRASSES IN NORTH AMERICA. RONALD PRESS, NEW YORK.

5499 SPRAGUE, R. (1957) - FUNGI ISOLATED FROM ROOTS AND CROWNS OF PEAR TREES. PL.DIS.REPTR 41, 74-76.

5500 SPRING, M.S. & STOKER, J.R. (1967) - THE BIOSYNTHESIS OF DICOUMAROL. BIO-CHEM.J. 103, 202-206.

5501 SPURR, H.W.JR. & SOUSA, A.A. (1974) - POTENTIAL INTERACTIONS OF ALDICARB AND ITS METABOLITES ON NONTARGET ORGANISMS IN THE ENVIRONMENT. J.EN-VIRONM.QUALITY 3, 130-133.

5502 SPUY, J.E.VAN DER, MATTHEE, F.N. & CRAFFORD, D.J.A. (1975) - THE HEAT RE-SISTANCE OF MOULDS PENICILLIUM VERMICULATUM DANGEARD AND PENICILLIUM BREFELDIANUM DODGE IN APPLE JUICE. PHYTOPHYLACTICA 7, 105-107.

5503 SREEKANTIAH, K.R. & JOHAR, D.S. (1963) - PECTOLYTIC ENZYME PRODUCTION BY FUNGI. 1. SCREENING OF ORGANISMS. FD SCI., MYSORE 12, 347-352.

5504 SREEKANTIAH, K.R., NAGARAJA RAO, K.S. & RAMACHANDRA RAO, T.N. (1975) - POST-HARVEST INFECTION OF APPLES BY TRICHOTHECIUM ROSEUM. INDIAN PHYTO-PATH. 27, 114-115.

5505 SREEKANTIAH, K.R., SHAH, V.K. & JOHAR, D.S. (1963) - PECTOLYTIC ENZYME PRODUCTION BY FUNGI. 2. EFFECT OF NUTRIENTS AND CULTURAL CONDITIONS ON THE SECRETION OF ENZYME. FD SCI., MYSORE 12, 353-357.

5506 SRINIVASAN, M.C. & THIRUMALACHAR, M.J. (1967) - EVALUATION OF TAXONOMIC CHARACTERS IN THE GENUS CONIDIOBOLUS, WITH KEY TO KNOWN SPECIES. MYCO-LOGIA 59, 698-713.

5507 SRIVASTAVA, D.N., ECHANDI, E. & WALKER, J.C. (1959) - PECTOLYTIC AND CEL-LULOLYTIC ENZYMES PRODUCED BY RHIZOPUS STOLONIFER. PHYTOPATHOLOGY 49, 145-148.

5508 SRIVASTAVA, H.P. (1971) - NEW RECORDS OF SOME ASCOMYCETES. INDIAN PHYTO-PATH. 24, 828-833.

5509 SRIVASTAVA, J.P. (1951) - EFFECT OF VARIOUS NITROGENOUS COMPOUNDS ON THE GROWTH OF ALTERNARIA TENUIS. J.INDIAN BOT.SOC. 30, 108-112.

5510 SRIVASTAVA, S.L., MISRA, L.C. & LAL, B. (1971) - PHYSICO-CHEMICAL AND MY-COFLORAL STUDIES ON RHIZOSPHERE OF OPHIOGLOSSUM RETICULATUM. INDIAN J. MYCOL.PL.PATH. 1, 30-35.

5511 SRIVASTAVA, S.N.S. (1953) - ON THE OCCURRENCE OF PHOMA CHRYSANTHEMICOLA HOLLOS ON CHRYSANTHEMUM SP. CURR.SCI. 22, 216.

5512 SRIVASTAVA, S.S. & BHARGAVA, K.S. (1966) - FUNGI ISOLATED FROM EUGENIA FOREST SOIL OF GORAKHPUR. PROC.INDIAN SCI.CONGR. 53 (3), 441 (ABS.).

5513   SRIVASTAVA, S.S. & BHARGAVA, K.S. (1966) - FUNGI COLONIZING LEAF LITTERS
       OF EUGENIA HEYNEANA. PROC.INDIAN SCI.CONGR. 53 (3), 441-442 (ABS.).

5514   SRIVASTAVA, V.B. (1971) - INVESTIGATION INTO THE RHIZOSPHERE MICROFLORA.
       8. LIGHT AND DARK TREATMENTS IN RELATION TO ROOT-REGION MICROFLORA.
       PL.SOIL 35, 463-470.

5515   STACK, M.E., EPPLEY, R.M., DREIFUSS, P.A. & POHLAND, A.E. (1977) - ISOLA-
       TIONS AND IDENTIFICATION OF XANTHOMEGNIN, VIOMELLEIN, RUBROSULPHIN, AND
       VIOPURPURIN AS METABOLITES OF PENICILLIUM VIRIDICATUM. APPL.ENVIRON.
       MICROBIOL. 33, 351-355.

5516   STADLER, D.R. (1952) - CHEMOTROPISM IN RHIZOPUS NIGRICANS. THE STALING RE-
       ACTION. J.CELL.COMP.PHYSIOL. 39, 449-474.

5517   STAGG, C.M. & FEATHER, M.S. (1973) - THE CHARACTERIZATION OF A CHITIN-ASSO-
       CIATED D-GLUCAN FROM THE CELL WALLS OF ASPERGILLUS NIGER. BIOCHIM.BIO-
       PHYS.ACTA 320, 64-72.

5518   STAHL, W.H. & PESSEN, H. (1953) - THE MICROBIOLOGICAL DEGRADATION OF PLAS-
       TICIZERS. 1. GROWTH ON ESTERS AND ALCOHOLS. APPL.MICROBIOL. 1, 30-35.

5519   STAIB, F. & BLISSE, A. (1974) - STELLUNGNAHME ZU SPOROTHRIX SCHENCKII VAR.
       LURIEI. EIN BEITRAG ZUM DIAGNOSTISCHEN WERT DER ASSIMILATION VON KRE-
       ATININ, KREATIN UND GUANIDINOESSIGSAEURE DURCH SPOROTHRIX SCHENCKII.
       ZENTBL.BAKT.PARASITKDE, ABT.1, 229, 261-263.

5520   STAIB, F., BLISSE, A. & RANDHAWA, H.S. (1972) - CREATINE AND CREATININE
       ASSIMILATION BY SPOROTHRIX SCHENCKII. ZENTBL.BAKT.PARASITKDE, ABT.1,
       221, 94-99.

5521   STAIB, F. & EVANGELINOS, P. (1968) - ZUM VORKOMMEN VON GEOPHILEN DERMATO-
       PHYTEN IM RAUM WUERZBURG. ZENTBL.BAKT.PARASITKDE, ABT.1, 207, 528-540.

5522   STAIB, F., GROSSE, G., MALE, O. & BLISSE, A. (1974) - ZUR VERWERTUNG VON
       KREATININ, KREATIN UND GUANIDINOESSIGSAEURE DURCH SPOROTHRIX SCHENCKII.
       Z.HAUTKR. 49, 607-613.

5523   STAIB, F., RANDHAWA, H.S. & BLISSE, A. (1973) - ASSIMILATION OF GUANIDO-
       ACETIC ACID BY SPOROTHRIX SCHENCKII. ZENTBL.BAKT.PARASITKDE, ABT.1, 224,
       237-240.

5524   STAMPS, D.J. (1953) - VARIATION IN A STRAIN OF PHYTOPHTHORA CACTORUM.
       TRANS.BR.MYCOL.SOC. 36, 248-259.

5525   STANGHELLINI, M.E. (1972) - EXOGENOUS NUTRIENT REQUIREMENTS FOR GERMINA-
       TION OF PYTHIUM APHANIDERMATUM OOSPORES. PHYTOPATHOLOGY 62, 791 (ABS.).

5526   STANGHELLINI, M.E. & BURR, T.J. (1973) - EFFECT OF SOIL WATER POTENTIAL ON
       DISEASE INCIDENCE AND OOSPORE GERMINATION OF PYTHIUM APHANIDERMATUM.
       PHYTOPATHOLOGY 63, 1496-1498.

5527   STANGHELLINI, M.E. & HANCOCK, J.G. (1970) - A QUANTITATIVE METHOD FOR THE
       ISOLATION OF PYTHIUM ULTIMUM FROM SOIL. PHYTOPATHOLOGY 60, 551-552.

5528   STANGHELLINI, M.E. & HANCOCK, J.G. (1971) - THE SPORANGIUM OF PYTHIUM UL-
       TIMUM AS A SURVIVAL STRUCTURE IN SOIL. PHYTOPATHOLOGY 61, 157-164.

5529   STANGHELLINI, M.E. & NIGH, E.L. (1972) - OCCURRENCE OF PYTHIUM APHANIDER-
       MATUM UNDER ARID SOIL CONDITIONS IN ARIZONA. PL.DIS.REPTR 56, 507-510.

5530   STANGHELLINI, M.E. & RUSSELL, J.D. (1971) - SURVIVAL AND GERMINATION OF
       OOSPORES OF PYTHIUM APHANIDERMATUM. PHYTOPATHOLOGY 61, 1324 (ABS.).

5531 STANGHELLINI, M.E. & RUSSELL, J.D. (1973) - GERMINATION IN VITRO OF PY-
     THIUM APHANIDERMATUM OOSPORES. PHYTOPATHOLOGY 63, 133-137.

5532 STANSLEY, P. & ANANENKO, N.H. (1949) - CANDIDULIN - AN ANTIBIOTIC FROM AS-
     PERGILLUS CANDIDUS. ARCHS BIOCHEM. 23, 256-261.

5533 STAPLETON, G.E., HOLLAENDER, A. & MARTIN, F.L. (1952) - MECHANISM OF LE-
     THAL AND MUTAGENIC ACTION OF IONIZING RADIATION ON ASPERGILLUS TERREUS.
     1. RELATIONSHIP OF RELATIVE BIOLOGICAL EFFICIENCY TO ION DENSITY. J.
     CELL.COMP.PHYSIOL. 39, 87-100.

5534 STARC, A. (1941) - MIKROBIOLOGISCHE UNTERSUCHUNGEN EINIGER PODSOLIGER BOE-
     DEN KROATIENS. ARCH.MIKROBIOL. 12, 329-352.

5535 STARRATT, A.N. & LOSCHIAVO, S.R. (1971) - AGGREGATION OF THE CONFUSED
     FLOUR BEETLE, TRIBOLIUM CONFUSUM, ELICITED BY MYCELIAL CONSTITUENTS OF
     THE FUNGUS NIGROSPORA SPHAERICA. J.INSECT PHYSIOL. 17, 407-414.

5536 STARRATT, A.N. & LOSCHIAVO, S.R. (1974) - THE PRODUCTION OF APHIDICOLIN BY
     NIGROSPORA SPHAERICA. CAN.J.MICROBIOL. 20, 416-417.

5537 STARRATT, A.N. & MADHOSINGH, C. (1967) - STEROL AND FATTY ACID COMPONENTS
     OF MYCELIUM OF FUSARIUM OXYSPORUM. CAN.J.MICROBIOL. 13, 1351-1355.

5538 STATHAKOS, D., ISAAKIDOU, I. & THOMOU, H. (1973) - PURIFICATION AND PROP-
     ERTIES OF NAD NUCLEOSIDASE FROM FUSARIUM NIVALE. BIOCHIM.BIOPHYS.ACTA
     302, 80-89.

5539 STAVY, R., STAVY, L. & GALUN, E. (1970) - PROTEIN SYNTHESIS IN AGED AND
     YOUNG ZONES OF TRICHODERMA COLONIES. BIOCHIM.BIOPHYS.ACTA 217, 468-476.

5540 STEADMAN, J.R. & COOK, G.E. (1974) - A SIMPLE METHOD FOR COLLECTING ASCO-
     SPORES OF WHETZELINIA SCLEROTIORUM. PL.DIS.REPTR 58, 190.

5541 STEADMAN, J.R. & NICKERSON, K.W. (1975) - DIFFERENTIAL INHIBITION OF SCLE-
     ROTIAL GERMINATION IN WHETZELINIA SCLEROTIORUM. MYCOPATHOLOGIA 57, 165-
     170.

5542 STEEKELENBURG, N.A.M.VAN (1973) - INFLUENCE OF LOW TEMPERATURES ON THE SUR-
     VIVAL OF PHYTOPHTHORA CINNAMOMI RANDS IN SOIL. MEDED.FAC.LANDBOUWWET.
     RIJKSUNIV.GENT 38, 1399-1405.

5543 STEELE, J.A., DAVIS, N.D. & DIENER, U.L. (1973) - EFFECT OF ZINC, COPPER,
     AND IRON ON OCHRATOXIN-A PRODUCTION. APPL.MICROBIOL. 25, 847-849.

5544 STEELE, J.A., MIROCHA, C.J. & PATHRE, S.V. (1976) - METABOLISM OF ZEARALE-
     NONE BY FUSARIUM ROSEUM GRAMINEARUM. J.AGRIC.FD CHEM. 24, 89-97.

5545 STEELE, S.D. (1973) - DOUBLE-MEMBRANED VESICLES IN GEOTRICHUM CANDIDUM.
     CAN.J.MICROBIOL. 19, 534-535.

5546 STEELE, S.D. & FRASER, T.W. (1973) - ULTRASTRUCTURAL CHANGES DURING GERMI-
     NATION OF GEOTRICHUM CANDIDUM ARTHROSPORES. CAN.J.MICROBIOL. 19, 1031-
     1034.

5547 STEELE, S.D. & FRASER, T.W. (1973) - THE ULTRASTRUCTURE OF GEOTRICHUM CAN-
     DIDUM HYPHAE. CAN.J.MICROBIOL. 19, 1507-1512.

5548 STEENSLAND, H. (1973) - CONTINUOUS CULTURE OF A SEWAGE FUNGUS FUSARIUM
     AQUAEDUCTUUM. ARCH.MIKROBIOL. 93, 287-294.

5549   STEFANOVIC, M. (1969) - DERMATOPHYTES AND OTHER FUNGI ISOLATED FROM THE
       SOIL IN SERBIA. MYKOSEN 12, 231-232.

5550   STEINBERG, R.A. (1937) - ROLE OF MOLYBDENUM IN THE UTILIZATION OF AMMONIUM
       AND NITRATE NITROGEN BY ASPERGILLUS NIGER. J.AGRIC.RES. 55, 891-902.

5551   STEINBERG, R.A. (1939) - EFFECTS OF NITROGEN COMPOUNDS AND TRACE ELEMENTS
       ON GROWTH OF ASPERGILLUS NIGER. J.AGRIC.RES. 59, 731-748.

5552   STEINBERG, R.A. (1939) - RELATION OF CARBON NUTRITION TO TRACE-ELEMENT AND
       ACCESSORY REQUIREMENTS OF ASPERGILLUS NIGER. J.AGRIC.RES. 59, 749-763.

5553   STEINBERG, R.A. (1942) - EFFECT OF TRACE ELEMENTS ON GROWTH OF ASPERGILLUS
       NIGER WITH AMINO ACIDS. J.AGRIC.RES. 64, 455-475.

5554   STEINBERG, R.A. (1950) - GROWTH ON SYNTHETIC NUTRIENT SOLUTIONS OF SOME
       FUNGI PATHOGENIC TO TOBACCO. AM.J.BOT. 37, 711-714.

5555   STEINBRENNER, K. & MATSCHKE, J. (1971) - EIN BEITRAG ZUR HUMINSTOFFSYNTHE-
       SE DURCH EINIGE BODENPILZE. ZENTBL.BAKT.PARASITKDE, ABT.2, 126, 585-603.

5556   STEINER, K. (1960) - UEBER DEN EINFLUSS VON SPURENELEMENTEN AUF WACHSTUM
       UND ENZYMBILDUNG VON ASPERGILLUS ORYZAE (AHLBURG) COHN. DISS.ETH, ZUE-
       RICH.

5557   STEINER, P.W. & MILLAR, R.L. (1974) - DEGRADATION OF MEDICARPIN AND SATI-
       VAN BY STEMPHYLIUM BOTRYOSUM. PHYTOPATHOLOGY 64, 586 (ABS.).

5558   STENERSEN, J. (1969) - DEGRADATION OF P32-BROMOPHOS BY MICROORGANISMS AND
       SEEDLINGS. BULL.ENVIRON.CONTAM.TOXICOL. 4, 104-112.

5559   STENTON, H. (1953) - THE SOIL FUNGI OF WICKEN FEN. TRANS.BR.MYCOL.SOC. 36,
       304-314.

5560   STENTON, H. (1958) - COLONIZATION OF ROOTS OF PISUM SATIVUM BY FUNGI.
       TRANS.BR.MYCOL.SOC. 41, 74-80.

5561   STEPHAN, B.R. (1967) - UNTERSUCHUNGEN UEBER DIE VARIABILITAET BEI COLLE-
       TOTRICHUM GLOEOSPORIOIDES PENZIG IN VERBINDUNG MIT HETEROKARYOSE. 1.
       MORPHOLOGISCHE VARIABILITAET BEI C. GLOEOSPORIOIDES PENZ. ZENTBL.BAKT.
       PARASITKDE, ABT.2, 121, 41-57.

5562   STEPHAN, B.R. (1967) - UNTERSUCHUNGEN UEBER DIE VARIABILITAET BEI COLLETO-
       TRICHUM GLOEOSPORUM. 2. CYTOLOGISCHE GRUNDLAGEN DER HETEROKARYOSE.
       ZENTBL.BAKT.PARASITKDE, ABT.2, 121, 58-72.

5563   STEPHAN, B.R. (1968) - UNTERSUCHUNGEN ZUM NACHWEIS DER HETEROKARYOSE BEI
       COLLETOTRICHUM GLOEOSPORIOIDES PENZIG UNTER VERWENDUNG AUXOTROPHER MU-
       TANTEN. ZENTBL.BAKT.PARASITKDE, ABT.2, 122, 420-435.

5564   STERN, A.M. (1952) - STUDIES ON THE PHYSIOLOGY OF THE MUCOR MUCEDO AND ITS
       ROLE IN THE FERMENTATION OF SOYBEAN CURD. DISS.ABSTR. 12, 6.

5565   STERNE, R.E., ZENTMYER, G.A. & BINGHAM, F.T. (1976) - EFFECT OF OSMOTIC
       POTENTIAL AND SPECIFIC IONS ON GROWTH OF PHYTOPHTHORA CINNAMOMI. PHY-
       TOPATHOLOGY 66, 1398-1402.

5566   STEVENS, B.J.H. & PAYNE, J. (1977) - CELLULASE AND XYLANASE PRODUCTION BY
       YEASTS OF THE GENUS TRICHOSPORON. J.GEN.MICROBIOL. 100, 381-393.

5567   STEVENS, F.L. (1928) - EFFECTS OF ULTRA-VIOLET RADIATION ON VARIOUS FUNGI.
       BOT.GAZ. 86, 210-225.

5568   STEVENS, F.L. (1931) - A COMPARATIVE STUDY OF SCLEROTIUM ROLFSII AND SCLE-
        ROTIUM DELPHINII. MYCOLOGIA 23, 204-222.

5569   STEVENSON, G. (1964) - THE GROWTH OF SEEDLINGS OF SOME PIONEER PLANTS AND
        THE MICROORGANISMS ASSOCIATED WITH THEIR ROOTS. TRANS.BR.MYCOL.SOC. 47,
        331-339.

5570   STEVENSON, I.L. (1954) - ANTIBIOTIC PRODUCTION BY ACTINOMYCETES IN SOIL
        DEMONSTRATED BY MORPHOLOGICAL CHANGES INDUCED IN HELMINTHOSPORIUM SATI-
        VUM. NATURE, LOND. 174, 598-599.

5571   STEVENSON, I.L. & BECKER, S.A.W.E. (1972) - THE FINE STRUCTURE AND DEVEL-
        OPMENT OF CHLAMYDOSPORES OF FUSARIUM OXYSPORUM. CAN.J.MICROBIOL. 18,
        997-1002.

5572   STEWARD, M.W. & PACKTER, N.M. (1965) - BIOSYNTHESIS OF GLIOROSEIN IN GLIO-
        CLADIUM ROSEUM. BIOCHEM.J. 95, 26C-28C.

5573   STEYAERT, R.L. (1949) - CONTRIBUTION A L'ETUDE MONOGRAPHIQUE DE PESTALOTIA
        ET MONOCHAETIA. BULL.JARD.BOT.ETAT BRUX. 19, 285-354.

5574   STEYN, P.S. (1970) - THE ISOLATION, STRUCTURE AND ABSOLUTE CONFIGURATION
        OF SECALONIC ACID-D, THE TOXIC METABOLITE OF PENICILLIUM OXALICUM.
        TETRAHEDRON 26, 51-57.

5575   STEYN, P.S. (1973) - THE STRUCTURES OF FIVE DIKETOPIPERAZINES FROM ASPER-
        GILLUS USTUS. TETRAHEDRON 29, 107-120.

5576   STEYN, P.S., HOLZAPFEL, C.W. & FERREIRA, N.P. (1970) - THE BIOSYNTHESIS OF
        THE OCHRATOXINS, METABOLITES OF ASPERGILLUS OCHRACEUS. PHYTOCHEMISTRY
        9, 1977-1983.

5577   STEYN, P.S. & VLEGGAAR, R. (1974) - AUSTOCYSTINS, SIX NOVEL DIHYDROFURO-
        (3',2':4,5)FURO(3,2-B)XANTHENONES FROM ASPERGILLUS USTUS. J.CHEM.SOC.
        PERKIN TRANS.I, 1974, 2250-2256.

5578   STICKINGS, C.E. (1959) - STUDIES IN THE BIOCHEMISTRY OF MICRO-ORGANISMS.
        106. METABOLITES OF ALTERNARIA TENUIS. THE STRUCTURE OF TENUAZONIC ACID.
        BIOCHEM.J. 72, 332-340.

5579   STICKINGS, C.E. & MAHMOODIAN, A. (1962) - METABOLITES OF PENICILLIUM FRE-
        QUENTANS AND THEIR SIGNIFICANCE FOR THE BIOSYNTHESIS OF SULOCHRIN. CHEM.
        IND., 1962, 1718-1719.

5580   STIERS, D.L. (1976) - THE FINE STRUCTURE OF ASCOSPORE FORMATION IN CERATO-
        CYSTIS FIMBRIATA. CAN.J.BOT. 54, 1714-1723.

5581   STIPANOVIC, R.D. & BELL, A.A. (1976) - PENTAKETIDE METABOLITES OF VERTI-
        CILLIUM DAHLIAE. 3. IDENTIFICATION OF (-)-3,4-DIHYDRO-3,8-DIHYDROXY-1
        (2H)-NAPHTHALENONE ((-)-VERMELONE) AS A PRECURSOR TO MELANIN. J.ORG.
        CHEM., 1976, 41, 2468-2469.

5582   STIPANOVIC, R.D. & BELL, A.A. (1977) - PENTAKETIDE METABOLITES OF VERTI-
        CILLIUM DAHLIAE. 2. ACCUMULATION OF NAPHTHOL DERIVATIVES BY THE ABERRANT
        -MELANIN MUTANT BRM-2. MYCOLOGIA 69, 164-172.

5583   STIPANOVIC, R.D. & SCHROEDER, H.W. (1975) - ZEARALENONE AND 8-HYDROXY-
        ZEARALENONE FROM FUSARIUM ROSEUM. MYCOPATHOLOGIA 57, 77-78.

5584   STIPANOVIC, R.D. & SCHROEDER, H.W. (1976) - PREECHINULIN, A METABOLITE OF
        ASPERGILLUS CHEVALIERI. TRANS.BR.MYCOL.SOC. 66, 178-179.

5585   STOCKDALE, PH.M. (1958) - OCCURRENCE OF MICROSPORUM GYPSEUM, KERATINOMYCES
       AJELLOI AND TRICHOPHYTON TERRESTRE IN SOME BRITISH SOILS. NATURE, LOND.
       182, 1754.

5586   STOCKDALE, PH.M. (1961) - NANNIZZIA INCURVATA GEN.NOV., SP.NOV., A PERFECT
       STATE OF MICROSPORUM GYPSEUM (BODIN) GUIART & GRIGORAKIS. SABOURAUDIA
       1, 41-44.

5587   STOCKDALE, PH.M. (1963) - THE MICROSPORUM GYPSEUM COMPLEX (NANNIZZIA IN-
       CURVATA STOCKD., N. GYPSEA (NANN.) COMB.NOV., N. FULVA SP.NOV.). SABOU-
       RAUDIA 3, 114-126.

5588   STOCKDALE, PH.M. (1968) - SEXUAL STIMULATION BETWEEN ARTHRODERMA SIMII
       STOCKD., MACKENZIE & AUSTWICK AND RELATED SPECIES. SABOURAUDIA 6, 176-
       181.

5589   STODDARD, J.L. & CARR, A.J.H. (1966) - PROPERTIES OF WILT-TOXINS PRODUCED
       BY VERTICILLIUM ALBO-ATRUM. ANN.APPL.BIOL. 58, 81-92.

5590   STODOLA, F.H., CABOT, C. & BENJAMIN, C.R. (1964) - STRUCTURE OF RAMULOSIN,
       A METABOLIC PRODUCT OF THE FUNGUS PESTALOTIA RAMULOSA. BIOCHEM.J. 93,
       92-97.

5591   STOKES, A. (1954) - UPTAKE AND TRANSLOCATION OF GRISEOFULVIN BY WHEAT SEED-
       LINGS. PL.SOIL 5, 132-142.

5592   STOLK, A.C. (1955) - THE GENERA ANIXIOPSIS AND PSEUDEUROTIUM. ANTONIE VAN
       LEEUWENHOEK 21, 65-79.

5593   STOLK, A. & SAMSON, R.A. (1972) - THE GENUS TALAROMYCES. STUDIES ON TALA-
       ROMYCES AND RELATED GENERA. 2. STUD.MYCOL., BAARN 2, 1-65.

5594   STOLK, A.C. (1965) - THERMOPHILIC SPECIES OF TALAROMYCES BENJAMIN AND THER-
       MOASCUS MIEHE. ANTONIE VAN LEEUWENHOEK 31, 262-276.

5595   STOLK, A.C. (1973) - PENICILLIUM DONKII SP.NOV. AND SOME OBSERVATIONS ON
       SCLEROTIAL STRAINS OF PENICILLIUM FUNICULOSUM. PERSOONIA 7, 333-337.

5596   STOLK, A.C. & MALLA, D.S. (1971) - PENICILLIUM INFLATUM SP.NOV. PERSOONIA
       6, 197-200.

5597   STOLK, A.C. & SCOTT DE B. (1967) - STUDIES ON THE GENUS EUPENICILLIUM 1.
       TAXONOMY AND NOMENCLATURE OF PENICILLIA IN RELATION TO THEIR SCLERO-
       TIOID ASCOCARPIC STATES. PERSOONIA 4, 391-405.

5598   STOLL, A., RENZ, J. & BRACK, A. (1951) - SPALTUNG VON HERZGLYKOSIDEN DURCH
       PILZENZYME. HELV.CHIM.ACTA 34, 397-401.

5599   STOLL, C. (1954) - UEBER STOFFWECHSEL UND BIOLOGISCH WIRKSAME STOFFE VON
       GIBBERELLA FUJIKUROI (SAW.) WOLL., DEM ERREGER DER BAKANAEKRANKHEIT.
       DISS.ETH, ZUERICH.

5600   STORCK, R. & ALEXOPOULOS, C.J. (1970) - DEOXYRIBONUCLEIC ACID OF FUNGI.
       BACT.REV. 34, 126-154.

5601   STOTT, W.T. & BULLERMAN, L.B. (1975) - INFLUENCE OF CARBOHYDRATE AND NITRO-
       GEN SOURCE ON PATULIN PRODUCTION BY PENICILLIUM PATULUM. APPL.MICROBIOL.
       30, 850-854.

5602   STOTZKY, G. & GOOS, R.D. (1965) - EFFECT OF HIGH CO2 AND LOW O2 TENSIONS
       ON THE SOIL MICROBIOTA. CAN.J.MICROBIOL. 11, 853-868.

5603 STOTZKY, G. & POST, A.H. (1967) - SOIL MINERALOGY AS POSSIBLE FACTOR IN
      GEOGRAPHIC DISTRIBUTION OF HISTOPLASMA CAPSULATUM. CAN.J.MICROBIOL. 13,
      1-7.

5604 STOTZKY, G. & REM, L.T. (1967) - INFLUENCE OF CLAY MINERALS ON MICROORGAN-
      ISMS. 4. MONTMORILLONITE AND KAOLINITE ON FUNGI. CAN.J.MICROBIOL. 13,
      1535-1550.

5605 STOUT, D.L. & SHAW, C.R. (1973) - COMPARATIVE ENZYME PATTERNS IN THAMNI-
      DIUM ELEGANS AND T. ANOMALUM. MYCOLOGIA 65, 803-808.

5606 STOUT, D.L. & SHAW, CH.R. (1974) - GENETIC DISTANCE AMONG CERTAIN SPECIES
      OF MUCOR. MYCOLOGIA 66, 969-977.

5607 STOVER, R. (1953) - MEASUREMENT OF COLONIZATION AND SURVIVAL OF SOIL FU-
      SARIA IN DETACHED PLANT TISSUE. NATURE, LOND. 172, 465.

5608 STOVER, R.H. (1966) - FUNGI ASSOCIATED WITH NEMATODE AND NON-NEMATODE LE-
      SIONS ON BANANA ROOTS. CAN.J.BOT. 44, 1703-1710.

5609 STOVOLD, G.E. (1974) - ROOT ROT CAUSED BY PYTHIUM IRREGULARE, AN IMPORTANT
      FACTOR IN THE DECLINE OF ESTABLISHED SUBTERRANEAN CLOVER PASTURES.
      AUST.J.AGRIC.RES. 25, 537-548.

5610 STRANKS, D.W. (1973) - INFLUENCE OF PHENETHYL ALCOHOL AND OTHER ORGANIC
      SOLVENTS ON CELLULASE PRODUCTION. CAN.J.MICROBIOL. 19, 1523-1526.

5611 STRANSKY, H. & AMBERGER, A. (1973) - ISOLIERUNG UND EIGENSCHAFTEN EINER
      CYANAMID-HYDRATASE (E.C.-GRUPPE 4.2.1) AUS MYROTHECIUM VERRUCARIA ALB.
      & SCHW. Z.PFLANZENPHYSIOL. 70, 74-87.

5612 STRETTON, H.M., FLENTJE, N.T. & MCKENZIE, A.R. (1967) - HOMOTHALLISM IN
      THANATEPHORUS CUCUMERIS. AUST.J.BIOL.SCI. 20, 113-120.

5613 STRETTON, H.M., MCKENZIE, A.R., BAKER, K.F. & FLENTJE, N.T. (1964) - FOR-
      MATION OF THE BASIDIAL STAGE OF SOME ISOLATES OF RHIZOCTONIA. PHYTO-
      PATHOLOGY 54, 1093-1095.

5614 STROEMNAES, O., GARBER, E.D. & BERAHA, L. (1964) - GENETICS OF PHYTOPATHO-
      GENIC FUNGI. 9. HETEROCARYOSIS AND THE PARASEXUAL CYCLE IN PENICILLIUM
      ITALICUM AND PENICILLIUM DIGITATUM. CAN.J.BOT. 42, 423-427.

5615 STRZELCZYK, E. (1964) - STUDIES ON THE RHIZOSPHERE MICROFLORA OF PLANTS
      RESISTANT AND SUSCEPTIBLE TO SOIL BORNE DISEASES. 2. EFFECT OF AMINO
      ACIDS AND VITAMINS ON GROWTH OF THIELAVIOPSIS BASICOLA (BERK. & BR.)
      FERR. AND FUSARIUM OXYSPORUM F. LINI (BOLLEY) SNYD. & HANS. ACTA MICRO-
      BIOL.POL. 13, 137-148.

5616 STRZELEC, A. (1973) - DEGRADATION OF SIMAZINE BY SOME SOIL FUNGI. PAM.PU-
      LAWSKI 58, 233-246.

5617 STUBBLEFIELD, R.D., SHOTWELL, O.L., SHANNON, G.M., WEISLEDER, D. & ROHWED-
      DER, W.K. (1970) - PARASITICOL, A NEW METABOLITE FROM ASPERGILLUS PARA-
      SITICUS. J.AGRIC.FD CHEM. 18, 391-393.

5618 STUTZENBERGER, F.J., KAUFMAN, A.J. & LOSSIN, R.D. (1970) - CELLULOLYTIC
      ACTIVITY IN MUNICIPAL SOLID WASTE COMPOSTING. CAN.J.MICROBIOL. 16, 553-
      560.

5619 SUBBA RAO, P.V., MOORE, K. & TOWERS, G.H.N. (1967) - THE CONVERSION OF
      TRYPTOPHAN TO 2,3-DIHYDROXYBENZOIC ACID AND CATECHOL BY ASPERGILLUS NI-
      GER. BIOCHEM.BIOPHYS.RES.COMMUNS 28, 1008-1012.

5620   SUBBA RAO, P.V., MOORE, K. & TOWERS, G.H.N. (1967) - O-PYROCATECHUIC ACID
       CARBOXYLYASE FROM ASPERGILLUS NIGER. ARCHS BIOCHEM.BIOPHYS. 122, 466-
       473.

5621   SUBERKROPP, K. & KLUG, M.J. (1976) - FUNGI AND BACTERIA ASSOCIATED WITH
       LEAVES DURING PROCESSING IN A WOODLAND STREAM. ECOLOGY 57, 707-719.

5622   SUBRAMANIAN, C.V. (1952) - FUNGI ISOLATED AND RECORDED FROM INDIAN SOILS.
       J.MADRAS UNIV., B, 22, 206-222.

5623   SUBRAMANIAN, C.V. (1953) - FUNGI IMPERFECTI FROM MADRAS. 4. PROC.INDIAN
       ACAD.SCI., SECT.B, 42, 96-105.

5624   SUBRAMANIAN, C.V. (1962) - FOOT ROT DISEASE IN WHEAT. CURR.SCI. 31, 46-48.

5625   SUBRAMANIAN, C.V. (1963) - DACTYLELLA, MONACROSPORIUM AND DACTYLINA. J.IN-
       DIAN BOT.SOC. 62, 291-300.

5626   SUBRAMANIAN, C.V. (1971) - HYPHOMYCETES, AN ACCOUNT OF INDIAN SPECIES, EX-
       CEPT CERCOSPORAE. ICAR, NEW DELHI, 930 PP.

5627   SUBRAMANIAN, C.V. (1972) - THE PERFECT STATES OF ASPERGILLUS. CURR.SCI.
       41, 755-761.

5628   SUBRAMANIAN, C.V. & JAIN, B.L. (1966) - A REVISION OF SOME GRAMINICOLOUS
       HELMINTHOSPORIA. CURR.SCI. 35, 352-355.

5629   SUBRAMANIAN, C.V. & TYAGI, P.D. (1968) - UTILIZATION OF VARIOUS FORMS OF
       NITROGEN BY DRECHSLERA SOROKINIANA, THE PATHOGEN CAUSING ROOT ROT DIS-
       EASE WHEAT. PROC.INDIAN ACAD.SCI., SECT.B, 68, 111-130.

5630   SUESS, A. & NETSZCH-LEHNER, A. (1969) - (EFFECT OF DIFFERENT MICROORGAN-
       ISMS ON THE INTENSITY OF DECOMPOSITION OF DIESEL-OIL COMPONENTS). Z.
       PFLERNAEHR.DUENG.BODENK. 123, 232-239.

5631   SUGIMOTO, T., MIURA, T. & KOBAYASI, J. (1959) - STUDIES ON THE SCLEROTIAL
       ROT OF CARROT ROOTS. MEM.FAC.AGRIC.HOKKAIDO UNIV. 3, 121-127.

5632   SUGIURA, M., ITO, A., OGISO, T., KATO, K. & ASANO, H. (1973) - STUDIES ON
       DEXTRANASE. PURIFICATION OF DEXTRANASE FROM PENICILLIUM FUNICULOSUM AND
       ITS ENZYMATIC PROPERTIES. BIOCHIM.BIOPHYS.ACTA 309, 357-368.

5633   SUGIYAMA, J. (1967) - MYCOFLORA IN CORE SAMPLES FROM STRATIGRAPHIC DRILL-
       INGS IN MIDDLE JAPAN. 2. THE GENUS ASPERGILLUS. J.FAC.SCI.TOKYO, SECT.3,
       9, 377-405.

5634   SUGIYAMA, J. (1969) - STUDIES ON HIMALAYAN YEASTS AND MOULDS. 2. MAMMARIA
       ECHINOBOTRYOIDES (HYPHOMYCETES) AND ITS ALLIES. TRANS.MYCOL.SOC.JAPAN
       9, 117-124.

5635   SUGIYAMA, J., KAWASAKI, Y. & KURATA, H. (1968) - WARDOMYCES SIMPLEX, A NEW
       HYPHOMYCETE FROM MILLED RICE. BOT.MAG., TOKYO 81, 243-250.

5636   SUGIYAMA, J., KAWASAKI, Y. & KURATA, H. (1969) - WARDOMYCES SIMPLEX (HYPHO-
       MYCETES) AND ITS ANNELLOSPORES. BOT.MAG., TOKYO 82, 353-358.

5637   SUGIYAMA, J., SUGIYAMA, Y. IIZUKA, H. & TORII, T. (1967) - REPORT OF THE
       JAPANESE SUMMER PARTIES IN DRY VALLEYS, VICTORIA LAND, 1963-65. 4. MY-
       COLOGICAL STUDIES OF THE ANTARCTIC FUNGI. 2. MYCOFLORA OF LAKE VANDA,
       AN ICE-FREE LAKE. ANTARCTIC REC. 28, 23-32.

5638 SULLIA, S.B. (1973) - EFFECT OF ROOT EXUDATES AND EXTRACTS ON RHIZOSPHERE FUNGI. PL.SOIL 39, 197-200.

5639 SUMI, M. (1928) - UEBER DIE CHEMISCHEN BESTANDTEILE DER SPOREN VON ASPERGILLUS ORYZAE. BIOCHEM.Z. 195, 161-174.

5640 SUMNER, J.L. (1970) - GROWTH AND SPORULATION OF MUCOR PUSILLUS. TRANS.BR. MYCOL.SOC. 55, 283-292.

5641 SUMNER, J.L. & COLOTELO, N. (1970) - THE FATTY ACID COMPOSITION OF SCLEROTIA. CAN.J.MICROBIOL. 16, 1171-1178.

5642 SUMNER, J.L. & EVANS, H.C. (1971) - THE FATTY ACID COMPOSITION OF DACTYLARIA AND SCOLECOBASIDIUM. CAN.J.MICROBIOL. 17, 7-11.

5643 SUMNER, J.L. & MORGAN, E.D. (1969) - THE FATTY ACID COMPOSITION OF SPORANGIOSPORES AND VEGETATIVE MYCELIUM OF TEMPERATURE-ADAPTED FUNGI IN THE ORDER MUCORALES. J.GEN.MICROBIOL. 59, 215-221.

5644 SUN, H.S., ALEXOPOULOS, C.J. & WILSON, G.B. (1954) - A CYTOTAXONOMIC STUDY OF THREE SPECIES OF GELASINOSPORA. CYTOLOGIA 19, 255-264.

5645 SUNDHEIM, L. (1972) - PHYSIOLOGIC SPECIALIZATION IN APHANOMYCES EUTEICHES. PHYSIOL.PL.PATH. 2, 301-306.

5646 SUNDHEIM, L. (1973) - BOTRYTIS FABAE, BOTRYTIS CINEREA AND ASCOCHYTA FABAE ON BROAD BEAN IN NORWAY. ACTA AGRIC.SCAND. 23, 43-51.

5647 SUPRUN, T.P., AVRAAMOVA, O.P. & BEKKER, Z.E. (1963) - (DISTRIBUTION OF SOIL FUNGI-ANTAGONISTS IN CENTRAL ASIA IN RELATION TO LOCAL ALTITUDE). BYULL.MOSK.OBSHCH.ISPYT.PRIR., OTD.BIOL. 68, 84-92.

5648 SUTTON, B.C. (1962) - COLLETOTRICHUM DEMATIUM AND C. TRICHELLUM. TRANS.BR. MYCOL.SOC. 45, 222-232.

5649 SUTTON, B.C. (1964) - PHOMA AND RELATED GENERA. TRANS.BR.MYCOL.SOC. 47, 497-509.

5650 SUTTON, B.C. (1969) - FOREST MICROFUNGI. 3. THE HETEROGENEITY OF PESTALOTIA DE NOT. SECTION SEXLOCULATAE KLEBAHN SENSU GUBA. CAN.J.BOT. 47, 2083-2094.

5651 SUTTON, B.C. (1971) - COELOMYCETES. 4. THE GENUS HARKNESSIA, AND SIMILAR FUNGI ON EUCALYPTUS. MYCOL.PAP. 123, 46 PP.

5652 SUTTON, B.C., PIROZYNSKI, K.A. & DEIGHTON, F.C. (1972) - MICRODOCHIUM SYD. CAN.J.BOT. 50, 1899-1907.

5653 SUZUKI, A., KANAOKA, M., ISOGAI, A., MURAKOSHI, S., ICHINOE, M. & TAMURA, M. (1977) - BASSIANOLIDE, A NEW INSECTICIDAL CYCLO-DEPSIPEPTIDE FROM BEAUVERIA BASSIANA AND VERTICILLIUM LECANII. TETRAHEDRON LETTERS, 1977 (25), 2167-2170.

5654 SUZUKI, A., KUYAMA, S., KODAIRA, Y. & TAMURA, S. (1966) - STRUCTURAL ELUCIDATION OF DESTRUXIN-A. AGRIC.BIOL.CHEM., TOKYO 30, 517-518.

5655 SUZUKI, A., TAGUCHI, H. & TAMURA, S. (1970) - ISOLATION AND STRUCTURE ELUCIDATION OF THREE NEW INSECTICIDAL CYCLODEPSIPEPTIDES, DESTRUXINS-C AND -D AND DESMETHYLDESTRUXIN-B, PRODUCED BY METARRHIZIUM ANISOPLIAE. AGRIC. BIOL.CHEM., TOKYO 34, 813-816.

5656   SUZUKI, A. & TAMURA, S. (1972) - ISOLATION AND STRUCTURE OF PROTODESTRUXIN
       FROM METARRHIZIUM ANISOPLIAE. AGRIC.BIOL.CHEM., TOKYO 36, 896-898.

5657   SUZUKI, H., LI, S. & LI, Y. (1970) - ALPHA-GALACTOSIDASE FROM MORTIERELLA
       VINACEA. CRYSTALLIZATION AND PROPERTIES. J.BIOL.CHEM. 245, 781-786.

5658   SUZUKI, K., SASSA, T., TANAKA, H., AOKI, H. & NAMIKI, M. (1968) - SCLERONE,
       A NEW METABOLITE OF SCLEROTINIA SCLEROTIORUM. AGRIC.BIOL.CHEM., TOKYO
       32, 1471-1475.

5659   SUZUKI, SH. & NIMURA, H. (1962) - ECOLOGICAL SPECIFICITY OF SOME AQUATIC
       HYPHOMYCETES IN JAPAN. JAP.J.ECOL. 12, 195-197.

5660   SUZUKI, T., TAKEDA, M. & TANABE, H. (1971) - A NEW MYCOTOXIN PRODUCED BY
       ASPERGILLUS CLAVATUS. BULL.CHEM.PHARM. 19, 1786-1788.

5661   SUZUKI, Y. & MARUMO, S. (1972) - FUNGAL METABOLISM OF (+)-EPOXYFARNESOL
       AND ITS ABSOLUTE STEREOCHEMISTRY. TETRAHEDRON LETTERS, 1972 (19), 1887-
       1890.

5662   SUZUKI, Y. & UCHIDA, K. (1971) - PRODUCTION OF 5-D-RIBOFLAVIN-ALPHA-D-GLU-
       CO-PYRANOSIDE IN GROWING CULTURES BY THE MOLD MUCOR. AGRIC.BIOL.CHEM.,
       TOKYO 35, 805-812.

5663   SVINNUFVUD, V.E. (1937) - UNTERSUCHUNGEN UEBER DIE BODENMIKROBIOLOGISCHEN
       UNTERSCHIEDE DER CAJANDERSCHEN WALDTYPEN. ACTA FOR.FENN. 44, 1-67.

5664   SWAN, D.C. & BARNETT, H.L. (1963) - THE EFFECT OF LIGHT ON SPORULATION OF
       EPICOCCUM NIGRUM. PROC.W.VA ACAD.SCI. 35, 46-50.

5665   SWART, H.J. (1959) - A COMPARATIVE STUDY OF THE GENERA GONYTRICHUM AND BI-
       SPOROMYCES. ANTONIE VAN LEEUWENHOEK 25, 439-444.

5666   SWART, H.J. (1964) - A STUDY OF THE PRODUCTION OF COREMIA IN THREE SPECIES
       OF THE GENUS TRICHURUS. ANTONIE VAN LEEUWENHOEK 30, 257-260.

5667   SWART, H.J. (1965) - CONIDIAL FORMATION IN HAPLOGRAPHIUM FULIGINEUM. TRANS.
       BR.MYCOL.SOC. 48, 459-461.

5668   SWART, H.J. (1975) - CALLOSITIES IN FUNGI. TRANS.BR.MYCOL.SOC. 64, 511-515.

5669   SWATEK, F.E. (1970) - ECOLOGY OF COCCIDIOIDES IMMITIS. MYCOPATH.MYCOL.APPL.
       41, 3-12.

5670   SWATEK, F.E. & OMIECZYNSKI, D.T. (1970) - ISOLATION AND IDENTIFICATION OF
       COCCIDIOIDES IMMITIS FROM NATURAL SOURCES. MYCOPATH.MYCOL.APPL. 41,
       155-166.

5671   SWIFT, M.E. (1929) - CONTRIBUTIONS TO A MYCOLOGICAL FLORA OF LOCAL SOILS.
       MYCOLOGIA 21, 204-221.

5672   SZANISZLO, P.J., COOPER, B.H. & VOGES, H.S. (1972) - CHEMICAL COMPOSITION
       OF THE HYPHAL WALLS OF THREE CHROMOMYCOSIS AGENTS. SABOURAUDIA 10, 94-
       102.

5673   SZEGI, J. (1967) - ADDITIONAL DATA TO THE HUMUS-DECOMPOSING ACTIVITY OF
       SOME ACTINOMYCES AND MICROSCOPICAL FUNGI. ACTA AGRON.HUNG. 16, 367-373.

5674   SZEGI, J. (1968) - DATA ON THE NITROGEN METABOLISM OF A FEW CELLULOSE DE-
       COMPOSING MICROSCOPIC FUNGI. ANNLS INST.PASTEUR, PARIS 115, 617-624.

5675 SZEGI, J. (1968) - (DATA ON THE NITROGEN NUTRITION OF SOME MICROSCOPIC
      FUNGI. 1. NATURE OF THE NITROGEN SOURCE AND C/N RATIO). AGROKEM.TALAJT.
      17, 255-264.

5676 SZEGI, J. (1970) - EFFECT OF SOME HERBICIDES ON THE GROWTH OF CELLULOSE
      DECOMPOSING MICROSCOPIC FUNGI. MEDED.FAC.LANDB.RIJKSUNIV.GENT 35, 559-
      561.

5677 SZEGI, J. & TIMAR, E. (1964) - (THE FORMATION OF STIMULATORY AND INHIBITORY
      SUBSTANCES BY CELLULOSE DECOMPOSING MICROORGANISMS). AGROKEM.TALAJT. 13,
      79-86.

5678 SZILVINYI, A.V. (1941) - MIKROBIOLOGISCHE BODENUNTERSUCHUNGEN IM LUNZER
      GEBIET. 3. ZENTBL.BAKT.PARASITKDE, ABT.2, 103, 133-189.

5679 SZTEJNBERG, A. & BLAKEMAN, J.P. (1973) - STUDIES ON LEACHING OF BOTRYTIS
      CINEREA CONIDIA AND DYE ABSORPTION BY BACTERIA IN RELATION TO COMPETI-
      TION FOR NUTRIENTS. J.GEN.MICROBIOL. 78, 15-22.

5680 TABAK, H.H. & COOKE, W.B. (1968) - GROWTH AND METABOLISM OF FUNGI IN AN
      ATMOSPHERE OF NITROGEN. MYCOLOGIA 60, 115-140.

5681 TABENKIN, B., LEMAHIEU, R.A., BERGER, J. & KIERSTEAD, R.W. (1969) - MICRO-
      BIOLOGICAL HYDROXYLATION OF CINERONE TO CINEROLONE. APPL.MICROBIOL. 17,
      714-717.

5682 TABER, R.A., PETTIT, R.E., TABER, W.A. & DOLLAHITE, J.W. (1968) - ISOLA-
      TION OF PITHOMYCES CHARTARUM IN TEXAS. MYCOLOGIA 60, 727-730.

5683 TAGUCHI, R., KIKUCHI, Y., SAKANO, Y. & KOBAYASHI, T. (1973) - STRUCTURAL
      UNIFORMITY OF PULLULAN PRODUCED BY SEVERAL STRAINS OF PULLULARIA PULLU-
      LANS. AGRIC.BIOL.CHEM., TOKYO 37, 1583-1588.

5684 TAGUCHI, R., SAKANO, Y., KIKUCHI, Y., SAKAMU, M. & KOBAYASHI, T. (1973) -
      SYNTHESIS OF PULLULAN BY ACETONE-DRIED CELLS AND CELL-FREE ENZYME FROM
      PULLULARIA PULLULANS, AND THE PARTICIPATION OF LIPID INTERMEDIATE.
      AGRIC.BIOL.CHEM., TOKYO 37, 1635-1641.

5685 TAKADA, M. (1969) - MATERIALS FOR THE FUNGUS FLORA OF JAPAN. 7. TRANS.MY-
      COL.SOC.JAPAN 9, 125-130.

5686 TAKADA, M. (1973) - NOTES ON SOIL-BORNE ASCOMYCETES. BULL.NATN.SCI.MUS.,
      TOKYO 16, 521-534.

5687 TAKADA, M. & UDAGAWA, S. (1970) - MATERIALS FOR THE FUNGUS FLORA OF JAPAN.
      TRANS.MYCOL.SOC.JAPAN 11, 53-56.

5688 TAKAGAWA, S. (1939) - STUDIES ON THE DECOMPOSITION OF PECTIN BY FUNGI.
      J.FERMENT.TECHNOL., OSAKA 17, 441-453.

5689 TAKAHASHI, C., YOSHIHIRA, K., NATORI, S., UMEDA, M., OHTZUBO, K. & SAITO,
      M. (1974) - TOXIC METABOLITES OF ASPERGILLUS CANDIDUS. EXPERIENTIA 30,
      529.

5690 TAKAHASHI, M. (1952) - A COMPARATIVE STUDY ON THE PATHOGENICITY OF TWO
      SPECIES OF AQUATIC PYTHIUM, P. APHANIDERMATUM AND P. MONOSPERMUM. ANN.
      PHYTOPATH.SOC.JAPAN 16, 19-22.

5691 TAKAHASHI, M. & KAWASE, Y. (1964) - (ECOLOGICAL AND TAXONOMIC STUDIES ON
      PYTHIUM AS PATHOGENIC SOIL FUNGI. 1. VERTICAL DISTRIBUTION OF SEVERAL
      PATHOGENIC FUNGI IN SOIL). ANN.PHYTOPATH.SOC.JAPAN 29, 155-161.

5692 TAKAHASHI, M. & OZAKI, T. (1965) - ECOLOGIC AND TAXONOMIC STUDIES ON PY-
      THIUM AS PATHOGENIC SOIL FUNGI. 6. THE ISOLATION METHODS OF PYTHIUM.
      BULL.UNIV.OSAKA PREF., SER.B, 17, 1-10.

5693 TAKAHASHI, M., TANAKA, Y., ICHITANI, T. & ALICBUSAN, R.V. (1972) - ECOLOG-
      IC AND TAXONOMIC STUDIES ON PYTHIUM AS PATHOGENIC SOIL FUNGI. 10. SEVERAL
      PYTHIUM CAUSING DAMPING-OFF OF SUGAR BEET SEEDLINGS. ANN.PHYTOPATH.SOC.
      JAPAN 38, 306-312.

5694 TAKASHIO, M. (1971) - OBTENTION DES FORMES SEXUEES DES CHAMPIGNONS PATHO-
      GENES. C.R. 1.MULTICOLL.EUROP.PARASITOL., RENNES, 469-475.

5695 TAKASHIO, M. (1972) - SEXUAL REPRODUCTION OF SOME ARTHRODERMA AND NANNIZ-
      ZIA ON DILUTED SABOURAUD AGAR WITH OR WITHOUT SALTS. MYKOSEN 15, 11-17.

5696 TAKEBE, I. (1966) - CHOLINE SULFATE AS A MAJOR SOLUBLE SULFUR COMPONENT OF
      CONIDIOSPORES OF ASPERGILLUS NIGER. J.GEN.APPL.MICROBIOL., TOKYO 6, 83-
      89.

5697 TAKEDA, N., SEO, S., OGIHARA, Y., SANKAWA, U., IITAKA, I., KITAGAWA, I. &
      SHIBATA, S. (1973) - STUDIES ON FUNGAL METABOLITES. 31. ANTHRAQUINONOID
      COLOURING MATTERS OF PENICILLIUM ISLANDICUM SOPP AND SOME OTHER FUNGI:
      (-)LUTEOSKYRIN, (-)RUBROSKYRIN, (+)RUGULOSIN AND THEIR RELATED COM-
      POUNDS. TETRAHEDRON 29, 3703-3719.

5698 TAKENAKA, S. & SETO, S. (1971) - THE BIOSYNTHESIS OF SEPEDONIN. 1. LABEL-
      ING PATTERN OF ANHYDROSEPEDONIN. AGRIC.BIOL.CHEM., TOKYO 35, 862-869.

5699 TAKENAKA, S. & SETO, S. (1974) - BIOSYNTHESIS OF SEPEDONIN BY CELL-FREE
      EXTRACT OF SEPEDONIUM CHRYSOSPERMUM. SCIENT.REP.RES.INST.TOHOKU UNIV.,
      SER.A, 25, 25-30.

5700 TAKENISHI, S. & TSUJISAKA, Y. (1973) - PENICILLIUM JANTHINELLUM BIOURGE,
      XYLANASE. PURIFICATION AND SOME PROPERTIES OF THREE XYLANASES FROM PE-
      NICILLIUM JANTHINELLUM BIOURGE. J.FERMENT.TECHNOL., OSAKA 51, 458-468.

5701 TAKENISHI, S. & TSUJISAKA, Y. (1973) - STRUCTURES OF THE OLIGOSACCHARIDES
      FROM THE ENZYMIC HYDROLYZATE OF RICE-STRAW ARABINOXYLAN BY A XYLANASE
      OF ASPERGILLUS NIGER. AGRIC.BIOL.CHEM., TOKYO 37, 1385-1391.

5702 TAKENISHI, S., TSUJISAKA, Y. & FUKUMOTO, J. (1973) - STUDIES ON HEMICEL-
      LULASES. 4. PURIFICATION AND PROPERTIES OF THE BETA-XYLOSIDASE PRODUCED
      BY ASPERGILLUS NIGER. J.BIOCHEM., TOKYO 73, 335-343.

5703 TAKEO, K. (1974) - ULTRASTRUCTURE OF POLYMORPHIC MUCOR AS OBSERVED BY
      MEANS OF FREEZE-ETCHING. 2. VEGETATIVE YEAST FORM GROWN UNDER ANAEROBIC
      CONDITIONS. ARCH.MICROBIOL. 99, 91-98.

5704 TAKEO, K. (1974) - ULTRASTRUCTURE OF POLYMORPHIC MUCOR AS OBSERVED BY
      MEANS OF FREEZE-ETCHING. 3. DORMANT SPORANGIOSPORE. ARCH.MICROBIOL. 99,
      99-107.

5705 TAKEO, K. & NISHIURA, M. (1974) - ULTRASTRUCTURE OF POLYMORPHIC MUCOR AS
      OBSERVED BY MEANS OF FREEZE-ETCHING. 1. VEGETATIVE GROWTH OF MYCELIUM
      AND ARTHROSPORES FORMATION IN SUBMERGED AND AERATED CULTURES. ARCH.MI-
      CROBIOL. 98, 175-185.

5706 TAKEUCHI, S., YONEHARA, H. & UMEZAWA, H. (1959) - STUDIES ON VARIOTIN, A
      NEW ANTIFUNGAL ANTIBIOTIC. 1. PREPARATIONS AND PROPERTIES OF VARIOTIN.
      J.ANTIBIOT., TOKYO, SER.A, 12, 195-200.

5707 TAKEUCHI, Y. & KITAHARA, M. (1966) - STRUCTURE OF GLUCO-OLIGOSACCHARIDES
      OBTAINED FROM THE PARTIAL ACID-HYDROLYZATE OF SCLEROTIA OF SCLEROTINIA
      LIBERTIANA. 1. SEPARATION OF OLIGOSACCHARIDES FROM THE ACID PARTIAL
      HYDROLYZATE OF DEFATTED SCLEROTIA. AGRIC.BIOL.CHEM., TOKYO 30, 523-528.

5708 TALBOT, P.H.B. (1965) - STUDIES OF 'PELLICULARIA' AND ASSOCIATED GENERA OF
      HYMENOMYCETES. PERSOONIA 3, 371-406.

5709 TALBOT, P.H.B. (1970) - TAXONOMY AND NOMENCLATURE OF THE PERFECT STATE.
      IN: RHIZOCTONIA SOLANI, BIOLOGY AND PATHOLOGY, SYMPOSIUM 1965; PARME-
      TER, J.JR. (ED.), UNIV.CALIFORNIA PRESS, BERKELEY, 20-31.

5710 TALBOYS, P.W. (1960) - A CULTURE-MEDIUM AIDING THE IDENTIFICATION OF VER-
      TICILLIUM ALBO-ATRUM AND V. DAHLIAE. PL.PATH. 9, 57-58.

5711 TALBOYS, P.W. & BUSCH, L.V. (1970) - PECTIC ENZYMES PRODUCED BY VERTICIL-
      LIUM SPECIES. TRANS.BR.MYCOL.SOC. 55, 367-381.

5712 TALBURT, D.E. & JOHNSON, G.T. (1972) - SOME METABOLIC EFFECTS OF RARE-
      EARTH CATIONS ON ASPERGILLUS NIGER CELLS. MYCOLOGIA 64, 551-559.

5713 TALIGOOLA, T.K., APINIS, A.E. & CHESTERS, C.G.C. (1972) - MICROFUNGI COLON-
      IZING COLLAPSED AERIAL PARTS OF PHRAGMITES COMMUNIS TRIN. IN WATER.
      NOVA HEDWIGIA 23, 465-472.

5714 TALLEY, P.J. & BLANK, L.M. (1941) - A CRITICAL STUDY OF THE NUTRITIONAL
      REQUIREMENTS OF PHYMATOTRICHUM OMNIVORUM. PL.PHYSIOL., LANCASTER 16, 1-
      18.

5715 TALLEY, P.J. & BLANK, L.M. (1942) - SOME FACTORS INFLUENCING THE UTILIZA-
      TION OF INORGANIC NITROGEN BY THE ROOT ROT FUNGUS. PL.PHYSIOL., LANCAS-
      TER 17, 52-68.

5716 TAMIYA, H. (1929) - STUDIEN UEBER DIE STOFFWECHSELPHYSIOLOGIE VON ASPER-
      GILLUS ORYZAE. 3. ACTA PHYTOCHIM., TOKYO 4, 227-295.

5717 TAMIYA, H. & USAMI, SH. (1940) - UEBER DAS WACHSTUM VON ASPERGILLUS ORYZAE
      BEI ZUGABE DER AMINOSAEUREN ALS ALLEINIGE KOHLENSTOFF UND STICKSTOFF-
      QUELLE. ACTA PHYTOCHIM., TOKYO 11, 262-298.

5718 TAMM, CH., BOEHNER, B. & ZUERCHER, W. (1972) - MYROCHROMANOL UND MYROCHRO-
      MANON, ZWEI WEITERE METABOLITEN VON MYROTHECIUM RORIDUM TODE EX FR.
      HELV.CHIM.ACTA 55, 510-518.

5719 TAMM, CH. & GUTZWILLER, J. (1962) - UEBER DIE VERRUCARINE UND RORIDINE. 2.
      PARTIALSTRUKTUR VON VERRUCARIN-A. HELV.CHIM.ACTA 45, 1726-1731.

5720 TAMURA, S., KUYAMA, S., KODAIRA, Y. & HIGASHIKAWA, S. (1964) - THE STRUC-
      TURE OF DESTRUXIN-B, A TOXIC METABOLITE OF OOSPORA DESTRUCTOR. AGRIC.
      BIOL.CHEM., TOKYO 28, 137-138.

5721 TAN, K.K. (1974) - COMPLETE REVERSIBILITY OF SPORULATION BY NEAR ULTRA-
      VIOLET AND BLUE LIGHT IN BOTRYTIS CINEREA. TRANS.BR.MYCOL.SOC. 63, 203-
      205.

5722 TAN, K.K. (1974) - BLUE LIGHT INHIBITION OF SPORULATION IN BOTRYTIS CINEREA.
      J.GEN.MICROBIOL. 82, 191-200.

5723 TAN, K.K. (1974) - RED-FAR-RED REVERSIBLE PHOTOREACTIVATION IN THE RECOV-
      ERY FROM BLUE-LIGHT INHIBITION OF SPORULATION IN BOTRYTIS CINEREA. J.
      GEN.MICROBIOL. 82, 201-202.

5724 TAN, K.K. (1975) - INTERACTION OF NEAR-ULTRAVIOLET, BLUE, RED, AND FAR-RED
      LIGHT IN SPORULATION OF BOTRYTIS CINEREA. TRANS.BR.MYCOL.SOC. 64, 215-
      222.

5725   TAN, K.K. (1975) - RECOVERY FROM THE BLUE-LIGHT INHIBITION OF SPORULATION
       IN BOTRYTIS CINEREA. TRANS.BR.MYCOL.SOC. 64, 223-228.

5726   TAN, K.K. & EPTON, H.A.S. (1973) - EFFECT OF LIGHT ON THE GROWTH AND SPOR-
       ULATION OF BOTRYTIS CINEREA. TRANS.BR.MYCOL.SOC. 61, 147-157.

5727   TAN, K.K. & EPTON, H.A.S. (1974) - FURTHER STUDIES ON LIGHT AND SPORULATION
       IN BOTRYTIS CINEREA. TRANS.BR.MYCOL.SOC. 62, 105-112.

5728   TANABE, M. & SUZUKI, K.T. (1974) - DETECTION OF C-C BOND FISSION DURING
       THE BIOSYNTHESIS OF THE FUNGAL TRIPRENYLPHENOL ASCOCHLORIN USING (1,2-
       13C)-ACETATE. CHEM.COMMUN., 1974 (11), 445-446.

5729   TANABE, M. & SUZUKI, K.T. (1974) - BIOSYNTHETIC STUDIES WITH CARBON-13,
       INCORPORATION PATTERN OF 1,2-13C-ACETATE INTO THE FUNGAL SESQUITERPENE
       OVALICIN. TETRAHEDRON LETTERS, 1974 (49/50), 4417-4420.

5730   TANAKA, K. (1966) - CHANGES IN ULTRASTRUCTURE OF ASPERGILLUS ORYZAE CONID-
       IA DURING GERMINATION. J.GEN.APPL.MICROBIOL., TOKYO 12, 239-246.

5731   TANAKA, K. & YANAGITA, T. (1963) - ELECTRON MICROSCOPY ON ULTRATHIN SEC-
       TIONS OF ASPERGILLUS NIGER. 1. FINE STRUCTURE OF HYPHAL CELLS. J.GEN.
       APPL.MICROBIOL., TOKYO 9, 101-118.

5732   TANAKA, K. & YANAGITA, T. (1963) - ELECTRON MICROSCOPY ON ULTRATHIN SEC-
       TIONS OF ASPERGILLUS NIGER. 2. FINE STRUCTURE OF CONIDIA-BEARING APPA-
       RATUS. J.GEN.APPL.MICROBIOL., TOKYO 9, 189-203.

5733   TANAKA, N. (1967) - VARIOTIN. J.ANTIBIOT., TOKYO 2, 216-221.

5734   TANDON, G.D. & MEHROTRA, B.S. (1970) - ADDITIONS TO PENICILLIA OF INDIA.
       2. GURUKULA KANGRI VISHWAVIDYALAYA J.SCIENT.RES. 2, 18-22.

5735   TANDON, M.P. & SRIVASTAVA, G. (1974) - SOME NEW FRUIT DISEASES. CURR.SCI.
       43, 795-796.

5736   TANDON, R.N. & BHARGAVA, S.N. (1962) - UTILIZATION OF MONOSACCHARIDES BY
       THREE PATHOGENIC FUNGI. LLOYDIA 25, 167-171.

5737   TANDON, R.N. & CHATURVEDI, C. (1962) - THE UTILIZATION OF AMINO ACIDS BY
       THREE IMPERFECT FUNGI. PHYTOPATH.Z. 45, 237-242.

5738   TANG, A., CURL, E.A. & RODRIGUEZ-KABANA, R. (1970) - EFFECT OF TRIFLURALIN
       ON INOCULUM DENSITY AND SPORE GERMINATION OF FUSARIUM OXYSPORUM F.SP.
       VASINFECTUM IN SOIL. PHYTOPATHOLOGY 60, 1082-1086.

5739   TANRIKUT, S. & VAUGHAN, E.K. (1951) - STUDIES ON THE PHYSIOLOGY OF SCLERO-
       TINIA SCLEROTIORUM. PHYTOPATHOLOGY 41, 1099-1103.

5740   TANSEY, M.R. (1971) - ISOLATION OF THERMOPHILIC FUNGI FROM SELF-HEATED,
       INDUSTRIAL WOOD-CHIP PILES. MYCOLOGIA 63, 537-547.

5741   TANSEY, M.R. (1971) - AGAR-DIFFUSION ASSAY OF CELLULOLYTIC ABILITY OF THER-
       MOPHILIC FUNGI. ARCH.MIKROBIOL. 77, 1-11.

5742   TANSEY, M.R. (1973) - ISOLATION OF THERMOPHILIC FUNGI FROM ALLIGATOR NEST-
       ING MATERIAL. MYCOLOGIA 65, 594-601.

5743   TANSEY, M.R. (1975) - ISOLATION OF THERMOPHILIC FUNGI FROM SNUFF. APPL.MI-
       CROBIOL. 29, 128-129.

5744   TANSEY, M.R. & APPLETON, J.A. (1975) - INHIBITION OF FUNGAL GROWTH BY GAR-
        LIC EXTRACT. MYCOLOGIA 67, 409-413.

5745   TANSEY, M.R. & BROCK, T.D. (1971) - ISOLATION OF THERMOPHILIC AND THERMO-
        TOLERANT FUNGI FROM HOT SPRING EFFLUENTS AND THERMAL SOILS OF YELLOW-
        STONE PARK. BACT.PROC. 71, 36.

5746   TANSEY, M.R. & BROCK, T.D. (1977) - MICROBIAL LIFE AT HIGH TEMPERATURES.
        ECOLOGICAL ASPECTS. ACADEMIC PRESS, NEW YORK.

5747   TANSEY, M.R. & JACK, M.A. (1976) - THERMOPHILIC FUNGI IN SUN-HEATED SOILS.
        MYCOLOGIA 68, 1061-1075.

5748   TARDIEUX, P., PEREA-DALLOS, M., FALCOU, J. & HERVECOTTU, Y. (1972) - PRE-
        LIMINARY STUDY ON THE EFFECT OF GAMMA IRRADIATION ON A FUNGAL POPULA-
        TION. AGROCHIMICA 16, 83-98.

5749   TARUNINA, T.A. & TIME, R.N. (1971) - (ISOLATION OF VERTICILLIUM NIGRESCENS
        PETHYB. FROM COTTON). MIKOL.FITOPAT. 5, 212-215.

5750   TATARENKO, E.S. (1954) - (THE INFLUENCE OF LIGHT ON THE DEVELOPMENT OF
        MOLD FUNGI). MIKROBIOLOGIYA 23, 29-33.

5751   TATSUNO, T., MORITA, Y., TSUNODA, H. & UMEDA, M. (1970) - RECHERCHES TOXI-
        COLOGIQUES DES SUBSTANCES METABOLIQUES DU FUSARIUM NIVALE. 7. LA TROI-
        SIEME SUBSTANCE METABOLIQUE DE F. NIVALE, LE DIACETATE DE NIVALENOL.
        CHEM.PHARM.BULL., TOKYO 18, 1485-1487.

5752   TATSUNO, T., SATO, M., KUBOTA, YU., KUBOTA, YA. & TSUNODA, H. (1971) -
        RECHERCHES TOXICOLOGIQUES DES SUBSTANCES METABOLIQUES DU FUSARIUM NIVA-
        LE. 8. LA QUATRIEME SUBSTANCE METABOLIQUE DE F. NIVALE. CHEM.PHARM.BULL.,
        TOKYO 19, 1498-1500.

5753   TAUBENHAUS, J.J. & EZEKIEL, W.N. (1936) - A RATING OF PLANTS WITH REFER-
        ENCE TO THEIR RELATIVE RESISTANCE OR SUSCEPTIBILITY TO PHYMATOTRICHUM
        ROOT ROT. BULL.TEXAS AGRIC.EXP.STN 527, 52 PP.

5754   TAYLOR, E.E. & MARSH, P.B. (1963) - CELLULOSE DECOMPOSITION BY PYTHIUM.
        CAN.J.MICROBIOL. 9, 353-358.

5755   TAYLOR, G.S. (1964) - FUSARIUM OXYSPORUM AND CYLINDROCARPON RADICICOLA IN
        RELATION TO THEIR ASSOCIATION WITH PLANT ROOTS. TRANS.BR.MYCOL.SOC. 47,
        381-391.

5756   TAYLOR, G.S. (1970) - THE SURVIVAL OF FUSARIUM NIVALE IN SOIL. ANNLS ACAD.
        SCI.FENN., SER.A, IV, 168, 66-70.

5757   TAYLOR, G.S. & PARKINSON, D. (1961) - THE GROWTH OF SAPROPHYTIC FUNGI ON
        ROOT SURFACES. PL.SOIL 15, 261-267.

5758   TAYLOR, G.S. & PARKINSON, D. (1964) - STUDIES ON FUNGI IN THE ROOT REGION.
        2. THE EFFECT OF CERTAIN ENVIRONMENTAL CONDITIONS ON THE DEVELOPMENT OF
        ROOT SURFACE MYCOFLORAS OF DWARF BEAN SEEDLINGS. PL.SOIL 20, 34-42.

5759   TAYLOR, G.S. & PARKINSON, D. (1965) - STUDIES ON FUNGI IN THE ROOT REGION.
        4. FUNGI ASSOCIATED WITH THE ROOTS OF PHASEOLUS VULGARIS. PL.SOIL 22,
        1-20.

5760   TAYLOR, H.I. & PARKINSON, D. (1971) - GROWTH AND ACTIVITY OF PENICILLIUM
        DECUMBENS UNDER DIFFERENT ENVIRONMENTAL CONDITIONS IN GLASS MICROBEAD
        MEDIA. CAN.J.MICROBIOL. 17, 967-973.

5761   TAYLOR, J. (1966) - GHOST SPOT OF APPLE LEAVES CAUSED BY ALTERNARIA TENUIS.
        PHYTOPATHOLOGY 56, 553-555.

5762   TAYLOR, J.B. (1971) - A SELECTIVE MEDIUM FOR THE ISOLATION OF BASIDIOMYCE-
        TES FROM DISEASED ROOTS, MYCORRHIZAS, AND SOIL. TRANS.BR.MYCOL.SOC. 56,
        313-314.

5763   TAYLOR, J.J. (1970) - FURTHER CLARIFICATION OF SPOROTRICHUM SPECIES. MY-
        COLOGIA 62, 797-825.

5764   TAYLOR, J.J. (1970) - A COMPARISON OF SOME CERATOCYSTIS SPECIES WITH SPO-
        ROTHRIX SCHENCKII. MYCOPATH.MYCOL.APPL. 42, 233-240.

5765   TAYLOR, J.J. (1976) - EX VIVO DETERMINATION OF POTENTIALLY VIRULENT SPORO-
        THRIX SCHENCKII. MYCOPATHOLOGIA 58, 107-114.

5766   TAYLOR, W.W., RADCLIFFE, F. & VANPEENEN, P.F.D. (1963/64) - THE ISOLATION
        OF PATHOGENIC FUNGI FROM THE SOILS OF EGYPT, THE SUDAN, AND ETHIOPIA.
        SABOURAUDIA 3, 235-238.

5767   TEAKLE, D.S. (1960) - SPECIES OF PYTHIUM IN QUEENSLAND. QD J.AGRIC.SCI.
        17, 15-31.

5768   TEH, J.S. (1974) - TOXICITY OF SHORT-CHAIN FATTY ACIDS AND ALCOHOLS TOWARDS
        CLADOSPORIUM RESINAE. APPL.MICROBIOL. 28, 840-844.

5769   TEH, J.S. (1975) - GLUCOSE TRANSPORT AND ITS INHIBITION BY SHORT-CHAIN
        N-ALKANES IN CLADOSPORIUM RESINAE. J.BACT. 122, 832-840.

5770   TEH, J.S. & LEE, K.H. (1974) - EFFECTS OF N-ALKANES ON CLADOSPORIUM RESI-
        NAE. CAN.J.MICROBIOL. 20, 971-976.

5771   TEITELL, L. (1958) - EFFECTS OF RELATIVE HUMIDITY ON VIABILITY OF CONIDIA
        OF ASPERGILLI. AM.J.BOT. 45, 748-753.

5772   TEMP, M. & HAGEDORN, D.J. (1964) - SOME EFFECTS OF CROPPING ON DISEASE
        INDICES OF APHANOMYCES EUTEICHES. PHYTOPATHOLOGY 54, 910 (ABS.).

5773   TEMP, M.W. & HAGEDORN, D.J. (1967) - INFLUENCE OF CROPPING PRACTICES ON
        APHANOMYCES ROOT ROT POTENTIAL OF WISCONSIN PEA FIELDS. PHYTOPATHOLOGY
        57, 667-670.

5774   TEMPEL, A. (1957) - SEROLOGICAL STUDIES ON FUSARIUM OXYSPORUM. NATURE,
        LOND. 180, 1483.

5775   TERADA, O., OHISHI, K. & KINOSHITA, S. (1960) - CITRIC ACID FORMATION BY
        TRICHODERMA VIRIDE. 1. ISOLATION, IDENTIFICATION AND DISTRIBUTION OF
        THE FUNGUS AND ITS ABILITY TO PRODUCE CITRIC ACID. AGRIC.BIOL.CHEM.,
        TOKYO 34, 160-170.

5776   TERASHITA, T. (1961) - STUDIES ON THE FUNGUS FLORA IN THE RHIZOSPHERE OF
        FOREST TREE SEEDLINGS. 1. ISOLATION OF FUSARIUM FROM THE RHIZOSPHERE OF
        JAPANESE RED PINE AND JAPANESE LARCH SEEDLINGS. BULL.GOVT FOREST EXP.
        STN MEGURO 128, 105-114.

5777   TERRACINA, F.C. (1974) - FINE STRUCTURE OF THE SEPTUM IN WALLEMIA SEBI.
        CAN.J.BOT. 52, 2587-2590.

5778   TERUI, M. & HARADA, Y. (1966) - EFFECT OF LOW TEMPERATURE TREATMENT OF
        SCLEROTIA ON APOTHECIAL PRODUCTION IN SCLEROTINIA SCLEROTIORUM. BULL.
        FAC.AGRIC.HIROSAKI UNIV. 12, 24-30.

5779 TETEREVNIKOVA-BABAYAN, D.N. & ABRAMYAN, DZH.G. (1966) - (RESULTS OF A STUDY
      OF THE EFFECT OF CERTAIN FUNGI OF THE RHIZOSPHERE ON TOMATO SEEDLINGS).
      BIOL.ZH.ARM. 193, 5-13.

5780 TEWARI, J.P. & SKOROPAD, W.P. (1975) - FINE STRUCTURE OF THE MACROCONIDIA
      OF FUSARIUM SOLANI. CAN.J.BOT. 53, 2134-2146.

5781 THAKUR, M.L. (1971) - THE EFFECT OF RELATIVE HUMIDITY ON OSMOTIC-TOLERANCE
      OF ALKALINE AND FERTILE SOIL ASPERGILLI. MICROBIOS 3, 49-53.

5782 THAKUR, M.L. (1973) - EFFECT OF OSMOTIC CONCENTRATION AND PH ON SCLEROTIA
      AND CLEISTOTHECIA PRODUCTION IN ALKALINE AND FERTILE SOIL ASPERGILLI.
      MICROBIOS 7, 215-220.

5783 THAKUR, R.N. & SASTRY, K.S.M. (1971) - STUDIES ON WILT DISEASE OF CROTALA-
      RIA MUCRONATA. INDIAN J.MYCOL.PL.PATH. 1, 84-86.

5784 THAKUR, S.B. (1977) - OCCURRENCE OF SPORES OF THERMOPHILIC FUNGI IN THE
      AIR AT BOMBAY. MYCOLOGIA 69, 197-199.

5785 THAKUR, S.B. (1977) - SURVIVAL OF SOME AQUATIC HYPHOMYCETES UNDER DRY CON-
      DITIONS. MYCOLOGIA 69, 843-845.

5786 THAMMAYYA, A. & MAYA SANYAL (1973) - MONOSPORIUM APIOSPERMUM CAUSING MYCE-
      TOMA PEDIS IN INDIA. INDIAN J.MED.RES. 61, 1289-1291.

5787 THANASSOULOPOULOS, C.C. & GIANNOPOLITIS, C.N. (1971) - IN VITRO SURVIVAL
      OF SCLEROTIA OF SCLEROTIUM ROLFSII SACC. PHYTOPATH.MEDIT. 10, 115-117.

5788 THAXTER, R. (1914) - NEW OR PECULIAR ZYGOMYCETES. 3. BLAKESLEA N.G.,
      DISSOPHORA N.G., HAPLOSPORANGIUM N.G. BOT.GAZ. 58, 353-366.

5789 THE, R. (1972) - UEBER DEN EINFLUSS DER TEMPERATUR AUF DIE MERKMALAUSBIL-
      DUNG EINIGER MUCORACEEN UND THAMNIDIACEEN. DISS.UNIV.SAARBRUECKEN.

5790 THEIMER, R.R. & RAU, W. (1972) - UNTERSUCHUNGEN UEBER DIE LICHTABHAENGIGE
      CAROTINOIDSYNTHESE. 8. DIE UNTERSCHIEDLICHEN WIRKUNGSMECHANISMEN VON
      LICHT UND MERCURIBENZOAT. PLANTA 106, 331-343.

5791 THIBAUT, M. (1970) - BIOTOPOLOGIE ET DIMORPHISME DU SPOROTRICHUM SCHENCKII
      (HEKTOEN & PERKINS 1900). ANNLS PARASIT.HUM.COMP. 45, 365-380.

5792 THIBAUT, M. (1970) - ETUDE MORPHOLOGIQUE DE LA PHASE MYCELIENNE DU SPORO-
      TRICHUM SCHENCKII (HEKTOEN & PERKINS, 1900) EN MICROSCOPE PHOTONIQUE.
      ANNLS PARASIT.HUM.COMP. 45, 509-516.

5793 THIBAUT, M. (1971) - TAXINOMIE, SYNONYMIE, HISTORIQUE ET REPARTITION GEO-
      GRAPHIQUE DU SPOROTRICHUM SCHENCKII. ANNLS PARASIT.HUM.COMP. 46, 93-102.

5794 THIBAUT, M. (1972) - LA FORME PARFAITE DU SPOROTRICHUM SCHENCKII (HEKTOEN
      & PERKINS 1900). DOLICHOASCUS SCHENCKII THIBAUT & ANSEL 1970 NOV.GEN.
      ANNLS PARASIT.HUM.COMP. 47, 431-441.

5795 THIBAUT, M. & ANSEL, M. (1973) - PREMIERES OBSERVATIONS SUR LE DOLICHOAS-
      CUS SCHENCKII, FORME SEXUEE DU SPOROTRICHUM SCHENCKII. ANNLS DERM.SYPH.
      100, 49-53.

5796 THIBAUT, M. & ANSEL, M. (1974) - OBSERVATIONS MICROSCOPIQUES SUR LES PHE-
      NOMENES DE SENESCENCE CHEZ LE SPOROTHRIX SCHENCKII. ANNLS PARASIT.HUM.
      COMP. 49, 109-117.

5797 THIELKE, C. (1958) - STUDIEN ZUR ENTWICKLUNGSPHYSIOLOGIE VON ASPERGILLUS.
      1. STERIGMENPROLIFERATION BEI ASPERGILLUS REPENS. PLANTA 51, 308-320.

5798 THIES, W.G. & PATTON, R.F. (1970) - AN EVALUATION OF PROPAGULES OF CYLIN-
      DROCLADIUM SCOPARIUM IN SOIL BY DIRECT ISOLATION. PHYTOPATHOLOGY 60,
      599-601.

5799 THIES, W.G. & PATTON, R.F. (1970) - THE BIOLOGY OF CYLINDROCLADIUM SCOPA-
      RIUM IN WISCONSIN FOREST TREE NURSERIES. PHYTOPATHOLOGY 60, 1662-1668.

5800 THIRUMALACHAR, M.J. & MISHRA, J.N. (1953) - SOME DISEASES OF ECONOMIC
      PLANTS IN BIHAR, INDIA. PL.PROT.BULL.F.A.O. 1, 145-146 AND 2, 11-12.

5801 THOMAS, A. & PARKINSON, D. (1967) - THE INITIATION OF THE RHIZOSPHERE MY-
      COFLORA OF DWARF BEAN PLANTS. CAN.J.MICROBIOL. 13, 439-446.

5802 THOMAS, R. (1959) - BIOSYNTHESIS OF ALTERNARIOL. PROC.CHEM.SOC., 1959, 88.

5803 THOMAS, R. (1961) - STUDIES IN THE BIOSYNTHESIS OF FUNGAL METABOLITES. 2.
      THE BIOSYNTHESIS OF ALTERNARIOL AND ITS RELATION TO OTHER FUNGAL PHENOLS.
      BIOCHEM.J. 78, 748-758.

5804 THOMPSON, K.V.A. & SIMMENS, S.C. (1962) - APPENDAGES ON THE SPORES OF MY-
      ROTHECIUM VERRUCARIA. NATURE, LOND. 193, 196-197.

5805 THORNTON, D.R. (1963) - THE PHYSIOLOGY AND NUTRITION OF SOME AQUATIC HY-
      PHOMYCETES. J.GEN.MICROBIOL. 33, 23-31.

5806 THORNTON, D.R. (1965) - AMINO ACID ANALYSIS OF FRESH LEAF LITTER AND THE
      NITROGEN NUTRITION OF SOME AQUATIC HYPHOMYCETES. CAN.J.MICROBIOL. 11,
      657-662.

5807 THORNTON, D.R. & FOX, M.H. (1968) - THE FREE AMINO ACID POOLS OF TWO AQUAT-
      IC HYPHOMYCETES. EXPERIENTIA 24, 393-394.

5808 THORNTON, M.L. (1971) - POTENTIAL FOR LONG-RANGE DISPERSAL OF AQUATIC PHY-
      COMYCETES BY INTERNAL TRANSPORT IN BIRDS. TRANS.BR.MYCOL.SOC. 57, 49-
      59.

5809 THORNTON, R.H. (1956) - NUTRITIONAL ASPECTS OF MORTIERELLA HYGROPHILA. NA-
      TURE, LOND. 177, 662.

5810 THORNTON, R.H. (1956) - RHIZOCTONIA IN NATURAL GRASSLAND SOIL. NATURE,
      LOND. 177, 230-231.

5811 THORNTON, R.H. (1956) - FUNGI OCCURRING IN MIXED OAKWOOD AND HEATH SOIL
      PROFILES. TRANS.BR.MYCOL.SOC. 39, 485-494.

5812 THORNTON, R.H. (1958) - BIOLOGICAL STUDIES OF SOME TUSSOCK-GRASSLAND SOILS.
      2. FUNGI. N.Z.JL AGRIC.RES. 1, 922-938.

5813 THORNTON, R.H. (1960) - GROWTH OF FUNGI IN SOME FOREST AND GRASSLAND SOILS
      IN: ECOLOGY OF SOIL FUNGI; PARKINSON, D. & WAID, J.S. (ED.), LIVERPOOL
      UNIV.PRESS, 84-91.

5814 THORNTON, R.H. (1960) - FUNGI OF SOME FOREST AND PASTURE SOILS. N.Z.JL
      AGRIC.RES. 3, 699-711.

5815 THORNTON, R.H. (1965) - STUDIES OF FUNGI IN PASTURE SOILS. 1. FUNGI ASSO-
      CIATED WITH LIVE ROOTS. N.Z.JL AGRIC.RES. 8, 417-447.

5816   THORNTON, R.H. & PERCIVAL, J.C. (1959) - A HEPATOTOXIN FROM SPORIDESMIUM
        BAKERI CAPABLE OF PRODUCING FACIAL ECZEMA DISEASES IN SHEEP. NATURE,
        LOND. 183, 63.

5817   THORNTON, R.H., SHIRLEY, G. & SALISBURY, R.M. (1968) - A NEPHROTOXIN FROM
        ASPERGILLUS FUMIGATUS AND ITS POSSIBLE RELATIONSHIP WITH NEW ZEALAND
        MUCOSAL DISEASE-LIKE SYNDROME IN CATTLE. N.Z.JL AGRIC.RES. 11, 1-14.

5818   THRONEBERRY, G.O. (1973) - SOME PHYSIOLOGICAL RESPONSES OF VERTICILLIUM
        ALBO-ATRUM TO ZINC. CAN.J.BOT. 51, 57-59.

5819   THROWER, L.B. (1954) - THE RHIZOSPHERE EFFECT SHOWN BY SOME VICTORIAN
        HEATHLAND PLANTS. AUST.J.BOT. 2, 246-267.

5820   THU HA NGUYEN, MATHUR, S.B. & NEERGAARD, P. (1973) - SEED-BORNE SPECIES OF
        MYROTHECIUM AND THEIR PATHOGENIC POTENTIAL. TRANS.BR.MYCOL.SOC. 61, 347-
        354.

5821   TICHOMIROVA, A.S., ZAGUSTINA, N.A. & MAKSIMOV, V.N. (1974) - (OPTIMIZATION
        OF THE MEDIUM FOR BETA-GALACTOSIDASE BIOSYNTHESIS BY ALTERNARIA TENUIS).
        PRIKL.BIOKHIM.MIKROBIOL. 10, 501-507.

5822   TIEDJE, J.M. & HAGEDORN, M.L. (1975) - DEGRADATION OF ALACHLOR BY A SOIL
        FUNGUS, CHAETOMIUM GLOBOSUM. J.AGRIC.FD CHEM. 23, 77-81.

5823   TILDEN, E.B., HATTON, E.H., FREEMAN, S., WILLIAMSON, W.A. & KOENIG, V.L.
        (1961) - PREPARATION AND PROPERTIES OF THE ENDOTOXINS OF ASPERGILLUS
        FUMIGATUS AND ASPERGILLUS FLAVUS. MYCOPATH.MYCOL.APPL. 14, 325-346.

5824   TILLMANNS, G. (1976) - OXIDATIVE TRANSFORMATIONEN VON PHENYLAMIDEN DURCH
        BODENPILZE AUS DER ORDNUNG MUCORALES. DISS.TECHN.UNIV.MUENCHEN.

5825   TIMONIN, M.I. (1940) - THE INTERACTION OF HIGHER PLANTS AND SOIL MICRO-OR-
        GANISMS. 1. MICROBIAL POPULATION OF RHIZOSPHERE OF SEEDLINGS OF CERTAIN
        CULTIVATED PLANTS. CAN.J.RES., SECT.C, 18, 307-317.

5826   TIMONIN, M.I. (1941) - THE INTERACTION OF HIGHER PLANTS AND SOIL MICRO-OR-
        GANISMS. 3. EFFECT OF BY-PRODUCTS OF PLANT GROWTH ON ACTIVITY OF FUNGI
        AND ACTINOMYCETES. SOIL SCI. 52, 395-413.

5827   TIMONIN, M.I. (1950) - SOIL MICROFLORA IN RELATION TO MANGANESE DEFICIENCY.
        CAN.J.AGRIC.SCI. 30, 324-325.

5828   TIMONIN, M.I., ILLMAN, W.I. & HARTGERINK, T. (1972) - OXIDATION OF MAN-
        GANOUS SALTS OF MANGANESE BY SOIL FUNGI. CAN.J.MICROBIOL. 18, 793- 799.

5829   TIMONIN, M.I., PETERSON, E.A. & ROUATT, J.W. (1974) - EFFECTS OF AMINO
        ACIDS AND SUBSTANCES FROM WHEAT ROOTS ON THE SOIL-BORNE PLANT PATHOGEN
        COCHLIOBOLUS SATIVUS. SOIL SCI. 118, 180-185.

5830   TINLINE, R.D. (1962) - COCHLIOBOLUS SATIVUS. 5. HETEROKARYOSIS AND PARA-
        SEXUALITY. CAN.J.BOT. 40, 425-438.

5831   TINLINE, R.D. (1971) - NUCLEAR DISTRIBUTION IN METARRHIZIUM ANISOPLIAE.
        MYCOLOGIA 63, 713-721.

5832   TINLINE, R.D. & DICKSON, J.G. (1958) - COCHLIOBOLUS SATIVUS. 1. PERITHE-
        CIAL DEVELOPMENT AND THE INHERITANCE OF SPORE COLOR AND MATING TYPE.
        MYCOLOGIA 50, 697-706.

5833   TINLINE, R.D. & NOVIELLO, C. (1971) - HETEROKARYOSIS IN THE ENTOMOGENOUS
        FUNGUS, METARRHIZIUM ANISOPLIAE. MYCOLOGIA 63, 701-712.

5834 TINLINE, R.D. & SAMBORSKI, D.J. (1959) - COCHLIOBOLUS SATIVUS. 2. PHOTO-
ACTIVATED PIGMENTATION. MYCOLOGIA 51, 77-88.

5835 TINNELL, W.H., JEFFERSON, B.L. & BENOIT, R.E. (1974) - THE ORGANIC NITRO-
GEN EXIGENCY OF AND EFFECTS OF MANGANESE ON COREMIA PRODUCTION IN PENI-
CILLIUM CLAVIGERUM AND PENICILLIUM CLAVIFORME. CAN.J.MICROBIOL. 20, 91-
96.

5836 TIRILLY, Y. (1976) - VARIATION SECTORIELLE CHEZ LE PHIALOPHORA CINERESCENS.
REVUE MYCOL. 40, 209-222.

5837 TIRILLY, Y. & LE PICARD, D. (1974) - VARIATIONS DU CONTENU NUCLEAIRE DANS
LE MYCELIUM ET LES SPORES DU PHIALOPHORA CINERESCENS. REVUE MYCOL. 38,
45-50.

5838 TIRILLY, Y. & MOREAU, C. (1976) - ETUDE COMPARATIVE DE QUELQUES PHIALOPHO-
RA VASCULAIRES DE PLANTES. BULL.TRIMEST.SOC.MYCOL.FR. 92, 349-358.

5839 TIRUNARAYANAN, M.O. & SIRSI, M. (1957) - ANTIBIOTICS FROM THE GENUS FUSA-
RIUM. ENNIATIN-B. 1. CULTURE STUDIES AND ANTIMICROBIAL ACTIVITY. J.IN-
DIAN INST.SCI. 39, 185-194.

5840 TIWARI, D.P. & AGRAWAL, P.D. (1972) - PHOMA EXIGUA FROM GRASSLAND SOIL OF
JABALPUR. CURR.SCI. 41, 77.

5841 TJITROSOMO, S. (1966) - THE MICROFUNGI OF FOREST AND PRAIRIE SOILS IN EAST
CENTRAL ILLINOIS. DISS.ABSTR., SER.B, 27, 707-708.

5842 TODOROVIC, M. (1963) - (CONTRIBUTION TO THE STUDY OF ANTAGONISTIC RELATION
OF ASPERGILLUS FUMIGATUS AND STACHYBOTRYS LOBULATA TO SOME MICROORGAN-
ISMS). ZEMLJ.BILJKA 12, 383-387.

5843 TOEPFER, H. & PIESCHE, K. (1973) - CHARAKTERISIERUNG EINER PROTEASE AUS
ASPERGILLUS OCHRACEUS. PHARMAZIE 28, 798 (ABS.).

5844 TOKUMASU, S. (1973) - RECORDS OF TWO ACREMONIUM SPECIES, APHANOCLADIUM ME-
LIOLAE, AND MONOCILLIUM MUCIDUM FROM JAPAN. TRANS.MYCOL.SOC.JAPAN 14,
161-164.

5845 TOKUMASU, S. (1973) - NOTES ON JAPANESE OIDIODENDRON (JAPANESE MICROSCOPIC
FUNGI II). TRANS.MYCOL.SOC.JAPAN 14, 246-255.

5846 TOKUMASU, S. (1974) - AN ANNOTATED LIST OF SOIL FUNGI OF SUGADAIRA, CEN-
TRAL JAPAN. BULL.SUGADAIRA BIOL.LAB. 6, 33-60.

5847 TOKUMASU, S. (1976) - ON THE NATURAL HABITATS OF OIDIODENDRON. TRANS.MY-
COL.SOC.JAPAN 17, 99-105.

5848 TOKUNAGA, M., TOKUNAGA, J. & HARADA, K. (1973) - SCANNING AND TRANSMISSION
ELECTRON MICROSCOPY OF STERIGMA AND CONIDIOSPORE FORMATION IN ASPERGIL-
LUS GROUP. J.ELECTRON MICROSC., CHIBA CY 22, 27-38.

5849 TOKUYAMA, T. & ASANO, K. (1975) - CHANGES OF THE INTRACELLULAR HYALURONIC
ACID-LIKE SUBSTANCE OF AUREOBASIDIUM PULLULANS. J.FERMENT.TECHNOL.,
OSAKA 53, 648-657.

5850 TOLBA, M.K. & SALAMA, A.M. (1957) - GROWTH, RESPIRATION, AND NITROGEN ME-
TABOLISM OF MYCELIAL MATS OF FUSARIUM OXYSPORUM AS AFFECTED BY VARYING
THE CATION OF NITRATE SALT IN CULTURE MEDIUM. PROC.IRAQI SCIENT.SOC. 1,
37-38.

5851 TOLBA, M.K. & SALAMA, A.M. (1960) - ON THE MECHANISM OF SUCROSE UTILIZA-
      TION BY MYCELIAL FELTS OF RHIZOCTONIA SOLANI. 1. UTILIZATION OF SUCROSE,
      MALTOSE, AND RAFFINOSE. ARCH.MIKROBIOL. 36, 23-30.

5852 TOLBA, M.K. & SALAMA, A.M. (1961) - ON THE MECHANISM OF SUCROSE UTILIZA-
      TION BY MYCELIAL FELTS OF RHIZOCTONIA SOLANI. 2. EFFECTS OF GLUCOSE,
      FRUCTOSE, SILVER NITRATE, SODIUM FLUORIDE, AND PREHEATING OF MYCELIAL
      MATS ON SUCROSE UTILIZATION. ARCH.MIKROBIOL. 38, 289-298.

5853 TOLER, R.W., DUKES, P.D. & JENKINS, S.F. (1965) - EFFECT OF OXYGEN AND
      CARBON DIOXIDE TENSIONS ON GROWTH OF FUSARIUM OXYSPORUM F. TRACHEIPHI-
      LUM IN VITRO. PHYTOPATHOLOGY 55, 502 (ABS.).

5854 TOLMSOFF, W.J. (1962) - RESPIRATORY ACTIVITIES OF CELL-FREE PARTICLES FROM
      PYTHIUM ULTIMUM, RHIZOCTONIA SOLANI, AND SUGAR BEET SEEDLINGS. PHYTO-
      PATHOLOGY 52, 755 (ABS.).

5855 TOLMSOFF, W.J. (1970) - METABOLISM OF RHIZOCTONIA SOLANI. IN: RHIZOCTONIA
      SOLANI, BIOLOGY AND PATHOLOGY, SYMPOSIUM 1965; PARMETER, J.JR. (ED.),
      UNIV.CALIFORNIA PRESS, BERKELEY, 93-107.

5856 TOMINAGA, Y. (1963) - STUDIES ON THE LIFE HISTORY OF JAPANESE PINE MUSH-
      ROOM, ARMILLARIA MATSUTAKE. BULL.HIROSHIMA AGRIC.COLL. 2, 105-145.

5857 TOMITA, Y., SUZUKI, H. & NISIZAWA, K. (1974) - FURTHER PURIFICATION AND
      PROPERTIES OF 'AVICELASE', A CELLULASE COMPONENT OF LESS RANDOM TYPE
      FROM TRICHODERMA VIRIDE. J.FERMENT.TECHNOL., OSAKA 52, 233-246.

5858 TOMLINSON, T.G. (1937) - THE ANAEROBIC METABOLISM OF THE MOULD FUNGI IN
      RELATION TO CITRIC ACID FORMATION. NEW PHYTOL. 38, 418-434.

5859 TOORN, J.VAN DER (1969) - THE BIODETERIORATION OF VINYL POLYMERS AND PLAS-
      TICIZERS. 1. ISOLATION OF MICRO-ORGANISMS AND EXPERIMENTS WITH POLYVI-
      NYL ALCOHOL. ZENTBL.BAKT.PARASITKDE, ABT.2, 123, 101-110.

5860 TORIELLO, C. & MARIAT, F. (1974) - ETUDE COMPAREE DES POLYOSIDES DES CHAM-
      PIGNONS CERATOCYSTIS STENOCERAS ET SPOROTHRIX SCHENCKII. COMPOSITION
      CHIMIQUE ET ANALYSE IMMUNOLOGIQUE. ANNLS MICROBIOL. 125A, 287-307.

5861 TOTH, J.A. (1973) - THE INFLUENCE OF SPORE NUMBER PER SURFACE UNIT ON THE
      COURSE OF GERMINATION IN SOME ASPERGILLUS SPECIES ON SOLID MEDIUM. ACTA
      BOT.ACAD.SCI.HUNG. 18, 385-389.

5862 TOTH, S. (1975) - RARE MICROSCOPIC FUNGI FROM HUNGARY. BOT.KOEZLEM. 62,
      13-18.

5863 TOUMANOFF, C. (1931) - ACTION DES CHAMPIGNONS ENTOMOPHYTES SUR LES ABEILLES.
      ANNLS PARASIT.HUM.COMP. 9, 464-482.

5864 TOUMANOFF, C. (1933) - ACTION DES CHAMPIGNONS ENTOMOPHYTES SUR LA PYRALE
      DU MAIS (PYRAUSTA NUBILALIS HUEN.). ANNLS PARASIT.HUM.COMP. 11, 129-143.

5865 TOUSSOUN, T.A. (1975) - FUSARIUM-SUPPRESSIVE SOILS. IN: BIOLOGY AND CON-
      TROL OF SOIL-BORNE PLANT PATHOGENS; BRUEHL, G.W. (ED.), ST.PAUL, MINNES.,
      145-151.

5866 TOUSSOUN, T.A., MENZINGER, W. & SMITH, R.S. (1969) - ROLE OF CONIFER LIT-
      TER IN ECOLOGY OF FUSARIUM - STIMULATION OF GERMINATION IN SOIL. PHYTO-
      PATHOLOGY 59, 1396-1399.

5867 TOUSSOUN, T.A., PATRICK, Z.A. & SNYDER, W.C. (1963) - INFLUENCE OF CROP
      RESIDUE DECOMPOSITION PRODUCTS ON THE GERMINATION OF FUSARIUM SOLANI F.
      PHASEOLI CHLAMYDOSPORES IN SOIL. NATURE, LOND. 197, 1314-1316.

5868   TOWNSEND, B.R. & WILLETTS, H.J. (1954) - THE DEVELOPMENT OF SCLEROTIA OF
       CERTAIN FUNGI. TRANS.BR.MYCOL.SOC. 37, 213-221.

5869   TOWNSEND, R.J., MOOS, M.O. & PECK, H.M. (1966) - ISOLATION AND CHARACTERI-
       ZATION OF HEPATOXINS FROM PENICILLIUM RUBRUM. J.PHARM.PHARMAC. 18, 471-
       473.

5870   TOWNSLEY, W.W. (1969) - GERMINATION AND RESPIRATION OF CURVULARIA GENICU-
       LATA AFTER FIVE YEARS STORAGE. PHYTOPATHOLOGY 59, 523-524.

5871   TOYAMA, K., KOGAWA, H., YAMAMOTO, H., SENMARU, H., ISHIOKA, H., SAITO, K.
       & TAMATSUKURI, T. (1975) - CADMIUM RESISTANT FILAMENTOUS FUNGI ISOLATED
       FROM MINE SOIL. ANN.PHYTOPATH.SOC.JAPAN 41, 108-109.

5872   TOYAMA, N. (1958) - CELLULOLYTIC ACTIVITIES OF TRICHODERMA KONINGI AND
       THEIR APPLICATION. BULL.FAC.AGRIC.MIYAZAKI UNIV. 33, 40-58.

5873   TOYAMA, N. (1960) - ISOLATION AND PROPERTIES OF CELLULASE FROM TRICHODERMA
       KONINGI. MEM.FAC.AGRIC.MIYAZAKI UNIV. 2, 100-138.

5874   TRAAEN, A.E. (1914) - UNTERSUCHUNGEN UEBER BODENPILZE AUS NORWEGEN. NYT
       MAG.NATURVID. 52, 20-121.

5875   TRAVASSOS, L.R., GORIN, P.A.J. & LLOYD, K.O. (1974) - DISCRIMINATION BE-
       TWEEN SPOROTHRIX SCHENCKII AND CERATOCYSTIS STENOCERAS RHAMNOMANNANS
       BY PROTON AND CARBON-13 MAGNETIC RESONANCE SPECTROSCOPY. INFECT.IMMUN.
       9, 674-680.

5876   TRAXLER, P. & TAMM, CH. (1970) - DIE STRUKTUR DES ANTIBIOTICUMS RORIDIN-H.
       VERRUCARINE UND RORIDINE. 20. HELV.CHIM.ACTA 53, 1846-1869.

5877   TRAXLER, P., ZUERCHER, W. & TAMM, CH. (1970) - DIE STRUKTUR DES ANTIBIOTI-
       CUMS RORIDIN-E. VERRUCARINE UND RORIDINE. 21. HELV.CHIM.ACTA 53, 2071-
       2085.

5878   TREGGI, G. & FALDI, G. (1952) - SOPRA UNA ALTERAZIONE DEI BULBI DI GLADIO-
       LO. AGRICOLTURA ITAL., PISA 52, 102-106.

5879   TRESCHOW, C. (1941) - THE VERTICILLIUM DISEASES OF CULTIVATED MUSHROOMS.
       DANSK BOT.ARK. 11 (1), 1-31.

5880   TRESNER, H.D., BACKUS, M.P. & CURTIS, J.T. (1954) - SOIL MICROFUNGI IN RE-
       LATION TO THE HARDWOOD FOREST CONTINUUM IN SOUTHERN WISCONSIN. MYCOLOGIA
       46, 314-333.

5881   TRESNER, H.D. & HAYES, J.A. (1971) - SODIUM CHLORIDE TOLERANCE OF TERRES-
       TRIAL FUNGI. APPL.MICROBIOL. 22, 210-213.

5882   TREVETHICK, J. & COOKE, R.C. (1973) - WATER RELATIONS IN SCLEROTIA OF SOME
       SCLEROTINIA AND SCLEROTIUM SPECIES. TRANS.BR.MYCOL.SOC. 60, 555-558.

5883   TREVETHICK, J. & COOKE, R.C. (1973) - NON-NUTRITIONAL FACTORS INFLUENCING
       SCLEROTIUM FORMATION IN SOME SCLEROTINIA AND SCLEROTIUM SPECIES. TRANS.
       BR.MYCOL.SOC. 60, 559-566.

5884   TRIBE, H.T. (1957) - ECOLOGY OF MICROORGANISMS IN SOIL AS OBSERVED DURING
       THEIR DEVELOPMENT UPON BURIED CELLULOSE FILM. IN: MICROBIAL ECOLOGY;
       WILLIAMS, R.E.O. & SPICER, C.C. (ED.), 7TH SYMP.SOC.GEN.MICROB., CAM-
       BRIDGE UNIV.PRESS, 287-298.

5885 TRIBE H.T. (1957) - ON THE PARASITISM OF SCLEROTINIA TRIFOLIORUM BY CONIO-
      THYRIUM MINITANS. TRANS.BR.MYCOL.SOC. 40, 489-499.

5886 TRIBE, H.T. (1960) - DECOMPOSITION OF BURIED CELLULOSE FILM, WITH SPECIAL
      REFERENCE TO THE ECOLOGY OF CERTAIN SOIL FUNGI. IN: ECOLOGY OF SOIL
      FUNGI; PARKINSON, D. & WAID, S.J. (ED.), LIVERPOOL UNIV.PRESS, 246-256.

5887 TRIBE, H.T. (1966) - INTERACTIONS OF SOIL FUNGI ON CELLULOSE FILM. TRANS.
      BR.MYCOL.SOC. 49, 457-466.

5888 TRINCI, A.P.J. (1969) - A KINETIC STUDY OF THE GROWTH OF ASPERGILLUS NIDU-
      LANS AND OTHER FUNGI. J.GEN.MICROBIOL. 57, 11-24.

5889 TRINCI, A.P.J. (1970) - KINETICS OF APICAL AND LATERAL BRANCHING IN ASPER-
      GILLUS NIDULANS AND GEOTRICHUM LACTIS. TRANS.BR.MYCOL.SOC. 55, 17-28.

5890 TRINCI, A.P.J. (1971) - INFLUENCE OF THE WIDTH OF THE PERIPHERAL GROWTH
      ZONE ON THE RADIAL GROWTH RATE OF FUNGAL COLONIES ON SOLID MEDIA. J.
      GEN.MICROBIOL. 67, 325-344.

5891 TRINCI, J.P. & COLLINGE, A.J. (1974) - SPORE FORMATION IN NITROGEN AND
      CARBON STARVED CULTURES OF GEOTRICHUM CANDIDUM AND MUCOR RACEMOSUS.
      TRANS.BR.MYCOL.SOC. 62, 351-358.

5892 TRIONE, E.J. & LEACH, CH.M. (1969) - LIGHT-INDUCED SPORULATION AND SPORO-
      GENIC SUBSTANCES IN FUNGI. PHYTOPATHOLOGY 59, 1077-1083.

5893 TRIONE, E.J., LEACH, C.M. & MUTCH, J.T. (1966) - SPOROGENIC SUBSTANCES
      ISOLATED FROM FUNGI. NATURE, LOND. 212, 163-164.

5894 TRIQUE, B. (1968) - CROISSANCE ET SPORULATION DE L'ASPERGILLUS VERSICOLOR
      (VUILL.) TIRABOSCHI ET DU PENICILLIUM CYCLOPIUM WESTL. EN FONCTION DES
      SOURCES DE CARBONE ET D'AZOTE. MEM.SOC.BOT.FR. 115, 101-109.

5895 TRIQUE, B. (1970) - CROISSANCE ET SPORULATION DE L'ASPERGILLUS VERSICOLOR
      (VUILL.) TIRABOSCHI ET DU PENICILLIUM CYCLOPIUM WESTL. EN CULTURE STA-
      TIONNAIRE OU AGITEE. REVUE MYCOL. 34, 365-375.

5896 TRIQUE, B. (1970) - PRODUCTION IN VITRO DE DIVERSES HYDROLASES PAR L'AS-
      PERGILLUS VERSICOLOR (VUILL.) TIRABOSCHI ET LE PENICILLIUM CYCLOPIUM
      WESTLING. ANNLS NUTR.ALIMENT. 24, 167-175.

5897 TROUVELOT, A. & CAMPOROTA, P. (1973) - RECHERCHES SUR LES FUSARIOSES. 7.
      RESULTATS DES RECHERCHES SUR LES ACIDES AMINES LIBRES DU THALLE DE DI-
      VERSES SOUCHES DE FUSARIUM. ANNLS PHYTOPATH. 5, 27-34.

5898 TRUSZKOWSKA, W. (1961) - (PRELIMINARY MYCOLOGICAL STUDY OF POPLAR ROOTS
      (POPULUS EUAMERICANA MARILANDICA) FROM DIFFERENT LOCALITIES IN TUREW.
      ACTA SOC.BOT.POL. 30, 395-421.

5899 TRUSZKOWSKA, W. (1967) - (MYCOLOGICAL ANALYSIS OF TOMATO SEEDS). ACTA MY-
      COL., WARSZAWA 3, 163-176.

5900 TRUSZKOWSKA, W., PUDELKO, S. & MOREAU, C. (1966) - ISOLEMENT DU PREUSSIA
      FLEISCHHAKII DANS LE SOL EN POLOGNE. REVUE MYCOL. 31, 45-47.

5901 TSAO, P.H. (1964) - EFFECT OF CERTAIN FUNGAL ISOLATION AGAR MEDIA ON THIE-
      LAVIOPSIS BASICOLA AND ON ITS RECOVERY IN SOIL DILUTION PLATES. PHYTO-
      PATHOLOGY 54, 548-555.

5902 TSAO, P.H., BHALLA, H.S. & ZENTMYER, G.A. (1975) - EFFECTS OF CERTAIN OR-
      GANIC AMENDMENTS ON SURVIVAL AND ACTIVITY OF PHYTOPHTHORA CINNAMOMI IN
      SOIL. PROC.AM.PHYTOPATH.SOC. 2, 40.

5903   TSAO, P.H. & BRICKER, J.L. (1966) – CHLAMYDOSPORES OF THIELAVIOPSIS BASI-
        COLA AS SURVIVING PROPAGULES IN NATURAL SOILS. PHYTOPATHOLOGY 56, 1012-
        1014.

5904   TSAO, P.H. & BRICKER, J.L. (1970) – ACROPETAL DEVELOPMENT IN THE CHAIN FOR-
        MATION OF CHLAMYDOSPORES OF THIELAVIOPSIS BASICOLA. MYCOLOGIA 62, 960-
        966.

5905   TSAO, P.H. & GUY, S.O. (1977) – INHIBITION OF MORTIERELLA AND PYTHIUM IN A
        PHYTOPHTHORA-ISOLATION MEDIUM CONTAINING HYMEXAZOL. PHYTOPATHOLOGY 67,
        796-801.

5906   TSAO, P.H. & OCANA, G. (1969) – SELECTIVE ISOLATION OF PHYTOPHTHORA FROM
        NATURAL SOILS ON AN IMPROVED ANTIBIOTIC MEDIUM. NATURE, LOND. 223, 636-
        638.

5907   TSAO, P.W. & TSAO, P.H. (1970) – ELECTRON MICROSCOPIC OBSERVATIONS ON THE
        SPORE WALL AND OPERCULUM FORMATION IN CHLAMYDOSPORES OF THIELAVIOPSIS
        BASICOLA. PHYTOPATHOLOGY 60, 613-616.

5908   TSCHANZ, A.T., HORST, R.K. & NELSON, P.E. (1975) – A SUBSTRATE FOR UNIFORM
        PRODUCTION OF PERITHECIA IN GIBBERELLA ZEAE. MYCOLOGIA 67, 1101-1108.

5909   TSCHANZ, A.T., HORST, R.K. & NELSON, P.E. (1976) – THE EFFECT OF ENVIRON-
        MENT ON SEXUAL REPRODUCTION OF GIBBERELLA ZEAE. MYCOLOGIA 68, 327-340.

5910   TSENG, T.C. & BATEMAN, D.F. (1969) – A PHOSPHATIDASE PRODUCED BY SCLERO-
        TIUM ROLFSII. PHYTOPATHOLOGY 59, 359-363.

5911   TSUCHIYA, H.M., JEANES, A., BRICKER, H.M. & WILHAM, C.A. (1952) – DEXTRAN-
        DEGRADING ENZYMES FROM MOLDS. J.BACT. 64, 513-519.

5912   TSUJISAKA, Y., HIYAMA, K., TAKENISHI, SH. & FUKUMOTO, J. (1972) – STUDIES
        ON THE HEMICELLULASES. 3. PURIFICATION AND SOME PROPERTIES OF MANNANASE
        FROM ASPERGILLUS NIGER VAN TIEGHEM SP. J.AGRIC.CHEM.SOC.JAPAN 46, 155-
        161.

5913   TSUJISAKA, Y., IWAI, M., FUKUMOTO, J. & OKAMOTO, Y. (1973) – INDUCED FOR-
        MATION OF LIPASE BY GEOTRICHUM CANDIDUM LINK. AGRIC.BIOL.CHEM., TOKYO
        37, 837-842.

5914   TSUJISAKA, Y., OKUMURA, S., TAKENISHI, S. & OKADA, S. (1973) – ENDOPOLYGA-
        LACTURONASE FROM ASPERGILLUS NIGER AND ITS ABILITY TO REMOVE SEGMENT
        SKIN FROM MANDARIN ORANGE. J.FERMENT.TECHNOL., OSAKA 51, 464-472.

5915   TSUKAHARA, T. (1968) – ELECTRON MICROSCOPY OF SWELLING AND GERMINATING
        CONIDIOSPORES OF ASPERGILLUS NIGER. SABOURAUDIA 6, 185-191.

5916   TSUKAHARA, T., YAMADA, M. & ITAGAKI, T. (1966) – MICROMORPHOLOGY OF CONID-
        IOSPORES OF ASPERGILLUS NIGER BY ELECTRON MICROSCOPY. JAPAN.J.MICROBIOL.
        10, 93-107.

5917   TSUNEDA, A. & SKOROPAD, W.P. (1977) – THE ALTERNARIA BRASSICAE - NECTRIA
        INVENTA HOST-PARASITE INTERFACE. CAN.J.BOT. 55, 448-454.

5918   TSURU, D., HIRAOKA, N., HIROSE, T. & FUKUMOTO, J. (1971) – STUDIES ON MOLD
        DEXTRANASES. 2. DEXTRANASE PRODUCTION BY A STRAIN OF ASPERGILLUS CAR-
        NEUS. AGRIC.BIOL.CHEM., TOKYO 35, 1727-1732.

5919   TU, C.C. & KIMBROUGH, J.W. (1975) – A MODIFIED SOIL-OVER-CULTURE METHOD
        FOR INDUCING BASIDIA IN THANATEPHORUS CUCUMERIS. PHYTOPATHOLOGY 65,
        730-731.

5920 TU, C.C. & KIMBROUGH, J.W. (1975) - MORPHOLOGY, DEVELOPMENT, AND CYTOCHEM-
     ISTRY OF THE HYPHAE AND SCLEROTIA OF SPECIES IN THE RHIZOCTONIA COMPLEX.
     CAN.J.BOT. 53, 2282-2296.

5921 TU, C.C. & KIMBROUGH, J.W. (1978) - SYSTEMATICS AND PHYLOGENY OF FUNGI IN
     THE RHIZOCTONIA COMPLEX. BOT.GAZ. 139, 454-466.

5922 TU, C.C., KIMBROUGH, J.W. & ALDRICH, H.C. (1977) - CYTOLOGY AND ULTRASTRUC-
     TURE OF THANATEPHORUS CUCUMERIS AND RELATED TAXA OF THE RHIZOCTONIA COM-
     PLEX. CAN.J.BOT. 55, 2419-2436.

5923 TU, C.C., ROBERTS, D.A. & KIMBROUGH, J.W. (1969) - HYPHAL FUSION, NUCLEAR
     CONDITION AND PERFECT STAGES OF THREE SPECIES OF RHIZOCTONIA. MYCOLOGIA
     61, 775-783.

5924 TUBAKI, K. (1955) - STUDIES ON JAPANESE HYPHOMYCETES. 2. FUNGICOLOUS GROUP.
     NAGAOA 5, 11-40.

5925 TUBAKI, K. (1957) - STUDIES ON JAPANESE HYPHOMYCETES. 3. AQUATIC GROUP.
     BULL.NATN.SCI.MUS., TOKYO 3, 249-268.

5926 TUBAKI, K. (1958) - STUDIES ON THE JAPANESE HYPHOMYCETES. 5. LEAF AND STEM
     GROUP WITH A DISCUSSION OF THE CLASSIFICATION OF HYPHOMYCETES AND THEIR
     PERFECT STAGES. J.HATTORI BOT.LAB. 21, 142-244.

5927 TUBAKI, K. (1960) - ON THE JAPANESE AQUATIC HYPHOMYCETES. SCUM AND FOAM
     GROUP, REFERRING TO THE PRELIMINARY SURVEY OF THE SNOW GROUP. NAGAOA 7,
     15-28.

5928 TUBAKI, K. (1962) - STUDIES ON A SLIME-FORMING FUNGUS IN POLLUTED WATER.
     TRANS.MYCOL.SOC.JAPAN 3, 29-35.

5929 TUBAKI, K. (1963) - NOTES ON JAPANESE HYPHOMYCETES. 1. CHLORIDIUM, CLONO-
     STACHYS, ISTHMOSPORA, PSEUDOBOTRYTIS, STACHYBOTRYS, AND STEPHANOMA.
     TRANS.MYCOL.SOC.JAPAN 4, 83-90.

5930 TUBAKI, K. (1965) - CONTRIBUTION TOWARDS THE FUNGUS FLORA OF AUSTRALIA AND
     NEW ZEALAND. A.REP.INST.FERMENT., OSAKA, 1963/64, 39-62.

5931 TUBAKI, K. (1969) - STUDIES ON JAPANESE MARINE FUNGI. LIGNICOLOUS GROUP
     (III), ALGICOLOUS GROUP AND A GENERAL CONSIDERATION. A.REP.INST.FERMENT.,
     OSAKA 4, 12-41.

5932 TUBAKI, K. (1973) - AQUATIC SEDIMENT AS A HABITAT OF EMERICELLOPSIS, WITH
     A DESCRIPTION OF AN UNDESCRIBED SPECIES OF CEPHALOSPORIUM. MYCOLOGIA
     65, 938-941.

5933 TUBAKI, K. & ITO, T. (1975) - DESCRIPTIVE CATALOGUE OF THE IFO FUNGUS COL-
     LECTION. 4. RES.COMMUNS INST.FERMENT., OSAKA 7, 113-142.

5934 TUBAKI, K., ITO, T. & MATSUDA, Y. (1974) - AQUATIC SEDIMENT AS A HABITAT OF
     THERMOPHILIC FUNGI. ANNALI MICROBIOL. 24, 199-207.

5935 TUBAKI, K. & YOKOYAMA, T. (1971) - SUCCESSIVE FUNGAL FLORA ON STERILIZED
     LEAVES IN THE LITTER OF FORESTS. 1. RES.COMMUNS INST.FERMENT., OSAKA 5,
     24-40.

5936 TUCKER, C.M. (1931) - TAXONOMY OF THE GENUS PHYTOPHTHORA DE BARY. BULL.RES.
     MO.AGRIC.EXP.STN 153, 208 PP.

5937   TUCKER, C.M. (1933) - THE DISTRIBUTION OF THE GENUS PHYTOPHTHORA. BULL.RES.
       MISS.AGRIC.EXP.STN 184, 80 PP.

5938   TULLOCH, M. (1972) - THE GENUS MYROTHECIUM TODE EX FR. MYCOL.PAP. 130, 1-
       42.

5939   TULLOCH, M. (1976) - THE GENUS METARRHIZIUM. TRANS.BR.MYCOL.SOC. 66, 407-
       411.

5940   TULLOCH, M. & LEACH, C.M. (1972) - A WORLD-WIDE SURVEY OF THE MICROFLORA
       OF DACTYLIS GLOMERATA SEED. ANN.APPL.BIOL. 72, 145-154.

5941   TUNG, K.K. & NORDIN, J.H. (1967) - EVIDENCE FOR A BURIED LOCATION OF NIGE-
       RAN IN THE CELL WALL OF ASPERGILLUS NIGER. BIOCHEM.BIOPHYS.RES.COMMUNS
       28, 519-524.

5942   TUREL, F. (1952) - DER EINFLUSS VON ANEURIN UND ZINK AUF DAS WACHSTUM UND
       DIE TOXINPRODUKTION VON FUSARIUM SOLANI. PHYTOPATH.Z. 19, 307-342.

5943   TURESSON, G. (1916) - THE PRESENCE AND SIGNIFICANCE OF MOULDS IN THE ALI-
       MENTARY CANAL OF MAN AND HIGHER ANIMALS. SV.BOT.TIDSKR. 10, 1-27.

5944   TURNER, E.M.C. (1957) - THE EFFECT OF SOME AMINO ACIDS ON THE GROWTH OF
       TWO VARIETIES OF OPHIOBOLUS GRAMINIS. J.GEN.MICROBIOL. 16, 531-533.

5945   TURNER, E.M.C. (1959) - INHIBITION OF GROWTH AND RESPIRATION OF OPHIOBOLUS
       GRAMINIS VAR. AVENAE AND ASPERGILLUS NIGER BY CYSTINE. NATURE, LOND.
       183, 1130-1131.

5946   TURNER, G.J. & TRIBE, H.T. (1975) - PRELIMINARY FIELD PLOT TRIALS ON BIO-
       LOGICAL CONTROL OF SCLEROTINIA TRIFOLIORUM BY CONIOTHYRIUM MINITANS.
       PL.PATH. 24, 109-113.

5947   TURNER, G.J. & TRIBE, H.T. (1976) - ON CONIOTHYRIUM MINITANS AND ITS PARA-
       SITISM OF SCLEROTINIA SPECIES. TRANS.BR.MYCOL.SOC. 66, 97-105.

5948   TURNER, M. (1963) - STUDIES IN THE GENUS MORTIERELLA. 1. MORTIERELLA ISA-
       BELLINA AND RELATED SPECIES. TRANS.BR.MYCOL.SOC. 46, 262-272.

5949   TURNER, M. & PUGH, G.J.F. (1961) - SPECIES OF MORTIERELLA FROM A SALT
       MARSH. TRANS.BR.MYCOL.SOC. 44, 243-252.

5950   TURNER, M.T. & BATEMAN, D.F. (1968) - MACERATION OF PLANT TISSUES SUSCEP-
       TIBLE AND RESISTANT TO SOFT-ROT PATHOGENS BY ENZYMES FROM COMPATIBLE
       HOST-PATHOGEN COMBINATIONS. PHYTOPATHOLOGY 58, 1509-1515.

5951   TURNER, P.D. (1965) - THE OCCURRENCE OF MICROSPORUM GYPSEUM IN CULTIVATED
       AND UNCULTIVATED SOILS IN HONG KONG. TRANS.BR.MYCOL.SOC. 48, 549-551.

5952   TUTT, S.F. & WILSON, W.T. (1975) - THE EFFECTS OF PENICILLIUM WAKSMANI
       GROWTH ON AMERICAN FOULBROOD INFECTED COMBS AND ADULT HONEYBEE ACTIVITY.
       J.INVERTEBR.PATH. 26, 283-287.

5953   TUVESON, R.W. (1964) - FURTHER OBSERVATIONS ON HYPHAL TIPS ISOLATED FROM
       HETEROCARYONS IN CEPHALOSPORIUM MYCOPHILUM. MYCOLOGIA 56, 831-840.

5954   TVEIT, M. (1956) - ISOLATION OF A CHETOMIN-LIKE SUBSTANCE FROM OAT SEED-
       LINGS INFECTED WITH CHAETOMIUM COCHLIODES. ACTA AGRIC.SCAND. 6, 13-16.

5955   TVEIT, M. & MOORE, M.B. (1954) - ISOLATES OF CHAETOMIUM THAT PROTECT OATS
       FROM HELMINTHOSPORIUM VICTORIAE. PHYTOPATHOLOGY 44, 686-689.

5956   TVEIT, M. & WOOD, R.K.S. (1955) - THE CONTROL OF FUSARIUM BLIGHT IN OAT
       SEEDLINGS WITH ANTAGONISTIC SPECIES OF CHAETOMIUM. ANN.APPL.BIOL. 43,
       538-552.

5957   TWEEDY, B.G., LOEPPKY, C. & ROSS, J.A. (1970) - METABOLISM OF 3-(P-BROMO-
       PHENYL)-1-METHOXY-1-METHYLUREA (METOBROMURON) BY SELECTED SOIL MICRO-
       ORGANISMS. J.AGRIC.FD CHEM. 18, 851-853.

5958   TWEEDY, B.G. & POWELL, D. (1963) - THE TAXONOMY OF ALTERNARIA AND SPECIES
       OF THIS GENUS ON APPLES. BOT.REV. 29, 405-412.

5959   TWEEDY, J.W. & SEGEL, I.H. (1971) - ATP-SULFURYLASE FROM PENICILLIUM CHRY-
       SOGENUM. 1. PURIFICATION AND CHARACTERIZATION. PREP.BIOCHEM. 1, 91-117.

5960   TYNER, L.E. (1940) - THE EFFECT OF CROP DEBRIS ON THE PATHOGENICITY OF
       CEREAL ROOT-ROTTING FUNGI. CAN.J.RES., SECT.C, 18, 289-306.

5961   TYNER, L.E. (1961) - COLONIZATION OF ORGANIC MATTER IN THE SOIL BY FUNGI.
       PHYTOPATHOLOGY 51, 625-634.

5962   TYNER, L.E. & MCKINNON, B.A. (1964) - FUNGI OF BARLEY SEED AND THEIR ASSO-
       CIATIVE EFFECTS. PHYTOPATHOLOGY 54, 506-508.

5963   TYPAS, M.A. & HEALE, J.B. (1976) - ACRIFLAVINE-INDUCED HYALINE VARIANTS OF
       VERTICILLIUM ALBO-ATRUM AND VERTICILLIUM DAHLIAE. TRANS.BR.MYCOL.SOC.
       66, 15-25.

5964   TYRELL, D. (1967) - THE FATTY ACID COMPOSITIONS OF 17 ENTOMOPHTHORA ISO-
       LATES. CAN.J.MICROBIOL. 13, 755-760.

5965   TYRRELL, D. (1969) - THE FATTY ACID COMPOSITION OF FOUR ENTOMOGENOUS IMPER-
       FECT FUNGI. CAN.J.MICROBIOL. 15, 818-820.

5966   TYRRELL, D. & MACLEOD, D.M. (1972) - A TAXONOMIC PROPOSAL REGARDING DELA-
       CROIXIA CORONATA (ENTOMOPHTHORACEAE). J.INVERTEBR.PATH. 20, 11-13.

5967   UDAGAWA, S. (1959) - TAXONOMIC STUDIES OF FUNGI ON STORED RICE GRAINS. 3.
       PENICILLIUM GROUP (PENICILLIA AND RELATED GENERA). 2. J.AGRIC.SCI.TOKYO
       5, 5-21.

5968   UDAGAWA, S. (1960) - A TAXONOMIC STUDY ON THE JAPANESE SPECIES OF CHAETO-
       MIUM. J.GEN.APPL.MICROBIOL., TOKYO 6, 223-251.

5969   UDAGAWA, S. (1962) - MICROASCUS SPECIES NEW TO THE MYCOFLORA OF JAPAN.
       J.GEN.APPL.MICROBIOL., TOKYO 8, 39-51.

5970   UDAGAWA, S. (1963) - NOTES ON SOME JAPANESE ASCOMYCETES. 1. TRANS.MYCOL.
       SOC.JAPAN 4, 94-102.

5971   UDAGAWA, S. (1963) - NEOCOSMOSPORA IN JAPAN. TRANS.MYCOL.SOC.JAPAN 12, 121-
       125.

5972   UDAGAWA, S. (1963) - MICROASCACEAE IN JAPAN. J.GEN.APPL.MICROBIOL., TOKYO
       9, 137-148.

5973   UDAGAWA, S. (1965) - NOTES ON SOME JAPANESE ASCOMYCETES. 2. TRANS.MYCOL.
       SOC.JAPAN 6, 78-90.

5974   UDAGAWA, S. & FURUYA, K. (1972) - NOTES ON SOME JAPANESE ASCOMYCETES. 10.
       TRANS.MYCOL.SOC.JAPAN 13, 49-56.

5975 UDAGAWA, S. & FURUYA, K. (1975) - MATERIAL FOR THE FUNGUS FLORA OF JAPAN.
19. TRANS.MYCOL.SOC.JAPAN 16, 215-221.

5976 UDAGAWA, S. & FURUYA, K. (1977) - NOTES ON SOME JAPANESE ASCOMYCETES. 15.
TRANS.MYCOL.SOC.JAPAN 18, 302-311.

5977 UDAGAWA, S. & HORIE, Y. (1971) - TAXONOMICAL NOTES ON MYCOGENOUS FUNGI. 1.
J.GEN.APPL.MICROBIOL., TOKYO 17, 141-159.

5978 UDAGAWA, S. & HORIE, Y. (1973) - SOME EUPENICILLIUM FROM SOILS OF NEW GUIN-
EA. TRANS.MYCOL.SOC.JAPAN 14, 370-387.

5979 UDAGAWA, S. & HORIE, Y. (1973) - SURFACE ORNAMENTATION OF ASCOSPORES IN
EUPENICILLIUM SPECIES. ANTONIE VAN LEEUWENHOEK 39, 313-319.

5980 UDAGAWA, S., ICHINOE, M. & KURATA, H. (1970) - OCCURRENCE AND DISTRIBUTION
OF MYCOTOXIN PRODUCERS IN JAPANESE FOODS. IN: TOXIC MICRO-ORGANISMS;
HERZBERG, M. (ED.), PROC.1ST U.S.-JAPAN. CONF., HONOLULU, 174-184.

5981 UDAGAWA, S. & KAWASAKI, Y. (1968) - NOTES ON SOME JAPANESE ASCOMYCETES. 6.
TRANS.MYCOL.SOC.JAPAN 8, 115-121.

5982 UDAGAWA, S. & TAKADA, M. (1968) - NOTES ON SOME JAPANESE ASCOMYCETES. 7.
TRANS.MYCOL.SOC.JAPAN 9, 12-17.

5983 UDAGAWA, S. & TAKADA, M. (1971) - SOIL AND COPROPHILOUS MICROFUNGI. BULL.
NATN.SCI.MUS., TOKYO 14, 501-515.

5984 UDAGAWA, S. & TAKADA, M. (1973) - MISCELLANEOUS NOTES ON MICROFUNGI. 13.
MYCOLOGICAL REPORTS FROM NEW GUINEA AND THE SOLOMON ISLANDS. BULL.NATN.
SCI.MUS., TOKYO 16, 317-330.

5985 UDEN, N.VAN & DO CARMO-SOUSA, L. (1959) - SOME PHYSIOLOGICAL PROPERTIES OF
GEOTRICHUM CANDIDUM. MYCOLOGIA 51, 595-598.

5986 UDUEBO, A.E. (1974) - EFFECT OF HIGH TEMPERATURE ON THE GROWTH, SPORULATION,
AND PIGMENT PRODUCTION OF BOTRYODIPLODIA THEOBROMAE. CAN.J.BOT. 52,
2631-2634.

5987 UDUEBO, A.E. & MADELIN, M.F. (1974) - GERMINATION OF CONIDIA OF BOTRYODI-
PLODIA THEOBROMAE IN RELATION TO AGE AND ENVIRONMENT. TRANS.BR.MYCOL.
SOC. 63, 33-44.

5988 UDUEBO, A.E. & MADELIN, M.F. (1974) - MATURATION IN VITRO OF CONIDIA OF
BOTRYODIPLODIA THEOBROMAE. TRANS.BR.MYCOL.SOC. 63, 45-56.

5989 UENO, K., GIAM, C.S. & TABER, W.A. (1974) - ABSENCE OF SPORIDESMIN IN A
TEXAS ISOLATE OF PITHOMYCES CHARTARUM. MYCOLOGIA 66, 360-362.

5990 UENO, T., YOSHIZAKO, F. & NISHIMURA, A. (1973) - THE FORMATION OF HOMOGEN-
TISIC ACID FROM PHENYLACETIC ACID BY AN ASPERGILLUS SP. CAN.J.MICROBIOL.
19, 393-395.

5991 UENO, Y. & ISHIKAWA, I. (1969) - PRODUCTION OF LUTEOSKYRIN, A HEPATOTOXIC
PIGMENT, BY PENICILLIUM ISLANDICUM SOPP. APPL.MICROBIOL. 18, 406-409.

5992 UENO, Y., SATO, N., ISHII, K., SAKAI, K. & ENOMOTO, M. (1972) - TOXICOLOG-
ICAL APPROACHES TO THE METABOLITES OF FUSARIA. 5. NEOSOLANIOL, T-2 TOXIN,
AND BUTENOLIDE, TOXIC METABOLITES OF FUSARIUM SPOROTRICHIOIDES NRRL 3510
AND FUSARIUM POAE 3287. JAPAN.J.EXP.MED. 42, 461-472.

5993 UENO, Y., SATO, N., ISHII, K., SAKAI, K., TSUNODA, H. & ENOMOTO, M. (1973)
- BIOLOGICAL AND CHEMICAL DETECTION OF TRICHOTHECENE MYCOTOXINS OF FUSA-
RIUM SPECIES. APPL.MICROBIOL. 25, 699-704.

5994 UENO, Y., UENO, I., SATO, N., IITOI, Y., SAITO, M., ENOMOTO, M. & TSUNODA,
      H. (1971) - TOXICOLOGICAL APPROACH TO (+)RUGULOSIN, AN ANTHRAQUINOID
      MYCOTOXIN OF PENICILLIUM RUGULOSUM THOM. JAPAN.J.EXP.MED. 41, 177-188.

5995 UEYAMA, A. (1972) - CHEMICAL BIOLOGY OF SEXUAL FACTORS IN THE FUNGI. 1.
      INDUCTION OF THE GAMETE INITIALS BY THE CULTURE EXTRACTS IN HETEROTHAL-
      LIC ABSIDIA GLAUCA HAGEM. TRANS.MYCOL.SOC.JAPAN 13, 66-70.

5996 UI, T. (1973) - ZONATION IN CULTURES OF RHIZOCTONIA SOLANI KUEHN UNDER
      CONTINUOUS DARKNESS. TRANS.MYCOL.SOC.JAPAN 14, 179-184.

5997 UI, T. & HOMMA, Y. (1974) - BEHAVIOUR OF RHIZOCTONIA SOLANI KUEHN DURING
      THE DECLINE AND DECAY OF INFECTED BEAN PLANTS. ANN.PHYTOPATH.SOC.JAPAN
      40, 392-400.

5998 UI, T., MITSUI, Y. & HARADA, Y. (1963) - STUDIES ON THE VICISSITUDES OF
      PELLICULARIA FILAMENTOSA IN SOIL. 2. THE ALTERNATION OF STRAINS OF RHI-
      ZOCTONIA SOLANI IN THE SOIL OF A PARTICULAR FLAX FIELD. ANN.PHYTOPATH.
      SOC.JAPAN 28, 270-279.

5999 UI, T., NAIKI, T. & AKIMOTO, M. (1976) - A SIEVING-FLOTATION TECHNIQUE
      USING HYDROGEN PEROXIDE SOLUTION FOR DETERMINATION OF SCLEROTIAL POPU-
      LATION OF RHIZOCTONIA SOLANI KUEHN IN SOIL. ANN.PHYTOPATH.SOC.JAPAN 42,
      46-48.

6000 UI, T. & OGOSHI, A. (1964) - (A COMPARISON OF TECHNIQUES FOR ISOLATING
      RHIZOCTONIA SOLANI FROM SOIL). MEM.FAC.AGRIC.HOKKAIDO UNIV. 5, 5-16.

6001 UJEVIC, I., KOVACIKOVA, E. & UROSEVIC, B. (1970) - GEGENSEITIGE BEZIEHUN-
      GEN ZWISCHEN EINIGEN PARASITISCHEN PILZEN, RHIZOBIUM UND ANDEREN MIKRO-
      ORGANISMEN IN DER LINSE (LENS ESCULALENTA MOENCH) UND BIOLOGISCHE SCHUTZ-
      MOEGLICHKEITEN. ZENTBL.BAKT.PARASITKDE, ABT.2, 125, 394-408.

6002 UJEVIC, I., STANEK, M., VACKE, J. & UROSEVIC, B. (1961) - (FUSARIUM MONI-
      LIFORME, ONE OF THE CAUSAL AGENTS OF DAMPING OFF AND WILT IN LUCERNE
      MEDICAGO SATIVA), AND THE INFLUENCE OF THE ANTAGONISTIC MICROFLORA ON
      THE COURSE OF THE DISEASE CAUSED BY THIS FUNGUS). ROSTL.VYROBA 7, 1365-
      1384.

6003 ULLOA, M. & HERRERA, T. (1973) - PHIALOPHORA RICHARDSIAE, UN HONGO CAUSANTE
      DE FEOSPOROTRICOSIS EN EL HOMBRE, AISLADO DEL POZOL. REVTA LATINOAM.MI-
      CROBIOL. 15, 199-201.

6004 ULSEN, F.W.VAN (1965) - SCHIMMELABORTUS BIJ RUNDEREN. TIJDSCHR.DIERENGE-
      NEESK. 80, 1081-1088.

6005 UMEDA, M., YAMASHITA, T., SAITO, M., SEKITA, S., TAKAHASHI, C., YOSHIHIRA,
      K., NATORI, S., KURATA, H. & UDAGAWA, S. (1974) - CHEMICAL AND CYTO-
      TOXICITY SURVEY ON THE METABOLITES OF TOXIC FUNGI. JAPAN.J.EXP.MED. 44,
      83-96.

6006 UOZUMI, T. (1969) - STUDIES ON THE AUTOLYSIS OF ASPERGILLUS ORYZAE. 5.
      PURIFICATION OF AN INTRACELLULAR NEW NUCLEASE. AGRIC.BIOL.CHEM., TOKYO
      33, 25.

6007 UPADHYAY, H.P. (1967) - SOIL FUNGI FROM NORTH-EAST BRAZIL. 3. PHYCOMYCE-
      TES. MYCOPATH.MYCOL.APPL. 31, 49-62.

6008 UPADHYAY, H.P. (1967) - SOIL FUNGI FROM NORTH-EAST AND NORTH BRAZIL. 6.
      NOVA HEDWIGIA 13, 227-234.

6009   UPADHYAY, H.P. (1969) - SOIL FUNGI FROM NORTH-EAST AND NORTH BRAZIL. 7.
       THE GENUS GONGRONELLA. NOVA HEDWIGIA 17, 65-73.

6010   UPDEGRAFF, D.M. (1971) - UTILIZATION OF CELLULOSE FROM WASTE PAPER BY MY-
       ROTHECIUM VERRUCARIA. BIOTECHNOL.BIOENG. 13, 77-97.

6011   UPITIS, V.V. (1956) - THE IMPORTANCE OF SOIL SAPROPHYTIC FUNGI FOR THE
       CONTROL OF PATHOGENS OF AGRICULTURAL PLANTS. SB.TRUD.ZASHCH.RAST.RIGA,
       1956, 181-190.

6012   UPSHALL, A. (1966) - SOMATICALLY UNSTABLE MUTANTS OF ASPERGILLUS NIDULANS.
       NATURE, LOND. 209, 1113-1115.

6013   UPSHALL, A. (1971) - PHENOTYPIC SPECIFICITY OF ANEUPLOID STATES IN ASPER-
       GILLUS NIDULANS. GENET.RES. 18, 167-171.

6014   UPSHER, F.J. (1975) - FUNGAL BIOLOGICAL FLORA. 3. CURVULARIA BOEDIJN. INT.
       BIODETERIOR.BULL. 11, 24-30.

6015   URAGUCHI, K., TATSUNO, T., SAKAI, F., TSUKIOKA, M., SAKAI, Y., YONEMITSU,
       O. & ITO, H. (1961) - ISOLATION OF TWO TOXIC AGENTS, LUTEOSKYRIN AND
       CHLORINE-CONTAINING PEPTIDE, FROM THE METABOLITES OF PENICILLIUM ISLAN-
       DICUM SOPP, WITH SOME PROPERTIES THEREOF. JAPAN J.EXP.MED. 31, 19-46.

6016   URAGUCHI, K., TATSUNO, T., TSUKIOKA, M., SAKAI, Y., SAKAI, F. & KOBAYASHI,
       Y. (1961) - TOXICOLOGICAL APPROACH TO THE METABOLITES OF PENICILLIUM
       ISLANDICUM SOPP GROWING ON THE YELLOWED RICE. JAPAN J.EXP.MED. 31, 1-18.

6017   URHAN, O. (1951) - LLAGA I MARCHITAMIENTO DEL CAFETO CAUSADO POR MYROTHE-
       CIUM RORIDUM. BOLN INF.COLOMBIA 2, 33-45.

6018   URRY, W.H., WEHRMEISTER, H.L., HODGE, E.B. & HIDY, P.H. (1966) - THE STRUC-
       TURE OF ZEARALENONE. TETRAHEDRON LETTERS, 1966 (27), 3109-3114.

6019   VAARAMA, A. & TAREN, N. (1959) - THE EFFECT OF GIBBERELLIC ACID AND FUNGI
       ON SPORE GERMINATION AND PROTONEMA GROWTH IN MOSSES. BOT.NOTISER 112,
       481-488.

6020   VAARTAJA, O. (1967) - DAMPING-OFF PATHOGENS IN SOUTH AUSTRALIAN NURSERIES.
       PHYTOPATHOLOGY 57, 765-768.

6021   VAARTAJA, O. (1968) - PYTHIUM AND MORTIERELLA IN SOILS OF ONTARIO FOREST
       NURSERIES. CAN.J.MICROBIOL. 14, 265-269.

6022   VAARTAJA, O. (1974) - INHIBITION OF PYTHIUM ULTIMUM IN MOLECULAR FRACTIONS
       FROM GEL FILTRATION OF SOIL EXTRACTS. CAN.J.MICROBIOL. 20, 1273-1280.

6023   VAARTAJA, O. (1976) - PYTHIUM SYLVATICUM IN CANADIAN FOREST NURSERIES.
       CAN.PL.DIS.SURV. 55, 101-102.

6024   VAARTAJA, O. & AGNIHOTRI, V.P. (1967) - INHIBITION OF PYTHIUM AND THANATHE-
       PHORUS (RHIZOCTONIA) BY LEACHATES FROM A NURSERY SOIL. PHYTOPATH.Z. 60,
       63-72.

6025   VAARTAJA, O. & AGNIHOTRI, V.P. (1969) - INTERACTIONS OF NUTRIENTS AND FOUR
       ANTIFUNGAL ANTIBIOTICS IN THEIR EFFECTS ON PYTHIUM SPECIES IN VITRO AND
       IN SOIL. PL.SOIL 30, 49-61.

6026   VAARTAJA, O. & AGNIHOTRI, V.P. (1970) - A COMPARISON OF RHIZOSPHERE FLORAS
       IN CONIFER BEDS TREATED WITH FUNGITOXICANTS. ZENTBL.BAKT.PARASITKDE,
       ABT.2, 124, 157-164.

6027 VAARTAJA, O. & BUMBIERIS, M. (1964) - ABUNDANCE OF PYTHIUM SPECIES IN NURS-
      ERY SOILS IN SOUTH AUSTRALIA. AUST.J.BIOL.SCI. 17, 436-445.

6028 VAARTAJA, O. & CRAM, W.H. (1956) - DAMPING-OFF PATHOGENS OF CONIFERS AND OF
      CARAGANA IN SASKATCHEWAN. PHYTOPATHOLOGY 46, 391-397.

6029 VAARTAJA, O. & SALISBURY, P.J. (1965) - MUTUAL EFFECTS IN VITRO OF MICRO-
      ORGANISMS ISOLATED FROM TREE SEEDLINGS, NURSERY SOIL, AND FORESTS. FOR-
      EST SCI. 11, 160-168.

6030 VAARTNOU, H., TEWARI, I. & HORRICKS, J. (1974) - FUNGI ASSOCIATED WITH DIS-
      EASES ON POLISH-TYPE RAPE IN ALBERTA. MYCOPATH.MYCOL.APPL. 52, 255-260.

6031 VAISEY, E.B. (1954) - OSMOPHILISM OF SPORENDONEMA EPIZOUM. J.FISH.RES.CAN.
      11, 901-903.

6032 VAKIL, J.R., RAGHAVENDRA RAO, M.R. & BHATTACHARYYA, P.K. (1961) - EFFECT
      OF CO2 ON THE GERMINATION OF CONIDIOSPORES OF ASPERGILLUS NIGER. ARCH.
      MIKROBIOL. 39, 53-57.

6033 VALADON, L.R.G. & COOKE, R.C. (1963) - CAROTENOID PIGMENTS OF THE NEMATODE
      -TRAPPING HYPHOMYCETE ARTHROBOTRYS OLIGOSPORA. PHYTOCHEMISTRY 2, 103-
      105.

6034 VALADON, L.R.G. & LODGE, E. (1970) - AUXINS AND OTHER COMPOUNDS OF CLADO-
      SPORIUM HERBARUM. TRANS.BR.MYCOL.SOC. 55, 9-15.

6035 VALENTA, J.R., DICUOLLO, C.J., FARE, L.R., MILLER, J.A. & PAGANO, J.F.
      (1974) - MICROBIAL TRANSFORMATION OF METHYL 5(6)-BUTYL-2-BENZIMIDAZOLE-
      CARBAMATE. APPL.MICROBIOL. 28, 995-998.

6036 VALENZUELA-PEREZ, J. & SMITH, J.E. (1971) - ROLE OF GLYCOLYSIS IN SPORULA-
      TION OF ASPERGILLUS NIGER IN SUBMERGED CULTURE. TRANS.BR.MYCOL.SOC. 57,
      111-119.

6037 VALLIER, M. (1959) - OBSERVATIONS MORPHOLOGIQUES ET CYTOLOGIQUES SUR LES
      MORTIERELLACEES DU GENRE HAPLOSPORANGIUM. REVUE GEN.BOT. 66, 165-209.

6038 VANBREUSEGHEM, R. (1952) - INTERET THEORIQUE ET PRATIQUE D'UN NOUVEAU DER-
      MATOPHYTE ISOLE DU SOL, KERATINOMYCES AJELLOI. BULL.ACAD.R.MED.BELG.,
      CL.SCI., SER.5, 38, 1068-1077.

6039 VANBREUSEGHEM, R. & BORGERS, G. (1951) - A PROPOS D'UNE SOUCHE DE SABOU-
      RAUDITES (MICROSPORUM) GYPSEUS ISOLEE AU CONGO BELGE. ANNLS SOC.BELGE
      MED.TROP. 21, 377-382.

6040 VANDAMME, E.J. & VOETS, J.P. (1972) - ETUDE COMPARATIVE D'UNE PENICILLINE
      V-ACYLASE FONGIQUE ET BACTERIENNE. MEDED.FAC.LANDBOUWWET.RIJKSUNIV.GENT
      37, 1185-1200.

6041 VAN ETTEN, H.D. & BATEMAN, D.F. (1969) - ENZYMATIC DEGRADATION OF GALACTAN,
      GALACTOMANNAN, AND XYLAN BY SCLEROTIUM ROLFSII. PHYTOPATHOLOGY 59, 968-
      972.

6042 VAN ETTEN, J.L., BULLA, L.A. & ST.JULIAN, G. (1974) - PHYSIOLOGICAL AND
      MORPHOLOGICAL CORRELATION OF RHIZOPUS STOLONIFER SPORE GERMINATION.
      J.BACT. 117, 882-887.

6043 VAN ETTEN, J.L. & GOTTLIEB, D. (1965) - BIOCHEMICAL CHANGES DURING THE
      GROWTH OF FUNGI. 2. ERGOSTEROL AND FATTY ACIDS IN PENICILLIUM ATROVENE-
      TUM. J.BACT. 89, 409-414.

6044 VAN ETTEN, J.L., ROKER, H.R. & DAVIES, E. (1972) - PROTEIN SYNTHESIS DURING
      FUNGAL SPORE GERMINATION - DIFFERENTIAL PROTEIN SYNTHESIS DURING GERMINA-
      TION OF BOTRYODIPLODIA THEOBROMAE SPORES. J.BACT. 112, 1029-1031.

6045 VARENNE, J., POLONSKY, J., CAGNOLI-BELLAVITA, N. & CECCHERELLI, P. (1971) -
      SUR L'ERGOSTEROL PRODUIT PAR L'OOSPORA VIRESCENS (LINK) WALLR. BIOCHI-
      MIE 53, 261-262.

6046 VARGHESE, G. (1972) - SOIL MICROFLORA OF PLANTATIONS AND NATURAL RAIN FOR-
      EST OF WEST MALAYSIA. MYCOPATH.MYCOL.APPL. 48, 43-61.

6047 VARSAVSKY, E. (1964) - OCCURRENCE OF KERATINOPHILIC HUMAN PATHOGENIC FUNGI
      IN SOILS OF ARGENTINA. MYCOPATH.MYCOL.APPL. 22, 81-90.

6048 VARTAPETYAN, B.B. & BOGDANOVA, I.P. (1964) - (TRANSFORMATION OF TANNIN OF
      THE TEA PLANT INDUCED BY PENICILLIUM EXPANSUM). MIKROBIOLOGIYA 53, 767-
      771.

6049 VAUGHN, R.H., BALATSOURAS, G.D., YORK, G.K. & NAGEL, C.W. (1957) - MEDIA
      FOR DETECTION OF PECTINOLYTIC MICRO-ORGANISMS ASSOCIATED WITH SOFTENING
      OF CUCUMBERS, OLIVES, AND OTHER PLANT TISSUES. FD RES. 22, 597-603.

6050 VEDROS, N.A. & COLMER, A.R. (1959) - THE USE OF SOIL PLAQUES TO GAUGE THE
      EFFECT OF SOME HERBICIDES ON THE FUNGAL FLORA OF MHOON SOIL. PROC.LA
      ACAD.SCI. 22, 82-89.

6051 VEEN, K.H. (1967) - A TECHNIQUE FOR MONOSPORE CULTURES AND THE DETERMINA-
      TION OF NUCLEUS NUMBERS IN METARRHIZIUM ANISOPLIAE. J.INVERTEBR.PATH.
      9, 276-278.

6052 VEEN, K.H. (1968) - RECHERCHES SUR LA MALADIE DUE A METARRHIZIUM ANISO-
      PLIAE, CHEZ LE CRIQUET PELERIN. MEDED.LANDBHOGESCH.WAGENINGEN 68 (5),
      1-77.

6053 VEEN, K.H. & FERRON, P. (1966) - A SELECTIVE MEDIUM FOR THE ISOLATION OF
      BEAUVERIA TENELLA AND OF METARRHIZIUM ANISOPLIAE. J.INVERTEBR.PATH. 8,
      268-269.

6054 VEEN, W.L.VAN (1973) - BIOLOGICAL OXIDATION OF MANGANESE IN SOILS. ANTONIE
      VAN LEEUWENHOEK 39, 657-662.

6055 VEGA, R.R., CORSINI, D. & LE TOURNEAU, D. (1970) - NONVOLATILE ORGANIC
      ACIDS PRODUCED BY SCLEROTINIA SCLEROTIORUM IN SYNTHETIC LIQUID MEDIA.
      MYCOLOGIA 62, 332-338.

6056 VEGA, R.R. & LE TOURNEAU, D. (1971) - TREHALOSE AND POLYOLS AS CARBON SOUR-
      CES FOR VERTICILLIUM SPP. PHYTOPATHOLOGY 61, 339-340.

6057 VELDKAMP, H. (1955) - A STUDY OF THE AEROBIC DECOMPOSITION OF CHITIN BY
      MICROORGANISMS. MEDED.LANDBHOGESCH.WAGENINGEN 55, 127-174.

6058 VENKATA RAM, C.S. (1951) - SEED-BORNE FUNGI AND LOSS OF SEEDLING VIGOUR IN
      COTTON. J.MADRAS UNIV., SECT.B, 21, 288-302.

6059 VENKATA RAM, C.S. (1955) - SOIL FUSARIA AND THEIR PATHOGENICITY. PROC.IN-
      DIAN ACAD.SCI., SECT.B, 42, 129-144.

6060 VENKATA RAM, C.S. (1956) - STUDIES ON CELLULOLYTIC ACTIVITY OF FUSARIA
      WITH REFERENCE TO BACTERIAL AND OTHER CELLULOSE SUBSTRATES. PROC.NATN.
      INST.SCI., INDIA, SECT.B, 22, 204-211.

6061 VENKATA RAM, C.S. (1957) - FUSARINIC ACID PRODUCTION BY FUSARIUM ORTHOCE-
RAS IN VITRO. EXPERIENTIA 13, 284.

6062 VENKATA RAM, C.S. (1959) - CELLULOLYTIC ACTIVITY AND FUNGAL NUTRITION WITH
SPECIAL REFERENCE TO DECOMPOSITION OF BACTERIAL CELLULOSE BY FUSARIUM
CULMORUM. PHYTOPATH.Z. 35, 122-134.

6063 VENKATARAYAN S.V. & DELVI M.H. (1951) - BLACK MOULD OF ONIONS IN STORAGE
CAUSED BY ASPERGILLUS NIGER. CURR.SCI. 20, 243-244.

6064 VERHOEFF, K. & WARREN, J.M. (1972) - IN VITRO AND IN VIVO PRODUCTION OF
CELL WALL DEGRADING ENZYMES BY BOTRYTIS CINEREA FROM TOMATO. NETH.J.PL.
PATH. 78, 179-185.

6065 VERMA, P.R., MORRALL, R.A.A. & TINLINE, R.D. (1974) - THE EPIDEMIOLOGY OF
COMMON ROOT ROT IN MANITOU WHEAT - DISEASE PROGRESSION DURING THE GROW-
ING SEASON. CAN.J.BOT. 52, 1757-1764.

6066 VERMA, P.R., TINLINE, R.D. & MORRALL, R.A.A. (1975) - THE EPIDEMIOLOGY OF
COMMON ROOT ROT IN MANITOU WHEAT. 2. EFFECTS OF TREATMENTS, PARTICULARLY
PHOSPHATE FERTILIZER, ON INCIDENCE AND INTENSITY OF DISEASE. CAN.J.BOT.
53, 1230-1238.

6067 VERMA, R.N. (1973) - RHIZOSPHERE MYCOFLORA OF TWO MEDICINAL LEGUMES OF
BHAGALPUR (BIHAR). PROC.INDIAN SCI.CONGR. 60, 364-365 (ABS.).

6068 VERMA, R.N. (1974) - SOME ADDITIONS TO INDIAN FUNGI - SOME NEW ACREMONIA.
CURR.SCI. 40, 360.

6069 VERMEIL, C., GORDEFF, A., LEROUX, M.-J., MORIN, O. & BOUC, M. (1971) -
BLASTOMYCOSE CHELOIDIENNE A AUREOBASIDIUM PULLULANS (DE BARY) ARNAUD EN
BRETAGNE. MYCOPATH.MYCOL.APPL. 43, 35-39.

6070 VERNON, T.R. (1935) - STUDIES ON THE MYCOLOGICAL PROBLEMS OF DAIRYING. 1.
THE SURFACE MOULDING OF BUTTER. J.DAIRY RES. 6, 154-167.

6071 VERNON, T.R. (1935) - STUDIES ON THE MYCOLOGICAL PROBLEMS OF DAIRYING. 2.
THE INTERNAL AND SUBSURFACE DISCOLORATIONS OF BUTTER. J.DAIRY RES. 6,
168-174.

6072 VERONA, O. & BERTOLDI, M.DE (1970) - ANNOTAZIONI SU DI ALCUNI FUNGHI DEL
TERRENO CAUSA DI ALTERAZIONI MACULICOLE DELLA CARTA. CELLULOSA E CARTA
NO.11, 9-17.

6073 VERONA, O. & CATELLA, E.F. (1942) - PRIME INDAGINI MICROBIOLOGICHE SOPRA I
TERRENI FORESTALI DI VALLOMBROSA. ANNALI FAC.AGRIC.UNIV.PISA 5, 336-385.

6074 VERONA, O. & FIRPI, M. (1971) - SUI MICROMICETI CARTICOLI DEI GENERI ALTER-
NARIA, ULOCLADIUM, STEMPHYLIUM. CELLULOSA E CARTA NO.8, 55-72.

6075 VERONA, O. & GAMBOGI, P. (1952) - UNA RICERCA SULL'AZIONE DELLA CITRININA
PRODOTTA DA PENICILLIUM CITRINUM SU FUNGI FITOPATOGENI. PHYTOPATH.Z.
19, 423-430.

6076 VERONA, O. & GAMBOGI, P. (1966) - COMPORTAMENTO CELLULOFILO DI ALCUNI MI-
CROMICETI DEL SUOLO. AGRICOLTURA ITAL., PISA 66, 107-114.

6077 VERONA, O. & GAMBOGI, P. (1970) - AZIONE DELLA CALCIOCIANAMIDE SULLA GER-
MINAZIONE DELLE SPORE E SULLO SVILUPPO MICELICO DI ALCUNI FUNGHI FITO-
PATOGENI. AGRICOLTURA ITAL., PISA 60, 24-33.

6078 VERONA, O. & PICCI, G. (1968) - UTILIZZAZIONE DI ALCUNI COMPOSTI AZOTATI
DA PARTE DI QUALCHE FUNGO CELLULOSOLITICO. AGRICOLTURA ITAL., PISA 68,
1-6.

6079   VERONA, O. & PICCI, G. (1968) - AZIONE DELLA CALCIOCIANAMIDE SU SCLEROTIUM
       ROLFSII SACC. AGRICOLTURA ITAL., PISA 68, 101-111.

6080   VERONA, O. & RAMBELLI, A. (1970) - MICROFUNGHI PRESENTI NELLA LETTIERA DI
       PINUS RADIATA. AGRICOLTURA ITAL., PISA 70, 138-146.

6081   VESCO, G.DAL (1963) - ISOLAMENTO DAL TERRENO DI DUE MONILIALI NUOVE PER
       L'ITALIA. G.BOT.ITAL. 70, 637-639.

6082   VESCO, G.DAL (1974/75) - FUNGHI DEL SUOLO DI UN PIANORO ACQUITRINOSO IN
       VALLE DI COGNE (AOSTA). ALLIONIA 20, 81-92.

6083   VESCO, G.DAL, FIUSSELLO, N. & RAMUS, M.V. (1971) - UTILIZZAZIONE DI GALLO-
       TANNINI ED ACIDO GALLICO DA PARTE DI ALCUNI ASPERGILLI E PENICILLI.
       ALLIONIA 17, 25-40.

6084   VESCO, G.DAL & PEYRONEL, B. (1968) - FUNGI ISOLATI DAL SUOLO DI DUE ISOLE
       DEL PACIFICO MERIDIONALE. ALLIONIA 14, 31-39.

6085   VESCO, G.DAL, PEYRONEL, B., BARGE, M.T. & VOLPIANO, N. (1967) - SULLA MICO-
       FLORA DELLO STERCO DI CONIGLIO (ORYCTOLAGUS CUNICULUS). ALLIONIA 13,
       107-127.

6086   VESSEY, J.C. & PEGG, G.F. (1973) - AUTOLYSIS AND CHITINASE PRODUCTION IN
       CULTURES OF VERTICILLIUM ALBO-ATRUM. TRANS.BR.MYCOL.SOC. 60, 133-143.

6087   VEY, A. & VAGO, C. (1972) - RECHERCHES SUR LES MALADIES ACTUELLES DES
       ECREVISSES EN FRANCE. ANNLS HYDROBIOL. 3, 59-64.

6088   VEZINA, C., SINGH, K. & SEHGAL, S.N. (1965) - SPORULATION OF FILAMENTOUS
       FUNGI IN SUBMERGED CULTURE. MYCOLOGIA 62, 722-736.

6089   VIDHYASEKARAN, P., MUTHUSWAMY, G. & SUBRAMANIAN, C.L. (1966) - ROLE OF SEED
       -BORNE MICROFLORA IN PADDY SEED SPOILAGE. 1. PRODUCTION OF HYDROLYTIC
       ENZYMES. INDIAN PHYTOPATH. 19, 333-341.

6090   VIGNAIS, P.M. & VIGNAIS, P.V. (1973) - FUSCIN, AN INHIBITOR OF MITOCHON-
       DRIAL SH-DEPENDENT TRANSPORT-LINKED FUNCTIONS. BIOCHIM.BIOPHYS.ACTA 325,
       357-374.

6091   VIJAYA KUMAR, C.S.K. & RAO, A.S. (1976) - AMINO ACIDS, ORGANIC ACIDS AND
       SUGARS PRESENT IN MYCELIUM OF ALTERNARIA TRITICINA AND ALTERNARIA TE-
       NUIS. TRANS.BR.MYCOL.SOC. 67, 498-499.

6092   VILLALOBOS, N. (1972) - ESTUDIO DE LA ACTIVIDAD AMILASICA EN VARIAS ESPE-
       CIES DEL GENERO VERTICILLIUM. REVTA ESP.FISIOL. 28, 273-279.

6093   VINCENT, P.G. & KULIK, M.M. (1970) - PYROLYSIS-GAS-LIQUID CHROMATOGRAPHY
       OF FUNGI. DIFFERENTIATION OF SPECIES AND STRAINS OF SEVERAL MEMBERS OF
       THE ASPERGILLUS FLAVUS GROUP. APPL.MICROBIOL. 20, 957-963.

6094   VINCENT, P.G. & KULIK, M.M. (1973) - PYROLYSIS-GAS-LIQUID CHROMATOGRAPHY
       OF FUNGI. NUMERICAL CHARACTERIZATION OF SPECIES VARIATION AMONG MEMBERS
       OF THE ASPERGILLUS GLAUCUS GROUP. MYCOPATH.MYCOL.APPL. 51, 251-265.

6095   VINING, L.C., KELLEHER, W.J. & SCHWARTING, A.E. (1962) - OOSPOREIN PRODUC-
       TION BY A STRAIN OF BEAUVERIA BASSIANA ORIGINALLY IDENTIFIED AS AMANITA
       MUSCARIA. CAN.J.MICROBIOL. 8, 931-933.

6096   VINING, L.K. & WEEKS, R.J. (1974) - A PRELIMINARY CHEMICAL AND PHYSICAL
       COMPARISON OF BLACKBIRD-STARLING ROOST SOILS WHICH DO OR DO NOT CONTAIN
       HISTOPLASMA CAPSULATUM. MYCOPATH.MYCOL.APPL. 54, 541-548.

6097   VINZE, V.L. (1962) - OXIDATION OF CARBOHYDRATES BY PENICILLIUM CHRYSOGENUM
       SPORES. HINDUSTAN ANTIBIOT.BULL. 5, 45-50.

6098   VISARATHANONTH, N. (1972) - CEPHALIOPHORA TROPICA THAXTER. CYTOLOGY AND CO-
       NIDIAL DEVELOPMENT. PHILIPP.AGRICST 56, 77-85.

6099   VISCHER, E.B. (1953) - THE STRUCTURES OF AURANTIO- AND RUBROGLIOCLADIN AND
       GLIOROSEIN. J.CHEM.SOC., 1953, 815-820.

6100   VISCHER, E.B., HOWLAND, S.R. & RAUDNITZ, H. (1950) - VIRIDIN. NATURE, LOND.
       165, 528.

6101   VISSER, S. & PARKINSON, D. (1975) - FUNGAL SUCCESSION ON ASPEN POPLAR LEAF
       LITTER. CAN.J.BOT. 53, 1640-1651.

6102   VISSER, S.A. (1970) - STUDIES ON ASPERGILLUS FLAVUS LINK AND ITS METABO-
       LITES. 7. INVESTIGATION INTO THE OPTIMUM CONDITIONS FOR THE FORMATION
       OF HUMIC COMPOUNDS IN ASPERGILLUS FLAVUS CULTURES AND SOME PROPERTIES
       OF THE PRODUCTS FORMED. W.AFR.J.BIOL.APPL.CHEM. 13, 1-13.

6103   VISSET, M.-F. (1972) - LES FORMES CONIDIENNES DU COMPLEXE MICROSPORUM GYP-
       SEUM OBSERVEES EN MICROSCOPIE ELECTRONIQUE A BALAYAGE. SABOURAUDIA 10,
       191-192.

6104   VISSET, M.-F. (1973) - L'ETUDE DES ULTRASCULPTURES DE SURFACE (MICROSCOPE
       ELECTRONIQUE A BALAYAGE), PERMET-ELLE D' ANALYSER LES COMPLEXES DE GYM-
       NOASCACEES. SABOURAUDIA 11, 124-126.

6105   VISSET, M.-F. (1974) - QUELQUES GYMNOASCACEAE OBSERVEES AU MICROSCOPE ELEC-
       TRONIQUE A BALAYAGE. MYCOPATH.MYCOL.APPL. 54, 377-383.

6106   VISSET, M.-F. (1974) - CONTRIBUTION A L'ETUDE DE LA REPARTITION DES CHAM-
       PIGNONS KERATINOPHILES TELLURIQUES DANS LE MASSIF ARMORICAIN. BULL.SOC.
       SCI.BRET. 48, 33-48.

6107   VISSET, M.-F. & VERMEIL, C. (1973) - CONTRIBUTION A LA CONNAISSANCE DES
       FUNGI KERATINOPHILES DE L'OUEST DE LA FRANCE. 5. ETUDE AU MICROSCOPE
       ELECTRONIQUE A BALAYAGE. MYCOPATH.MYCOL.APPL. 49, 89-100.

6108   VITTAL, B.P.R. (1976) - STUDIES ON LITTER FUNGI. 1. MYCOFLORA OF ATLANTIA
       AND GYMNOSPORIA LITTER. PROC.INDIAN ACAD.SCI., SECT.B, 83, 133-138.

6109   VITTIMBERGA, B.M. (1963) - THE MUCONOMYCINS. 1. STUDIES ON THE STRUCTURE
       OF MUCONOMYCIN-A, A NEW BIOLOGICALLY ACTIVE COMPOUND. J.ORG.CHEM. 28,
       1786-1789.

6110   VLEGGAAR, R., STEYN, P.S. & NAGEL, D.W. (1974) - CONSTITUTION AND ABSOLUTE
       CONFIGURATION OF AUSTDIOL, THE MAIN TOXIC METABOLITE FROM ASPERGILLUS
       USTUS. J.CHEM.SOC.PERKIN TRANS.I, 1974 (1), 45-49.

6111   VOEROES, J. (1958) - FUNGISTATIC ACTIVITY OF THE SPECIES SPHAEROPSIDALES
       AND MELANCONIALES. ACTA MICROBIOL.ACAD.SCI.HUNG. 5, 261-266.

6112   VOEROES, J. (1965) - STREPTOMYCIN SENSITIVITY OF OOMYCETES DUE TO THE IN-
       CREASED ABSORPTION OF STREPTOMYCIN BY THEIR MYCELIA. PHYTOPATH.Z. 54,
       249-257.

6113   VOEROES, J. (1969) - CONIOTHYRIUM MINITANS CAMPBELL, A NEW HYPERPARASITIC
       FUNGUS IN HUNGARY. ACTA PHYTOPATH.ACAD.SCI.HUNG. 4, 221-227.

6114 VOGT, R. (1945) - ZUR PHYSIOLOGIE DER PATHOGENEN SCHIMMELPILZE ABSIDIA
      LICHTHEIMI UND ABSIDIA RAMOSA MIT BESONDERER·BERUECKSICHTIGUNG DES
      WIRKSTOFFBEDUERFNISSES. MITT.NATURFORSCH.GES.BERN 3, 53-118.

6115 VOINOVA-RAIKOVA, Z., BAKALIVANOV, D., CHANOVA, D. & STRATIEVA, A. (1969) -
      (BETA-INDOLEACETIC ACID IN SOME SOIL MICROORGANISMS). POCHVOZN.AGROKHIM.
      4, 85-90.

6116 VOLGER, C. (1959) - ERFAHRUNGEN MIT FUNGIZIDEN BEIZMITTELN, PRAEPARATEN
      ZUR KEIMLINGSBEHANDLUNG UND BODENDESINFEKTIONSMITTELN IM KONIFEREN-SAAT-
      BEET. FORSTW.ZENTBL. 78, 231-243.

6117 VOLZ, P.A. (1971) - A PRELIMINARY STUDY OF KERATINOPHILIC FUNGI FROM ABACO
      ISLAND, THE BAHAMAS. MYCOPATH.MYCOL.APPL. 43, 337-339.

6118 VOLZ, P.A. (1976) - THERMOTOLERANT FUNGI ASSOCIATED WITH TAIWAN HOT SPRINGS.
      PHYTOLOGIA 33, 154-163.

6119 VOLZ, P.A., HSU, Y.-C., LIU, C.-H., HO, S.-M. & CHEN, Z.-C. (1975) - THE
      KERATINOPHILIC FUNGI OF TAIWAN. TAIWANIA 20, 23-31.

6120 VONK, J.W. & KAARS SIJPESTEIJN, A. (1973) - STUDIES ON THE METHYLATION OF
      MERCURIC CHLORIDE BY PURE CULTURES OF BACTERIA AND FUNGI. ANTONIE VAN
      LEEUWENHOEK 39, 505-513.

6121 VRIES, G.A.DE (1952) - CONTRIBUTION TO THE KNOWLEDGE OF THE GENUS CLADOSPO-
      RIUM. DISS.UNIV.UTRECHT, REPRINT J.CRAMER, LEHRE (1967).

6122 VRIES, G.A.DE (1962) - KERATINOPHILIC FUNGI AND THEIR ACTION. ANTONIE VAN
      LEEUWENHOEK 28, 122-133.

6123 VRIES, G.A.DE (1969) - DAS PROBLEM - APHANOASCUS ZUKAL ODER ANIXIOPSIS HAN-
      SEN. MYKOSEN 12, 111-122.

6124 VRIES, G.A.DE & CORMANE, R.H. (1969) - A STUDY ON THE POSSIBLE RELATION-
      SHIPS BETWEEN CERTAIN MORPHOLOGICAL AND PHYSIOLOGICAL PROPERTIES OF AS-
      PERGILLUS FUMIGATUS AND ITS PRESENCE IN OR ON HUMAN AND ANIMAL (PULMO-
      NARY) TISSUE. MYCOPATH.MYCOL.APPL. 39, 241-253.

6125 VRIES, G.A.DE & KLEINE-NATROP, H.E. (1957) - SPOROTRICHUM CEREBRIFORME
      NOV.SPEC. MYCOPATH.MYCOL.APPL. 8, 154-160.

6126 VRIES, O.M.H.DE & WESSELS, J.G.H. (1973) - EFFECTIVENESS OF A LYTIC ENZYME
      PREPARATION FROM TRICHODERMA VIRIDE IN RELEASING SPHEROPLASTS FROM FUN-
      GI, PARTICULARLY BASIDIOMYCETES. ANTONIE VAN LEEUWENHOEK 39, 397-400.

6127 VROEY, C.DE (1971) - ON THE ROLE OF KERATIN IN THE ECOLOGY OF KERATINOPHIL-
      IC SOIL FUNGI. MYKOSEN 14, 546 (ABS.).

6128 VYAS, K.M. & SAKSENA, S.B. (1973) - STUDIES ON MYCELIAL RESPIRATION OF
      SCLEROTIUM ROLFSII. PROC.INDIAN ACAD.SCI., SECT.B, 39, 569-575.

6129 WAELCHLI, O. (1976) - DER EINFLUSS VON HEFEEXTRAKT AUF DEN CELLULOSEABBAU
      DURCH SCHIMMELPILZE. MATER.ORG. 11, 19-31.

6130 WAHLROOS, OE. & VIRTANEN, A.I. (1958) - ON THE ANTIFUNGAL EFFECT OF BENZ-
      OXAZOLINONE AND 6-METHOXYBENZOXAZOLINONE, RESPECTIVELY, ON FUSARIUM NI-
      VALE. ACTA CHEM.SCAND. 12, 124-128.

6131 WAID, J.S. (1954) - OCCURRENCE OF AQUATIC HYPHOMYCETES UPON THE ROOT SUR-
      FACES OF BEECH GROWN IN WOODLAND SOILS. TRANS.BR.MYCOL.SOC. 37, 420-421.

6132   WAID, J.S. (1956) - ROOT DISSECTION. A METHOD OF STUDYING THE DISTRIBUTION
       OF ACTIVE MYCELIA WITHIN ROOT TISSUE. NATURE, LOND. 178, 1477-1478.

6133   WAID, J.S. (1957) - DISTRIBUTION OF FUNGI WITHIN DECOMPOSING TISSUES OF
       RYEGRASS ROOTS. TRANS.BR.MYCOL.SOC. 40, 391-406.

6134   WAID, J.S. (1974) - DECOMPOSITION OF ROOTS. IN: BIOLOGY OF PLANT LITTER DE-
       COMPOSITION; DICKINSON, C.H. & PUGH, G.J.H. (ED.), ACADEMIC PRESS, LON-
       DON, NEW YORK, 175-211.

6135   WAINWRIGHT, M. & PUGH, G.J.F. (1974) - THE EFFECTS OF FUNGICIDES ON CER-
       TAIN CHEMICAL AND MICROBIAL PROPERTIES OF SOILS. SOIL BIOL.BIOCHEM. 6,
       263-267.

6136   WAINWRIGHT, M. & PUGH, G.J.F. (1975) - EFFECT OF FUNGICIDES ON THE NUMBERS
       OF MICRO-ORGANISMS AND FREQUENCY OF CELLULOLYTIC FUNGI IN SOILS. PL.
       SOIL 43, 561-572.

6137   WAKSMAN, S.A. (1916) - SOIL FUNGI AND THEIR ACTIVITIES. SOIL SCI. 2, 103-
       155.

6138   WAKSMAN, S.A. (1917) - IS THERE ANY FUNGUS FLORA OF THE SOIL? SOIL SCI. 3,
       565-589.

6139   WAKSMAN, S.A. (1944) - PURIFICATION AND ANTIBACTERIAL ACTIVITY OF FUMIGA-
       CIN AND CLAVACIN. SCIENCE, N.Y. 99, 220-221.

6140   WAKSMAN, S.A. & BUGIE, E. (1944) - CHAETOMIN, A NEW ANTIBIOTIC SUBSTANCE
       PRODUCED BY CHAETOMIUM COCHLIODES. 1. FORMATION AND PROPERTIES. J.BACT.
       48, 527-530.

6141   WAKSMAN, S.A. & HORNING, E.S. (1943) - DISTRIBUTION OF ANTAGONISTIC FUNGI
       IN NATURE AND THEIR ANTIBIOTIC ACTION. MYCOLOGIA 35, 47-65.

6142   WAKSMAN, S.A., HORNING, E.S. & SPENCER, E.L. (1943) - TWO ANTAGONISTIC
       FUNGI, ASPERGILLUS FUMIGATUS AND ASPERGILLUS CLAVATUS, AND THEIR ANTI-
       BIOTIC SUBSTANCES. J.BACT. 45, 233-248.

6143   WAKSMAN, S.A. & SCHATZ, A. (1943) - STRAIN SPECIFICITY AND PRODUCTION OF
       ANTIBIOTIC SUBSTANCES. PROC.NATN.ACAD.SCI., U.S.A. 29, 74-79.

6144   WALBEEK, W.VAN, CLADEMENOS, T. & THATCHER, F.S. (1969) - INFLUENCE OF RE-
       FRIGERATION ON AFLATOXIN PRODUCTION BY STRAINS OF ASPERGILLUS FLAVUS.
       CAN.J.MICROBIOL. 15, 629-632.

6145   WALBEEK, W.VAN, SCOTT, P.M., HARWIG, J. & LAWRENCE, J.W. (1969) - PENICIL-
       LIUM VIRIDICATUM WESTLING - A NEW SOURCE OF OCHRATOXIN-A. CAN.J.MICRO-
       BIOL. 15, 1281-1285.

6146   WALBEEK, W.VAN, SCOTT, P.M. & THATCHER, F.S. (1968) - MYCOTOXINS FROM FOOD
       -BORNE FUNGI. CAN.J.MICROBIOL. 14, 131-137.

6147   WALKER, J. (1972) - TYPE STUDIES ON GAEUMANNOMYCES GRAMINIS AND RELATED
       FUNGI. TRANS.BR.MYCOL.SOC. 58, 427-457.

6148   WALKER, J. (1975) - TAKE-ALL DISEASES OF GRAMINEAE. A REVIEW OF RECENT
       WORK. REV.PL.PATH. 54, 113-144.

6149   WALKER, J.A. & MAUDE, R.B. (1975) - NATURAL OCCURRENCE AND GROWTH OF GLIO-
       CLADUM ROSEUM ON THE MYCELIUM AND SCLEROTIA OF BOTRYTIS ALLII. TRANS.
       BR.MYCOL.SOC. 65, 335-338.

6150 WALKER, J.D. & COONEY, J.J. (1973) - ALIPHATIC HYDROCARBONS OF CLADOSPO-
      RIUM RESINAE CULTURED ON GLUCOSE, GLUTAMIC ACID, AND HYDROCARBONS. APPL.
      MICROBIOL. 26, 705-708.

6151 WALKER, J.D. & COONEY, J.J. (1973) - OXIDATION OF N-ALKANES BY CLADOSPO-
      RIUM RESINAE. CAN.J.MICROBIOL. 19, 1325-1330.

6152 WALKER, J.D. & COONEY, J.J. (1973) - PATHWAY OF N-ALKANE OXIDATION IN CLA-
      DOSPORIUM RESINAE. J.BACT. 115, 635-639.

6153 WALKER, J.D. & COONEY, J.J. (1975) - EFFECTS OF POORLY METABOLIZED HYDRO-
      CARBONS ON SUBSTRATE OXIDATION BY CLADOSPORIUM RESINAE. J.APPL.BACT. 39,
      189-196.

6154 WALKER, J.R.L. (1968) - STUDIES ON THE DIPHENOL OXIDASE OF THE PHYTOPATHO-
      GENIC FUNGUS GLOMERELLA CINGULATA. INHIBITION BY QUATERNARY AMMONIUM
      COMPOUNDS. PHYTOCHEMISTRY 7, 1231-1240.

6155 WALKER, R.F. & THRONEBERRY, G.O. (1971) - LIPID CONTENT OF VERTICILLIUM
      ALBO-ATRUM. PHYTOCHEMISTRY 10, 2979-2982.

6156 WALKER, T.K., HALL, A.N. & HOPTON, J.W. (1951) - CHROMATOGRAPHIC DETECTION
      OF PYRUVIC, DIMETHYLPYRUVIC AND ALPHA-KETOGLUTARIC ACIDS IN CULTURES OF
      ASPERGILLUS NIGER ON VARIOUS SUBSTRATES. NATURE, LOND. 168, 1042-1043.

6157 WALKEY, D.G.A. & HARVEY, R. (1965) - COPROPHILOUS ISOLATES OF NECTRIA COC-
      CINEA. TRANS.BR.MYCOL.SOC. 48, 35-37.

6158 WALLBRIDGE, A. & PINEGAR, J.A. (1975) - FUNGI ASSOCIATED WITH CROWN-ROT
      DISEASE OF BANANAS FROM ST.LUCIA IN THE WINDWARD ISLANDS. TRANS.BR.MY-
      COL.SOC. 64, 247-254.

6159 WALLIS, F.M. & JOUBERT, J.J. (1974) - GERMINATION OF PENICILLIUM CITRINUM
      SPORES ON VARIOUS BETA-GLUCOSIDES AND THE DISTRIBUTION OF BETA-GLUCOSI-
      DASES IN FILAMENTOUS FUNGI. TRANS.BR.MYCOL.SOC. 62, 519-525.

6160 WALLNOEFFER, P.R., KOENIGER, M., SAFE, S. & HUTZINGER, O. (1972) - THE ME-
      TABOLISM OF THE SYSTEMIC FUNGICIDE CARBOXIN (VITAVAX) BY RHIZOPUS JAPO-
      NICUS. INT.J.ENVIRON.ANAL.CHEM. 2, 37-43.

6161 WALSH, J.H. (1970) - A RAPID METHOD FOR THE INSPECTION OF PHIALOSPORE SUR-
      FACES OF TRICHODERMA BY ELECTRON MICROSCOPY. TRANS.BR.MYCOL.SOC. 55,
      491-493.

6162 WALSH, J.H. & HARLEY, J.L. (1962) - SUGAR ABSORPTION BY CHAETOMIUM GLOBO-
      SUM. NEW PHYTOL. 61, 299-313.

6163 WALSH, J.H. & STEWART, C.S. (1971) - EFFECT OF TEMPERATURE, OXYGEN AND CAR-
      BON DIOXYDE ON CELLULOLYTIC ACTIVITY OF SOME FUNGI. TRANS.BR.MYCOL.SOC.
      57, 75-84.

6164 WALSTAD, J.D., ANDERSON, R.F. & STAMBAUGH, W.J. (1970) - EFFECTS OF EN-
      VIRONMENTAL CONDITIONS ON TWO SPECIES OF MUSCARDINE FUNGI (BEAUVERIA
      BASSIANA AND METARRHIZIUM ANISOPLIAE). J.INVERTEBR.PATH. 16, 221-226.

6165 WALT, J.P.VAN DER (1970) - A NOTE ON CHLAMYDOSPORE FORMATION IN TRICHOSPO-
      RON CUTANEUM. MYCOPATH.MYCOL.APPL. 41, 233-235.

6166 WANG, C.J.K. (1961) - PRELIMINARY REPORT ON THE FUNGOUS FLORA OF PULP AND
      PAPER IN NEW YORK. TAPPI 44, 785-788.

6167   WANG, C.J.K. (1964) - STUDIES ON TRICHOSPORIUM HETEROMORPHUM NANNFELDT.
       CAN.J.BOT. 42, 1011-1016.

6168   WANG, C.J.K. (1965) - FUNGI OF PULP AND PAPER IN NEW YORK. TECH.PUBLS N.Y.
       ST.COLL.FOR. 87, 115 PP.

6169   WANG, C.J.K. (1966) - ANNELLOPHORES IN TORULA JEANSELMEI. MYCOLOGIA 58,
       614-621.

6170   WANG, C.J.K. & BROWNELL, S. (1967) - PRELIMINARY STUDIES OF SOME PHYSIOLOG-
       ICAL PROPERTIES OF TORULA JEANSELMEI. J.BACT. 94, 597-599.

6171   WANG, D.T. (1954) - INHIBITION OF FLAX SEED GERMINATION BY SUBSTANCES PRO-
       DUCED BY PHOMA EXIGUA. M.SC.THESIS UNIV.SASKATCHEWAN, SASKATOON.

6172   WANG, H.L., ELLIS, J.J. & HESSELTINE, C.W. (1972) - ANTIBACTERIAL ACTIVITY
       PRODUCED BY MOLDS COMMONLY USED IN ORIENTAL FOOD FERMENTATION. MYCOLO-
       GIA 64, 218-221.

6173   WANG, H.L., VESPA, J.B. & HESSELTINE, C.W. (1974) - ACID PROTEASE PRODUC-
       TION BY FUNGI USED IN SOYBEAN FOOD FERMENTATION. APPL.MICROBIOL. 27,
       906-911.

6174   WANG, M.C. & BARTNICKI-GARCIA, S. (1970) - STRUCTURE AND COMPOSITION OF
       WALLS OF THE YEAST FORM OF VERTICILLIUM ALBO-ATRUM. J.GEN.MICROBIOL.
       64, 41-54.

6175   WANG, M.C. & KEEN, N.T. (1970) - PURIFICATION AND CHARACTERIZATION OF EN-
       DOPOLYGALACTURONASE FROM VERTICILLIUM ALBO-ATRUM. ARCHS BIOCHEM.BIOPHYS.
       141, 749-757.

6176   WANG, S.-Y.C. & LE TOURNEAU, D. (1967) - THE EFFECT OF CARBOHYDRATES ON
       MYCELIAL GROWTH AND SCLEROTIAL PRODUCTION BY SCLEROTINIA SCLEROTIORUM.
       PHYTOPATHOLOGY 57, 1010 (ABS.).

6177   WANG, S.-Y.C. & LE TOURNEAU, D. (1971) - CARBON SOURCES, GROWTH, SCLERO-
       TIUM FORMATION AND CARBOHYDRATE COMPOSITION OF SCLEROTINIA SCLEROTIORUM.
       ARCH.MIKROBIOL. 80, 219-233.

6178   WANG, S.-Y.C. & LE TOURNEAU, D. (1972) - AMINO ACIDS AS NITROGEN SOURCES
       FOR GROWTH AND SCLEROTIUM FORMATION IN SCLEROTINIA SCLEROTIORUM. TRANS.
       BR.MYCOL.SOC. 59, 509-512.

6179   WANG, S.-Y.C. & LE TOURNEAU, D. (1972) - MANNITOL BIOSYNTHESIS IN SCLERO-
       TINIA SCLEROTIORUM. ARCH.MIKROBIOL. 81, 91-99.

6180   WANG, S.-Y.C. & LE TOURNEAU, D. (1972) - TREHALASE FROM SCLEROTINIA SCLERO-
       TIORUM. ARCH.MIKROBIOL. 87, 235-241.

6181   WANG, S.-Y.C. & LE TOURNEAU, D. (1973) - PENTITOL OXIDOREDUCTASES IN SCLE-
       ROTINIA SCLEROTIORUM. ARCH.MIKROBIOL. 93, 87-90.

6182   WARCUP, J.H. (1951) - THE ECOLOGY OF SOIL FUNGI. TRANS.BR.MYCOL.SOC. 34,
       376-399.

6183   WARCUP, J.H. (1951) - SOIL STEAMING - A SELECTIVE METHOD FOR THE ISOLATION
       OF ASCOMYCETES FROM SOIL. TRANS.BR.MYCOL.SOC. 34, 515-518.

6184   WARCUP, J.H. (1951) - EFFECT OF PARTIAL STERILIZATION BY STEAM OR FORMALIN
       ON THE FUNGUS FLORA OF AN OLD FOREST NURSERY SOIL. TRANS.BR.MYCOL.SOC.
       34, 520-532.

6185 WARCUP, J.H. (1952) - EFFECT OF PARTIAL STERILIZATION BY STEAM OR FORMALIN ON DAMPING-OFF OF SITKA SPRUCE. TRANS.BR.MYCOL.SOC. 35, 248-262.

6186 WARCUP, J.H. (1957) - STUDIES ON THE OCCURRENCE AND ACTIVITY OF FUNGI IN A WHEAT-FIELD SOIL. TRANS.BR.MYCOL.SOC. 40, 237-260.

6187 WARCUP, J.H. & BAKER, K.F. (1963) - OCCURRENCE OF DORMANT ASCOSPORES IN SOIL. NATURE, LOND. 197, 1317-1318.

6188 WARCUP, J.H. & TALBOT, P.H.B. (1962) - ECOLOGY AND IDENTITY OF MYCELIA ISOLATED FROM SOIL. TRANS.BR.MYCOL.SOC. 45, 495-518.

6189 WARCUP, J.H. & TALBOT, P.H.B. (1967) - PERFECT STATES OF RHIZOCTONIAS ASSOCIATED WITH ORCHIDS. NEW PHYTOL. 66, 631-641.

6190 WARD, A.C. & PACKTER, N.M. (1974) - RELATIONSHIP BETWEEN FATTY-ACID AND PHENOL SYNTHESIS IN ASPERGILLUS FUMIGATUS. EUR.J.BIOCHEM. 46, 323-333.

6191 WARD, E.W.B. & HENRY, A.W. (1961) - COMPARATIVE RESPONSE OF TWO SAPROPHYTIC AND TWO PLANT PARASITIC SOIL FUNGI TO TEMPERATURE, HYDROGEN ION CONCENTRATION, AND NUTRITIONAL FACTORS. CAN.J.BOT. 39, 65-79.

6192 WARD, J.E. (1971) - THERMOPHILIC MICROFUNGI FROM FOREST SOILS. J.ELISHA MITCHELL SCIENT.SOC. 87, 156.

6193 WARD, J.E.JR. & COWLEY, G.T. (1972) - THERMOPHILIC FUNGI OF SOME CENTRAL SOUTH CAROLINA FOREST SOILS. MYCOLOGIA 64, 200-205.

6194 WARDLAW, C.W. (1932) - OBSERVATIONS ON THE PYCNIDIUM OF BOTRYODIPLODIA THEOBROMAE PAT. ANN.BOT. 46, 229-238.

6195 WARMELO, K.T.VAN (1971) - SOMATIC NUCLEAR DIVISION IN STEMPHYLIUM BOTRYOSUM. BOTHALIA 10, 329-334.

6196 WARMELO, K.T.VAN (1971) - CONIDIAL NUCLEATION IN STEMPHYLIUM BOTRYOSUM. BOTHALIA 10, 335-339.

6197 WARMELO, K.T.VAN (1976) - SCANNING ELECTRON MICROSCOPY OF NEOCOSMOSPORA ASCOSPORES. MYCOLOGIA 68, 1181-1187.

6198 WARNER, G. & FRENCH, D.W. (1969) - DISSEMINATION OF FUNGI BY MIGRATORY BIRDS. SURVIVAL AND RECOVERY OF FUNGI FROM BIRDS. CAN.J.BOT. 48, 907-910.

6199 WARNOCK, D.W. (1971) - ASSAY OF FUNGAL MYCELIUM IN GRAINS OF BARLEY, INCLUDING THE USE OF THE FLUORESCENT ANTIBODY TECHNIQUE FOR INDIVIDUAL FUNGAL SPECIES. J.GEN.MICROBIOL. 67, 197-205.

6200 WARNOCK, D.W. (1973) - USE OF IMMUNOFLUORESCENCE TO DETECT MYCELIUM OF ALTERNARIA, ASPERGILLUS AND PENICILLIUM IN BARLEY GRAINS. TRANS.BR.MYCOL.SOC. 61, 547-552.

6201 WARREN, H.L. & KOMMEDAHL, T. (1973) - FERTILIZATION AND WHEAT REFUSE EFFECTS ON FUSARIUM SPECIES ASSOCIATED WITH WHEAT ROOTS IN MINNESOTA. PHYTOPATHOLOGY 63, 103-108.

6202 WARREN, H.L. & KOMMEDAHL, T. (1973) - ROOT-INFECTING SPECIES OF FUSARIUM IN SOIL AND IN THE ROOTS, RHIZOSPHERES, AND RESIDUES OF OATS. PHYTOPATHOLOGY 63, 1401-1403.

6203 WARREN, H.L. & KOMMEDAHL, T. (1973) - FUSARIUM SPECIES IN ROOTS AND SOIL ASSOCIATED WITH MONOCULTURE OF SOYBEANS IN MINNESOTA. PL.DIS.REPTR 57, 912-914.

6204   WARREN, J.R. (1948) - AN UNDESCRIBED SPECIES OF PAPULOSPORA PARASITIC ON
        RHIZOCTONIA SOLANI. MYCOLOGIA 40, 391-401.

6205   WASSERMANN, O. (1969) - UNTERSUCHUNGEN UEBER DEN ANTIBIOTISCHEN EINFLUSS
        VON BAKTERIEN UND PILZEN AUF DAS WACHSTUM VON VENTURIA INAEQUALIS (CKE.)
        WINT. IN VITRO. ZENTBL.BAKT.PARASITKDE, ABT.2, 123, 30-55.

6206   WASTIE, R.L. (1972) - SECONDARY LEAF FALL OF HEVEA BRASILIENSIS - FACTORS
        AFFECTING THE PRODUCTION, GERMINATION AND VIABILITY OF SPORES OF COLLE-
        TOTRICHUM GLOEOSPORIOIDES. ANN.APPL.BIOL. 72, 273-282.

6207   WASTIE, R.L. (1972) - SECONDARY LEAF FALL OF HEVEA BRASILIENSIS METEOROLOG-
        ICAL AND OTHER FACTORS AFFECTING INFECTION BY COLLETOTRICHUM GLOEOSPO-
        RIOIDES. ANN.APPL.BIOL. 72, 283-293.

6208   WASTIE, R.L. & JANARDHANAN, P.S. (1970) - PATHOGENICITY OF COLLETOTRICHUM
        GLOEOSPORIOIDES, C. DEMATIUM AND C. CRASSIPES TO LEAVES OF HEVEA BRASI-
        LIENSIS. TRANS.BR.MYCOL.SOC. 54, 150-152.

6209   WATANABE, H., YOKOE, M. & HARADA, T. (1974) - FORMATION OF A RED PIGMENT(S)
        FROM TRYPTOPHAN BY PENICILLIUM PURPUROGENUM W 59. J.FERMENT.TECHNOL.,
        OSAKA 52, 360-363.

6210   WATANABE, T. (1971) - FUNGI ISOLATED FROM THE RHIZOSPHERE SOILS OF WILTED
        PINEAPPLE PLANTS IN OKINAWA. TRANS.MYCOL.SOC.JAPAN 12, 35-47.

6211   WATANABE, T. (1974) - FUNGI ISOLATED FROM UNDERGROUND PARTS OF SUGAR CANE
        IN RELATION TO POOR RATOONING IN TAIWAN. 2. PYTHIUM AND PYTHIOGETON.
        TRANS.MYCOL.SOC.JAPAN 15, 343-357.

6212   WATANABE, T. (1975) - FUNGI ISOLATED FROM THE UNDERGROUND PARTS OF SUGAR
        CANE IN RELATION TO THE POOR RATOONING IN TAIWAN. 3. MUCORALES. TRANS.
        MYCOL.SOC.JAPAN 16, 18-27.

6213   WATANABE, T. (1975) - FUNGI ISOLATED FROM THE UNDERGROUND PARTS OF SUGAR
        CANE IN RELATION TO POOR RATOONING IN TAIWAN. 6. PAPULASPORA. TRANS.MY-
        COL.SOC.JAPAN 16, 264-267.

6214   WATANABE, T. (1975) - TETRACLADIUM SETIGERUM, AN AQUATIC HYPHOMYCETE ASSO-
        CIATED WITH GENTIAN AND STRAWBERRY ROOTS. TRANS.MYCOL.SOC.JAPAN 16, 348-
        350.

6215   WATANABE, T. & SHIYOMI, M. (1975) - HYPHAL MORPHOLOGY OF RHIZOCTONIA SOLA-
        NI AND RELATED FUNGI ISOLATED FROM SUGAR CANE IN TAIWAN. TRANS.MYCOL.
        SOC.JAPAN 16, 253-263.

6216   WATERHOUSE, G.M. (1963) - KEY TO THE SPECIES OF PHYTOPHTHORA DE BARY. MY-
        COL.PAP. 92, 22 PP.

6217   WATERHOUSE, G.M. (1967) - KEY TO PYTHIUM. MYCOL.PAP. 109, 1-15.

6218   WATERHOUSE, G.M. (1968) - THE GENUS PYTHIUM. DIAGNOSES AND FIGURES FROM
        THE ORIGINAL PAPERS. MYCOL.PAP. 110, 1-71.

6219   WATERHOUSE, G.M. (1970) - THE GENUS PHYTOPHTHORA DE BARY. MYCOL.PAP. 122,
        59 PP.

6220   WATKINS, G.M. (1950) - GERMINATION OF SCLEROTIA OF SCLEROTIUM ROLFSII AF-
        TER STORAGE AT VARIOUS HUMIDITY LEVELS. PHYTOPATHOLOGY 40, 31 (ABS.).

6221 WATKINS, G.M. (1961) - PHYSIOLOGY OF SCLEROTIUM ROLFSII, WITH EMPHASIS ON PARASITISM. PHYTOPATHOLOGY 51, 110-113.

6222 WATKINS, G.M. & WATKINS, M.O. (1940) - A STUDY OF THE PATHOGENIC ACTION OF PHYMATOTRICHUM OMNIVORUM. AM.J.BOT. 27, 251-262.

6223 WATLING, R. (1963) - THE FUNGAL SUCCESSION ON HAWK PELLETS. TRANS.BR.MYCOL. SOC. 46, 81-90.

6224 WATLING, R. (1969) - THE FIRST RECORD OF NECTRIA RADICICOLA IN BRITAIN. NOTES R.BOT.GDN EDINBURGH 29, 263-264.

6225 WATLING, R. (1973) - ON FOUR BRITISH HYPHOMYCETES. TRANS.BOT.SOC.EDINBURGH 42, 83-87.

6226 WATSON, A.G. (1973) - LUTTE BIOLOGIQUE CONTRE LA FONTE DES SEMIS DE LA LAITUE CAUSEE PAR PYTHIUM ULTIMUM. PUBLS STNS FED.ESSAIS AGRIC. 1002, 4 PP.

6227 WATSON, A.K. & MILTIMORE, J.E. (1975) - PARASITISM OF THE SCLEROTIA OF SCLEROTINIA SCLEROTIORUM BY MICROSPHAEROPSIS CENTAUREAE. CAN.J.BOT. 53, 2458-2461.

6228 WATSON, J.H. & STOJANOVIC, B.J. (1965) - SYNTHESIS AND BONDING OF SOIL AGGREGATES AS AFFECTED BY MICROFLORA AND ITS METABOLIC PRODUCTS. SOIL SCI. 100, 57-62.

6229 WEAKLY, H.E., MCCALLA, T.M. & HASKINS, F.A. (1967) - SIZE DISTRIBUTION OF SOIL AGGREGATES AS INFLUENCED BY MICROORGANISMS. SOIL SCI. 103, 75-77.

6230 WEAVER, D.J. (1974) - GROWTH AND PRODUCTION OF MICROSCLEROTIA OF TWO CY-LINDROCLADIUM SPECIES WITH VARIOUS CARBON AND NITROGEN SOURCES. CAN.J. BOT. 52, 1665-1668.

6231 WEBB, B.D., THIERS, H.D. & RICHARDSON, L.R. (1959) - STUDIES IN FEED SPOIL-AGE INHIBITION OF MOLD GROWTH BY GAMMA RADIATION. APPL.MICROBIOL. 7, 329-333.

6232 WEBB, H.M., GAFOOR, A. & HEALE, J.B. (1972) - PROTEIN AND ENZYME PATTERNS IN STRAINS OF VERTICILLIUM. TRANS.BR.MYCOL.SOC. 59, 393-402.

6233 WEBER, D.J. & GUNASEKARAN, M. (1972) - EFFECT OF TRYPTOPHAN AND DIMETHYL SULFOXIDE ON SPORULATION OF RHIZOPUS ARRHIZUS. PHYTOPATHOLOGY 62, 797 (ABS.).

6234 WEBER, D.J. & OGAWA, J.M. (1965) - THE SPECIFICITY OF PROLINE IN THE GER-MINATION OF SPORES OF RHIZOPUS ARRHIZUS. PHYTOPATHOLOGY 55, 262-266.

6235 WEBER, G.F. (1931) - BLIGHT OF CARROTS CAUSED BY SCLEROTIUM ROLFSII, WITH GEOGRAPHIC DISTRIBUTION AND HOST RANGE OF THE FUNGUS. PHYTOPATHOLOGY 21, 1129-1140.

6236 WEBSTER, J. (1952) - SPORE PROJECTION IN THE HYPHOMYCETE NIGROSPORA SPHAE-RICA. NEW PHYTOL. 51, 229-235.

6237 WEBSTER, J. (1956) - SUCCESSION OF FUNGI ON DECAYING COCKSFOOT CULMS. 1. J.ECOL. 44, 517-544.

6238 WEBSTER, J. (1957) - SUCCESSION OF FUNGI ON DECAYING COCKSFOOT CULMS. 2. J.ECOL. 45, 1-30.

6239 WEBSTER, J. (1959) - TRICELLULA AQUATICA SP.NOV., AN AQUATIC HYPHOMYCMTE. TRANS.BR.MYCOL.SOC. 42, 416-420.

6240 WEBSTER, J. (1964) - CULTURE STUDIES ON HYPOCREA AND TRICHODERMA. 1. COMPARISON OF THE PERFECT STATES OF H. GELATINOSA, H. RUFA, AND H. SPEC. 1. TRANS.BR.MYCOL.SOC. 47, 75-96.

6241 WEBSTER, J. (1970) - COPROPHILOUS FUNGI. TRANS.BR.MYCOL.SOC. 54, 161-180.

6242 WEBSTER, J. (1975) - FURTHER STUDIES OF SPORULATION OF AQUATIC HYPHOMYCETES IN RELATION TO AERATION. TRANS.BR.MYCOL.SOC. 64, 119-128.

6243 WEBSTER, J. & DIX, N.J. (1960) - SUCCESSION OF FUNGI ON DECAYING COCKSFOOT CULMS. 3. TRANS.BR.MYCOL.SOC. 43, 85-99.

6244 WEBSTER, J. & HALE, R. (1972) - PERITHECIA OF HYPOCREA RUFA IN SOIL PLATES. TRANS.BR.MYCOL.SOC. 58, 531-532.

6245 WEBSTER, J. & LOMAS, N. (1964) - DOES TRICHODERMA VIRIDE PRODUCE GLIOTOXIN AND VIRIDIN? TRANS.BR.MYCOL.SOC. 47, 535-549.

6246 WEBSTER, J. & LUCAS, M.T. (1961) - OBSERVATIONS ON BRITISH SPECIES OF PLEOSPORA. 2. TRANS.BR.MYCOL.SOC. 44, 417-436.

6247 WEBSTER, J. & RIFAI, M.A. (1968) - CULTURE STUDIES ON HYPOCREA AND TRICHODERMA. 4. HYPOCREA PILULIFERA SP.NOV. TRANS.BR.MYCOL.SOC. 51, 511-514.

6248 WEBSTER, J. & TOWFIK FATMA HASSAN (1972) - SPORULATION OF AQUATIC HYPHOMYCETES IN RELATION TO AERATION. TRANS.BR.MYCOL.SOC. 59, 353-364.

6249 WEBSTER, R.K. & BUTLER, E.E. (1967) - A MORPHOLOGICAL AND BIOLOGICAL CONCEPT OF THE SPECIES CERATOCYSTIS FIMBRIATA. CAN.J.BOT. 45, 1457-1468.

6250 WEBSTER, R.K. & NELSON, R.R. (1968) - THE GENETICS COCHLIOBOLUS SPICIFERUS. 1. GENETIC INHIBITION OF PERITHECIAL AND ASCUS FORMATION. CAN.J. BOT. 46, 196-202.

6251 WEETE, J.D., LAWLER, G.C. & LASETER, J.L. (1973) - TOTAL LIPID AND STEROL COMPONENTS OF RHIZOPUS ARRHIZUS. IDENTIFICATION AND METABOLISM. ARCHS BIOCHEM.BIOPHYS. 155, 411-419.

6252 WEHNER, F.C. & RABIE, C.J. (1970) - THE MICROORGANISMS IN NUTS AND DRIED FRUITS. PHYTOPHYLACTICA 2, 165-170.

6253 WEIDENSAUL, T.C. & WOOD, F.A. (1973) - SOURCES OF SPECIES OF FUSARIUM IN NORTHERN HARDWOOD FORESTS. PHYTOPATHOLOGY 63, 367-371.

6254 WEIDENSAUL, T.C. & WOOD, F.A. (1974) - RESPONSE OF FUSARIUM SOLANI TO CONSTANT AND FLUCTUATING TEMPERATURES AND ITS RELATIONSHIP TO FUSARIUM CANKER OF SUGAR MAPLE. PHYTOPATHOLOGY 64, 1018-1024.

6255 WEIJER, J. & WEISBERG, S.H. (1966) - KARYOKINESIS OF THE SOMATIC NUCLEUS OF ASPERGILLUS NIDULANS. 1. THE JUVENILE CHROMOSOME CYCLE (FEULGEN STAINING). CAN.J.GENET.CYTOL. 8, 361-374.

6256 WEIJMAN, A.C.M. & HOOG, G.S.DE (1975) - ON THE SUBDIVISION OF THE GENUS CERATOCYSTIS. ANTONIE VAN LEEUWENHOEK 41, 353-360.

6257 WEIK, K.L. & PAPPELIS, A.J. (1964) - GROWTH OF CEPHALIOPHORA TROPICA IN RESPONSE TO VARIOUS NITROGEN SOURCES. MYCOLOGIA 56, 650-655.

6258 WEINBERGER, M. & BOLLAG, J.M. (1972) - DEGRADATION OF CHLORBROMURON AND RELATED COMPOUNDS BY THE FUNGUS RHIZOCTONIA SOLANI. APPL.MICROBIOL. 24, 750-754.

6259 WEINDLING, R. (1932) - TRICHODERMA LIGNORUM AS A PARASITE OF OTHER SOIL FUNGI. PHYTOPATHOLOGY 22, 837-845.

6260 WEINDLING, R. & FAWCETT, H.S. (1936) - EXPERIMENTS IN THE CONTROL OF RHIZOCTONIA DAMPING-OFF OF CITRUS SEEDLINGS. HILGARDIA 10, 1-16.

6261 WEINHOLD, A.R. (1977) - POPULATION OF RHIZOCTONIA SOLANI IN AGRICULTURAL SOILS DETERMINED BY A SCREENING PROCEDURE. PHYTOPATHOLOGY 67, 566-569.

6262 WEINHOLD, A.R. & BOWMAN, T. (1974) - REPRESSION OF VIRULENCE IN RHIZOCTONIA SOLANI BY GLUCOSE AND 3-0-METHYL GLUCOSE. PHYTOPATHOLOGY 64, 985-990.

6263 WEISBERG, S.H. & TURIAN, G. (1971) - ULTRASTRUCTURE OF ASPERGILLUS NIDULANS CONIDIA AND CONIDIAL LOMASOMES. PROTOPLASMA 72, 55-67.

6264 WEISBERG, S.H. & TURIAN, G. (1974) - THE MEMBRANEOUS TYPE OF LOMASOME (MEMBRANOSOME) IN THE HYPHAE OF ASPERGILLUS NIDULANS. PROTOPLASMA 79, 377-389.

6265 WEISS, S. & NORD, F.F. (1949) - ON THE MECHANISM OF ENZYMIC ACTION. 37. SOLANIONE, A PIGMENT FROM FUSARIUM SOLANI D2 PURPLE. ARCHS BIOCHEM. 22, 288-313.

6266 WEISS, U., STRELITZ, F., FLON, H. & ASHESHOV, A.N. (1958) - ANTIBIOTIC COMPOUNDS WITH ACTION AGAINST BACTERIAL VIRUSES - NEOHYDROXYASPERGILLIC ACID. ARCHS BIOCHEM.BIOPHYS. 74, 150-157.

6267 WEITZMAN, I. (1963/64) - VARIATION IN MICROSPORUM GYPSEUM. 1. A GENETIC STUDY OF PLEOMORPHISM. SABOURAUDIA 3, 195-204.

6268 WEITZMAN, I., ALLDERDICE, P.W. & SILVA-HUTNER, M. (1970) - CHROMOSOME NUMBERS IN SPECIES OF NANNIZZIA AND ARTHRODERMA. MYCOLOGIA 62, 89-97.

6269 WEITZMAN, I., GORDON, M. & ROSENTHAL, S.A. (1971) - DETERMINATION OF THE PERFECT STATE, MATING TYPE AND ELASTASE ACTIVITY IN CLINICAL ISOLATES OF THE MICROSPORUM GYPSEUM COMPLEX. J.INVEST.DERM. 57, 278-282.

6270 WEITZMAN, I. & SILVA-HUTNER, M. (1967) - NON-KERATINOUS AGAR MEDIA AS SUBSTRATES FOR THE ASCIGEROUS STATE IN CERTAIN MEMBERS OF THE GYMNOASCACEAE PATHOGENIC FOR MAN AND ANIMALS. SABOURAUDIA 5, 335-340.

6271 WELCH, A.W.JR., JENKINS, S.F.JR. & AVERRE, C.W. (1975) - TRICHOTHECIUM FRUIT ROT ON GREENHOUSE TOMATOES IN NORTH CAROLINA. PL.DIS.REPTR 59, 255-257.

6272 WELFRINGER, A. & PERCEBOIS, G. (1975) - SIX CAS D'ONYXIS DU GROS ORTEIL A SCOPULARIOPSIS BREVICAULIS. BULL.SOC.FR.MYCOL.MED. 4, 37-40.

6273 WELLING, B. (1969) - SVAMPFLORA OG SPIREEVNE HOS BYG. TIDSSKR.PLAVL 73, 291-308.

6274 WELLING, B. (1974) - ASPERGILLUS AND PENICILLIUM SPECIES ON STORED DANISH BARLEY GRAIN. TIDSSKR.PLAVL 78, 1-8.

6275 WELLS, H.D., BELL, D.K. & JAWORSKI, C.A. (1972) - EFFICACY OF TRICHODERMA HARZIANUM AS A BIOCONTROL FOR SCLEROTIUM ROLFSII. PHYTOPATHOLOGY 62, 442-447.

6276   WELLS, H.D., BELL, D.K. & JAWORKSI, C.A. (1972) - TRICHODERMA HARZIANUM, A
        BIOCONTROL FOR SCLEROTIUM ROLFSII. PHYTOPATHOLOGY 62, 808 (ABS.).

6277   WELLS, J.M. (1967) - GROWTH AND PRODUCTION OF PECTIC AND CELLULOLYTIC EN-
        ZYMES BY RHIZOPUS STOLONIFER. PHYTOPATHOLOGY 57, 1010 (ABS.).

6278   WELLS, J.M. (1968) - GROWTH OF RHIZOPUS STOLONIFER IN LOW-OXYGEN ATMOSPHERES
        AND PRODUCTION OF PECTIC AND CELLULOLYTIC ENZYMES. PHYTOPATHOLOGY 58,
        1598-1602.

6279   WELLS, J.M. & PAYNE, J.A. (1975) - TOXIGENIC ASPERGILLUS AND PENICILLIUM
        ISOLATED FROM WEEVIL-DAMAGED CHESTNUTS. APPL.MICROBIOL. 30, 536-540.

6280   WELLS, J.M. & SPALDING, D.H. (1973) - GROWTH AND INFECTIVITY OF GEOTRICHUM
        CANDIDUM IN LOW-OXYGEN AND HIGH-CARBON DIOXIDE ATMOSPHERES. PHYTOPATHOL-
        OGY 63, 449 (ABS.).

6281   WELLS, J.M. & UOTA, M. (1970) - GERMINATION AND GROWTH OF FIVE FUNGI IN
        LOW-OXYGEN AND HIGH-CARBON DIOXIDE ATMOSPHERES. PHYTOPATHOLOGY 60, 50-
        53.

6282   WELTY, R.E. & LUCAS, G.B. (1968) - FUNGI ISOLATED FROM DAMAGED FLUE-CURED
        TOBACCO. APPL.MICROBIOL. 16, 851-854.

6283   WELTZIEN, H.C. (1961) - ACREMONIELLA ATRA UND ANDERE PILZE ALS SAMENBEWOH-
        NER BEI ALEXANDRINERKLEE. Z.PFLKRANKH.PFLPATH.PFLSCHUTZ 68, 642-646.

6284   WELTZIEN, H.C. (1963) - UNTERSUCHUNGEN UEBER DIE URSACHEN DER KEIMHEMMUNG
        VON PILZSPOREN IM BODEN. ZENTBL.BAKT.PARASITKDE, ABT.2, 116, 131-170.

6285   WELVAERT, W. & VELDEMAN, R. (1955) - SCHIMMELFLORA VAN KLEI - EN BOSGROND.
        MEDED.LANDBHOGESCH.OPZOEKSTNS GENT 20, 193-210.

6286   WEN-SHION CHANG, USAMI, S. & TAKETOMI, N. (1965) - STUDIES ON CELLULASE.
        1. ISOLATION OF CELLULOSE DECOMPOSING ORGANISMS, AND EFFECTS OF PH AND
        TEMPERATURE ON CELLULASE ACTIVITIES. HAKKO KYOKAISHI 23, 375-377.

6287   WENSLEY, R.N. (1953) - MICROBIOLOCIGAL STUDIES OF THE ACTION OF SOME SELEC-
        TED SOIL FUMIGANTS. CAN.J.BOT. 31, 277-308.

6288   WENSLEY, R.N. (1956) - THE PEACH REPLANT PROBLEM IN ONTARIO. 4. FUNGI AS-
        SOCIATED WITH REPLANT FAILURE AND THEIR IMPORTANCE IN FUMIGATED AND NON-
        FUMIGATED SOILS. CAN.J.BOT. 34, 967-981.

6289   WENT, J.C. & DE JONG, F. (1966) - DECOMPOSITION OF CELLULOSE IN SOILS.
        ANTONIE VAN LEEUWENHOEK 32, 39-56.

6290   WERESUB, L.K. & LECLAIR, P.M. (1971) - ON PAPULASPORA AND BULBILLIFEROUS
        BASIDIOMYCETES BURGOA AND MINIMEDUSA. CAN.J.BOT. 49, 2203-2214.

6291   WERESUB, L.K., MALLOCH, D. & PIROZYNSKI, K.A. (1974) - RESPONSE TO HAWKS-
        WORTH AND SUTTON'S PROPOSALS FOR ART.59. TAXON 23, 569-578.

6292   WERGIN, W.P. (1972) - ULTRASTRUCTURAL COMPARISON OF MICROBODIES IN PATHO-
        GENIC AND SAPROPHYTIC HYPHAE OF FUSARIUM OXYSPORUM F.SP. LYCOPERSICI.
        PHYTOPATHOLOGY 62, 1043-1051.

6293   WERGIN, W.P., DUNKLE, L.D., VAN ETTEN, J.L., ST.JULIAN, G. & BULLA, L.A.
        (1973) - MICROSCOPIC OBSERVATION OF GERMINATION AND SEPTUM FORMATION IN
        PYCNIDIOSPORES OF BOTRYODIPLODIA THEOBROMAE. DEV.BIOL. 32, 1-14.

6294   WERKENTHIN, F.C. (1916) - FUNGUS FLORA OF TEXAS SOILS. PHYTOPATHOLOGY 6,
        241-253.

6295 WERKMAN, B.A. & ENDE, H.VAN DEN (1974) - TRISPORIC ACID SYNTHESIS IN HO-
      MOTHALLIC AND HETEROTHALLIC MUCORALES. J.GEN.MICROBIOL. 82, 273-278.

6296 WERTH, R., SABWE-MUBANGU, J., GATTI, F. & BASTIN, J.P. (1972) - DEUXIEME
      CAS DE RHINO-ENTOMOPHTOROMYCOSE DUE A ENTOMOPHTHORA CORONATA OBSERVE EN
      REPUBLIQUE DU ZAIRE. ANNLS SOC.BELGE MED.TROP. 52, 343-355.

6297 WESSEL, H. (1975) - BEITRAEGE ZUR BIOLOGIE UND EPIDEMIOLOGIE VON GLOMEREL-
      LA CINGULATA (STONEM.) SPAULD. & V. SCHRENK UND PEZICULA ALBA GUTHRIE
      AUF APFELSAEMLINGSBLAETTERN. DISS.UNIV.BONN.

6298 WEST, B. (1967) - NUTRITION OF PHIALOPHORA VERRUCOSA A126. MYCOPATH.MYCOL.
      APPL. 31, 12-16.

6299 WEST, E. (1961) - SCLEROTIUM ROLFSII, HISTORY, TAXONOMY, HOST RANGE, AND
      DISTRIBUTION. PHYTOPATHOLOGY 51, 108-109.

6300 WESTE, G. (1965) - INFECTION OF WHEAT ROOTS BY ASCOSPORES OF OPHIOBOLUS
      GRAMINIS. PHYTOPATH.Z. 52, 204-206.

6301 WESTE, G. (1970) - FACTORS AFFECTING VEGETATIVE GROWTH AND THE PRODUCTION
      OF PERITHECIA IN CULTURE BY OPHIOBOLUS GRAMINIS. 1. VARIATIONS IN MEDIA
      AND AGE OF MYCELIUM. AUST.J.BOT. 18, 1-10.

6302 WESTE, G. (1970) - FACTORS AFFECTING VEGETATIVE GROWTH AND THE PRODUCTION
      OF PERITHECIA IN CULTURE BY OPHIOBOLUS GRAMINIS. 2. VARIATIONS IN LIGHT
      AND TEMPERATURE. AUST.J.BOT. 18, 11-28.

6303 WESTE, G. (1975) - THE DISTRIBUTION OF PHYTOPHTHORA CINNAMOMI WITHIN THE
      NATIONAL PARK, WILSON'S PROMONTORY, VICTORIA. AUST.J.BOT. 23, 67-76.

6304 WESTE, G. (1975) - PATHOGENICITY OF PHYTOPHTHORA CINNAMOMI TOWARDS NOTHO-
      FAGUS CUNNINGHAMII. AUST.J.BOT. 23, 277-284.

6305 WESTE, G. (1975) - COMPARATIVE PATHOGENICITY OF ROOT PARASITES TO WHEAT
      SEEDLINGS. TRANS.BR.MYCOL.SOC. 64, 43-54.

6306 WESTE, G. & MARKS, G.C. (1974) - THE DISTRIBUTION OF PHYTOPHTHORA CINNAMO-
      MI IN VICTORIA. TRANS.BR.MYCOL.SOC. 63, 559-572.

6307 WESTE, G. & RUPPIN, P. (1975) - FACTORS AFFECTING THE POPULATION DENSITY
      OF PHYTOPHTHORA CINNAMOMI IN NATIVE FORESTS OF THE BRISBANE RANGES,
      VICTORIA. AUST.J.BOT. 23, 77-86.

6308 WESTE, G. & TAYLOR, P. (1971) - THE INVASION OF NATIVE FOREST BY PHYTO-
      PHTHORA CINNAMOMI. 1. BRISBANE RANGES, VICTORIA. AUST.J.BOT. 19, 281-294.

6309 WESTE, G. & THROWER, L.B. (1963) - PRODUCTION OF PERITHECIA AND MICROCONID-
      IA IN CULTURE BY OPHIOBOLUS GRAMINIS. PHYTOPATHOLOGY 53, 354.

6310 WESTE, G. & THROWER, L.B. (1971) - THE EFFECT OF ADDED NITRATE ON THE
      GROWTH OF OPHIOBOLUS GRAMINIS. PL.SOIL 35, 161-172.

6311 WESTLAKE, D.W.S. & SPENCER, J.F.T. (1966) - THE UTILIZATION OF FLAVONOID
      COMPOUNDS BY YEASTS AND YEAST-LIKE FUNGI. CAN.J.MICROBIOL. 12, 165-174.

6312 WETTER, C. (1954) - UEBER EIN VERFAHREN ZUR QUANTITATIVEN BESTIMMUNG VON
      MANGAN IM BODEN MIT HILFE VON ASPERGILLUS NIGER. LANDW.FORSCH. 6, 114-
      119.

6313 WHEELER, B.E.J. (1972) - EFFECT OF ETHANOL ON PRODUCTION OF SCLEROTIA BY
      SCLEROTIUM ROLFSII. TRANS.BR.MYCOL.SOC. 59, 453-461.

6314 WHEELER, B.E.J. & SHARAN, N. (1965) - THE PRODUCTION OF SCLEROTIA BY SCLE-
      ROTIUM ROLFSII. 1. EFFECTS OF VARYING THE SUPPLY OF NUTRIENTS IN AN
      AGAR MEDIUM. TRANS.BR.MYCOL.SOC. 48, 291-301.

6315 WHEELER, B.E.J. & WALLER, J.M. (1965) - THE PRODUCTION OF SCLEROTIA BY
      SCLEROTIUM ROLFSII. 2. THE RELATIONSHIP BETWEEN MYCELIAL GROWTH AND INI-
      TIATION OF SCLEROTIA. TRANS.BR.MYCOL.SOC. 48, 303-314.

6316 WHEELER, H.E. & MCGAHEN, J.W. (1952) - GENETICS OF GLOMERELLA. 10. GENES
      AFFECTING SEXUAL REPRODUCTION. AM.J.BOT. 39, 110-119.

6317 WHEELER, J.E. & HINE, R.B. (1972) - INFLUENCE OF SOIL TEMPERATURE AND MOIS-
      TURE ON SURVIVAL AND GROWTH OF STRANDS OF PHYMATOTRICHUM OMNIVORUM. PHY-
      TOPATHOLOGY 62, 828-832.

6318 WHEELER, M.H., TOLMSOFF, W.J. & MEOLA, S. (1976) - ULTRASTRUCTURE OF MEL-
      ANIN FORMATION IN VERTICILLIUM DAHLIAE WITH (+)-SCYTALONE AS A BIOSYN-
      THETIC INTERMEDIATE. CAN.J.MICROBIOL. 22, 702-711.

6319 WHITAKER, A. & MORTON, A.G. (1971) - AMINO ACID TRANSPORT IN PENICILLIUM
      GRISEOFULVUM. TRANS.BR.MYCOL.SOC. 56, 353-369.

6320 WHITE, E.C. (1943) - ANTIBACTERIAL FILTRATES FROM CULTURES OF ASPERGILLUS
      FLAVIPES. PROC.SOC.EXP.BIOL.MED. 54, 258-259.

6321 WHITE, E.C. & HILL, J.H. (1943) - STUDIES ON ANTIBACTERIAL PRODUCTS FORMED
      BY MOLDS. 1. ASPERGILLIC ACID, A PRODUCT OF A STRAIN OF ASPERGILLUS FLA-
      VUS. J.BACT. 45, 433-443.

6322 WHITE, E.P. (1967) - ISOLATION OF (+)-2-ACETAMIDO-2,5-DIHYDRO-5-OXOFURAN
      FROM FUSARIUM EQUISETI. J.CHEM.SOC.(C), 1967, 346-347.

6323 WHITE, E.P. (1972) - 2,5-DIOXOPIPERAZINES FROM THE FUNGAL GENERA ENTOLOMA
      AND FUSARIUM. N.Z.JL SCI. 15, 178-181.

6324 WHITE, N.H. (1941) - PHYSIOLOGICAL STUDIES OF THE FUNGUS OPHIOBOLUS GRAMI-
      NIS. 1. GROWTH FACTOR REQUIREMENTS. J.COUN.SCI.IND.RES. 14, 137-146.

6325 WHITE, N.H., CHILVERS, G.A. & EVANS, G. (1962) - ANTIFUNGAL ACTIVITY OF
      CYLINDROCARPON RADICICOLA. NATURE, LOND. 195, 406-407.

6326 WHITE, W.L., DARBY, R.T., STECHERT, G.M. & SANDERSON, K. (1948) - ASSAY OF
      CELLULOLYTIC ACTIVITY OF MOLDS ISOLATED FROM FABRICS AND RELATED ITEMS
      EXPOSED IN THE TROPICS. MYCOLOGIA 40, 34-84.

6327 WHITE, W.L. & DOWNING, M.H. (1947) - THE IDENTITY OF METARRHIZIUM GLUTINO-
      SUM. MYCOLOGIA 39, 546-555.

6328 WHITE, W.L. & DOWNING, M.H. (1951) - COCCOSPORA AGRICOLA, ITS SPECIFIC STA-
      TUS, RELATIONSHIPS, AND CELLULOLYTIC ACTIVITY. MYCOLOGIA 43, 645-657.

6329 WHITE, W.L. & DOWNING, M.H. (1953) - HUMICOLA GRISEA, A SOIL-INHABITING,
      CELLULOLYTIC HYPHOMYCETE. MYCOLOGIA 45, 951-963.

6330 WHITE, W.L., MANDELS, G.R. & SIU, R.G.H. (1950) - FUNGI IN RELATION TO THE
      DEGRADATION OF WOOLLEN FABRICS. MYCOLOGIA 42, 199-223.

6331 WHITE, W.L., SIU, R.G.H. & REESE, E.T. (1948) - THE BLACK ASPERGILLI IN RE-
      LATION TO CELLULOSIC SUBSTRATA. BULL.TORREY BOT.CLUB 75, 604-632.

6332   WHITE, W.L., YEAGER, C.C. & SHOTTS, H. (1949) - HISTORY, DISTRIBUTION AND
       ECONOMIC SIGNIFICANCE OF THE CELLULOSE-DESTROYING FUNGUS MEMNONIELLA
       ECHINATA. FARLOWIA 3, 399-423.

6333   WHITEHOUSE, H.L.K. (1974) - GENETIC ANALYSIS OF RECOMBINATION AT THE G LO-
       CUS IN SORDARIA FIMICOLA. GENET.RES. 24, 251-280.

6334   WHITNEY, E.D. (1974) - SYNERGISTIC EFFECT OF PYTHIUM ULTIMUM AND THE ADDI-
       TIVE EFFECT OF PENICILLIUM APHANIDERMATUM WITH HETERODERA SCHACHTII ON
       SUGAR BEET. PHYTOPATHOLOGY 64, 380-383.

6335   WHITESIDE, W.C. (1957) - PERITHECIAL INITIALS OF CHAETOMIUM. MYCOLOGIA 49,
       420-425.

6336   WHITESIDE, W.C. (1961) - MORPHOLOGICAL STUDIES IN THE CHAETOMIACEAE. 1.
       MYCOLOGIA 53, 512-523.

6337   WHITESIDE, W.C. (1962) - MORPHOLOGICAL STUDIES IN THE CHAETOMIACEAE. 2.
       MYCOLOGIA 54, 152-159.

6338   WHITNEY, H.S. (1964) - SPORULATION OF THANATEPHORUS CUCUMERIS (RHIZOCTONIA
       SOLANI) IN THE LIGHT AND IN THE DARK. PHYTOPATHOLOGY 54, 874-875.

6339   WHITNEY, H.S. & PARMETER, J.R. (1963) - SYNTHESIS OF HETEROCARYONS IN RHI-
       ZOCTONIA SOLANI. CAN.J.BOT. 41, 879-886.

6340   WHITNEY, N.J. & MORTIMORE, C.G. (1959) - AN ANTIFUNGAL SUBSTANCE IN THE
       CORN PLANT AND ITS EFFECT ON GROWTH OF TWO STALK-ROTTING FUNGI. NATURE,
       LOND. 183, 341.

6341   WHITNEY, N.J. & MORTIMORE, C.G. (1959) - ISOLATION OF THE ANTIFUNGAL SUB-
       STANCE, 6-METHOXYBENZOXAZOLINONE, FROM FIELD CORN (ZEA MAYS) IN CANADA.
       NATURE, LOND. 184, 1320.

6342   WHITNEY, P., CHAPMAN, J.M. & HEALE, J.B. (1969) - CARBOXYMETHYLCELLULASE
       PRODUCTION BY VERTICILLIUM ALBO-ATRUM. J.GEN.MICROBIOL. 56, 215-225.

6343   WHITNEY, P.J., VAUGHAN, J.G. & HEALE, J.B. (1968) - A DISC ELECTROPHORETIC
       STUDY OF THE PROTEINS OF VERTICILLIUM ALBO-ATRUM, VERTICILLIUM DAHLIAE,
       AND FUSARIUM OXYSPORUM WITH REFERENCE TO THEIR TAXONOMY. J.EXP.BOT. 19,
       415-426.

6344   WHITTLE, A.M. (1977) - MYCOFLORA OF CONES AND SEEDS OF PINUS SYLVESTRIS.
       TRANS.BR.MYCOL.SOC. 69, 47-57.

6345   WICKERHAM, L.J. & KURTZMAN, C.P. (1975) - SYNERGISTIC COLOR VARIANTS OF
       AUREOBASIDIUM PULLULANS. MYCOLOGIA 67, 342-361.

6346   WICKLOW, D.T. (1968) - ASPERGILLUS FUMIGATUS FRESENIUS ISOLATED FROM ORNI-
       THOGENIC SOIL COLLECTED AT HALLETT STATION, ANTARCTICA. CAN.J.MICROBIOL.
       14, 717-719.

6347   WICKLOW, D.T. (1973) - MICROFUNGAL POPULATIONS IN SURFACE SOILS OF MANIPU-
       LATED PRAIRIE STANDS. ECOLOGY 54, 1302-1310.

6348   WICKLOW, D.T. & MALLOCH, D. (1971) - STUDIES IN THE GENUS THELEBOLUS. TEM-
       PERATURE OPTIMA FOR GROWTH AND ASCOCARP DEVELOPMENT. MYCOLOGIA 63, 118-
       131.

6349   WICKLOW, D.T. & MOORE, V. (1974) - EFFECT OF INCUBATION TEMPERATURE ON THE
       COPROPHILOUS FUNGAL SUCCESSION. TRANS.BR.MYCOL.SOC. 62, 411-415.

6350   WICKLOW, D.T. & WHITTINGHAM, W.F. (1974) - SOIL MICROFUNGAL CHANGES AMONG
       THE PROFILES OF DISTURBED CONIFER-HARDWOOD FORESTS. ECOLOGY 55, 3-16.

6351   WICKLOW, M.C., BOLLEN, W.B. & DENISON, W.C. (1974) - COMPARISON OF SOIL MI-
       CROFUNGI IN 40-YEAR-OLD STANDS OF PURE ALDER, PURE CONIFER, AND ALDER-
       CONIFER MIXTURES. SOIL BIOL.BIOCHEM. 6, 73-78.

6352   WIDDEN, P. & PARKINSON, D. (1973) - FUNGI FROM CANADIAN CONIFEROUS FOREST
       SOILS. CAN.J.BOT. 51, 2275-2290.

6353   WIDDEN, P. & PARKINSON, D. (1975) - THE EFFECTS OF A FOREST FIRE ON SOIL
       MICROFUNGI. SOIL BIOL.BIOCHEM. 7, 125-138.

6354   WIDRA, A., RHODES, H.J. & POTTER, B. (1966) - ASCOSPOROGENESIS IN NANNIZ-
       ZIA GRUBYIA INDUCED BY ALPHA-KERATOSE. BACT.PROC., 1966, 75.

6355   WIEBE, C. & WINKELMANN, G. (1975) - KINETIC STUDIES ON THE SPECIFICITY OF
       CHELATE-IRON UPTAKE IN ASPERGILLUS. J.BACT. 123, 837-842.

6356   WIERINGA, K.T. (1956) - THE MICROORGANISMS DECOMPOSING PECTIC SUBSTANCES
       IN THE DEW RETTING PROCESS OF FLAX. NETH.J.AGRIC.SCI. 4, 204-209.

6357   WIESNER, B.P. (1942) - BACTERICIDAL EFFECTS OF ASPERGILLUS CLAVATUS. NA-
       TURE, LOND. 149, 356-357.

6358   WIJKMAN, N. (1931) - UEBER EINIGE NEUE, DURCH SCHIMMELPILZE GEBILDETE SUB-
       STANZEN. LIEBIGS ANNL.CHEMIE 485, 61-73.

6359   WILCOXSON, R.D. & SUBBARAYUDU, S. (1968) - TRANSLOCATION AND ACCUMULATION
       OF PHOSPHORUS-32 IN SCLEROTIA OF SCLEROTIUM ROLFSII. CAN.J.BOT. 46, 85-
       88.

6360   WILEY, B.J. & FENNELL, D.I. (1973) - ASCOCARPS OF ASPERGILLUS STROMATOIDES,
       A. NIVEUS, AND A. FLAVIPES. MYCOLOGIA 65, 752-760.

6361   WILEY, B.J. & SIMMONS, E.G. (1973) - NEW SPECIES AND A NEW GENUS OF PLECTO-
       MYCETES WITH ASPERGILLUS STATES. MYCOLOGIA 65, 934-938.

6362   WILHELM, S. (1950) - VERTICAL DISTRIBUTION OF VERTICILLIUM ALBO-ATRUM IN
       SOILS. PHYTOPATHOLOGY 40, 368-376.

6363   WILHELM, S. (1955) - LONGEVITY OF THE VERTICILLIUM WILT FUNGUS IN THE LAB-
       ORATORY AND FIELD. PHYTOPATHOLOGY 45, 180-181.

6364   WILHELM, S. (1965) - PYTHIUM ULTIMUM AND THE SOIL FUMIGATION GROWTH RE-
       SPONSE. PHYTOPATHOLOGY 55, 1016-1020.

6365   WILKINS, W.H. & HARRIS, G.C.M. (1944) - INVESTIGATIONS INTO THE PRODUCTION
       OF BACTERIOSTATIC SUBSTANCES BY FUNGI. TRANS.BR.MYCOL.SOC. 27, 113-120.

6366   WILKINSON, S. & SPILSBURY, J.F. (1965) - GLIOTOXIN FROM ASPERGILLUS CHEVA-
       LIERI (MANGIN) THOM & CHURCH. NATURE, LOND. 206, 619.

6367   WILKINSON, V. (1969) - ECOLOGICAL EFFECTS OF DIQUAT. NATURE, LOND. 224,
       618-619.

6368   WILLCOX, J. & TRIBE, H.T. (1974) - FUNGAL PARASITISM IN CYSTS OF HETERODE-
       RA. TRANS.BR.MYCOL.SOC. 62, 585-594.

6369   WILLETTS, A.J. (1973) - MICROBIAL METABOLISM OF ALKYLBENZENE SULPHONATES.
       FUNGAL METABOLISM OF 1-PHENYLUNDECANE-P-SULPHONATE AND 1-PHENYLDODECANE-
       P-SULPHONATE. ANTONIE VAN LEEUWENHOEK 39, 585-597.

6370   WILLETTS, H.J. (1961) - A COMPARISON BETWEEN OPHIOBOLUS GRAMINIS AND OPHI-
OBOLUS GRAMINIS VAR. AVENAE. TRANS.BR.MYCOL.SOC. 44, 504-510.

6371   WILLETTS, H.J. (1969) - STRUCTURE OF THE OUTER SURFACES OF SCLEROTIA OF
CERTAIN FUNGI. ARCH.MIKROBIOL. 69, 48-53.

6372   WILLETTS, H.J. & WONG, A.L. (1971) - ONTOGENIC DIVERSITY OF SCLEROTIA OF
SCLEROTINIA SCLEROTIORUM AND RELATED SPECIES. TRANS.BR.MYCOL.SOC. 57,
515-524.

6373   WILLIAMS, C.N. (1959) - SPORE SIZE IN RELATION TO CULTURE CONDITIONS. TRANS.
BR.MYCOL.SOC. 42, 213-222.

6374   WILLIAMS, G.H. & WESTERN, J.H. (1965) - THE BIOLOGY OF SCLEROTINIA TRIFOLI-
ORUM AND OTHER SPECIES OF SCLEROTIUM-FORMING FUNGI. 1. APOTHECIUM FORMA-
TION FROM SCLEROTIA. ANN.APPL.BIOL. 56, 253-260.

6375   WILLIAMS, G.H. & WESTERN, J.H. (1965) - THE BIOLOGY OF SCLEROTINIA TRIFOLI-
ORUM ERIKSS. AND OTHER SPECIES OF SCLEROTIUM-FORMING FUNGI. 2. THE SUR-
VIVAL OF SCLEROTIA IN SOIL. ANN.APPL.BIOL. 56, 261-268.

6376   WILLIAMS, J.I. & PUGH, G.J.F. (1971) - FUNGAL BIOLOGICAL FLORA. 1. GLIOMA-
STIX MURORUM AND G. MURORUM VAR. FELINA. INT.BIODETERIOR.BULL. 7, 37-41.

6377   WILLIAMS, J.I. & PUGH, G.J.F. (1974) - FUNGAL BIOLOGICAL FLORA CHRYSOSPO-
RIUM PANNORUM (LINK) HUGHES 1958. INT.BIODETERIOR.BULL. 10, 75-80.

6378   WILLIAMS, J.I. & PUGH, G.J.F. (1975) - RESISTANCE OF CHRYSOSPORIUM PANNO-
RUM TO AN ORGANOMERCURY FUNGICIDE. TRANS.BR.MYCOL.SOC. 64, 255-263.

6379   WILLIAMS, L.E. & SCHMITTHENNER, A.F. (1962) - EFFECT OF CROP ROTATION ON
SOIL FUNGUS POPULATIONS. PHYTOPATHOLOGY 52, 241-247.

6380   WILLIAMS, R.J. & ABATENI AYANABA (1975) - INCREASED INCIDENCE OF PYTHIUM
STEM ROT IN COWPEAS TREATED WITH BENOMYL AND RELATED FUNGICIDES. PHYTO-
PATHOLOGY 65, 217-218.

6381   WILLIAMS, S.T. (1963) - THE DISTRIBUTION OF FUNGI IN THE HORIZONS OF A POD-
SOLISED SOIL. IN: SOIL ORGANISMS; DOEKSEN, J. & DRIFT, J. VAN DER (ED.),
NORTH HOLLAND PUBL.CO., AMSTERDAM, 158-166.

6382   WILLIAMS, S.T., GRAY, T.R.G. & HITCHEN, P. (1965) - HETEROTHALLIC FORMATION
OF ZYGOSPORES IN MORTIERELLA MARBURGENSIS. TRANS.BR.MYCOL.SOC. 48, 129-
133.

6383   WILLIAMS, S.T. & PARKINSON, D. (1964) - STUDIES OF FUNGI IN A PODZOL. 1.
NATURE AND FLUCTUATION OF THE FUNGUS FLORA OF THE MINERAL HORIZONS. J.
SOIL SCI. 15, 331-341.

6384   WILLOUGHBY, L.G. & ARCHER, J.F. (1973) - THE FUNGAL SPORA OF A FRESHWATER
STREAM AND ITS COLONIZATION PATTERN ON WOOD. FRESHWATER BIOL. 3, 219-
239.

6385   WILSENACH, R. & KESSEL, M. (1965) - MICROPORES IN THE CROSSWALL OF GEOTRI-
CHUM CANDIDUM. NATURE, LOND. 207, 545-546.

6386   WILSENACH, R. & KESSEL, M. (1965) - THE ROLE OF LOMASOMES IN WALL FORMATION.
IN PENICILLIUM VERMICULATUM. J.GEN.MICROBIOL. 40, 401-404.

6387   WILSON, B.J. (1966) - TOXINS OTHER THAN AFLATOXINS PRODUCED BY ASPERGILLUS
FLAVUS. BACT.REV. 30, 478-484.

6388   WILSON, B.J. (1971) - MISCELLANEOUS ASPERGILLUS TOXINS. IN: MICROBIAL TOX-
       INS, VOL.6, FUNGAL TOXINS; CIEGLER, A., KADIS, S. & AJL, S.J. (ED.),
       ACADEMIC PRESS, NEW YORK, LONDON, 207-295.

6389   WILSON, B.J., CAMPBELL, T.C., HAYES, A, W. & HANLIN, R.T. (1968) - INVES-
       TIGATION OF REPORTED AFLATOXIN PRODUCTION BY FUNGI OUTSIDE THE ASPERGIL-
       LUS FLAVUS GROUP. APPL.MICROBIOL. 16, 819-821.

6390   WILSON, B.J., HARRIS, T.M. & HAYES, A.W. (1967) - MYCOTOXINS FROM PENICIL-
       LIUM PUBERULUM. J.BACT. 93, 1737-1738.

6391   WILSON, B.J. & WILSON, CH.H. (1962) - EXTRACTION AND PRELIMINARY CHARAC-
       TERIZATION OF A HEPATOTOXIC SUBSTANCE FROM CULTURES OF PENICILLIUM RU-
       BRUM. J.BACT. 84, 283-290.

6392   WILSON, B.J., WILSON, CH.H. & HAYES, A.W. (1968) - TREMORGENIC TOXIN FROM
       PENICILLIUM CYCLOPIUM GROWN ON FOOD MATERIALS. NATURE, LOND. 220, 77-78.

6393   WILSON, B.J., YANG, D.T.C. & HARRIS, TH.M. (1973) - PRODUCTION, ISOLATION
       AND PRELIMINARY TOXICITY STUDIES OF BREVIANAMIDE-A FROM CULTURES OF PE-
       NICILLIUM VIRIDICATUM. APPL.MICROBIOL. 26, 633-635.

6394   WILSON, D.M. & NUOVO, G.J. (1973) - PATULIN PRODUCTION IN APPLES DECAYED
       BY PENICILLIUM EXPANSUM. APPL.MICROBIOL. 26, 124-125.

6395   WILSON, J.M. & GRIFFIN, D.M. (1975) - RESPIRATION AND RADIAL GROWTH OF
       SOIL FUNGI AT TWO OSMOTIC POTENTIALS. SOIL BIOL.BIOCHEM. 7, 269-274.

6396   WILSON, K., PADHYE, A.A. & CARMICHAEL, J.W. (1969) - ANTIFUNGAL ACTIVITY
       OF WALLEMIA ICHTHYOPHAGA (= HEMISPORA STELLATA VUILL. = TORULA EPIZOA
       CORDA). ANTONIE VAN LEEUWENHOEK 35, 529-532.

6397   WILSON, K.S. & PORTER, C.L. (1958) - THE PATHOGENICITY OF VERTICILLIUM AL-
       BO-ATRUM AS AFFECTED BY MUCK SOIL ANTAGONISTS. APPL.MICROBIOL. 6, 155-
       159.

6398   WINDELS, C.E. & KOMMEDAHL, T. (1974) - POPULATION DIFFERENCES IN INDIGENOUS
       FUSARIUM SPECIES BY CORN CULTURE OF PRAIRIE SOIL. AM.J.BOT. 61, 141-145.

6399   WINDELS, M.B. & KOMMEDAHL, T. (1976) - ASSOCIATION OF FUSARIUM SPECIES WITH
       PICNIC BEETLES ON CORN EARS. PHYTOPATHOLOGY 66, 328-331.

6400   WINDISCH, S. (1951) - ZUR BIOLOGIE UND SYSTEMATIK DES MILCHSCHIMMELS UND
       EINIGER AEHNLICHER FORMEN. 1. DER MILCHSCHIMMEL (ENDOMYCES LACTIS) UND
       ENDOMYCES MAGNUSII. BEITR.BIOL.PFL. 28, 69-130.

6401   WINDISCH, S. (1965) - UEBER ZWEI NEUE PILZARTEN. PROTENDOMYCOPSIS DOMSCHII
       N.G., N.SP. UND ENDOMYCES LAIBACHII N.SP. BEITR.BIOL.PFL. 41, 337-358.

6402   WINITZKY, J. (1948) - LAS ESPECIES DE ASPERGILLI EN MUESTRAS DE TIERRA Y
       AIRE DE LA CIUDAD DE BUENOS AIRES. REVTA INVEST.AGRIC., B.AIRES 2, 97-
       104.

6403   WINITZKY, J. (1952) - LAS ESPECIES DE ASPERGILLI EN MUESTRAS DE TIERRA Y
       AIRE DE LA ESTEPA PAMPEANA. REVTA INVEST.AGRIC., B.AIRES 5, 303-316.

6404   WINITZKY, J. (1953) - LAS ESPECIES DE ASPERGILLUS EN MUESTRAS DE TIERRA Y
       AIRE DEL 'PARQUE MESOPOTAMICO' Y DE LA 'SELVA MISIONERA'. REVTA INVEST.
       AGRIC., B.AIRES 7, 341-354.

6405 WINITZKY, J. (1957) - LAS ESPECIES DE ASPERGILLI EN MUESTRAS DE TIERRA Y AIRE DEL PARQUE CHAQUENO. REVTA INVEST.AGRIC., B.AIRES 11, 149-162.

6406 WINTER, A.G. (1949) - UNTERSUCHUNGEN UEBER DIE BEZIEHUNGEN ZWISCHEN OPHIO-BOLUS GRAMINIS UND ANDEREN ORGANISMEN MIT HILFE DER AUFWUCHSPLATTENME-THODE. ARCH.MIKROBIOL. 14, 240-270.

6407 WINTER, W.F., MATHUR, S.B. & NEERGAARD, P. (1974) - SEEDBORNE ORGANISMS OF ARGENTINA - A SURVEY. PL.DIS.REPTR 58, 507-511.

6408 WIRTH, J. & KLOSER, R. (1972) - RELATIONSHIPS IN PENICILLIUM AURANTIO-VI-RENS. PHYTOCHEMISTRY 11, 2615.

6409 WIRTH, J.C., ANAND, S.R. & ZOLTAN, L.K. (1964) - THE FATTY ACIDS OF MICRO-SPORUM GYPSEUM. CAN.J.MICROBIOL. 10, 811-812.

6410 WITKAMP, M. (1969) - ENVIRONMENTAL EFFECTS ON MICROBIAL TURNOVER OF SOME MINERAL ELEMENTS. 1. ABIOTIC FACTORS. SOIL BIOL.BIOCHEM. 1, 167-176.

6411 WOELKERLING, W.J. & BAXTER, J.W. (1968) - AQUATIC HYPHOMYCETES OF WISCON-SIN. DISTRIBUTION AND ECOLOGY. MYCOPATH.MYCOL.APPL. 35, 33-36.

6412 WOGAN, G.N.(ED.) (1965) - MYCOTOXINS IN FOODSTUFFS. MASS.INST.TECHNOL. PRESS, CAMBRIDGE, MASS.

6413 WOGAN, G.N. (1966) - MYCOTOXIN CONTAMINATION OF FOODSTUFFS. IN: SYMPOSIUM OF THE DIVISION OF AGRICULTURAL AND FOOD CHEMISTRY; AM.CHEM.SOC., WASH-INGTON, D.C., ADV.CHEM.SER.57, 195-215.

6414 WOHLRAB, G., TUVESON, R.W. & OLMSTED, C.E. (1963) - FUNGAL POPULATION FROM EARLY STAGES OF SUCCESSION IN INDIANA DUNE SAND. ECOLOGY 44, 734-740.

6415 WOLF, D.C. & MARTIN, J.P. (1975) - MICROBIAL DECOMPOSITION OF RING-14C ATRAZINE, CYANURIC ACID, AND 2-CHLORO-4,6-DIAMINO-S-TRIAZINE. J.ENVIRON. QUALITY 4, 134-139.

6416 WOLF, E. (1954) - BEITRAG ZUR SYSTEMATIK DER GATTUNG MORTIERELLA UND MORTIE-RELLA-ARTEN ALS MYKORRHIZAPILZE BEI ERICACEEN. ZENTBL.BAKT.PARASITKDE, ABT.2, 107, 523-548.

6417 WOLF, F.A. (1949) - TWO UNUSUAL CONIDIAL FUNGI. MYCOLOGIA 41, 561-564.

6418 WOLF, F.T. (1951) - THE CULTIVATION OF TWO SPECIES OF ENTOMOPHTHORA ON SYN-THETIC MEDIA. BULL.TORREY BOT.CLUB 78, 211-220.

6419 WOLF, F.T., BRYDEN, R.R. & MACLAREN, J.A. (1950) - THE NUTRITION OF MONO-SPORIUM APIOSPERMUM. MYCOLOGIA 42, 233-241.

6420 WOLLENWEBER, H.W. (1913) - RAMULARIA, MYCOSPHAERELLA, NECTRIA, CALONECTRIA. EINE MORPHOLOGISCH-PATHOLOGISCHE STUDIE ZUR ABGRENZUNG VON PILZGRUPPEN MIT CYLINDRISCHEN UND SICHELFOERMIGEN KONIDIENFORMEN. PHYTOPATHOLOGY 3, 197-242.

6421 WOLLENWEBER, H.W. (1920) - DER KARTOFFELSCHORF. ARB.FORSCHINST.KARTBAU, BERL. 2, 1-102.

6422 WOLLENWEBER, H.W. (1928) - UEBER FRUCHTFORMEN DER KREBSERREGENDEN NECTRIA-CEEN. Z.PARASITKDE 1, 138-173.

6423 WOLLENWEBER, H.W. & HOCHAPFEL, H. (1937) - BEITRAEGE ZUR KENNTNIS PARASI-TAERER UND SAPROPHYTISCHER PILZE. 4. CONIOTHYRIUM UND SEINE BEZIEHUNG ZUR FRUCHTFAEULE. Z.PARASITKDE 9, 600-637.

6424 WOLLENWEBER, H.W. & REINKING, O. (1935) - DIE FUSARIEN. P.PAREY, BERLIN.

6425 WOLLENWEBER, H.W. & REINKING, O. (1935) - DIE VERBREITUNG DER FUSARIEN IN
      DER NATUR. FRIEDLAENDER, BERLIN.

6426 WOLTZ, S.S. & LITTRELL, R.H. (1968) - PRODUCTION OF YELLOW STRAPLEAF OF
      CHRYSANTHEMUM AND SIMILAR DISEASES WITH AN ANTIMETABOLITE PRODUCED BY
      ASPERGILLUS WENTII. PHYTOPATHOLOGY 58, 1476-1480.

6427 WONG, A.-L. & WILLETTS, H.J. (1973) - ELECTROPHORETIC STUDIES OF SOLUBLE
      PROTEINS AND ENZYMES OF SCLEROTINIA SPECIES. TRANS.BR.MYCOL.SOC. 61,
      167-178.

6428 WONG, A.-L. & WILLETTS, H.J. (1975) - A TAXONOMIC STUDY OF SCLEROTINIA
      SCLEROTIORUM AND RELATED SPECIES - MYCELIAL INTERACTIONS. J.GEN.MICRO-
      BIOL. 88, 339-344.

6429 WONG, A.-L. & WILLETTS, H.J. (1975) - ELECTROPHORETIC STUDIES OF AUSTRAL-
      ASIAN, NORTH AMERICAN AND EUROPEAN ISOLATES OF SCLEROTINIA SCLEROTIO-
      RUM AND RELATED SPECIES. J.GEN.MICROBIOL. 90, 355-359.

6430 WONG, P.T.W. & WALKER, J. (1975) - GERMINATING PHIALIDIC CONIDIA OF GAEU-
      MANNOMYCES GRAMINIS AND PHIALOPHORA-LIKE FUNGI FROM GRAMINEAE. TRANS.
      BR.MYCOL.SOC. 65, 41-47.

6431 WOOD, F.C. (1937 AND 1939) - STUDIES ON 'DAMPING-OFF' OF CULTIVATED MUSH-
      ROOMS AND ITS ASSOCIATION WITH FUSARIUM SPECIES. PHYTOPATHOLOGY 27, 85-
      94 AND 29, 728-739.

6432 WOOD, F.H. (1973) - NEMATODE-TRAPPING FUNGI FROM A TUSSOCK GRASSLAND SOIL
      IN NEW ZEALAND. N.Z.JL BOT. 11, 231-240.

6433 WOOD, H.A., BOZARTH, R.F. & MISLIVEC, P.B. (1971) - VIRUSLIKE PARTICLES
      ASSOCIATED WITH AN ISOLATE OF PENICILLIUM BREVI-COMPACTUM. VIROLOGY 44,
      592-598.

6434 WOOD, R.K.S. (1951) - THE CONTROL OF DISEASES OF LETTUCE BY THE USE OF AN-
      TAGONISTIC ORGANISMS. 2. THE CONTROL OF RHIZOCTONIA SOLANI. ANN.APPL.
      BIOL. 38, 217-230.

6435 WOOD, T.M. (1968) - CELLULOLYTIC ENZYME SYSTEM OF TRICHODERMA KONINGII.
      SEPARATION OF COMPONENTS ATTACKING NATIVE COTTON. BIOCHEM.J. 109, 217-
      227.

6436 WOOD-BAKER, A. (1955) - EFFECTS OF OXYGEN-NITROGEN MIXTURES ON THE SPORE
      GERMINATION OF MUCORACEOUS MOULDS. TRANS.BR.MYCOL.SOC. 38, 291-297.

6437 WOODBURY, W., CHI, C.C. & HANSON, E.W. (1962) - PECTIC ENZYME PRODUCTION
      BY THREE FUSARIUM SPP. FROM RED CLOVER. PHYTOPATHOLOGY 52, 33 (ABS.).

6438 WOODIN, T.S. & SEGEL, J.H. (1968) - ISOLATION AND CHARACTERIZATION OF GLU-
      TATHIONE REDUCTASE FROM PENICILLIUM CHRYSOGENUM. BIOCHIM.BIOPHYS.ACTA
      167, 64-77.

6439 WOOTTON, L.M.O. & PRAMER, D. (1966) - VALINE-INDUCED MORPHOGENESIS IN AR-
      THROBOTRYS CONOIDES. BACT.PROC., 1966, 75.

6440 WORF, G.L. & HAGEDORN, D.J. (1961) - A TECHNIQUE FOR STUDYING RELATIVE
      SOIL POPULATIONS OF TWO FUSARIUM PATHOGENS OF GARDEN PEAS. PHYTOPATHOL-
      OGY 51, 805-806.

6441 WORONIN, M. (1864/65) - ZUR ENTWICKLUNGSGESCHICHTE DES ASCOBOLUS PULCHER-
      RIMUS UND EINIGER PEZIZEN. ABH.SENCKENB.NATURFORSCH.GES.5, (4), 333-344.

6442 WRIGHT, D.E. (1969) - PHYTOTOXICITY OF SPORIDESMIN. N.Z.JL AGRIC.RES. 12,
      271-274.

6443 WRIGHT, D.S.C. & ABRAHAMSON, J.P. (1970) - ELECTRON MICROSCOPIC STUDY OF
      VERTICILLIUM DAHLIAE KLEB. AS A PATHOGEN OF TOBACCO (NICOTIANA TABACUM
      L.). N.Z.JL BOT. 8, 326-343.

6444 WRIGHT, E. & BOLLEN, W.B. (1961) - MICROFLORA OF DOUGLAS-FIR FOREST SOIL.
      ECOLOGY 42, 825-828.

6445 WRIGHT, J.E., GODEAS, A.M. & BERTONI, M.D. (1971) - MICOFLORA DEL SUELO DE
      LA ARGENTINA. 2. ALGUNAS FORMAS ASCOSPORICAS DE LA PROVINCIA DE BUENOS
      AIRES. BOLN SOC.ARGENT.BOT. 14, 43-56.

6446 WRIGHT, J.E. & MARCHAND, S. (1972) - MICOFLORA DEL SUELO DE LA ARGENTINA.
      3. DOS INTERESANTES GENEROS SINEMATICOS - TRICHURUS Y DORATOMYCES. BOLN
      SOC.ARGENT.BOT. 14, 305-310.

6447 WRIGHT, J.L.C., MCINNES, A.G., SMITH, D.G. & VINING, L.C. (1970) - STRUC-
      TURE OF SEPEDONIN, A TROPOLONE METABOLITE OF SEPEDONIUM CHRYSOSPERMUM
      FRIES. CAN.J.CHEM. 48, 2702-2708.

6448 WRIGHT, J.M. (1951) - PHYTOTOXIC EFFECTS OF SOME ANTIBIOTICS. ANN.BOT. 15,
      493-499.

6449 WRIGHT, J.M. (1955) - THE PRODUCTION OF ANTIBIOTICS IN SOIL. 2. PRODUCTION
      OF GRISEOFULVIN BY PENICILLIUM NIGRICANS. ANN.APPL.BIOL. 43, 288-296.

6450 WRIGHT, J.M. (1956) - A STUDY OF THE FREE-LIVING AND ROOT-SURFACE FUNGI IN
      CULTIVATED AND FALLOW SOIL IN HONG KONG. PL.SOIL 8, 132-140.

6451 WRIGHT, J.M. (1956) - THE PRODUCTION OF ANTIBIOTICS IN SOIL. 4. PRODUCTION
      OF ANTIBIOTICS IN COATS OF SEED SOWN IN SOIL. ANN.APPL.BIOL. 44, 561-
      566.

6452 WU, M.T., AYRES, J.C., KOEHLER, P.E. & CHASSIS, G. (1974) - TOXIC METABO-
      LITE PRODUCED BY ASPERGILLUS WENTII. APPL.MICROBIOL. 27, 337-339.

6453 WUEST, P.J., BAKER, K.F. & CONWAY, W.S. (1970) - SENSITIVITY OF SELECTED
      MUSHROOM PATHOGENS TO AERATED STEAM. PHYTOPATHOLOGY 60, 1274-1275.

6454 WUEST, P.J. & MOORE, R.K. (1972) - ADDITIONAL DATA ON THE THERMAL SENSI-
      TIVITY OF SELECTED FUNGI ASSOCIATED WITH AGARICUS BISPORUS. PHYTOPATHOL-
      OGY 62, 1470-1472.

6455 WUNDER, W. (1973) - DER DURCH AFLATOXINE HERVORGERUFENE LEBERKREBS BEI DER
      REGENBOGENFORELLE. Z.LEBENSMITTELUNTERS.FORSCH. 151, 250-255.

6456 WURTZ, T. & JOCKUSCH, H. (1975) - SEXUAL DIFFERENTIATION IN MUCOR. TRISPO-
      RIC ACID RESPONSE MUTANT AND MUTANTS BLOCKED IN ZYGOSPORE DEVELOPMENT.
      DEV.BIOL. 43, 213-220.

6457 WYLLIE, T.D. (1961) - HOST-PARASITE RELATIONSHIPS BETWEEN SOYBEAN AND RHI-
      ZOCTONIA SOLANI. DISS.ABSTR. 21, 2854.

6458 WYLLIE, T.D. (1962) - EFFECT OF METABOLIC BY-PRODUCTS OF RHIZOCTONIA SOLA-
      NI ON THE ROOTS OF CHIPPEWA SOYBEAN SEEDLINGS. PHYTOPATHOLOGY 52, 202-
      206.

6459   WYLLIE, T.D. & DEVAY, J.E. (1970) - IMMUNOLOGICAL COMPARISON OF ISOLATES
        OF VERTICILLIUM ALBO-ATRUM AND V. NIGRESCENS PATHOGENIC TO COTTON. PHY-
        TOPATHOLOGY 60, 1682-1686.

6460   WYNSTON, L.K. & TILDEN, E.B. (1963) - CHROMATOGRAPHIC FRACTIONATION OF AS-
        PERGILLUS ENDOTOXINS. MYCOPATH.MYCOL.APPL. 20, 272-283.

6461   XENOPOULOS, S. & MILLAR, C. (1977) - PYCNIDIUM PRODUCTION BY AUREOBASIDIUM
        PULLULANS TYPE-CULTURES. TRANS.BR.MYCOL.SOC. 68, 127-130.

6462   YADAV, A.S. (1966) - THE ECOLOGY OF MICROFUNGI ON DECAYING STEMS OF HERA-
        CLEUM SPHONDYLIUM. TRANS.BR.MYCOL.SOC. 49, 471-485.

6463   YADAV, A.S. & MADELIN, M.F. (1968) - THE ECOLOGY OF MICROFUNGI ON DECAYING
        STEMS OF URTICA DIOICA. TRANS.BR.MYCOL.SOC. 51, 249-259.

6464   YADAV, A.S. & MADELIN, M.F. (1968) - EXPERIMENTAL STUDIES ON MICROFUNGI
        FROM DECAYING STEMS OF HERACLEUM SPHONDYLIUM AND URTICA DIOICA. TRANS.
        BR.MYCOL.SOC. 51, 261-267.

6465   YAMADA, K., IIBUCHI, S. & MINODA, Y. (1967) - STUDIES ON TANNIN HYDROLASE
        OF MICROORGANISMS. 1. ISOLATION AND IDENTIFICATION OF PRODUCING MOLDS
        AND STUDIES ON THE CONDITIONS OF CULTIVATION. J.FERMENT.TECHNOL., OSAKA
        45, 233-240.

6466   YAMAMOTO, S., MINODA, Y. & YAMADA, K. (1973) - FORMATION AND SOME PROPER-
        TIES OF THE ACID PHOSPHATASE IN ASPERGILLUS TERREUS. AGRIC.BIOL.CHEM.,
        TOKYO 37, 2719-2726.

6467   YAMAMOTO, W. (1959) - SOME SPECIES OF CLADOSPORIUM FROM JAPAN. SCI.REP.
        HYOGO UNIV.AGRIC., SER.AGRIC.BIOL. 4, 1-6.

6468   YAMAMOTO, Y., SHINYA, M. & OOHATA, Y. (1970) - STUDIES ON THE METABOLIC
        PRODUCTS OF A STRAIN OF ASPERGILLUS FUMIGATUS (DH 413). 4. BIOSYNTHESIS
        OF TOLUQUINONES AND CHEMICAL STRUCTURES OF NEW METABOLITES. CHEM.PHARM.
        BULL., TOKYO 18, 561-569.

6469   YAMANE, H., MUROFUSHI, N. & TAKAHASHI, N. (1974) - STRUCTURE OF A NEW NOR-
        KAURENOLIDE FROM GIBBERELLA FUJIKUROI. AGRIC.BIOL.CHEM., TOKYO 38, 207-
        210.

6470   YAMAZAKI, M., MAEBAYASHI, Y. & MIYAKI, K. (1970) - PRODUCTION OF OCHRATOX-
        IN-A BY ASPERGILLUS OCHRACEUS ISOLATED IN JAPAN FROM MOLDY RICE. APPL.
        MICROBIOL. 20, 452-454.

6471   YAMAZAKI, M., MAEBAYASHI, Y. & MIYAKI, K. (1971) - THE ISOLATION OF SECA-
        LONIC ACID A FROM ASPERGILLUS OCHRACEUS CULTURE ON RICE. CHEM.PHARM.
        BULL., TOKYO 19, 199-201.

6472   YAMAZAKI, M., MAEBAYASHI, Y. & MIYAKI, K. (1972) - ISOLATION OF A NEW TYPE
        OF PYRAZINE METABOLITE FROM ASPERGILLUS OCHRACEUS WILH. CHEM.PHARM.BULL.,
        TOKYO 20, 2274-2276.

6473   YAMAZAKI, M., MAEBAYASHI, Y. & MIYAKI, K. (1972) - ISOLATION OF A NEW META-
        BOLITE, 6-METHOXY-8HYDROXYISOCOUMARIN-3-CARBOXYLIC ACID FROM ASPERGIL-
        LUS OCHRACEUS WILH. CHEM.PHARM.BULL. 20, 2276-2278.

6474   YAMAZAKI, M., SUZUKI, SH. & MIYAKI, K. (1971) - TREMORGENIC TOXINS FROM
        ASPERGILLUS FUMIGATUS FRES. CHEM.PHARM.BULL., TOKYO 19, 1739-1740.

6475   YANAGITA, T. & KOGANE, F. (1963) - SITE OF BIOSYNTHESIS OF SULFUR COMPOUNDS
        IN GROWING COLONIES OF ASPERGILLUS NIGER. J.GEN.APPL.MICROBIOL., TOKYO
        9, 331-336.

6476 YANG, B.-Y. & LIU, C.-H. (1972) - PRELIMINARY STUDIES ON TAIWAN MUCORALES. 1. TAIWANIA 17, 293-303.

6477 YANG, C.Y. (1969) - STIMULATION OF SOME RHIZOSPHERE FUNGI BY FOUR SPECIES OF PYTHIUM. PHYTOPATHOLOGY 59, 1058 (ABS.).

6478 YANG, C.Y. (1970) - ENZYME-INDUCED GERMINATION OF APHANOMYCES OOSPORES. PHYTOPATHOLOGY 60, 1320 (ABS.).

6479 YANG, C.Y. & MITCHELL, J.E. (1965) - CATION EFFECT ON REPRODUCTION OF PYTHIUM SPP. PHYTOPATHOLOGY 55, 1127-1131.

6480 YANG, C.Y. & MITCHELL, J.E. (1966) - EFFECT OF COMPONENTS OF PEPTONE ON THE GROWTH AND DIFFERENTIATION OF APHANOMYCES EUTEICHES. PHYTOPATHOLOGY 56, 907 (ABS.).

6481 YANG, C.Y. & SCHOULTIES, C.L. (1972) - A SIMPLE CHEMICALLY DEFINED MEDIUM FOR THE GROWTH OF APHANOMYCES EUTEICHES AND SOME OTHER OOMYCETES. MYCOPATH.MYCOL.APPL. 46, 5-15.

6482 YANG, D.T.C. & WILSON, B.J. (1970) - ERGOSTEROL PRODUCTION BY PENICILLIUM CYCLOPIUM. J.CHINESE CHEM.SOC. 17, 185.

6483 YANG, S.M. (1959) - AN INVESTIGATION ON THE HOST RANGE AND SOME ECOLOGICAL ASPECTS ON THE SCLEROTINIA DISEASE OF THE RAPE PLANT. ACTA PHYTOPATH. SIN. 5, 111-122.

6484 YARWOOD, C.E. (1946) - ISOLATION OF THIELAVIOPSIS BASICOLA FROM SOIL BY MEANS OF CARROT DISKS. MYCOLOGIA 38, 346-348.

6485 YARWOOD, C.E. (1974) - HABITATS OF THIELAVIOPSIS IN CALIFORNIA. PL.DIS. REPTR 58, 54-56.

6486 YATES, S.G., TOOKEY, H.L., ELLIS, J.J. & BURKHARDT, H.J. (1967) - TOXIC BUTENOLIDE BY FUSARIUM NIVALE (FRIES) CESATI ISOLATED FROM TALL FESCUE (FESTUCA ARUNDINACEA SCHREB.). TETRAHEDRON LETTERS, 1967 (7), 621-625.

6487 YATES, S.G., TOOKEY, H.L., ELLIS, J.J. & BURKHARDT, H.J. (1968) - MYCOTOXINS PRODUCED BY FUSARIUM NIVALE ISOLATED FROM TALL FESCUE (FESTUCA ARUNDINACEA). PHYTOCHEMISTRY 7, 139-146.

6488 YEN, C.M. & HOWARD, D.H. (1970) - GERMINATION OF BLASTOSPORES OF HISTOPLASMA CAPSULATUM. SABOURAUDIA 8, 242-252.

6489 YENDOL, W.G. (1968) - FACTORS AFFECTING GERMINATION OF ENTOMOPHTHORA CONIDIA. J.INVERTEBR.PATH. 10, 116-121.

6490 YENDOL, W.G. & HAMLEN, R.A. (1973) - ECOLOGY OF ENTOMOGENOUS VIRUSES AND FUNGI. ANN.N.Y.ACAD.SCI. 217, 18-30.

6491 YENDOL, W.G., MILLER, E.M. & BEHNKE, C.N. (1968) - TOXIC SUBSTANCES FROM ENTOMOPHTHORACEOUS FUNGI. J.INVERTEBR.PATH. 10, 313-319.

6492 YENDOL, W.G. & PASCHKE, J.D. (1965) - PATHOLOGY OF AN ENTOMOPHTHORA INFECTION IN THE EASTERN SUBTERRANEAN TERMITE RETICULITERMES FLAVIPES (KOLLAR). J.INVERTEBR.PATH. 7, 414-422.

6493 YLIMAEKI, A. (1967) - ROOT ROT AS A CAUSE OF RED CLOVER DECLINE IN LEYS IN FINLAND. ANNLS AGRIC.FENN. 6, 7-59.

6494   YLIMAEKI, A. (1969) - TYPHULA BLIGHT OF CLOVERS. ANNLS AGRIC.FENN., SER.
       PHYTOPATH. 8, 30-37.

6495   YLIMAEKI, A. (1970) - THE MICROFLORA OF CEREAL SEEDS IN FINLAND. ANNLS
       AGRIC.FENN. 9, 293-295.

6496   YODER, D.L. & LOCKWOOD, J.L. (1973) - FUNGAL SPORE GERMINATION ON NATURAL
       AND STERILE SOIL. J.GEN.MICROBIOL. 74, 107-117.

6497   YOKOYAMA, S. & ICHISHIMA, E. (1972) - A NEW TYPE OF ACID CARBOXYPEPTIDASE
       OF MOLDS OF THE GENUS PENICILLIUM. AGRIC.BIOL.CHEM., TOKYO 36, 1259-
       1261.

6498   YOKOYAMA, S., OOBAYASHI, A., TANABE, O., SUGAWARA, S., ARAKI, E. & ICHI-
       SHIMA, E. (1974) - PRODUCTION AND SOME PROPERTIES OF A NEW TYPE OF ACID
       CARBOXYPEPTIDASE OF PENICILLIUM MOLDS. APPL.MICROBIOL. 27, 953-960.

6499   YOKOYAMA, T. & TUBAKI, K. (1973) - SOME HYPHOMYCETES FROM PAPUA AND NEW
       GUINEA. BULL.NATN.SCI.MUS., TOKYO 16, 655-660.

6500   YOKOYAMA, T., TUBAKI, K. & ITO, T. (1975) - DESCRIPTIVE CATALOGUE OF IFO
       FUNGUS COLLECTION IV. RES COMMUNS INST.FERMENT., OSAKA 7, 113-142.

6501   YOSHIDA, H. & TAMIYA, N. (1971) - ACID PHOSPHATASES FROM FUSARIUM MONILI-
       FORME. PURIFICATION AND ENZYMATIC PROPERTIES. J.BIOCHEM. 69, 525-534.

6502   YOSHIDA, T. & ALEXANDER, M. (1970) - NITROUS OXIDE FORMATION BY NITROSOMO-
       NAS EUROPAEA AND HETEROTROPHIC MICROORGANISMS. PROC.SOIL SCI.SOC.AM. 34,
       880-882.

6503   YOSHIMURA, M., YAMANAKA, S., MITSUGI, K. & HIROSE, Y. (1975) - PRODUCTION
       OF MONASCUS-PIGMENT IN A SUBMERGED CULTURE. AGRIC.BIOL.CHEM., TOKYO 39,
       1789-1795.

6504   YOSHIZAWA, T., TSUCHIYA, Y., MOROOKA, N. & SAWADA, Y. (1975) - MALFORMIN-
       A1 AS A MAMMALIAN TOXICANT FROM ASPERGILLUS NIGER. AGRIC.BIOL.CHEM.,
       TOKYO 39, 1325-1326.

6505   YOUATT, G. (1958) - FUNGAL CELLULASES. 9. GROWTH OF STACHYBOTRYS ATRA ON
       CELLULOSE AND PRODUCTION OF A BETA-GLUCOSIDASE HYDROLYSING CELLOBIOSE.
       AUST.J.BIOL.SCI. 11, 209-217.

6506   YOUNG, E.M. (1930) - PHYSIOLOGICAL STUDIES IN RELATION TO THE TAXONOMY OF
       MONASCUS SPP. TRANS.WIS.ACAD.SCI. 25, 227-244.

6507   YOUNG, E.M. (1931) - THE MORPHOLOGY AND CYTOLOGY OF MONASCUS RUBER. AM.J.
       BOT. 18, 499-517.

6508   YOUNG, H.C. & BENNETT, C.W. (1922) - GROWTH OF SOME PARASITIC FUNGI IN
       SYNTHETIC CULTURE MEDIA. AM.J.BOT. 9, 459-469.

6509   YOUNG, R.E., PRATT, H.K. & BIALE, J.B. (1951) - IDENTIFICATION OF ETHYLENE
       AS A VOLATILE PRODUCT OF THE FUNGUS PENICILLIUM DIGITATUM. PL.PHYSIOL.,
       LANCASTER 26, 304-310.

6510   YOUSSEF, Y.A. (1974) - ON THE FUNGAL FLORA OF LIBYAN SOILS. ARCH.MIKROBIOL.
       99, 167-171.

6511   YOUSSEF, Y.A. & MANKARIOS, A.T. (1968) - STUDIES ON THE RHIZOSPHERE MYCO-
       FLORA OF BROAD BEAN AND COTTON. MYCOPATH.MYCOL.APPL. 35, 389-400.

6512   YU-DI YANG, C. & MITCHELL, J.E. (1965) - CATION EFFECT ON REPRODUCTION OF
       PYTHIUM SPECIES. PHYTOPATHOLOGY 55, 1127-1131.

6513 YUE, Y.N., KIANG, F.S., FANG, T.Y. & WANG, C.Y. (1963) - STUDIES ON THE
      PHYSIOLOGY OF CELLULOSE-DECOMPOSING FUNGUS OF TRICHODERMA KONINGI OUDE-
      MANS. ACTA BOT.SIN. 11, 191-199.

6514 YUILL, E. (1950) - THE NUMBERS OF NUCLEI IN CONIDIA OF ASPERGILLI. TRANS.
      BR.MYCOL.SOC. 33, 324-331.

6515 YUILL, J.L. (1952) - POLYSACCHARIDE PRODUCTION BY ASPERGILLUS NIGER. A
      STRAIN RICH IN MYCODEXTRAN. CHEM.IND., 1952, 755-756.

6516 YUNG, C. & STENTON, H. (1964) - A STUDY OF THE PHYCOMYCETES IN THE SOILS
      OF HONG KONG. TRANS.BR.MYCOL.SOC. 47, 127-139.

6517 YURCHENKO, L.V., ZAKHAROV, I.A. & LEVITIN, M.M. (1974) - (GENETICS AND SE-
      LECTION OF BEAUVERIA BASSIANA (BALS.) VUILL., AN ENTOMOPATHOGENIC FUN-
      GUS). GENETIKA 10, 95-101.

6518 YUSEF, H.M. & ALLAM, M.E. (1967) - THE EFFECT OF LIGHT AND GROWTH AND SPOR-
      ULATION OF CERTAIN FUNGI. MYCOPATH.MYCOL.APPL. 33, 81-89.

6519 YUSEF, H.M. & ALLAM, M.E. (1967) - THE CARBON AND NITROGEN NUTRITION OF
      CERTAIN FUNGI. CAN.J.MICROBIOL. 13, 1097-1106.

6520 ZABAWSKI, J. (1967) - (STUDIES ON THE MYCOFLORA OF SPHAGNUM BOG ZIELENIEC).
      ZESZ.PROBL.POSTEP.NAUK ROLN. 76, 355-400.

6521 ZACHARIAH, A.T., HANSEN, H.N. & SNYDER, W.C. (1956) - THE INFLUENCE OF EN-
      VIRONMENTAL FACTORS ON CULTURAL CHARACTERS OF FUSARIUM SPECIES. MYCO-
      LOGIA 48, 459-467.

6522 ZACHARIAH, K. & FITZ-JAMES, P.C. (1967) - THE STRUCTURE OF PHIALIDES IN
      PENICILLIUM CLAVIFORME. CAN.J.MICROBIOL. 13, 249-256.

6523 ZACHARIAH, K. & METITIRI, P.O. (1970) - THE EFFECT OF MUTATION ON CELL
      PROLIFERATION AND NUCLEAR BEHAVIOR IN PENICILLIUM CLAVIFORME BAINIER.
      PROTOPLASMA 69, 331-339.

6524 ZACHARUK, R.Y. (1970) - FINE STRUCTURE OF THE FUNGUS METARRHIZIUM ANISO-
      PLIAE INFECTING THREE SPECIES OF LARVAL ELATERIDAE (COLEOPTERA). J.INVER-
      TEBR.PATH. 15, 63-80.

6525 ZACHARUK, R.Y. (1970) - FINE STRUCTURE OF THE FUNGUS METARRHIZIUM ANISO-
      PLIAE INFECTING THREE SPECIES OF LARVAL ELATERIDAE (COLEOPTERA). 2. CO-
      NIDIAL GERM TUBES AND APPRESSORIA. J.INVERTEBR.PATH. 15, 81-91.

6526 ZACHARUK, R.Y. (1970) - FINE STRUCTURE OF THE FUNGUS METARRHIZIUM ANISO-
      PLIAE INFECTING THREE SPECIES OF LARVAL ELATERIDAE (COLEOPTERA). 3. PEN-
      ETRATION OF THE HOST INTEGUMENT. J.INVERTEBR.PATH. 15, 372- 396.

6527 ZACHARUK, R.Y. (1971) - FINE STRUCTURE OF THE FUNGUS METARRHIZIUM ANISO-
      PLIAE INFECTING THREE SPECIES OF LARVAL ELATERIDAE (COLEOPTERA). 4. DE-
      VELOPMENT WITHIN THE HOST. CAN.J.MICROBIOL. 17, 524-529.

6528 ZAEHNER, H., KELLER-SCHIERLEIN, W., HUETTER, R., HESS-LEISINGER, K. &
      DEER, A. (1963) - STOFFWECHSELPRODUKTE VON MIKROORGANISMEN. 40. SIDERA-
      MINE AUS ASPERGILLACEEN. ARCH.MIKROBIOL. 45, 119-135.

6529 ZAGULYAYEVA, Z.A. (1971) - (PHYSIOLOGY OF CELLULOSE DECOMPOSING MICROMYCE-
      TES). MIKOL.FITOPAT. 5, 385-389.

6530 ZAJIC, J.E. & LEDUY, A. (1973) - FLOCCULANT AND CHEMICAL PROPERTIES OF A
      POLYSACCHARIDE FROM PULLULARIA PULLULANS. APPL.MICROBIOL. 25, 628-635.

6531 ZALESKI, K. (1927) - UEBER DIE IN POLEN GEFUNDENEN ARTEN DER GRUPPE PENI-
      CILLIUM LINK. 1. 2. UND 3. BULL.ACAD.POL.SCI., MATH.NAT., SER.D, 417-
      563.

6532 ZALESKI, K., BLASZCZAK, W. & GLASER, T. (1960) - (STUDIES ON THE BIOLOGY
      AND PATHOGENICITY OF FOUR FUSARIUM SPECIES FROM LUPINES AND OF TWO
      STRAINS OF RHIZOCTONIA SOLANI, AND ATTEMPTS OF THEIR CONTROL IN GREEN
      HOUSE CONDITIONS). PR.KOM.NAUK ROLN.LESN., POZNAN 5, 1-63.

6533 ZALIKHANOVA, F.A. (1971) - (RESERVOIRS OF DERMATOMYCOSIS AGENTS AND THEIR
      ROLE IN DISTRIBUTION OF CATTLE TRICHOPHYTOSIS). TRUDY VSES.NAUCHNO-
      ISSLED.INST.VET.SAN. 38, 50-55.

6534 ZALIKHANOVA, F.A. (1971) - (KERATINOPHILIC DERMATOPHYTES IN SOIL SAMPLES
      FROM THE KARBADINO-BALKARSKOI ASSR). TRUDY VSES.NAUCHNO-ISSLED.INST.VET.
      SAN. 38, 56-62.

6535 ZAMBETTAKIS, C. (1954) - RECHERCHES SUR LA SYSTEMATIQUE DES SPHAEROPSIDA-
      LES-PHAEODIDYMAE. BULL.TRIMEST.SOC.MYCOL.FR. 70, 219-349.

6536 ZAMORA, J.R.C. (1977) - ISOLATION OF HISTOPLASMA CAPSULATUM FROM THE AIR
      IN THE AGUAS BUENAS CAVES, AGUAS BUENAS, PUERTO RICO. MYCOPATHOLOGIA
      60, 163-165.

6537 ZAMORA, J.R.C. (1977) - ISOLATION OF HISTOPLASMA CAPSULATUM FROM THE TIS-
      SUES OF BATS CAPTURED IN THE AGUAS BUENAS CAVES, AGUAS BUENAS, PUERTO
      RICO. MYCOPATHOLOGIA 60, 167-169.

6538 ZAPATER, R.C., ALBESI, E.J. & GARCIA, G.H. (1975) - MYCOTIC KERATITIS BY
      DRECHSLERA SPICIFERA. SABOURAUDIA 13, 295-298.

6539 ZAPATER, R.C. & ARRECHEA, A. (1975) - MYCOTIC KERATITIS BY FUSARIUM - A
      REVIEW AND REPORT OF TWO CASES. OPHTHALMOLOGICA, BASEL 170, 1-12.

6540 ZAPATER, R.C., ARRECHEA, A.DE & GUEVARA, V.H. (1972) - QUERATOMICOSIS POR
      FUSARIUM DIMERUM. SABOURAUDIA 10, 274-275.

6541 ZARKA, A.M.E. (1963) - A RAPID METHOD FOR THE ISOLATION AND DETECTION OF
      RHIZOCTONIA SOLANI FROM NATURALLY INFESTED AND ARTIFICIALLY INOCULATED
      SOILS. MEDED.LANDBHOGESCH.WAGENINGEN 28, 877-885.

6542 ZAROOGIAN, G.E. & CURTIS, R.W. (1964) - SIMILARITY AMONG PLANT GROWTH IN-
      HIBITORS PRODUCED BY PENICILLIUM THOMII, PENICILLIUM OXALICUM, AND BYS-
      SOCHLAMYS NIVEA. NATURE, LOND. 201, 1142.

6543 ZAROOGIAN, G.E. & CURTIS, R.W. (1964) - ISOLATION AND IDENTIFICATION OF
      ASYMMETRIN. PL.CELL PHYSIOL. 5, 291-296.

6544 ZAROR, L. (1973) - MICROSPORUM GYPSEUM AND KERATINOMYCES AJELLOI FROM
      CHILEAN SOILS. MYCOPATH.MYCOL.APPL. 51, 103.

6545 ZAROR, Z.C. (1972) - DERMATOFITOS EN LOS SUELOS DE CHILE (ESTUDIO PRELIM-
      INAR). BOLN INST.BACT.CHILE 14, 31-35.

6546 ZATTLER, F. & CHROMETZKA, P. (1960) - ZUR BIOLOGIE VON VERTICILLIUM ALBO-
      ATRUM R. & B., DEM ERREGER DER WELKEKRANKHEIT DES HOPFENS. PRAKT.PFLBAU
      PFLSCHUTZ 55, 17-23.

6547 ZAWADA, J.W. & SUTCLIFFE, J.F. (1974) - UREASE ACTIVITY IN ASPERGILLUS TA-
      MARII. ANN.BOT. 38, 1093-1102.

6548   ZEIDLER, G. & MARGALITH, P. (1972) - SYNCHRONIZED SPORULATION IN PENICIL-
        LIUM DIGITATUM (SACC.). CAN.J.MICROBIOL. 18, 1685-1690.

6549   ZEIDLER, G. & MARGALITH, P. (1973) - MODIFICATION OF THE SPORULATION CYCLE
        IN PENICILLIUM DIGITATUM (SACC.). CAN.J.MICROBIOL. 19, 481-483.

6550   ZELLER, L. (1968) - CHRYSOSPORIUM SPECIES FROM THE "BARADLA" CAVE IN AGG-
        TELEK. MYCOPATH.MYCOL.APPL. 34, 296-301.

6551   ZELLER, L. (1968) - MUCORALES FROM THE "BARADLA" CAVE IN AGGTELEK. ANNLS
        UNIV.SCIENT.BPEST.ROLANDO EOETVOES, SECT.BIOL. 9-10, 387-399.

6552   ZELLER, L. (1970) - ARTHRODERMA SPECIES FROM THE "BARADLA" CAVE IN AGG-
        TELEK. ANNLS UNIV.SCIENT.BPEST.ROLANDO EOETVOES, SECT.BIOL. 12,
        235-240.

6553   ZEL'TSER, S.SH., AVAZKHODZHAEV, M.KH. & DARIEV, R.S. (1974) - (BIOLOGICAL
        ROLE OF THE EXTRACELLULAR POLYSACCHARIDE OF THE FUNGUS VERTICILLIUM
        DAHLIAE IN THE PATHOGENESIS OF COTTON WILT). MIKOL.FITOPAT. 8, 143-144.

6554   ZENTMYER, G.A. (1952) - A SUBSTANCE STIMULATING SEXUAL REPRODUCTION IN
        PHYTOPHTHORA CINNAMOMI. PHYTOPATHOLOGY 42, 24 (ABS.).

6555   ZENTMYER, G.A. (1961) - CHEMOTAXIS OF ZOOSPORES FOR ROOT EXUDATES. SCIENCE,
        N.Y. 133, 1595.

6556   ZENTMYER, G.A. (1965) - BACTERIAL STIMULATION OF SPORANGIUM PRODUCTION IN
        PHYTOPHTHORA CINNAMOMI. SCIENCE, N.Y. 150, 1178-1179.

6557   ZENTMYER, G.A. & ERWIN, D.C. (1970) - DEVELOPMENT AND REPRODUCTION OF PHY-
        TOPHTHORA. PHYTOPATHOLOGY 60, 1120-1127.

6558   ZENTMYER, G.A., GILPATRICK, J.D. & THORN, W.A. (1960) - METHODS OF ISOLAT-
        ING PHYTOPHTHORA CINNAMOMI FROM SOIL AND FROM HOST TISSUE. PHYTOPATHOL-
        OGY 50, 87 (ABS.).

6559   ZENTMYER, G.A., LEARY, J.V., KLURE, L.J. & GRANTHAM, G.L. (1976) - VARIA-
        BILITY IN GROWTH OF PHYTOPHTHORA CINNAMOMI IN RELATION TO TEMPERATURE.
        PHYTOPATHOLOGY 66, 982-986.

6560   ZENTMYER, G.A. & MARSHALL, L.A. (1959) - FACTORS AFFECTING SPORANGIAL PRO-
        DUCTION BY PHYTOPHTHORA CINNAMOMI. PHYTOPATHOLOGY 49, 556 (ABS.).

6561   ZENTMYER, G.A. & MIRCETICH, S.M. (1966) - SAPROPHYTISM AND PERSISTENCE IN
        SOIL BY PHYTOPHTHORA CINNAMOMI. PHYTOPATHOLOGY 56, 710-712.

6562   ZETSCHE, K. (1961) - CHEMISCH-PHYSIOLOGISCHE UNTERSUCHUNGEN UEBER DIE HY-
        DROXYLIERUNG VON STEROIDEN DURCH PILZE DER GATTUNG CURVULARIA. ARCH.
        MIKROBIOL. 38, 237-271.

6563   ZHDANOVA, N.N. (1963) - (OCCURRENCE OF DARK HYPHOMYCETES IN MAIZE RHIZO-
        SPHERE IN THE REGION OF THE STEPPE AND FOREST STEPPE OF THE UKRAINIAN
        SSR). MYKROBIOL.ZH. 25 (4), 28-34.

6564   ZHDANOVA, N.N. (1966) - (RARE AND NEW SPECIES OF FUNGI OF THE DEMATIACEAE
        ISOLATED FROM THE RHIZOSPHERE OF MAIZE FROM DIFFERENT CLIMATIC ZONES OF
        THE UKRAINIAN SSR). MYKROBIOL.ZH. 28 (1), 36-40.

6565   ZHDANOVA, N.N., GAVRYUSHINA, A.I. & POKHODENKO, V.D. (1974) - (RELATION OF
        SOME DEMATIACEAE SPECIES AND MUTANTS TO OXYGEN CONTENT IN THE AIR ME-
        DIUM). IZV.AKAD.NAUK SSSR, SER.BIOL. 4, 602-606.

6566 ZHDANOVA, N.N., GAVRYUSHINA, A.I. & VASILEVSKAYA, A.I. (1973) - (EFFECT OF
      GAMMA- AND UV-IRRADIATION ON SURVIVAL OF CLADOSPORIUM SP. AND OIDIODEN-
      DRON CEREALIS). MYKROBIOL.ZH. 35, 449-452.

6567 ZHDANOVA, N.N. & POKHODENKO, V.D. (1973) - (POSSIBLE PARTICIPATION OF MELA-
      NIN PIGMENT IN PROTECTION OF FUNGAL CELL FROM DEHYDRATION). MIKROBIOLO-
      GIYA 42, 848-853.

6568 ZICKLER, D. (1973) - FINE STRUCTURE OF CHROMOSOME PAIRING IN TEN ASCOMYCE-
      TES - MEIOTIC AND PREMEIOTIC (MITOTIC) SYNAPTONEMAL COMPLEXES. CHROMO-
      SOMA 40, 401-416.

6569 ZIEGLER, H. & BOEHME, H. (1976) - ZUR PROBLEMATIK DER PRAEPARATION VON DE-
      FINIERTEN PILZANTIGENEN. DERM.MSCHR. 162, 87-92.

6570 ZIEGLER, H., BOEHME, H., HEIDUK, U., SCHWELLA, M. & KEMPNY, J. (1970) -
      DIE VERWERTUNG VON AMYLUM SOLUBILE ALS HAUPTKOHLENSTOFFQUELLE DURCH DER-
      MATOPHYTEN UND SCHIMMELPILZE. DERM.MSCHR. 156, 52-66.

6571 ZIMENKO, T.G. (1972) - MICROFLORA OF PEAT SOILS. IN: MICROFLORA OF SOILS
      IN THE NORTHERN AND CENTRAL USSR.; MISHUSTIN, E.N. (ED.), ISRAEL PRO-
      GRAM SCIENT.TRANSL., JERUSALEM, 159-196.

6572 ZIMMERMANN, G. (1974) - UNTERSUCHUNGEN UEBER ART UND URSACHEN VON VERFAER-
      BUNGEN AN BERGAHORN-STAMMHOLZ (ACER PSEUDOPLATANUS L.). FORSTWISS.ZENTBL.
      93, 247-261.

6573 ZOGG, H. (1951) - STUDIEN UEBER DIE PATHOGENITAET VON ERREGERGEMISCHEN BEI
      GETREIDEFUSSKRANKHEITEN. PHYTOPATH.Z. 18, 1-54.

6574 ZOGG, H. (1959) - STUDIEN UEBER DIE BIOLOGISCHE BODENENTSEUCHUNG. 2. BEEIN-
      FLUSSUNG DER PATHOGENITAET VON OPHIOBOLUS GRAMINIS DURCH DIE MIKROFLO-
      REN VERSCHIEDENER BOEDEN MIT VERSCHIEDENEN FRUCHTFOLGEN. PHYTOPATH.Z.
      34, 432-444.

6575 ZOGG, H. (1962) - STUDIEN UEBER DIE BIOLOGISCHE BODENENTSEUCHUNG. 3. BEEIN-
      FLUSSUNG DER PATHOGENITAET VON OPHIOBOLUS GRAMINIS AUF LEBENDEM UND TO-
      TEM WIRTSPFLANZENGEWEBE DURCH DIE MIKROFLORA EINER BESTIMMTEN ACKERERDE.
      PHYTOPATH.Z. 46, 87-96.

6576 ZOGG, H. (1963) - STUDIEN UEBER DIE BIOLOGISCHE BODENENTSEUCHUNG. 4. ELI-
      MINIERUNG VON OPHIOBOLUS GRAMINIS IM BODEN UNTER ANWESENHEIT VERSCHIE-
      DENARTIGER MONOKOTYLER UND DIKOTYLER FUTTERPFLANZEN. PHYTOPATH.Z. 48,
      272-286.

6577 ZOGG, H. (1969) - CROP ROTATION AND BIOLOGICAL SOIL DISINFECTION. QUAL.PL.
      MAT.VEGET. 18, 256-273.

6578 ZOGG, H. & JAEGGI, W. (1974) - STUDIES ON THE BIOLOGICAL SOIL DISINFECTION.
      7. CONTRIBUTION TO THE TAKE-ALL DECLINE (GAEUMANNOMYCES GRAMINIS) IMI-
      TATED BY MEANS OF LABORATORY TRIALS AND SOME OF ITS POSSIBLE MECHANISMS.
      PHYTOPATH.Z. 81, 160-169.

6579 ZONNEVELD, B.J.M. (1971) - BIOCHEMICAL ANALYSIS OF THE CELL WALL OF ASPER-
      GILLUS NIDULANS. BIOCHIM.BIOPHYS.ACTA 249, 506-614.

6580 ZONNEVELD, B.J.M. (1972) - A NEW TYPE OF ENZYME, AN EXO-SPLITTING ALPHA-1,
      3-GLUCANASE FROM NON-INDUCED CULTURES OF ASPERGILLUS NIDULANS. BIOCHIM.
      BIOPHYS.ACTA 258, 541-547.

6581 ZONNEVELD, B.J.M. (1972) - MORPHOGENESIS IN ASPERGILLUS NIDULANS. THE SIG-
      NIFICANCE OF ALPHA-1,3-GLUCAN OF THE CELL WALL AND ALPHA-1,3-GLUCANASE
      FOR CLEISTOTHECIUM DEVELOPMENT. BIOCHIM.BIOPHYS.ACTA 273, 174-184.

6582 ZONNEVELD, B.J.M. (1974) - ALPHA-1,3 GLUCAN SYNTHESIS CORRELATED WITH AL-
PHA-1,3 GLUCANASE SYNTHESIS, CONIDIATION AND FRUCTIFICATION IN MORPHO-
GENETIC MUTANTS OF ASPERGILLUS NIDULANS. J.GEN.MICROBIOL. 81, 445-451.

6583 ZONNEVELD, B.J.M. (1975) - SEXUAL DIFFERENTIATION IN ASPERGILLUS NIDULANS.
THE REQUIREMENT FOR MANGANESE AND ITS EFFECT ON ALPHA-1,3 GLUCAN SYN-
THESIS AND DEGRADATION. ARCH.MICROBIOL. 105, 101-104.

6584 ZONNEVELD, B.J.M. (1975) - SEXUAL DIFFERENTIATION IN ASPERGILLUS NIDULANS.
THE REQUIREMENT FOR MANGANESE AND THE CORRELATION BETWEEN PHOSPHOGLUCO-
MUTASE AND THE SYNTHESIS OF RESERVE MATERIAL. ARCH.MICROBIOL. 105, 105-
108.

6585 ZONNEVELD, B.J.M. (1976) - THE EFFECT OF GLUCOSE AND MANGANESE ON ADENO-
SINE-3,5-MONOPHOSPHATE LEVELS DURING GROWTH AND DIFFERENTIATION OF AS-
PERGILLUS NIDULANS. ARCH.MICROBIOL. 108, 41-44.

6586 ZUB, J. (1960) - (A KIND OF FUNGUS NEW IN POLAND. CONIOTHYRIUM MINITANS
CAMPB., SUPER-PARASITE OF CANKER OF CLOVER (SCLEROTINIA TRIFOLIORUM
ERIKSS.). BIUL.INST.OCHR.ROSLIN, 171-180.

6587 ZUERCHER, W. & TAMM, CH. (1966) - ISOLIERUNG VON 2-DEHYDROVERRUCARIN-A ALS
METABOLIT VON MYROTHECIUM RORIDUM. HELV.CHIM.ACTA 49, 2594-2597.

6588 ZYCHA, H., SIEPMANN, R. & LINNEMANN, G. (1969) - MUCORALES. EINE BESCHREI-
BUNG ALLER GATTUNGEN UND ARTEN DIESER PILZGRUPPE. J.CRAMER, LEHRE, 355
PP.

6589 ANONYMOUS (1963) - FERRIRUBIN AND DESFERRIRUBIN. CIBA LTD.BELG. PAT.
633,631.

6590 ANONYMOUS (1964) - PLANT PATHOLOGY, PATH.REP.DEP.AGRIC.MAURITIUS, 63-67.

6591 ANONYMOUS (1965) - ANTIBIOTICS, SANDOZ LTD, NETH.APPL. 6,606,173.

6592 ANONYMOUS (1965) - ANTIFUNGAL COMPOUND BY FERMENTATION. BR.PAT. 1,006,724.

6593 ANONYMOUS (1966) - A NEW ANTIBIOTIC. UPJOHN CO., NETH.APPL. 6,516,312.

INDEX OF FUNGAL NAMES

Names and pages of fully treated fungi are printed in bold face, other recognized names in roman letters, synonyms in italics. Figures preceded by letter k refer to the "Key to the genera" in Vol. 2.